THE CALCULUS
with analytic geometry
SECOND EDITION

THE CALCULUS
with analytic geometry
SECOND EDITION

Louis Leithold
UNIVERSITY OF SOUTHERN CALIFORNIA

HARPER & ROW, PUBLISHERS
NEW YORK, EVANSTON, SAN FRANCISCO, LONDON

Cover art: "Calculus," an etching and engraving by Stanley William Hayter (Courtesy La Tortue Galerie, Santa Monica, Calif.)

Art for chapter headings: details from "Hydroides," an engraving by Stanley William Hayter

STANDARD BOOK NUMBER: 06-043959-9

LIBRARY OF CONGRESS CATALOG CARD NUMBER: 74-168364

To my son, Gordon Marc Leithold

Contents

ACKNOWLEDGMENTS

Reviewers

Professor William D. Bandes, San Diego Mesa College
Professor Archie D. Brock, East Texas State University
Professor Reuben W. Farley, Virginia Commonwealth University
Professor Jacob Golightly, Jacksonville University
Professor Albert Herr, Drexel University
Professor Gordon L. Miller, Wisconsin State University
Professor William W. Mitchell, Jr., Phoenix College
Professor Roger B. Nelsen, Lewis and Clark College
Sister Madeleine Rose, Holy Names College
Professor George W. Schultz, St. Petersburg Junior College
Professor Donald R. Sherbert, University of Illinois
Professor John Vadney, Fulton-Montgomery Community College
Professor David Whitman, San Diego State College

Production Staff at Harper & Row

Blake Vance, Mathematics Editor
Howard Boyer, Special Projects Editor
Karen Judd, Production Editor
Rita Naughton, Designer

Assistants for Answers to Exercises

Jacqueline Dewar, University of Southern California
Kenneth Kast, University of Southern California

Cover and Chapter Opening Artist

Stanley William Hayter, Atelier 17, Paris, France

To these people and to all the users of the first edition who have suggested changes, I express my deep appreciation.

L. L.

Preface

This textbook is available either in one volume or in two parts: Part I consists of the first fourteen chapters, and Part II comprises Chapters 14 through 18 (Chapter 14 on Infinite Series is included in both parts to make the use of the two-volume set more flexible). The material in Part I consists of the differential and integral calculus of functions of a single variable and plane analytic geometry, and it may be covered in a one-year course of nine or ten semester hours or twelve quarter hours. The second part is suitable for a course consisting of five or six semester hours or eight quarter hours. It includes the calculus of several variables and a treatment of vectors in the plane, as well as in three dimensions, with a vector approach to solid analytic geometry.

The second edition, like the first, can be used for courses designed for prospective mathematics majors as well as for those having students whose primary interest is in engineering, the physical sciences, or non-technical fields. It is assumed that the reader has a knowledge of high-school algebra and geometry.

The objectives of the first edition have been maintained. I have endeavored to achieve a healthy balance between the presentation of elementary calculus from a rigorous approach and that from the older, intuitive, and computational point of view. Bearing in mind that a textbook should be written for the student, I have attempted to keep the presentation geared to a beginner's experience and maturity and to leave no step unexplained or omitted. I desire that the reader be aware that proofs of theorems are necessary and that these proofs be well motivated and carefully explained so that they are understandable to the student who has achieved an average mastery of the preceding sections of the book. If a theorem is stated without proof, I have generally augmented the discussion by both figures and examples, and in such cases I have always stressed that what is presented is an illustration of the content of the theorem and is not a proof.

Major changes in the second edition occur in the chapters on trigonometric functions, infinite series, and multiple integration; these chapters have been completely rewritten and expanded to include additional subject matter. Other changes include the following: (1) the rewording in certain sections and the addition of examples to clarify the explanations; (2) a reordering of some topics, such as placing the chapter on infinite series at the conclusion of the study of the calculus of functions of single variable, unifying the discussion of functions, limits, and continuity into a single chapter, incorporating the presentation of hyperbolic functions with that of the trigonometric functions, and treating vectors in space immediately following vectors in the plane; (3) additional applications of the calculus including some to the fields of economics and business; (4) a complete revision of the exercise sets so that there is a larger number of theoretical problems, as well as some more challenging ones and those giving a wider variety of applications; (5) the addition of a set of Review Exercises at the end of each chapter; (6) the use of color to clarify the figures, emphasize the statements of definitions and theorems, and improve the overall design of the book.

Basic facts about the real-number system are given in Chapter 1. I have avoided presenting sophisticated, tricky arguments merely for the purpose of showing that some of the properties can be derived from others. It has been my experience that few students of beginning calculus are capable of appreciating such discussions and that these considerations belong to a course in abstract algebra. Chapter 1 also gives an introduction to analytic geometry, and it includes the traditional material on straight lines as well as a discussion of the circle and the parabola. These sections may be omitted by those who have already had a course in analytic geometry.

Chapter 2 is the heart of any first course in the calculus. I have defined a function as a set of ordered pairs and have used this idea to point up the concept of a function as a correspondence between sets of real numbers. The notion of a limit of a function is first given a step-by-step motivation, which brings the reader from computing the value of a function near a number, through an intuitive discussion of the limiting process, up to a rigorous epsilon–delta definition. A sequence of examples progressively graded in difficulty is included. All the limit theorems are stated, and some proofs are presented in the text, while other proofs have been outlined in the exercises. In the discussion of continuity, I have used as examples and counterexamples "common, everyday" functions and have avoided those that would have little intuitive meaning for the reader.

In Chapter 3, before giving the formal definition of a derivative, I have defined the tangent line to a curve and instantaneous velocity in rectilinear motion in order to demonstrate in advance that the concept of a derivative is of wide application, both geometrical and physical. Theorems on differentiation are proved and illustrated by examples. Chapter 4 gives the traditional applications of the derivative to problems involving related rates, maxima and minima, and curve sketching, as well as some to business and economics.

The antiderivative is treated in Chapter 5. I use the term "antidifferentiation" instead of indefinite integration, but the standard notation $\int f(x)\ dx$ is retained so that the reader will not be given a bizarre new notation that would make the reading of standard references difficult. This notation will suggest to the student that some relation must exist between definite integrals, introduced in Chapter 6, and antiderivatives, but I see no harm in this as long as he is presented with the theoretically proper view of the definite integral as the limit of sums. Exercises involving the evaluation of definite integrals by finding limits of sums are given in Chapter 6, to impress upon the reader that this is how they are calculated. The introduction of the definite integral follows the definition of the measure of the area under a curve as a limit of sums. Elementary properties of the definite integral are derived and the fundamental theorem of the calculus is proved. It is emphasized that this is a theorem, and an important one, because it provides us with an alternative to computing limits of sums. It is also emphasized that the definite integral is in no sense some special type of antiderivative. In Chapter 7, I have given numerous applications of definite integrals. The presentation stresses not only the manipulative techniques but also the fundamental principles involved. In each application, the definitions of the new terms are intuitively motivated and explained.

The treatment of logarithmic and exponential functions in Chapter 8 is the modern approach. The natural logarithm is defined as an integral, and after the discussion of the inverse of a function, the exponential function is defined as the inverse of the natural logarithm function. An irrational power of a real number is then defined. The trigonometric functions are defined in Chapter 9 as functions assigning numbers to numbers. The important trigonometric identities are derived and used to obtain the formulas for the derivatives and integrals of these functions. Sections on the differentiation and integration of the trigonometric functions as well as of the inverse trigonometric functions are followed by two sections on hyperbolic functions. The geometric interpretation of the hyperbolic functions is postponed until Chapter 15 because it involves the use of parametric equations.

Chapter 10, on techniques of integration, involves one of the most important computational aspects of the calculus. I have explained the theoretical backgrounds of each different method after an introductory motivation. The mastery of integration techniques depends upon the examples, and I have used as illustrations problems that the student will certainly meet in practice, those which require patience and persistence to solve. The material on the approximation of definite integrals includes the statement of theorems for computing the bounds of the error involved in these approximations. The theorems and the problems that go with them, being self-contained, can be omitted from a course if the instructor so wishes.

Polar coordinates and some of their applications are given in Chapter 11. In Chapter 12, conics are treated as a unified subject to impress upon the reader their natural and close relationship to each other. Equations of the conics in polar coordinates are treated first, and the cartesian equations are derived from the polar equations. The topics of indeterminate forms, improper integrals, and Taylor's formula, and the computational techniques involved are presented in Chapter 13.

I have attempted in Chapter 14 to give as complete a treatment of infinite series as is feasible in an elementary calculus text. In addition to the customary computational material, I have included the proof of the equivalence of convergence and boundedness of monotonic sequences based on the completeness property of the real numbers and the proofs of the computational processes involving differentiation and integration of power series.

The first five sections of Chapter 15 on vectors in the plane can be taken up after Chapter 3 if it is desired to introduce vectors earlier in the course. The approach to vectors is modern, and it serves both as an introduction to the viewpoint of linear algebra and to that of classical vector analysis. The applications are to physics and geometry. Chapter 16 treats vectors in three-dimensional space and, if desired, the topics in the first three sections of this chapter may be studied concurrently with the corresponding topics of Chapter 15.

Limits, continuity, and differentiation of functions of several variables are considered in Chapter 17. The discussion and examples are applied mainly to functions of two and three variables; however, statements of most of the definitions and theorems are extended to functions of n variables. Applications to the solution of extrema problems and an introduction to Lagrange multipliers are presented as well as a section on applications of the partial derivative in economics. The double integral of a function of two variables and the triple integral of a function of three variables, along with some applications to physics, engineering, and geometry, are given in Chapter 18.

LOUIS LEITHOLD

1

Real Numbers and Introduction to Analytic Geometry

1.1 REAL NUMBERS AND INEQUALITIES

The real number system can be completely described by a set of axioms. With these axioms we can derive the properties of the real numbers from which follow the familiar algebraic operations of addition, subtraction, multiplication, and division, as well as the algebraic concepts of solving equations, factoring, and so forth. In this book we are not concerned with showing how such properties are derived from the axioms because these considerations belong to a course in abstract algebra. However, because elementary calculus involves real numbers, you should be familiar with some of the fundamental properties of the real number system given below.

1.1.1 Sum and product

If a and b are any real numbers, there is one and only one real number, denoted by $a + b$, called their *sum,* and there is one and only one real number, denoted by ab (or $a \times b$, or $a \cdot b$), called their *product.*

1.1.2 Commutative laws

If a and b are any real numbers,

$$a + b = b + a \quad \text{and} \quad ab = ba$$

1.1.3 Associative laws

If a, b, and c are any real numbers,

$$a + (b + c) = (a + b) + c \quad \text{and} \quad a(bc) = (ab)c$$

1.1.4 Distributive law

If a, b, and c are any real numbers,

$$a(b + c) = ab + ac$$

1

1.1.5 Existence of identity elements There exist two distinct real numbers 0 and 1 such that for every real number a

$$a + 0 = a \quad \text{and} \quad a \cdot 1 = a$$

1.1.6 Existence of negatives Every real number a has a *negative*, denoted by $-a$, such that

$$a + (-a) = 0$$

1.1.7 Existence of reciprocals Every real number $a \neq 0$ has a *reciprocal*, denoted by $1/a$, such that

$$a \cdot \frac{1}{a} = 1$$

1.1.8 Definition of subtraction If a and b are any real numbers, the *difference* between a and b, denoted by $a - b$, is defined by

$$a - b = a + (-b)$$

1.1.9 Definition of division If a is any real number, and b is any real number except 0, the *quotient* of a and b is defined by

$$\frac{a}{b} = a \cdot \frac{1}{b}$$

To enable us to refer to one real number being greater (or less) than another, we introduce the concept of a real number being *positive* and an *order relation*.

1.1.10 Axiom of order In the set of real numbers, there exists a subset called the *positive numbers* such that

(i) if a is any real number, exactly one of these three statements holds: $a = 0$; a is positive; $-a$ is positive.
(ii) the sum of two positive numbers is positive.
(iii) the product of two positive numbers is positive.

1.1.11 Definition The real number a is *negative* if and only if $-a$ is positive.

1.1.12 Definition The symbols $<$ ("is less than") and $>$ ("is greater than") are defined as follows:

(i) $a < b$ if and only if $b - a$ is positive.
(ii) $a > b$ if and only if $a - b$ is positive.

1.1.13 Definition The symbols $\leq$ ("is less than or equal to") and $\geq$ ("is greater than or equal to") are defined as follows:

(i) $a \leq b$ if and only if either $a < b$ or $a = b$.
(ii) $a \geq b$ if and only if either $a > b$ or $a = b$.

Expressions such as $a < b$, $a > b$, $a \le b$, and $a \ge b$ are called *inequalities*. Some examples are $2 < 7$, $-5 < 6$, $-5 < -4$, $14 > 8$, $2 > -4$, $-3 > -6$, $5 \ge 3$, $-10 \le -7$. In particular, $a < b$ and $a > b$ are called *strict* inequalities, whereas $a \le b$ and $a \ge b$ are called *nonstrict* inequalities.

The following properties can be proved by using 1.1.1 through 1.1.13.

1.1.14 Property (i) $a > 0$ if and only if a is positive.
(ii) $a < 0$ if and only if a is negative.
(iii) $a > 0$ if and only if $-a < 0$.
(iv) $a < 0$ if and only if $-a > 0$.

1.1.15 Property If $a < b$ and $b < c$, then $a < c$.

EXAMPLE: $3 < 6$ and $6 < 14$; so $3 < 14$.

1.1.16 Property If $a < b$, then $a + c < b + c$, if c is any real number.

EXAMPLE: $4 < 7$; so $4 + 5 < 7 + 5$; and $4 - 5 < 7 - 5$.

1.1.17 Property If $a < b$ and $c < d$, then $a + c < b + d$.

EXAMPLE: $2 < 6$ and $-3 < 1$; so $2 + (-3) < 6 + 1$.

1.1.18 Property If $a < b$, and c is any positive number, then $ac < bc$.

EXAMPLE: $2 < 5$; so $2 \cdot 4 < 5 \cdot 4$.

1.1.19 Property If $a < b$, and c is any negative number, then $ac > bc$.

EXAMPLE: $2 < 5$; so $2(-4) > 5(-4)$.

1.1.20 Property If $0 < a < b$ and $0 < c < d$, then $ac < bd$.

EXAMPLE: $0 < 4 < 7$ and $0 < 8 < 9$; so $4(8) < 7(9)$.

Property 1.1.18 states that if both members of an inequality are multiplied by a positive number, the direction of the inequality remains unchanged, whereas Property 1.1.19 states that if both members of an inequality are multiplied by a negative number, the direction of the inequality is reversed. Properties 1.1.18 and 1.1.19 also hold for division, because dividing both members of an inequality by a number d is equivalent to multiplying both members by $1/d$.

To illustrate the type of proof that is usually given, we present a proof of Property 1.1.17:

Since $a < b$, $b - a$ is positive   (by 1.1.12(i)).

Since $c < d$, $d - c$ is positive   (by 1.1.12(i)).

Hence, $(b - a) + (d - c)$ is positive   (by 1.1.10(ii)).

Therefore, $(b + d) - (a + c)$ is positive   (by 1.1.3, 1.1.2, and 1.1.8).

Therefore, $a + c < b + d$ (by 1.1.12(i)).

The following properties are similar to Properties 1.1.15 to 1.1.20 except that the direction of the inequality is reversed.

1.1.21 Property   If $a > b$ and $b > c$, then $a > c$.

EXAMPLE: $8 > 4$ and $4 > -2$; so $8 > -2$.

1.1.22 Property   If $a > b$, then $a + c > b + c$, if c is any real number.

EXAMPLE: $3 > -5$; so $3 - 4 > -5 - 4$.

1.1.23 Property   If $a > b$ and $c > d$, then $a + c > b + d$.

EXAMPLE: $7 > 2$ and $3 > -5$; so $7 + 3 > 2 + (-5)$.

1.1.24 Property   If $a > b$ and if c is any positive number, then $ac > bc$.

EXAMPLE: $-3 > -7$; so $(-3)4 > (-7)4$.

1.1.25 Property   If $a > b$ and if c is any negative number, then $ac < bc$.

EXAMPLE: $-3 > -7$; so $(-3)(-4) < (-7)(-4)$.

1.1.26 Property   If $a > b > 0$ and $c > d > 0$, then $ac > bd$.

EXAMPLE: $4 > 3 > 0$ and $7 > 6 > 0$; so $4(7) > 3(6)$.

From Axiom 1.1.10 and Definition 1.1.11, it follows that a real number is either a positive number, a negative number, or zero. Any real number can be classified as a *rational* number or an *irrational* number. A rational number is any number that can be expressed as the ratio of two integers. That is, a rational number is a number of the form p/q, where p and q are integers and $q \neq 0$. The rational numbers consist of the following:

The *integers* (positive, negative, and zero)

$$\ldots, -5, -4, -3, -2, -1, 0, 1, 2, 3, 4, 5, \ldots$$

The positive and negative *fractions* such as

$$\tfrac{2}{7} \qquad -\tfrac{4}{5} \qquad \tfrac{83}{5}$$

The positive and negative *terminating decimals* such as

$$2.36 = \frac{236}{100} \qquad -0.003251 = -\frac{3,251}{1,000,000}$$

The positive and negative *nonterminating repeating decimals* such as

$$0.333\ldots = \tfrac{1}{3} \qquad -0.549549549\ldots = -\tfrac{61}{111}$$

The real numbers which are not rational numbers are called *irrational numbers*. These are positive and negative *nonterminating, nonrepeating* decimals, for example,

$$\sqrt{3} = 1.732\ldots \qquad \pi = 3.14159\ldots \qquad \tan 140° = -0.8391\ldots$$

The set of all real numbers is denoted by R_1. R_1 can be represented geometrically by points on a horizontal line, called an *axis*, which is illustrated in Fig. 1.1.1.

Figure 1.1.1

A point on the axis is chosen to represent the number 0. This point is called the *origin*. A unit of distance is selected. Then each positive number n is represented by the point at a distance of n units to the right of the origin, and each negative number n is represented by the point at a distance of $-n$ units to the left of the origin. (It should be noted that if n is negative, then $-n$ is positive.) There is a one-to-one correspondence between R_1 and the points on the axis; that is, to each real number there corresponds a unique point on the axis, and with each point on the axis there is associated only one real number. So the points on the axis are identified with the numbers they represent, and we shall use the same symbol for both the number and the point representing that number on the axis. Because of the one-to-one correspondence, we identify R_1 with the axis, and we call R_1 the *number line*.

Figure 1.1.2

We see that $a < b$ if and only if the point representing the number a is to the left of the point representing the number b. Similarly, $a > b$ if and only if the point representing a is to the right of the point representing b. For instance, the number 2 is less than the number 5 and the point 2 is to the left of the point 5. We could also write $5 > 2$ and say that the point 5 is to the right of the point 2.

Figure 1.1.3

A number x is between a and b if $a < x$ and $x < b$. We can write this as a continued inequality as follows:

$$a < x < b \tag{1}$$

The continued inequality (1) denotes an *open interval.*

1.1.27 Definition   The *open interval* from a to b, denoted by (a, b), is the set of all real numbers x such that $a < x < b$.

The *closed interval* from a to b consists of all numbers between, and including, a and b.

1.1.28 Definition   The *closed interval* from a to b, denoted by $[a, b]$, is the set of all real numbers x such that $a \le x \le b$.

Figure 1.1.2 illustrates the open interval (a, b), and Fig. 1.1.3 illustrates the closed interval $[a, b]$.

The *interval half-open on the left* consists of all numbers between *a* and *b* as well as *b*, but not *a*.

1.1.29 Definition   The *interval half-open on the left,* denoted by (*a*, *b*], is the set of all real numbers *x* such that $a < x \le b$.

We define an *interval half-open on the right* in a similar way.

1.1.30 Definition   The *interval half-open on the right,* denoted by [*a*, *b*), is the set of all real numbers *x* such that $a \le x < b$.

a   *b*

Figure 1.1.4

a   *b*

Figure 1.1.5

a

Figure 1.1.6

b

Figure 1.1.7

Figure 1.1.4 illustrates the interval (*a*, *b*], and Fig. 1.1.5 illustrates the interval [*a*, *b*).

We shall use the symbol $+\infty$ ("positive infinity") and the symbol $-\infty$ ("negative infinity"); however, care must be taken not to confuse these symbols with real numbers, for they do not obey the properties of the real numbers.

The notation $(a, +\infty)$ denotes the set of all numbers greater than *a*. We can also state that $(a, +\infty)$ is the set of all real numbers *x* such that $x > a$. Similarly, $(-\infty, b)$ denotes the set of all numbers less than *b*; or, $(-\infty, b)$ is the set of all real numbers *x* such that $x < b$. Figure 1.1.6 illustrates the interval $(a, +\infty)$, and Fig. 1.1.7 illustrates the interval $(-\infty, b)$.

The interval $[a, +\infty)$ is the set of all real numbers *x* such that $x \ge a$; and $(-\infty, b]$ is the set of all real numbers *x* such that $x \le b$. Finally, $(-\infty, +\infty)$ denotes the set of all real numbers.

For each of the intervals (*a*, *b*), [*a*, *b*], [*a*, *b*), and (*a*, *b*] the numbers *a* and *b* are called the *endpoints* of the interval. The closed interval [*a*, *b*] contains both its endpoints, whereas the open interval (*a*, *b*) contains neither endpoint. The interval [*a*, *b*) contains its left endpoint but not its right one, and the interval (*a*, *b*] contains its right endpoint but not its left one. An open interval can be thought of as one which contains none of its endpoints, and a closed interval can be regarded as one which contains all of its endpoints. Consequently, the interval $[a, +\infty)$ is considered to be a closed interval because it contains its only endpoint *a*. Similarly, $(-\infty, b]$ is a closed interval, whereas $(a, +\infty)$ and $(-\infty, b)$ are open. The intervals [*a*, *b*) and (*a*, *b*] are neither open nor closed. Since the interval $(-\infty, +\infty)$ has no endpoints, it can be considered as both containing them and not containing them, and hence is thought of as being both open and closed.

Let us now solve some inequalities and express the solutions as intervals.

EXAMPLE 1: Find all real numbers satisfying the inequality

$2 + 3x < 5x + 8$

SOLUTION: If *x* is a number such that

$2 + 3x < 5x + 8$

then

$$2 + 3x - 2 < 5x + 8 - 2 \quad \text{(by 1.1.16)}$$

or

$$3x < 5x + 6$$

Then, adding $-5x$ to both members of this inequality, we have

$$-2x < 6 \quad \text{(by 1.1.16)}$$

Dividing on both sides of this inequality by -2 and reversing the direction of the inequality, we obtain

$$x > -3 \quad \text{(by 1.1.19)}$$

What we have proved is that if

$$2 + 3x < 5x + 8$$

then

$$x > -3$$

Each of the steps is reversible; that is, if we start with

$$x > -3$$

we multiply on each side by -2, reverse the direction of the inequality, and obtain

$$-2x < 6$$

Then we add $5x$ and 2 to both members of the inequality, and we get

$$2 + 3x < 5x + 8$$

Therefore, we can conclude that

$$2 + 3x < 5x + 8 \quad \textit{if and only if} \quad x > -3$$

So the interval solution of the given inequality is $(-3, +\infty)$, which is illustrated in Fig. 1.1.8.

Figure 1.1.8

EXAMPLE 2: Find all real numbers satisfying the inequality

$$4 < 3x - 2 \le 10$$

Figure 1.1.9

SOLUTION: Adding 2 to each member of the inequality, we obtain

$$6 < 3x \le 12$$

Dividing each member by 3, we get

$$2 < x \le 4$$

Each step is reversible; so the interval solution is $(2, 4]$, as is illustrated in Fig. 1.1.9.

EXAMPLE 3:   Find all real numbers satisfying the inequality

$$\frac{7}{x} > 2 \qquad x \neq 0$$

SOLUTION: We wish to multiply both members of the inequality by x. However, the direction of the inequality that results will depend upon whether x is positive or negative. So we must consider two cases.

Case 1: x is positive; that is, $x > 0$.

Multiplying on both sides by x, we obtain

$$7 > 2x$$

Dividing on both sides by 2, we get

$$\tfrac{7}{2} > x \quad \text{or, equivalently,} \quad x < \tfrac{7}{2}$$

Therefore, since the above steps are reversible, the solution of Case 1 is the set of all numbers x such that $x > 0$ and $x < \tfrac{7}{2}$; that is, $0 < x < \tfrac{7}{2}$, which is the interval $(0, \tfrac{7}{2})$.

Case 2: x is negative; that is, $x < 0$.

Multiplying on both sides by x and reversing the direction of the inequality, we find

$$7 < 2x$$

Dividing on both sides by 2, we have

$$\tfrac{7}{2} < x \quad \text{or, equivalently,} \quad x > \tfrac{7}{2}$$

Again, because the above steps are reversible, the solution of Case 2 is the set of all numbers x such that $x < 0$ and $x > \tfrac{7}{2}$. But it is impossible to find a value for x satisfying both of these inequalities. Hence, Case 2 has no solution.

From Cases 1 and 2 we conclude that the solution of the given inequality is the open interval $(0, \tfrac{7}{2})$, which is illustrated in Fig. 1.1.10.

Figure 1.1.10

EXAMPLE 4:   Find all real numbers satisfying the inequality

$$\frac{x}{x - 3} < 4 \qquad x \neq 3$$

SOLUTION: To multiply both members of the inequality by $x - 3$, we must consider two cases, as in Example 3.

Case 1: $x - 3 > 0$; that is, $x > 3$.

Multiplying on both sides of the inequality by $x - 3$, we get

$$x < 4x - 12$$

Adding $-4x$ to both members, we obtain

$$-3x < -12$$

Dividing on both sides by -3 and reversing the direction of the inequality, we have

$$x > 4$$

Thus, the solution of Case 1 is the set of all numbers x such that $x > 3$ and $x > 4$. This is the set of all x such that $x > 4$, or the interval $(4, +\infty)$.

Case 2: $x - 3 < 0$; that is, $x < 3$.

Multiplying on both sides by $x - 3$ and reversing the direction of the inequality, we have

$$x > 4x - 12$$

or

$$-3x > -12$$

or

$$x < 4$$

Therefore, x must be less than 4 and also less than 3. Thus, the solution of Case 2 is the interval $(-\infty, 3)$.

If the solutions for Cases 1 and 2 are combined, we obtain all numbers x in the two intervals $(-\infty, 3)$ and $(4, +\infty)$ or, more simply, all numbers x *not* in the closed interval $[3, 4]$. This solution is illustrated in Fig. 1.1.11.

Figure 1.1.11

EXAMPLE 5:   Find all real numbers satisfying the inequality

$$(x + 3)(x + 4) > 0$$

SOLUTION: The inequality will be satisfied when both factors have the same sign, that is, if $x + 3 > 0$ and $x + 4 > 0$, or if $x + 3 < 0$ and $x + 4 < 0$. Let us consider the two cases.

Case 1: $x + 3 > 0$ and $x + 4 > 0$. That is,

$$x > -3 \quad \text{and} \quad x > -4$$

Thus, both inequalities hold if $x > -3$, which is the interval $(-3, +\infty)$.

Case 2: $x + 3 < 0$ and $x + 4 < 0$. That is,

$$x < -3 \quad \text{and} \quad x < -4$$

Both inequalities hold if $x < -4$, which is the interval $(-\infty, -4)$. Therefore, if we combine the solutions for Cases 1 and 2, we have the two intervals $(-\infty, -4)$ and $(-3, +\infty)$ or, equivalently, all x *not* in the closed interval $[-4, -3]$.

Exercises 1.1

In Exercises 1 through 22, find all real numbers satisfying the inequality. Give the interval solution, and illustrate the solution on the number line.

1. $5x + 2 > x - 6$

2. $3 - x < 5 + 3x$

3. $\frac{2}{3}x - \frac{1}{2} < 0$

4. $3x - 5 < \dfrac{3}{4}x + \dfrac{1-x}{3}$

5. $13 \geq 2x - 3 \geq 5$

6. $2 \leq 5 - 3x < 11$

7. $2 > -3 - 3x \geq -7$

8. $\dfrac{5}{x} < \dfrac{3}{4}$

9. $\dfrac{4}{x} - 3 > \dfrac{2}{x} - 7$

10. $\dfrac{2}{1-x} \leq 1$

11. $x^2 > 4$

12. $x^2 \leq 9$

13. $(x-3)(x+5) > 0$

14. $x^2 - 3x + 2 > 0$

15. $1 - x - 2x^2 \geq 0$

16. $x^2 + 3x + 1 > 0$

17. $4x^2 + 9x < 9$

18. $2x^2 - 6x + 3 < 0$

19. $\dfrac{1}{x+1} < \dfrac{2}{3x-1}$

20. $\dfrac{x+1}{2-x} < \dfrac{x}{3+x}$

21. $\dfrac{1}{3x-7} \geq \dfrac{4}{3-2x}$

22. $x^3 + 1 > x^2 + x$

23. Prove Property 1.1.15.

24. Prove Property 1.1.16.

25. Prove Properties 1.1.18 and 1.1.19.

26. If $a > b \geq 0$, prove that $a^2 > b^2$.

27. If a and b are nonnegative numbers, and $a^2 > b^2$, prove that $a > b$.

28. Prove that if $a \geq 0$ and $b \geq 0$, then $a^2 = b^2$ if and only if $a = b$.

29. Prove that if $b > a > 0$ and $c > 0$, then

$$\dfrac{a+c}{b+c} > \dfrac{a}{b}$$

30. Prove that if $x < y$, then $x < \tfrac{1}{2}(x+y) < y$.

1.2 ABSOLUTE VALUE
1.2.1 Definition

The absolute value of x, denoted by $|x|$, is defined as

$$|x| = x \quad \text{if } x > 0$$
$$|x| = -x \quad \text{if } x < 0$$
$$|0| = 0$$

Thus, the absolute value of a positive number or zero is equal to the number itself. The absolute value of a negative number is the corresponding positive number because the negative of a negative number is positive. For example,

$$|3| = 3 \qquad |-5| = -(-5) = 5 \qquad |8 - 14| = |-6| = -(-6) = 6$$

We see from the definition that the absolute value of a number is either a positive number or zero; that is, it is nonnegative.

In terms of geometry, the absolute value of a number x is its distance from 0, without regard to direction. In general, $|a - b|$ is the distance between a and b without regard to direction, that is, without regard to which is the larger number. Refer to Fig. 1.2.1.

We have the following properties of absolute values.

Figure 1.2.1

1.2.2 Theorem $|x| < a$ if and only if $-a < x < a$, where $a > 0$.

1.2.3 Corollary $|x| \leq a$ if and only if $-a \leq x \leq a$, where $a > 0$.

1.2.4 Theorem $|x| > a$ if and only if $x > a$ or $x < -a$, where $a > 0$.

1.2.5 Corollary $|x| \geq a$ if and only if $x \geq a$ or $x \leq -a$, where $a > 0$.

The proof of a theorem that has an "if and only if" qualification requires two parts, as illustrated in the following proof of Theorem 1.2.2.

PART 1:   Prove that $|x| < a$ if $-a < x < a$, where $a > 0$. Here, we have to consider two cases: $x \geq 0$ and $x < 0$.

Case 1: $x \geq 0$.
    Then $|x| = x$. Because $x < a$, we conclude that $|x| < a$.

Case 2: $x < 0$.
    Then $|x| = -x$. Because $-a < x$, we apply Property 1.1.19 and obtain $a > -x$ or, equivalently, $-x < a$. But because $-x = |x|$, we have $|x| < a$.
    In both cases, then,

$$|x| < a \quad \text{if} \quad -a < x < a, \qquad \text{where } a > 0$$

PART 2:   Prove that $|x| < a$ only if $-a < x < a$, where $a > 0$. Here we must show that whenever the inequality $|x| < a$ holds, the inequality $-a < x < a$ also holds. Assume that $|x| < a$ and consider the two cases $x \geq 0$ and $x < 0$.

Case 1: $x \geq 0$.
    Then $|x| = x$. Because $|x| < a$, we conclude that $x < a$. Also, because $a > 0$, it follows from Property 1.1.25 that $-a < 0$. Thus, we have $-a < 0 \leq x < a$, or $-a < x < a$.

Case 2: $x < 0$.
    Then $|x| = -x$. Because $|x| < a$, we conclude that $-x < a$. Also, because $x < 0$, it follows from Property 1.1.19 that $0 < -x$. Therefore, we have $-a < 0 < -x < a$, or $-a < -x < a$, which by applying Property 1.1.19 yields $-a < x < a$.
    In both cases,

$$|x| < a \quad \text{only if} \quad -a < x < a, \qquad \text{where } a > 0 \qquad ■$$

The proof of Theorem 1.2.4 is left for the reader (see Exercise 27).
    The following examples illustrate the solution of equations and inequalities involving absolute values.

EXAMPLE 1: Solve for x:

$$|3x + 2| = 5.$$

SOLUTION: This equation will be satisfied if either

$$3x + 2 = 5 \quad \text{or} \quad 3x + 2 = -5$$

Considering each equation separately, we have

$$x = 1 \quad \text{and} \quad x = -\tfrac{7}{3}$$

which are the two solutions to the given equation.

EXAMPLE 2: Solve for x:

$$|2x - 1| = |4x + 3|.$$

SOLUTION: This equation will be satisfied if either

$$2x - 1 = 4x + 3 \quad \text{or} \quad 2x - 1 = -(4x + 3)$$

Solving the first equation, we have $x = -2$; solving the second, we get $x = -\tfrac{1}{3}$, thus giving us two solutions to the original equation.

EXAMPLE 3: Solve for x:

$$|5x + 4| = -3.$$

SOLUTION: Because the absolute value of a number may never be negative, this equation has no solution.

EXAMPLE 4: Find all real numbers satisfying the inequality

$$|x - 5| < 4.$$

SOLUTION: If x is a number such that

$$|x - 5| < 4$$

then

$$-4 < x - 5 < 4 \quad \text{(by 1.2.2)}$$

Adding 5 to each member of the preceding inequality, we obtain

$$1 < x < 9$$

Because each step is reversible, we can conclude that

$$|x - 5| < 4 \quad \text{if and only if} \quad 1 < x < 9$$

So, the interval solution of the given inequality is (1, 9), which is illustrated in Fig. 1.2.2.

Figure 1.2.2

EXAMPLE 5: Find all real numbers satisfying the inequality

$$\left| \frac{3 - 2x}{2 + x} \right| \le 4$$

SOLUTION: By Corollary 1.2.3, the given inequality is equivalent to

$$-4 \le \frac{3 - 2x}{2 + x} \le 4$$

If we multiply by $2 + x$, we must consider two cases, depending upon whether $2 + x$ is positive or negative.

Case 1: $2 + x > 0$ or $x > -2$.

Then we have

$$-4(2 + x) \le 3 - 2x \le 4(2 + x)$$

or

$$-8 - 4x \le 3 - 2x \le 8 + 4x$$

So, if $x > -2$, then also $-8 - 4x \le 3 - 2x$ and $3 - 2x \le 8 + 4x$. We solve these two inequalities. The first inequality is

$$-8 - 4x \le 3 - 2x$$

Adding $2x + 8$ to both members gives

$$-2x \le 11$$

Dividing both members by -2 and reversing the inequality sign, we obtain

$$x \ge -\tfrac{11}{2}$$

The second inequality is

$$3 - 2x \le 8 + 4x$$

Adding $-4x - 3$ to both members gives

$$-6x \le 5$$

Dividing both members by -6 and reversing the inequality sign, we obtain

$$x \ge -\tfrac{5}{6}$$

Therefore, if $x > -2$, then the original inequality holds if and only if $x \ge -\tfrac{11}{2}$ and $x \ge -\tfrac{5}{6}$.

Because all three inequalities $x > -2$, $x \ge -\tfrac{11}{2}$, and $x \ge -\tfrac{5}{6}$ must be satisfied by the same value of x, we have $x \ge -\tfrac{5}{6}$, or the interval $[-\tfrac{5}{6}, +\infty)$.

Case 2: $2 + x < 0$ or $x < -2$.

Thus, we have

$$-4(2 + x) \ge 3 - 2x \ge 4(2 + x)$$

or

$$-8 - 4x \ge 3 - 2x \ge 8 + 4x$$

Considering the left inequality, we have

$$-8 - 4x \ge 3 - 2x$$

or

$$-2x \ge 11$$

or

$$x \le -\tfrac{11}{2}$$

From the right inequality we have

$$3 - 2x \geq 8 + 4x$$

or

$$-6x \geq 5$$

or

$$x \leq -\tfrac{5}{6}$$

Therefore, if $x < -2$, the original inequality holds if and only if $x \leq -\tfrac{11}{2}$ and $x \leq -\tfrac{5}{6}$.

Because all three inequalities must be satisfied by the same value of x, we have $x \leq -\tfrac{11}{2}$, or the interval $(-\infty, -\tfrac{11}{2}]$.

Combining the solutions of Case 1 and Case 2, we have as the solution the two intervals $(-\infty, -\tfrac{11}{2}]$ and $[-\tfrac{5}{6}, +\infty)$ or, more simply, all x not in the interval $(-\tfrac{11}{2}, -\tfrac{5}{6})$.

EXAMPLE 6:   Find all real numbers satisfying the inequality

$$|3x + 2| > 5$$

SOLUTION: By Theorem 1.2.4, the given inequality is equivalent to

$$3x + 2 > 5 \quad \text{or} \quad 3x + 2 < -5 \tag{1}$$

That is, the given inequality will be satisfied if either of the inequalities in (1) is satisfied.

Considering the first inequality, we have

$$3x + 2 > 5$$

or

$$x > 1$$

Therefore, the interval $(1, +\infty)$ is a solution.

From the second inequality, we have

$$3x + 2 < -5$$

or

$$x < -\tfrac{7}{3}$$

Hence, the interval $(-\infty, -\tfrac{7}{3})$ is a solution.

The solution of the given inequality consists of the two intervals $(-\infty, -\tfrac{7}{3})$ and $(1, +\infty)$ or, equivalently, all x *not* in the closed interval $[-\tfrac{7}{3}, 1]$.

The reader may recall from algebra that the symbol $\sqrt{a}$, where $a \geq 0$, is defined as the unique nonnegative number x such that $x^2 = a$. We read $\sqrt{a}$ as "the principal square root of a." For example,

$$\sqrt{4} = 2 \qquad \sqrt{0} = 0 \qquad \sqrt{\tfrac{9}{25}} = \tfrac{3}{5}$$

NOTE: $\sqrt{4} \neq -2$; -2 is a square root of 4, but $\sqrt{4}$ denotes only the positive square root of 4.

Because we are concerned only with real numbers in this book, $\sqrt{a}$ is not defined if $a < 0$. From the definition of $\sqrt{a}$, it follows that

$$\sqrt{x^2} = |x|$$

For example, $\sqrt{5^2} = 5$ and $\sqrt{(-3)^2} = 3$.

The following theorems about absolute value will be useful later.

1.2.6 Theorem   If a and b are any numbers, then

$$|ab| = |a| \cdot |b|$$

Expressed in words, this equation states that the absolute value of the product of two numbers is the product of the absolute values of the two numbers.

PROOF:

$$|ab| = \sqrt{(ab)^2}$$
$$= \sqrt{a^2 b^2}$$
$$= \sqrt{a^2} \cdot \sqrt{b^2}$$
$$= |a| \cdot |b|$$

1.2.7 Theorem   If a is any number and b is any number except 0,

$$\left|\frac{a}{b}\right| = \frac{|a|}{|b|}$$

That is, the absolute value of the quotient of two numbers is the quotient of the absolute values of the two numbers.

The proof of Theorem 1.2.7 is left to the reader (see Exercise 28).

1.2.8 Theorem
The Triangle Inequality

If a and b are any numbers, then

$$|a + b| \le |a| + |b|$$

PROOF: We consider four cases.

Case 1: $a \ge 0$ and $b \ge 0$.
   Then $|a| = a$, $|b| = b$, and $|a + b| = a + b = |a| + |b|$; thus, the theorem holds.

Case 2: $a < 0$ and $b < 0$.
   Then $|a| = -a$, $|b| = -b$, and $|a + b| = -(a + b) = (-a) + (-b) = |a| + |b|$, and so the theorem holds.

Case 3: $a \ge 0$ and $b < 0$.

Then $|a| = a$, $|b| = -b$. Therefore,

$$|a + b| = a + b \qquad \text{if } a + b \geq 0$$

or

$$|a + b| = -(a + b) \quad \text{if } a + b < 0$$

But, $a + b < a + (-b) = |a| + |b|$, because $b < 0$ and $a \geq 0$; also, $-(a + b)$ $= (-a) + (-b) \leq a + (-b) = |a| + |b|$, because $b < 0$ and $a \geq 0$. In either case, $|a + b| \leq |a| + |b|$, and the theorem holds.

Case 4: $a < 0$ and $b \geq 0$.

The proof of this case is identical with the proof of Case 3. Therefore, for all the cases we have

$$|a + b| \leq |a| + |b| \qquad \blacksquare$$

Theorem 1.2.8 has two important corollaries which we now state and prove.

1.2.9 Corollary   If a and b are any numbers, then

$$|a - b| \leq |a| + |b|$$

PROOF: $|a - b| = |a + (-b)| \leq |a| + |(-b)| = |a| + |b|$. $\qquad \blacksquare$

1.2.10 Corollary   If a and b are any numbers, then

$$|a| - |b| \leq |a - b|$$

PROOF: $|a| = |(a - b) + b| \leq |a - b| + |b|$; thus, subtracting $|b|$ from both members of the inequality, we have

$$|a| - |b| \leq |a - b| \qquad \blacksquare$$

Exercises 1.2

In Exercises 1 through 10, solve for x.

1. $|4x + 3| = 7$

2. $|3x - 8| = 4$

3. $|5 - 2x| = 11$

4. $|4 + 3x| = 1$

5. $|5x - 3| = |3x + 5|$

6. $|x - 2| = |3 - 2x|$

7. $|7x| = 4 - x$

8. $2x + 3 = |4x + 5|$

9. $\left|\dfrac{x + 2}{x - 2}\right| = 5$

10. $\left|\dfrac{3x + 8}{2x - 3}\right| = 4$

In Exercises 11 through 14, find all the values of x for which the number is real.

11. $\sqrt{8x - 5}$

12. $\sqrt{x^2 - 16}$

13. $\sqrt{x^2 - 5x + 4}$

14. $\sqrt{x^2 + 2x - 1}$

In Exercises 15 through 26, find all real numbers satisfying the given inequality; give the interval solution; illustrate the solution on the real line.

15. $|x + 4| < 7$

16. $|2x - 5| < 3$

17. $|3x - 4| \leq 2$

18. $|6 - 2x| \geq 7$

19. $|2x - 5| > 3$

20. $|3 + 2x| < |4 - x|$

21. $|x + 4| \leq |2x - 6|$

22. $|3x| > |6 - 3x|$

23. $|9 - 2x| \geq |4x|$

24. $\left| \dfrac{6 - 5x}{3 + x} \right| \leq \dfrac{1}{2}$

25. $\left| \dfrac{x + 2}{2x - 3} \right| < 4$

26. $\left| \dfrac{5}{2x - 1} \right| \geq \left| \dfrac{1}{x - 2} \right|$

27. Prove Theorem 1.2.4.

28. Prove Theorem 1.2.7.

In Exercises 29 through 32, solve for x and use absolute value bars to write the answer.

29. $\dfrac{x - a}{x + a} > 0$

30. $\dfrac{a - x}{a + x} \geq 0$

31. $\dfrac{x - 2}{x - 4} > \dfrac{x + 2}{x}$

32. $\dfrac{x + 5}{x + 6} < \dfrac{x - 5}{x - 6}$

33. Prove Theorem 1.2.8 by adding corresponding members of the inequalities $-|a| \leq a \leq |a|$ and $-|b| \leq b \leq |b|$, and then applying Corollary 1.2.3.

34. Prove that if a and b are any numbers, then $|a - b| \leq |a| + |b|$. (HINT: Write $a - b$ as $a + (-b)$ and use Theorem 1.2.8.)

35. Prove that if a and b are any numbers, then $|a| - |b| \leq |a - b|$. (HINT: Let $|a| = |(a - b) + b|$, and use Theorem 1.2.8.)

36. What single inequality is equivalent to the following two inequalities: $a > b + c$ and $a > b - c$?

1.3 THE NUMBER PLANE AND GRAPHS OF EQUATIONS

Ordered pairs of real numbers will now be considered. Any two real numbers form a *pair,* and when the order of the pair of real numbers is designated, we call it an *ordered pair of real numbers.* If x is the first real number and y is the second real number, we denote this ordered pair by writing them in parentheses with a comma separating them as (x, y). Note that the ordered pair $(3, 7)$ is different from the ordered pair $(7, 3)$.

1.3.1 Definition

The set of all ordered pairs of real numbers is called the *number plane,* and each ordered pair (x, y) is called a *point* in the number plane. The number plane is denoted by R_2.

Just as we can identify R_1 with points on an axis (a one-dimensional space), we can identify R_2 with points in a geometric plane (a two-dimensional space). The method we use with R_2 is the one attributed to the French mathematician René Descartes (1596–1650), who is credited with the invention of analytic geometry in 1637.

A horizontal line is chosen in the geometric plane and is called the x axis. A vertical line is chosen and is called the y axis. The point of intersection of the x axis and the y axis is called the *origin* and is denoted by the letter O. A unit of length is chosen (usually the unit length on each axis is the same). We establish the positive direction on the x axis to the right of the origin, and the positive direction on the y axis above the origin.

We now associate an ordered pair of real numbers (x, y) with a point P in the geometric plane. The distance of P from the y axis (considered as positive if P is to the right of the y axis and negative if P is to the left of the y axis) is called the *abscissa* (or *x coordinate*) of P and is denoted by x. The distance of P from the x axis (considered as positive if P is above the x axis and negative if P is below the x axis) is called the *ordinate* (or *y coordinate*) of P and is denoted by y. The abscissa and the ordinate of a point are called the *rectangular cartesian coordinates* of the point. There is a one-to-one correspondence between the points in a geometric plane and R_2; that is, with each point there corresponds a unique ordered pair (x, y), and with each ordered pair (x, y) there is associated only one point. This one-to-one correspondence is called a *rectangular cartesian coordinate system*. Figure 1.3.1 illustrates a rectangular cartesian coordinate system with some points plotted.

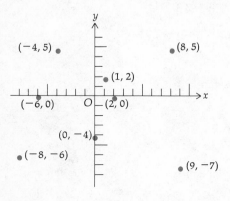

Figure 1.3.1

The x and y axes are called the *coordinate axes*. They divide the plane into four parts, called *quadrants*. The first quadrant is the one in which the abscissa and the ordinate are both positive, that is, the upper right quadrant. The other quadrants are numbered in the counterclockwise direction, with the fourth, for example, being the lower right quadrant.

Because of the one-to-one correspondence, we identify R_2 with the geometric plane. For this reason we call an ordered pair (x, y) a *point*. Similarly, we refer to a "line" in R_2 as the set of all points corresponding to a line in the geometric plane, and we use other geometric terms for sets of points in R_2.

Consider the equation

$$y = x^2 - 2 \qquad (1)$$

where (x, y) is a point in R_2. We call this an equation in R_2.

By a solution of this equation, we mean an ordered pair of numbers, one for x and one for y, which satisfies the equation. For example, if x is replaced by 3 in Eq. (1), we see that $y = 7$; thus, $x = 3$ and $y = 7$ constitutes a solution of this equation. If any number is substituted for x in the right side of Eq. (1), we obtain a corresponding value for y. It is seen, then, that Eq. (1) has an unlimited number of solutions. Table 1.3.1 gives a few such solutions.

Table 1.3.1

x	0	1	2	3	4	-1	-2	-3	-4
$y = x^2 - 2$	-2	-1	2	7	14	-1	2	7	14

Figure 1.3.2

If we plot the points having as coordinates the number pairs (x, y) satisfying Eq. (1), we have a sketch of the graph of the equation. In Fig. 1.3.2 we have plotted points whose coordinates are the number pairs obtained from Table 1.3.1. These points are connected by a smooth curve. Any point (x, y) on this curve has coordinates satisfying Eq. (1). Also, the coordinates of any point not on this curve do not satisfy the equation. We have the following general definition.

1.3.2 Definition   The *graph of an equation* in R_2 is the set of all points (x, y) in R_2 whose coordinates are numbers satisfying the equation.

We sometimes call the graph of an equation the *locus* of the equation. The graph of an equation in R_2 is also called a *curve*. Unless otherwise stated, an equation with two unknowns, x and y, is considered an equation in R_2.

EXAMPLE 1:   Draw a sketch of the graph of the equation

$$y^2 - x - 2 = 0 \qquad (2)$$

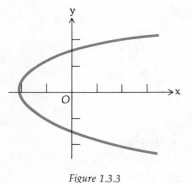

Figure 1.3.3

SOLUTION: Solving Eq. (2) for y, we have

$$y = \pm\sqrt{x + 2} \qquad (3)$$

Equations (3) are equivalent to the two equations

$$y = \sqrt{x + 2} \qquad (4)$$

$$y = -\sqrt{x + 2} \qquad (5)$$

The coordinates of all points that satisfy Eq. (3) will satisfy either Eq. (4) or (5), and the coordinates of any point that satisfies either Eq. (4) or (5) will satisfy Eq. (3). Table 1.3.2 gives some of these values of x and y.

Table 1.3.2

x	0	0	1	1	2	2	3	3	−1	−1	−2
y	$\sqrt{2}$	$-\sqrt{2}$	$\sqrt{3}$	$-\sqrt{3}$	2	−2	$\sqrt{5}$	$-\sqrt{5}$	1	−1	0

Note that for any value of $x < -2$ there is no real value for y. Also, for each value of $x > -2$ there are two values for y. A sketch of the graph of Eq. (2) is shown in Fig. 1.3.3. The graph is a *parabola*.

EXAMPLE 2:   Draw sketches of the graphs of the equations

$$y = \sqrt{x + 2} \qquad (6)$$
and
$$y = -\sqrt{x + 2}$$

SOLUTION: Equation (6) is the same as Eq. (4). The value of y is non-negative; hence, the graph of Eq. (6) is the upper half of the graph of Eq. (3). A sketch of this graph is shown in Fig. 1.3.4.

Similarly, the graph of the equation

$$y = -\sqrt{x + 2}$$

a sketch of which is shown in Fig. 1.3.5, is the lower half of the parabola of Fig. 1.3.3.

Figure 1.3.4   Figure 1.3.5

EXAMPLE 3: Draw a sketch of the graph of the equation

$$y = |x + 3| \qquad (7)$$

SOLUTION: From the definition of the absolute value of a number, we have

$$y = x + 3 \quad \text{if} \quad x + 3 \geq 0$$

and

$$y = -(x + 3) \quad \text{if} \quad x + 3 < 0$$

or, equivalently,

$$y = x + 3 \quad \text{if} \quad x \geq -3$$

and

$$y = -(x + 3) \quad \text{if} \quad x < -3$$

Table 1.3.3 gives some values of x and y satisfying Eq. (7).

Table 1.3.3

x	0	1	2	3	−1	−2	−3	−4	−5	−6	−7	−8	−9
y	3	4	5	6	2	1	0	1	2	3	4	5	6

Figure 1.3.6

A sketch of the graph of Eq. (7) is shown in Fig. 1.3.6.

EXAMPLE 4: Draw a sketch of the graph of the equation

$$(x - 2y + 3)(y - x^2) = 0 \quad (8)$$

SOLUTION: By the property of real numbers that $ab = 0$ if and only if $a = 0$ or $b = 0$, we have from Eq. (8)

$$x - 2y + 3 = 0 \qquad (9)$$

and

$$y - x^2 = 0 \qquad (10)$$

The coordinates of all points that satisfy Eq. (8) will satisfy either Eq. (9) or Eq. (10), and the coordinates of any point that satisfies either

Figure 1.3.7

Eq. (9) or (10) will satisfy Eq. (8). Therefore, the graph of Eq. (8) will consist of the graphs of Eqs. (9) and (10). Table 1.3.4 gives some values of x and y satisfying Eq. (9), and Table 1.3.5 gives some values of x and y satisfying Eq. (10). A sketch of the graph of Eq. (8) is shown in Fig. 1.3.7.

Table 1.3.4

x	0	1	2	3	-1	-2	-3	-4	-5
y	$\frac{3}{2}$	2	$\frac{5}{2}$	3	1	$\frac{1}{2}$	0	$-\frac{1}{2}$	-1

Table 1.3.5

x	0	1	2	3	-1	-2	-3
y	0	1	4	9	1	4	9

1.3.3 Definition   An *equation of a graph* is an equation which is satisfied by the coordinates of those, and only those, points on the graph.

For example, in R_2, $y = 8$ is an equation whose graph consists of those points having an ordinate of 8. This is a line which is parallel to the x axis, and 8 units above the x axis.

In drawing a sketch of the graph of an equation, it is often helpful to consider properties of *symmetry* of a graph.

1.3.4 Definition   Two points P and Q are said to be *symmetric with respect to a line* if and only if the line is the perpendicular bisector of the line segment PQ. Two points P and Q are said to be *symmetric with respect to a third point* if and only if the third point is the midpoint of the line segment PQ.

In particular, the points $(3, 2)$ and $(3, -2)$ are symmetric with respect to the x axis, the points $(3, 2)$ and $(-3, 2)$ are symmetric with respect to the y axis, and the points $(3, 2)$ and $(-3, -2)$ are symmetric with respect to the origin. In general, the points (x, y) and $(x, -y)$ are symmetric with respect to the x axis, the points (x, y) and $(-x, y)$ are symmetric with respect to the y axis, and the points (x, y) and $(-x, -y)$ are symmetric with respect to the origin.

1.3.5 Definition   The graph of an equation is symmetric with respect to a line l if and only if for every point P on the graph there is a point Q, also on the graph, such that P and Q are symmetric with respect to l. The graph of an equation is symmetric with respect to a point R if and only if for every point P on the graph there is a point S, also on the graph, such that P and S are symmetric with respect to R.

From Definition 1.3.5 it follows that if a point (x, y) is on a graph which is symmetric with respect to the x axis, then the point $(x, -y)$ also must be on the graph. And, if both the points (x, y) and $(x, -y)$ are on the graph, then the graph is symmetric with respect to the x axis. Therefore, the coordinates of the point $(x, -y)$ as well as (x, y) must satisfy an equation of the graph. Hence, we may conclude that the graph of an equation in x and y is symmetric with respect to the x axis if and only if an equivalent equation is obtained when y is replaced by $-y$ in the equation. We have thus proved part (i) in the following theorem. The proofs of parts (ii) and (iii) are similar.

1.3.6 Theorem
Tests for Symmetry

The graph of an equation in x and y is

(i) symmetric with respect to the x axis if and only if an equivalent equation is obtained when y is replaced by $-y$ in the equation;

(ii) symmetric with respect to the y axis if and only if an equivalent equation is obtained when x is replaced by $-x$ in the equation;

(iii) symmetric with respect to the origin if and only if an equivalent equation is obtained when x is replaced by $-x$ and y is replaced by $-y$ in the equation.

The graph in Fig. 1.3.2 is symmetric with respect to the y axis, and for Eq. (1) an equivalent equation is obtained when x is replaced by $-x$. In Example 1 we have Eq. (2) for which an equivalent equation is obtained when y is replaced by $-y$, and its graph sketched in Fig. 1.3.3 is symmetric with respect to the x axis. The following example gives a graph which is symmetric with respect to the origin.

EXAMPLE 4:   Draw a sketch of the graph of the equation

$$xy = 1 \qquad (11)$$

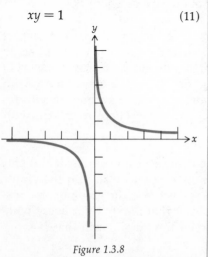

Figure 1.3.8

SOLUTION: We see that if in Eq. (11) x is replaced by $-x$ and y is replaced by $-y$, an equivalent equation is obtained; hence, by Theorem 1.3.6(iii) the graph is symmetric with respect to the origin. Table 1.3.6 gives some values of x and y satisfying Eq. (11).

Table 1.3.6

x	1	2	3	4	$\frac{1}{2}$	$\frac{1}{3}$	$\frac{1}{4}$	-1	-2	-3	-4	$-\frac{1}{2}$	$-\frac{1}{3}$	$-\frac{1}{4}$
y	1	$\frac{1}{2}$	$\frac{1}{3}$	$\frac{1}{4}$	2	3	4	-1	$-\frac{1}{2}$	$-\frac{1}{3}$	$-\frac{1}{4}$	-2	-3	-4

From Eq. (11) we obtain $y = 1/x$. We see that as x increases through positive values, y decreases through positive values and gets closer and closer to zero. As x decreases through positive values, y increases through positive values and gets larger and larger. As x increases through negative values (i.e., x takes on the values $-4, -3, -2, -1, -\frac{1}{2}$, etc.), y takes on negative values having larger and larger absolute values. A sketch of the graph is shown in Fig. 1.3.8.

Exercises 1.3

In Exercises 1 through 6, plot the given point P and such of the following points as may apply:
(a) The point Q such that the line through Q and P is perpendicular to the x axis and is bisected by it. Give the coordinates of Q.
(b) The point R such that the line through P and R is perpendicular to and is bisected by the y axis. Give the coordinates of R.
(c) The point S such that the line through P and S is bisected by the origin. Give the coordinates of S.
(d) The point T such that the line through P and T is perpendicular to and is bisected by the 45° line through the origin bisecting the first and third quadrants. Give the coordinates of T.

1. $P(1,-2)$
2. $P(-2,2)$
3. $P(2,2)$
4. $P(-2,-2)$
5. $P(-1,-3)$
6. $P(0,-3)$

In Exercises 7 through 28 draw a sketch of the graph of the equation.

7. $y = 2x + 5$
8. $y = 4x - 3$
9. $y = \sqrt{x-3}$
10. $y = -\sqrt{x-3}$
11. $y^2 = x - 3$
12. $y = 5$
13. $x = -3$
14. $x = y^2 + 1$
15. $y = |x - 5|$
16. $y = -|x + 2|$
17. $y = |x| - 5$
18. $y = -|x| + 2$
19. $4x^2 + 9y^2 = 36$
20. $4x^2 - 9y^2 = 36$
21. $y = 4x^3$
22. $y^2 = 4x^3$
23. $4x^2 - y^2 = 0$
24. $3x^2 - 13xy - 10y^2 = 0$
25. $4x^2 + y^2 = 0$
26. $(2x + y - 1)(4y + x^2) = 0$
27. $x^4 - 5x^2y + 4y^2 = 0$
28. $(y^2 - x + 2)(y + \sqrt{x-4}) = 0$

29. Draw a sketch of the graph of each of the following equations:
(a) $y = \sqrt{2x}$
(b) $y = -\sqrt{2x}$
(c) $y^2 = 2x$

30. Draw a sketch of the graph of each of the following equations:
(a) $y = \sqrt{-2x}$
(b) $y = -\sqrt{-2x}$
(c) $y^2 = -2x$

31. Draw a sketch of the graph of each of the following equations:
(a) $x + 3y = 0$
(b) $x - 3y = 0$
(c) $x^2 - 9y^2 = 0$

32. (a) Write an equation whose graph is the x axis. (b) Write an equation whose graph is the y axis. (c) Write an equation whose graph is the set of all points on either the x axis or the y axis.

33. (a) Write an equation whose graph consists of all points having an abscissa of 4. (b) Write an equation whose graph consists of all points having an ordinate of -3.

34. Prove that a graph that is symmetric with respect to both coordinate axes is also symmetric with respect to the origin.

35. Prove that a graph that is symmetric with respect to any two perpendicular lines is also symmetric with respect to their point of intersection.

1.4 DISTANCE FORMULA AND MIDPOINT FORMULA   If A is the point (x_1, y) and B is the point (x_2, y) (i.e., A and B have the same ordinate but different abscissas), then the directed distance from A to B, denoted by $\overline{AB}$, is defined as $x_2 - x_1$. Following are some examples, which are illustrated in Fig. 1.4.1(a), (b), and (c).

Figure 1.4.1

Figure 1.4.2

If A is the point (3, 4) and B is the point (9, 4), then $\overline{AB} = 9 - 3 = 6$. If A is the point (−8, 0) and B is the point (6, 0), then $\overline{AB} = 6 - (-8) = 14$. If A is the point (4, 2) and B is the point (1, 2), then $\overline{AB} = 1 - 4 = -3$. We see that $\overline{AB}$ is positive if B is to the right of A, and $\overline{AB}$ is negative if B is to the left of A.

If C is the point (x, y_1) and D is the point (x, y_2), then the directed distance from C to D, denoted by $\overline{CD}$, is defined as $y_2 - y_1$. The following examples are illustrated in Fig. 1.4.2(a) and (b).

If C is the point (1, −2) and D is the point (1, −8), then $\overline{CD} = -8 - (-2) = -6$. If C is the point (−2, −3) and D is the point (−2, 4), then $\overline{CD} = 4 - (-3) = 7$. The number $\overline{CD}$ is positive if D is above C, and $\overline{CD}$ is negative if D is below C.

We consider a directed distance $\overline{AB}$ as the signed distance traveled by a particle that starts at A and travels to B. In such a case, the abscissa of the particle changes from x_1 to x_2, and we use the notation Δx ("delta x") to denote this change; that is,

$$\Delta x = x_2 - x_1$$

Therefore, $\overline{AB} = \Delta x$.

It is important to note that the symbol Δx denotes the difference between the abscissa of B and the abscissa of A, and it does not mean "delta multiplied by x."

Similarly, if we consider a particle moving along a line parallel to the y axis from a point $C(x, y_1)$ to a point $D(x, y_2)$, then the ordinate of the particle changes from y_1 to y_2. We denote this change by Δy or

$$\Delta y = y_2 - y_1$$

Thus, $\overline{CD} = \Delta y$.

Now let $P_1(x_1, y_1)$ and $P_2(x_2, y_2)$ be any two points in the plane. We wish to obtain a formula for finding the nonnegative distance between these two points. We shall denote this distance by $|\overline{P_1P_2}|$. We use absolute-value bars because we are concerned only with the length, which is a nonnegative number, of the line segment between the two points P_1 and

P_2. To derive the formula, we note that $|\overline{P_1P_2}|$ is the length of the hypotenuse of a right triangle P_1MP_2. This is illustrated in Fig. 1.4.3 for P_1 and P_2, both of which are in the first quadrant.

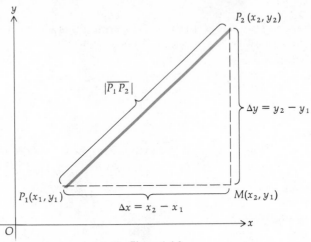

Figure 1.4.3

Using the Pythagorean theorem, we have

$$|\overline{P_1P_2}|^2 = |\Delta x|^2 + |\Delta y|^2$$

So

$$|\overline{P_1P_2}| = \sqrt{|\Delta x|^2 + |\Delta y|^2}$$

or

$$|\overline{P_1P_2}| = \sqrt{(x_2 - x_1)^2 + (y_2 - y_1)^2} \tag{1}$$

Formula (1) holds for all possible positions of P_1 and P_2 in all four quadrants. The length of the hypotenuse will always be $|\overline{P_1P_2}|$, and the lengths of the two legs will always be $|\Delta x|$ and $|\Delta y|$ (see Exercises 1 and 2). We state this result as a theorem.

1.4.1 Theorem   The undirected distance between the two points $P_1(x_1, y_1)$ and $P_2(x_2, y_2)$ is given by

$$|\overline{P_1P_2}| = \sqrt{(x_2 - x_1)^2 + (y_2 - y_1)^2}$$

EXAMPLE 1: If a point $P(x, y)$ is such that its distance from $A(3, 2)$ is always twice its distance from $B(-4, 1)$, find an equation which the coordinates of P must satisfy.

SOLUTION: From the statement of the problem

$$|\overline{PA}| = 2|\overline{PB}|$$

Using formula (1), we have

$$\sqrt{(x - 3)^2 + (y - 2)^2} = 2\sqrt{(x + 4)^2 + (y - 1)^2}$$

Squaring on both sides, we have

$$x^2 - 6x + 9 + y^2 - 4y + 4 = 4(x^2 + 8x + 16 + y^2 - 2y + 1)$$

or

$$3x^2 + 3y^2 + 38x - 4y + 55 = 0$$

EXAMPLE 2:   Show that the triangle with vertices at $A(-2, 4)$,
$B(-5, 1)$, and $C(-6, 5)$ is
isosceles.

C(-6, 5)

A(-2, 4)

B(-5, 1)

O   x

Figure 1.4.4

SOLUTION: The triangle is shown in Fig. 1.4.4.

$$|\overline{BC}| = \sqrt{(-6+5)^2 + (5-1)^2} = \sqrt{1+16} = \sqrt{17}$$
$$|\overline{AC}| = \sqrt{(-6+2)^2 + (5-4)^2} = \sqrt{16+1} = \sqrt{17}$$
$$|\overline{BA}| = \sqrt{(-2+5)^2 + (4-1)^2} = \sqrt{9+9} = 3\sqrt{2}$$

Therefore,

$$|\overline{BC}| = |\overline{AC}|$$

Hence, triangle ABC is isosceles.

EXAMPLE 3:   Prove analytically
that the lengths of the diagonals
of a rectangle are equal.

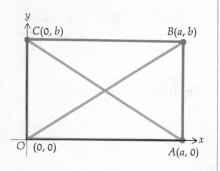

y
C(0, b)   B(a, b)

O (0, 0)   A(a, 0)   x

Figure 1.4.5

SOLUTION: Draw a general rectangle. Because we can choose the coordinate axes anywhere in the plane, and because the choice of the position
of the axes does not affect the truth of the theorem, we take the origin at
one vertex, the x axis along one side, and the y axis along another side.
This procedure simplifies the coordinates of the vertices on the two axes.
Refer to Fig. 1.4.5.

Now the hypothesis and the conclusion of the theorem can be stated.
Hypothesis: $OABC$ is a rectangle with diagonals OB and AC.
Conclusion: $|\overline{OB}| = |\overline{AC}|$.

PROOF:

$$|\overline{OB}| = \sqrt{(a-0)^2 + (b-0)^2} = \sqrt{a^2 + b^2}$$
$$|\overline{AC}| = \sqrt{(0-a)^2 + (b-0)^2} = \sqrt{a^2 + b^2}$$

Therefore,

$$|\overline{OB}| = |\overline{AC}|$$

Let $P_1(x_1, y_1)$ and $P_2(x_2, y_2)$ be the endpoints of a line segment. We
shall denote this line segment by P_1P_2. This is not to be confused with the
notation $\overline{P_1P_2}$, which denotes the directed distance from P_1 to P_2. That is,

$\overline{P_1P_2}$ denotes a number, whereas P_1P_2 is a line segment. Let $P(x, y)$ be the midpoint of the line segment P_1P_2. Refer to Fig. 1.4.6.

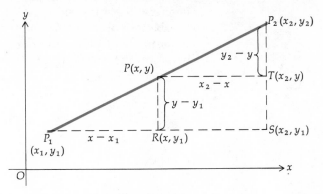

Figure 1.4.6

In Fig. 1.4.6 we see that triangles P_1RP and PTP_2 are congruent. Therefore, $|\overline{P_1R}| = |\overline{PT}|$, and so $x - x_1 = x_2 - x$, giving us

$$x = \frac{x_1 + x_2}{2} \tag{2}$$

Similarly, $|\overline{RP}| = |\overline{TP_2}|$. Then $y - y_1 = y_2 - y$, and therefore

$$y = \frac{y_1 + y_2}{2} \tag{3}$$

Hence, the coordinates of the midpoint of a line segment are, respectively, the average of the abscissas and the average of the ordinates of the endpoints of the line segment.

In the derivation of formulas (2) and (3) it was assumed that $x_2 > x_1$ and $y_2 > y_1$. The same formulas are obtained by using any orderings of these numbers (see Exercises 3 and 4).

EXAMPLE 4: Prove analytically that the line segments joining the midpoints of the opposite sides of any quadrilateral bisect each other.

SOLUTION: Draw a general quadrilateral. Take the origin at one vertex and the x axis along one side. This method simplifies the coordinates of the two vertices on the x axis. See Fig. 1.4.7.

Hypothesis: $OABC$ is a quadrilateral. M is the midpoint of OA, N is the midpoint of CB, R is the midpoint of OC, and S is the midpoint of AB.

Conclusion: MN and RS bisect each other.

PROOF: To prove that two line segments bisect each other, we show that they have the same midpoint. Using formulas (2) and (3), we obtain the coordinates of M, N, R, and S. M is the point $(\frac{1}{2}a, 0)$, N is the point $(\frac{1}{2}(b + d), \frac{1}{2}(c + e))$, R is the point $(\frac{1}{2}d, \frac{1}{2}e)$, and S is the point $(\frac{1}{2}(a + b), \frac{1}{2}c)$.

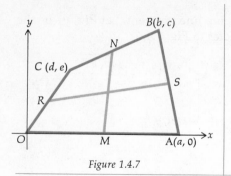

Figure 1.4.7

The abscissa of the midpoint of MN is $\frac{1}{2}[\frac{1}{2}a + \frac{1}{2}(b+d)] = \frac{1}{4}(a+b+d)$.
The ordinate of the midpoint of MN is $\frac{1}{2}[0 + \frac{1}{2}(c+e)] = \frac{1}{4}(c+e)$.
Therefore, the midpoint of MN is the point $(\frac{1}{4}(a+b+d), \frac{1}{4}(c+e))$.
The abscissa of the midpoint of RS is $\frac{1}{2}[\frac{1}{2}d + \frac{1}{2}(a+b)] = \frac{1}{4}(a+b+d)$.
The ordinate of the midpoint of RS is $\frac{1}{2}[\frac{1}{2}e + \frac{1}{2}c] = \frac{1}{4}(c+e)$.
Therefore, the midpoint of RS is the point $(\frac{1}{4}(a+b+d), \frac{1}{4}(c+e))$.
Thus, the midpoint of MN is the same point as the midpoint of RS.
Therefore, MN and RS bisect each other. ∎

Exercises 1.4

1. Derive distance formula (1) if P_1 is in the third quadrant and P_2 is in the second quadrant. Draw a figure.

2. Derive distance formula (1) if P_1 is in the second quadrant and P_2 is in the fourth quadrant. Draw a figure.

3. Derive midpoint formulas (2) and (3) if P_1 is in the first quadrant and P_2 is in the third quadrant.

4. Derive midpoint formulas (2) and (3) if $P_1(x_1, y_1)$ and $P_2(x_2, y_2)$ are both in the second quadrant and $x_2 > x_1$ and $y_1 > y_2$.

5. Find the length of the medians of the triangle having vertices $A(2, 3)$, $B(3, -3)$, and $C(-1, -1)$.

6. Find the midpoints of the diagonals of the quadrilateral whose vertices are $(0, 0)$, $(0, 4)$, $(3, 5)$, and $(3, 1)$.

7. Prove that the triangle with vertices $A(3, -6)$, $B(8, -2)$, and $C(-1, -1)$ is a right triangle. Find the area of the triangle. (HINT: Use the converse of the Pythagorean theorem.)

8. Prove that the points $A(6, -13)$, $B(-2, 2)$, $C(13, 10)$, and $D(21, -5)$ are the vertices of a square. Find the length of a diagonal.

9. By using distance formula (1), prove that the points $(-3, 2)$, $(1, -2)$, and $(9, -10)$ lie on a line.

10. If one end of a line segment is the point $(-4, 2)$ and the midpoint is $(3, -1)$, find the coordinates of the other end of the line segment.

11. The abscissa of a point is -6, and its distance from the point $(1, 3)$ is $\sqrt{74}$. Find the ordinate of the point.

12. Determine whether or not the points $(14, 7)$, $(2, 2)$, and $(-4, -1)$ lie on a line by using distance formula (1).

13. If two vertices of an equilateral triangle are $(-4, 3)$ and $(0, 0)$, find the third vertex.

14. Find an equation that must be satisfied by the coordinates of any point that is equidistant from the two points $(-3, 2)$ and $(4, 6)$.

15. Find an equation that must be satisfied by the coordinates of any point whose distance from the point $(5, 3)$ is always two units greater than its distance from the point $(-4, -2)$.

16. Given the two points $A(-3, 4)$ and $B(2, 5)$, find the coordinates of a point P on the line through A and B such that P is (a) twice as far from A as from B, and (b) twice as far from B as from A.

17. Find the coordinates of the three points that divide the line segment from $A(-5, 3)$ to $B(6, 8)$ into four equal parts.

18. If r_1 and r_2 are positive integers, prove that the coordinates of the point $P(x, y)$, which divides the line segment P_1P_2 in the ratio r_1/r_2—that is, $|\overline{P_1P}|/|\overline{P_1P_2}| = r_1/r_2$—are given by

$$x = \frac{(r_2 - r_1)x_1 + r_1 x_2}{r_2} \quad \text{and} \quad y = \frac{(r_2 - r_1)y_1 + r_1 y_2}{r_2}$$

In Exercises 19 through 23, use the formulas of Exercise 18 to find the coordinates of point P.

19. The point P is on the line segment between points $P_1(1, 3)$ and $P_2(6, 2)$ and is three times as far from P_2 as it is from P_1.

20. The point P is on the line segment between points $P_1(1, 3)$ and $P_2(6, 2)$ and is three times as far from P_1 as it is from P_2.

21. The point P is on the line through P_1 and P_2 and is three times as far from $P_2(6, 2)$ as it is from $P_1(1, 3)$ but is not between P_1 and P_2.

22. The point P is on the line through P_1 and P_2 and is three times as far from $P_1(1, 3)$ as it is from $P_2(6, 2)$ but is not between P_1 and P_2.

23. The point P is on the line through $P_1(-3, 5)$ and $P_2(-1, 2)$ so that $\overline{PP_1} = 4 \cdot \overline{P_1P_2}$.

24. (a) Find an equation whose graph consists of all points that are at a distance of 4 units from the point $(1, 3)$. (b) Draw a sketch of the graph of the equation found in (a).

25. (a) Find an equation whose graph consists of all points equidistant from the points $(-1, 2)$ and $(3, 4)$. (b) Draw a sketch of the graph of the equation found in (a).

26. Prove analytically that the sum of the squares of the distances of any point from two opposite vertices of any rectangle is equal to the sum of the squares of its distances from the other two vertices.

27. Prove analytically that the line segment joining the midpoints of two opposite sides of any quadrilateral and the line segment joining the midpoints of the diagonals of the quadrilateral bisect each other.

28. Prove analytically that the midpoint of the hypotenuse of any right triangle is equidistant from each of the three vertices.

29. Prove analytically that if the lengths of two of the medians of a triangle are equal, the triangle is isosceles.

1.5 EQUATIONS OF A LINE

1.5.1 Definition

If $P_1(x_1, y_1)$ and $P_2(x_2, y_2)$ are any two distinct points on line l, which is not parallel to the y axis, then the *slope* of l, denoted by m, is given by

$$m = \frac{y_2 - y_1}{x_2 - x_1} \tag{1}$$

In Eq. (1), $x_2 \neq x_1$ since l is not parallel to the y axis.

The value of m computed from Eq. (1) is independent of the choice of the two points P_1 and P_2 on l. To show this, suppose we choose two different points, $\bar{P}_1(\bar{x}_1, \bar{y}_1)$ and $\bar{P}_2(\bar{x}_2, \bar{y}_2)$, and compute a number $\bar{m}$ from Eq. (1).

$$\bar{m} = \frac{\bar{y}_2 - \bar{y}_1}{\bar{x}_2 - \bar{x}_1}$$

We shall show that $\bar{m} = m$. Refer to Fig. 1.5.1. Triangles $\bar{P}_1\bar{R}\bar{P}_2$ and P_1RP_2 are similar, so the lengths of corresponding sides are proportional. Therefore,

$$\frac{\bar{y}_2 - \bar{y}_1}{\bar{x}_2 - \bar{x}_1} = \frac{y_2 - y_1}{x_2 - x_1}$$

or

$$\bar{m} = m$$

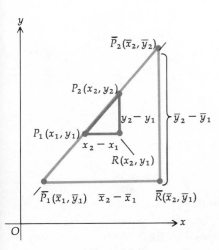

Figure 1.5.1

Hence, we conclude that the value of m computed from Eq. (1) is the same number no matter what two points on l are selected.

In Fig. 1.5.1, $x_2 > x_1$, $y_2 > y_1$, $\bar{x}_2 > \bar{x}_1$, and $\bar{y}_2 > \bar{y}_1$. The discussion above is valid for any ordering of these pairs of numbers since Definition 1.5.1 holds for any ordering.

In Sec. 1.4 we defined $\Delta y = y_2 - y_1$ and $\Delta x = x_2 - x_1$. Substituting these values into Eq. (1), we have

$$m = \frac{\Delta y}{\Delta x}$$

Multiplying on both sides of this equation by Δx, we obtain

$$\Delta y = m \, \Delta x \tag{2}$$

It is seen from Eq. (2) that if we consider a particle moving along line l, the change in the ordinate of the particle is proportional to the change in the abscissa, and the constant of proportionality is the slope of the line.

If the slope of a line is positive, then as the abscissa of a point on the line increases, the ordinate increases. Such a line is shown in Fig. 1.5.2. In Fig. 1.5.3, we have a line whose slope is negative. For this line, as the abscissa of a point on the line increases, the ordinate decreases. Note that if the line is parallel to the x axis, then $y_2 = y_1$ and so $m = 0$.

If the line is parallel to the y axis, $x_2 = x_1$; thus, Eq. (1) is meaningless because we cannot divide by zero. This is the reason that lines parallel to the y axis, or vertical lines, are excluded in Definition 1.5.1. We say that a vertical line does not have a slope.

Figure 1.5.2

Figure 1.5.3

EXAMPLE 1:   Let l be the line through the points $P_1(2, 3)$ and $P_2(4, 7)$. Find the slope of l.

SOLUTION: The slope of l, by Definition 1.5.1, is given by

$$m = \frac{7 - 3}{4 - 2} = 2$$

Figure 1.5.4

Refer to Fig. 1.5.4. If $P(x, y)$ and $Q(x + \Delta x, y + \Delta y)$ are any two points on l, then

$$\frac{\Delta y}{\Delta x} = 2$$

or

$$\Delta y = 2 \, \Delta x$$

Thus, if a particle is moving along the line l, the change in the ordinate is twice the change in the abscissa. That is, if the particle is at $P_2(4, 7)$ and the abscissa is increased by one unit, then the ordinate is increased by two units, and the particle is at the point $P_3(5, 9)$. Similarly, if the particle is at $P_1(2, 3)$ and the abscissa is decreased by three units, then the ordinate is decreased by six units, and the particle is at the point $P_4(-1, -3)$.

Since two points $P_1(x_1, y_1)$ and $P_2(x_2, y_2)$ determine a unique line, we should be able to obtain an equation of the line through these two points. Consider $P(x, y)$ any point on the line. We want an equation that is satisfied by x and y if and only if $P(x, y)$ is on the line through $P_1(x_1, y_1)$ and $P_2(x_2, y_2)$. We distinguish two cases.

Case 1: $x_2 = x_1$.

In this case the line through P_1 and P_2 is parallel to the y axis, and all points on this line have the same abscissa. So $P(x, y)$ is any point on the line if and only if

$$x = x_1 \tag{3}$$

Equation (3) is an equation of a line parallel to the y axis. Note that this equation is independent of y; that is, the ordinate may have any value whatsoever, and the point $P(x, y)$ is on the line whenever the abscissa is x_1.

Case 2: $x_2 \neq x_1$.

The slope of the line through P_1 and P_2 is given by

$$m = \frac{y_2 - y_1}{x_2 - x_1} \tag{4}$$

If $P(x, y)$ is any point on the line except (x_1, y_1), the slope is also given by

$$m = \frac{y - y_1}{x - x_1} \tag{5}$$

The point P will be on the line through P_1 and P_2 if and only if the value of m from Eq. (4) is the same as the value of m from Eq. (5), that is, if and only if

$$\frac{y - y_1}{x - x_1} = \frac{y_2 - y_1}{x_2 - x_1}$$

Multiplying on both sides of this equation by $(x - x_1)$, we obtain

$$y - y_1 = \frac{y_2 - y_1}{x_2 - x_1}(x - x_1) \tag{6}$$

Equation (6) is satisfied by the coordinates of P_1 as well as by the coordinates of any other point on the line through P_1 and P_2.

Equation (6) is called the *two-point* form of an equation of the line. It gives an equation of the line if two points on the line are known.

If in Eq. (6) we replace $(y_2 - y_1)/(x_2 - x_1)$ by m, we get

$$y - y_1 = m(x - x_1) \tag{7}$$

Equation (7) is called the *point-slope* form of an equation of the line. It gives an equation of the line if a point $P_1(x_1, y_1)$ on the line and the slope m of the line are known.

If we choose the particular point $(0, b)$ (i.e., the point where the line intersects the y axis) for the point (x_1, y_1) in Eq. (7), we have

$$y - b = m(x - 0)$$

or

$$y = mx + b \qquad\qquad (8)$$

The number b, which is the ordinate of the point where the line intersects the y axis, is called the y *intercept* of the line. Consequently, Eq. (8) is called the *slope-intercept* form of an equation of the line. This form is especially important because it enables us to find the slope of a line from its equation. It is also important because it expresses the y coordinate explicitly in terms of the x coordinate.

| EXAMPLE 2: Given the line having the equation $3x + 4y = 7$, find the slope of the line. | SOLUTION: Solving the equation for y, we have $$y = -\tfrac{3}{4}x + \tfrac{7}{4}$$ Comparing this equation with Eq. (8), we see that $m = -\tfrac{3}{4}$ and $b = \tfrac{7}{4}$. Therefore, the slope is $-\tfrac{3}{4}$. |

Another form of an equation of a line is the one involving the intercepts of a line. We define the x *intercept* of a line as the abscissa of the point at which the line intersects the x axis. The x intercept is denoted by a. If the x intercept a and the y intercept b are given, we have two points $(a, 0)$ and $(0, b)$ on the line. Applying Eq. (6), the two-point form, we have

$$y - 0 = \frac{b - 0}{0 - a}(x - a)$$

or

$$-ay = bx - ab$$

or

$$bx + ay = ab$$

Dividing by ab, if $a \neq 0$ and $b \neq 0$, we obtain

$$\frac{x}{a} + \frac{y}{b} = 1 \qquad\qquad (9)$$

Equation (9) is called the *intercept* form of an equation of the line. Obviously it does not apply to a line through the origin, because for such a line both a and b are zero.

EXAMPLE 3: The point (2, 3) bisects that portion of a line which is cut off by the coordinate axes. Find an equation of the line.

Figure 1.5.5

SOLUTION: Refer to Fig. 1.5.5. If a is the x intercept of the line and b is the y intercept of the line, then the point (2, 3) is the midpoint of the line segment joining $(a, 0)$ and $(0, b)$. By the midpoint formulas, we have

$$2 = \frac{a+0}{2} \quad \text{and} \quad 3 = \frac{0+b}{2}$$

Then

$$a = 4 \quad \text{and} \quad b = 6$$

The intercept form, Eq. (9), gives us

$$\frac{x}{4} + \frac{y}{6} = 1$$

or

$$3x + 2y = 12$$

1.5.2 Theorem   The graph of the equation

$$Ax + By + C = 0 \tag{10}$$

where A, B, and C are constants and where not both A and B are zero, is a straight line.

PROOF: Consider the two cases $B \neq 0$ and $B = 0$.

Case 1: $B \neq 0$.
Because $B \neq 0$, we divide on both sides of Eq. (10) by B and obtain

$$y = -\frac{A}{B} x - \frac{C}{B} \tag{11}$$

Equation (11) is an equation of a straight line because it is in the slope-intercept form, where $m = -A/B$ and $b = -C/B$.

Case 2: $B = 0$.
Because $B = 0$, we may conclude that $A \neq 0$ and thus have

$$Ax + C = 0$$

or

$$x = -\frac{C}{A} \tag{12}$$

Equation (12) is in the form of Eq. (3), and so the graph is a straight line parallel to the y axis. This completes the proof. ■

Because the graph of Eq. (10) is a straight line, it is called a *linear equation*. Equation (10) is the general equation of the first degree in x and y.

Because two points determine a line, to draw a sketch of the graph of a straight line from its equation we need only determine the coordinates of two points on the line, plot the two points, and then draw the line. Any two points will suffice, but it is usually convenient to plot the two points where the line intersects the two axes (which are given by the intercepts).

EXAMPLE 4:   Given line l_1, having the equation $2x - 3y = 12$, and line l_2, having the equation $4x + 3y = 6$, draw a sketch of each of the lines. Then find the coordinates of the point of intersection of l_1 and l_2.

SOLUTION: To draw a sketch of the graph of l_1, we find the intercepts a and b. In the equation of l_1, we substitute 0 for x and get $b = -4$. In the equation of l_1, we substitute 0 for y and get $a = 6$. Similarly, we obtain the intercepts a and b for l_2, and for l_2 we have $a = \frac{3}{2}$ and $b = 2$. The two lines are plotted in Fig. 1.5.6.

To find the coordinates of the point of intersection of l_1 and l_2, we solve the two equations simultaneously. Because the point must lie on both lines, its coordinates must satisfy both equations. If both equations are put in the slope-intercept form, we have

$$y = \tfrac{2}{3}x - 4 \quad \text{and} \quad y = -\tfrac{4}{3}x + 2$$

Eliminating y gives

$$\tfrac{2}{3}x - 4 = -\tfrac{4}{3}x + 2$$

or

$$2x - 12 = -4x + 6$$

or

$$6x = 18$$

or

$$x = 3$$

So

$$y = \tfrac{2}{3}(3) - 4$$

or

$$y = -2$$

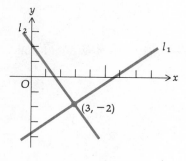

Figure 1.5.6

Therefore, the point of intersection is $(3, -2)$.

1.5.3 Theorem

If l_1 and l_2 are two distinct nonvertical lines having slopes m_1 and m_2, respectively, then l_1 and l_2 are parallel if and only if $m_1 = m_2$.

PROOF: Let an equation of l_1 be $y = m_1x + b_1$, and let an equation of l_2 be $y = m_2x + b_2$. Because there is an "if and only if" qualification, the proof consists of two parts.

PART 1:   Prove that l_1 and l_2 are parallel if $m_1 = m_2$.

Assume that l_1 and l_2 are not parallel. Let us show that this assumption leads to a contradiction. If l_1 and l_2 are not parallel, then they intersect.

Call this point of intersection $P(x_0, y_0)$. The coordinates of P must satisfy the equations of l_1 and l_2, and so we have

$$y_0 = m_1 x_0 + b_1 \quad \text{and} \quad y_0 = m_2 x_0 + b_2$$

But $m_1 = m_2$, which gives

$$y_0 = m_1 x_0 + b_1 \quad \text{and} \quad y_0 = m_1 x_0 + b_2$$

from which it follows that $b_1 = b_2$. So, if $m_1 = m_2$ and $b_1 = b_2$, then both lines l_1 and l_2 have the same equation, $y = m_1 x + b_1$, and so the lines are the same. But this contradicts the hypothesis that l_1 and l_2 are distinct lines. Therefore, our assumption is false. So we conclude that l_1 and l_2 are parallel.

PART 2: Prove that l_1 and l_2 are parallel only if $m_1 = m_2$. Here we must show that if l_1 and l_2 are parallel, then $m_1 = m_2$.

Assume that $m_1 \neq m_2$. Solving the equations for l_1 and l_2 simultaneously, we get, upon eliminating y,

$$m_1 x + b_1 = m_2 x + b_2$$

from which it follows that

$$(m_1 - m_2)x = b_2 - b_1$$

Because we have assumed that $m_1 \neq m_2$, this gives

$$x = \frac{b_2 - b_1}{m_1 - m_2}$$

Hence, l_1 and l_2 have a point of intersection, which contradicts the hypothesis that l_1 and l_2 are parallel. So our assumption is false, and therefore $m_1 = m_2$. ∎

In Fig. 1.5.7, the two lines l_1 and l_2 are perpendicular. We state and prove the following theorem on the slopes of two perpendicular lines.

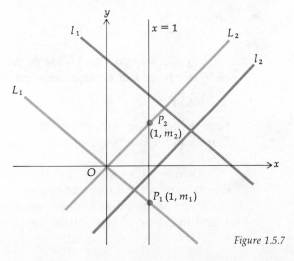

Figure 1.5.7

1.5.4 Theorem   If neither line l_1 nor line l_2 is vertical, then l_1 and l_2 are perpendicular i and only if the product of their slopes is -1. That is, if m_1 is the slope o l_1 and m_2 is the slope of l_2, then l_1 and l_2 are perpendicular if and only i $m_1 m_2 = -1$.

PROOF:

PART 1:   Prove that l_1 and l_2 are perpendicular only if $m_1 m_2 = -1$.

Let L_1 be the line through the origin parallel to l_1 and let L_2 be the line through the origin parallel to l_2. See Fig. 1.5.7. Therefore, by Theorem 1.5.3, the slope of line L_1 is m_1 and the slope of line L_2 is m_2. Because neither L_1 nor L_2 is vertical, these two lines intersect the line $x = 1$ at points P_1 and P_2, respectively. The abscissa of both P_1 and P_2 is 1. Let $\bar{y}$ be the ordinate of P_1. Since L_1 contains the points $(0, 0)$ and $(1, \bar{y})$ and its slope is m_1 we have from Definition 1.5.1

$$m_1 = \frac{\bar{y} - 0}{1 - 0}$$

and so $\bar{y} = m_1$. Similarly, the ordinate of P_2 is shown to be m_2.

Applying the Pythagorean theorem to right triangle $P_1 O P_2$, we get

$$|\overline{OP_1}|^2 + |\overline{OP_2}|^2 = |\overline{P_1 P_2}|^2 \tag{13}$$

By applying the distance formula, we obtain

$$|\overline{OP_1}|^2 = (1 - 0)^2 + (m_1 - 0)^2 = 1 + m_1{}^2$$

$$|\overline{OP_2}|^2 = (1 - 0)^2 + (m_2 - 0)^2 = 1 + m_2{}^2$$

$$|\overline{P_1 P_2}|^2 = (1 - 1)^2 + (m_2 - m_1)^2 = m_2{}^2 - 2m_1 m_2 + m_1{}^2$$

Substituting into Eq. (13) gives

$$(1 + m_1{}^2) + (1 + m_2{}^2) = m_2{}^2 - 2m_1 m_2 + m_1{}^2$$

$$2 = -2m_1 m_2$$

$$m_1 m_2 = -1$$

PART 2:   Prove that l_1 and l_2 are perpendicular if $m_1 m_2 = -1$. Starting with $m_1 m_2 = -1$, we can reverse the steps of the proof of Part 1 and obtain

$$|\overline{OP_1}|^2 + |\overline{OP_2}|^2 = |\overline{P_1 P_2}|^2$$

from which it follows, from the converse of the Pythagorean theorem, that L_1 and L_2 are perpendicular; hence, l_1 and l_2 are perpendicular.   ∎

Theorem 1.5.4 states that if two lines are perpendicular and neither one is vertical, the slope of one of the lines is the negative reciprocal of the slope of the other line. For example, if line l_1 is perpendicular to line l_2 and the slope of l_1 is $\frac{2}{3}$, then the slope of l_2 must be $-\frac{3}{2}$.

EXAMPLE 5:   Prove by means of slopes that the four points $A(6, 2)$, $B(8, 6)$, $C(4, 8)$, and $D(2, 4)$ are the vertices of a rectangle.

Figure 1.5.8

SOLUTION: See Fig. 1.5.8. Let

$$m_1 = \text{the slope of } AB = \frac{6-2}{8-6} = 2.$$

$$m_2 = \text{the slope of } BC = \frac{8-6}{4-8} = -\frac{1}{2}.$$

$$m_3 = \text{the slope of } DC = \frac{8-4}{4-2} = 2.$$

$$m_4 = \text{the slope of } AD = \frac{4-2}{2-6} = -\frac{1}{2}.$$

Because

$$m_1 = m_3, \; AB \parallel DC.$$

$$m_2 = m_4, \; BC \parallel AD.$$

$$m_1 m_2 = -1, \; AB \perp BC.$$

Therefore, quadrilateral $ABCD$ has opposite sides parallel and two adjacent sides perpendicular, and we conclude that $ABCD$ is a rectangle.

EXAMPLE 6:   Given the line l having the equation

$$2x + 3y - 5 = 0$$

find an equation of the line perpendicular to line l and passing through the point $A(-1, 3)$.

SOLUTION: Because the required line is perpendicular to line l, its slope must be the negative reciprocal of the slope of l. We find the slope of l by putting its equation into the slope-intercept form. Solving the given equation for y, we obtain

$$y = -\tfrac{2}{3}x + \tfrac{5}{3}$$

Therefore, the slope of l is $-\tfrac{2}{3}$, and the slope of the required line is $\tfrac{3}{2}$. Because we also know that the required line contains the point $(-1, 3)$, we use the point-slope form, which gives

$$y - 3 = \tfrac{3}{2}(x + 1)$$

or

$$2y - 6 = 3x + 3$$

or

$$3x - 2y + 9 = 0$$

Exercises 1.5

In Exercises 1 through 4, find the slope of the line through the given points.

1. $(2, -3)$, $(-4, 3)$

2. $(5, 2)$, $(-2, -3)$

3. $(\tfrac{1}{3}, \tfrac{1}{2})$, $(-\tfrac{5}{6}, \tfrac{2}{3})$

4. $(-2.1, 0.3)$, $(2.3, 1.4)$

In Exercises 5 through 14, find an equation of the line satisfying the given conditions.

5. The slope is 4 and through the point $(2, -3)$.

6. Through the two points $(3, 1)$ and $(-5, 4)$.

7. Through the point $(-3, -4)$ and parallel to the y axis.

8. Through the point $(1, -7)$ and parallel to the x axis.

9. The x intercept is -3, and the y intercept is 4.

10. Through $(1, 4)$ and parallel to the line whose equation is $2x - 5y + 7 = 0$.

11. Through $(-2, -5)$ and having a slope of $\sqrt{3}$.

12. Through the origin and bisecting the angle between the axes in the first and third quadrants.

13. Through the origin and bisecting the angle between the axes in the second and fourth quadrants.

14. The slope is -2, and the x intercept is 4.

15. Find an equation of the line through the points $(1, 3)$ and $(2, -2)$, and put the equation in the intercept form.

16. Find an equation of the line through the points $(3, -5)$ and $(1, -2)$, and put the equation in the slope-intercept form.

17. Show by means of slopes that the points $(-4, -1)$, $(3, \frac{8}{3})$, $(8, -4)$, and $(2, -9)$ are the vertices of a trapezoid.

18. Three consecutive vertices of a parallelogram are $(-4, 1)$, $(2, 3)$, and $(8, 9)$. Find the coordinates of the fourth vertex.

19. For each of the following sets of three points, determine by means of slopes if the points are on a line: (a) $(2, 3)$, $(-4, -7)$, $(5, 8)$; (b) $(-3, 6)$, $(3, 2)$, $(9, -2)$; (c) $(2, -1)$, $(1, 1)$, $(3, 4)$; and (d) $(4, 6)$, $(1, 2)$, $(-5, -4)$.

20. Prove by means of slopes that the three points $A(3, 1)$, $B(6, 0)$, and $C(4, 4)$ are the vertices of a right triangle, and find the area of the triangle.

21. Given the line l having the equation $2y - 3x = 4$ and the point $P(1, -3)$, find (a) an equation of the line through P and perpendicular to l; (b) the shortest distance from P to line l.

22. If A, B, C, and D are constants, show that (a) the lines $Ax + By + C = 0$ and $Ax + By + D = 0$ are parallel and (b) the lines $Ax + By + C = 0$ and $Bx - Ay + D = 0$ are perpendicular.

23. Given the line l, having the equation $Ax + By + C = 0$, $B \neq 0$, find (a) the slope, (b) the y intercept, (c) the x intercept, (d) an equation of the line through the origin perpendicular to l.

24. Find an equation of the line which has equal intercepts and which passes through the point $(8, -6)$.

25. Find equations of the three medians of the triangle having vertices $A(3, -2)$, $B(3, 4)$, and $C(-1, 1)$, and prove that they meet in a point.

26. Find equations of the perpendicular bisectors of the sides of the triangle having vertices $A(-1, -3)$, $B(5, -3)$, and $C(5, 5)$, and prove that they meet in a point.

27. Find an equation of each of the lines through the point $(3, 2)$, which forms with the coordinate axes a triangle of area 12.

28. Let l_1 be the line having the equation $A_1x + B_1y + C_1 = 0$, and let l_2 be the line having the equation $A_2x + B_2y + C_2 = 0$. If l_1 is not parallel to l_2 and if k is any constant, the equation

$$A_1x + B_1y + C_1 + k(A_2x + B_2y + C_2) = 0$$

represents an unlimited number of lines. Prove that each of these lines contains the point of intersection of l_1 and l_2.

29. Given an equation of l_1 is $2x + 3y - 5 = 0$ and an equation of l_2 is $3x + 5y - 8 = 0$, by using Exercise 28 and without finding the coordinates of the point of intersection of l_1 and l_2, find an equation of the line through this point of intersection and (a) passing through the point $(1, 3)$; (b) parallel to the x axis; (c) parallel to the y axis; (d) having slope -2; (e) perpendicular to the line having the equation $2x + y = 7$; (f) forming an isosceles triangle with the coordinate axes.

0. Find an equation of each straight line that is perpendicular to the line having the equation $5x - y = 1$ and that forms with the coordinate axes a triangle having an area of measure 5.

1. Prove analytically that the diagonals of a rhombus are perpendicular.

2. Prove analytically that the line segments joining consecutive midpoints of the sides of any quadrilateral form a parallelogram.

3. Prove analytically that the diagonals of a parallelogram bisect each other.

4. Prove analytically that if the diagonals of a quadrilateral bisect each other, then the quadrilateral is a parallelogram.

1.6 THE CIRCLE

1.6.1 Definition   A *circle* is the set of all points in a plane equidistant from a fixed point. The fixed point is called the *center* of the circle, and the measure of the constant equal distance is called the *radius* of the circle.

1.6.2 Theorem   The circle with center at the point $C(h, k)$ and radius r has as an equation

$$(x - h)^2 + (y - k)^2 = r^2 \tag{1}$$

PROOF: The point $P(x, y)$ lies on the circle if and only if

$$|\overline{PC}| = r$$

that is, if and only if

$$\sqrt{(x - h)^2 + (y - k)^2} = r$$

This is true if and only if

$$(x - h)^2 + (y - k)^2 = r^2$$

which is Eq. (1). Equation (1) is satisfied by the coordinates of those and only those points which lie on the given circle. Hence, (1) is an equation of the circle.   ∎

From Definition 1.3.2, it follows that the graph of Eq. (1) is the circle with center at (h, k) and radius r.

If the center of the circle is at the origin, then $h = k = 0$; therefore, its equation is $x^2 + y^2 = r^2$.

EXAMPLE 1:   Find an equation of the circle with center at $(2, -3)$ and radius equal to 4.

SOLUTION: The circle is shown in Fig. 1.6.1. In this example, $h = 2$, $k = -3$, $r = 4$. Substituting into Eq. (1), we have

$$(x - 2)^2 + [y - (-3)]^2 = 4^2$$

or

$$(x - 2)^2 + (y + 3)^2 = 16$$

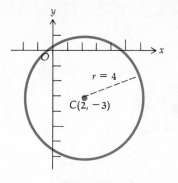

Figure 1.6.1

Squaring and then combining terms, we have

$$x^2 - 4x + 4 + y^2 + 6y + 9 = 16$$

or

$$x^2 + y^2 - 4x + 6y - 3 = 0$$

EXAMPLE 2: Given the equation

$$x^2 + y^2 + 6x - 2y - 15 = 0$$

prove that the graph of this equation is a circle, and find its center and radius.

SOLUTION: The given equation may be written as

$$(x^2 + 6x) + (y^2 - 2y) = 15$$

Completing the squares of the terms in parentheses by adding 9 and on both sides of the equation, we have

$$(x^2 + 6x + 9) + (y^2 - 2y + 1) = 15 + 9 + 1$$

or

$$(x + 3)^2 + (y - 1)^2 = 25$$

Comparing this equation with Eq. (1), we see that this is an equation of a circle with its center at $(-3, 1)$ and a radius of 5.

In Eq. (1), removing parentheses and combining terms gives

$$x^2 + y^2 - 2hx - 2ky + (h^2 + k^2 - r^2) = 0 \tag{2}$$

Equation (2) is of the form

$$x^2 + y^2 + Dx + Ey + F = 0 \tag{3}$$

where $D = -2h$, $E = -2k$, and $F = h^2 + k^2 - r^2$

Equation (3) is called the *general form* of an equation of a circle whereas Eq. (1) is called the *center-radius form*. Because every circle has a center and a radius, its equation can be put in the center-radius form and hence into the general form.

We now consider the question of whether or not the graph of every equation of the form

$$x^2 + y^2 + Dx + Ey + F = 0$$

is a circle. To determine this, we shall attempt to write this equation in the center-radius form. We rewrite the equation as

$$x^2 + y^2 + Dx + Ey = -F$$

and complete the squares of the terms in parentheses by adding $\frac{1}{4}D^2$ and $\frac{1}{4}E^2$ on both sides, thus giving us

$$(x^2 + Dx + \tfrac{1}{4}D^2) + (y^2 + Ey + \tfrac{1}{4}E^2) = -F + \tfrac{1}{4}D^2 + \tfrac{1}{4}E^2$$

or

$$(x + \tfrac{1}{2}D)^2 + (y + \tfrac{1}{2}E)^2 = \tfrac{1}{4}(D^2 + E^2 - 4F) \tag{4}$$

Equation (4) is in the form of Eq. (1) if and only if

$$\tfrac{1}{4}(D^2 + E^2 - 4F) = r^2$$

We now consider three cases, namely, $(D^2 + E^2 - 4F)$ as positive, zero, and negative.

Case 1: $(D^2 + E^2 - 4F) > 0$.

Then $r^2 = \frac{1}{4}(D^2 + E^2 - 4F)$, and so Eq. (4) is an equation of a circle having a radius equal to $\frac{1}{2}\sqrt{D^2 + E^2 - 4F}$ and its center at $(-\frac{1}{2}D, -\frac{1}{2}E)$.

Case 2: $D^2 + E^2 - 4F = 0$.

Equation (4) is then of the form

$$(x + \tfrac{1}{2}D)^2 + (y + \tfrac{1}{2}E)^2 = 0. \tag{5}$$

Because the only real values of x and y satisfying Eq. (5) are $x = -\frac{1}{2}D$ and $y = -\frac{1}{2}E$, the graph is the point $(-\frac{1}{2}D, -\frac{1}{2}E)$. Comparing Eq. (5) with Eq. (1), we see that $h = -\frac{1}{2}D$, $k = -\frac{1}{2}E$, and $r = 0$. Thus, this point can be called a *point-circle*.

Case 3: $(D^2 + E^2 - 4F) < 0$.

Then Eq. (4) has a negative number on the right side and the sum of the squares of two real numbers on the left side. There are no real values of x and y that satisfy such an equation; consequently, we say there is no real locus.

Before stating the results of these three cases as a theorem, we observe that an equation of the form

$$Ax^2 + Ay^2 + Dx + Ey + F = 0 \qquad \text{where } A \neq 0 \tag{6}$$

can be written in the form of Eq. (3) by dividing by A, thereby obtaining

$$x^2 + y^2 + \frac{D}{A}x + \frac{E}{A}y + \frac{F}{A} = 0$$

Equation (6) is a special case of the general equation of the second degree:

$$Ax^2 + Bxy + Cy^2 + Dx + Ey + F = 0$$

in which the coefficients of x^2 and y^2 are equal and which has no xy term. We have, then, the following theorem.

1.6.3 Theorem   The graph of any second-degree equation in R_2 in x and y, in which the coefficients of x^2 and y^2 are equal and in which there is no xy term, i either a circle, a point-circle, or no real locus.

EXAMPLE 3: Determine the graph of the equation

$$2x^2 + 2y^2 + 12x - 8y + 31 = 0$$

SOLUTION: The equation is of the form (6), and therefore the graph is either a circle, a point-circle, or no real locus. If the equation is put in the form of Eq. (1), we have

$$x^2 + y^2 + 6x - 4y + \tfrac{31}{2} = 0$$

$$(x^2 + 6x) + (y^2 - 4y) = -\tfrac{31}{2}$$

$$(x^2 + 6x + 9) + (y^2 - 4y + 4) = -\tfrac{31}{2} + 9 + 4$$

$$(x + 3)^2 + (y - 2)^2 = -\tfrac{5}{2}$$

Therefore, there is no real locus.

EXAMPLE 4: Find an equation of the circle through the three points $A(4, 5)$, $B(3, -2)$, and $C(1, -4)$.

SOLUTION: The general form of an equation of the circle is

$$x^2 + y^2 + Dx + Ey + F = 0$$

Because the three points A, B, and C must lie on the circle, the coordinates of these points must satisfy the equation. So we have

$$16 + 25 + 4D + 5E + F = 0$$

$$9 + 4 + 3D - 2E + F = 0$$

$$1 + 16 + D - 4E + F = 0$$

or

$$4D + 5E + F = -41$$

$$3D - 2E + F = -13$$

$$D - 4E + F = -17$$

Solving these three equations simultaneously, we get

$$D = 7 \qquad E = -5 \qquad F = -44$$

Thus, an equation of the circle is

$$x^2 + y^2 + 7x - 5y - 44 = 0$$

In the following example we have a line which is tangent to a circle. The definition of the tangent line to a general curve at a specific point is given in Sec. 3.1. However, for a circle we use the definition from plane geometry which states that a tangent line at a point P on the circle is the line intersecting the circle at only the point P.

EXAMPLE 5:   Find an equation of the circle with its center at the point $C(1, 6)$ and tangent to the line l having the equation $x - y - 1 = 0$.

SOLUTION: See Fig. 1.6.2. Given that $h = 1$ and $k = 6$, if we find r, we can obtain an equation of the circle by using the center-radius form.

Let l_1 be the line through C and the point P, which is the point of tangency of line l with the circle.

$$r = |\overline{PC}|$$

Hence, we must find the coordinates of P. We do this by finding an equation of l_1 and then finding the point of intersection of l_1 with l. Since l_1 is along a diameter of the circle, and l is tangent to the circle, l_1 is perpendicular to l. Because the slope of l is 1, the slope of l_1 is -1. Therefore, using the point-slope form of an equation of a line, we obtain as an equation of l_1

$$y - 6 = -1(x - 1)$$

or

$$x + y - 7 = 0$$

Solving this equation simultaneously with the given equation of l, namely,

$$x - y - 1 = 0$$

we get $x = 4$ and $y = 3$. Thus, P is the point $(4, 3)$. Therefore,

$$r = |\overline{PC}| = \sqrt{(4 - 1)^2 + (3 - 6)^2}$$

or

$$r = \sqrt{18}$$

So, an equation of the circle is

$$(x - 1)^2 + (y - 6)^2 = (\sqrt{18})^2$$

or

$$x^2 + y^2 - 2x - 12y + 19 = 0$$

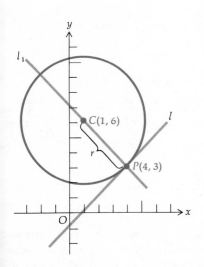

Figure 1.6.2

Exercises 1.6

In Exercises 1 through 4, find an equation of the circle with center at C and radius r. Write the equation in both the center-radius form and the general form.

1. $C(4, -3)$, $r = 5$

2. $C(0, 0)$, $r = 8$

3. $C(-5, -12)$, $r = 3$

4. $C(-1, 1)$, $r = 2$

In Exercises 5 through 10, find an equation of the circle satisfying the given conditions.

5. Center is at $(1, 2)$ and through the point $(3, -1)$.

6. Center is at $(-2, 5)$ and tangent to the line $x = 7$.

7. Center is at $(-3, -5)$ and tangent to the line $12x + 5y - 4 = 0$.

8. Through the three points $(2, 8)$, $(7, 3)$, and $(-2, 0)$.

9. Tangent to the line $3x + y + 2 = 0$ at $(-1, 1)$ and through the point $(3, 5)$.

10. Tangent to the line $3x + 4y - 16 = 0$ at $(4, 1)$ and with a radius of 5. (Two possible circles.)

In Exercises 11 through 14, find the center and radius of each circle, and draw a sketch of the graph.

11. $x^2 + y^2 - 6x - 8y + 9 = 0$ 12. $2x^2 + 2y^2 - 2x + 2y + 7 = 0$

13. $3x^2 + 3y^2 + 4y - 7 = 0$ 14. $x^2 + y^2 - 10x - 10y + 25 = 0$

In Exercises 15 through 20, determine whether the graph is a circle, a point-circle, or no real locus.

15. $x^2 + y^2 - 2x + 10y + 19 = 0$ 16. $4x^2 + 4y^2 + 24x - 4y + 1 = 0$ 17. $x^2 + y^2 - 10x + 6y + 36 = 0$

18. $x^2 + y^2 + 2x - 4y + 5 = 0$ 19. $36x^2 + 36y^2 - 48x + 36y - 119 = 0$ 20. $9x^2 + 9y^2 + 6x - 6y + 5 = 0$

21. Find an equation of the common chord of the two circles $x^2 + y^2 + 4x - 6y - 12 = 0$ and $x^2 + y^2 + 8x - 2y + 8 = 0$. (HINT: If the coordinates of a point satisfy two different equations, then the coordinates also satisfy the difference of the two equations.)

22. Find the points of intersection of the two circles in Exercise 21.

23. Find an equation of the line which is tangent to the circle $x^2 + y^2 - 4x + 6y - 12 = 0$ at the point $(5, 1)$.

24. Find an equation of each of the two lines having slope $-\frac{4}{3}$ which are tangent to the circle $x^2 + y^2 + 2x - 8y - 8 = 0$.

25. From the origin, chords of the circle $x^2 + y^2 + 4x = 0$ are drawn. Prove that the set of midpoints of these chords is a circle.

26. Prove analytically that a line from the center of any circle bisecting any chord is perpendicular to the chord.

27. Prove analytically that an angle inscribed in a semicircle is a right angle.

28. Given the line $y = mx + b$ tangent to the circle $x^2 + y^2 = r^2$, find an equation involving m, b, and r.

1.7 THE PARABOLA

A *conic section* is a curve of intersection of a plane with a right circular cone of two nappes. There are three types of curves that occur in this way: the parabola, the ellipse (including the circle as a special case), and the hyperbola. The resulting curve depends on the inclination of the axis of the cone to the cutting plane. In this section we study the parabola; the ellipse and the hyperbola are discussed in Chapter 12.

When the cutting plane is parallel to an element of the cone, a parabola is obtained. Following is the analytic definition of a parabola.

1.7.1 Definition

A *parabola* is the set of all points in a plane equidistant from a fixed point and a fixed line. The fixed point is called the *focus*, and the fixed line is called the *directrix*.

We now derive an equation of a parabola from the definition. In order for this equation to be as simple as possible, we choose the x axis as perpendicular to the directrix and containing the focus. The origin is taken as the point on the x axis midway between the focus and the directrix. It should be stressed that we are choosing the axes (*not* the parabola) in a special way. See Fig. 1.7.1.

Let p be the directed distance $\overline{OF}$. The focus is the point $F(p, 0)$, and the directrix is the line having the equation $x = -p$. A point $P(x, y)$ is on the parabola if and only if P is equidistant from F and the directrix. That is, if $Q(-p, y)$ is the foot of the perpendicular line from P to the directrix, then P is on the parabola if and only if

$$|\overline{FP}| = |\overline{QP}|$$

Because

$$|\overline{FP}| = \sqrt{(x - p)^2 + y^2}$$

and

$$|\overline{QP}| = \sqrt{(x + p)^2 + (y - y)^2}$$

P is on the parabola if and only if

$$\sqrt{(x - p)^2 + y^2} = \sqrt{(x + p)^2}$$

By squaring on both sides of the equation, we obtain

$$x^2 - 2px + p^2 + y^2 = x^2 + 2px + p^2$$

or

$$y^2 = 4px$$

This result is stated as a theorem.

1.7.2 Theorem An equation of the parabola having its focus at $(p, 0)$ and as its directrix the line $x = -p$ is

$$y^2 = 4px \tag{1}$$

In Fig. 1.7.1, p is positive; p may be negative, however, because it is the directed distance $\overline{OF}$. Figure 1.7.2 shows a parabola for $p < 0$.

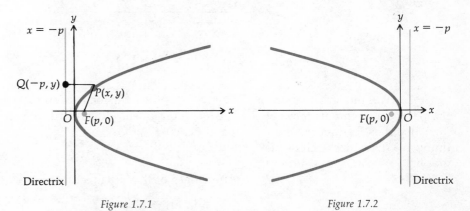

Figure 1.7.1   Figure 1.7.2

From Figs. 1.7.1 and 1.7.2, we see that for the equation $y^2 = 4px$ the parabola opens to the right if $p > 0$ and to the left if $p < 0$. The point midway between the focus and the directrix on the parabola is called the *vertex.* The vertex of the parabolas in Figs. 1.7.1 and 1.7.2 is the origin The line through the vertex and the focus is called the *axis* of the parabola The axis of the parabolas in Figs. 1.7.1 and 1.7.2 is the *x* axis.

In the above derivation, if the *x* axis and the *y* axis are interchanged then the focus is at the point $F(0, p)$, and the directrix is the line having the equation $y = -p$. An equation of this parabola is $x^2 = 4py$, and the result is stated as a theorem.

1.7.3 Theorem An equation of the parabola having its focus at $(0, p)$ and as its directrix the line $y = -p$ is

$$x^2 = 4py \qquad (2$$

If $p > 0$, the parabola opens upward as shown in Fig. 1.7.3; and if $p < 0$, the parabola opens downward as shown in Fig. 1.7.4. In each case the vertex is at the origin, and the *y* axis is the axis of the parabola.

When we draw a sketch of the graph of a parabola, it is helpful to draw the chord through the focus, perpendicular to the axis of the parabola. This chord is called the *latus rectum* of the parabola. The length of the latus rectum is $|4p|$. (See Exercise 17.)

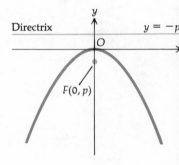

Figure 1.7.3   *Figure 1.7.4*

EXAMPLE 1: Find an equation of the parabola having its focus at $(0, -3)$ and as its directrix the line $y = 3$. Draw a sketch of the graph.

SOLUTION: Since the focus is on the *y* axis and is also below the directrix the parabola opens downward, and $p = -3$. Hence, an equation of the parabola is

$$x^2 = -12y$$

The length of the latus rectum is

$$|4(-3)| = 12$$

A sketch of the graph is shown in Fig. 1.7.5.

Any point on the parabola is equidistant from the focus and the directrix. In Fig. 1.7.5, three such points (P_1, P_2, and P_3) are shown, and we have

$$|\overline{FP_1}| = |\overline{P_1Q_1}| \qquad |\overline{FP_2}| = |\overline{P_2Q_2}| \qquad |\overline{FP_3}| = |\overline{P_3Q_3}|$$

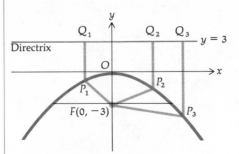

Figure 1.7.5

EXAMPLE 2: Given the parabola having the equation

$$y^2 = 7x$$

find the coordinates of the focus, an equation of the directrix, and the length of the latus rectum. Draw a sketch of the graph.

SOLUTION: The given equation is of the form of Eq. (1); so

$$4p = 7$$

or

$$p = \tfrac{7}{4}$$

Because $p > 0$, the parabola opens to the right. The focus is at the point $F(\tfrac{7}{4}, 0)$. An equation of the directrix is $x = -\tfrac{7}{4}$. The length of the latus rectum is 7. A sketch of the graph is shown in Fig. 1.7.6.

Figure 1.7.6

Exercises 1.7

For each of the parabolas in Exercises 1 through 8, find the coordinates of the focus, an equation of the directrix, and the length of the latus rectum. Draw a sketch of the curve.

1. $x^2 = 4y$
2. $y^2 = 6x$
3. $y^2 = -8x$
4. $x^2 = -16y$
5. $x^2 + y = 0$
6. $y^2 - 5x = 0$
7. $2y^2 - 9x = 0$
8. $3x^2 + 4y = 0$

In Exercises 9 through 16, find an equation of the parabola having the given properties.

9. Focus, $(5, 0)$; directrix, $x = -5$.

10. Focus, $(0, 4)$; directrix, $y = -4$.

11. Focus, $(0, -2)$; directrix, $y - 2 = 0$.

12. Focus, $(-\frac{5}{3}, 0)$; directrix, $5 - 3x = 0$.

13. Focus, $(\frac{1}{2}, 0)$; directrix, $2x + 1 = 0$.

14. Focus, $(0, \frac{2}{3})$; directrix, $3y + 2 = 0$.

15. Vertex, $(0, 0)$; opens to the left; length of latus rectum $= 6$.

16. Vertex, $(0, 0)$; opens upward; length of latus rectum $= 3$.

17. Prove that the length of the latus rectum of a parabola is $|4p|$.

18. Find an equation of the parabola having its vertex at the origin, the x axis as its axis, and passing through the point $(2, -4)$.

19. Find an equation of the parabola having its vertex at the origin, the y axis as its axis, and passing through the point $(-2, -4)$.

20. A parabolic arch has a height of 20 ft and a width of 36 ft at the base. If the vertex of the parabola is at the top of the arch, at what height above the base is it 18 ft wide?

21. The cable of a suspension bridge hangs in the form of a parabola when the load is uniformly distributed horizontally. The distance between two towers is 1500 ft, the points of support of the cable on the towers are 220 ft above the roadway, and the lowest point on the cable is 70 ft above the roadway. Find the vertical distance to the cable from a point in the roadway 150 ft from the foot of a tower.

22. Assume that water issuing from the end of a horizontal pipe, 25 ft above the ground, describes a parabolic curve, the vertex of the parabola being at the end of the pipe. If, at a point 8 ft below the line of the pipe, the flow of water has curved outward 10 ft beyond a vertical line through the end of the pipe, how far beyond this vertical line will the water strike the ground?

23. A reflecting telescope has a parabolic mirror for which the distance from the vertex to the focus is 30 ft. If the distance across the top of the mirror is 64 in., how deep is the mirror at the center?

24. Using Definition 2.7.1, find an equation of the parabola having as its directrix the line $y = 4$ and as its focus the point $(-3, 8)$.

25. Using Definition 2.7.1, find an equation of the parabola having as its directrix the line $x = -3$ and as its focus the point $(2, 5)$.

26. Find all points on the parabola $y^2 = 8x$ such that the foot of the perpendicular drawn from the point to the directrix, the focus, and the point itself are vertices of an equilateral triangle.

27. Find an equation of the circle passing through the vertex and the endpoints of the latus rectum of the parabola $x^2 = -8y$.

28. Prove analytically that the circle having as its diameter the latus rectum of a parabola is tangent to the directrix of the parabola.

29. A focal chord of a parabola is a line segment through the focus and with its endpoints on the parabola. If A and B are the endpoints of a focal chord of a parabola, and if C is the point of intersection of the directrix with a line through the vertex and point A, prove that the line through C and B is parallel to the axis of the parabola.

30. Prove that the distance from the midpoint of a focal chord (see Exercise 29) of a parabola to the directrix is half the length of the focal chord.

1.8 TRANSLATION OF AXES

The shape of a curve is not affected by the position of the coordinate axes; however, an equation of the curve is affected. For example, if a circle with a radius of 3 has its center at the point $(4, -1)$, then an equation of this circle is

$$(x - 4)^2 + (y + 1)^2 = 9$$

or

$$x^2 + y^2 - 8x + 2y + 8 = 0$$

However, if the origin is at the center, the same circle has a simpler equation, namely,

$$x^2 + y^2 = 9$$

If we may take the coordinate axes as we please, they are generally chosen in such a way that the equations will be as simple as possible. If the axes are given, however, we often wish to find a simpler equation of a given curve referred to another set of axes.

In general, if in the plane with given x and y axes, new coordinate axes are chosen parallel to the given ones, we say that there has been a *translation of axes* in the plane.

In particular, let the given x and y axes be translated to the x' and y' axes, having origin (h, k) with respect to the given axes. Also, assume that the positive numbers are on the same side of the origin on the x' and y' axes as they are on the x and y axes (see Fig. 1.8.1).

A point P in the plane, having coordinates (x, y) with respect to the given coordinate axes, will have coordinates (x', y') with respect to the new axes. To obtain relationships between these two sets of coordinates, we draw a line through P parallel to the y axis and the y' axis, and also a line through P parallel to the x axis and the x' axis. Let the first line intersect the x axis at the point A and the x' axis at the point A', and the second line intersect the y axis at the point B and the y' axis at the point B'.

With respect to the x and y axes, the coordinates of P are (x, y), the coordinates of A are $(x, 0)$, and the coordinates of A' are (x, k). Because $\overline{A'P} = \overline{AP} - \overline{AA'}$, we have

$$y' = y - k$$

or

$$y = y' + k$$

With respect to the x and y axes, the coordinates of B are $(0, y)$, and the coordinates of B' are (h, y). Because $\overline{B'P} = \overline{BP} - \overline{BB'}$, we have

$$x' = x - h$$

or

$$x = x' + h$$

These results are stated as a theorem.

Figure 1.8.1

1.8.1 Theorem   If (x, y) represents a point P with respect to a given set of axes, and (x', y') is a representation of P after the axes are translated to a new origin having coordinates (h, k) with respect to the given axes, then

$$x = x' + h \quad \text{and} \quad y = y' + k \tag{1}$$

or

$$x' = x - h \quad \text{and} \quad y' = y - k \tag{2}$$

Equations (1) or (2) are called the *equations of translating the axes*.

If an equation of a curve is given in x and y, then an equation in x' and y' is obtained by replacing x by $(x' + h)$ and y by $(y' + k)$. The graph of the equation in x and y, with respect to the x and y axes, is exactly the same set of points as the graph of the corresponding equation in x' and y' with respect to the x' and y' axes.

EXAMPLE 1:   Given the equation $x^2 + 10x + 6y + 19 = 0$, find an equation of the graph with respect to the x' and y' axes after a translation of axes to the new origin $(-5, 1)$.

Figure 1.8.2

SOLUTION: A point P, represented by (x, y) with respect to the old axes, has the representation (x', y') with respect to the new axes. Then by Eqs. (1), with $h = -5$ and $k = 1$, we have

$$x = x' - 5 \quad \text{and} \quad y = y' + 1$$

Substituting these values of x and y into the given equation, we obtain

$$(x' - 5)^2 + 10(x' - 5) + 6(y' + 1) + 19 = 0$$

or

$$x'^2 - 10x' + 25 + 10x' - 50 + 6y' + 6 + 19 = 0$$

or

$$x'^2 = -6y'$$

The graph of this equation with respect to the x' and y' axes is a parabola with its vertex at the origin, opening downward, and with $4p = -6$. The graph with respect to the x and y axes is, then, a parabola having its vertex at $(-5, 1)$, its focus at $(-5, -\frac{1}{2})$, and as its directrix the line $y = \frac{5}{2}$ (see Fig. 1.8.2).

The above example illustrates how an equation can be reduced to a simpler form by a suitable translation of axes. In general, equations of the second degree which contain no term involving xy can be simplified by a translation of axes. This is illustrated in the following example.

EXAMPLE 2:   Given the equation $9x^2 + 4y^2 - 18x + 32y + 37 = 0$, translate the axes so the equation of the graph with respect to the x' and y' axes contains no first-degree terms.

SOLUTION: We rewrite the given equation:

$$9(x^2 - 2x) + 4(y^2 + 8y) = -37$$

Completing the squares of the terms in parentheses by adding $9 \cdot 1$ and $4 \cdot 16$ on both sides of the equation, we have

$$9(x^2 - 2x + 1) + 4(y^2 + 8y + 16) = -37 + 9 + 64$$

Figure 1.8.3

or

$$9(x-1)^2 + 4(y+4)^2 = 36$$

Then, if we let $x' = x - 1$ and $y' = y + 4$, we obtain

$$9x'^2 + 4y'^2 = 36$$

From Eq. (2), we see that the substitutions of $x' = x - 1$ and $y' = y + 4$ result in a translation of axes to a new origin of $(1, -4)$. In Fig. 1.8.3, we have a sketch of the graph of the equation in x' and y' with respect to the x' and y' axes.

We shall now apply the translation of axes to finding the general equation of a parabola having its directrix parallel to a coordinate axis and its vertex at the point (h, k). In particular, let the directrix be parallel to the y axis. If the vertex is at point $V(h, k)$, then the directrix has the equation $x = h - p$, and the focus is at the point $F(h + p, k)$. Let the x' and y' axes be such that the origin O' is at $V(h, k)$ (see Fig. 1.8.4).

An equation of the parabola in Fig. 1.8.4 with respect to the x' and y' axes is

$$y'^2 = 4px'$$

To obtain an equation of this parabola with respect to the x and y axes, we replace x' by $(x - h)$ and y' by $(y - k)$ from Eq. (2), which gives us

$$(y - k)^2 = 4p(x - h)$$

The axis of this parabola is parallel to the x axis.

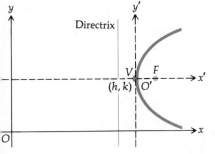

Figure 1.8.4

Similarly, if the directrix of a parabola is parallel to the x axis and the vertex is at $V(h, k)$, then its focus is at $F(h, k + p)$ and the directrix has the equation $y = k - p$, and an equation of the parabola with respect to the x and y axes is

$$(x - h)^2 = 4p(y - k)$$

The axis of this parabola is parallel to the y axis. We have proved, then, the following theorem.

1.8.2 Theorem   If p is the directed distance from the vertex to the focus, an equation of the parabola with its vertex at (h, k) and with its axis parallel to the x axis is

$$(y - k)^2 = 4p(x - h) \tag{3}$$

A parabola with the same vertex and with its axis parallel to the y axis has for an equation

$$(x - h)^2 = 4p(y - k) \tag{4}$$

EXAMPLE 3:   Find an equation of the parabola having as its directrix the line $y = 1$ and as its focus the point $F(-3, 7)$.

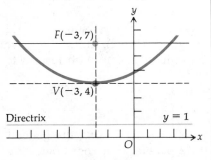

Figure 1.8.5

SOLUTION: Since the directrix is parallel to the x axis, the axis will be parallel to the y axis, and the equation will have the form (4).

Since the vertex V is halfway between the directrix and the focus, V has coordinates $(-3, 4)$. The directed distance from the vertex to the focus is p, and so

$$p = 7 - 4 = 3$$

Therefore, an equation is

$$(x + 3)^2 = 12(y - 4)$$

Squaring and simplifying, we have

$$x^2 + 6x - 12y + 57 = 0$$

A sketch of the graph of this parabola is shown in Fig. 1.8.5.

EXAMPLE 4:   Given the parabola having the equation

$$y^2 + 6x + 8y + 1 = 0$$

find the vertex, the focus, an equation of the directrix, an equation of the axis, and the length of the latus rectum, and draw a sketch of the graph.

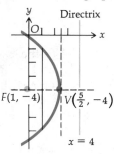

Figure 1.8.6

SOLUTION: Rewrite the given equation as

$$y^2 + 8y = -6x - 1$$

Completing the square of the terms involving y on the left side of this equation by adding 16 on both sides, we obtain

$$y^2 + 8y + 16 = -6x + 15$$

or

$$(y + 4)^2 = -6(x - \tfrac{5}{2})$$

Comparing this equation with (3), we let

$$k = -4 \qquad h = \tfrac{5}{2}$$

and

$$4p = -6 \quad \text{or} \quad p = -\tfrac{3}{2}$$

Therefore, the vertex is at $(\tfrac{5}{2}, -4)$; an equation of the axis is $y = -4$; the focus is at $(1, -4)$; an equation of the directrix is $x = 4$; and the length of the latus rectum is 6. A sketch of the graph is shown in Fig. 1.8.6.

Exercises 1.8

In Exercises 1 through 8, find a new equation of the graph of the given equation after a translation of axes to the new origin as indicated. Draw the original and the new axes and a sketch of the graph.

1. $x^2 + y^2 + 6x + 4y = 0$; $(-3, -2)$

2. $x^2 + y^2 - 10x + 4y + 13 = 0$; $(5, -2)$

3. $y^2 - 6x + 9 = 0$; $(\tfrac{3}{2}, 0)$

4. $y^2 + 3x - 2y + 7 = 0$; $(-2, 1)$

5. $x^2 + 4y^2 + 4x + 8y + 4 = 0$; $(-2, -1)$

6. $25x^2 + y^2 - 50x + 20y - 500 = 0$; $(1, -10)$

7. $y - 4 = 2(x - 1)^3$; $(1, 4)$

8. $(y + 1)^2 = 4(x - 2)^3$; $(2, -1)$

In Exercises 9 through 12, translate the axes so that an equation of the graph with respect to the new axes will contain no first-degree terms. Draw the original and the new axes and a sketch of the graph.

9. $x^2 + 4y^2 - 16x + 24y + 84 = 0$

10. $16x^2 + 25y^2 - 32x - 100y - 284 = 0$

11. $3x^2 - 2y^2 + 6x - 8y - 11 = 0$

12. $x^2 - y^2 + 14x - 8y - 35 = 0$

In Exercises 13 through 18, find the vertex, the focus, an equation of the axis, and an equation of the directrix of the given parabola. Draw a sketch of the graph.

13. $x^2 + 6x + 4y + 8 = 0$

14. $4x^2 - 8x + 3y - 2 = 0$

15. $y^2 + 6x + 10y + 19 = 0$

16. $3y^2 - 8x - 12y - 4 = 0$

17. $2y^2 = 4y - 3x$

18. $y = 3x^2 - 3x + 3$

In Exercises 19 through 28, find an equation of the parabola having the given properties. Draw a sketch of the graph.

19. Vertex at $(2, 4)$; focus at $(-3, 4)$.

20. Vertex at $(1, -3)$; directrix, $y = 1$.

21. Focus at $(-1, 7)$; directrix, $y = 3$.

22. Focus at $(-\frac{3}{4}, 4)$; directrix, $x = -\frac{5}{4}$.

23. Vertex at $(3, -2)$; axis, $x = 3$; length of the latus rectum is 6.

24. Axis parallel to the x axis; through the points $(1, 2)$, $(5, 3)$, and $(11, 4)$.

25. Vertex at $(-4, 2)$; axis, $y = 2$; through the point $(0, 6)$.

26. Directrix, $x = -2$; axis, $y = 4$; length of the latus rectum is 8.

27. Directrix, $x = 4$; axis, $y = 4$; through the point $(9, 7)$.

28. Endpoints of the latus rectum are $(1, 3)$ and $(7, 3)$.

29. Given the parabola having the equation $y = ax^2 + bx + c$, with $a \neq 0$, find the coordinates of the vertex.

30. Find the coordinates of the focus of the parabola in Exercise 29.

31. Find an equation of every parabola containing the points $A(-3, -4)$ and $B(5, -4)$, such that points A and B are each 5 units from the focus.

32. Given the equation $4x^3 - 12x^2 + 12x - 3y - 10 = 0$, translate the axes so that the equation of the graph with respect to the new axes will contain no second-degree term and no constant term. Draw a sketch of the graph and the two sets of axes. (HINT: Let $x = x' + h$ and $y = y' + k$ in the given equation.)

33. Given the equation $x^3 + 3x^2 - y^2 + 3x + 4y - 3 = 0$, translate the axes so that the equation of the graph with respect to the new axes will contain no first-degree term and no constant term. Draw a sketch of the graph and the two sets of axes (see hint for Exercise 32).

34. If a parabola has its focus at the origin and the x axis is its axis, prove that it must have an equation of the form $y^2 = 4kx + 4k^2$, $k \neq 0$.

1.9 INEQUALITIES IN THE PLANE

Expressions of the form $Ax + By + C > 0$, $Ax + By + C \geq 0$, $Ax + By + C < 0$, and $Ax + By + C \leq 0$, where A and B are not both zero, are inequalities of the first degree in the number plane R_2. By the graph of such an inequality, we mean the set of all points (x, y) in R_2 whose coordinates satisfy the inequality.

Every line in a plane divides the plane into two regions, one on each side of the line, and each of these regions is called a *half plane*. We show

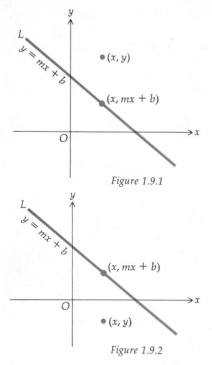

Figure 1.9.1

Figure 1.9.2

that the graph of a strict inequality of the first degree in R_2 is a half plane.

Let L be the line having the equation $Ax + By + C = 0$. If $B \neq 0$, then L is nonvertical and its equation can be written as $y = mx + b$, where $m = -A/B$ and $b = -C/B$. If (x, y) is any point in R_2, it follows from the axiom of order (1.1.10) that exactly one of the following statements holds: $y = mx + b$, $y > mx + b$, or $y < mx + b$.

Now, $y > mx + b$ if and only if the point (x, y) is above the point $(x, mx + b)$ on line L (see Fig. 1.9.1), and $y < mx + b$ if and only if the point (x, y) is below the point $(x, mx + b)$ on L (see Fig. 1.9.2). Hence, the line L divides the plane into two regions. One region is the half plane above line L, which is the graph of the inequality $y > mx + b$, and the other region is the half plane below L, which is the graph of the inequality $y < mx + b$.

If $B = 0$, then L is a vertical line and its equation can be written as $x = a$, where $a = -C/A$. If (x, y) is any point in R_2, it follows from the axiom of order (1.1.10) that exactly one of the following statements is true: $x = a$, $x > a$, or $x < a$. The point (x, y) is to the right of the point (a, y) if and only if $x > a$; hence, the graph of the inequality $x > a$ is the half plane lying to the right of the line $x = a$. Similarly, the graph of $x < a$ is the half plane lying to the left of the line $x = a$, because $x < a$ if and only if the point (x, y) is to the left of the point (a, y). We have proved the following theorem.

1.9.1 Theorem   The graph of any strict inequality of the first degree in R_2 is a half plane. In particular,

(i) the graph of $y > mx + b$ is the half plane lying above the line $y = mx + b$;

(ii) the graph of $y < mx + b$ is the half plane lying below the line $y = mx + b$;

(iii) the graph of $x > a$ is the half plane lying to the right of the line $x = a$;

(iv) the graph of $x < a$ is the half plane lying to the left of the line $x = a$.

Figure 1.9.3

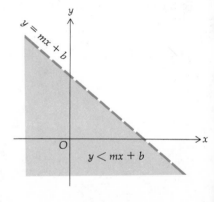

Figure 1.9.4

To draw a sketch of the graph of a strict inequality we shade the appropriate half plane. Figures 1.9.3 and 1.9.4 show sketches of the graphs of $y > mx + b$ and $y < mx + b$, respectively. The graph of the line $y = mx + b$ is indicated by a broken line to show that it is not part of the graph.

EXAMPLE 1: Draw a sketch of the graph of the inequality

$$x - 2y + 8 > 0.$$

SOLUTION: The given inequality is equivalent to $y < \frac{1}{2}x + 4$. The required sketch is shown in Fig. 1.9.5, which is the half plane below the line $y = \frac{1}{2}x + 4$.

Figure 1.9.5

A *closed half plane* is a half plane together with the line bounding it, and it is the graph of a nonstrict inequality.

EXAMPLE 2: Draw a sketch of the graph of the inequality

$$6x + 3y - 4 \geq 0.$$

SOLUTION: Writing the given inequality as $y \geq -2x + \frac{4}{3}$, we see that the graph is the closed half plane consisting of the line $y = -2x + \frac{4}{3}$ and the half plane above it. The sketch is shown in Fig. 1.9.6.

Figure 1.9.6

Two intersecting lines divide the points of the plane into four regions. Each of these regions is the intersection of two half planes and is defined by a pair of linear inequalities. For example, the two inequalities

$$2x - y - 3 > 0 \quad \text{and} \quad x - 3y - 4 < 0$$

describe the region which is the intersection of the half plane below the

Figure 1.9.7

line $y = 2x - 3$ and the half plane above the line $y = \frac{1}{3}x - \frac{4}{3}$. This is the darkly shaded region shown in Fig. 1.9.7.

The above is an example of a region defined by a system of two linear inequalities. We now give an example involving a system of three linear inequalities.

EXAMPLE 3:   Draw a sketch of the region defined by the inequalities

$$8x - 3y + 15 > 0$$
$$x + 4y - 20 \le 0$$
$$x - y \le 0$$

Figure 1.9.8

SOLUTION: Each of the inequalities defines a half plane, two of which are closed. Let L_1 be a line having the equation $8x - 3y + 15 = 0$, L_2 the line having the equation $x + 4y - 20 = 0$, and L_3 the line having the equation $x - y = 0$. The lines L_1 and L_2 intersect at the point $P(0, 5)$, L_1 and L_3 intersect at $Q(-3, -3)$, and L_2 and L_3 intersect at $R(4, 4)$. See Fig. 1.9.8. The first inequality, $y < \frac{8}{3}x + 5$, defines the half plane below line L_1. The inequality $y \le -\frac{1}{4}x + 5$ defines the half plane below L_2 together with L_2, and $y \ge x$ defines the half plane above L_3 together with L_3. The region, whose points satisfy all three inequalities, consists of the interior of triangle PQR and the points on line segments PR and QR, excluding the points P and Q.

The following example illustrates a procedure which can be extended to an arbitrary number of linear inequalities. Such systems occur in the fields of economics, statistics, science, and engineering, among others. In practice, many unknowns are usually involved as well as a large number of inequalities, and electronic computers do most of the work.

EXAMPLE 4:   Find the region, if there is one, whose points satisfy each of the inequalities:

$$x - y - 2 \le 0 \qquad (1)$$

SOLUTION: Let lines L_1, L_2, L_3, L_4, and L_5 have the following equations, which are obtained from inequalities (1) through (5), respectively:

$$L_1: y = x - 2$$
$$L_2: y = -\frac{6}{7}x + \frac{25}{7}$$

$6x + 7y - 25 \leq 0$ (2)

$5x - 4y + 48 \geq 0$ (3)

$9x + 5y - 60 \leq 0$ (4)

$x + 3y + 2 \geq 0$ (5)

$L_3\colon y = \frac{5}{4}x + 12$

$L_4\colon y = -\frac{9}{5}x + 12$

$L_5\colon y = -\frac{1}{3}x - \frac{2}{3}$

We proceed to determine if there are any points which satisfy each of the inequalities. Solving simultaneously the equations for L_1 and L_2 we obtain the point of intersection $P(3, 1)$. We check to see if the coordinates of this point satisfy inequalities (3), (4), (5), and we see that they do. The coordinates of P then satisfy each of the five inequalities, and hence P is in the required region. We find the point of intersection of L_1 and L_3 to be $Q(-56, -58)$. The coordinates of Q satisfy inequalities (2) and (4) but not (5). So the point Q is not in the required region.

Continuing on, we see that L_1 and L_4 intersect at the point $R(5, 3)$, and the coordinates of R satisfy inequalities (3) and (5) but not (2). L_1 and L_5 intersect at the point $S(1, -1)$ and the coordinates of this point satisfy the three inequalities (2), (3), and (4). Therefore, the point S is in the required region. Taking the equations in pairs, we have ten points of intersection. We see that the point of intersection of L_2 and L_3, which is $T(-4, 7)$, and the point of intersection of L_3 and L_5, which is $U(-8, 2)$, are in the required region. The other remaining points are not. Then we have four points, P, S, T, and U, whose coordinates satisfy all five inequalities. We plot these four points and the five lines, as shown in Fig. 1.9.9. Considering the closed half planes defined by inequalities (1) through (5), we see that the interior and the sides of the quadrilateral $PSTU$ give us all the points whose coordinates satisfy the given system.

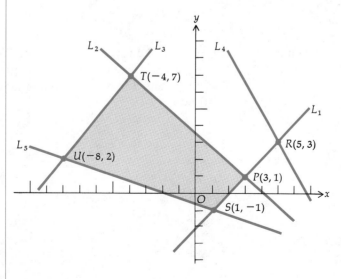

Figure 1.9.9

The inequalities

$$y \leq Ax^2 + Bx + C$$

and

$$y \geq Ax^2 + Bx + C$$

are quadratic inequalities, and we can draw a sketch of their graphs by a method similar to that for linear inequalities. The following example illustrates the method.

EXAMPLE 5: Draw a sketch of the region defined by the inequality $$y < 2x^2 - 8x + 5$$	SOLUTION: By equating the two members of the given inequality, we obtain the equation $y = 2x^2 - 8x + 5$, which is equivalent to $y + 3 = 2(x - 2)^2$. A sketch of the graph of this parabola is shown in Fig. 1.9.10 by a broken curve, because the parabola is not part of the graph of the inequality. The required region is below the parabola and is shaded in the figure.

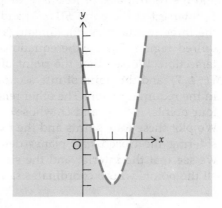

Figure 1.9.10

EXAMPLE 6: Draw a sketch of the region defined by the system of inequalities $$x^2 - 4 \leq y \leq 4 - x^2 \qquad |x| > 1$$	SOLUTION: The given system consists of the four inequalities $x^2 - 4 \leq y$, $y \leq 4 - x^2$, $x > 1$, and $x < -1$. The graph of each of these inequalities is shaded in Fig. 1.9.11. The triple-shaded region in the figure is the one required.

Figure 1.9.11

Consider now a circle having its center at $C(h, k)$ and radius r. All the points (x, y) whose coordinates satisfy the equation

$$\sqrt{(x - h)^2 + (y - k)^2} = r$$

are r units from C and hence lie on the circle. The points whose coordinates satisfy the inequality

$$\sqrt{(x - h)^2 + (y - k)^2} < r \tag{6}$$

are at a distance less than r units from C, and these points are in the region called the *interior* of the circle. Similarly, the points whose coordinates satisfy the inequality

$$\sqrt{(x - h)^2 + (y - k)^2} > r \tag{7}$$

are in the region called the *exterior* of the circle because these points are at a distance greater than r units from C. By squaring both members of inequalities (6) and (7), we have the following theorem.

1.9.2 Theorem   The graph of the inequality

$$(x - h)^2 + (y - k)^2 < r^2$$

is the interior of the circle having center at (h, k) and radius r, and the graph of the inequality

$$(x - h)^2 + (y - k)^2 > r^2$$

is the exterior of the circle.

In Figs. 1.9.12 and 1.9.13 we have shaded the interior and exterior, respectively, of the circle whose center is at $(-2, 1)$ and whose radius is 3.

Figure 1.9.12

Figure 1.9.13

Exercises 1.9

In Exercises 1 through 16, draw a sketch of the graph of the given inequality.

1. $y > 3x - 1$
2. $y \leq 3x - 1$
3. $3x - 5 \geq 0$
4. $y + 6 < 0$
5. $2x - 4y + 5 \leq 0$
6. $3y - x - 8 > 0$
7. $9x + 3y - 7 \geq 0$
8. $5x - 2y + 6 \geq 0$
9. $y - 4x^2 < 0$

10. $2x^2 + 9y \geq 0$ 11. $x^2 - 4y + 8 \geq 0$ 12. $x^2 + 4y + 6x + 8 < 0$

13. $x^2 + y^2 < 16$ 14. $x^2 + y^2 \geq 25$ 15. $x^2 + y^2 \geq 2(3y - 2x)$

16. $3x^2 + 3y^2 - 6x + 8y < 1$

In Exercises 17 through 38, draw a sketch of the region (if any) defined by the given system of inequalities.

17. $2x + y \leq 4, y - 2x \leq 4$ 18. $2x + y \geq 4, y - 2x \geq 4$

19. $-1 < x - y \leq 2$ 20. $3 + y \leq x \leq y - 4$

21. $4x + 3y - 7 > 0, 6x - y - 5 < 0$ 22. $6x - 2y - 7 \leq 0, 4x + y - 6 \geq 0$

23. $4 < x^2 + y^2 < 9$ 24. $x^2 + y^2 \leq 36, x \geq 3, y \leq 3$

25. $x - 2y - 4 < 0, y > 11 - 6x, 4x + 5y < 29$ 26. $x - y - 1 \leq 0, x + y + 1 \geq 0, x - y + 1 \geq 0, x + y - 1 \leq 0$

27. $x^2 - y + 4 > 0, x - y \leq 4$ 28. $x^2 - y + 1 < 0, x + y - 4 > 0$

29. $x^2 + y^2 \geq 16, y > x^2$ 30. $x^2 - 3 \leq y \leq 3 - x^2$

31. $x^2 + y^2 \leq 25, x^2 - y - 3 \leq 0, x^2 + y - 3 \leq 0$ 32. $16 \leq x^2 + y^2 \leq 25, x^2 + 2 \leq y \leq x^2 + 4$

33. $4 \leq x^2 + y^2 \leq 9, |x - y| \leq 1$ 34. $4 \leq x^2 + y^2 \leq 9, |x| + 2 \leq y \leq |x| + 3$

35. $x \geq 0, y \geq 0, y \leq 3, x + y - 5 \leq 0, 2x + y - 8 \leq 0$ 36. $x \geq 0, y \geq 0, y - x + 1 \geq 0, x + y - 5 \leq 0, x + 3y - 8 \leq 0$

37. $x \geq 1, y \leq 0, 2x - y - 4 \leq 0, 3x - y - 4 \leq 0, x + y - 7 \leq 0$

38. $1 - x - y \leq 0, x \geq 3 - y, y \geq 2, 2x + y - 1 \geq 0, x \leq 2, y \leq 6$

In Exercises 39 through 44, define the given region by a single inequality or a system of inequalities.

39. The closed half plane bounded by $3x - 4y + 5 = 0$ and containing the point $(-4, 1)$.

40. The half plane below the line $2x + 3y - 6 = 0$ and to the right of the y axis.

41. The region containing the interior and sides of the triangle having vertices at $(2, 2)$, $(3, 6)$, and $(4, 1)$.

42. The region containing the interior and sides of the quadrilateral having vertices at $(-3, 4)$, $(-3, 6)$, $(-1, 8)$, and $(2, 6)$.

43. The region which is exterior to the circle having its center at $(-3, 4)$ and a radius of 2 and interior to the circle having its center at $(-3, 4)$ and a radius of 6.

44. The region that is common to the interiors of the circles $x^2 + y^2 - 10x - 6y + 18 = 0$ and $x^2 + y^2 - 10x + 6y + 18 = 0$.

Review Exercises (Chapter 1)

In Exercises 1 through 6 find all real numbers satisfying the given inequality. Give the interval solution and illustrate the solution on the number line.

1. $8 < 5x + 4 \leq 10$ 2. $\dfrac{x}{x - 1} > \dfrac{1}{4}$ 3. $2x^2 + x < 3$

4. $\dfrac{3}{x + 4} < \dfrac{2}{x - 5}$ 5. $|3 + 5x| \leq 9$ 6. $\left| \dfrac{2 - 3x}{3 + x} \right| \geq \dfrac{1}{4}$

7. Define the following sets of points by either an equation or an inequality: (a) the point circle $(3, -5)$; (b) the set of all points whose distance from the point $(3, -5)$ is less than 4; (c) the set of all points whose distance from the point $(3, -5)$ is at least 5.

8. Prove that the points $(1, -1)$, $(3, 2)$, and $(7, 8)$ are collinear in two ways: (a) by using the distance formula; (b) by using slopes.

9. Find equations of the lines passing through the origin that are tangent to the circle having its center at $(2, 1)$ and a radius of 2.

10. Prove that the quadrilateral having vertices at $(1, 2)$, $(5, -1)$, $(11, 7)$, and $(7, 10)$ is a rectangle.

11. Determine the values of k and h if $3x + ky + 2 = 0$ and $5x - y + h = 0$ are equations of the same line.

12. Show that the triangle with vertices at $(-8, 1)$, $(-1, -6)$ and $(2, 4)$ is isosceles and find its area.

13. Two vertices of a parallelogram are at $(-3, 4)$ and $(2, 3)$ and its center is at $(0, -1)$. Find the other two vertices.

14. Two opposite vertices of a square are at $(3, -4)$ and $(9, -4)$. Find the other two vertices.

15. Determine all values of k for which the graphs of the two equations $x^2 + y^2 = k$ and $x + y = k$ intersect.

16. Prove that if x is any real number, $|x| < x^2 + 1$.

17. Find an equation of the circle circumscribed about the triangle having sides on the lines $x - 3y + 2 = 0, 3x - 2y + 6 = 0$, and $2x + y - 3 = 0$.

18. Find an equation of the circle having as its diameter the common chord of the two circles $x^2 + y^2 + 2x - 2y - 14 = 0$ and $x^2 + y^2 - 4x + 4y - 2 = 0$.

19. Find an equation of the parabola having vertex at $(5, 1)$, axis parallel to the y axis and through the point $(9, 3)$.

20. Show that any equation of the form $xy + ax + by + c = 0$ can always be written in the form $x'y' = k$ by a translation of the axes, and determine the value of k.

21. Any section of a parabolic mirror made by passing a plane through the axis of the mirror is a segment of a parabola. The altitude of the segment is 12 in. and the length of the base is 18 in. A section of the mirror made by a plane perpendicular to its axis is a circle. Find the circumference of the circular plane section if the plane perpendicular to the axis is 3 in. from the vertex.

22. Find an equation of the line through the point of intersection of the lines $5x + 6y - 4 = 0$ and $x - 3y + 2 = 0$ and perpendicular to the line $x - 4y - 20 = 0$ without finding the point of intersection of the two lines. (HINT: See Exercise 28 in Exercises 1.5.)

23. The sides of a parallelogram are on the lines $x + 2y - 10 = 0, 3x - y + 20 = 0, x + 2y - 15 = 0$, and $3x - y + 10 = 0$. Find the equations of the diagonals without finding the vertices of the parallelogram. (HINT: See Exercise 28 in Exercises 1.5.)

24. Draw a sketch of the region defined by the inequalities: $2x - y \geq 1, x + y \leq 2$, and $x - 2y \geq 2$.

25. Draw a sketch of the region defined by the inequalities: $9 \leq x^2 + y^2 \leq 25$, and $x^2 + 1 \leq y \leq x^2 + 2$.

26. Prove that the two lines $A_1x + B_1y + C_1 = 0$ and $A_2x + B_2y + C_2 = 0$ are parallel if and only if $A_1B_2 - A_2B_1 = 0$.

27. Prove analytically that the three medians of any triangle meet in a point.

28. Prove analytically that the line segment joining the midpoints of any two sides of a triangle is parallel to the third side and that its length is one-half the length of the third side.

29. Prove analytically that if the diagonals of a rectangle are perpendicular, then the rectangle is a square.

30. Prove analytically that the set of points equidistant from two given points is the perpendicular bisector of the line segment joining the two points.

31. In a triangle the point of intersection of the medians, the point of intersection of the altitudes, and the center of the circumscribed circle are collinear. Find these three points and prove they are collinear for the triangle having vertices at $(2, 8)$, $(5, -1)$, and $(6, 6)$.

32. Find the length of a side of an equilateral triangle having a vertex at the origin and inscribed in the parabola $x^2 = 4py$.

33. The directrix of the parabola $y^2 = 4px$ is tangent to a circle having the focus of the parabola as its center. Find an equation of the circle and the points of intersection of the two curves.

34. Prove that the midpoints of all chords parallel to a fixed chord of a parabola lie on a line which is parallel to the axis of the parabola.

35. The points P and Q are on the parabola $y^2 = 4px$ and the line segment PQ is perpendicular to the axis of the parabola. If the length of PQ is $8|p|$, prove that the lines OP and OQ are perpendicular.

36. Line segments are drawn from a fixed point P to all points on a fixed circle C. Determine the curve on which the midpoints of these line segments lie.

2

Functions, Limits, and Continuity

2.1 FUNCTIONS AND THEIR GRAPHS

We intuitively consider a quantity y to be a function of another quantity x if there is some rule by which a unique value is assigned to y by a corresponding value of x. Familiar examples of such relationships are given by equations such as

$$y = 2x^2 + 5 \tag{1}$$

and

$$y = \sqrt{x^2 - 9} \tag{2}$$

It is not necessary that x and y be related by an equation in order for a functional relationship to exist between them. For example, if y is the number of cents in the postage of an airmail letter, and if x is the number of ounces in the weight of the letter, then y is a function of x. For this functional relationship, there is no equation involving x and y; however, the relationship between x and y may be given by means of a table, such as Table 2.1.1.

Table 2.1.1

x: number of ounces in the weight of the letter	$0 < x \leq 1$	$1 < x \leq 2$	$2 < x \leq 3$	$3 < x \leq 4$	$4 < x \leq 5$	$5 < x \leq 6$
y: number of cents in airmail postage	11	22	33	44	55	66

The formal definition makes the concept of a function precise.

2.1.1 Definition   A *function* is a set of ordered pairs of numbers (x, y) in which no two distinct ordered pairs have the same first number. The set of all possible values of x is called the *domain* of the function, and the set of all possible values of y is called the *range* of the function.

In Definition 2.1.1, the restriction that no two distinct ordered pairs can have the same first number assures us that y is unique for a specific value of x.

Equation (1) defines a function. Let us call this function f. The equation gives the rule by which a unique value of y can be determined whenever x is given: that is, multiply the number x by itself, then multiply that product by 2, and add 5. The function f is the set of all ordered pairs (x, y) such that x and y satisfy Eq. (1). The numbers x and y are called *variables*. Because for the function f values are assigned to x and because the value of y is dependent upon the choice of x, we call x the *independent variable* and y the *dependent variable*. The domain of the function is the set of all possible values of the independent variable, and the range of the function is the set of all possible values of the dependent variable. For the function f under consideration, the domain is the set of all real numbers which can be denoted with interval notation as $(-\infty, +\infty)$. The smallest value that y can assume is 5 (when $x = 0$). The range of f is then the set of all positive numbers greater than or equal to 5, which is $[5, +\infty)$.

Now, let g be the function which is the set of all ordered pairs (x, y) defined by Eq. (2): $y = \sqrt{x^2 - 9}$. Because the numbers are confined to real numbers, y is a function of x only for $x \geq 3$ or $x \leq -3$ (or simply $|x| \geq 3$) because for any x satisfying either of these inequalities a unique value of y is determined. However, if x is in the interval $-3 < x < 3$, a square root of a negative number is obtained, and hence no real number y exists. Therefore, we must restrict x, and we say that the function g is the set of all ordered pairs (x, y) such that

$$y = \sqrt{x^2 - 9} \quad \text{and} \quad |x| \geq 3$$

The domain of g is $(-\infty, -3]$ and $[3, +\infty)$, and the range of g is $[0, +\infty)$.

It should be stressed that in order to have a function there must be *exactly one value* of the dependent variable for a value of the independent variable in the domain of the function.

2.1.2 Definition   If f is a function, then the *graph* of f is the set of all points (x, y) in R_2 for which (x, y) is an ordered pair in f.

Hence, the graph of a function is a curve which is the set of all points in R_2 whose cartesian coordinates are given by the ordered pairs of numbers (x, y). Because for each value of x in the domain of the function there corresponds a unique value of y, no vertical line can intersect the graph of the function at more than one point.

EXAMPLE 1:   Let f be the function which is the set of all ordered pairs (x, y) such that

$$y = \sqrt{5 - x}$$

Find the domain and range of f, and draw a sketch of the graph of f.

SOLUTION: A sketch of the graph of f is shown in Fig. 2.1.1. The domain of f is the set of all real numbers less than or equal to 5, which is $(-\infty, 5]$, and the range of f is the set of all nonnegative real numbers, which is $[0, +\infty)$.

Figure 2.1.1

EXAMPLE 2:   Let g be the function which is the set of all ordered pairs (x, y) such that

$$y = \begin{cases} -3 & \text{if } x \le -1 \\ 1 & \text{if } -1 < x \le 2 \\ 4 & \text{if } 2 < x \end{cases}$$

Find the domain and range of g, and draw a sketch of the graph of g.

SOLUTION: The domain of g is $(-\infty, +\infty)$, while the range of g consists of the three numbers -3, 1, and 4. A sketch of the graph is shown in Fig. 2.1.2.

Figure 2.1.2

Note in Fig. 2.1.2 that there is a break at $x = -1$ and another at $x = 2$. We say that g is discontinuous at -1 and 2. Continuous and discontinuous functions are considered in Sec. 2.11.

EXAMPLE 3:   Let h be the function which is the set of all ordered pairs (x, y) such that

$$y = |x|$$

Find the domain and range of h, and draw a sketch of the graph of h.

SOLUTION: The domain of h is $(-\infty, +\infty)$, and the range of h is $[0, +\infty)$. A sketch of the graph of h is shown in Fig. 2.1.3.

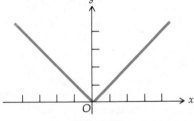

Figure 2.1.3

EXAMPLE 4:   Let F be the function which is the set of all ordered pairs (x, y) such that

$$y = \begin{cases} 3x - 2 & \text{if } x < 1 \\ x^2 & \text{if } 1 \le x \end{cases}$$

Find the domain and range of F, and draw a sketch of the graph of F.

SOLUTION: A sketch of the graph of F is shown in Fig. 2.1.4. The domain of F is $(-\infty, +\infty)$, and the range of F is $(-\infty, +\infty)$.

Figure 2.1.4

EXAMPLE 5:   Let G be the function which is the set of all ordered pairs (x, y) such that

$$y = \frac{x^2 - 9}{x - 3}$$

Find the domain and range of G, and draw a sketch of the graph of G.

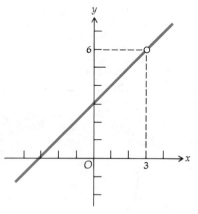

Figure 2.1.5

SOLUTION: A sketch of the graph is shown in Fig. 2.1.5. Because a value for y is determined for each value of x except $x = 3$, the domain of G consists of all real numbers except 3. When $x = 3$, both the numerator and denominator are zero, and 0/0 is undefined.

Factoring the numerator into $(x - 3)(x + 3)$, we obtain

$$y = \frac{(x - 3)(x + 3)}{(x - 3)}$$

or $y = x + 3$, provided that $x \ne 3$. In other words, the function G consists of all ordered pairs (x, y) such that

$$y = x + 3 \quad \text{and} \quad x \ne 3$$

The range of G consists of all real numbers except 6. The graph consists of all points on the line $y = x + 3$ except the point $(3, 6)$.

EXAMPLE 6:   Let H be the function which is the set of all ordered pairs (x, y) such that

SOLUTION: A sketch of the graph of this function is shown in Fig. 2.1.6. The graph consists of the point $(3, 2)$ and all points on the line $y = x + 3$ except the point $(3, 6)$. Function H is defined for all values of x, and there-

$$y = \begin{cases} x+3 & \text{if } x \neq 3 \\ 2 & \text{if } x = 3 \end{cases}$$

Find the domain and range of H, and draw a sketch of the graph of H.

fore the domain of H is $(-\infty, +\infty)$. The range of H consists of all real numbers except 6.

Figure 2.1.6

EXAMPLE 7:   Let ϕ be the function which is the set of all ordered pairs (x, y) such that

$$y = \frac{(x^2 + 3x - 4)(x^2 - 9)}{(x^2 + x - 12)(x + 3)}$$

Find the domain and range of ϕ, and draw a sketch of the graph of ϕ.

Figure 2.1.7

SOLUTION: A sketch of the graph of this function is shown in Fig. 2.1.7. Factoring the numerator and denominator, we obtain

$$y = \frac{(x+4)(x-1)(x-3)(x+3)}{(x+4)(x-3)(x+3)}$$

We see that the denominator is zero for $x = -4, -3$, and 3; therefore, ϕ is undefined for these three values of x. For values of $x \neq -4, -3$, or 3, we may divide numerator and denominator by the common factors and obtain

$$y = x - 1 \quad \text{if} \quad x \neq -4, -3, \text{ or } 3$$

Therefore, the domain of ϕ is the set of all real numbers except -4, -3, and 3, and the range of ϕ is the set of all real numbers except those values of $(x - 1)$ obtained by replacing x by $-4, -3$, or 3, that is, all real numbers except $-5, -4$, and 2. The graph of this function is the straight line $y = x - 1$, with the points $(-4, -5)$, $(-3\ -4)$, and $(3, 2)$ deleted.

EXAMPLE 8:   Let f be the function which is the set of all ordered pairs (x, y) such that

$$y = \begin{cases} x^2 & \text{if } x \neq 2 \\ 7 & \text{if } x = 2 \end{cases}$$

Find the domain and range of f, and draw a sketch of the graph of f.

SOLUTION: A sketch of the graph of f is shown in Fig. 2.1.8. The graph consists of the point $(2, 7)$ and all points on the parabola $y = x^2$, except the point $(2, 4)$. Function f is defined for all values of x, and so the domain of f is $(-\infty, +\infty)$. The range of f consists of all nonnegative real numbers.

Figure 2.1.8

EXAMPLE 9:   Let h be the function which is the set of all ordered pairs (x, y) such that

$$y = \begin{cases} x - 1 & \text{if } x < 3 \\ 2x + 1 & \text{if } 3 \leq x \end{cases}$$

Find the domain and range of h, and draw a sketch of the graph of h.

SOLUTION: A sketch of the graph of h is shown in Fig. 2.1.9. The domain of h is $(-\infty, +\infty)$. The values of y are either less than 2 or greater than or equal to 7. So the range of h is $(-\infty, 2)$ and $[7, +\infty)$ or, equivalently, all real numbers not in $[2, 7)$.

Figure 2.1.9

EXAMPLE 10:   Let g be the function which is the set of all ordered pairs (x, y) such that

$$y = \sqrt{x(x-2)}$$

Find the domain and range of g, and draw a sketch of the graph of g.

Figure 2.1.10

SOLUTION: Because $\sqrt{x(x-2)}$ is not a real number when $x(x-2) < 0$, the domain of g consists of the values of x for which $x(x-2) \geq 0$. This inequality will be satisfied when one of the following two cases holds: $x \geq 0$ and $x - 2 \geq 0$; or $x \leq 0$ and $x - 2 \leq 0$.

Case 1: $x \geq 0$ and $x - 2 \geq 0$.

    That is,

$$x \geq 0 \quad \text{and} \quad x \geq 2$$

Both inequalities hold if $x \geq 2$, which is the interval $[2, +\infty)$.

Case 2: $x \leq 0$ and $x - 2 \leq 0$.
    That is,

$$x \leq 0 \quad \text{and} \quad x \leq 2$$

Both inequalities hold if $x \leq 0$, which is the interval $(-\infty, 0]$.

    Combining the solutions for the two cases, we obtain for the domain of g the two intervals $(-\infty, 0]$ and $[2, +\infty)$. The range of g is the interval $[0, +\infty)$. Figure 2.1.10 shows a sketch of the graph of g.

Exercises 2.1

In each of the following exercises, the function is the set of all ordered pairs (x, y) satisfying the given equation. Find the domain and range of the function, and draw a sketch of the graph of the function.

1. $f: y = 3x - 1$

2. $g: y = x^2 + 2$

3. $F: y = 3x^2 - 6$

4. $G: y = \sqrt{x+1}$

5. $h: y = \sqrt{3x - 4}$

6. $f: y = \sqrt{4 - x^2}$

7. $g: y = \sqrt{x^2 - 4}$

8. $H: y = |x - 3|$

9. $\phi: y = |3x + 2|$

10. $F: y = \dfrac{4x^2 - 1}{2x + 1}$

11. $G: y = \begin{cases} -2 & \text{if } x \leq 3 \\ 2 & \text{if } 3 < x \end{cases}$

12. $h: y = \begin{cases} -4 & \text{if } x < -2 \\ -1 & \text{if } -2 \leq x \leq 2 \\ 3 & \text{if } 2 < x \end{cases}$

13. $f: y = \begin{cases} 2x - 1 & \text{if } x \neq 2 \\ 0 & \text{if } x = 2 \end{cases}$

14. $\phi: y = \begin{cases} \sqrt{25 - x^2} & \text{if } x \leq 5 \\ x - 5 & \text{if } 5 < x \end{cases}$

15. $H: y = \begin{cases} x^2 - 4 & \text{if } x < 3 \\ 2x - 1 & \text{if } 3 \leq x \end{cases}$

16. $g: y = \begin{cases} 6x + 7 & \text{if } x \leq -2 \\ 4 - x & \text{if } -2 < x \end{cases}$

17. $F: y = \dfrac{(x+1)(x^2 + 3x - 10)}{x^2 + 6x + 5}$

18. $G: y = \dfrac{(x^2 + 3x - 4)(x^2 - 5x + 6)}{(x^2 - 3x + 2)(x - 3)}$

19. $f: y = \sqrt{x^2 - 3x - 4}$

20. $h: y = \sqrt{6x^2 - 5x - 4}$

21. $g: y = \dfrac{x^3 - 2x^2}{x - 2}$

22. $f: y = \dfrac{x^3 - x^2 - 13x - 3}{x + 3}$

23. $h: y = \dfrac{x^3 + 9x^2 + 27x + 35}{x + 5}$

24. $F: y = \dfrac{x^4 - 3x^3 - 11x^2 + 23x + 6}{x^2 + x - 6}$

2.2 FUNCTION NOTATION AND OPERATIONS ON FUNCTIONS

If f is the function having as its domain values of x and as its range values of y, the symbol $f(x)$ (read "f of x") denotes the particular value of y which corresponds to the value of x. Therefore, in Example 1 of Sec. 2.1, we may write $f(x) = \sqrt{5 - x}$; because when $x = 1$, $\sqrt{5 - x} = 2$, we write $f(1) = 2$. Similarly, $f(-6) = \sqrt{11}$, $f(0) = \sqrt{5}$, and so on. In Example 2 of Sec. 2.1, because the function is denoted by g, we would use the symbol $g(x)$ to denote the function value corresponding to x; thus, we have $g(-5) = -3$, $g(0) = 1$, $g(2) = 1$, $g(17) = 4$, and so on.

When defining a function, the domain of the independent variable must be given either explicitly or implicitly. For example, if we are given

$$f(x) = 3x^2 - 5x + 2$$

it is implied that x can be any real number. However, if we are given

$$f(x) = 3x^2 - 5x + 2 \qquad 1 \le x \le 10$$

then the domain of f consists of all real numbers between and including one and ten.

Similarly, if g is defined by the equation

$$g(x) = \frac{5x - 2}{x + 4}$$

it is implied that $x \ne -4$, because the quotient is undefined for $x = -4$; hence, the domain of g is the set of all real numbers except -4.

If we are given

$$h(x) = \sqrt{9 - x^2}$$

it is implied that x is in the closed interval $-3 \le x \le 3$, because $\sqrt{9 - x^2}$ is undefined (i.e., not a real number) for $x > 3$ or $x < -3$. So the domain of h is $[-3, +3]$, and the range of h is $[0, 3]$.

EXAMPLE 1: Given that f is the function defined by $f(x) = x^2 + 3x - 4$, find: (a) $f(0)$; (b) $f(2)$; (c) $f(h)$; (d) $f(2h)$; (e) $f(2x)$; (f) $f(x + h)$; (g) $f(x) + f(h)$.

SOLUTION:

(a) $f(0) = 0^2 + 3 \cdot 0 - 4 = -4$
(b) $f(2) = 2^2 + 3 \cdot 2 - 4 = 6$
(c) $f(h) = h^2 + 3h - 4$
(d) $f(2h) = (2h)^2 + 3(2h) - 4 = 4h^2 + 6h - 4$
(e) $f(2x) = (2x)^2 + 3(2x) - 4 = 4x^2 + 6x - 4$
(f) $f(x + h) = (x + h)^2 + 3(x + h) - 4$
$\qquad = x^2 + 2hx + h^2 + 3x + 3h - 4$
$\qquad = x^2 + (2h + 3)x + (h^2 + 3h - 4)$
(g) $f(x) + f(h) = (x^2 + 3x - 4) + (h^2 + 3h - 4)$
$\qquad = x^2 + 3x + (h^2 + 3h - 8)$

EXAMPLE 2: Given

$$g(x) = \sqrt{3x - 1}$$

find

$$\frac{g(x + h) - g(x)}{h} \qquad h \ne 0$$

SOLUTION:

$$\frac{g(x + h) - g(x)}{h} = \frac{\sqrt{3(x + h) - 1} - \sqrt{3x - 1}}{h}$$

$$= \frac{(\sqrt{3x + 3h - 1} - \sqrt{3x - 1})(\sqrt{3x + 3h - 1} + \sqrt{3x - 1})}{h(\sqrt{3x + 3h - 1} + \sqrt{3x - 1})}$$

$$= \frac{(3x + 3h - 1) - (3x - 1)}{h(\sqrt{3x + 3h - 1} + \sqrt{3x - 1})}$$

$$= \frac{3h}{h(\sqrt{3x + 3h - 1} + \sqrt{3x - 1})}$$

$$= \frac{3}{\sqrt{3x + 3h - 1} + \sqrt{3x - 1}}$$

In the second step of this solution, the numerator and denominator were multiplied by the conjugate of the numerator in order to rationalize the numerator, and this gave a common factor of h in the numerator and the denominator.

We now consider operations (i.e., addition, subtraction, multiplication, division) on functions. The functions obtained from these operations—called the sum, the difference, the product, and the quotient of the original functions—are defined as follows.

2.2.1 Definition   Given the two functions f and g:

(i) their *sum*, denoted by $(f + g)$, is the function defined by $(f + g)(x) = f(x) + g(x)$;

(ii) their *difference*, denoted by $(f - g)$, is the function defined by $(f - g)(x) = f(x) - g(x)$;

(iii) their *product*, denoted by $(f \cdot g)$, is the function defined by $(f \cdot g)(x) = f(x) \cdot g(x)$;

(iv) their *quotient*, denoted by (f/g), is the function defined by $(f/g)(x) = f(x)/g(x)$.

In each case the *domain* of the resulting function consists of those values of x common to the domains of f and g, with the exception that in case (iv) the values of x for which $g(x) = 0$ are excluded.

EXAMPLE 3:   Given that f is the function defined by $f(x) = \sqrt{x + 1}$ and g is the function defined by $g(x) = \sqrt{x - 4}$, find: (a) $(f + g)(x)$; (b) $(f - g)(x)$; (c) $(f \cdot g)(x)$; (d) $(f/g)(x)$. In each case, determine the domain of the resulting function.

SOLUTION:

(a) $(f + g)(x) = \sqrt{x + 1} + \sqrt{x - 4}$
(b) $(f - g)(x) = \sqrt{x + 1} - \sqrt{x - 4}$
(c) $(f \cdot g)(x) = \sqrt{x + 1} \cdot \sqrt{x - 4}$

(d) $(f/g)(x) = \dfrac{\sqrt{x + 1}}{\sqrt{x - 4}}$

The domain of f is $[-1, +\infty)$, and the domain of g is $[4, +\infty)$. So in parts (a), (b), and (c) the domain of the resulting function is $[4, +\infty)$. In part (d) the denominator is zero when $x = 4$; thus, 4 is excluded from the domain, and the domain is therefore $(4, +\infty)$.

To indicate the product of a function f multiplied by itself, or $f \cdot f$, we write f^2. For example, if f is defined by $f(x) = 3x$, then f^2 is the function defined by $f^2(x) = (3x)(3x) = 9x^2$.

In addition to combining two functions by the operations given in Definition 2.2.1, we shall consider the *composite function* of two given functions.

2.2.2 Definition   Given the two functions f and g, the *composite function*, denoted by $f \circ g$, is defined by

$$(f \circ g)(x) = f(g(x))$$

and the domain of $f \circ g$ is the set of all numbers x in the domain of g such that $g(x)$ is in the domain of f.

EXAMPLE 4: Given that f is defined by $f(x) = \sqrt{x}$ and g is defined by $g(x) = 2x - 3$, find $F(x)$ if $F = f \circ g$, and find the domain of F.

SOLUTION: $F(x) = (f \circ g)(x) = f(g(x))$

$$= f(2x - 3)$$

$$= \sqrt{2x - 3}$$

The domain of g is $(-\infty, +\infty)$, and the domain of f is $[0, +\infty)$. So the domain of F is the set of real numbers for which $2x - 3 \geq 0$ or, equivalently, $[\frac{3}{2}, +\infty)$.

EXAMPLE 5: Given that f is defined by $f(x) = \sqrt{x}$ and g is defined by $g(x) = x^2 - 1$, find:
(a) $f \circ f$; (b) $g \circ g$; (c) $f \circ g$; (d) $g \circ f$. Also find the domain of the composite function in each part.

SOLUTION: The domain of f is $[0, +\infty)$, and the domain of g is $(-\infty, +\infty)$.

(a) $(f \circ f)(x) = f(f(x)) = f(\sqrt{x}) = \sqrt{\sqrt{x}} = \sqrt[4]{x}$
   The domain of $f \circ f$ is $[0, +\infty)$.
(b) $(g \circ g)(x) = g(g(x)) = g(x^2 - 1) = (x^2 - 1)^2 - 1 = x^4 - 2x^2$
   The domain of $g \circ g$ is $(-\infty, +\infty)$.
(c) $(f \circ g)(x) = f(g(x)) = f(x^2 - 1) = \sqrt{x^2 - 1}$
   The domain of $f \circ g$ consists of the two intervals $(-\infty, -1]$ and $[1, +\infty)$ or, equivalently, all x not in $(-1, 1)$.
(d) $(g \circ f)(x) = g(f(x)) = g(\sqrt{x}) = (\sqrt{x})^2 - 1 = x - 1$
   The domain of $g \circ f$ is $[0, +\infty)$. Note that even though $x - 1$ is defined for all values of x, the domain of $g \circ f$, by Definition 2.2.2, is the set of all numbers x in the domain of f such that $f(x)$ is in the domain of g.

A function f is said to be an *even* function if for every x in the domain of f, $f(-x) = f(x)$; and f is said to be an *odd* function if for every x in the domain of f, $f(-x) = -f(x)$, it being understood that $-x$ is in the domain of f whenever x is. In particular, if f is the function defined by $f(x) = 3x^4 - 2x^2 + 7$, then $f(-x) = 3(-x)^4 - 2(-x)^2 + 7 = 3x^4 - 2x^2 + 7 = f(x)$, and so f is an even function. The function g for which $g(x) = 2x^5 + 5x^3 - 8x$ is an odd function since $g(-x) = 2(-x)^5 + 5(-x)^3 - 8(-x) = -2x^5 - 5x^3 + 8x = -(2x^5 + 5x^3 - 8x) = -g(x)$. Furthermore, the function h for which $h(x) = 2x^4 + 5x^3 - x^2 + 8$ is neither even nor odd.

From the definition of an even function and Theorem 1.3.6(ii) it follows that the graph of an even function is symmetric with respect to the y axis. From Theorem 1.3.6(iii) and the definition of an odd function, we see that the graph of an odd function is symmetric with respect to the origin.

Exercises 2.2

1. Given $f(x) = 2x^2 + 5x - 3$, find:

   (a) $f(-2)$ (b) $f(-1)$ (c) $f(0)$ (d) $f(3)$

   (e) $f(h + 1)$ (f) $f(2x^2)$ (g) $f(x^2 - 3)$ (h) $f(x + h)$

   (i) $f(x) + f(h)$ (j) $\dfrac{f(x + h) - f(x)}{h}$, $h \neq 0$

2. Given $g(x) = 3x^2 - 4$, find:

   (a) $g(-4)$ (b) $g(\frac{1}{2})$ (c) $g(x^2)$ (d) $g(3x^2 - 4)$

   (e) $g(x - h)$ (f) $g(x) - g(h)$ (g) $\dfrac{g(x + h) - g(x)}{h}$, $h \neq 0$

3. Given $F(x) = \sqrt{2x + 3}$, find:

   (a) $F(-1)$ (b) $F(4)$ (c) $F(\frac{1}{2})$

   (d) $F(30)$ (e) $F(2x + 3)$ (f) $\dfrac{F(x + h) - F(x)}{h}$, $h \neq 0$

4. Given $G(x) = \sqrt{2x^2 + 1}$, find:

   (a) $G(-2)$ (b) $G(0)$ (c) $G(\frac{1}{3})$

   (d) $G(\frac{4}{7})$ (e) $G(2x^2 - 1)$ (f) $\dfrac{G(x + h) - G(x)}{h}$, $h \neq 0$

5. Given

$$f(x) = \begin{cases} \dfrac{|x|}{x} & \text{if } x \neq 0 \\ 1 & \text{if } x = 0 \end{cases}$$

   find: (a) $f(1)$; (b) $f(-1)$; (c) $f(4)$; (d) $f(-4)$; (e) $f(-x)$; (f) $f(x + 1)$; (g) $f(x^2)$; (h) $f(-x^2)$.

6. Given $f(t) = \dfrac{|3 + t| - |t| - 3}{t}$ express $f(t)$ without absolute-value bars if (a) $t \geq 0$; (b) $-3 \leq t < 0$; (c) $t < -3$.

In Exercises 7 through 12 the functions f and g are defined. In each problem define the following functions and determine the domain of the resulting function: (a) $f + g$; (b) $f - g$; (c) $f \cdot g$; (d) f/g; (e) g/f; (f) $f \circ g$; (g) $g \circ f$.

7. $f(x) = x - 5$; $g(x) = x^2 - 1$ 8. $f(x) = \sqrt{x}$; $g(x) = x^2 + 1$ 9. $f(x) = \dfrac{x+1}{x-1}$; $g(x) = \dfrac{1}{x}$

10. $f(x) = \sqrt{x - 2}$; $g(x) = \dfrac{1}{x}$ 11. $f(x) = \sqrt{x^2 - 1}$; $g(x) = \sqrt{x - 1}$ 12. $f(x) = |x|$; $g(x) = |x - 3|$

13. For each of the following functions, determine whether f is even, odd, or neither.

(a) $f(x) = 2x^4 - 3x^2 + 1$ (b) $f(x) = 5x^3 - 7x$ (c) $f(s) = s^2 + 2s + 2$

(d) $f(x) = x^6 - 1$ (e) $f(t) = 5t^7 + 1$ (f) $f(x) = |x|$

(g) $f(y) = \dfrac{y^3 - y}{y^2 + 1}$ (h) $f(x) = \dfrac{x - 1}{x + 1}$

14. Prove that if f and g are both odd functions, then $(f + g)$ and $(f - g)$ are also odd functions.

15. Prove that if f and g are both odd functions, then $f \cdot g$ and f/g are both even functions.

16. Prove that any function can be expressed as the sum of an even function and an odd function by writing

$$f(x) = \tfrac{1}{2}[f(x) + f(-x)] + \tfrac{1}{2}[f(x) - f(-x)]$$

and showing that the function having function values $\tfrac{1}{2}[f(x) + f(-x)]$ is an even function and the function having function values $\tfrac{1}{2}[f(x) - f(-x)]$ is an odd function.

17. Use the result of Exercise 16 to express the functions defined by the following equations as the sum of an even function and an odd function: (a) $f(x) = x^2 + 2$; (b) $f(x) = x^3 - 1$; (c) $f(x) = x^4 + x^3 - x + 3$; (d) $f(x) = 1/x$; (e) $f(x) = (x - 1)/(x + 1)$; (f) $f(x) = |x| + |x - 1|$.

18. There is one function that is both even and odd. What is it?

19. Determine whether the composite function $f \circ g$ is odd or even in each of the following cases: (a) f and g are both even; (b) f and g are both odd; (c) f is even and g is odd; (d) f is odd and g is even.

20. The function g is defined by $g(x) = x^2$. Define a function f such that $(f \circ g)(x) = x$ if (a) $x \geq 0$; (b) $x < 0$.

21. Find the domain and range of $f \circ g$ and formulas for $(f \circ g)(x)$ if

$$f(x) = \begin{cases} 0 & \text{if } x < 0 \\ 2x & \text{if } 0 \leq x \leq 1 \\ 0 & \text{if } x > 1 \end{cases} \quad \text{and} \quad g(x) = \begin{cases} 1 & \text{if } x < 0 \\ \tfrac{1}{2}x & \text{if } 0 \leq x \leq 1 \\ 1 & \text{if } x > 1 \end{cases}$$

22. Find the domain and range of $g \circ f$ and formulas for $(g \circ f)(x)$ for the functions of Exercise 21.

23. Find the domain and range of $f \circ g$ and formulas for $(f \circ g)(x)$ if

$$f(x) = \begin{cases} 0 & \text{if } x < 0 \\ x^2 & \text{if } 0 \leq x \leq 1 \\ 0 & \text{if } x > 1 \end{cases} \quad \text{and} \quad g(x) = \begin{cases} 1 & \text{if } x < 0 \\ 2x & \text{if } 0 \leq x \leq 1 \\ 1 & \text{if } x > 1 \end{cases}$$

24. If $f(x) = x^2$, find two functions g for which $(f \circ g)(x) = 4x^2 - 12x + 9$.

25. If $f(x) = x^2 + 2x + 2$, find two functions g for which $(f \circ g)(x) = x^2 - 4x + 5$.

2.3 TYPES OF FUNCTIONS AND SOME SPECIAL FUNCTIONS

If the range of a function f consists of only one number, then f is called a *constant function*. So if $f(x) = c$, and if c is any real number, then f is a constant function and its graph is a straight line parallel to the x axis at a directed distance of c units from the x axis.

If a function f is defined by

$$f(x) = a_0 x^n + a_1 x^{n-1} + a_2 x^{n-2} + \cdots + a_{n-1} x + a_n$$

where n is a nonnegative integer, and $a_0, a_1, \ldots, a_n$ are real numbers ($a_0 \neq 0$), then f is called a *polynomial function* of degree n. Thus, the function f defined by

$$f(x) = 3x^5 - x^2 + 7x - 1$$

is a polynomial function of degree 5.

If the degree of a polynomial function is 1, then the function is called a *linear function;* if the degree is 2, the function is called a *quadratic function;* and if the degree is 3, the function is called a *cubic function.* So the function f defined by $f(x) = 3x + 4$ is a linear function. The function g defined by $g(x) = 5x^2 - 8x + 1$ is a quadratic function. The function h defined by $h(x) = 8x^3 - x + 4$ is a cubic function. If the degree of a polynomial function is zero, the function is a constant function.

The general linear function is defined by

$$f(x) = mx + b$$

where m and b are constants and $m \neq 0$. The graph of this function is a straight line having m as its slope and b as its y intercept.

The particular linear function defined by

$$f(x) = x$$

is called the *identity function.* The general quadratic function is defined by

$$f(x) = ax^2 + bx + c$$

where a, b, and c are constants and $a \neq 0$. The graph of the quadratic function is a parabola, which opens upward if $a > 0$ and downward if $a < 0$.

If a function can be expressed as the quotient of two polynomial functions, the function is called a *rational function.* For example, the function f defined by

$$f(x) = \frac{x^3 - x^2 + 5}{x^2 - 9}$$

is a rational function, for which the domain is the set of all real numbers except 3 and -3.

An *algebraic function* is a function formed by a finite number of algebraic operations on the identity function and the constant function. These algebraic operations include addition, subtraction, multiplication, division, raising to powers, and extracting roots. An example of an algebraic function is the function f defined by

$$f(x) = \frac{(x^2 - 3x + 1)^3}{\sqrt{x^4 + 1}}$$

In addition to algebraic functions, *transcendental functions* are considered in elementary calculus. Examples of transcendental functions are trigonometric functions, logarithmic functions, and exponential functions, which are discussed in later chapters. The following examples illustrate some special functions.

EXAMPLE 1: f is the function defined by

$$f(x) = 11n \quad \text{if} \quad n - 1 < x \leq n$$

where n is a positive integer. This is the function referred to in Table 2.1.1. Draw a sketch of the graph of this function.

SOLUTION: From the definition of the function it follows that

$$f(x) = 11 \quad \text{if} \quad 0 < x \leq 1$$
$$f(x) = 22 \quad \text{if} \quad 1 < x \leq 2$$
$$f(x) = 33 \quad \text{if} \quad 2 < x \leq 3$$
$$f(x) = 44 \quad \text{if} \quad 3 < x \leq 4$$

and so on. See Fig. 2.3.1.

Figure 2.3.1

In the following example, the symbol $[\![x]\!]$ is used. $[\![x]\!]$ is defined as the greatest integer which is less than or equal to x. Therefore, $[\![1]\!] = 1$, $[\![1.3]\!] = 1$, $[\![\tfrac{1}{2}]\!] = 0$, $[\![-4.2]\!] = -5$, $[\![-8]\!] = -8$, $[\![9.8]\!] = 9$. The function F defined by $F(x) = [\![x]\!]$ is called the *greatest integer function*.

EXAMPLE 2: F is the greatest integer function, defined by $F(x) = [\![x]\!] = n$, if $n \leq x < n + 1$, where n is an integer. Draw a sketch of the graph of F. State the domain and range of F.

Figure 2.3.2

SOLUTION: A sketch of the graph is shown in Fig. 2.3.2, where $y = [\![x]\!]$.

$$-5 \leq x < -4 \qquad [\![x]\!] = -5$$
$$-4 \leq x < -3 \qquad [\![x]\!] = -4$$
$$-3 \leq x < -2 \qquad [\![x]\!] = -3$$
$$-2 \leq x < -1 \qquad [\![x]\!] = -2$$
$$-1 \leq x < 0 \qquad [\![x]\!] = -1$$
$$0 \leq x < 1 \qquad [\![x]\!] = 0$$
$$1 \leq x < 2 \qquad [\![x]\!] = 1$$
$$2 \leq x < 3 \qquad [\![x]\!] = 2$$
$$3 \leq x < 4 \qquad [\![x]\!] = 3$$
$$4 \leq x < 5 \qquad [\![x]\!] = 4$$

The domain of F is the set of all real numbers. The range of F consists of all the integers.

EXAMPLE 3:   G is the function
defined by $G(x) = [[x]] - x$.
Draw a sketch of the graph of G.
State the domain and range of G.

Figure 2.3.3

SOLUTION:

If $0 \leq x < 1$,	$[[x]] = 0$;	so $G(x) = -x$.
If $1 \leq x < 2$,	$[[x]] = 1$;	so $G(x) = 1 - x$.
If $2 \leq x < 3$,	$[[x]] = 2$;	so $G(x) = 2 - x$.
If $-1 \leq x < 0$,	$[[x]] = -1$;	so $G(x) = -1 - x$.

and so on.

A sketch of the graph is shown in Fig. 2.3.3. The domain of G is the
set of all real numbers, and the range of G is $(-1, 0]$.

Exercises 2.3

For each of the functions in the following exercises, draw a sketch of the graph and state the domain and range. In Exercises 3 through 14, the function U is the unit step function defined in Exercise 1 and the function sgn is the signum function defined in Exercise 2.

1. U is the function defined by $U(t) = \begin{cases} 0 & \text{if } t < 0 \\ 1 & \text{if } t \geq 0 \end{cases}$

   This function U is called the *unit step function.*

2. The *signum function* (or *sign function*), denoted by sgn, is defined by

   $$\text{sgn } x = \begin{cases} -1 & \text{if } x < 0 \\ 0 & \text{if } x = 0 \\ 1 & \text{if } x > 0 \end{cases}$$

   sgn x is read "signum of x."

3. $f(x) = U(x - 1)$

4. $g(x) = U(x) - U(x - 1)$

5. $g(x) = \text{sgn}(x + 1) - \text{sgn}(x - 1)$

6. $f(x) = \text{sgn } x^2 - \text{sgn } x$

7. $h(x) = x \cdot U(x)$

8. $F(x) = (x + 1) \cdot U(x + 1)$

9. $G(x) = (x + 1) \cdot U(x + 1) - x \cdot U(x)$

10. $h(x) = \text{sgn } x - U(x)$

11. $F(x) = x - 2 \text{ sgn } x$

12. $f(x) = \text{sgn } x + x \cdot U(x)$

13. $f(x) = \text{sgn } x \cdot U(x + 1)$

14. $G(x) = \text{sgn}(U(x))$

15. $f(x) = |x| + |x - 1|$

16. $g(x) = |x| \cdot |x - 1|$

17. $G(x) = x - [[x]]$

18. $F(x) = [[x + 2]]$

19. $h(x) = [[x^2]]$

20. $H(x) = |x| + [[x]]$

21. $g(x) = \dfrac{[[x]]}{|x|}$

22. $f(x) = (x - [[x]])^2$

23. $f(x) = 2 + (-1)^n$, where $n = [[x]]$

24. $h(x) = \dfrac{|x|}{[[x]]}$

2.4 THE LIMIT OF A FUNCTION

Consider the function f defined by the equation

$$f(x) = \frac{(2x + 3)(x - 1)}{(x - 1)} \tag{1}$$

f is defined for all values of x except $x = 1$. Furthermore, if $x \neq 1$, the numerator and denominator can be divided by $(x - 1)$ to obtain

$$f(x) = 2x + 3 \qquad x \neq 1 \qquad\qquad (2)$$

We shall investigate the function values, $f(x)$, when x is close to 1 but not equal to 1. First, let x take on the values 0, 0.25, 0.50, 0.75, 0.9, 0.99, 0.999, 0.9999, and so on. We are taking values of x closer and closer to 1, but less than 1; in other words, the variable x is approaching 1 through values that are less than 1. We illustrate this in Table 2.4.1. Now, let the variable

Table 2.4.1

x	0	0.25	0.5	0.75	0.9	0.99	0.999	0.9999	0.99999
$f(x) = 2x + 3$ $(x \neq 1)$	3	3.5	4	4.5	4.8	4.98	4.998	4.9998	4.99998

x approach 1, through values that are greater than 1; that is, let x take on the values 2, 1.75, 1.5, 1.25, 1.1, 1.01, 1.001, 1.0001, 1.00001, and so on. Refer to Table 2.4.2.

Table 2.4.2

x	2	1.75	1.5	1.25	1.1	1.01	1.001	1.0001	1.00001
$f(x) = 2x + 3$ $(x \neq 1)$	7	6.5	6.0	5.5	5.2	5.02	5.002	5.0002	5.00002

We see from both tables that as x gets closer and closer to 1, $f(x)$ gets closer and closer to 5; and the closer x is to 1, the closer $f(x)$ is to 5. For instance, from Table 2.4.1, when $x = 0.9$, $f(x) = 4.8$; that is, when x is 0.1 less than 1, $f(x)$ is 0.2 less than 5. When $x = 0.999$, $f(x) = 4.998$; or when x is 0.001 less than 1, $f(x)$ is 0.002 less than 5. Furthermore, when $x = 0.9999$, $f(x) = 0.49998$; or when x is 0.0001 less than 1, $f(x)$ is 0.0002 less than 5.

Table 2.4.2 shows that when $x = 1.1$, $f(x) = 5.2$; or when x is 0.1 greater than 1, $f(x)$ is 0.2 greater than 5. When $x = 1.001$, $f(x) = 5.002$; or when x is 0.001 greater than 1, $f(x)$ is 0.002 greater than 5. When $x = 1.0001$, $f(x) = 5.0002$; or when x is 0.0001 greater than 1, $f(x)$ is 0.0002 greater than 5.

Therefore, from the two tables, we see that when x differs from 1 by ± 0.001 (i.e., $x = 0.999$ or $x = 1.001$), $f(x)$ differs from 5 by ± 0.002 [i.e., $f(x) = 4.998$ or $f(x) = 5.002$]. And when x differs from 1 by ± 0.0001, $f(x)$ differs from 5 by ± 0.0002.

Now, looking at the situation another way, we consider the values of $f(x)$ first. We see that we can make the value of $f(x)$ as close to 5 as we please by taking x close enough to 1. Another way of saying this is that we can make the absolute value of the difference between $f(x)$ and 5 as small as we please by making the absolute value of the difference between x and 1 small enough. That is, $|f(x) - 5|$ can be made as small as we please by making $|x - 1|$ small enough.

A more precise way of noting this is by using two symbols for these small differences. The symbols usually used are ϵ (epsilon) and δ (delta). So we state that $|f(x) - 5|$ will be less than ϵ whenever $|x - 1|$ is less than δ and $|x - 1| \neq 0$ (since $x \neq 1$). It is important to realize that the size of δ depends on the size of ϵ. Still another way of phrasing this is: Given any positive number ϵ, we can make $|f(x) - 5| < \epsilon$ by taking $|x - 1|$ small enough; that is, there is some sufficiently small positive number δ such that

$$|f(x) - 5| < \epsilon \quad \text{whenever} \quad 0 < |x - 1| < \delta \tag{3}$$

We see from the two tables that $|f(x) - 5| = 0.2$ when $|x - 1| = 0.1$. So, given $\epsilon = 0.2$, we take $\delta = 0.1$ and state that

$$|f(x) - 5| < 0.2 \quad \text{whenever} \quad 0 < |x - 1| < 0.1$$

This is statement (3), with $\epsilon = 0.2$ and $\delta = 0.1$.

Also, $|f(x) - 5| = 0.002$ when $|x - 1| = 0.001$. Hence, if $\epsilon = 0.002$, we take $\delta = 0.001$, and then

$$|f(x) - 5| < 0.002 \quad \text{whenever} \quad 0 < |x - 1| < 0.001$$

This is statement (3), with $\epsilon = 0.002$ and $\delta = 0.001$.

Similarly, if $\epsilon = 0.0002$, we take $\delta = 0.0001$ and state that

$$|f(x) - 5| < 0.0002 \quad \text{whenever} \quad 0 < |x - 1| < 0.0001$$

This is statement (3), with $\epsilon = 0.0002$ and $\delta = 0.0001$.

We could go on and give ϵ any small positive value, and find a suitable value for δ such that $|f(x) - 5|$ will be less than ϵ whenever $|x - 1|$ is less than δ and $x \neq 1$ (or $|x - 1| > 0$). Now, because for any $\epsilon > 0$ we can find a $\delta > 0$ such that $|f(x) - 5| < \epsilon$ whenever $0 < |x - 1| < \delta$, we state that the limit of $f(x)$ as x approaches 1 is equal to 5 or, expressed in symbols,

$$\lim_{x \to 1} f(x) = 5 \tag{4}$$

You will note that we state $0 < |x - 1|$. This condition is imposed because we are concerned only with values of $f(x)$ for x close to 1, but not for $x = 1$. As a matter of fact, this function is not defined for $x = 1$.

Let us see what this means geometrically for the particular function defined by Eq. (1). Figure 2.4.1 illustrates the geometric significance of ϵ and δ. We see that $f(x)$ on the vertical axis will lie between $5 - \epsilon$ and $5 + \epsilon$ whenever x on the horizontal axis lies between $1 - \delta$ and $1 + \delta$; or

$$|f(x) - 5| < \epsilon \quad \text{whenever} \quad 0 < |x - 1| < \delta$$

Another way of stating this is that $f(x)$ on the vertical axis can be restricted to lie between $5 - \epsilon$ and $5 + \epsilon$ by restricting x on the horizontal axis to lie between $1 - \delta$ and $1 + \delta$.

Figure 2.4.1

Note that the values of ϵ are chosen arbitrarily and can be as small as desired, and that the value of a δ is dependent on the ϵ chosen. We should also point out that the smaller the value of ϵ, the smaller will be the corresponding value of δ.

Summing up for this example, we state that $\lim_{x \to 1} f(x) = 5$ because for any $\epsilon > 0$, however small, there exists a $\delta > 0$ such that

$$|f(x) - 5| < \epsilon \quad \text{whenever} \quad 0 < |x - 1| < \delta$$

We are now in a position to define the limit of a function in general.

2.4.1 Definition   Let f be a function which is defined at every number in some open interval I containing a, except possibly at the number a itself. The *limit of* $f(x)$ *as x approaches a is L,* written as

$$\lim_{x \to a} f(x) = L \tag{5}$$

if for any $\epsilon > 0$, however small, there exists a $\delta > 0$ such that

$$|f(x) - L| < \epsilon \quad \text{whenever} \quad 0 < |x - a| < \delta \tag{6}$$

In words, Definition 2.4.1 states that the function values $f(x)$ approach a limit L as x approaches a number a if the absolute value of the difference between $f(x)$ and L can be made as small as we please by taking x sufficiently near a, but not equal to a.

It is important to realize that in the above definition nothing is mentioned about the value of the function when $x = a$. That is, it is not necessary that the function be defined for $x = a$ in order for the $\lim_{x \to a} f(x)$ to exist.

In particular, we saw in our example that

$$\lim_{x \to 1} \frac{(2x + 3)(x - 1)}{(x - 1)} = 5$$

but that

$$\frac{(2x + 3)(x - 1)}{(x - 1)}$$

is not defined for $x = 1$. However, the first sentence in Definition 2.4.1 requires that the function of our example be defined at all numbers except 1 in some open interval containing 1.

We now consider some examples of finding a δ which corresponds to a specific ϵ in some simple cases.

EXAMPLE 1:   Let the function f be defined by the equation

$$f(x) = 4x - 1$$

Given $\lim_{x \to 3} f(x) = 11$, find a δ for

SOLUTION:

$$|f(x) - 11| = |(4x - 1) - 11|$$
$$= |4x - 12|$$
$$= 4|x - 3|$$

$\epsilon = 0.01$ such that

$$|f(x) - 11| < 0.01$$

whenever

$$0 < |x - 3| < \delta$$

Therefore, we want

$$4|x - 3| < 0.01 \quad \text{whenever} \quad 0 < |x - 3| < \delta$$

or

$$|x - 3| < 0.0025 \quad \text{whenever} \quad 0 < |x - 3| < \delta$$

If we take $\delta = 0.0025$, we have

$$|(4x - 1) - 11| < 0.01 \quad \text{whenever} \quad 0 < |x - 3| < 0.0025 \tag{7}$$

It is important to realize that in this example any positive number less than 0.0025 can be used in place of 0.0025 as the required δ. That is, if $0 < \gamma < 0.0025$ and statement (7) holds, then

$$|(4x - 1) - 11| < 0.01 \quad \text{whenever} \quad 0 < |x - 3| < \gamma \tag{8}$$

because every number x satisfying the inequality $0 < |x - 3| < \gamma$ also satisfies the inequality $0 < |x - 3| < 0.0025$.

The solution of Example 1 consisted of finding a δ for a specific ϵ. If for any ϵ we can find a δ that will work, we shall have established that the value of the limit is 11. We do this in the next example.

EXAMPLE 2:   Using Definition 2.4.1, prove that

$$\lim_{x \to 3} (4x - 1) = 11$$

SOLUTION: We must show that for any $\epsilon > 0$ there exists a $\delta > 0$ such that

$$|(4x - 1) - 11| < \epsilon \quad \text{whenever} \quad 0 < |x - 3| < \delta$$

From Example 1, we note that

$$|(4x - 1) - 11| = |4x - 12|$$

$$= 4|x - 3|$$

Therefore, we want

$$4|x - 3| < \epsilon \quad \text{whenever} \quad 0 < |x - 3| < \delta$$

or, equivalently,

$$|x - 3| < \tfrac{1}{4}\epsilon \quad \text{whenever} \quad 0 < |x - 3| < \delta$$

So if we choose $\delta = \tfrac{1}{4}\epsilon$, we have

$$4|x - 3| < 4\delta \quad \text{whenever} \quad 0 < |x - 3| < \delta$$

or

$$4|x - 3| < 4 \cdot \tfrac{1}{4}\epsilon \quad \text{whenever} \quad 0 < |x - 3| < \delta$$

or

$$4|x - 3| < \epsilon \quad \text{whenever} \quad 0 < |x - 3| < \delta$$

giving us

$$|(4x - 1) - 11| < \epsilon \quad \text{whenever} \quad 0 < |x - 3| < \delta$$

if $\delta = \frac{1}{4}\epsilon$. This proves that $\lim\limits_{x \to 3} (4x - 1) = 11$.

In particular, if $\epsilon = 0.01$, then we take $\delta = 0.01/4$, or 0.0025, which corresponds to our result in Example 1.

Any positive number $\delta' < \frac{1}{4}\epsilon$ can be used in place of $\frac{1}{4}\epsilon$ as the required δ in this example.

EXAMPLE 3: **Using Definition 2.4.1, prove that**

$$\lim_{x \to 2} x^2 = 4$$

SOLUTION: We must show that for any $\epsilon > 0$ there exists a $\delta > 0$ such that

$$|x^2 - 4| < \epsilon \quad \text{whenever} \quad 0 < |x - 2| < \delta$$

Factoring, we get

$$|x^2 - 4| = |x - 2| \cdot |x + 2|$$

We want to show that $|x^2 - 4|$ is small when x is close to 2. To do this, we first find an upper bound for the factor $|x + 2|$. If x is close to 2, we know that the factor $|x - 2|$ is small, and that the factor $|x + 2|$ is close to 4. Because we are considering values of x close to 2, we can concern ourselves with only those values of x for which $|x - 2| < 1$; that is, we are requiring the δ, for which we are looking, to be less than or equal to 1. The inequality

$$|x - 2| < 1$$

is equivalent to

$$-1 < x - 2 < 1$$

which is equivalent to

$$1 < x < 3$$

or

$$3 < x + 2 < 5$$

This means that if $|x - 2| < 1$, then $3 < |x + 2| < 5$; therefore, we have

$$|x^2 - 4| = |x - 2| \cdot |x + 2| < |x - 2| \cdot 5 \quad \text{whenever} \quad |x - 2| < 1$$

Now we want

$$|x - 2| \cdot 5 < \epsilon \quad \text{or, equivalently,} \quad |x - 2| < \tfrac{1}{5}\epsilon$$

Thus, if we choose δ to be the smaller of 1 and $\frac{1}{5}\epsilon$, then whenever $|x - 2| < \delta$, it follows that $|x - 2| < \frac{1}{5}\epsilon$ and $|x + 2| < 5$ (because this is true when $|x - 2| < 1$) and so $|x^2 - 4| < (\frac{1}{5}\epsilon) \cdot (5)$. Therefore, we conclude that

$$|x^2 - 4| < \epsilon \quad \text{whenever} \quad 0 < |x - 2| < \delta$$

if δ is the smaller of the two numbers 1 and $\frac{1}{5}\epsilon$, which we write as $\delta = \min(1, \frac{1}{5}\epsilon)$.

EXAMPLE 4:   Using Definition 2.4.1, prove that

$$\lim_{t \to 7} \frac{8}{t-3} = 2$$

SOLUTION: We must show that for any $\epsilon > 0$ there exists a $\delta > 0$ such that

$$\left| \frac{8}{t-3} - 2 \right| < \epsilon \quad \text{whenever} \quad 0 < |t-7| < \delta$$

Now

$$\left| \frac{8}{t-3} - 2 \right| = \left| \frac{8 - 2(t-3)}{t-3} \right|$$

$$= \left| \frac{14 - 2t}{t-3} \right|$$

$$= \frac{2 \cdot |7-t|}{|t-3|}$$

$$= |t-7| \cdot \frac{2}{|t-3|}$$

We wish to show that $|8/(t-3) - 2|$ is small when t is close to 7. We proceed to find some upper bound for the fraction $2/|t-3|$. By requiring the δ for which we are looking to be less than or equal to 1, we can say that whenever $|t-7| < \delta$, then certainly $|t-7| < 1$. The inequality

$$|t-7| < 1$$

is equivalent to

$$-1 < t-7 < 1$$

which is equivalent to

$$3 < t-3 < 5$$

or

$$3 < |t-3| < 5$$

Therefore, whenever $|t-7| < 1$, $|t-3| > 3$, and because we have shown that $|8/(t-3) - 2| = |t-7| \cdot 2/|t-3|$, we have

$$\left| \frac{8}{t-3} - 2 \right| = |t-7| \cdot \frac{2}{|t-3|} < |t-7| \cdot \frac{2}{3} \quad \text{whenever} \quad |t-7| < 1$$

We want then $|t-7| \cdot \frac{2}{3} < \epsilon$ or, equivalently, $|t-7| < \frac{3}{2}\epsilon$. Consequently, we take δ as the smaller of 1 and $\frac{3}{2}\epsilon$, which assures us that whenever $|t-7| < \delta$, then $|t-7| < \frac{3}{2}\epsilon$ and $|t-3| > 3$ (because this is true when $|t-7| < 1$). This gives us

$$\left| \frac{8}{t-3} - 2 \right| < |t-7| \cdot \frac{2}{3} < \frac{3}{2}\epsilon \cdot \frac{2}{3}$$

or

$$\left| \frac{8}{t-3} - 2 \right| < \epsilon$$

whenever $0 < |t - 7| < \delta$, and where $\delta = \min(1, \frac{3}{2}\epsilon)$. We have therefore proved that $\lim_{t \to 7} [8/(t-3)] = 2$.

The following theorem states that a function cannot approach two different limits at the same time. It is called a *uniqueness theorem* because it guarantees that if the limit of a function exists, it is unique.

2.4.2 Theorem   If $\lim_{x \to a} f(x) = L_1$ and $\lim_{x \to a} f(x) = L_2$, then $L_1 = L_2$.

PROOF: We shall assume that $L_1 \neq L_2$ and show that this assumption leads to a contradiction. Because $\lim_{x \to a} f(x) = L_1$, it follows from Definition 2.4.1 that for any $\epsilon > 0$ there exists a $\delta_1 > 0$ such that

$$|f(x) - L_1| < \epsilon \quad \text{whenever} \quad 0 < |x - a| < \delta_1 \tag{9}$$

Also, because $\lim_{x \to a} f(x) = L_2$, we know that there exists a $\delta_2 > 0$ such that

$$|f(x) - L_2| < \epsilon \quad \text{whenever} \quad 0 < |x - a| < \delta_2 \tag{10}$$

Now, writing $L_1 - L_2$ as $L_1 - f(x) + f(x) - L_2$ and applying the triangle inequality, we have

$$|L_1 - L_2| = |[L_1 - f(x)] + [f(x) - L_2]|$$
$$\leq |L_1 - f(x)| + |f(x) - L_2| \tag{11}$$

So from (9), (10), and (11) we may conclude that for any $\epsilon > 0$ there exists a $\delta_1 > 0$ and a $\delta_2 > 0$ such that

$$|L_1 - L_2| < \epsilon + \epsilon \quad \text{whenever} \quad 0 < |x - a| < \delta_1 \text{ and } 0 < |x - a| < \delta_2 \tag{12}$$

If δ is the smaller of δ_1 and δ_2, then $\delta \leq \delta_1$ and $\delta \leq \delta_2$, and (12) states that for any $\epsilon > 0$ there exists a $\delta > 0$ such that

$$|L_1 - L_2| < 2\epsilon \quad \text{whenever} \quad 0 < |x - a| < \delta \tag{13}$$

However, if we take $\epsilon = \frac{1}{2}|L_1 - L_2|$, then (13) states that there exists a $\delta > 0$ such that

$$|L_1 - L_2| < |L_1 - L_2| \quad \text{whenever} \quad 0 < |x - a| < \delta \tag{14}$$

Because (14) is a contradiction, our assumption is false. So $L_1 = L_2$, and the theorem is proved. ∎

Exercises 2.4

In Exercises 1 through 8, we are given $f(x)$, a, and L, as well as $\lim_{x \to a} f(x) = L$. Determine a number δ for the given ϵ such that $|f(x) - L| < \epsilon$ whenever $0 < |x - a| < \delta$.

1. $\lim_{x \to 3} (2x + 4) = 10$; $\epsilon = 0.01$

2. $\lim_{x \to 2} (4x - 5) = 3$; $\epsilon = 0.001$

3. $\lim_{x \to -1} (3 - 4x) = 7$; $\epsilon = 0.02$

4. $\lim\limits_{x \to -2} (2 + 5x) = -8$; $\epsilon = 0.002$

5. $\lim\limits_{x \to 3} x^2 = 9$; $\epsilon = 0.005$

6. $\lim\limits_{x \to 4} \sqrt{x} = 2$; $\epsilon = 0.005$

7. $\lim\limits_{x \to -2} \dfrac{x^2 - 4}{x + 2} = -4$; $\epsilon = 0.01$

8. $\lim\limits_{x \to 1/3} \dfrac{9x^2 - 1}{3x - 1} = 2$; $\epsilon = 0.01$

In Exercises 9 through 29, establish the limit by using Definition 2.4.1; that is, for any $\epsilon > 0$, find a $\delta > 0$, such that

$$|f(x) - L| < \epsilon \quad \text{whenever} \quad 0 < |x - a| < \delta$$

9. $\lim\limits_{x \to 1} (5x - 3) = 2$

10. $\lim\limits_{x \to -2} (7 - 2x) = 11$

11. $\lim\limits_{x \to 3} \dfrac{x^2 - 9}{x - 3} = 6$

12. $\lim\limits_{x \to 4} \dfrac{\sqrt{x} - 2}{x - 4} = \dfrac{1}{4}$

13. $\lim\limits_{x \to 1} x^2 = 1$

14. $\lim\limits_{x \to -3} x^2 = 9$

15. $\lim\limits_{x \to 3} \dfrac{4}{x - 1} = 2$

16. $\lim\limits_{x \to 6} \dfrac{x}{x - 3} = 2$

17. $\lim\limits_{x \to 5} \dfrac{2}{x - 4} = 2$

18. $\lim\limits_{x \to -4} \dfrac{1}{x + 3} = -1$

19. $\lim\limits_{x \to 5} (x^2 - 3x) = 10$

20. $\lim\limits_{x \to 2} (x^2 + 2x - 1) = 7$

21. $\lim\limits_{x \to -3} (5 - x - x^2) = -1$

22. $\lim\limits_{x \to 1/2} \dfrac{3 + 2x}{5 - x} = \dfrac{8}{9}$

23. $\lim\limits_{x \to 4} \sqrt{x + 5} = 3$

24. $\lim\limits_{x \to 1} \dfrac{1}{\sqrt{5 - x}} = \dfrac{1}{2}$

25. Prove that $\lim\limits_{x \to a} x^2 = a^2$ if a is any positive number.

26. Prove that $\lim\limits_{x \to a} x^2 = a^2$ if a is any negative number.

27. Prove that $\lim\limits_{x \to a} \sqrt{x} = \sqrt{a}$ if a is any positive number.

28. Prove that $\lim\limits_{x \to a} \sqrt[3]{x} = \sqrt[3]{a}$. (HINT: $a^3 - b^3 = (a - b)(a^2 + ab + b^2)$.)

29. Prove that if $\lim\limits_{x \to a} f(x)$ exists and is L, then $\lim\limits_{x \to a} |f(x)|$ exists and is $|L|$.

2.5 THEOREMS ON LIMITS OF FUNCTIONS

In order to find limits of functions in a straightforward manner, we shall need some theorems. The proofs of the theorems are based on Definition 2.4.1. These theorems, as well as other theorems on limits of functions appearing in later sections of this chapter, will be labeled "limit theorems" and will be so designated as they are presented.

2.5.1 Limit theorem 1   If m and b are any constants,

$$\lim_{x \to a} (mx + b) = ma + b$$

PROOF: To prove this theorem, we use Definition 2.4.1. For any $\epsilon > 0$, we must prove that there exists a $\delta > 0$ such that

$$|(mx + b) - (ma + b)] < \epsilon \quad \text{whenever} \quad 0 < |x - a| < \delta \tag{1}$$

Case 1: $m \neq 0$.

Because $|(mx + b) - (ma + b)| = |mx - ma| = |m| \cdot |x - a|$, we want to find a $\delta > 0$ for any $\epsilon > 0$ such that

$$|m| \cdot |x - a| < \epsilon \quad \text{whenever} \quad 0 < |x - a| < \delta$$

or, because $m \neq 0$,

$$|x - a| < \frac{\epsilon}{|m|} \quad \text{whenever} \quad 0 < |x - a| < \delta \tag{2}$$

Statement (2) will hold if we take $\delta = \epsilon/|m|$. So we conclude that

$$|(mx + b) - (ma + b)| < \epsilon \quad \text{whenever} \quad 0 < |x - a| < \delta \quad \text{if} \quad \delta = \frac{\epsilon}{|m|}$$

This proves the theorem for Case 1.

Case 2: $m = 0$.

If $m = 0$, then $|(mx + b) - (ma + b)| = 0$ for all values of x. So we take δ to be any positive number, and statement (1) holds. This proves the theorem for Case 2. ∎

2.5.2 Limit theorem 2   If c is a constant, then for any number a,

$$\lim_{x \to a} c = c$$

PROOF: This follows immediately from Limit theorem 1 by taking $m = 0$ and $b = c$. ∎

2.5.3 Limit theorem 3

$$\lim_{x \to a} x = a$$

PROOF: This also follows immediately from Limit theorem 1 by taking $m = 1$ and $b = 0$. ∎

2.5.4 Limit theorem 4   If $\lim_{x \to a} f(x) = L$ and $\lim_{x \to a} g(x) = M$, then

$$\lim_{x \to a} [f(x) \pm g(x)] = L \pm M$$

PROOF: We shall prove this theorem using the plus sign. Given

$$\lim_{x \to a} f(x) = L \tag{3}$$

and

$$\lim_{x \to a} g(x) = M \tag{4}$$

we wish to prove that

$$\lim_{x \to a} [f(x) + g(x)] = L + M \tag{5}$$

To prove Eq. (5), we must use Definition 2.4.1; that is, for any $\epsilon > 0$ we must prove that there exists a $\delta > 0$ such that

$$|(f(x) + g(x) - (L + M)| < \epsilon \quad \text{whenever} \quad 0 < |x - a| < \delta \qquad (6)$$

Because we are given Eq. (3), we know from the definition of a limit, that for $\tfrac{1}{2}\epsilon > 0$ there exists a $\delta_1 > 0$ such that

$$|f(x) - L| < \tfrac{1}{2}\epsilon \quad \text{whenever} \quad 0 < |x - a| < \delta_1$$

Similarly, from Eq. (4), for $\tfrac{1}{2}\epsilon > 0$ there exists a $\delta_2 > 0$ such that

$$|g(x) - M| < \tfrac{1}{2}\epsilon \quad \text{whenever} \quad 0 < |x - a| < \delta_2$$

Now, let δ be the smaller of the two numbers δ_1 and δ_2. Therefore, $\delta \le \delta_1$ and $\delta \le \delta_2$. So we can say

$$|f(x) - L| < \tfrac{1}{2}\epsilon \quad \text{whenever} \quad 0 < |x - a| < \delta$$

and

$$|g(x) - M| < \tfrac{1}{2}\epsilon \quad \text{whenever} \quad 0 < |x - a| < \delta$$

Hence, we have

$$|[f(x) + g(x)] - (L + M)| = |(f(x) - L) + (g(x) - M)|$$
$$\le |f(x) - L| + |g(x) - M|$$
$$< \tfrac{1}{2}\epsilon + \tfrac{1}{2}\epsilon = \epsilon \quad \text{whenever} \quad 0 < |x - a| < \delta$$

In this way, we have obtained statement (6), thereby proving that

$$\lim_{x \to a} [f(x) + g(x)] = L + M$$

The proof of Limit theorem 4 using the minus sign is left for the reader (see Exercise 24).   ∎

Limit theorem 4 can be extended to any finite number of functions.

2.5.5 Limit theorem 5   If $\lim_{x \to a} f_1(x) = L_1$, $\lim_{x \to a} f_2(x) = L_2$, . . . , and $\lim_{x \to a} f_n(x) = L_n$, then

$$\lim_{x \to a} [f_1(x) \pm f_2(x) \pm \cdots \pm f_n(x)] = L_1 \pm L_2 \pm \cdots \pm L_n$$

This theorem may be proved by applying Limit theorem 4 and mathematical induction (see Exercise 25).

2.5.6 Limit theorem 6   If $\lim_{x \to a} f(x) = L$ and $\lim_{x \to a} g(x) = M$, then

$$\lim_{x \to a} f(x) \cdot g(x) = L \cdot M$$

The proof of this theorem is more sophisticated than those of the preceding theorems, and it is often omitted from a beginning calculus text. We have outlined the proof in Exercises 27 and 28, with some steps left to be supplied by the reader.

Limit theorem 6 also can be extended to any finite number of functions by applying mathematical induction.

2.5.7 Limit theorem 7   If $\lim\limits_{x \to a} f_1(x) = L_1$, $\lim\limits_{x \to a} f_2(x) = L_2$, . . . , and $\lim\limits_{x \to a} f_n(x) = L_n$, then

$$\lim_{x \to a} [f_1(x) \cdot f_2(x) \cdot \cdot \cdot \cdot \cdot f_n(x)] = L_1 \cdot L_2 \cdot \cdot \cdot \cdot \cdot L_n$$

The proof is left for the reader (see Exercise 29).

2.5.8 Limit theorem 8   If $\lim\limits_{x \to a} f(x) = L$ and n is any positive integer, then

$$\lim_{x \to a} [f(x)]^n = L^n$$

The proof follows immediately from Limit theorem 7 by taking

$$f(x) = f_1(x) = f_2(x) = \cdot \cdot \cdot = f_n(x) \quad \text{and} \quad L = L_1 = L_2 = \cdot \cdot \cdot = L_n$$

2.5.9 Limit theorem 9   If $\lim\limits_{x \to a} f(x) = L$ and $\lim\limits_{x \to a} g(x) = M$, and $M \neq 0$, then

$$\lim_{x \to a} \frac{f(x)}{g(x)} = \frac{L}{M}$$

The proof, based on Definition 2.4.1, is also frequently omitted from a beginning calculus text. However, a proof is given in Sec. 2.12. Although we are postponing the proof, we apply this theorem when necessary.

2.5.10 Limit theorem 10   If $\lim\limits_{x \to a} f(x) = L$, then

$$\lim_{x \to a} \sqrt[n]{f(x)} = \sqrt[n]{L}$$

if $L > 0$ and n is any positive integer, or if $L \leq 0$ and n is a positive odd integer.

A proof of this theorem is given in Sec. 2.12, and as is the case with the preceding theorem, we apply it when necessary.

Following are some examples illustrating the application of the above theorems. To indicate the limit theorem being used, we use the abbreviation "L.T." followed by the theorem number; for example, "L.T. 2" refers to Limit theorem 2.

EXAMPLE 1: Find

$$\lim_{x \to 3} (x^2 + 7x - 5)$$

and, when applicable, indicate the limit theorems which are being used.

SOLUTION:

$$\lim_{x \to 3} (x^2 + 7x - 5) = \lim_{x \to 3} x^2 + \lim_{x \to 3} 7x - \lim_{x \to 3} 5 \qquad \text{(L.T. 5)}$$

$$= \lim_{x \to 3} x \cdot \lim_{x \to 3} x + \lim_{x \to 3} 7 \cdot \lim_{x \to 3} x - \lim_{x \to 3} 5 \qquad \text{(L.T. 6)}$$

$$= 3 \cdot 3 + 7 \cdot 3 - 5 \qquad \text{(L.T. 3 and L.T. 2)}$$

$$= 9 + 21 - 5$$

$$= 25$$

It is important, at this point, to realize that the limit in Example 1 was evaluated by direct application of the theorems on limits. For the function f defined by $f(x) = x^2 + 7x - 5$, we see that $f(3) = 3^2 + 7 \cdot 3 - 5 = 25$, which is the same as $\lim_{x \to 3} (x^2 + 7x - 5)$. It is not always true that we have $\lim_{x \to a} f(x) = f(a)$ (see Example 4). In Example 1, $\lim_{x \to 3} f(x) = f(3)$ because the function f is continuous at $x = 3$. We discuss the meaning of continuous functions in Sec. 2.11.

EXAMPLE 2: Find

$$\lim_{x \to 2} \sqrt{\frac{x^3 + 2x + 3}{x^2 + 5}}$$

and when applicable indicate the limit theorems being used.

SOLUTION:

$$\lim_{x \to 2} \sqrt{\frac{x^3 + 2x + 3}{x^2 + 5}} = \sqrt{\lim_{x \to 2} \frac{x^3 + 2x + 3}{x^2 + 5}} \qquad \text{(L.T. 10)}$$

$$= \sqrt{\frac{\lim_{x \to 2} (x^3 + 2x + 3)}{\lim_{x \to 2} (x^2 + 5)}} \qquad \text{(L.T. 9)}$$

$$= \sqrt{\frac{\lim_{x \to 2} x^3 + \lim_{x \to 2} 2x + \lim_{x \to 2} 3}{\lim_{x \to 2} x^2 + \lim_{x \to 2} 5}} \qquad \text{(L.T. 5)}$$

$$= \sqrt{\frac{(\lim_{x \to 2} x)^3 + \lim_{x \to 2} 2 \cdot \lim_{x \to 2} x + \lim_{x \to 2} 3}{(\lim_{x \to 2} x)^2 + \lim_{x \to 2} 5}}$$

$$\text{(L.T. 7 and L.T. 8)}$$

$$= \sqrt{\frac{2^3 + 2 \cdot 2 + 3}{2^2 + 5}} \qquad \text{(L.T. 3 and L.T. 2)}$$

$$= \sqrt{\frac{8 + 4 + 3}{9}}$$

$$= \frac{\sqrt{15}}{3}$$

EXAMPLE 3:   Find

$$\lim_{x \to 3} \frac{x^3 - 27}{x - 3}$$

and, when applicable, indicate the limit theorems being used.

SOLUTION: Here we have a more difficult problem since Limit theorem 9 cannot be applied to the quotient $(x^3 - 27)/(x - 3)$ because $\lim_{x \to 3} (x - 3) = 0$. However, factoring the numerator, we obtain

$$\frac{x^3 - 27}{x - 3} = \frac{(x - 3)(x^2 + 3x + 9)}{x - 3}$$

This quotient is $(x^2 + 3x + 9)$ if $x \neq 3$ (since if $x \neq 3$ we can divide the numerator and denominator by $(x - 3)$).

When evaluating $\lim_{x \to 3} [(x^3 - 27)/(x - 3)]$, we are considering values of x close to 3, but not equal to 3. Therefore, it is possible to divide the numerator and denominator by $(x - 3)$. The solution to this problem takes the following form:

$$\lim_{x \to 3} \frac{x^3 - 27}{x - 3} = \lim_{x \to 3} \frac{(x - 3)(x^2 + 3x + 9)}{x - 3}$$

$$= \lim_{x \to 3} (x^2 + 3x + 9) \quad \text{dividing numerator and denominator by } (x - 3) \text{ since } x \neq 3$$

$$= \lim_{x \to 3} x^2 + \lim_{x \to 3} (3x + 9) \qquad \text{(L.T. 4)}$$

$$= (\lim_{x \to 3} x)^2 + 18 \qquad \text{(L.T. 8 and L.T. 1)}$$

$$= 3^2 + 18 \qquad \text{(L.T. 3)}$$

$$= 27$$

Note that in Example 3 $(x^3 - 27)/(x - 3)$ is not defined when $x = 3$, but $\lim_{x \to 3} [(x^3 - 27)/(x - 3)]$ exists and is equal to 27.

EXAMPLE 4:   Given that f is the function defined by

$$f(x) = \begin{cases} x - 3 & \text{if } x \neq 4 \\ 5 & \text{if } x = 4 \end{cases}$$

find $\lim_{x \to 4} f(x)$.

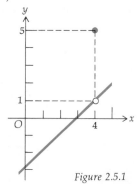

Figure 2.5.1

SOLUTION: When evaluating $\lim_{x \to 4} f(x)$, we are considering values of x close to 4 but not equal to 4. Thus, we have

$$\lim_{x \to 4} f(x) = \lim_{x \to 4} (x - 3)$$

$$= 1 \qquad \text{(L.T. 1)}$$

In this example, $\lim_{x \to 4} f(x) = 1$ but $f(4) = 5$; therefore, $\lim_{x \to 4} f(x) \neq f(4)$.

This is an example of a function which is discontinuous at $x = 4$. In terms of geometry, this means that there is a break in the graph of the function at the point where $x = 4$ (see Fig. 2.5.1). The graph of the function consists of the isolated point $(4, 5)$ and the straight line whose equation is $y = x - 3$, with the point $(4, 1)$ deleted.

Exercises 2.5

In Exercises 1 through 17, find the value of the limit, and when applicable indicate the limit theorems being used.

1. $\lim\limits_{x \to 2} (x^2 + 2x - 1)$

2. $\lim\limits_{y \to -1} (y^3 - 2y^2 + 3y - 4)$

3. $\lim\limits_{t \to 2} \dfrac{t^2 - 5}{2t^3 + 6}$

4. $\lim\limits_{x \to -1} \dfrac{2x + 1}{x^2 - 3x + 4}$

5. $\lim\limits_{y \to -2} \dfrac{y^3 + 8}{y + 2}$

6. $\lim\limits_{s \to 1} \dfrac{s^3 - 1}{s - 1}$

7. $\lim\limits_{x \to -3} \dfrac{x^2 + 5x + 6}{x^2 - x - 12}$

8. $\lim\limits_{x \to 4} \dfrac{3x^2 - 17x + 20}{4x^2 - 25x + 36}$

9. $\lim\limits_{r \to 1} \sqrt{\dfrac{8r + 1}{r + 3}}$

10. $\lim\limits_{x \to 2} \sqrt{\dfrac{x^2 + 3x + 4}{x^3 + 1}}$

11. $\lim\limits_{y \to -3} \sqrt{\dfrac{y^2 - 9}{2y^2 + 7y + 3}}$

12. $\lim\limits_{t \to -3/2} \sqrt{\dfrac{8t^3 - 27}{4t^2 - 9}}$

13. $\lim\limits_{x \to 0} \dfrac{\sqrt{x + 2} - \sqrt{2}}{x}$ (HINT: Rationalize the numerator.)

14. $\lim\limits_{t \to 0} \dfrac{2 - \sqrt{4 - t}}{t}$

15. $\lim\limits_{h \to 0} \dfrac{\sqrt[3]{h + 1} - 1}{h}$

16. $\lim\limits_{x \to -2} \dfrac{x^3 - x^2 - x + 10}{x^2 + 3x + 2}$

17. $\lim\limits_{x \to 3} \dfrac{2x^3 - 5x^2 - 2x - 3}{4x^3 - 13x^2 + 4x - 3}$

18. If $f(x) = x^2 + 5x - 3$, show that $\lim\limits_{x \to 2} f(x) = f(2)$.

19. If $F(x) = 2x^3 + 7x - 1$, show that $\lim\limits_{x \to -1} F(x) = F(-1)$.

20. If $g(x) = (x^2 - 4)/(x - 2)$, show that $\lim\limits_{x \to 2} g(x) = 4$ but that $g(2)$ is not defined.

21. If $h(x) = (\sqrt{x + 9} - 3)/x$, show that $\lim\limits_{x \to 0} h(x) = \tfrac{1}{6}$ but that $h(0)$ is not defined.

22. Given that f is the function defined by

$$f(x) = \begin{cases} 2x - 1 & \text{if } x \neq 2 \\ 1 & \text{if } x = 2 \end{cases}$$

(a) Find $\lim\limits_{x \to 2} f(x)$, and show that $\lim\limits_{x \to 2} f(x) \neq f(2)$.
(b) Draw a sketch of the graph of f.

23. Given that f is the function defined by

$$f(x) = \begin{cases} x^2 - 9 & \text{if } x \neq -3 \\ 4 & \text{if } x = -3 \end{cases}$$

(a) Find $\lim\limits_{x \to -3} f(x)$, and show that $\lim\limits_{x \to -3} f(x) \neq f(-3)$.
(b) Draw a sketch of the graph of f.

24. Using Definition 2.4.1, prove that if

$$\lim\limits_{x \to a} f(x) = L \quad \text{and} \quad \lim\limits_{x \to a} g(x) = M$$

then

$$\lim\limits_{x \to a} [f(x) - g(x)] = L - M$$

25. Prove Limit theorem 5 by applying Limit theorem 4 and mathematical induction.

26. Prove that if $\lim\limits_{x \to a} f(x) = L$, then $\lim\limits_{x \to a} (f(x) - L) = 0$.

27. Using Definition 2.4.1, prove that if

$$\lim_{x \to a} f(x) = L \quad \text{and} \quad \lim_{x \to a} g(x) = 0$$

then

$$\lim_{x \to a} f(x) \cdot g(x) = 0$$

(HINT: In order to prove that $\lim_{x \to a} f(x) \cdot g(x) = 0$, we must show that for any $\epsilon > 0$ there exists a $\delta > 0$ such that $|f(x) \cdot g(x)| < \epsilon$ whenever $0 < |x - a| < \delta$. First show that there is a $\delta_1 > 0$ such that $|f(x)| < 1 + |L|$ whenever $0 < |x - a| < \delta_1$, by applying Definition 2.4.1 to $\lim_{x \to a} f(x) = L$, with $\epsilon = 1$ and $\delta = \delta_1$, and then use the triangle inequality. Then show that there is a $\delta_2 > 0$ such that $|g(x)| < \epsilon/(1 + |L|)$ whenever $0 < |x - a| < \delta_2$, by applying Definition 2.4.1 to $\lim_{x \to a} g(x) = 0$. By taking δ as the smaller of the two numbers δ_1 and δ_2, the theorem is proved.)

28. Prove Limit theorem 6: If $\lim_{x \to a} f(x) = L$ and $\lim_{x \to a} g(x) = M$, then

$$\lim_{x \to a} [f(x) \cdot g(x)] = L \cdot M$$

(HINT: Write $f(x) \cdot g(x) = [f(x) - L]g(x) + L[g(x) - M] + L \cdot M$. Apply Limit theorem 5 and the results of Exercises 26 and 27.)

29. Prove Limit theorem 7 by applying Limit theorem 6 and mathematical induction.

30. Prove that, if $f(x) = g(x)$ for all values of x except $x = a$, then $\lim_{x \to a} f(x) = \lim_{x \to a} g(x)$ if the limits exist.

2.6 ONE-SIDED LIMITS

When considering $\lim_{x \to a} f(x)$ we are concerned with values of x in an open interval containing a but not at a itself, that is, at values of x close to a and either greater than a or less than a. However, suppose, for example, that we have the function f for which $f(x) = \sqrt{x - 4}$. Because $f(x)$ does not exist if $x < 4$, f is not defined on any open interval containing 4. Hence, we cannot consider $\lim_{x \to 4} \sqrt{x - 4}$. However, if x is restricted to values greater than 4, the value of $\sqrt{x - 4}$ can be made as close to 0 as we please by taking x sufficiently close to 4 but greater than 4. In such a case as this, we let x approach 4 from the right and consider the *one-sided limit from the right* or the *right-hand limit,* which we now define.

2.6.1 Definition   Let f be a function which is defined at every number in some open interval (a, c). Then the *limit of $f(x)$, as x approaches a from the right, is L,* written

$$\lim_{x \to a^+} f(x) = L$$

if for any $\epsilon > 0$, however small, there exists a $\delta > 0$ such that

$$|f(x) - L| < \epsilon \quad \text{whenever} \quad 0 < x - a < \delta \tag{1}$$

Note that in statement (1) there are no absolute-value bars around $x - a$ since $x - a > 0$, because $x > a$.

It follows from Definition 2.6.1 that

$$\lim_{x \to 4^-} \sqrt{x - 4} = 0$$

If when considering the limit of a function the independent variable x is restricted to values less than a number a, we say that x approaches a from the left; the limit is called the *one-sided limit from the left* or the *left-hand limit*.

2.6.2 Definition Let f be a function which is defined at every number in some open interval (d, a). Then the *limit of $f(x)$, as x approaches a from the left, is L*, written

$$\lim_{x \to a^-} f(x) = L$$

if for any $\epsilon > 0$, however small, there exists a $\delta > 0$ such that

$$|f(x) - L| < \epsilon \quad \text{whenever} \quad -\delta < x - a < 0$$

We can refer to $\lim_{x \to a} f(x)$ as the *two-sided limit,* or the *undirected limit,* to distinguish it from the one-sided limits.

Limit theorems 1–10 given in Sec. 2.5 remain unchanged when "$x \to a$" is replaced by "$x \to a^+$" or "$x \to a^-$."

EXAMPLE 1: Let f be defined by

$$f(x) = \operatorname{sgn} x = \begin{cases} -1 & \text{if } x < 0 \\ 0 & \text{if } x = 0 \\ 1 & \text{if } 0 < x \end{cases}$$

(a) Draw a sketch of the graph of f. (b) Determine $\lim_{x \to 0^-} f(x)$ if it exists. (c) Determine $\lim_{x \to 0^+} f(x)$ if it exists.

SOLUTION: A sketch of the graph is shown in Fig. 2.6.1. $\lim_{x \to 0^-} f(x) = -1$ since, if x is any number less than 0, $f(x)$ has the value -1. Similarly, $\lim_{x \to 0^+} f(x) = +1$.

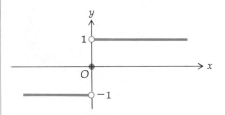

Figure 2.6.1

In the above example $\lim_{x \to 0^-} f(x) \neq \lim_{x \to 0^+} f(x)$. Because the left-hand limit and the right-hand limit are not equal, we say that the two-sided limit, $\lim_{x \to 0} f(x)$, does not exist. The concept of the two-sided limit failing to exist because the two one-sided limits are unequal is stated in the following theorem.

2.6.3 Theorem $\lim_{x \to a} f(x)$ exists and is equal to L if and only if $\lim_{x \to a^-} f(x)$ and $\lim_{x \to a^+} f(x)$ both exist and both are equal to L.

The proof of this theorem is left for the reader (see Exercise 16).

EXAMPLE 2:   Let g be defined by

$$g(x) = \begin{cases} |x| & \text{if } x \neq 0 \\ 2 & \text{if } x = 0 \end{cases}$$

(a) Draw a sketch of the graph of g. (b) Find $\lim_{x \to 0} g(x)$ if it exists.

SOLUTION: A sketch of the graph is shown in Fig. 2.6.2.

$$\lim_{x \to 0^-} g(x) = \lim_{x \to 0^-} (-x) = 0 \quad \text{and} \quad \lim_{x \to 0^+} g(x) = \lim_{x \to 0^+} x = 0$$

Therefore, by Theorem 2.6.3 $\lim_{x \to 0} g(x)$ exists and is equal to 0. Note that $g(0) = 2$, which has no effect on $\lim_{x \to 0} g(x)$.

Figure 2.6.2

EXAMPLE 3:   Let h be defined by

$$h(x) = \begin{cases} 4 - x^2 & \text{if } x \leq 1 \\ 2 + x^2 & \text{if } 1 < x \end{cases}$$

(a) Draw a sketch of the graph of h. (b) Find each of the following limits if they exist: $\lim_{x \to 1^-} h(x)$, $\lim_{x \to 1^+} h(x)$, $\lim_{x \to 1} h(x)$.

SOLUTION: A sketch of the graph is shown in Fig. 2.6.3.

$$\lim_{x \to 1^-} h(x) = \lim_{x \to 1^-} (4 - x^2) = 3$$

$$\lim_{x \to 1^+} h(x) = \lim_{x \to 1^+} (2 + x^2) = 3$$

Therefore, by Theorem 2.6.3 $\lim_{x \to 1} h(x)$ exists and is equal to 3. Note that $h(1) = 3$.

Figure 2.6.3

Exercises 2.6

In Exercises 1 through 10, draw a sketch of the graph and find the indicated limit if it exists; if the limit does not exist, give the reason.

1. $f(x) = \begin{cases} 2 & \text{if } x < 1 \\ -1 & \text{if } x = 1 \\ -3 & \text{if } 1 < x \end{cases}$; (a) $\lim\limits_{x \to 1^+} f(x)$; (b) $\lim\limits_{x \to 1^-} f(x)$; (c) $\lim\limits_{x \to 1} f(x)$

2. $g(s) = \begin{cases} s + 3 & \text{if } s \leq -2 \\ 3 - s & \text{if } -2 < s \end{cases}$; (a) $\lim\limits_{s \to -2^+} g(s)$; (b) $\lim\limits_{s \to -2^-} g(s)$; (c) $\lim\limits_{s \to -2} g(s)$

3. $h(x) = \begin{cases} 2x + 1 & \text{if } x < 3 \\ 10 - x & \text{if } 3 \leq x \end{cases}$; (a) $\lim\limits_{x \to 3^+} h(x)$; (b) $\lim\limits_{x \to 3^-} h(x)$; (c) $\lim\limits_{x \to 3} h(x)$

4. $F(x) = \begin{cases} x^2 & \text{if } x \leq 2 \\ 8 - 2x & \text{if } 2 < x \end{cases}$; (a) $\lim\limits_{x \to 2^+} F(x)$; (b) $\lim\limits_{x \to 2^-} F(x)$; (c) $\lim\limits_{x \to 2} F(x)$

5. $f(r) = \begin{cases} 2r + 3 & \text{if } r < 1 \\ 2 & \text{if } r = 1 \\ 7 - 2r & \text{if } 1 < r \end{cases}$; (a) $\lim\limits_{r \to 1^+} f(r)$; (b) $\lim\limits_{r \to 1^-} f(r)$; (c) $\lim\limits_{r \to 1} f(r)$

6. $g(t) = \begin{cases} 3 + t^2 & \text{if } t < -2 \\ 0 & \text{if } t = -2 \\ 11 - t^2 & \text{if } -2 < t \end{cases}$; (a) $\lim\limits_{t \to -2^+} g(t)$; (b) $\lim\limits_{t \to -2^-} g(t)$; (c) $\lim\limits_{t \to -2} g(t)$

7. $F(x) = |x - 5|$; (a) $\lim\limits_{x \to 5^+} F(x)$; (b) $\lim\limits_{x \to 5^-} F(x)$; (c) $\lim\limits_{x \to 5} F(x)$

8. $f(x) = 3 + |2x - 4|$; (a) $\lim\limits_{x \to 2^+} f(x)$; (b) $\lim\limits_{x \to 2^-} f(x)$; (c) $\lim\limits_{x \to 2} f(x)$

9. $f(x) = \dfrac{|x|}{x}$; (a) $\lim\limits_{x \to 0^+} f(x)$; (b) $\lim\limits_{x \to 0^-} f(x)$; (c) $\lim\limits_{x \to 0} f(x)$

10. The absolute value of the signum function (see Exercise 2 in Exercises 2.3).

    (a) $\lim\limits_{x \to 0^+} |\text{sgn } x|$; (b) $\lim\limits_{x \to 0^-} |\text{sgn } x|$; (c) $\lim\limits_{x \to 0} |\text{sgn } x|$.

11. F is the function of Exercise 11 in Exercises 2.3. Find, if they exist:

    (a) $\lim\limits_{x \to 0^+} F(x)$; (b) $\lim\limits_{x \to 0^-} F(x)$; (c) $\lim\limits_{x \to 0} F(x)$.

12. h is the function of Exercise 10 in Exercises 2.3. Find, if they exist: (a) $\lim\limits_{x \to 0^+} h(x)$; (b) $\lim\limits_{x \to 0^-} h(x)$; (c) $\lim\limits_{x \to 0} h(x)$.

13. Find, if they exist: (a) $\lim\limits_{x \to 2^+} [\![x]\!]$; (b) $\lim\limits_{x \to 2^-} [\![x]\!]$; (c) $\lim\limits_{x \to 2} [\![x]\!]$.

14. Let $G(x) = [\![x]\!] + [\![4 - x]\!]$. Draw a sketch of the graph of G. Find, if they exist: (a) $\lim\limits_{x \to 3^+} G(x)$; (b) $\lim\limits_{x \to 3^-} G(x)$; (c) $\lim\limits_{x \to 3} G(x)$.

15. Given

$$f(x) = \begin{cases} x^2 + 3 & \text{if } x \leq 1 \\ x + 1 & \text{if } x > 1 \end{cases} \quad \text{and} \quad g(x) = \begin{cases} x^2 & \text{if } x \leq 1 \\ 2 & \text{if } x > 1 \end{cases}$$

    (a) Show that $\lim\limits_{x \to 1^-} f(x)$ and $\lim\limits_{x \to 1^+} f(x)$ both exist but are not equal, and hence $\lim\limits_{x \to 1} f(x)$ does not exist.
    (b) Show that $\lim\limits_{x \to 1^-} g(x)$ and $\lim\limits_{x \to 1^+} g(x)$ both exist but are not equal, and hence $\lim\limits_{x \to 1} g(x)$ does not exist.
    (c) Find formulas for $f(x) \cdot g(x)$.
    (d) Prove that $\lim\limits_{x \to 1} f(x) \cdot g(x)$ exists by showing that $\lim\limits_{x \to 1^-} f(x) \cdot g(x) = \lim\limits_{x \to 1^+} f(x) \cdot g(x)$.

16. Prove Theorem 2.6.3.

2.7 LIMITS AT INFINITY

Figure 2.7.1

Consider the function f defined by the equation

$$f(x) = \frac{2x^2}{x^2 + 1}$$

A sketch of the graph of this function is shown in Fig. 2.7.1. Let x take on the values 0, 1, 2, 3, 4, 5, 10, 100, 1000, and so on, allowing x to increase without bound. The corresponding function values are given in Table 2.7.1.

Table 2.7.1

x	0	1	2	3	4	5	10	100	1000
$f(x) = \dfrac{2x^2}{x^2+1}$	0	1	$\dfrac{8}{5}$	$\dfrac{18}{10}$	$\dfrac{32}{17}$	$\dfrac{50}{26}$	$\dfrac{200}{101}$	$\dfrac{20{,}000}{10{,}001}$	$\dfrac{2{,}000{,}000}{1{,}000{,}001}$

We see from Table 2.7.1 that as x increases through positive values, the function values $f(x)$ get closer and closer to 2. In particular, when $x = 4$,

$$2 - \frac{2x^2}{x^2 + 1} = 2 - \frac{32}{17} = \frac{2}{17}$$

Therefore, the difference between 2 and $f(x)$ is $\frac{2}{17}$ when $x = 4$. When $x = 100$,

$$2 - \frac{2x^2}{x^2 + 1} = 2 - \frac{20{,}000}{10{,}001} = \frac{2}{10{,}001}$$

Hence, the difference between 2 and $f(x)$ is $2/10{,}001$ when $x = 100$.

Continuing on, we intuitively see that we can make the value of $f(x)$ as close to 2 as we please by taking x large enough. In other words, we can make the difference between 2 and $f(x)$ as small as we please by taking x large enough; or going a step further, for any $\epsilon > 0$, however small, we can find a number $N > 0$ such that $|f(x) - 2| < \epsilon$ whenever $x > N$.

When an independent variable x is increasing without bound through positive values, we write "$x \to +\infty$." From the illustrative example above, then, we can say that

$$\lim_{x \to +\infty} \frac{2x^2}{x^2 + 1} = 2$$

In general, we have the following definition.

2.7.1 Definition   Let f be a function which is defined at every number in some interval $(a, +\infty)$. The *limit of* $f(x)$, *as x increases without bound, is L,* written

$$\lim_{x \to +\infty} f(x) = L \qquad (1)$$

if for any $\epsilon > 0$, however small, there exists a number $N > 0$ such that

$$|f(x) - L| < \epsilon \quad \text{whenever} \quad x > N$$

NOTE: It should be stressed again (as in Sec. 1.1) that $+\infty$ is not a real number; hence, when we write $x \to +\infty$, it does not have the same meaning as, for instance, $x \to 1000$. The symbolism "$x \to +\infty$" indicates the behavior of the variable x. However, we can read Eq. (1) as "the limit of $f(x)$ as x approaches positive infinity is L," bearing in mind this note.

Now let us consider the same function and let x take on the values $0, -1, -2, -3, -4, -5, -10, -100, -1000$, and so on, allowing x to decrease through negative values without bound. Table 2.7.2 gives the corresponding function values of $f(x)$.

Table 2.7.2

x	0	-1	-2	-3	-4	-5	-10	-100	-1000
$f(x) = \dfrac{2x^2}{x^2+1}$	0	1	$\dfrac{8}{5}$	$\dfrac{18}{10}$	$\dfrac{32}{17}$	$\dfrac{50}{26}$	$\dfrac{200}{101}$	$\dfrac{20{,}000}{10{,}001}$	$\dfrac{2{,}000{,}000}{1{,}000{,}001}$

Note that the function values are the same for the negative numbers as for the corresponding positive numbers. So we intuitively see that as x decreases without bound, $f(x)$ approaches 2, and formally we say that for any $\epsilon > 0$, however small, we can find a number $N < 0$ such that $|f(x) - 2| < \epsilon$ whenever $x < N$. Using the symbolism "$x \to -\infty$" to denote that the variable x is decreasing without bound, we write

$$\lim_{x \to -\infty} \frac{2x^2}{x^2+1} = 2 \tag{2}$$

In general, we have the following definition.

2.7.2 Definition Let f be a function which is defined at every number in some interval $(-\infty, a)$. The *limit of $f(x)$, as x decreases without bound, is L*, written

$$\lim_{x \to -\infty} f(x) = L$$

if for any $\epsilon > 0$, however small, there exists a number $N < 0$ such that

$$|f(x) - L| < \epsilon \quad \text{whenever} \quad x < N$$

NOTE: As in the note following Definition 2.7.1, the symbolism "$x \to -\infty$" only indicates the behavior of the variable x, but we can read Eq. (2) as "the limit of $f(x)$ as x approaches negative infinity is L."

Limit theorems 2, 4, 5, 6, 7, 8, 9, and 10 given in Sec. 2.5 remain unchanged when "$x \to a$" is replaced by $x \to +\infty$ or $x \to -\infty$. We have the following additional limit theorem.

2.7.3 Limit theorem 11 If r is any positive integer, then

$$\text{(i)} \lim_{x \to +\infty} \frac{1}{x^r} = 0 \qquad \text{(ii)} \lim_{x \to -\infty} \frac{1}{x^r} = 0$$

PROOF OF (i):   To prove part (i), we must show that Definition 2.7.1 holds for $f(x) = 1/x^r$ and $L = 0$; that is, we must show that for any $\epsilon > 0$ there exists a number $N > 0$ such that

$$\left|\frac{1}{x^r} - 0\right| < \epsilon \quad \text{whenever} \quad x > N$$

or, equivalently,

$$|x|^r > \frac{1}{\epsilon} \quad \text{whenever} \quad x > N$$

or, equivalently, since $r > 0$,

$$|x| > \left(\frac{1}{\epsilon}\right)^{1/r} \quad \text{whenever} \quad x > N$$

In order for the above to hold, take $N = (1/\epsilon)^{1/r}$. Thus, we can conclude that

$$\left|\frac{1}{x^r} - 0\right| < \epsilon \quad \text{whenever} \quad x > N, \text{ if } N = \left(\frac{1}{\epsilon}\right)^{1/r}$$

This proves part (i).   ∎

The proof of part (ii) is analogous and is left for the reader (see Exercise 16).

EXAMPLE 1:   Find

$$\lim_{x \to +\infty} \frac{4x - 3}{2x + 5}$$

and when applicable indicate the limit theorems being used.

SOLUTION: To use Limit theorem 11, we divide the numerator and the denominator by x, thus giving us

$$\lim_{x \to +\infty} \frac{4x - 3}{2x + 5} = \lim_{x \to +\infty} \frac{4 - 3/x}{2 + 5/x}$$

$$= \frac{\lim\limits_{x \to +\infty} (4 - 3/x)}{\lim\limits_{x \to +\infty} (2 + 5/x)} \qquad \text{(L.T.9)}$$

$$= \frac{\lim\limits_{x \to +\infty} 4 - \lim\limits_{x \to +\infty} (3/x)}{\lim\limits_{x \to +\infty} 2 + \lim\limits_{x \to +\infty} (5/x)} \qquad \text{(L.T. 4)}$$

$$= \frac{\lim\limits_{x \to +\infty} 4 - \lim\limits_{x \to +\infty} 3 \cdot \lim\limits_{x \to +\infty} (1/x)}{\lim\limits_{x \to +\infty} 2 + \lim\limits_{x \to +\infty} 5 \cdot \lim\limits_{x \to +\infty} (1/x)} \qquad \text{(L.T. 6)}$$

$$= \frac{4 - 3 \cdot 0}{2 + 5 \cdot 0} \qquad \text{(L.T. 2 and L.T. 11)}$$

$$= 2$$

EXAMPLE 2:   Find

$$\lim_{x \to -\infty} \frac{2x^2 - x + 5}{4x^3 - 1}$$

and when applicable indicate the limit theorems being used.

SOLUTION: To use Limit theorem 11, we divide the numerator and the denominator by the highest power of x occurring in either the numerator or denominator, which in this case is x^3. So we have

$$\lim_{x \to -\infty} \frac{2x^2 - x + 5}{4x^3 - 1} = \lim_{x \to -\infty} \frac{2/x - 1/x^2 + 5/x^3}{4 - 1/x^3}$$

$$= \frac{\lim_{x \to -\infty} (2/x - 1/x^2 + 5/x^3)}{\lim_{x \to -\infty} (4 - 1/x^3)} \qquad \text{(L.T. 9)}$$

$$= \frac{\lim_{x \to -\infty} (2/x) - \lim_{x \to -\infty} (1/x^2) + \lim_{x \to -\infty} (5/x^3)}{\lim_{x \to -\infty} 4 - \lim_{x \to -\infty} (1/x^3)} \qquad \text{(L.T. 5)}$$

$$= \frac{\lim_{x \to -\infty} 2 \cdot \lim_{x \to -\infty} (1/x) - \lim_{x \to -\infty} (1/x^2) + \lim_{x \to -\infty} 5 \cdot \lim_{x \to -\infty} (1/x^3)}{\lim_{x \to -\infty} 4 - \lim_{x \to -\infty} (1/x^3)} \qquad \text{(L.T. 6)}$$

$$= \frac{2 \cdot 0 - 0 + 5 \cdot 0}{4 - 0} \qquad \text{(L.T. 2 and L.T. 11)}$$

$$= 0$$

EXAMPLE 3:   Find

$$\lim_{x \to +\infty} \frac{3x + 4}{\sqrt{2x^2 - 5}}$$

and when applicable indicate the limit theorems being used.

SOLUTION: We divide the numerator and the denominator of the fraction by x. In the denominator we let $x = \sqrt{x^2}$ since we are considering only positive values of x.

$$\lim_{x \to +\infty} \frac{3x + 4}{\sqrt{2x^2 - 5}} = \lim_{x \to +\infty} \frac{3 + 4/x}{\sqrt{2x^2 - 5}/\sqrt{x^2}}$$

$$= \frac{\lim_{x \to +\infty} (3 + 4/x)}{\lim_{x \to +\infty} \sqrt{2 - 5/x^2}} \qquad \text{(L.T. 9)}$$

$$= \frac{\lim_{x \to +\infty} (3 + 4/x)}{\sqrt{\lim_{x \to +\infty} (2 - 5/x^2)}} \qquad \text{(L.T. 10)}$$

$$= \frac{\lim_{x \to +\infty} 3 + \lim_{x \to +\infty} (4/x)}{\sqrt{\lim_{x \to +\infty} 2 - \lim_{x \to +\infty} (5/x^2)}} \qquad \text{(L.T. 4)}$$

$$= \frac{\lim_{x \to +\infty} 3 + \lim_{x \to +\infty} 4 \cdot \lim_{x \to +\infty} (1/x)}{\sqrt{\lim_{x \to +\infty} 2 - \lim_{x \to +\infty} 5 \cdot \lim_{x \to +\infty} (1/x^2)}} \qquad \text{(L.T. 6)}$$

$$= \frac{3 + 4 \cdot 0}{\sqrt{2 - 5 \cdot 0}}$$

(L.T. 2 and L.T. 11

$$= \frac{3}{\sqrt{2}}$$

EXAMPLE 4:   Find

$$\lim_{x \to -\infty} \frac{3x + 4}{\sqrt{2x^2 - 5}}$$

SOLUTION: The function is the same as the one in Example 3; however since we are considering negative values of x, in this case $\sqrt{x^2} = -x$ or, equivalently, $-\sqrt{x^2} = x$. Hence, in the first step when we divide numerator and denominator by x, we let $x = -\sqrt{x^2}$ in the denominator, and we have

$$\lim_{x \to -\infty} \frac{3x + 4}{\sqrt{2x^2 - 5}} = \lim_{x \to -\infty} \frac{3 + 4/x}{\sqrt{2x^2 - 5}/(-\sqrt{x^2})}$$

$$= \frac{\lim\limits_{x \to -\infty} (3 + 4/x)}{\lim\limits_{x \to -\infty} (-\sqrt{2 - 5/x^2})}$$

$$= \frac{\lim\limits_{x \to -\infty} 3 + \lim\limits_{x \to -\infty} (4/x)}{-\sqrt{\lim\limits_{x \to -\infty} (2 - 5/x^2)}}$$

The remaining steps are similar to those in the solution of Example 3, and in the denominator we obtain $-\sqrt{2}$ instead of $\sqrt{2}$. Hence, the limit is $-3/\sqrt{2}$.

Exercises 2.7

In Exercises 1 through 12, find the limits, and when applicable indicate the limit theorems being used.

1. $\lim\limits_{x \to +\infty} \dfrac{2x + 1}{5x - 2}$

2. $\lim\limits_{s \to +\infty} \dfrac{4s^2 + 3}{2s^2 - 1}$

3. $\lim\limits_{x \to +\infty} \dfrac{x + 4}{3x^2 - 5}$

4. $\lim\limits_{x \to +\infty} \dfrac{x^2 - 2x + 5}{7x^3 + x + 1}$

5. $\lim\limits_{y \to +\infty} \dfrac{\sqrt{y^2 + 4}}{y + 4}$

6. $\lim\limits_{x \to -\infty} \dfrac{\sqrt{x^2 + 4}}{x + 4}$

7. $\lim\limits_{x \to -\infty} \dfrac{4x^3 + 2x^2 - 5}{8x^3 + x + 2}$

8. $\lim\limits_{x \to +\infty} \dfrac{3x^4 - 7x^2 + 2}{2x^4 + 1}$

9. $\lim\limits_{x \to +\infty} (\sqrt{x^2 + 1} - x)$

10. $\lim\limits_{x \to +\infty} (\sqrt{x^2 + x} - x)$

11. $\lim\limits_{x \to -\infty} (\sqrt[3]{x^3 + x} - \sqrt[3]{x^3 + 1})$

12. $\lim\limits_{t \to +\infty} \dfrac{\sqrt{t + \sqrt{t + \sqrt{t}}}}{\sqrt{t + 1}}$

For the functions defined in Exercises 13 and 14, prove that $\lim\limits_{x \to +\infty} f(x) = 1$ by applying Definition 2.7.1; that is, for any $\epsilon > 0$, show that there exists a number $N > 0$ such that $|f(x) - 1| < \epsilon$ whenever $x > N$.

13. $f(x) = \dfrac{x}{x - 1}$

14. $f(x) = \dfrac{x^2 + 2x}{x^2 - 1}$

15. Prove that

$$\lim_{x \to -\infty} \frac{8x + 3}{2x - 1} = 4$$

by showing that for any $\epsilon > 0$ there exists a number $N < 0$, such that

$$\left| \frac{8x + 3}{2x - 1} - 4 \right| < \epsilon$$

whenever $x < N$.

16. Prove Limit theorem 11(ii) (2.7.3).

2.8 INFINITE LIMITS   Let f be the function defined by

$$f(x) = \frac{3}{(x - 2)^2}$$

A sketch of the graph of this function is in Fig. 2.8.1.

We investigate the function values of f when x is close to 2. Letting x approach 2 from the right, we have the values of $f(x)$ given in Table 2.8.1. From this table we intuitively see that as x gets closer and closer

Figure 2.8.1

Table 2.8.1

x	3	$\frac{5}{2}$	$\frac{7}{3}$	$\frac{9}{4}$	$\frac{21}{10}$	$\frac{201}{100}$	$\frac{2001}{1000}$
$f(x) = \dfrac{3}{(x-2)^2}$	3	12	27	48	300	30,000	3,000,000

to 2 through values greater than 2, $f(x)$ increases without bound; in other words, we can make $f(x)$ as large as we please by taking x close enough to 2. We write

$$\lim_{x \to 2^+} \frac{3}{(x - 2)^2} = +\infty$$

If we let x approach 2 from the left, we have the values of $f(x)$ given in Table 2.8.2. We intuitively see from this table that as x gets closer and

Table 2.8.2

x	1	$\frac{3}{2}$	$\frac{5}{3}$	$\frac{7}{4}$	$\frac{19}{10}$	$\frac{199}{100}$	$\frac{1999}{1000}$
$f(x) = \dfrac{3}{(x-2)^2}$	3	12	27	48	300	30,000	3,000,000

closer to 2, through values less than 2, $f(x)$ increases without bound; so we write

$$\lim_{x \to 2^-} \frac{3}{(x-2)^2} = +\infty$$

Therefore, as x approaches 2 from either the right or the left, $f(x)$ increases without bound, and we write

$$\lim_{x \to 2} \frac{3}{(x-2)^2} = +\infty$$

We have the following definition.

2.8.1 Definition   Let f be a function which is defined at every number in some open interval I containing a, except possibly at the number a itself. *As x approaches a, $f(x)$ increases without bound*, which is written

$$\lim_{x \to a} f(x) = +\infty \tag{1}$$

if for any number $N > 0$ there exists a $\delta > 0$ such that $f(x) > N$ whenever $0 < |x - a| < \delta$.

NOTE: Equation (1) can be read as "the limit of $f(x)$ as x approaches a is positive infinity." In such a case the limit does not exist, but the symbolism "$+\infty$" indicates the behavior of the function values $f(x)$ as x gets closer and closer to a.

In words, Definition 2.8.1 states that we can make $f(x)$ as large as we please (i.e., greater than any positive number N) by taking x sufficiently close to a.

In an analogous manner, we can indicate the behavior of a function whose function values decrease without bound. To lead up to this, we consider the function g defined by the equation

$$g(x) = \frac{-3}{(x-2)^2}$$

A sketch of the graph of this function is in Fig. 2.8.2.

The function values given by $g(x) = -3/(x-2)^2$ are the negatives of the function values given by $f(x) = 3/(x-2)^2$. So for the function g as x approaches 2, either from the right or the left, $g(x)$ decreases without bound, and we write

$$\lim_{x \to 2} \frac{-3}{(x-2)^2} = -\infty$$

In general, we have the following definition.

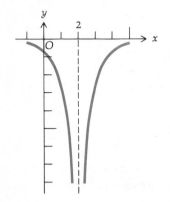

Figure 2.8.2

2.8.2 Definition   Let f be a function which is defined at every number in some open interval I containing a, except possibly at the number a itself. *As x approaches a, $f(x)$ decreases without bound*, which is written

$$\lim_{x \to a} f(x) = -\infty \tag{2}$$

if for any number $N < 0$ there exists a $\delta > 0$ such that $f(x) < N$ whenever $0 < |x - a| < \delta$.

NOTE: Equation (2) can be read as "the limit of $f(x)$ as x approaches a is negative infinity," noting again that the limit does not exist and the symbolism "$-\infty$" indicates only the behavior of the function values as x approaches a.

We can consider one-sided limits which are "infinite." In particular, $\lim_{x \to a^+} f(x) = +\infty$ if f is defined at every number in some open interval (a, c) and if for any number $N > 0$ there exists a $\delta > 0$ such that $f(x) > 0$ whenever $0 < x - a < \delta$. Similar definitions can be given if $\lim_{x \to a^-} f(x) = +\infty$, $\lim_{x \to a^+} f(x) = -\infty$, and $\lim_{x \to a^-} f(x) = -\infty$.

Now suppose that h is the function defined by the equation

$$h(x) = \frac{2x}{x - 1} \qquad (3)$$

y

O 1 x

Figure 2.8.3

A sketch of the graph of this function is in Fig. 2.8.3. By referring to Figs. 2.8.1, 2.8.2, and 2.8.3, note the difference in the behavior of the function whose graph is sketched in Fig. 2.8.3 from the functions of the other two figures. We see that

$$\lim_{x \to 1^-} \frac{2x}{x - 1} = -\infty$$

and

$$\lim_{x \to 1^+} \frac{2x}{x - 1} = +\infty$$

That is, for the function defined by Eq. (3), as x approaches 1 through values less than 1, the function values decrease without bound, and as x approaches 1 through values greater than 1, the function values increase without bound. To refer to the two-sided limit of this function at 1, we use the concept of "unsigned infinity," which we denote by ∞. We have the following definition.

2.8.3 Definition

$$\lim_{x \to a} f(x) = \infty \qquad (4)$$

is equivalent to

$$\lim_{x \to a} |f(x)| = +\infty$$

NOTE: Equation (4) can be read as "the limit of $f(x)$ as x approaches a is unsigned infinity."

Since

$$\lim_{x \to 1} \left| \frac{2x}{x-1} \right| = +\infty$$

we can write, from Definition 2.8.3,

$$\lim_{x \to 1} \frac{2x}{x-1} = \infty$$

"Infinite" limits at infinity can be considered. There are formal definitions for each of the following.

$$\lim_{x \to +\infty} f(x) = +\infty \qquad \lim_{x \to -\infty} f(x) = +\infty$$

$$\lim_{x \to +\infty} f(x) = -\infty \qquad \lim_{x \to -\infty} f(x) = -\infty$$

$$\lim_{x \to +\infty} f(x) = \infty \qquad \lim_{x \to -\infty} f(x) = \infty$$

For example, $\lim_{x \to +\infty} f(x) = +\infty$ if the function f is defined on some interval $(a, +\infty)$ and if for any number $N > 0$ there exists an $M > 0$ such that $f(x) > N$ whenever $x > M$. The other definitions are left for the reader (see Exercise 17).

Before giving some examples, we need two limit theorems involving "infinite" limits.

2.8.4 Limit theorem 12   If r is any positive integer, then

(i) $\lim_{x \to 0} \dfrac{1}{x^r} = \infty$

(ii) $\lim_{x \to 0^+} \dfrac{1}{x^r} = +\infty$

(iii) $\lim_{x \to 0^-} \dfrac{1}{x^r} = \begin{cases} -\infty & \text{if } r \text{ is odd} \\ +\infty & \text{if } r \text{ is even} \end{cases}$

PROOF: According to Definition 2.8.3, part (i) will be true if

$$\lim_{x \to 0} \left| \frac{1}{x^r} \right| = +\infty \tag{4}$$

If parts (ii) and (iii) are true, then Eq. (4) follows; thus, part (i) will be true. Therefore, we prove part (ii) first. We must show that for any $N > 0$ there exists a $\delta > 0$ such that

$$\frac{1}{x^r} > N \quad \text{whenever} \quad 0 < x < \delta$$

or, equivalently, because $x > 0$ and $N > 0$,

$$x^r < \frac{1}{N} \quad \text{whenever} \quad 0 < x < \delta$$

or, equivalently, since $r > 0$,

$$x < \left(\frac{1}{N}\right)^{1/r} \quad \text{whenever} \quad 0 < x < \delta$$

The above statement holds if $\delta = (1/N)^{1/r}$. We conclude that

$$\frac{1}{x^r} > N \quad \text{whenever} \quad 0 < x < \delta, \text{ if } \delta = \left(\frac{1}{N}\right)^{1/r} \qquad\blacksquare$$

The proof of (iii) is analogous and is left for the reader (see Exercise 23).

2.8.5 Limit theorem 13   If a is any real number, and if $\lim\limits_{x \to a} f(x) = 0$ and $\lim\limits_{x \to a} g(x) = c$, where c is a constant not equal to 0, then

(i) if $c > 0$ and if $f(x) \to 0$ through positive values of $f(x)$,

$$\lim_{x \to a} \frac{g(x)}{f(x)} = +\infty$$

(ii) if $c > 0$ and if $f(x) \to 0$ through negative values of $f(x)$,

$$\lim_{x \to a} \frac{g(x)}{f(x)} = -\infty$$

(iii) if $c < 0$ and if $f(x) \to 0$ through positive values of $f(x)$,

$$\lim_{x \to a} \frac{g(x)}{f(x)} = -\infty$$

(iv) if $c < 0$ and if $f(x) \to 0$ through negative values of $f(x)$,

$$\lim_{x \to a} \frac{g(x)}{f(x)} = +\infty$$

The theorem is also valid if "$x \to a$" is replaced by "$x \to a^+$," "$x \to a^-$," "$x \to +\infty$," or "$x \to -\infty$."

PROOF: We prove part (i) and leave the proofs of the other parts for the reader (see Exercises 24–26). To prove that

$$\lim_{x \to a} \frac{g(x)}{f(x)} = +\infty$$

we must show that for any $N > 0$ there exists a $\delta > 0$ such that

$$\frac{g(x)}{f(x)} > N \quad \text{whenever} \quad 0 < |x - a| < \delta \qquad (5)$$

Since $\lim\limits_{x \to a} g(x) = c > 0$, by taking $\epsilon = \frac{1}{2}c$ in Definition 2.4.1, it follows that there exists a $\delta_1 > 0$ such that

$$|g(x) - c| < \tfrac{1}{2}c \quad \text{whenever} \quad 0 < |x - a| < \delta_1$$

By applying Theorem 1.2.2 to the above inequality, it follows that there exists a $\delta_1 > 0$ such that

$$-\tfrac{1}{2}c < g(x) - c < \tfrac{1}{2}c \quad \text{whenever} \quad 0 < |x - a| < \delta_1$$

or, equivalently,

$$\tfrac{1}{2}c < g(x) < \tfrac{3}{2}c \quad \text{whenever} \quad 0 < |x - a| < \delta_1$$

So there exists a $\delta_1 > 0$ such that

$$g(x) > \tfrac{1}{2}c \quad \text{whenever} \quad 0 < |x - a| < \delta_1 \tag{6}$$

Now $\lim\limits_{x \to a} f(x) = 0$. Thus, for any $\epsilon > 0$, there exists a $\delta_2 > 0$ such that

$$|f(x)| < \epsilon \quad \text{whenever} \quad 0 < |x - a| < \delta_2$$

Since $f(x)$ is approaching zero through positive values of $f(x)$, we can remove the absolute-value bars around $f(x)$; hence, for any $\epsilon > 0$ there exists a $\delta_2 > 0$ such that

$$f(x) < \epsilon \quad \text{whenever} \quad 0 < |x - a| < \delta_2 \tag{7}$$

From statements (6) and (7) we can conclude that for any $\epsilon > 0$ there exist a $\delta_1 > 0$ and a $\delta_2 > 0$ such that

$$\frac{g(x)}{f(x)} > \frac{\tfrac{1}{2}c}{\epsilon} \quad \text{whenever} \quad 0 < |x - a| < \delta_1 \quad \text{and} \quad 0 < |x - a| < \delta_2$$

Hence, if $\epsilon = c/2N$ and $\delta = \min(\delta_1, \delta_2)$, then

$$\frac{g(x)}{f(x)} > \frac{\tfrac{1}{2}c}{c/2N} = N \quad \text{whenever} \quad 0 < |x - a| < \delta$$

which is statement (5). Hence, part (i) is proved.   ∎

EXAMPLE 1: Find:

(a) $\lim\limits_{x \to 3^+} \dfrac{x^2 + x + 2}{x^2 - 2x - 3}$

(b) $\lim\limits_{x \to 3^-} \dfrac{x^2 + x + 2}{x^2 - 2x - 3}$

(c) $\lim\limits_{x \to 3} \dfrac{x^2 + x + 2}{x^2 - 2x - 3}$

SOLUTION:

(a) $\lim\limits_{x \to 3^+} \dfrac{x^2 + x + 2}{x^2 - 2x - 3} = \lim\limits_{x \to 3^+} \dfrac{x^2 + x + 2}{(x - 3)(x + 1)}$

The limit of the numerator is 14, which can be easily verified.

$$\lim_{x \to 3^+} (x - 3)(x + 1) = \lim_{x \to 3^+} (x - 3) \cdot \lim_{x \to 3^+} (x + 1)$$

$$= 0 \cdot 4 = 0$$

The limit of the denominator is 0, and the denominator is approaching 0 through positive values. Then applying Limit theorem 13(i), we obtain

$$\lim_{x \to 3^+} \frac{x^2 + x + 2}{x^2 - 2x - 3} = +\infty$$

(b) $\lim\limits_{x \to 3^-} \dfrac{x^2 + x + 2}{x^2 - 2x - 3} = \lim\limits_{x \to 3^-} \dfrac{x^2 + x + 2}{(x - 3)(x + 1)}$

As in part (a), the limit of the numerator is 14.

$$\lim_{x \to 3^-} (x - 3)(x + 1) = \lim_{x \to 3^-} (x - 3) \cdot \lim_{x \to 3^-} (x + 1)$$

$$= 0 \cdot 4 = 0$$

In this case, the limit of the denominator is zero, but the denominator is approaching zero through negative values. Applying Limit theorem 13(ii), we have

$$\lim_{x \to 3^-} \frac{x^2 + x + 2}{x^2 - 2x - 3} = -\infty$$

(c) $\lim\limits_{x \to 3} \dfrac{x^2 + x + 2}{x^2 - 2x - 3} = \infty$ because $\lim\limits_{x \to 3} \left| \dfrac{x^2 + x + 2}{x^2 - 2x - 3} \right| = +\infty$

EXAMPLE 2:   Find

$$\lim_{x \to +\infty} \frac{x^2}{x + 1}$$

SOLUTION: Dividing the numerator and the denominator by x^2, we obtain

$$\lim_{x \to +\infty} \frac{x^2}{x + 1} = \lim_{x \to +\infty} \frac{1}{1/x + 1/x^2}$$

Evaluating the limit of the denominator, we have

$$\lim_{x \to +\infty} \left(\frac{1}{x} + \frac{1}{x^2} \right) = \lim_{x \to +\infty} \frac{1}{x} + \lim_{x \to +\infty} \frac{1}{x^2} = 0 + 0 = 0$$

Therefore, the limit of the denominator is 0, and the denominator is approaching 0 through positive values.

The limit of the numerator is 1, and so by Limit theorem 13(i) it follows that

$$\lim_{x \to +\infty} \frac{x^2}{x + 1} = +\infty$$

EXAMPLE 3:   Find

$$\lim_{x \to +\infty} \frac{2x - x^2}{3x + 5}$$

SOLUTION: $\lim\limits_{x \to +\infty} \dfrac{2x - x^2}{3x + 5} = \lim\limits_{x \to +\infty} \dfrac{2/x - 1}{3/x + 5/x^2}$

We consider the limits of the numerator and the denominator separately.

$$\lim_{x \to +\infty} \left(\frac{2}{x} - 1 \right) = \lim_{x \to +\infty} \frac{2}{x} - \lim_{x \to +\infty} 1 = 0 - 1 = -1$$

$$\lim_{x \to +\infty} \left(\frac{3}{x} + \frac{5}{x^2} \right) = \lim_{x \to +\infty} \frac{3}{x} + \lim_{x \to +\infty} \frac{5}{x^2} = 0 + 0 = 0$$

Therefore, we have the limit of a quotient in which the limit of the numerator is -1 and the limit of the denominator is 0, where the denominator is approaching 0 through positive values. By Limit theorem 13(iii) it follows that

$$\lim_{x \to +\infty} \frac{2x - x^2}{3x + 5} = -\infty$$

Remember that because $+\infty$, $-\infty$, and ∞ are not numbers, the Limit theorems 1–10 of Sec. 2.5 do not hold for "infinite" limits. However, we do have the following properties regarding such limits. The proofs are left for the reader (see Exercises 28–30).

2.8.6 Theorem If $\lim_{x \to a} f(x) = \infty$ and $\lim_{x \to a} g(x) = c$, where c is any constant, then

$$\lim_{x \to a} [f(x) + g(x)] = \infty$$

The theorem holds if ∞ is replaced by $+\infty$ or $-\infty$. Furthermore, the theorem is valid if "$x \to a$" is replaced by "$x \to a^+$," "$x \to a^-$," "$x \to +\infty$," or "$x \to -\infty$."

2.8.7 Theorem If $\lim_{x \to a} f(x) = +\infty$ and $\lim_{x \to a} g(x) = c$, where c is any constant except 0, then

(i) if $c > 0$, $\lim_{x \to a} f(x) \cdot g(x) = +\infty$.

(ii) if $c < 0$, $\lim_{x \to a} f(x) \cdot g(x) = -\infty$.

The theorem is valid if "$x \to a$" is replaced by "$x \to a^+$," "$x \to a^-$," "$x \to +\infty$," or "$x \to -\infty$."

2.8.8 Theorem If $\lim_{x \to a} f(x) = -\infty$ and $\lim_{x \to a} g(x) = c$, where c is any constant except 0, then

(i) if $c > 0$, $\lim_{x \to a} f(x) \cdot g(x) = -\infty$.

(ii) if $c < 0$, $\lim_{x \to a} f(x) \cdot g(x) = +\infty$.

The theorem is valid if "$x \to a$" is replaced by "$x \to a^+$," "$x \to a^-$," "$x \to +\infty$," or "$x \to -\infty$."

Exercises 2.8

In Exercises 1 through 12, evaluate the limit.

1. $\lim\limits_{x \to 4} \dfrac{x}{x-4}$

2. $\lim\limits_{x \to 3} \dfrac{4x^2}{9-x^2}$

3. $\lim\limits_{t \to 2^+} \dfrac{t+2}{t^2-4}$

4. $\lim\limits_{t \to 2^-} \dfrac{t+2}{t^2-4}$

5. $\lim\limits_{t \to 2} \dfrac{t+2}{t^2-4}$

6. $\lim\limits_{x \to 0^+} \dfrac{\sqrt{3+x^2}}{x}$

7. $\lim\limits_{x \to 0^-} \dfrac{\sqrt{3+x^2}}{x}$

8. $\lim\limits_{x \to 0} \dfrac{\sqrt{3+x^2}}{x}$

9. $\lim\limits_{x \to 3^+} \dfrac{\sqrt{x^2-9}}{x-3}$

10. $\lim\limits_{x \to 4^-} \dfrac{\sqrt{16-x^2}}{x-4}$

11. $\lim\limits_{y \to +\infty} \dfrac{2y^3-4}{5y+3}$

12. $\lim\limits_{x \to -\infty} \dfrac{5x^3-12x+7}{4x^2-1}$

13. $\lim\limits_{x \to 3^-} \dfrac{[\![x]\!]-x}{3-x}$

14. $\lim\limits_{x \to 1^-} \dfrac{[\![x^2]\!]-1}{x^2-1}$

15. $\lim\limits_{x \to 0} \left(\dfrac{1}{x}-\dfrac{1}{x^2}\right)$

16. $\lim\limits_{s \to 2} \left(\dfrac{1}{s-2}-\dfrac{3}{s^2-4}\right)$

17. Give a definition for each of the following: (a) $\lim\limits_{x \to +\infty} f(x) = -\infty$; (b) $\lim\limits_{x \to -\infty} f(x) = +\infty$; (c) $\lim\limits_{x \to -\infty} f(x) = -\infty$; (d) $\lim\limits_{x \to +\infty} f(x) = \infty$; (e) $\lim\limits_{x \to -\infty} f(x) = \infty$.

18. Prove that $\lim\limits_{x \to 2} \dfrac{3}{(x-2)^2} = +\infty$ by using Definition 2.8.1.

19. Prove that $\lim\limits_{x \to 4} \dfrac{-2}{(x-4)^2} = -\infty$ by using Definition 2.8.2.

20. Prove that

$$\lim_{x \to -3} \left|\frac{5-x}{3+x}\right| = +\infty$$

by using Definition 2.8.1, and then apply Definition 2.8.3 to prove that

$$\lim_{x \to -3} \frac{5-x}{3+x} = \infty$$

21. Prove that $\lim\limits_{x \to +\infty} (x^2-4) = +\infty$ by showing that for any $N > 0$ there exists an $M > 0$ such that $(x^2-4) > N$ whenever $x > M$.

22. Prove that $\lim\limits_{x \to +\infty} (6-x-x^2) = -\infty$ by applying the definition in Exercise 17(a).

23. Prove Theorem 2.8.4(iii).

24. Prove Theorem 2.8.5(ii).

25. Prove Theorem 2.8.5(iii).

26. Prove Theorem 2.8.5(iv).

27. Prove Theorem 2.8.5(i) if "$x \to a$" is replaced by "$x \to +\infty$."

28. Prove Theorem 2.8.6.

29. Prove Theorem 2.8.7.

30. Prove Theorem 2.8.8.

2.9 HORIZONTAL AND VERTICAL ASYMPTOTES

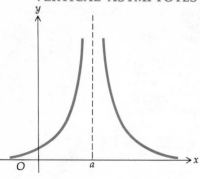

Figure 2.9.1

An aid in drawing the sketch of the graph of a function is to find, if there are any, the *horizontal* and *vertical asymptotes* of the graph. Consider the function f defined by

$$f(x) = \frac{1}{(x-a)^2} \tag{1}$$

A sketch of the graph of f is in Fig. 2.9.1. Any line parallel to and above the x axis will intersect this graph in two points: one point to the left of the line $x = a$ and one point to the right of this line. Thus, for any $k > 0$, no matter how large, the line $y = k$ will intersect the graph of f in two points; the distance of these two points from the line $x = a$ gets smaller and smaller as k gets larger and larger. The line $x = a$ is called a *vertical asymptote* of the graph of f. Following is the definition of a vertical asymptote.

2.9.1 Definition The line $x = a$ is said to be a *vertical asymptote* of the graph of the function f if at least one of the following statements is true:

(i) $\lim\limits_{x \to a^+} f(x) = +\infty$.

(ii) $\lim\limits_{x \to a^+} f(x) = -\infty$.

(iii) $\lim\limits_{x \to a^-} f(x) = +\infty$.

(iv) $\lim\limits_{x \to a^-} f(x) = -\infty$.

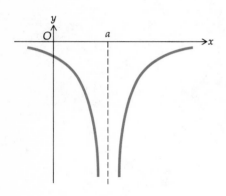

Figure 2.9.2

For the function defined by Eq. (1), both parts (i) and (iii) of the above definition are true. If g is the function defined by

$$g(x) = -\frac{1}{(x-a)^2}$$

then both parts (ii) and (iv) are true, and the line $x = a$ is a vertical asymptote of the graph of g. This is shown in Fig. 2.9.2.

A *horizontal asymptote* of a graph is a line parallel to the x axis.

2.9.2 Definition The line $y = b$ is said to be a *horizontal asymptote* of the graph of the function f if at least one of the following statements is true:

(i) $\lim\limits_{x \to +\infty} f(x) = b$.

(ii) $\lim\limits_{x \to -\infty} f(x) = b$.

EXAMPLE 1:   Find the horizontal asymptotes of the graph of the function f defined by

$$f(x) = \frac{x}{\sqrt{x^2+1}}$$

SOLUTION: First we consider $\lim\limits_{x \to +\infty} f(x)$, and we have

$$\lim_{x \to +\infty} f(x) = \lim_{x \to +\infty} \frac{x}{\sqrt{x^2+1}}$$

To evaluate this limit we write $x = \sqrt{x^2}$ ($x > 0$, because $x \to +\infty$) and then nd draw a sketch of the graph.

divide the numerator and the denominator, under the radical sign, by x^2.

$$\lim_{x \to +\infty} \frac{x}{\sqrt{x^2+1}} = \lim_{x \to +\infty} \frac{\sqrt{x^2}}{\sqrt{x^2+1}}$$

$$= \lim_{x \to +\infty} \sqrt{\frac{1}{1+1/x^2}}$$

$$= \sqrt{\frac{1}{1+\lim_{x \to +\infty}(1/x^2)}}$$

$$= 1$$

Therefore, by Definition 2.9.2(i), the line $y = 1$ is a horizontal asymptote.

Now we consider $\lim_{x \to -\infty} f(x)$; in this case we write $x = -\sqrt{x^2}$ because if $x \to -\infty$, $x < 0$. So we have

$$\lim_{x \to -\infty} f(x) = \lim_{x \to -\infty} \frac{-\sqrt{x^2}}{\sqrt{x^2+1}}$$

$$= \lim_{x \to -\infty} -\sqrt{\frac{1}{1+1/x^2}}$$

$$= -\sqrt{\frac{1}{1+\lim_{x \to -\infty}(1/x^2)}}$$

$$= -1$$

Accordingly, by Definition 2.9.2(ii), the line $y = -1$ is a horizontal asymptote. A sketch of the graph is in Fig. 2.9.3.

Figure 2.9.3

EXAMPLE 2: Find the vertical and horizontal asymptotes of the graph of the equation $xy^2 - 2y^2 - 4x = 0$, and draw a sketch of the graph.

SOLUTION: Solving the given equation for y, we obtain

$$y = \pm 2 \sqrt{\frac{x}{x-2}} \tag{2}$$

Equation (2) defines two functions:

$$y = f_1(x) \quad \text{where } f_1 \text{ is defined by} \quad f_1(x) = +2\sqrt{\frac{x}{x-2}}$$

and

$$y = f_2(x) \quad \text{where } f_2 \text{ is defined by} \quad f_2(x) = -2\sqrt{\frac{x}{x-2}}$$

The graph of the given equation is composed of the graphs of the two functions f_1 and f_2. The domains of the two functions consist of those values of x for which $x/(x-2) \geq 0$. By using the result of Example 10, Sec. 2.1, and excluding $x = 2$, we see that the domains of f_1 and f_2 are the two intervals $(-\infty, 0]$ and $(2, +\infty)$.

Now, consider f_1. Because

$$\lim_{x \to 2^+} f_1(x) = \lim_{x \to 2^+} 2\sqrt{\frac{x}{x-2}} = +\infty$$

by Definition 2.9.1(i) the line $x = 2$ is a vertical asymptote of the graph of f_1.

$$\lim_{x \to +\infty} f_1(x) = \lim_{x \to +\infty} 2\sqrt{\frac{x}{x-2}} = \lim_{x \to +\infty} 2\sqrt{\frac{1}{1-2/x}} = 2$$

So by Definition 2.9.2(i), the line $y = 2$ is a horizontal asymptote of the graph of f_1.

Similarly, $\lim_{x \to -\infty} f_1(x) = 2$. A sketch of the graph of f_1 is shown in Fig. 2.9.4.

Figure 2.9.4

$$\lim_{x \to 2^+} f_2(x) = \lim_{x \to 2^+} \left[-2\sqrt{\frac{x}{x-2}} \right] = -\infty$$

Hence, by Definition 2.9.1(ii) the line $x = 2$ is a vertical asymptote of the graph of f_2.

$$\lim_{x \to +\infty} f_2(x) = \lim_{x \to +\infty} \left[-2\sqrt{\frac{x}{x-2}} \right] = \lim_{x \to +\infty} \left[-2\sqrt{\frac{1}{1-2/x}} \right] = -2$$

So by Definition 2.9.2(i) the line $y = -2$ is a horizontal asymptote of the graph of f_2.

Also, $\lim_{x \to -\infty} f_2(x) = -2$. A sketch of the graph of f_2 is shown in Fig. 2.9.5.

The graph of the given equation consists of the graphs of f_1 and f_2, and a sketch is shown in Fig. 2.9.6.

Figure 2.9.5

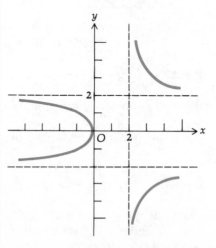

Figure 2.9.6

Exercises 2.9

In Exercises 1 through 14, find the horizontal and vertical asymptotes of the graph of the function defined by the given equation, and draw a sketch of the graph.

1. $f(x) = \dfrac{4}{x-5}$

2. $f(x) = \dfrac{-2}{x+3}$

3. $g(x) = \dfrac{-3}{(x+2)^2}$

4. $F(x) = \dfrac{5}{x^2 + 8x + 16}$

5. $f(x) = \dfrac{1}{x^2 + 5x - 6}$ *

6. $G(x) = \dfrac{2x}{6x^2 + 11x - 10}$

7. $h(x) = \dfrac{4x^2}{x^2 - 9}$

8. $f(x) = \dfrac{x^2}{4 - x^2}$

9. $f(x) = \dfrac{2}{\sqrt{x^2 - 4}}$

10. $g(x) = \dfrac{-1}{\sqrt{x^2 + 5x + 6}}$

11. $F(x) = \dfrac{-3x}{\sqrt{x^2 + 3}}$

12. $h(x) = \dfrac{x}{\sqrt{x^2 - 9}}$

13. $f(x) = \dfrac{4x^2}{\sqrt{x^2 - 2}}$

14. $f(x) = \dfrac{-3x^2}{\sqrt{x^2 + 7x + 10}}$

In Exercises 15 through 21, find the horizontal and vertical asymptotes of the graph of the given equation, and draw a sketch of the graph.

15. $3xy - 2x - 4y - 3 = 0$

16. $2xy + 4x - 3y + 6 = 0$

17. $x^2y^2 - x^2 + 4y^2 = 0$

18. $2xy^2 + 4y^2 - 3x = 0$

19. $(y^2 - 1)(x - 3) = 6$

20. $xy^2 + 3y^2 - 9x = 0$

21. $x^2y + 6xy - x^2 + 2x + 9y + 3 = 0$

2.10 ADDITIONAL THEOREMS ON LIMITS OF FUNCTIONS

There are two limits that we need in order to prove Limit theorems 9 and 10 in Sec. 2.12. They are given in the following two theorems.

2.10.1 Theorem If a is any number except zero,

$$\lim_{x \to a} \frac{1}{x} = \frac{1}{a}$$

PROOF: We need to consider two cases: $a > 0$ and $a < 0$. We prove the theorem if $a > 0$ and leave the proof for $a < 0$ to the reader (see Exercise 1).

So, if a is any positive number, from Definition 2.4.1 we must show that for any $\epsilon > 0$ there exists a $\delta > 0$ such that

$$\left| \frac{1}{x} - \frac{1}{a} \right| < \epsilon \quad \text{whenever} \quad 0 < |x - a| < \delta$$

Now

$$\left| \frac{1}{x} - \frac{1}{a} \right| = \left| \frac{x - a}{ax} \right| = \frac{|x - a|}{|a||x|}$$

and because $a > 0$, we have

$$\left| \frac{1}{x} - \frac{1}{a} \right| = |x - a| \cdot \frac{1}{a|x|} \tag{1}$$

We proceed to find some upper bound for the fraction $1/a|x|$. If we require the δ for which we are looking to be less than or equal to $\frac{1}{2}a$, then certainly whenever $|x - a| < \delta$, we know $|x - a| < \frac{1}{2}a$. The inequality

$$|x - a| < \tfrac{1}{2}a$$

is equivalent to

$$-\tfrac{1}{2}a < x - a < \tfrac{1}{2}a$$

which is equivalent to

$$\tfrac{1}{2}a < x < \tfrac{3}{2}a$$

or, since $a > 0$,

$$\tfrac{1}{2}a < |x| < \tfrac{3}{2}a$$

Hence, whenever $|x - a| < \frac{1}{2}a$, $|x| > \frac{1}{2}a$. So from Eq. (1) we have

$$\left|\frac{1}{x} - \frac{1}{a}\right| = |x - a| \cdot \frac{1}{a|x|} < |x - a| \cdot \frac{1}{a \cdot \frac{1}{2}a} = |x - a| \cdot \frac{2}{a^2}$$

whenever

$$|x - a| < \tfrac{1}{2}a$$

We want then $|x - a| \cdot (2/a^2) < \epsilon$ or, equivalently, $|x - a| < \frac{1}{2}a^2\epsilon$. Hence, we take δ as the smaller of $\frac{1}{2}a$ and $\frac{1}{2}a^2\epsilon$, which assures us that whenever $|x - a| < \delta$, then $|x - a| < \frac{1}{2}a^2\epsilon$ and $|x| > \frac{1}{2}a$ (because this is true when $|x - a| < \frac{1}{2}a$). This gives us

$$\left|\frac{1}{x} - \frac{1}{a}\right| = |x - a| \cdot \frac{1}{a|x|} < \tfrac{1}{2}a^2\epsilon \cdot \frac{1}{a \cdot \frac{1}{2}a}$$

or

$$\left|\frac{1}{x} - \frac{1}{a}\right| < \epsilon$$

whenever $0 < |x - a| < \delta$, and where $\delta = \min(\frac{1}{2}a, \frac{1}{2}a^2\epsilon)$. Hence, we have proved that $\lim\limits_{x \to a} (1/x) = 1/a$ if a is any positive number.   ∎

The proof of the next theorem makes use of the following formula, where n is any positive integer.

$$a^n - b^n = (a - b)(a^{n-1} + a^{n-2}b + a^{n-3}b^2 + \cdots + a^2b^{n-3} + ab^{n-2} + b^{n-1}) \quad (2)$$

The proof of Eq. (2) follows.

$$a(a^{n-1} + a^{n-2}b + \cdots + ab^{n-2} + b^{n-1}) = a^n + a^{n-1}b + \cdots + a^2b^{n-2} + ab^{n-1} \quad (3)$$

$$b(a^{n-1} + a^{n-2}b + \cdots + ab^{n-2} + b^{n-1}) = a^{n-1}b + \cdots + a^2b^{n-2} + ab^{n-1} + b^n \quad (4)$$

Subtracting terms of Eq. (4) from terms of Eq. (3) gives us Eq. (2).

2.10.2 Theorem   If n is a positive integer, then

$$\lim_{x \to a} \sqrt[n]{x} = \sqrt[n]{a}$$

if either

   (i) a is any positive number, or
   (ii) a is a negative number or zero and n is odd.

PROOF: We prove part (i) and leave the proof of part (ii) to the reader (see Exercise 2).

Letting a be any positive number and using Definition 2.4.1, we must show that for any $\epsilon > 0$ there exists a $\delta > 0$ such that

$$|\sqrt[n]{x} - \sqrt[n]{a}| < \epsilon \quad \text{whenever} \quad 0 < |x - a| < \delta$$

To express $|\sqrt[n]{x} - \sqrt[n]{a}|$ in terms of $|x - a|$, we use Eq. (2). We have

$$|\sqrt[n]{x} - \sqrt[n]{a}| = \left| \frac{(x^{1/n} - a^{1/n})[(x^{1/n})^{n-1} + (x^{1/n})^{n-2}a^{1/n} + \cdots + x^{1/n}(a^{1/n})^{n-2} + (a^{1/n})^{n-1}]}{(x^{1/n})^{n-1} + (x^{1/n})^{n-2}a^{1/n} + \cdots + x^{1/n}(a^{1/n})^{n-2} + (a^{1/n})^{n-1}} \right|$$

Applying Eq. (2) to the numerator, we have

$$|\sqrt[n]{x} - \sqrt[n]{a}| = |x - a| \cdot \frac{1}{|x^{(n-1)/n} + x^{(n-2)/n}a^{1/n} + \cdots + x^{1/n}a^{(n-2)/n} + a^{(n-1)/n}|} \tag{5}$$

We wish to find an upper bound for the fraction on the right side of Eq. (5). If we require the δ for which we are looking to be less than or equal to a, then whenever $|x - a| < \delta$, we know that $|x - a| < a$, which is equivalent to

$$-a < x - a < a$$

or

$$0 < x < 2a$$

So, whenever $|x - a| < a$, then $x > 0$. Therefore, if in the denominator of the fraction on the right side of Eq. (5) the x is replaced by 0, we obtain $1/a^{(n-1)/n}$, which is greater than the fraction appearing in Eq. (5). Hence, whenever $|x - a| < a$, we have

$$|\sqrt[n]{x} - \sqrt[n]{a}| < |x - a| \cdot \frac{1}{a^{(n-1)/n}}$$

We want, then, $|x - a| \cdot 1/a^{(n-1)/n} < \epsilon$ or, equivalently, $|x - a| < a^{(n-1)/n}\epsilon$. Thus, we take δ as the smaller of a and $a^{(n-1)/n}\epsilon$, which assures us that whenever $|x - a| < \delta$, then $|x - a| < a^{(n-1)/n}\epsilon$ and $x > 0$. Therefore,

$$|\sqrt[n]{x} - \sqrt[n]{a}|$$

$$= |x - a| \cdot \frac{1}{|x^{(n-1)/n} + x^{(n-2)/n}a^{1/n} + \cdots + x^{1/n}a^{(n-2)/n} + a^{(n-1)/n}|}$$

$$< a^{(n-1)/n}\epsilon \cdot \frac{1}{a^{(n-1)/n}}$$

$$= \epsilon$$

whenever $0 < |x - a| < \delta$, where $\delta = \min(a, a^{(n-1)/n}\epsilon)$. We have therefore proved that $\lim\limits_{x \to a} \sqrt[n]{x} = \sqrt[n]{a}$, if a is any positive number. ∎

To illustrate Theorem 2.10.2, from part (i) it follows that $\lim\limits_{x \to 5} \sqrt{x} = \sqrt{5}$ and $\lim\limits_{x \to 16} \sqrt[4]{x} = 2$; from part (ii) it follows that $\lim\limits_{x \to -27} \sqrt[3]{x} = -3$. We do not consider a limit such as $\lim\limits_{x \to -4} \sqrt{x}$ because $\sqrt{x}$ is not defined on any open interval containing -4.

We now discuss five theorems which are needed to prove some important theorems in later chapters. After the statement of each theorem, an example is given to illustrate it.

2.10.3 Theorem   If $\lim\limits_{x \to a} f(x)$ exists and is positive, then there is an open interval containing a such that $f(x) > 0$ for every $x \neq a$ in the interval.

To illustrate this theorem, consider the function f defined by

$$f(x) = \frac{5}{2x - 1}$$

A sketch of the graph of f is in Fig. 2.10.1. Because $\lim\limits_{x \to 3} f(x) = 1$, and $1 > 0$, according to Theorem 2.10.3 there is an open interval containing 3 such that $f(x) > 0$ for every $x \neq 3$ in the interval. Such an interval is $(2, 4)$. Actually, any open interval (a, b) for which $\frac{1}{2} \leq a < 3$ and $b > 3$ will suffice.

PROOF OF THEOREM 2.10.3:   Let $L = \lim\limits_{x \to a} f(x)$. By hypothesis, $L > 0$. Applying Definition 2.4.1 and taking $\epsilon = \frac{1}{2}L$, we know there is a $\delta > 0$ such that

$$|f(x) - L| < \tfrac{1}{2}L \quad \text{whenever} \quad 0 < |x - a| < \delta \tag{6}$$

Also, $|f(x) - L| < \frac{1}{2}L$ is equivalent to $-\frac{1}{2}L < f(x) - L < \frac{1}{2}L$, which in turn is equivalent to

$$\tfrac{1}{2}L < f(x) < \tfrac{3}{2}L \tag{7}$$

Also, $0 < |x - a| < \delta$ is equivalent to $-\delta < x - a < \delta$ but $x \neq a$, which in turn is equivalent to

$$a - \delta < x < a + \delta \quad \text{but} \quad x \neq a$$

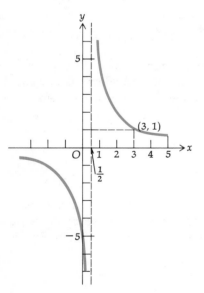

Figure 2.10.1

which is equivalent to stating that

$$x \text{ is in the open interval } (a - \delta, a + \delta) \quad \text{but} \quad x \neq a \qquad (8)$$

From statements (7) and (8), we can replace (6) by the statement $\frac{1}{2}L < f(x) < \frac{3}{2}L$ when x is in the open interval $(a - \delta, a + \delta)$ but $x \neq a$.

Since $L > 0$, we have the conclusion $f(x) > 0$ for every $x \neq a$ in the open interval $(a - \delta, a + \delta)$. ∎

Figure 2.10.2

2.10.4 Theorem If $\lim_{x \to a} f(x)$ exists and is negative, there is an open interval containing a such that $f(x) < 0$ for every $x \neq a$ in the interval.

The proof of this theorem is similar to the proof of Theorem 2.10.3 and is left for the reader (see Exercise 3). Theorem 2.10.4 is illustrated by the function g defined by

$$g(x) = \frac{6 - x}{3 - 2x}$$

Figure 2.10.2 shows a sketch of the graph of g. $\lim_{x \to 2} g(x) = -4 < 0$; hence, by Theorem 2.10.4 there is an open interval containing 2 such that $g(x) < 0$ for every $x \neq 2$ in the interval. Such an interval is $(\frac{3}{2}, 3)$. Any open interval (a, b) for which $\frac{3}{2} \le a < 2$ and $2 < b \le 6$ will suffice.

The following theorem is sometimes referred to as the *squeeze theorem*.

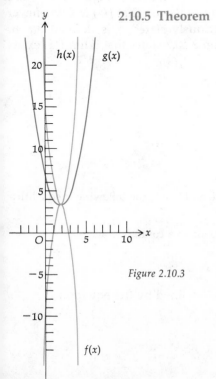

Figure 2.10.3

2.10.5 Theorem Suppose that the functions f, g, and h are defined on some open interval I containing a except possibly at a itself, and that $f(x) \le g(x) \le h(x)$ for all x in I for which $x \neq a$. Also suppose that $\lim_{x \to a} f(x)$ and $\lim_{x \to a} h(x)$ both exist and are equal to L. Then $\lim_{x \to a} g(x)$ also exists and is equal to L.

The proof is left for the reader (see Exercise 4). To illustrate Theorem 2.10.5, consider the functions f, g, and h defined by

$$f(x) = -4(x - 2)^2 + 3$$

$$g(x) = \frac{(x - 2)(x^2 - 4x + 7)}{x - 2}$$

$$h(x) = 4(x - 2)^2 + 3$$

The graphs of the functions f and h are parabolas having their vertex at $(2, 3)$. The graph of g is a parabola with its vertex $(2, 3)$ deleted. Sketches of these graphs are shown in Fig. 2.10.3. The function g is not defined when $x = 2$; however, for all $x \neq 2$, $f(x) \le g(x) \le h(x)$. Furthermore, $\lim_{x \to 2} f(x) = 3$ and $\lim_{x \to 2} h(x) = 3$. The hypothesis of Theorem 2.10.5 is therefore satisfied, and it follows that $\lim_{x \to 2} g(x) = 3$.

Figure 2.10.4

2.10.6 Theorem   Suppose that the function f is defined on some open interval I containing a, except possibly at a. Also suppose that there is some number M for which there is a $\delta > 0$ such that $f(x) \le M$ whenever $0 < |x - a| < \delta$. Then, if $\lim\limits_{x \to a} f(x)$ exists and is equal to L, $L \le M$.

The proof is left for the reader (see Exercise 5). Figure 2.10.4 shows a sketch of the graph of a function f satisfying the hypothesis of Theorem 2.10.6. From the figure we see that $f(1)$ is not defined, but f is defined on the open interval $(\frac{1}{2}, \frac{3}{2})$ except at 1. Furthermore, $f(x) \le \frac{9}{4}$, whenever $0 < |x - 1| < \frac{1}{2}$. Thus, we can conclude from Theorem 2.10.6 that if $\lim\limits_{x \to 1} f(x)$ exists and is L, then $L \le \frac{9}{4}$. From the figure we observe that there is an L and it is 2.

2.10.7 Theorem   Suppose that the function f is defined on some open interval I containing a, except possibly at a. Also suppose that there is some number M for which there is a $\delta > 0$ such that $f(x) \ge M$ whenever $0 < |x - a| < \delta$. Then if $\lim\limits_{x \to a} f(x)$ exists and is equal to L, $L \ge M$.

The proof is left for the reader (see Exercise 6). Figure 2.10.4 also illustrates Theorem 2.10.7. From the figure we see that $f(x) \ge \frac{3}{2}$ whenever $0 < |x - 1| < \frac{1}{2}$; and, because as previously stated, f is defined on the open interval $(\frac{1}{2}, \frac{3}{2})$ except at 1, Theorem 2.10.7 states that if $\lim\limits_{x \to 1} f(x)$ exists and is L, then $L \ge \frac{3}{2}$.

Exercises 2.10

1. Prove Theorem 2.10.1 if $a < 0$.

2. Prove Theorem 2.10.2 if a is a negative number or zero and n is odd.

3. Prove Theorem 2.10.4.

4. Prove Theorem 2.10.5. (HINT: First show that when $|x - a|$ is sufficiently small, and $\epsilon > 0$, the following inequalities must hold: $L - \epsilon < f(x) < L + \epsilon$, and $L - \epsilon < h(x) < L + \epsilon$.)

5. Prove Theorem 2.10.6. (HINT: Assume $M < L$, and show that this assumption leads to a contradiction.)

6. Prove Theorem 2.10.7.

2.11 CONTINUITY OF A FUNCTION AT A NUMBER   In Sec. 2.4 we considered the function f defined by the equation

$$f(x) = \frac{(2x + 3)(x - 1)}{x - 1}$$

Figure 2.11.1

We noted that f is defined for all values of x except 1. A sketch of the graph consisting of all points on the line $y = 2x + 3$ except $(1, 5)$ is shown in Fig. 2.11.1. There is a break in the graph at the point $(1, 5)$, and we state that the function f is *discontinuous* at the number 1.

If we define $f(1) = 2$, for instance, the function is defined for all values of x, but there is still a break in the graph, and the function is still discontinuous at 1. If we define $f(1) = 5$, however, there is no break in the graph, and the function f is said to be *continuous* at all values of x. We have the following definition.

2.11.1 Definition   The function f is said to be *continuous* at the number a if and only if the following three conditions are satisfied:

(i) $f(a)$ exists.
(ii) $\lim\limits_{x \to a} f(x)$ exists.
(iii) $\lim\limits_{x \to a} f(x) = f(a)$.

If one or more of these three conditions fails to hold at a, the function f is said to be *discontinuous* at a.

We now consider some examples of discontinuous functions. In each example we draw a sketch of the graph, determine the points where there is a break in the graph, and show which of the three conditions in Definition 2.11.1 fails to hold at each discontinuity.

EXAMPLE 1:   Let f be defined as follows:

$$f(x) = \begin{cases} \dfrac{(2x + 3)(x - 1)}{x - 1} & \text{if } x \neq 1 \\ 2 & \text{if } x = 1 \end{cases}$$

Figure 2.11.2

SOLUTION: A sketch of the graph of this function is given in Fig. 2.11.2. We see that there is a break in the graph at the point where $x = 1$, and so we investigate there the conditions of Definition 2.11.1.

$f(1) = 2$; therefore, condition (i) is satisfied.
$\lim\limits_{x \to 1} f(x) = 5$; therefore, condition (ii) is satisfied.
$\lim\limits_{x \to 1} f(x) = 5$, but $f(1) = 2$; therefore, condition (iii) is not satisfied.

We conclude that f is discontinuous at 1.

Note that if in Example 1 $f(1)$ is defined to be 5, then $\lim\limits_{x \to 1} f(x) = f(1)$ and f would be continuous at 1.

EXAMPLE 2: **Let f be defined by**

$$f(x) = \frac{1}{x-2}$$

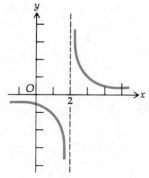

Figure 2.11.3

SOLUTION: A sketch of the graph of f is given in Fig. 2.11.3. There is a break in the graph at the point where $x = 2$, and so we investigate there the conditions of Definition 2.11.1.

$f(2)$ is not defined; therefore, condition (i) is not satisfied. We conclude that f is discontinuous at 2.

EXAMPLE 3: **Let g be defined by**

$$g(x) = \begin{cases} \dfrac{1}{x-2} & \text{if } x \neq 2 \\ 3 & \text{if } x = 2 \end{cases}$$

Figure 2.11.4

SOLUTION: A sketch of the graph of g is shown in Fig. 2.11.4. Investigating the three conditions of Definition 2.11.1 at 2 we have the following.

$g(2) = 3$; therefore, condition (i) is satisfied.

$\lim\limits_{x \to 2^-} g(x) = -\infty$, and $\lim\limits_{x \to 2^+} g(x) = +\infty$; therefore, condition (ii) is not satisfied.

Thus, g is discontinuous at 2.

EXAMPLE 4: **Let h be defined by**

$$h(x) = \begin{cases} 3 + x & \text{if } x \leq 1 \\ 3 - x & \text{if } 1 < x \end{cases}$$

SOLUTION: A sketch of the graph of h is shown in Fig. 2.11.5. Because there is a break in the graph at the point where $x = 1$, we investigate the conditions of Definition 2.11.1 at 1. We have the following.

$h(1) = 4$; therefore, condition (i) is satisfied.

$$\lim_{x \to 1^-} h(x) = \lim_{x \to 1^-} (3 + x) = 4$$

$$\lim_{x \to 1^+} h(x) = \lim_{x \to 1^+} (3 - x) = 2$$

Figure 2.11.5

Because $\lim_{x \to 1^-} h(x) \neq \lim_{x \to 1^+} h(x)$, we conclude that $\lim_{x \to 1} h(x)$ does not exist; therefore, condition (ii) fails to hold at 1.

Hence, h is discontinuous at 1.

EXAMPLE 5: Let F be defined by

$$F(x) = \begin{cases} |x - 3| & \text{if } x \neq 3 \\ 2 & \text{if } x = 3 \end{cases}$$

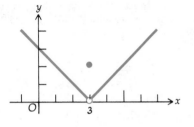

Figure 2.11.6

SOLUTION: A sketch of the graph of F is shown in Fig. 2.11.6. We investigate the three conditions of Definition 2.11.1 at the point where $x = 3$. We have

$F(3) = 2$; therefore, condition (i) is satisfied.

$\lim_{x \to 3^-} F(x) = 0$ and $\lim_{x \to 3^+} F(x) = 0$. So $\lim_{x \to 3} F(x)$ exists and is 0; therefore, condition (ii) is satisfied.

$\lim_{x \to 3} F(x) = 0$ but $F(3) = 2$; therefore, condition (iii) is not satisfied.

Therefore, F is discontinuous at 3.

It should be apparent that the geometric notion of a break in the graph of a certain point is synonymous with the analytic concept of a function being discontinuous at a certain value of the independent variable.

After the solution of Example 1 we mentioned that if $f(1)$ had been defined to be 5, then f would be continuous at 1. This illustrates the concept of a *removable discontinuity*. In general, suppose that f is a function which is discontinuous at the number a, but for which $\lim_{x \to a} f(x)$ exists. Then either $f(a) \neq \lim_{x \to a} f(x)$ or else $f(a)$ does not exist. Such a discontinuity is called a removable discontinuity because if f were redefined at a so that $f(a) = \lim_{x \to a} f(x)$, f becomes continuous at a. If the discontinuity is not removable it is called an *essential discontinuity*.

EXAMPLE 6:   In each of the Examples 1 through 5, determine if the discontinuity is removable or essential.

SOLUTION: In Example 1 the function is discontinuous at 1 but $\lim_{x \to 1} f(x) = 5$. By redefining $f(1) = 5$, we have $\lim_{x \to 1} f(x) = f(1)$, and so the discontinuity is removable.

In Example 2, the function f is discontinuous at 2. $\lim\limits_{x \to 2} f(x)$ does not exist; hence, the discontinuity is essential.

In Example 3, $\lim\limits_{x \to 2} g(x)$ does not exist, and so the discontinuity is essential.

In Example 4, the function h is discontinuous because $\lim\limits_{x \to 1} h(x)$ does not exist, and so again the discontinuity is essential.

In Example 5, $\lim\limits_{x \to 3} F(x) = 0$, but $F(3) = 2$, and so F is discontinuous at 3. However, if $F(3)$ is redefined to be 0, then the function is continuous at 3, and so the discontinuity is removable.

Exercises 2.11

In Exercises 1 through 22 draw a sketch of the graph of the function; then by observing where there are breaks in the graph, determine the values of the independent variable at which the function is discontinuous and show why Definition 2.11.1 is not satisfied at each discontinuity.

1. $f(x) = \begin{cases} \dfrac{5}{x-4} & \text{if } x \neq 4 \\ 1 & \text{if } x = 4 \end{cases}$

2. $g(x) = \begin{cases} \dfrac{1}{x+2} & \text{if } x \neq -2 \\ 0 & \text{if } x = -2 \end{cases}$

3. $F(x) = \dfrac{x^2 + x - 6}{x + 3}$

4. $h(x) = \dfrac{x^4 - 16}{x^2 - 4}$

5. $g(x) = \begin{cases} \dfrac{x^2 + x - 6}{x + 3} & \text{if } x \neq -3 \\ 1 & \text{if } x = -3 \end{cases}$

6. $f(x) = \dfrac{x^3 - 2x^2 - 11x + 12}{x^2 - 5x + 4}$

7. $h(x) = \dfrac{x + 3}{x^2 + x - 6}$

8. $g(x) = \dfrac{x^2 - 4}{x^4 - 16}$

9. $f(x) = \begin{cases} -1 & \text{if } x < 0 \\ 0 & \text{if } x = 0 \\ x & \text{if } 0 < x \end{cases}$

10. $H(x) = \begin{cases} 1 + x & \text{if } x \leq -2 \\ 2 - x & \text{if } -2 < x \leq 2 \\ 2x - 1 & \text{if } 2 < x \end{cases}$

11. $f(x) = |2x + 5|$

12. $G(x) = \begin{cases} |2x + 5| & \text{if } x \neq -\frac{5}{2} \\ 3 & \text{if } x = -\frac{5}{2} \end{cases}$

13. $f(x) = \dfrac{x - 3}{|x - 3|}$

14. $F(x) = \begin{cases} \dfrac{x - 3}{|x - 3|} & \text{if } x \neq 3 \\ 0 & \text{if } x = 3 \end{cases}$

15. $g(x) = \begin{cases} 2x + 3 & \text{if } x \leq 1 \\ 8 - 3x & \text{if } 1 < x < 2 \\ x + 3 & \text{if } 2 \leq x \end{cases}$

16. $f(x) = \begin{cases} \dfrac{x^2 + x - 2}{x + 2} & \text{if } x \neq -2 \\ -3 & \text{if } x = -2 \end{cases}$

17. The greatest integer function. (See Example 2 in Sec. 2.3.)

18. The unit step function. (See Exercise 1 in Exercises 2.3.)

19. The signum function. (See Exercise 2 in Exercises 2.3.)

20. The function of Exercise 4 in Exercises 2.3.

21. The function of Exercise 13 in Exercises 2.3.

22. The function of Exercise 12 in Exercises 2.3.

In Exercises 23 through 30 prove that the function is discontinuous at the number a. Then determine if the discontinuity is removable or essential. If the discontinuity is removable, define $f(a)$ so that the discontinuity is removed.

23. $f(x) = \dfrac{9x^2 - 4}{3x - 2}; \ a = \dfrac{2}{3}$

24. $f(s) = \begin{cases} \dfrac{1}{s + 5} & \text{if } s \neq -5 \\ 0 & \text{if } s = -5 \end{cases}; \ a = -5$

25. $f(x) = \begin{cases} |x - 3| & \text{if } x \neq 3 \\ 2 & \text{if } x = 3 \end{cases}; \ a = 3$

26. $f(x) = \begin{cases} \dfrac{x^2 - 4x + 3}{x - 3} & \text{if } x \neq 3 \\ 5 & \text{if } x = 3 \end{cases}; \ a = 3$

27. $f(x) = \dfrac{\sqrt{2 + \sqrt[3]{x}} - 2}{x - 8}; \ a = 8$

28. $f(y) = \dfrac{\sqrt{y + 5} - \sqrt{5}}{y}; \ a = 0$

29. $f(t) = \begin{cases} t^2 - 4 & \text{if } t \leq 2 \\ t & \text{if } t > 2 \end{cases}; \ a = 2$

30. $f(x) = \dfrac{\sqrt[3]{x + 1} - 1}{x}; \ a = 0$

31. Let f be the function defined by
$$f(x) = \begin{cases} |x - [\![x]\!]| & \text{if } [\![x]\!] \text{ is even} \\ |x - [\![x + 1]\!]| & \text{if } [\![x]\!] \text{ is odd} \end{cases}$$
Draw a sketch of the graph of f. At what numbers is f discontinuous?

32. The function f is defined by
$$f(x) = \lim_{n \to +\infty} \frac{2nx}{1 - nx}$$
Draw a sketch of the graph of f. At what values of x is f discontinuous?

2.12 THEOREMS ON CONTINUITY

By applying Definition 2.11.1 and limit theorems, we have the following theorem about functions which are continuous at a number.

2.12.1 Theorem   If f and g are two functions which are continuous at the number a, then

    (i) $f + g$ is continuous at a.
    (ii) $f - g$ is continuous at a.
    (iii) $f \cdot g$ is continuous at a.
    (iv) f/g is continuous at a, provided that $g(a) \neq 0$.

To illustrate the kind of proof required for each part of this theorem, we prove part (i):

Because f and g are continuous at a, from Definition 2.11.1 we have

$$\lim_{x \to a} f(x) = f(a) \tag{1}$$

and

$$\lim_{x \to a} g(x) = g(a) \tag{2}$$

Therefore, from Eqs. (1) and (2) and Limit theorem 4, we have

$$\lim_{x \to a} [f(x) + g(x)] = f(a) + g(a) \tag{3}$$

Equation (3) is the condition that $f + g$ is continuous at a, which furnishes the proof of (i).

The proofs of parts (ii), (iii), and (iv) are left for the reader (see Exercises 1–3).

2.12.2 Theorem A polynomial function is continuous at every number.

To prove this theorem, consider the polynomial function f defined by

$$f(x) = b_0 x^n + b_1 x^{n-1} + b_2 x^{n-2} + \cdots + b_{n-1} x + b_n \qquad b_0 \neq 0$$

where n is a nonnegative integer, and $b_0, b_1, \ldots, b_n$ are real numbers. By successive applications of limit theorems, we can show that if a is any number

$$\lim_{x \to a} f(x) = b_0 a^n + b_1 a^{n-1} + b_2 a^{n-2} + \cdots + b_{n-1} a + b_n$$

from which it follows that

$$\lim_{x \to a} f(x) = f(a)$$

thus establishing the theorem. The details of the proof are left for the reader (see Exercise 4).

2.12.3 Theorem A rational function is continuous at every number in its domain.

PROOF: If f is a rational function, it can be expressed as the quotient of two polynomial functions. So f can be defined by

$$f(x) = \frac{g(x)}{h(x)}$$

where g and h are two polynomial functions, and the domain of f consists of all numbers except those for which $h(x) = 0$.

If a is any number in the domain of f, then $h(a) \neq 0$; and so by Limit theorem 9,

$$\lim_{x \to a} f(x) = \frac{\lim_{x \to a} g(x)}{\lim_{x \to a} h(x)} \qquad (4)$$

Because g and h are polynomial functions, by Theorem 2.12.2 they are continuous at a, and so $\lim_{x \to a} g(x) = g(a)$ and $\lim_{x \to a} h(x) = h(a)$. Consequently, from Eq. (4) we have

$$\lim_{x \to a} f(x) = \frac{g(a)}{h(a)}$$

Thus, we can conclude that f is continuous at every number in its domain. ■

Definition 2.11.1 states that the function f is continuous at the number a if $f(a)$ exists, if $\lim_{x \to a} f(x)$ exists, and if

$$\lim_{x \to a} f(x) = f(a) \tag{5}$$

Definition 2.4.1 states that $\lim_{x \to a} f(x) = L$ if for any $\epsilon > 0$ there exists a $\delta > 0$ such that

$$|f(x) - L| < \epsilon \quad \text{whenever} \quad 0 < |x - a| < \delta$$

Applying this definition to Eq. (5), we have $\lim_{x \to a} f(x) = f(a)$ if for any $\epsilon > 0$ there exists a $\delta > 0$ such that

$$|f(x) - f(a)| < \epsilon \quad \text{whenever} \quad 0 < |x - a| < \delta \tag{6}$$

If f is continuous at a, we know that $f(a)$ exists; thus, in statement (6) it is not necessary that $|x - a| > 0$ because when $x = a$, statement (6) obviously holds. We have, then, the following definition of continuity of a function by using ϵ and δ notation.

2.12.4 Definition   The function f is said to be continuous at the number a if f is defined on some open interval containing a and if for any $\epsilon > 0$ there exists a $\delta > 0$ such that

$$|f(x) - f(a)| < \epsilon \quad \text{whenever} \quad |x - a| < \delta$$

This alternate definition is used in proving the following important theorem regarding the limit of a composite function.

2.12.5 Theorem   If $\lim_{x \to a} g(x) = b$ and if the function f is continuous at b,

$$\lim_{x \to a} (f \circ g)(x) = f(b)$$

or, equivalently,

$$\lim_{x \to a} f(g(x)) = f(\lim_{x \to a} g(x))$$

PROOF: Because f is continuous at b, we have the following statement from Definition 2.12.4: For any $\epsilon_1 > 0$ there exists a $\delta_1 > 0$ such that

$$|f(y) - f(b)| < \epsilon_1 \quad \text{whenever} \quad |y - b| < \delta_1 \tag{7}$$

Because $\lim_{x \to a} g(x) = b$, for any $\delta_1 > 0$ there exists a $\delta_2 > 0$ such that

$$|g(x) - b| < \delta_1 \quad \text{whenever} \quad 0 < |x - a| < \delta_2 \tag{8}$$

Whenever $0 < |x - a| < \delta_2$, we replace y in statement (7) by $g(x)$ and obtain the following: For any $\epsilon_1 > 0$ there exists a $\delta_1 > 0$ such that

$$|f(g(x)) - f(b)| < \epsilon_1 \quad \text{whenever} \quad |g(x) - b| < \delta_1 \tag{9}$$

From statements (9) and (8), we conclude that for any $\epsilon_1 > 0$ there exists a $\delta_2 > 0$ such that

$$|f(g(x)) - f(b)| < \epsilon_1 \quad \text{whenever} \quad 0 < |x - a| < \delta_2$$

from which it follows that

$$\lim_{x \to a} f(g(x)) = f(b)$$

or, equivalently,

$$\lim_{x \to a} f(g(x)) = f(\lim_{x \to a} g(x)) \qquad \blacksquare$$

An immediate application of Theorem 2.12.5 is in proving Limit theorems 9 and 10, the proofs of which were deferred until now. We restate these theorems and prove them, but before the statement of each theorem a special case is given as an example.

EXAMPLE 1:   By using Theorem 2.12.5 and not Limit theorem 9 (limit of a quotient), find

$$\lim_{x \to 2} \frac{4x - 3}{x^2 + 2x + 5}$$

SOLUTION: Let the functions f and g be defined by

$$f(x) = 4x - 3 \quad \text{and} \quad g(x) = x^2 + 2x + 5$$

We consider $f(x)/g(x)$ as the product of $f(x)$ and $1/g(x)$ and use Limit theorem 6 (limit of a product). First of all, though, we must find $\lim_{x \to 2} 1/g(x)$ and this we do by considering $1/g(x)$ as a composite function value.

If h is the function defined by $h(x) = 1/x$, then the composite function $h \circ g$ is the function defined by $h(g(x)) = 1/g(x)$. Now

$$\lim_{x \to 2} g(x) = \lim_{x \to 2} (x^2 + 2x + 5) = 13$$

To use Theorem 2.12.5, h must be continuous at 13, which follows from Theorem 2.10.1. We have, then,

$$\lim_{x \to 2} \frac{1}{x^2 + 2x + 5} = \lim_{x \to 2} \frac{1}{g(x)}$$

$$= \lim_{x \to 2} h(g(x))$$

$$= h(\lim_{x \to 2} g(x)) \quad \text{(by Theorem 2.12.5)}$$

$$= h(13)$$

$$= \tfrac{1}{13}$$

Therefore, by using Limit theorem 6, we have

$$\lim_{x \to 2} \frac{4x - 3}{x^2 + 2x + 5} = \lim_{x \to 2} (4x - 3) \cdot \lim_{x \to 2} \frac{1}{x^2 + 2x + 5}$$

$$= 5 \cdot \tfrac{1}{13}$$

$$= \tfrac{5}{13}$$

Limit theorem 9   If $\lim\limits_{x \to a} f(x) = L$ and if $\lim\limits_{x \to a} g(x) = M$ and $M \neq 0$, then

$$\lim_{x \to a} \frac{f(x)}{g(x)} = \frac{L}{M}$$

PROOF: Let h be the function defined by $h(x) = 1/x$. Then the composite function $h \circ g$ is defined by $h(g(x)) = 1/g(x)$. The function h is continuous everywhere except at 0, which follows from Theorem 2.10.1. Hence,

$$\lim_{x \to a} \frac{1}{g(x)} = \lim_{x \to a} h(g(x))$$

$$= h(\lim_{x \to a} g(x)) \quad \text{(by Theorem 2.12.5)}$$

$$= h(M)$$

$$= \frac{1}{M}$$

Applying Limit theorem 6 and the above result, we have

$$\lim_{x \to a} \frac{f(x)}{g(x)} = \lim_{x \to a} f(x) \cdot \lim_{x \to a} \frac{1}{g(x)}$$

$$= L \cdot \frac{1}{M}$$

$$= \frac{L}{M} \qquad\qquad \blacksquare$$

EXAMPLE 2: By using Theorem 2.12.5 and not Limit theorem 10, find

$$\lim_{x \to 7} \sqrt[4]{3x - 5}$$

SOLUTION: Let the functions f and h be defined by

$$f(x) = 3x - 5 \quad \text{and} \quad h(x) = \sqrt[4]{x}$$

The composite function $h \circ f$ is defined by $h(f(x)) = \sqrt[4]{3x - 5}$. $\lim\limits_{x \to 7} f(x) = \lim\limits_{x \to 7} (3x - 5) = 16$; so, to use Theorem 2.12.5 for the composite function $h \circ f$, h must be continuous at 16, which follows from Theorem 2.10.2(i). The solution, then, is as follows.

$$\lim_{x \to 7} \sqrt[4]{3x - 5} = \lim_{x \to 7} h(f(x))$$

$$= h(\lim_{x \to 7} f(x)) \quad \text{(by Theorem 2.12.5)}$$

$$= h(16)$$

$$= \sqrt[4]{16}$$

$$= 2$$

Limit theorem 10   If $\lim\limits_{x \to a} f(x) = L$, *then*

$$\lim_{x \to a} \sqrt[n]{f(x)} = \sqrt[n]{L}$$

if $L > 0$ *and* n *is any positive integer, or if* $L \leq 0$ *and* n *is a positive odd integer.*

PROOF: Let h be the function defined by $h(x) = \sqrt[n]{x}$. Then the composite function $h \circ f$ is defined by $h(f(x)) = \sqrt[n]{f(x)}$. From Theorem 2.10.2 it follows that h is continuous at L if $L > 0$ and n is any positive integer or if $L \leq 0$ and n is a positive odd integer. Therefore, we have

$$\lim_{x \to a} \sqrt[n]{f(x)} = \lim_{x \to a} h(f(x))$$

$$= h(\lim_{x \to a} f(x)) \quad \text{(by Theorem 2.12.5)}$$

$$= \sqrt[n]{\lim_{x \to a} f(x)}$$

$$= \sqrt[n]{L} \qquad \blacksquare$$

Another application of Theorem 2.12.5 is in proving that *a continuous function of a continuous function is continuous.* This is now stated as a theorem.

2.12.6 Theorem   If the function g is continuous at a and the function f is continuous at $g(a)$, then the composite function $f \circ g$ is continuous at a.

PROOF: Because g is continuous at a we have

$$\lim_{x \to a} g(x) = g(a) \tag{10}$$

Now f is continuous at $g(a)$; thus, we can apply Theorem 2.12.5 to the composite function $f \circ g$, thereby giving us

$$\lim_{x \to a} (f \circ g)(x) = \lim_{x \to a} f(g(x))$$

$$= f(\lim_{x \to a} g(x))$$

$$= f(g(a)) \quad \text{(by Eq. (10))}$$

$$= (f \circ g)(a)$$

which proves that $f \circ g$ is continuous at a. $\qquad \blacksquare$

Theorem 2.12.6 enables us to determine the numbers for which a particular function is continuous. The following example illustrates this.

EXAMPLE 3:   Given

$$h(x) = \sqrt{4 - x^2}$$

determine the values of x for which h is continuous.

SOLUTION: If $g(x) = 4 - x^2$ and $f(x) = \sqrt{x}$, then $h(x) = (f \circ g)(x)$. Because g is a polynomial function, g is continuous everywhere. Furthermore, f is continuous at every positive number. Therefore, by Theorem 2.12.6, h is continuous at every number x for which $g(x) > 0$, that is, when $4 - x^2 > 0$. Hence, h is continuous at every number in the open interval $(-2, 2)$.

Exercises 2.12

1. Prove Theorem 2.12.1(ii).

2. Prove Theorem 2.12.1(iii).

3. Prove Theorem 2.12.1(iv).

4. Prove Theorem 2.12.2, showing step by step which limit theorems are used.

In Exercises 5 through 10 show the application of Theorem 2.12.5 to find the limit.

5. $\lim\limits_{x \to 3} \dfrac{1}{x^2 - 2x + 2}$

6. $\lim\limits_{t \to -1} \dfrac{t + 4}{t - 2}$

7. $\lim\limits_{y \to -4} \sqrt[3]{3y + 4}$

8. $\lim\limits_{x \to 2} \sqrt{x^3 + 1}$

9. $\lim\limits_{x \to 7} \dfrac{x^2 - 4}{\sqrt[3]{x^2 + 5x - 3}}$

10. $\lim\limits_{x \to 3} \dfrac{x + 3}{\sqrt[3]{1 - x^2}}$

In Exercises 11 through 26 determine all values of x for which the given function is continuous. Indicate which theorems you apply.

11. $f(x) = x^2(x + 3)^3$

12. $f(x) = (x - 5)^3(x^2 + 4)^5$

13. $g(x) = \dfrac{x^3 - 1}{x^2 - 4}$

14. $h(x) = \dfrac{x + 2}{x^3 - 7x - 6}$

15. $F(x) = \dfrac{x^2 + 2x - 8}{x^3 + 6x^2 + 5x - 12}$

16. $g(x) = \sqrt{x^2 + 4}$

17. $f(x) = \sqrt{x^2 - 16}$

18. $F(x) = \sqrt{16 - x^2}$

19. $h(x) = \sqrt{\dfrac{x + 4}{x - 4}}$

20. $f(x) = \sqrt{\dfrac{4 - x}{4 + x}}$

21. $f(x) = |x - 5|$

22. $g(x) = |9 - x^2|$

23. $f(x) = x^2(x^{-2} + x^{-1/2})^3$

24. $G(x) = \left(\dfrac{x^2}{x^2 - 4} - \dfrac{1}{x}\right)^{1/3}$

25. $g(x) = [\![\sqrt{1 - x^2}]\!]$

26. $F(x) = 1 - x + [\![x]\!] - [\![1 - x]\!]$

27. Prove that if the function f is continuous at t, then $\lim\limits_{h \to 0} f(t - h) = f(t)$.

28. Prove that if f is continuous at a and g is discontinuous at a, then $f + g$ is discontinuous at a.

29. If

$$f(x) = \begin{cases} -x & \text{if } x < 0 \\ 1 & \text{if } x \geq 0 \end{cases} \quad \text{and} \quad g(x) = \begin{cases} 1 & \text{if } x < 0 \\ x & \text{if } x \geq 0 \end{cases}$$

prove that f and g are both discontinuous at 0 but that the product $f \cdot g$ is continuous at 0.

30. Give an example of two functions that are both discontinuous at a number a, but the sum of the two functions is continuous at a.

31. Give an example to show that the product of two functions f and g may be continuous at a number a where f is continuous at a but g is discontinuous at a.

32. If the function g is continuous at a number a and the function f is discontinuous at a, is it possible for the quotient of the two functions, f/g, to be continuous at a? Prove your answer.

2.13 CONTINUITY ON AN INTERVAL

In Example 3 of Sec. 2.12 we showed that the function h, for which $h(x) = \sqrt{4 - x^2}$, is continuous at every number in the open interval $(-2, 2)$. Because of this fact, we say that h is continuous on the open interval $(-2, 2)$. Following is the general definition of continuity on an open interval.

2.13.1 Definition A function is said to be *continuous on an open interval* if and only if it is continuous at every number in the open interval.

EXAMPLE 1: If $f(x) = 1/(x - 3)$, on what open intervals is f continuous?

SOLUTION: The function f is continuous at every number except 3. Hence, by Definition 2.13.1, f is continuous on every open interval which does not contain the number 3.

We refer again to the function h for which $h(x) = \sqrt{4 - x^2}$. We know that h is continuous on the open interval $(-2, 2)$. However, because h is not defined on any open interval containing either -2 or 2, we cannot consider $\lim_{x \to -2} h(x)$ or $\lim_{x \to 2} h(x)$. Hence, to discuss the question of the continuity of h on the closed interval $[-2, 2]$, we must extend the concept of continuity to include continuity at an endpoint of a closed interval. We do this by first defining *right-hand continuity* and *left-hand continuity*.

2.13.2 Definition The function f is said to be *continuous from the right at the number a* if and only if the following three conditions are satisfied:

(i) $f(a)$ exists.
(ii) $\lim_{x \to a^+} f(x)$ exists.
(iii) $\lim_{x \to a^+} f(x) = f(a)$.

2.13.3 Definition The function f is said to be *continuous from the left at the number a* if and only if the following three conditions are satisfied:

(i) $f(a)$ exists.
(ii) $\lim_{x \to a^-} f(x)$ exists.
(iii) $\lim_{x \to a^-} f(x) = f(a)$.

2.13.4 Definition   A function whose domain includes the closed interval $[a, b]$ is said to be continuous on $[a, b]$ if and only if it is continuous on the open interval (a, b), as well as continuous from the right at a and continuous from the left at b.

EXAMPLE 2:   **Prove that the function h, for which $h(x) = \sqrt{4 - x^2}$, is continuous on the closed interval $[-2, 2]$.**

SOLUTION: The function h is continuous on the open interval $(-2, 2)$ and

$$\lim_{x \to -2^+} \sqrt{4 - x^2} = 0 = h(-2)$$

and

$$\lim_{x \to 2^-} \sqrt{4 - x^2} = 0 = h(2)$$

Thus, by Definition 2.13.4, h is continuous on the closed interval $[-2, 2]$.

2.13.5 Definition   (i) A function whose domain includes the interval half-open on the right $[a, b)$ is said to be continuous on $[a, b)$ if and only if it is continuous on the open interval (a, b) and continuous from the right at a.

(ii) A function whose domain includes the interval half-open on the left $(a, b]$ is said to be continuous on $(a, b]$ if and only if it is continuous on the open interval (a, b) and continuous from the left at b.

EXAMPLE 3:   **Given f is the function defined by**

$$f(x) = \sqrt{\frac{2 - x}{3 + x}}$$

determine whether f is continuous or discontinuous on each of the following intervals: $(-3, 2)$, $[-3, 2]$, $[-3, 2)$, $(-3, 2]$.

SOLUTION: We first determine the domain of f. The domain of f is the set of all numbers for which $(2 - x)/(3 + x)$ is nonnegative. Thus, any values of x for which the numerator and the denominator of this fraction have opposite signs are excluded from the domain. The numerator changes sign when $x = 2$, and the denominator changes sign when $x = -3$. We make use of Table 2.13.1 to determine when the fraction is positive, negative, zero, or undefined, from which we are able to determine the values of x for which $f(x)$ exists. The domain of f is then the interval half-open on the left $(-3, 2]$. The function f is continuous on the open interval $(-3, 2)$. It is continuous from the left at 2 because

$$\lim_{x \to 2^-} \sqrt{\frac{2 - x}{3 + x}} = 0 = f(2)$$

However, f is not continuous from the right at -3 because

$$\lim_{x \to -3^+} \sqrt{\frac{2 - x}{3 + x}} = +\infty$$

We conclude that f is continuous on $(-3, 2]$ and discontinuous on $[-3, 2]$ and $[-3, 2)$.

Table 2.13.1

	$2 - x$	$3 + x$	$\dfrac{2 - x}{3 + x}$	$f(x)$
$x < -3$	$+$	$-$	$-$	does not exist
$x = -3$	5	0	undefined	does not exist
$-3 < x < 2$	$+$	$+$	$+$	$+$
$x = 2$	0	5	0	0
$2 < x$	$-$	$+$	$-$	does not exist

EXAMPLE 4: Given $g(x) = [\![x]\!]$ and $1 \leq x \leq 3$. Discuss the continuity of g.

Figure 2.13.1

SOLUTION: Figure 2.13.1 shows a sketch of the graph of g. Suppose that u is any number in $(1, 2)$. Then $[\![u]\!] = 1$, and $\lim_{x \to u} [\![x]\!] = 1$. Hence, if $1 < u < 2$, $\lim_{x \to u} g(x) = g(u)$, and so g is continuous on $(1, 2)$.

$$\lim_{x \to 1^+} g(x) = \lim_{x \to 1^+} [\![x]\!] = 1 = g(1)$$

Therefore, g is continuous from the right at 1. But

$$\lim_{x \to 2^-} g(x) = \lim_{x \to 2^-} [\![x]\!] = 1$$

and $g(2) = 2$. So g is not continuous from the left at 2. The function g is therefore continuous on the interval half-open on the right $[1, 2)$.

Similarly, g is continuous at every number u for which $2 < u < 3$. At 2, g is continuous from the right since $\lim_{x \to 2^+} g(x) = g(2)$, but g is not continuous from the left at 3 because $\lim_{x \to 3^-} g(x) = 2$ and $g(3) = 3$. Hence, g is also continuous on the interval $[2, 3)$.

Exercises 2.13

In Exercises 1 through 16 determine whether the function is continuous or discontinuous on each of the indicated intervals.

1. $f(x) = \dfrac{2}{x + 5}$; $(3, 7)$, $[-6, 4]$, $(-\infty, 0)$, $(-5, +\infty)$, $[-5, +\infty)$, $[-10, -5)$.

2. $f(r) = \dfrac{r + 3}{r^2 - 4}$; $(0, 4]$, $(-2, 2)$, $(-\infty, -2]$, $(2, +\infty)$, $[-4, 4]$, $(-2, 2]$.

3. $g(x) = \sqrt{x^2 - 9}$; $(-\infty, -3)$, $(-\infty, -3]$, $(3, +\infty)$, $[3, +\infty)$, $(-3, 3)$.

4. $f(x) = [\![x]\!]$; $(-\frac{1}{2}, \frac{1}{2})$, $(\frac{1}{4}, \frac{1}{2})$, $(1, 2)$, $[1, 2)$, $(1, 2]$.

5. $f(t) = \dfrac{|t - 1|}{t - 1}$; $(-\infty, 1)$, $(-\infty, 1]$, $[-1, 1]$, $(-1, +\infty)$, $(1, +\infty)$.

6. $h(x) = \begin{cases} 2x - 3 & \text{if } x < -2 \\ x - 5 & \text{if } -2 \le x \le 1 \\ 3 - x & \text{if } 1 < x \end{cases}$; $(-\infty, 1)$, $(-2, +\infty)$, $(-2, 1)$, $[-2, 1)$.

7. $f(x) = \sqrt{4 - x^2}$; $(-2, 2)$, $[-2, 2]$, $[-2, 2)$, $(-2, 2]$, $(-\infty, -2]$, $(2, +\infty)$.

8. $f(x) = \sqrt{\dfrac{2 + x}{2 - x}}$; $(-2, 2)$, $[-2, 2]$, $[-2, 2)$, $(-2, 2]$, $(-\infty, -2)$, $[2, +\infty)$.

9. $F(y) = \dfrac{1}{\sqrt{3 + 2y - y^2}}$; $(-1, 3)$, $[-1, 3]$, $[-1, 3)$, $(-1, 3]$.

10. $f(x) = \sqrt{3 + 2x - x^2}$; $(-1, 3)$, $[-1, 3]$, $[-1, 3)$, $(-1, 3]$.

11. $G(x) = \sqrt{\dfrac{9 - x^2}{4 - x}}$; $(-\infty, -3)$, $(-3, 3)$, $[-3, 3]$, $[-3, 3)$, $[3, 4]$, $(3, 4]$, $[4, +\infty)$, $(4, +\infty)$.

12. $g(x) = \sqrt{\dfrac{2 + x}{25 - x^2}}$; $(-\infty, -5)$, $(-\infty, -5]$, $[-5, -2]$, $[-2, 5]$, $[-2, 5)$, $(-2, 5]$, $(-2, 5)$, $[5, +\infty)$, $(5, +\infty)$.

In Exercises 13 through 20 determine the intervals on which the given function is continuous.

13. $f(x) = \dfrac{1}{x^2 - 4}$

14. $g(y) = \dfrac{4}{y + 1}$

15. $h(x) = \sqrt{x^2 - x - 12}$

16. $F(x) = \sqrt{\dfrac{x - 5}{x + 6}}$

17. The function of Exercise 5 in Exercises 2.3.

18. The function of Exercise 6 in Exercises 2.3.

19. The function of Exercise 21 in Exercises 2.3.

20. The function of Exercise 24 in Exercises 2.3.

In Exercises 21 through 28, functions f and g are defined. In each exercise define $f \circ g$, and determine all values of x for which $f \circ g$ is continuous.

21. $f(x) = x^3$; $g(x) = \sqrt{x}$

22. $f(x) = x^2$; $g(x) = x^2 - 3$

23. $f(x) = \sqrt{x}$; $g(x) = \dfrac{1}{x - 2}$

24. $f(x) = \sqrt{x}$; $g(x) = x + 1$

25. $f(x) = \dfrac{1}{x - 2}$; $g(x) = \sqrt{x}$

26. $f(x) = \sqrt[3]{x}$; $g(x) = \sqrt{x + 1}$

27. $f(x) = \dfrac{x + 1}{x - 1}$; $g(x) = \sqrt{x}$

28. $f(x) = \sqrt{x + 1}$; $g(x) = \sqrt[3]{x}$

In Exercises 29 through 32, find the values of the constants c and k that make the function continuous on $(-\infty, +\infty)$ and draw a sketch of the graph of the resulting function.

29. $f(x) = \begin{cases} 3x + 7 & \text{if } x \le 4 \\ kx - 1 & \text{if } 4 < x \end{cases}$

30. $f(x) = \begin{cases} kx - 1 & \text{if } x < 2 \\ kx^2 & \text{if } 2 \le x \end{cases}$

31. $f(x) = \begin{cases} x & \text{if } x \le 1 \\ cx + k & \text{if } 1 < x < 4 \\ -2x & \text{if } 4 \le x \end{cases}$

32. $f(x) = \begin{cases} x + 2c & \text{if } x < -2 \\ 3cx + k & \text{if } -2 \le x \le 1 \\ 3x - 2k & \text{if } 1 < x \end{cases}$

33. Given that f is defined by

$$f(x) = \begin{cases} g(x) & \text{if } a \le x < b \\ h(x) & \text{if } b \le x \le c \end{cases}$$

If g is continuous on $[a, b)$, and h is continuous on $[b, c]$, can we conclude that f is continuous on $[a, c]$? If your answer is yes, prove it. If your answer is no, what additional condition or conditions would assure continuity of f on $[a, c]$?

34. If f is the function defined by $f(x) = \sqrt[n]{x^m}$, where m and n are positive integers, prove that f is continuous on the interval $[0, +\infty)$.

Review Exercises (Chapter 2)

In Exercises 1 through 4, for the given functions f and g, define the following functions and determine the domain of the resulting function: (a) $f + g$; (b) $f - g$; (c) $f \cdot g$; (d) f/g; (e) g/f; (f) $f \circ g$; (g) $g \circ f$.

1. $f(x) = x^2 - 4$ and $g(x) = 4x - 3$.

2. $f(x) = \sqrt{x + 2}$ and $g(x) = x^2 + 4$.

3. $f(x) = 1/(x - 3)$ and $g(x) = x/(x + 1)$.

4. $f(x) = \sqrt{x}$ and $g(x) = 1/x^2$.

In Exercises 5 through 10, evaluate the limit, and when applicable indicate the limit theorems being used.

5. $\lim\limits_{x \to 2} (3x^2 - 4x + 5)$

6. $\lim\limits_{h \to 1} \dfrac{h^2 - 4}{3h^3 + 6}$

7. $\lim\limits_{t \to 0} \dfrac{\sqrt{9 - t} - 3}{t}$

8. $\lim\limits_{y \to -4} \sqrt{\dfrac{5y + 4}{y - 5}}$

9. $\lim\limits_{x \to +\infty} \dfrac{8x^3 - 5x^2 + 3}{2x^3 + 7x - 4}$

10. $\lim\limits_{x \to -\infty} \dfrac{\sqrt{x^2 + 5}}{2x - 4}$

In Exercises 11 through 14, draw a sketch of the graph and discuss the continuity of the function.

11. $f(x) = \sqrt{4x^2 - 9}$

12. $g(x) = \sqrt{\dfrac{x - 3}{4 - x}}$

13. $h(x) = \sqrt{(x - 3)(4 - x)}$

14. $F(x) = \dfrac{|x^2 - 4|}{x + 2}$

In Exercises 15 and 16 find $(f \circ g)(x)$ and discuss the continuity of $f \circ g$ if f is the signum function (see Exercise 2 in Exercises 2.3) and g is the given function.

15. $g(x) = x^2 + 1$

16. $g(x) = x^2 - x$

In Exercises 17 through 22, establish the limit by using Definition 2.4.1; that is, for any $\epsilon > 0$ find a $\delta > 0$ such that $|f(x) - L| < \epsilon$ whenever $0 < |x - a| < \delta$.

17. $\lim\limits_{x \to -2} (8 - 3x) = 14$

18. $\lim\limits_{x \to 3} (2x^2 - x - 6) = 9$

19. $\lim\limits_{t \to 4} \sqrt{t - 3} = 1$

20. $\lim\limits_{y \to 5} \dfrac{3}{2y - 1} = \dfrac{1}{3}$

21. $\lim\limits_{x \to 3} \dfrac{5 + 3x}{2x + 1} = 2$

22. $\lim\limits_{x \to -2} x^3 = -8$

23. Prove that $\lim\limits_{t \to 2^+} \sqrt{t^2 - 4} = 0$ by showing that for any $\epsilon > 0$ there exists a $\delta > 0$ such that $\sqrt{t^2 - 4} < \epsilon$ whenever $0 < t - 2 < \delta$.

24. Prove that

$$\lim\limits_{x \to +\infty} \dfrac{4x + 7}{2x - 5} = 2$$

by showing that for any $\epsilon > 0$ there exists an $M > 0$ such that

$$\left| \dfrac{4x + 7}{2x - 5} - 2 \right| < \epsilon \qquad \text{whenever } x > M$$

25. If $f(x) = (|x| - x)/x$, evaluate:

   (a) $\lim\limits_{x \to 0^-} f(x)$; (b) $\lim\limits_{x \to 0^+} f(x)$; (c) $\lim\limits_{x \to 0} f(x)$.

26. Prove that $x \operatorname{sgn} x = |x|$.

In Exercises 27 through 33 evaluate the limit.

27. $\lim\limits_{x \to 9} \dfrac{2\sqrt{x} - 6}{x - 9}$

28. $\lim\limits_{s \to 7} \dfrac{5 - \sqrt{4 + 3s}}{7 - s}$

29. $\lim\limits_{t \to 0} \dfrac{\sqrt[3]{(t + a)^2} - \sqrt[3]{a^2}}{t}$

30. $\lim\limits_{x \to 8} \dfrac{\sqrt{7 + \sqrt[3]{x}} - 3}{x - 8}$

31. $\lim\limits_{x \to 0} \dfrac{\sqrt[4]{x^4 + 1} - \sqrt{x^2 + 1}}{x^2}$

   $\left(\text{HINT: Write } \dfrac{\sqrt[4]{x^4 + 1} - \sqrt{x^2 + 1}}{x^2} = \dfrac{1 - \sqrt{x^2 + 1}}{x^2} + \dfrac{\sqrt[4]{x^4 + 1} - 1}{x^2}.\right)$

32. $\lim\limits_{t \to +\infty} (\sqrt{t^2 + t} - \sqrt{t^2 + 4})$

33. $\lim\limits_{x \to 1^+} \dfrac{[\![x^2]\!] - [\![x]\!]^2}{x^2 - 1}$

34. Draw a sketch of the graph of f if $f(x) = [\![1 - x^2]\!]$ and $-2 \le x \le 2$. (a) Does $\lim\limits_{x \to 0} f(x)$ exist? (b) Is f continuous at 0?

35. Draw a sketch of the graph of g if $g(x) = (x - 1)[\![x]\!]$, and $0 \le x \le 2$.

   (a) Does $\lim\limits_{x \to 1} g(x)$ exist? (b) Is g continuous at 1?

36. Give an example of a function for which $\lim\limits_{x \to 0} |f(x)|$ exists but $\lim\limits_{x \to 0} f(x)$ does not exist.

37. Give an example of a function whose domain is the set of all real numbers and that (a) is continuous at every number except 0; (b) continuous at every number except 0 and 1; (c) continuous from the left at 1 but discontinuous from the right at 1.

38. Give an example of a function f that is discontinuous at 1 for which (a) $\lim\limits_{x \to 1} f(x)$ exists but $f(1)$ does not exist; (b) $f(1)$ exists but $\lim\limits_{x \to 1} f(x)$ does not exist; (c) $\lim\limits_{x \to 1} f(x)$ and $f(1)$ both exist but are not equal.

39. Let f be the function defined by

   $$f(x) = \begin{cases} 1 & \text{if } x \text{ is an integer} \\ 0 & \text{if } x \text{ is not an integer} \end{cases}$$

   (a) Draw a sketch of the graph of f. (b) For what values of a does $\lim\limits_{x \to a} f(x)$ exist? (c) At what numbers is f continuous?

40. If the function g is continuous at a and f is continuous at $g(a)$, is the composite function $f \circ g$ continuous at a? Why?

41. If $f(x) = 2x/\sqrt{x^2 - 6x - 7}$, find the horizontal and vertical asymptotes of the graph of f and draw a sketch of the graph.

42. (a) Prove that if $\lim\limits_{h \to 0} f(x + h) = f(x)$ then $\lim\limits_{h \to 0} f(x + h) = \lim\limits_{h \to 0} f(x - h)$. (b) Show that the converse of the theorem in (a) is not true by giving an example of a function for which $\lim\limits_{h \to 0} f(x + h) = \lim\limits_{h \to 0} f(x - h)$ but $\lim\limits_{h \to 0} f(x + h) \neq f(x)$.

43. If the domain of f is the set of all real numbers, and f is continuous at 0, prove that if $f(a + b) = f(a) \cdot f(b)$ for all a and b, then f is continuous at every number.

44. If the domain of f is the set of all real numbers and f is continuous at 0, prove that if $f(a + b) = f(a) + f(b)$ for all a and b, then f is continuous at every number.

3

The Derivative

3.1 THE TANGENT LINE

Figure 3.1.1

Figure 3.1.2

Many of the important problems in calculus depend on the problem of finding the tangent line to a given curve at a specific point on the curve. If the curve is a circle, we know from plane geometry that the tangent line at a point P on the circle is defined as the line intersecting the circle at only one point P. This definition does not suffice for a curve in general. For example, in Fig. 3.1.1 the line which we wish to be the tangent line to the curve at point P intersects the curve at another point Q.

In this section we arrive at a suitable definition of the tangent line to the graph of a function at a point on the graph. We proceed by considering how we should define the slope of the tangent line at a point, because if we know the slope of a line and a point on the line, the line is determined.

Let the function f be continuous at x_1. We wish to define the slope of the tangent line to the graph of f at $P(x_1, f(x_1))$. Let $Q(x_2, f(x_2))$ be another point on the graph of f such that x_2 is also in I. Draw a line through P and Q. Any line through two points on a curve is called a *secant line*; therefore, the line through P and Q is a secant line. See Fig. 3.1.2. In the figure, Q is to the right of P. However, Q may be on either the right or left side of P.

Let us denote the difference of the abscissas of Q and P by Δx so that

$$\Delta x = x_2 - x_1$$

Δx may be either positive or negative. The slope of the secant line PQ then is given by

$$m_{PQ} = \frac{f(x_2) - f(x_1)}{\Delta x}$$

Because $x_2 = x_1 + \Delta x$, we can write the above equation as

$$m_{PQ} = \frac{f(x_1 + \Delta x) - f(x_1)}{\Delta x} \tag{1}$$

Now, think of point P as being fixed, and move point Q along the curve toward P; that is, Q approaches P. This is equivalent to stating that Δx approaches zero. As this occurs, the secant line turns about the fixed point P. If this secant line has a limiting position, it is this limiting position which we wish to be the tangent line to the graph at P. So we want the slope of the tangent line to the graph at P to be the limit of m_{PQ} as Δx approaches zero, if this limit exists. If $\lim\limits_{\Delta x \to 0} m_{PQ} = \infty$, then as Δx approaches zero the line PQ approaches the line through P which is parallel to the y axis. In this case we would want the tangent line to the graph at P to be the line $x = x_1$. The preceding discussion leads us to the following definition.

3.1.1 Definition   If the function f is continuous at x_1, then the *tangent line* to the graph of f at the point $P(x_1, f(x_1))$ is

    (i) the line through P having slope $m(x_1)$, given by

$$m(x_1) = \lim_{\Delta x \to 0} \frac{f(x_1 + \Delta x) - f(x_1)}{\Delta x} \tag{1}$$

    if this limit exists; or

    (ii) the line $x = x_1$ if $\lim\limits_{\Delta x \to 0} \dfrac{f(x_1 + \Delta x) - f(x_1)}{\Delta x} = \infty$

If neither (i) nor (ii) of Definition 3.1.1 holds, then there is no tangent line to the graph of f at the point $P(x_1, f(x_1))$.

EXAMPLE 1: Find the slope of the tangent line to the curve $y = x^2 - 4x + 3$ at the point (x_1, y_1).

SOLUTION: $f(x) = x^2 - 4x + 3$; therefore, $f(x_1) = x_1^2 - 4x_1 + 3$, and $f(x_1 + \Delta x) = (x_1 + \Delta x)^2 - 4(x_1 + \Delta x) + 3$. From Eq. (1), we have

$$m(x_1) = \lim_{\Delta x \to 0} \frac{f(x_1 + \Delta x) - f(x_1)}{\Delta x}$$

$$= \lim_{\Delta x \to 0} \frac{[(x_1 + \Delta x)^2 - 4(x_1 + \Delta x) + 3] - [x_1^2 - 4x_1 + 3]}{\Delta x}$$

$$= \lim_{\Delta x \to 0} \frac{x_1^2 + 2x_1 \, \Delta x + (\Delta x)^2 - 4x_1 - 4 \, \Delta x + 3 - x_1^2 + 4x_1 - 3}{\Delta x}$$

$$= \lim_{\Delta x \to 0} \frac{2x_1 \, \Delta x + (\Delta x)^2 - 4 \, \Delta x}{\Delta x}$$

Because $\Delta x \neq 0$, we can divide the numerator and the denominator by Δx and obtain

$$m(x_1) = \lim_{\Delta x \to 0} (2x_1 + \Delta x - 4)$$

or

$$m(x_1) = 2x_1 - 4 \tag{2}$$

Figure 3.1.3

We now draw a sketch of the graph of the equation in Example 1. We plot some points and a segment of the tangent line at some points. We take values of x arbitrarily and compute the corresponding value of y from the given equation, as well as the value of m from Eq. (2). The results are given in Table 3.1.1, and a sketch of the graph is shown in Fig. 3.1.3. It is important to determine the points where the graph has a horizontal tangent. Because a horizontal line has a slope of zero, these points are found by setting $m(x_1) = 0$ and solving for x_1. Doing this calculation for this example, we have $2x_1 - 4 = 0$, which gives $x_1 = 2$. Therefore, at the point having an abscissa of 2, the tangent line will be parallel to the x axis.

Table 3.1.1

x	y	m
2	−1	0
1	0	−2
0	3	−4
−1	8	−6
3	0	2
4	3	4
5	8	6

EXAMPLE 2: Find an equation of the tangent line to the curve of Example 1 at the point (4, 3).

SOLUTION: Because the slope of the tangent line at any point (x_1, y_1) is given by

$$m(x_1) = 2x_1 - 4$$

the slope of the tangent line at the point (4, 3) is $m(4) = 2(4) - 4 = 4$. Therefore, an equation of the desired line, if we use the point-slope form, is

$$y - 3 = 4(x - 4)$$

or

$$4x - y - 13 = 0$$

3.1.2 Definition   The *normal line* to a curve at a given point is the line perpendicular to the tangent line at that point.

EXAMPLE 3:   Find an equation of the normal line to the curve $y = \sqrt{x-3}$ which is parallel to the line $6x + 3y - 4 = 0$.

SOLUTION: Let l be the given line. To find the slope of l, we write its equation in the slope-intercept form, which is

$$y = -2x + \tfrac{4}{3}$$

Therefore, the slope of l is -2, and the slope of the desired normal line is also -2 because the two lines are parallel.

To find the slope of the tangent line to the given curve at any point (x_1, y_1), we apply Definition 3.1.1 with $f(x) = \sqrt{x-3}$, and we have

$$m(x_1) = \lim_{\Delta x \to 0} \frac{\sqrt{x_1 + \Delta x - 3} - \sqrt{x_1 - 3}}{\Delta x}$$

To evaluate this limit, we rationalize the numerator.

$$m(x_1) = \lim_{\Delta x \to 0} \frac{(\sqrt{x_1 + \Delta x - 3} - \sqrt{x_1 - 3})(\sqrt{x_1 + \Delta x - 3} + \sqrt{x_1 - 3})}{\Delta x(\sqrt{x_1 + \Delta x - 3} + \sqrt{x_1 - 3})}$$

$$= \lim_{\Delta x \to 0} \frac{\Delta x}{\Delta x(\sqrt{x_1 + \Delta x - 3} + \sqrt{x_1 - 3})}$$

Dividing numerator and denominator by Δx (since $\Delta x \neq 0$), we obtain

$$m(x_1) = \lim_{\Delta x \to 0} \frac{1}{\sqrt{x_1 + \Delta x - 3} + \sqrt{x_1 - 3}}$$

$$= \frac{1}{2\sqrt{x_1 - 3}}$$

Because the normal line at a point is perpendicular to the tangent line at that point, the product of their slopes is -1. Hence, the slope of the normal line at (x_1, y_1) is given by

$$-2\sqrt{x_1 - 3}$$

As shown above, the slope of the desired line is -2. So we solve the equation

$$-2\sqrt{x_1 - 3} = -2$$

giving us

$$x_1 = 4$$

Therefore, the desired line is the line through point $(4, 1)$ on the curve and has a slope of -2. Using the point-slope form of an equation of a line, we obtain

$$y - 1 = -2(x - 4)$$

or

$$2x + y - 9 = 0$$

Refer to Fig. 3.1.4, which shows a sketch of the curve together with the line l, the normal line PN at $(4, 1)$, and the tangent line PT at $(4, 1)$.

Figure 3.1.4

Exercises 3.1

In Exercises 1 through 8, find the slope of the tangent line to the graph at the point (x_1, y_1). Make a table of values of x, y, and m at various points on the graph, and include in the table all points where the graph has a horizontal tangent. Draw a sketch of the graph.

1. $y = 9 - x^2$
2. $y = x^2 - 6x + 9$
3. $y = 7 - 6x - x^2$
4. $y = \frac{1}{4}x^2$
5. $y = x^3 - 3x$
6. $y = x^3 - x^2 - x + 10$
7. $y = 4x^3 - 13x^2 + 4x - 3$
8. $y = \sqrt{x+1}$

In Exercises 9 through 18, find an equation of the tangent line and an equation of the normal line to the given curve at the indicated point. Draw a sketch of the curve together with the resulting tangent line and normal line.

9. $y = x^2 - 4x - 5$; $(-2, 7)$
10. $y = x^2 + 2x + 1$; $(1, 4)$
11. $y = \frac{1}{8}x^3$; $(4, 8)$
12. $y = 2x - x^3$; $(-2, 4)$
13. $y = \sqrt{9 - 4x}$; $(-4, 5)$
14. $y = \sqrt{4x - 3}$; $(3, 3)$
15. $y = \dfrac{6}{x}$; $(3, 2)$
16. $y = -\dfrac{8}{\sqrt{x}}$; $(4, -4)$
17. $y = \sqrt[3]{x}$; $(8, 2)$

18. $y = \sqrt[3]{5 - x}$; $(-3, 2)$

19. Find an equation of the tangent line to the curve $y = 2x^2 + 3$ that is parallel to the line $8x - y + 3 = 0$.

20. Find an equation of the normal line to the curve $y = x^3 - 3x$ that is parallel to the line $2x + 18y - 9 = 0$.

21. Find an equation of the tangent line to the curve $y = \sqrt{4x - 3} - 1$ that is perpendicular to the line $x + 2y - 11 = 0$.

22. Find an equation of each line through the point $(3, -2)$ that is tangent to the curve $y = x^2 - 7$.

23. Find an equation of each line through the point $(2, -6)$ that is tangent to the curve $y = 3x^2 - 8$.

24. Prove analytically that there is no line through the point $(1, 2)$ that is tangent to the curve $y = 4 - x^2$.

3.2 INSTANTANEOUS VELOCITY IN RECTILINEAR MOTION

Consider a particle moving along a straight line. Such a motion is called *rectilinear motion*. One direction is chosen arbitrarily as positive, and the opposite direction is negative. For simplicity, we assume that the motion of the particle is along a horizontal line, with distance to the right as positive and distance to the left as negative. Select some point on the line and denote it by the letter O. Let f be the function determining the directed distance of the particle from O at any particular time.

To be more specific, let s feet be the directed distance of the particle from O at t seconds of time. Then f is the function defined by the equation

$$s = f(t) \tag{1}$$

which gives the directed distance from the point O to the particle at a particular instant of time. Equation (1) is called an *equation of motion* of the particle.

In particular, let

$$s = t^2 + 2t - 3$$

Then, when $t = 0$, $s = -3$; therefore, the particle is 3 ft to the left of point O when $t = 0$. When $t = 1$, $s = 0$; so the particle is at point O at 1 sec. When $t = 2$, $s = 5$; so the particle is 5 ft to the right of point O at 2 sec. When $t = 3$, $s = 12$; so the particle is 12 ft to the right of point O at 3 sec.

Figure 3.2.1 illustrates the various positions of the particle for specific values of t.

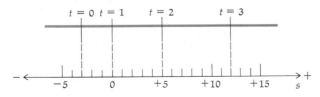

Figure 3.2.1

Between the time for $t = 1$ and $t = 3$, the particle moves from the point where $s = 0$ to the point where $s = 12$; thus, in the 2-sec interval the change in the directed distance from O is 12 ft. The average velocity of the particle is the ratio of the change in the directed distance from a fixed point to the change in the time. So the number of feet per second in the average velocity of the particle from $t = 1$ to $t = 3$ is $\frac{12}{2} = 6$. From $t = 0$ to $t = 2$, the change in the directed distance from O of the particle is 8 ft, and so the number of feet per second in the average velocity of the particle in this 2-sec interval is $\frac{8}{2} = 4$.

The average velocity of the particle is obviously not constant; and the average velocity supplies no specific information about the motion of the particle at any particular instant. For example, if a person is driving a car a distance of 70 miles in the same direction, and it takes him 2 hr, we say his average velocity in traveling that distance is 35 mi/hr. However, from this information we cannot conclude anything about the speed-ometer reading of the car at any particular time in the 2-hr period. The speedometer reading at a specific time is referred to as the *instantaneous velocity*. The following discussion enables us to arrive at a definition of what is meant by "instantaneous velocity."

Let Eq. (1) define s (the number of feet in the directed distance of the particle from point O) as a function of t (the number of seconds in the time). When $t = t_1$, $s = s_1$. The change in the directed distance from O is $(s - s_1)$ ft over the interval of time $(t - t_1)$ sec, and the number of feet per second in the average velocity of the particle over this interval of time is given by

$$\frac{s - s_1}{t - t_1}$$

or, because $s = f(t)$ and $s_1 = f(t_1)$, the average velocity is found from

$$\frac{f(t) - f(t_1)}{t - t_1}$$

Now the shorter the interval is from t_1 to t, the closer the average velocity will be to what we would intuitively think of as the instantaneous veloc-ity at t_1.

For example, if the speedometer reading of a car as it passes a point P_1 is 40 mi/hr and if a point P is, for instance, 100 ft from P_1, then the average velocity of the car as it travels this 100 ft will very likely be close to 40 mi/hr because the variation of the velocity of the car along this short stretch is probably slight. Now, if the distance from P_1 to P were shortened to 50 ft, the average velocity of the car in this interval would be even closer to the speedometer reading of the car as it passes P_1. We can con-tinue this process, and the speedometer reading at P_1 can be represented as the limit of the average velocity between P_1 and P as P approaches P_1. We have, then, the following definition.

3.2.1 Definition   If f is a function given by the equation

$$s = f(t) \tag{1}$$

and a particle is moving along a straight line so that s is the number of units in the directed distance of the particle from a fixed point at t units of time, then the *instantaneous velocity* of the particle at time t_1 sec is $v(t_1)$ units of velocity where

$$v(t_1) = \lim_{t \to t_1} \frac{f(t) - f(t_1)}{t - t_1} \tag{2}$$

if this limit exists.

Because $t \neq t_1$, we can write

$$t = t_1 + \Delta t \tag{3}$$

and conclude that

$$\text{"}t \to t_1\text{"} \quad \text{is equivalent to} \quad \text{"}\Delta t \to 0\text{"} \tag{4}$$

From Eqs. (2) and (3) and statement (4), we obtain the following expression for $v(t_1)$:

$$v(t_1) = \lim_{\Delta t \to 0} \frac{f(t_1 + \Delta t) - f(t_1)}{\Delta t} \tag{5}$$

if this limit exists.

Formula (5) can be substituted for formula (2) in the definition of instantaneous velocity.

The instantaneous velocity may be either positive or negative, depending on whether the particle is moving along the line in the positive or the negative direction. When the instantaneous velocity is zero, the particle is at rest.

The *speed* of a particle at any time is defined as the absolute value of the instantaneous velocity. Hence, the speed is a nonnegative number. The terms "speed" and "instantaneous velocity" are often confused. It should be noted that the speed indicates only how fast the particle is moving, whereas the instantaneous velocity also tells us the direction of motion.

EXAMPLE 1:   A particle is moving along a straight line according to the equation of motion

$$s = 2t^3 - 4t^2 + 2t - 1$$

Determine the intervals of time when the particle is moving to the right and when it is moving to the left. Also determine the instant when the particle reverses its direction.

SOLUTION: $f(t) = 2t^3 - 4t^2 + 2t - 1$.

Applying formula (2) in the definition of the instantaneous velocity of the particle at t_1, we have

$$v(t_1) = \lim_{t \to t_1} \frac{f(t) - f(t_1)}{t - t_1}$$

$$= \lim_{t \to t_1} \frac{(2t^3 - 4t^2 + 2t - 1) - (2t_1^3 - 4t_1^2 + 2t_1 - 1)}{t - t_1}$$

$$= \lim_{t \to t_1} \frac{2(t^3 - t_1^3) - 4(t^2 - t_1^2) + 2(t - t_1)}{t - t_1}$$

$$= \lim_{t \to t_1} \frac{2(t - t_1)[(t^2 + tt_1 + t_1^2) - 2(t + t_1) + 1]}{t - t_1}$$

Dividing the numerator and the denominator by $t - t_1$ (because $t \neq t_1$), we obtain

$$v(t_1) = \lim_{t \to t_1} 2(t^2 + tt_1 + t_1^2 - 2t - 2t_1 + 1)$$

$$= 2(t_1^2 + t_1^2 + t_1^2 - 2t_1 - 2t_1 + 1)$$

$$= 2(3t_1^2 - 4t_1 + 1)$$

$$= 2(3t_1 - 1)(t_1 - 1)$$

The instantaneous velocity is zero when $t_1 = \frac{1}{3}$ and $t_1 = 1$. Therefore, the particle is at rest at these two times. The particle is moving to the right when $v(t_1)$ is positive, and it is moving to the left when $v(t_1)$ is negative. We determine the sign of $v(t_1)$ for various intervals of t_1, and the results are given in Table 3.2.1.

Table 3.2.1

	$3t_1 - 1$	$t_1 - 1$	Conclusion
$t_1 < \frac{1}{3}$	−	−	$v(t_1)$ is positive, and the particle is moving to the right
$t_1 = \frac{1}{3}$	0	−	$v(t_1)$ is zero, and the particle is changing direction from right to left
$\frac{1}{3} < t_1 < 1$	+	−	$v(t_1)$ is negative, and the particle is moving to the left
$t_1 = 1$	+	0	$v(t_1)$ is zero, and the particle is changing direction from left to right
$1 < t_1$	+	+	$v(t_1)$ is positive, and the particle is moving to the right

The motion of the particle, indicated in Fig. 3.2.2, is along the horizontal line; however, the behavior of the motion is indicated above the line. The accompanying Table 3.2.2 gives values of s and v for specific values of t.

Table 3.2.2

t	s	v
-1	-9	16
0	-1	2
$\frac{1}{3}$	$-\frac{19}{27}$	0
1	0	0
2	3	10

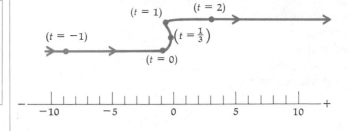

In the above example, $v(t_1)$ can also be found by applying formula (5). (See Exercise 1.)

EXAMPLE 2:   A ball is thrown vertically upward from the ground with an initial velocity of 64 ft/sec. If the positive direction

SOLUTION: $v(t_1) =$ the number of feet per second in the instantaneous velocity of the ball at t_1 sec.

$$s = f(t) \qquad \text{where } f(t) = -16t^2 + 64t$$

of the distance from the starting point is up, the equation of motion is

$$s = -16t^2 + 64t$$

If t is the number of seconds in the time which has elapsed since the ball was thrown, and s is the number of feet in the distance of the ball from the starting point at t sec, find: (a) the instantaneous velocity of the ball at the end of 1 sec; (b) the instantaneous velocity of the ball at the end of 3 sec; (c) how many seconds it takes the ball to reach its highest point; (d) how high the ball will go; (e) the speed of the ball at the end of 1 sec and at the end of 3 sec; (f) how many seconds it takes the ball to reach the ground; (g) the instantaneous velocity of the ball when it reaches the ground. At the end of 1 sec is the ball rising or falling? At the end of 3 sec is the ball rising or falling?

Figure 3.2.3

Applying formula (2), we find that

$$v(t_1) = \lim_{t \to t_1} \frac{f(t) - f(t_1)}{t - t_1}$$

$$= \lim_{t \to t_1} \frac{-16t^2 + 64t - (-16t_1{}^2 + 64t_1)}{t - t_1}$$

$$= \lim_{t \to t_1} \frac{-16(t^2 - t_1{}^2) + 64(t - t_1)}{t - t_1}$$

Dividing the numerator and the denominator by $t - t_1$ (because $t \neq t_1$), we obtain

$$v(t_1) = \lim_{t \to t_1} [-16(t + t_1) + 64] = -32t_1 + 64$$

(a) $v(1) = -32(1) + 64 = 32$; so at the end of 1 sec the ball is rising with an instantaneous velocity of 32 ft/sec.

(b) $v(3) = -32(3) + 64 = -32$; so at the end of 3 sec the ball is falling with an instantaneous velocity of -32 ft/sec.

(c) The ball reaches its highest point when the direction of motion changes, that is, when $v(t_1) = 0$. Setting $v(t_1) = 0$, we obtain

$$-32t_1 + 64 = 0 \quad \text{or} \quad t_1 = 2$$

(d) When $t = 2$, $s = 64$; therefore, the ball reaches a highest point of 64 ft above the starting point.

(e) $|v(t_1)| = $ the number of feet per second in the speed of the ball at t_1 sec.

$$|v(1)| = 32 \quad \text{and} \quad |v(3)| = 32$$

(f) The ball will reach the ground when $s = 0$. Setting $s = 0$, we have $-16t^2 + 64t = 0$, from which we obtain $t = 0$ and $t = 4$. Therefore, the ball will reach the ground in 4 sec.

(g) $v(4) = -64$; when the ball reaches the ground, its instantaneous velocity is -64 ft/sec.

Table 3.2.3

t	s	v
0	0	64
$\frac{1}{2}$	28	48
1	48	32
2	64	0
3	48	-32
$\frac{7}{2}$	28	-48
4	0	-64

Table 3.2.3 gives values of s and v for some specific values of t. The

motion of the ball is indicated in Fig. 3.2.3. The motion is assumed to be in a straight vertical line, and the behavior of the motion is indicated to the left of the line.

Exercises 3.2

1. Apply formula (5) to find $v(t_1)$ for the rectilinear motion in Example 1.

2. Apply formula (5) to find $v(t_1)$ for the rectilinear motion in Example 2.

In Exercises 3 through 8, a particle is moving along a horizontal line according to the given equation of motion, where s ft is the directed distance of the particle from a point O at t sec. Find the instantaneous velocity $v(t_1)$ ft/sec at t_1 sec; and then find $v(t_1)$ for the particular value of t_1 given.

3. $s = 3t^2 + 1$; $t_1 = 3$ 4. $s = 8 - t^2$; $t_1 = 5$ 5. $s = \sqrt{t+1}$; $t_1 = 3$

6. $s = \dfrac{1}{4t}$; $t_1 = \dfrac{1}{2}$ 7. $s = \dfrac{2}{\sqrt{5t+6}}$; $t_1 = 2$ 8. $s = \sqrt[3]{t+2}$; $t_1 = 6$

In Exercises 9 through 12, the motion of a particle is along a horizontal line according to the given equation of motion, where s ft is the directed distance of the particle from a point O at t sec. The positive direction is to the right. Determine the intervals of time when the particle is moving to the right and when it is moving to the left. Also determine when the particle reverses its direction. Show the behavior of the motion by a figure similar to Fig. 3.2.2, choosing values of t at random but including the values of t when the particle reverses its direction.

9. $s = t^3 + 3t^2 - 9t + 4$ 10. $s = 2t^3 - 3t^2 - 12t + 8$

11. $s = \dfrac{1+t}{4+t^2}$ 12. $s = \dfrac{t}{1+t^2}$

13. If an object falls from rest, its equation of motion is $s = -16t^2$, where t is the number of seconds in the time that has elapsed since the object left the starting point, s is the number of feet in the distance of the object from the starting point at t sec, and the positive direction is upward. If a stone is dropped from a building 256 ft high, find: (a) the instantaneous velocity of the stone 1 sec after it is dropped; (b) the instantaneous velocity of the stone 2 sec after it is dropped; (c) how long it takes the stone to reach the ground; (d) the instantaneous velocity of the stone when it reaches the ground.

14. If a stone is thrown vertically upward from the ground with an initial velocity of 32 ft/sec, the equation of motion is $s = -16t^2 + 32t$, where t sec is the time that has elapsed since the stone was thrown, s ft is the distance of the stone from the starting point at t sec, and the positive direction is upward. Find: (a) the average velocity of the stone during the time interval: $\frac{3}{4} \le t \le \frac{5}{4}$; (b) the instantaneous velocity of the stone at $\frac{3}{4}$ sec and at $\frac{5}{4}$ sec; (c) the speed of the stone at $\frac{3}{4}$ sec and at $\frac{5}{4}$ sec; (d) the average velocity of the stone during the time interval: $\frac{1}{2} \le t \le \frac{3}{4}$; (e) how many seconds it will take the stone to reach the highest point; (f) how high the stone will go; (g) how many seconds it will take the stone to reach the ground; (h) the instantaneous velocity of the stone when it reaches the ground. Show the behavior of the motion by a figure similar to Fig. 3.2.3.

15. If a ball is given a push so that it has an initial velocity of 24 ft/sec down a certain inclined plane, then $s = 24t + 10t^2$, where s ft is the distance of the ball from the starting point at t sec and the positive direction is down the inclined plane. (a) What is the instantaneous velocity of the ball at t_1 sec? (b) How long does it take for the velocity to increase to 48 ft/sec?

16. A rocket is fired vertically upward, and it is s ft above the ground t sec after being fired, where $s = 560t - 16t^2$ and the positive direction is upward. Find (a) the velocity of the rocket 2 sec after being fired, and (b) how long it takes for the rocket to reach its maximum height.

3.3 THE DERIVATIVE OF A FUNCTION

In Sec. 3.1 the slope of the tangent line to the graph of $y = f(x)$ at the point $(x_1, f(x_1))$ is defined by

$$m(x_1) = \lim_{\Delta x \to 0} \frac{f(x_1 + \Delta x) - f(x_1)}{\Delta x} \tag{1}$$

In Sec. 3.2 we learned that if a particle is moving along a straight line so that its directed distance s units from a fixed point at t units of time is given by $s = f(t)$, then if $v(t_1)$ units of velocity is the instantaneous velocity of the particle at t_1 units of time,

$$v(t_1) = \lim_{\Delta t \to 0} \frac{f(t_1 + \Delta t) - f(t_1)}{\Delta t} \tag{2}$$

The limits in formulas (1) and (2) are of the same form. This type of limit occurs in other problems too, and it is given a specific name.

3.3.1 Definition

The derivative of the function f is that function, denoted by f', such that its function value at any number x in the domain of f is given by

$$f'(x) = \lim_{\Delta x \to 0} \frac{f(x + \Delta x) - f(x)}{\Delta x} \tag{3}$$

if this limit exists. (f' is read "f prime," and $f'(x)$ is read "f prime of x.")

Another symbol that is used instead of $f'(x)$ is $D_x f(x)$, which is read "the derivative of f of x with respect to x."

If $y = f(x)$, then $f'(x)$ is the derivative of y with respect to x, and we use the notation $D_x y$. The notation y' is also used for the derivative of y with respect to an independent variable, if the independent variable is understood.

If x_1 is a particular number in the domain of f, then

$$f'(x_1) = \lim_{\Delta x \to 0} \frac{f(x_1 + \Delta x) - f(x_1)}{\Delta x} \tag{4}$$

if this limit exists. Comparing formulas (1) and (4), note that the slope of the tangent line to the graph of $y = f(x)$ at the point $(x_1, f(x_1))$ is precisely the derivative of f evaluated at x_1.

If a particle is moving along a straight line according to the equation of motion $s = f(t)$, then upon comparing formulas (2) and (4), it is seen that $v(t_1)$ in the definition of instantaneous velocity of the particle at t_1 is the derivative of f evaluated at t_1 or, equivalently, the derivative of s with respect to t evaluated at t_1.

EXAMPLE 1: Given $f(x) = 3x^2 + 12$, find the derivative of f.

SOLUTION: If x is any number in the domain of f, from Eq. (3) we obtain

$$f'(x) = \lim_{\Delta x \to 0} \frac{f(x + \Delta x) - f(x)}{\Delta x}$$

$$= \lim_{\Delta x \to 0} \frac{[3(x + \Delta x)^2 + 12] - (3x^2 + 12)}{\Delta x}$$

$$= \lim_{\Delta x \to 0} \frac{3x^2 + 6x \, \Delta x + 3(\Delta x)^2 + 12 - 3x^2 - 12}{\Delta x}$$

$$= \lim_{\Delta x \to 0} \frac{6x \, \Delta x + 3(\Delta x)^2}{\Delta x} = \lim_{\Delta x \to 0} (6x + 3 \, \Delta x)$$

$$= 6x$$

Therefore, the derivative of f is the function f' defined by $f'(x) = 6x$. The domain of f' is the set of all real numbers, which is the same as the domain of f.

In Sec. 3.2 we showed that the limit

$$\lim_{\Delta t \to 0} \frac{f(t_1 + \Delta t) - f(t_1)}{\Delta t}$$

is equivalent to

$$\lim_{t \to t_1} \frac{f(t) - f(t_1)}{t - t_1}$$

Therefore, an alternative formula to (4) for $f'(x_1)$ is given by

$$f'(x_1) = \lim_{x \to x_1} \frac{f(x) - f(x_1)}{x - x_1} \tag{5}$$

EXAMPLE 2:   For the function f of Example 1, find the derivative of f at 2 in three ways: (a) apply formula (4); (b) apply formula (5); (c) substitute 2 for x in the expression for $f'(x)$ in Example 1.

SOLUTION: (a) Applying formula (4), we have

$$f'(2) = \lim_{\Delta x \to 0} \frac{f(2 + \Delta x) - f(2)}{\Delta x}$$

$$= \lim_{\Delta x \to 0} \frac{[3(2 + \Delta x)^2 + 12] - [3(2)^2 + 12]}{\Delta x}$$

$$= \lim_{\Delta x \to 0} \frac{12 + 12 \, \Delta x + 3(\Delta x)^2 + 12 - 12 - 12}{\Delta x}$$

$$= \lim_{\Delta x \to 0} \frac{12 \, \Delta x + 3(\Delta x)^2}{\Delta x}$$

$$= \lim_{\Delta x \to 0} (12 + 3 \, \Delta x)$$

$$= 12$$

(b) From formula (5) we obtain

$$f'(2) = \lim_{x \to 2} \frac{f(x) - f(2)}{x - 2}$$

$$= \lim_{x \to 2} \frac{(3x^2 + 12) - 24}{x - 2}$$

$$= \lim_{x \to 2} \frac{3x^2 - 12}{x - 2}$$

$$= 3 \lim_{x \to 2} \frac{(x - 2)(x + 2)}{x - 2}$$

$$= 3 \lim_{x \to 2} (x + 2)$$

$$= 12$$

(c) Because, from Example 1, $f'(x) = 6x$, we obtain $f'(2) = 12$.

If the function f is given by the equation $y = f(x)$, we can let

$$\Delta y = f(x + \Delta x) - f(x)$$

and write $D_x y$ in place of $f'(x)$, so that from formula (3) we have

$$D_x y = \lim_{\Delta x \to 0} \frac{\Delta y}{\Delta x} \qquad (6)$$

A derivative is sometimes indicated by the notation dy/dx. But we avoid this symbolism until we have defined what is meant by dy and dx.

EXAMPLE 3: Given

$$y = \frac{2 + x}{3 - x}$$

find $D_x y$.

SOLUTION:

$$D_x y = \lim_{\Delta x \to 0} \frac{\Delta y}{\Delta x}$$

$$= \lim_{\Delta x \to 0} \frac{f(x + \Delta x) - f(x)}{\Delta x}$$

$$= \lim_{\Delta x \to 0} \frac{(2 + x + \Delta x)/(3 - x - \Delta x) - (2 + x)/(3 - x)}{\Delta x}$$

$$= \lim_{\Delta x \to 0} \frac{(3 - x)(2 + x + \Delta x) - (2 + x)(3 - x - \Delta x)}{\Delta x (3 - x - \Delta x)(3 - x)}$$

$$= \lim_{\Delta x \to 0} \frac{(6 + x - x^2 + 3\,\Delta x - x\,\Delta x) - (6 + x - x^2 - 2\,\Delta x - x\,\Delta x)}{\Delta x (3 - x - \Delta x)(3 - x)}$$

$$= \lim_{\Delta x \to 0} \frac{5\,\Delta x}{\Delta x (3 - x - \Delta x)(3 - x)}$$

$$= \lim_{\Delta x \to 0} \frac{5}{(3 - x - \Delta x)(3 - x)}$$

$$= \frac{5}{(3 - x)^2}$$

EXAMPLE 4:   Given $f(x) = x^{2/3}$, find $f'(x)$.

SOLUTION:

$$f'(x) = \lim_{\Delta x \to 0} \frac{f(x + \Delta x) - f(x)}{\Delta x} = \lim_{\Delta x \to 0} \frac{(x + \Delta x)^{2/3} - x^{2/3}}{\Delta x}$$

We rationalize the numerator in order to obtain a common factor of Δx in the numerator and the denominator; this yields

$$f'(x) = \lim_{\Delta x \to 0} \frac{[(x + \Delta x)^{2/3} - x^{2/3}][(x + \Delta x)^{4/3} + (x + \Delta x)^{2/3}x^{2/3} + x^{4/3}]}{\Delta x[(x + \Delta x)^{4/3} + (x + \Delta x)^{2/3}x^{2/3} + x^{4/3}]}$$

$$= \lim_{\Delta x \to 0} \frac{(x + \Delta x)^2 - x^2}{\Delta x[(x + \Delta x)^{4/3} + (x + \Delta x)^{2/3}x^{2/3} + x^{4/3}]}$$

$$= \lim_{\Delta x \to 0} \frac{x^2 + 2x(\Delta x) + (\Delta x)^2 - x^2}{\Delta x[(x + \Delta x)^{4/3} + (x + \Delta x)^{2/3}x^{2/3} + x^{4/3}]}$$

$$= \lim_{\Delta x \to 0} \frac{2x(\Delta x) + (\Delta x)^2}{\Delta x[(x + \Delta x)^{4/3} + (x + \Delta x)^{2/3}x^{2/3} + x^{4/3}]}$$

$$= \lim_{\Delta x \to 0} \frac{2x + \Delta x}{(x + \Delta x)^{4/3} + (x + \Delta x)^{2/3}x^{2/3} + x^{4/3}}$$

$$= \frac{2x}{x^{4/3} + x^{2/3}x^{2/3} + x^{4/3}}$$

$$= \frac{2x}{3x^{4/3}}$$

$$= \frac{2}{3x^{1/3}}$$

Note that $f'(0)$ does not exist even though f is continuous at 0. A sketch of the graph of f is shown in Fig. 3.3.1.

Figure 3.3.1

If for the function of Example 4 we evaluate

$$\lim_{\Delta x \to 0} \frac{f(x_1 + \Delta x) - f(x_1)}{\Delta x} \qquad \text{at } x_1 = 0$$

we have

$$\lim_{\Delta x \to 0} \frac{f(0 + \Delta x) - f(0)}{\Delta x} = \lim_{\Delta x \to 0} \frac{(\Delta x)^{2/3} - 0}{\Delta x}$$

$$= \lim_{\Delta x \to 0} \frac{1}{(\Delta x)^{1/3}}$$

$$= \infty$$

Therefore, we conclude that the tangent line to the graph of f at the origin is the y axis.

Example 4 shows that $f'(x)$ can exist for some values of x in the domain of f but fails to exist for other values of x in the domain of f. We have the following definition.

3.3.2 Definition   The function f is said to be *differentiable* at x_1 if $f'(x_1)$ exists.

From Definition 3.3.2 it follows that the function of Example 4 is differentiable at every number except 0.

3.3.3 Definition   A function is said to be *differentiable* if it is differentiable at every number in its domain.

Exercises 3.3

In Exercises 1 through 10, find $f'(x)$ for the given function by applying formula (3) of this section.

1. $f(x) = 4x^2 + 5x + 3$

2. $f(x) = x^3$

3. $f(x) = \sqrt{x}$

4. $f(x) = \sqrt{3x + 5}$

5. $f(x) = \dfrac{1}{x + 1}$

6. $f(x) = \sqrt{3x}$

7. $f(x) = \dfrac{1}{x^2} - x$

8. $f(x) = \dfrac{3}{1 + x^2}$

9. $f(x) = \dfrac{1}{\sqrt{x + 1}}$

10. $f(x) = \sqrt[3]{2x + 3}$

In Exercises 11 through 16, find $f'(a)$ for the given value of a by applying formula (4) of this section.

11. $f(x) = 1 - x^2$; $a = 3$

12. $f(x) = \dfrac{4}{5x}$; $a = 2$

13. $f(x) = \dfrac{2}{x^3}$; $a = 6$

14. $f(x) = \dfrac{2}{\sqrt{x}} - 1$; $a = 4$

15. $f(x) = \sqrt{x^2 - 9}$; $a = 5$

16. $f(x) = \dfrac{1}{x} + x + x^2$; $a = -3$

In Exercises 17 through 22, find $f'(a)$ for the given value of a by applying formula (5) of this section.

17. $f(x) = 3x + 2$; $a = -3$

18. $f(x) = x^2 - x + 4$; $a = 4$

19. $f(x) = 2 - x^3$; $a = -2$

20. $f(x) = \sqrt{1 + 9x}$; $a = 7$

21. $f(x) = \dfrac{1}{\sqrt{2x + 3}}$; $a = 3$

22. $f(x) = \dfrac{1}{\sqrt[3]{x}} - x$; $a = -8$

23. Given $f(x) = \sqrt[3]{x - 1}$, find $f'(x)$. Is f differentiable at 1? Draw a sketch of the graph of f.

24. Given $f(x) = \sqrt[3]{(4x - 3)^2}$, find $f'(x)$. Is f differentiable at $\frac{3}{4}$? Draw a sketch of the graph of f.

25. If g is continuous at a and $f(x) = (x - a)g(x)$, find $f'(a)$. (HINT: Use Eq. (5).)

26. Let f be a function whose domain is the set of all real numbers and $f(a + b) = f(a) \cdot f(b)$ for all a and b. Furthermore, suppose that $f(0) = 1$ and $f'(0)$ exists. Prove that $f'(x)$ exists for all x and that $f'(x) = f'(0) \cdot f(x)$.

27. If f is differentiable at a, prove that

$$f'(a) = \lim_{\Delta x \to 0} \frac{f(a + \Delta x) - f(a - \Delta x)}{2\,\Delta x}$$

(HINT: $f(a + \Delta x) - f(a - \Delta x) = f(a + \Delta x) - f(a) + f(a) - f(a - \Delta x)$.)

28. Let f be a function such that $|f(x)| \le x^2$ for all x. Prove that f is differentiable at 0 and that $f'(0) = 0$. (HINT: Use Theorem 2.10.5.)

3.4 DIFFERENTIABILITY AND CONTINUITY   The function of Example 4 of Sec. 3.3 is continuous at the number zero but is not differentiable there. Hence, it may be concluded that continuity of a function at a number does not imply differentiability of the function at that number. However, differentiability *does* imply continuity, which is given by the next theorem.

3.4.1 Theorem   If a function f is differentiable at x_1, then f is continuous at x_1.

PROOF: To prove that f is continuous at x_1, we must show that the three conditions of Definition 2.11.1 hold there. That is, we must show that (i) $f(x_1)$ exists; (ii) $\lim_{x \to x_1} f(x)$ exists; and (iii) $\lim_{x \to x_1} f(x) = f(x_1)$.

By hypothesis, f is differentiable at x_1. Therefore, $f'(x_1)$ exists. Because by formula (5) of Sec. 3.3

$$f'(x_1) = \lim_{x \to x_1} \frac{f(x) - f(x_1)}{x - x_1} \tag{1}$$

we conclude that $f(x_1)$ must exist; otherwise, the above limit has no meaning. Therefore, condition (i) holds at x_1. Now, let us consider

$$\lim_{x \to x_1} [f(x) - f(x_1)]$$

We can write

$$\lim_{x \to x_1} [f(x) - f(x_1)] = \lim_{x \to x_1} \left[(x - x_1) \cdot \frac{f(x) - f(x_1)}{x - x_1} \right] \tag{2}$$

Because

$$\lim_{x \to x_1} (x - x_1) = 0 \quad \text{and} \quad \lim_{x \to x_1} \frac{f(x) - f(x_1)}{x - x_1} = f'(x_1)$$

we apply the theorem on the limit of a product (Theorem 2.5.6) to the right side of Eq. (2), and we have

$$\lim_{x \to x_1} [f(x) - f(x_1)] = \lim_{x \to x_1} (x - x_1) \cdot \lim_{x \to x_1} \frac{f(x) - f(x_1)}{x - x_1} = 0 \cdot f'(x_1)$$

so that

$$\lim_{x \to x_1} [f(x) - f(x_1)] = 0$$

Then we have

$$\lim_{x \to x_1} f(x) = \lim_{x \to x_1} [f(x) - f(x_1) + f(x_1)]$$

$$= \lim_{x \to x_1} [f(x) - f(x_1)] + \lim_{x \to x_1} f(x_1)$$

$$= 0 + f(x_1)$$

which gives us

$$\lim_{x \to x_1} f(x) = f(x_1) \tag{3}$$

From Eq. (3) we may conclude that conditions (ii) and (iii) for continuity of f at x_1 hold. Therefore, the theorem is proved.   ∎

As previously stated, Example 4 of Sec. 3.3 shows that the converse of the above theorem is not true. Before giving an additional example of a function which is continuous at a number but which is not differentiable there, the concept of a *one-sided derivative* is introduced.

3.4.2 Definition   If the function f is defined at x_1, then the *derivative from the right* of f at x_1, denoted by $f'_+(x_1)$, is defined by

$$f'_+(x_1) = \lim_{\Delta x \to 0^+} \frac{f(x_1 + \Delta x) - f(x_1)}{\Delta x} \qquad (4)$$

or, equivalently,

$$f'_+(x_1) = \lim_{x \to x_1^+} \frac{f(x) - f(x_1)}{x - x_1} \qquad (5)$$

if the limit exists.

3.4.3 Definition   If the function f is defined at x_1, then the *derivative from the left* of f at x_1, denoted by $f'_-(x_1)$, is defined by

$$f'_-(x_1) = \lim_{\Delta x \to 0^-} \frac{f(x_1 + \Delta x) - f(x_1)}{\Delta x} \qquad (6)$$

or, equivalently,

$$f'_-(x_1) = \lim_{x \to x_1^-} \frac{f(x) - f(x_1)}{x - x_1} \qquad (7)$$

if the limit exists.

EXAMPLE 1:   Let f be the function defined by

$$f(x) = \begin{cases} 2x - 1 & \text{if } x < 3 \\ 8 - x & \text{if } 3 \le x \end{cases}$$

(a) Draw a sketch of the graph of f. (b) Prove that f is continuous at 3. (c) Find $f'_-(3)$ and $f'_+(3)$. (d) Is f differentiable at 3?

SOLUTION: (a) A sketch of the graph is shown in Fig. 3.4.1.

(b) To prove that f is continuous at 3, we verify the three conditions for continuity at a number:

(i) $f(3) = 5$

(ii) $\lim\limits_{x \to 3^-} f(x) = \lim\limits_{x \to 3^-} (2x - 1) = 5$

$\lim\limits_{x \to 3^+} f(x) = \lim\limits_{x \to 3^+} (8 - x) = 5$

Therefore,

$\lim\limits_{x \to 3} f(x) = 5$

(iii) $\lim\limits_{x \to 3} f(x) = f(3)$

(3, 5)

Figure 3.4.1

Because conditions (i), (ii), and (iii) all hold at 3, f is continuous at 3.

(c) $f'_-(3) = \lim\limits_{\Delta x \to 0^-} \dfrac{f(3 + \Delta x) - f(3)}{\Delta x}$

$\quad = \lim\limits_{\Delta x \to 0^-} \dfrac{[2(3 + \Delta x) - 1] - 5}{\Delta x}$

$\quad = \lim\limits_{\Delta x \to 0^-} \dfrac{6 + 2\,\Delta x - 6}{\Delta x}$

$\quad = \lim\limits_{\Delta x \to 0^-} \dfrac{2\,\Delta x}{\Delta x}$

$\quad = \lim\limits_{\Delta x \to 0^-} 2$

$\quad = 2$

$f'_+(3) = \lim\limits_{\Delta x \to 0^+} \dfrac{f(3 + \Delta x) - f(3)}{\Delta x}$

$\quad = \lim\limits_{\Delta x \to 0^+} \dfrac{[8 - (3 + \Delta x)] - 5}{\Delta x}$

$\quad = \lim\limits_{\Delta x \to 0^+} \dfrac{8 - 3 - \Delta x - 5}{\Delta x}$

$\quad = \lim\limits_{\Delta x \to 0^+} \dfrac{-\Delta x}{\Delta x}$

$\quad = \lim\limits_{\Delta x \to 0^+} (-1)$

$\quad = -1$

(d) Because

$$\lim\limits_{\Delta x \to 0^-} \dfrac{f(3 + \Delta x) - f(3)}{\Delta x} \neq \lim\limits_{\Delta x \to 0^+} \dfrac{f(3 + \Delta x) - f(3)}{\Delta x}$$

we conclude that

$$\lim\limits_{\Delta x \to 0} \dfrac{f(3 + \Delta x) - f(3)}{\Delta x}$$

does not exist. Hence, f is not differentiable at 3. However, the derivative from the left and the derivative from the right both exist at 3.

The function in Example 1 gives us another illustration of a function which is continuous at a number but not differentiable there.

Exercises 3.4

In Exercises 1 through 14, do each of the following: (a) Draw a sketch of the graph of the function; (b) determine if f is continuous at x_1; (c) find $f'_-(x_1)$ and $f'_+(x_1)$ if they exist; (d) determine if f is differentiable at x_1.

1. $f(x) = \begin{cases} x+2 & \text{if } x \le -4 \\ -x-6 & \text{if } x > -4 \end{cases}$
   $x_1 = -4$

2. $f(x) = \begin{cases} 3-2x & \text{if } x < 2 \\ 3x-7 & \text{if } x \ge 2 \end{cases}$
   $x_1 = 2$

3. $f(x) = |x-3|$; $x_1 = 3$

4. $f(x) = 1 + |x+2|$; $x_1 = -2$

5. $f(x) = \begin{cases} -1 & \text{if } x < 0 \\ x-1 & \text{if } x \ge 0 \end{cases}$
   $x_1 = 0$

6. $f(x) = \begin{cases} x & \text{if } x \le 0 \\ x^2 & \text{if } x > 0 \end{cases}$
   $x_1 = 0$

7. $f(x) = \begin{cases} x^2 & \text{if } x \le 0 \\ -x^2 & \text{if } x > 0 \end{cases}$
   $x_1 = 0$

8. $f(x) = \begin{cases} x^2 - 4 & \text{if } x < 2 \\ \sqrt{x-2} & \text{if } x \ge 2 \end{cases}$
   $x_1 = 2$

9. $f(x) = \begin{cases} \sqrt{1-x} & \text{if } x < 1 \\ (1-x)^2 & \text{if } x \ge 1 \end{cases}$
   $x_1 = 1$

10. $f(x) = \begin{cases} x^2 & \text{if } x < -1 \\ -1-2x & \text{if } x \ge -1 \end{cases}$
    $x_1 = -1$

11. $f(x) = \sqrt[3]{x+1}$; $x_1 = -1$

12. $f(x) = (x-2)^{-2}$; $x_1 = 2$

13. $f(x) = \begin{cases} 5-6x & \text{if } x \le 3 \\ -4-x^2 & \text{if } x > 3 \end{cases}$
    $x_1 = 3$

14. $f(x) = \begin{cases} -x^{2/3} & \text{if } x \le 0 \\ x^{2/3} & \text{if } x > 0 \end{cases}$
    $x_1 = 0$

15. Given $f(x) = |x|$, draw a sketch of the graph of f. Prove that f is continuous at 0. Prove that f is not differentiable at 0, but that $f'(x) = |x|/x$ for all $x \ne 0$. (HINT: Let $|x| = \sqrt{x^2}$.)

16. Given $f(x) = \sqrt{9-x^2}$, prove that f is continuous on the closed interval $[-3, 3]$. Prove that neither the derivative from the right at -3 nor the derivative from the left at 3 exist. Draw a sketch of the graph.

17. Given $f(x) = x^{3/2}$, prove that $f'_+(0)$ exists and find its value. Prove that f is continuous from the right at 0. Draw a sketch of the graph.

18. Given $f(x) = (1-x^2)^{3/2}$, prove that f is continuous on the closed interval $[-1, 1]$. Prove that $f'(x)$ exists for all values of x in the open interval $(-1, 1)$, and that both $f'_+(-1)$ and $f'_-(1)$ exist. Draw a sketch of the graph of f on $[-1, 1]$.

19. Find the values of a and b so that $f'(1)$ exists if

$$f(x) = \begin{cases} x^2 & \text{if } x < 1 \\ ax+b & \text{if } x \ge 1 \end{cases}$$

20. Given $f(x) = [\![x]\!]$, find $f'(x_1)$ if x_1 is not an integer. Prove by applying Theorem 3.4.1 that $f'(x_1)$ does not exist if x_1 is an integer. If x_1 is an integer, what can you say about $f'_-(x_1)$ and $f'_+(x_1)$?

21. Given $f(x) = (x-1)[\![x]\!]$. Draw a sketch of the graph of f for x in $[0, 2]$. Find: (a) $f'_-(1)$; (b) $f'_+(1)$; (c) $f'(1)$.

22. Given

$$f(x) = \begin{cases} 0 & \text{if } x \le 0 \\ x^n & \text{if } x > 0 \end{cases}$$

where n is a positive integer. (a) For what values of n is f differentiable for all values of x? (b) For what values of n is f' continuous for all values of x?

23. Given $f(x) = \text{sgn } x$. (a) Prove that $f'_+(0) = +\infty$ and $f'_-(0) = +\infty$. (b) Prove that $\lim_{x \to 0^+} f'(x) = 0$ and $\lim_{x \to 0^-} f'(x) = 0$.

24. Let the function f be defined by

$$f(x) = \begin{cases} \dfrac{g(x) - g(a)}{x - a} & \text{if } x \neq a \\ g'(a) & \text{if } x = a \end{cases}$$

Prove that if $g'(a)$ exists, f is continuous at a.

3.5 SOME THEOREMS ON DIFFERENTIATION OF ALGEBRAIC FUNCTIONS

The operation of finding the derivative of a function is called *differentiation,* which can be performed by applying Definition 3.3.1. However, because this process is usually rather lengthy, we state and prove some theorems which enable us to find the derivative of certain functions more easily. These theorems are proved by applying Definition 3.3.1. Following the proof of each theorem, we state the corresponding formula of differentiation.

3.5.1 Theorem If c is a constant and if $f(x) = c$ for all x, then

$$f'(x) = 0$$

PROOF:

$$f'(x) = \lim_{\Delta x \to 0} \frac{f(x + \Delta x) - f(x)}{\Delta x}$$

$$= \lim_{\Delta x \to 0} \frac{c - c}{\Delta x}$$

$$= \lim_{\Delta x \to 0} 0$$

$$= 0 \qquad \blacksquare$$

$$D_x(c) = 0 \tag{1}$$

The derivative of a constant is zero.

EXAMPLE 1: Given $y = 5$, find $D_x y$.

SOLUTION: $D_x y = 0$.

3.5.2 Theorem If n is a positive integer and if $f(x) = x^n$, then

$$f'(x) = nx^{n-1}$$

PROOF:

$$f'(x) = \lim_{\Delta x \to 0} \frac{f(x + \Delta x) - f(x)}{\Delta x}$$

$$= \lim_{\Delta x \to 0} \frac{(x + \Delta x)^n - x^n}{\Delta x}$$

Applying the binomial theorem to $(x + \Delta x)^n$, we have

$$f'(x) = \lim_{\Delta x \to 0} \frac{\left[x^n + nx^{n-1}\,\Delta x + \dfrac{n(n-1)}{2!}\,x^{n-2}(\Delta x)^2 + \cdots + nx(\Delta x)^{n-1} + (\Delta x)^n \right] - x^n}{\Delta x}$$

$$= \lim_{\Delta x \to 0} \frac{nx^{n-1}\,\Delta x + \dfrac{n(n-1)}{2!}\,x^{n-2}(\Delta x)^2 + \cdots + nx(\Delta x)^{n-1} + (\Delta x)^n}{\Delta x}$$

Dividing the numerator and the denominator by Δx, we have

$$f'(x) = \lim_{\Delta x \to 0} \left[nx^{n-1} + \frac{n(n-1)}{2!}\,x^{n-2}(\Delta x) + \cdots + nx(\Delta x)^{n-2} + (\Delta x)^{n-1} \right]$$

Every term, except the first, has a factor of Δx; therefore, every term, except the first, approaches zero as Δx approaches zero. So we obtain

$$f'(x) = nx^{n-1} \qquad \blacksquare$$

$$D_x(x^n) = nx^{n-1} \tag{2}$$

EXAMPLE 2: Given $f(x) = x^8$, find $f'(x)$.

SOLUTION: $f'(x) = 8x^7$.

EXAMPLE 3: Given $f(x) = x$, find $f'(x)$.

SOLUTION: $f'(x) = 1 \cdot x^0 = 1 \cdot 1 = 1$.

3.5.3 **Theorem**   If f is a function, c is a constant, and g is the function defined by

$$g(x) = c \cdot f(x)$$

then if $f'(x)$ exists,

$$g'(x) = c \cdot f'(x)$$

PROOF:

$$g'(x) = \lim_{\Delta x \to 0} \frac{g(x + \Delta x) - g(x)}{\Delta x}$$

$$= \lim_{\Delta x \to 0} \frac{cf(x + \Delta x) - cf(x)}{\Delta x}$$

$$= \lim_{\Delta x \to 0} c \cdot \left[\frac{f(x + \Delta x) - f(x)}{\Delta x} \right]$$

$$= c \cdot \lim_{\Delta x \to 0} \frac{f(x + \Delta x) - f(x)}{\Delta x}$$

$$= cf'(x)$$

$$D_x[c \cdot f(x)] = c \cdot D_x f(x) \tag{3}$$

The derivative of a constant times a function is the constant times the derivative of the function if this derivative exists.

By combining Theorems 3.5.2 and 3.5.3 we obtain the following result: If $f(x) = cx^n$, where n is a positive integer and c is a constant,

$$f'(x) = cnx^{n-1}$$

$$D_x(cx^n) = cnx^{n-1} \tag{4}$$

EXAMPLE 4: Given $f(x) = 5x^7$, find $f'(x)$.

SOLUTION: $f'(x) = 5 \cdot 7x^6 = 35x^6$.

3.5.4 Theorem   If f and g are functions and if h is the function defined by

$$h(x) = f(x) + g(x)$$

then if $f'(x)$ and $g'(x)$ exist,

$$h'(x) = f'(x) + g'(x)$$

PROOF:

$$h'(x) = \lim_{\Delta x \to 0} \frac{h(x + \Delta x) - h(x)}{\Delta x}$$

$$= \lim_{\Delta x \to 0} \frac{[f(x + \Delta x) + g(x + \Delta x)] - [f(x) + g(x)]}{\Delta x}$$

$$= \lim_{\Delta x \to 0} \frac{[f(x + \Delta x) - f(x)] + [g(x + \Delta x) - g(x)]}{\Delta x}$$

$$= \lim_{\Delta x \to 0} \frac{f(x + \Delta x) - f(x)}{\Delta x} + \lim_{\Delta x \to 0} \frac{g(x + \Delta x) - g(x)}{\Delta x}$$

$$= f'(x) + g'(x)$$

$$D_x[f(x) + g(x)] = D_x f(x) + D_x g(x) \tag{5}$$

The derivative of the sum of two functions is the sum of their derivatives if these derivatives exist.

The result of the preceding theorem can be extended to any finite number of functions, by mathematical induction, and this is stated as another theorem.

3.5.5 Theorem   The derivative of the sum of a finite number of functions is equal to the sum of their derivatives if these derivatives exist.

From the preceding theorems the derivative of any polynomial function can be found easily.

EXAMPLE 5:   Given

$$f(x) = 7x^4 - 2x^3 + 8x + 5$$

find $f'(x)$.

SOLUTION:

$$f'(x) = D_x(7x^4 - 2x^3 + 8x + 5)$$
$$= D_x(7x^4) + D_x(-2x^3) + D_x(8x) + D_x(5)$$
$$= 28x^3 - 6x^2 + 8$$

3.5.6 Theorem   If f and g are functions and if h is the function defined by

$$h(x) = f(x)g(x)$$

then if $f'(x)$ and $g'(x)$ exist,

$$h'(x) = f(x)g'(x) + g(x)f'(x)$$

PROOF:

$$h'(x) = \lim_{\Delta x \to 0} \frac{h(x + \Delta x) - h(x)}{\Delta x}$$

$$= \lim_{\Delta x \to 0} \frac{f(x + \Delta x) \cdot g(x + \Delta x) - f(x) \cdot g(x)}{\Delta x}$$

We subtract and add $f(x + \Delta x) \cdot g(x)$ in the numerator, thereby giving us

$$h'(x) = \lim_{\Delta x \to 0} \frac{f(x + \Delta x) \cdot g(x + \Delta x) - f(x + \Delta x) \cdot g(x) + f(x + \Delta x) \cdot g(x) - f(x) \cdot g(x)}{\Delta x}$$

$$= \lim_{\Delta x \to 0} \left[f(x + \Delta x) \cdot \frac{g(x + \Delta x) - g(x)}{\Delta x} + g(x) \cdot \frac{f(x + \Delta x) - f(x)}{\Delta x} \right]$$

$$= \lim_{\Delta x \to 0} \left[f(x + \Delta x) \cdot \frac{g(x + \Delta x) - g(x)}{\Delta x} \right]$$

$$+ \lim_{\Delta x \to 0} \left[g(x) \cdot \frac{f(x + \Delta x) - f(x)}{\Delta x} \right]$$

$$= \lim_{\Delta x \to 0} f(x + \Delta x) \cdot \lim_{\Delta x \to 0} \frac{g(x + \Delta x) - g(x)}{\Delta x}$$

$$+ \lim_{\Delta x \to 0} g(x) \cdot \lim_{\Delta x \to 0} \frac{f(x + \Delta x) - f(x)}{\Delta x}$$

Because f is differentiable at x, by Theorem 3.4.1, f is continuous at x; therefore, $\lim_{\Delta x \to 0} f(x + \Delta x) = f(x)$. Also,

$$\lim_{\Delta x \to 0} \frac{g(x + \Delta x) - g(x)}{\Delta x} = g'(x)$$

$$\lim_{\Delta x \to 0} \frac{f(x + \Delta x) - f(x)}{\Delta x} = f'(x)$$

and

$$\lim_{\Delta x \to 0} g(x) = g(x)$$

thus giving us

$$h'(x) = f(x)g'(x) + g(x)f'(x)$$

$$D_x[f(x)g(x)] = f(x) \cdot D_x g(x) + g(x) \cdot D_x f(x) \tag{6}$$

The derivative of the product of two functions is the first function times the derivative of the second function plus the second function times the derivative of the first function if these derivatives exist.

EXAMPLE 6: Given

$$h(x) = (2x^3 - 4x^2)(3x^5 + x^2)$$

find $h'(x)$.

SOLUTION:

$$h'(x) = (2x^3 - 4x^2)(15x^4 + 2x) + (3x^5 + x^2)(6x^2 - 8x)$$

$$= (30x^7 - 60x^6 + 4x^4 - 8x^3) + (18x^7 - 24x^6 + 6x^4 - 8x^3)$$

$$= 48x^7 - 84x^6 + 10x^4 - 16x^3$$

In this example, note that if we multiply first and then perform the differentiation, the same result is obtained. Doing this, we have

$$h(x) = 6x^8 - 12x^7 + 2x^5 - 4x^4$$

Thus,

$$h'(x) = 48x^7 - 84x^6 + 10x^4 - 16x^3$$

3.5.7 Theorem If f and g are functions and if h is the function defined by

$$h(x) = \frac{f(x)}{g(x)} \qquad \text{where } g(x) \neq 0$$

then if $f'(x)$ and $g'(x)$ exist,

$$h'(x) = \frac{g(x)f'(x) - f(x)g'(x)}{[g(x)]^2}$$

PROOF:

$$h'(x) = \lim_{\Delta x \to 0} \frac{h(x + \Delta x) - h(x)}{\Delta x}$$

$$= \lim_{\Delta x \to 0} \frac{\dfrac{f(x + \Delta x)}{g(x + \Delta x)} - \dfrac{f(x)}{g(x)}}{\Delta x}$$

$$= \lim_{\Delta x \to 0} \frac{f(x + \Delta x) \cdot g(x) - f(x) \cdot g(x + \Delta x)}{\Delta x \cdot g(x) \cdot g(x + \Delta x)}$$

Subtracting and adding $f(x) \cdot g(x)$ in the numerator, we obtain

$$h'(x) = \lim_{\Delta x \to 0} \frac{f(x + \Delta x) \cdot g(x) - f(x) \cdot g(x) - f(x) \cdot g(x + \Delta x) + f(x) \cdot g(x)}{\Delta x \cdot g(x) \cdot g(x + \Delta x)}$$

$$= \lim_{\Delta x \to 0} \frac{\left[g(x) \cdot \dfrac{f(x + \Delta x) - f(x)}{\Delta x} \right] - \left[f(x) \cdot \dfrac{g(x + \Delta x) - g(x)}{\Delta x} \right]}{g(x) \cdot g(x + \Delta x)}$$

$$= \frac{\displaystyle\lim_{\Delta x \to 0} g(x) \cdot \lim_{\Delta x \to 0} \dfrac{f(x + \Delta x) - f(x)}{\Delta x} - \lim_{\Delta x \to 0} f(x) \cdot \lim_{\Delta x \to 0} \dfrac{g(x + \Delta x) - g(x)}{\Delta x}}{\displaystyle\lim_{\Delta x \to 0} g(x) \cdot \lim_{\Delta x \to 0} g(x + \Delta x)}$$

$$= \frac{g(x) \cdot f'(x) - f(x) \cdot g'(x)}{g(x) \cdot g(x)}$$

$$= \frac{g(x)f'(x) - f(x)g'(x)}{[g(x)]^2} \qquad \blacksquare$$

$$D_x \left[\frac{f(x)}{g(x)} \right] = \frac{g(x)D_x f(x) - f(x)D_x g(x)}{[g(x)]^2} \qquad (7)$$

The derivative of the quotient of two functions is the fraction having as its denominator the square of the original denominator, and as its numerator the denominator times the derivative of the numerator minus the numerator times the derivative of the denominator if these derivatives exist.

EXAMPLE 7: Given

$$h(x) = (2x^3 + 4)/(x^2 - 4x + 1)$$

find $h'(x)$.

SOLUTION:

$$h'(x) = \frac{(x^2 - 4x + 1)(6x^2) - (2x^3 + 4)(2x - 4)}{(x^2 - 4x + 1)^2}$$

$$= \frac{6x^4 - 24x^3 + 6x^2 - 4x^4 + 8x^3 - 8x + 16}{(x^2 - 4x + 1)^2}$$

$$= \frac{2x^4 - 16x^3 + 6x^2 - 8x + 16}{(x^2 - 4x + 1)^2}$$

3.5.8 Theorem   If $f(x) = x^{-n}$, where $-n$ is a negative integer and $x \neq 0$, then

$$f'(x) = -nx^{-n-1}$$

PROOF: If $-n$ is a negative integer, then n is a positive integer. We write

$$f(x) = \frac{1}{x^n}$$

Applying Theorem 3.5.7, we have

$$f'(x) = \frac{x^n \cdot 0 - 1 \cdot nx^{n-1}}{(x^n)^2} = \frac{-nx^{n-1}}{x^{2n}} = -nx^{n-1-2n}$$

$$= -nx^{-n-1}$$ ∎

EXAMPLE 8:   Given

$$f(x) = \frac{3}{x^5}$$

find $f'(x)$.

SOLUTION: $f(x) = 3x^{-5}$. Hence,

$$f'(x) = 3(-5x^{-6}) = -15x^{-6} = -\frac{15}{x^6}$$

If r is any positive or negative integer it follows from Theorems 3.5.2 and 3.5.8 that

$$D_x(x^r) = rx^{r-1} \tag{8}$$

and from Theorems 3.5.2, 3.5.3, and 3.5.8 we obtain

$$D_x(cx^r) = crx^{r-1} \tag{9}$$

Exercises 3.5

In Exercises 1 through 26, differentiate the given function by applying the theorems of this section.

1. $f(x) = x^3 - 3x^2 + 5x - 2$
2. $f(x) = 3x^4 - 5x^2 + 1$
3. $f(x) = \frac{1}{8}x^8 - x^4$
4. $g(x) = x^7 - 2x^5 + 5x^3 - 7x$
5. $F(t) = \frac{1}{4}t^4 - \frac{1}{2}t^2$
6. $H(x) = \frac{1}{3}x^3 - x + 2$
7. $v(r) = \frac{4}{3}\pi r^3$
8. $G(y) = y^{10} + 7y^5 - y^3 + 1$
9. $F(x) = x^2 + 3x + \frac{1}{x^2}$

10. $f(x) = x^4 - 5 + x^{-2} + 4x^{-4}$

11. $g(x) = \dfrac{3}{x^2} + \dfrac{5}{x^4}$

12. $H(x) = \dfrac{5}{6x^5}$

13. $f(s) = \sqrt{3}(s^3 - s^2)$

14. $g(x) = (2x^2 + 5)(4x - 1)$

15. $f(x) = (2x^4 - 1)(5x^3 + 6x)$

16. $g(x) = (4x^2 + 3)^2$

17. $H(x) = \dfrac{x^2 + 2x + 1}{x^2 - 2x + 1}$

18. $F(y) = \dfrac{2y + 1}{3y + 4}$

19. $f(x) = \dfrac{x}{x - 1}$

20. $f(x) = (x^2 - 3x + 2)(2x^3 + 1)$

21. $h(x) = \dfrac{5x}{1 + 2x^2}$

22. $g(x) = \dfrac{x^4 - 2x^2 + 5x + 1}{x^4}$

23. $f(x) = \dfrac{x^3 - 8}{x^3 + 8}$

24. $f(x) = \dfrac{x^2 - a^2}{x^2 + a^2}$

25. $f(x) = \dfrac{2x + 1}{x + 5}(3x - 1)$

26. $g(x) = \dfrac{x^3 + 1}{x^2 + 3}(x^2 - 2x^{-1} + 1)$

27. If f, g, and h are functions and if $\phi(x) = f(x) \cdot g(x) \cdot h(x)$, prove that if $f'(x)$, $g'(x)$, and $h'(x)$ exist, $\phi'(x) = f(x) \cdot g(x) \cdot h'(x) + f(x) \cdot g'(x) \cdot h(x) + f'(x) \cdot g(x) \cdot h(x)$. (HINT: Apply Theorem 3.5.6 twice.)

Use the result of Exercise 27 to differentiate the functions in Exercises 28 through 31.

28. $f(x) = (x^2 + 3)(2x - 5)(3x + 2)$

29. $h(x) = (3x + 2)^2(x^2 - 1)$

30. $g(x) = (3x^3 + x^{-3})(x + 3)(x^2 - 5)$

31. $\phi(x) = (2x^2 + x + 1)^3$

32. Find an equation of the tangent line to the curve $y = 8/(x^2 + 4)$ at the point $(2, 1)$.

33. Find an equation of each of the lines through the point $(-1, 2)$ which is a tangent line to the curve $y = (x - 1)/(x + 3)$.

34. Find an equation of each of the tangent lines to the curve $3y = x^3 - 3x^2 + 6x + 4$, which is parallel to the line $2x - y + 3 = 0$.

35. Find an equation of each of the normal lines to the curve $y = x^3 - 4x$ which is parallel to the line $x + 8y - 8 = 0$.

36. An object is moving along a straight line according to the equation of motion $s = 3t/(t^2 + 9)$, with $t \geq 0$, where s ft is the directed distance of the object from the starting point at t sec. (a) What is the instantaneous velocity of the object at t_1 sec? (b) What is the instantaneous velocity at 1 sec? (c) At what time is the instantaneous velocity zero?

3.6 THE DERIVATIVE OF A COMPOSITE FUNCTION

Suppose that y is a function of u and u, in turn, is a function of x. For example, let

$$y = f(u) = u^5 \qquad (1)$$

and

$$u = g(x) = 2x^3 - 5x^2 + 4 \qquad (2)$$

Equations (1) and (2) together define y as a function of x because if we replace u in (1) by the right side of (2) we have

$$y = h(x) = f(g(x)) = (2x^3 - 5x^2 + 4)^5$$

where h is a composite function which was defined previously (refer to Definition 2.2.2).

We now state and prove a theorem for finding the derivative of a composite function. This theorem is known as the *chain rule*.

3.6.1 Theorem   If y is a function of u, defined by $y = f(u)$, and $D_u y$ exists, and if u is a
Chain Rule   function of x, defined by $u = g(x)$, and $D_x u$ exists, then y is a function of
x and $D_x y$ exists and is given by

$$D_x y = D_u y \cdot D_x u$$

PROOF: From Eq. (6) of Sec. 3.3, we have

$$D_u y = \lim_{\Delta u \to 0} \frac{\Delta y}{\Delta u}$$

Hence, when $|\Delta u|$ is small (close to zero but not equal to zero) the
difference

$$\frac{\Delta y}{\Delta u} - D_u y$$

is numerically small. Denoting the difference by η, we have

$$\frac{\Delta y}{\Delta u} - D_u y = \eta \qquad \text{if } \Delta u \neq 0$$

or, equivalently,

$$\frac{\Delta y}{\Delta u} = D_u y + \eta \qquad \text{if } \Delta u \neq 0$$

The above equation defines η as a function of Δu, provided that $\Delta u \neq 0$.
Letting $\eta = F(\Delta u)$ and solving for $F(\Delta u)$, we obtain

$$F(\Delta u) = \frac{\Delta y}{\Delta u} - D_u y \qquad \text{if } \Delta u \neq 0 \tag{3}$$

Equation (3) defines $F(\Delta u)$ provided that $\Delta u \neq 0$. Now, as we see later,
we want the function F to be continuous at 0, and so we define $F(0)$ to be
$\lim_{\Delta u \to 0} F(\Delta u)$. From Eq. (3) we have

$$\lim_{\Delta u \to 0} F(\Delta u) = \lim_{\Delta u \to 0} \frac{\Delta y}{\Delta u} - \lim_{\Delta u \to 0} D_u y$$

$$= D_u y - D_u y$$

$$= 0$$

Hence, we define $F(0) = 0$, and we have

$$F(\Delta u) = \begin{cases} \dfrac{\Delta y}{\Delta u} - D_u y & \text{if } \Delta u \neq 0 \\ 0 & \text{if } \Delta u = 0 \end{cases}$$

Solving Eq. (3) for Δy, we obtain

$$\Delta y = D_u y \cdot \Delta u + \Delta u \cdot F(\Delta u) \qquad \text{if } \Delta u \neq 0 \tag{4}$$

Note that Eq. (4) also holds if $\Delta u = 0$ because we have $\Delta y = 0$ (remember that $\Delta y = f(u + \Delta u) - f(u)$).

Dividing on both sides of Eq. (4) by Δx, where $\Delta x \neq 0$, we obtain

$$\frac{\Delta y}{\Delta x} = D_u y \cdot \frac{\Delta u}{\Delta x} + \frac{\Delta u}{\Delta x} \cdot F(\Delta u)$$

Taking the limit on both sides of the above equation as Δx approaches zero and applying limit theorems, we have

$$\lim_{\Delta x \to 0} \frac{\Delta y}{\Delta x} = \lim_{\Delta x \to 0} D_u y \cdot \lim_{\Delta x \to 0} \frac{\Delta u}{\Delta x} + \lim_{\Delta x \to 0} \frac{\Delta u}{\Delta x} \cdot \lim_{\Delta x \to 0} F(\Delta u)$$

or

$$D_x y = D_u y \cdot D_x u + D_x u \cdot \lim_{\Delta x \to 0} F(\Delta u) \qquad (5)$$

We now show that $\lim_{\Delta x \to 0} F(\Delta u) = 0$ by making use of Theorem 2.12.5. We first express Δu as a function of Δx. Because

$$\lim_{\Delta x \to 0} \frac{\Delta u}{\Delta x} = D_x u$$

it follows that when $|\Delta x|$ is small and $\Delta x \neq 0$, $\Delta u / \Delta x$ differs from $D_x u$ by a small number which depends on Δx, which is called $\phi(\Delta x)$. Hence, we write

$$\frac{\Delta u}{\Delta x} = D_x u + \phi(\Delta x) \qquad \text{if } \Delta x \neq 0$$

and multiplying by Δx we obtain

$$\Delta u = D_x u \cdot \Delta x + \phi(\Delta x) \cdot \Delta x \qquad \text{if } \Delta x \neq 0$$

The above equation expresses Δu as a function of Δx. Calling this function G, we have

$$G(\Delta x) = D_x u \cdot \Delta x + \phi(\Delta x) \cdot \Delta x \qquad \text{if } \Delta x \neq 0$$

Hence, $F(\Delta u) = F(G(\Delta x))$, and

$$\lim_{\Delta x \to 0} F(\Delta u) = \lim_{\Delta x \to 0} F(G(\Delta x))$$

Because $\lim_{\Delta x \to 0} G(\Delta x) = 0$ and F is continuous at 0 (remember that we made it so), we can apply Theorem 2.12.5, to the right side of the above equation and we have

$$\lim_{\Delta x \to 0} F(\Delta u) = F(\lim_{\Delta x \to 0} G(\Delta x))$$

$$= F(0)$$

$$= 0$$

So in Eq. (5) if we replace $\lim\limits_{\Delta x \to 0} F(\Delta u)$ by 0 we obtain

$$D_x y = D_u y \cdot D_x u + D_x u \cdot 0$$

or

$$D_x y = D_u y \cdot D_x u$$ ∎

Now let us apply the chain rule to our previous example.

EXAMPLE 1: Given

$$y = (2x^3 - 5x^2 + 4)^5$$

find $D_x y$.

SOLUTION: Considering y as a function of u, where u is a function of x, we have

$$y = u^5 \qquad \text{where } u = 2x^3 - 5x^2 + 4$$

Therefore, from the chain rule,

$$D_x y = D_u y \cdot D_x u = 5u^4(6x^2 - 10x)$$
$$= 5(2x^3 - 5x^2 + 4)^4(6x^2 - 10x)$$

EXAMPLE 2: Given

$$f(x) = \frac{1}{4x^3 + 5x^2 - 7x + 8}$$

find $f'(x)$.

SOLUTION: Write $f(x) = (4x^3 + 5x^2 - 7x + 8)^{-1}$, and apply the chain rule to obtain

$$f'(x) = -1(4x^3 + 5x^2 - 7x + 8)^{-2}(12x^2 + 10x - 7)$$
$$= \frac{-12x^2 - 10x + 7}{(4x^3 + 5x^2 - 7x + 8)^2}$$

EXAMPLE 3: Given

$$f(x) = \left(\frac{2x + 1}{3x - 1}\right)^4$$

find $f'(x)$.

SOLUTION: Applying the chain rule, we have

$$f'(x) = 4\left(\frac{2x + 1}{3x - 1}\right)^3 \frac{(3x - 1)(2) - (2x + 1)(3)}{(3x - 1)^2}$$
$$= \frac{4(2x + 1)^3(-5)}{(3x - 1)^5}$$
$$= -\frac{20(2x + 1)^3}{(3x - 1)^5}$$

EXAMPLE 4: Given

$$f(x) = (3x^2 + 2)^2(x^2 - 5x)^3$$

find $f'(x)$.

SOLUTION: Consider f as the product of the two functions g and h, where

$$g(x) = (3x^2 + 2)^2 \quad \text{and} \quad h(x) = (x^2 - 5x)^3$$

Using Theorem 3.5.6 for the derivative of the product of two functions, we have

$$f'(x) = g(x)h'(x) + h(x)g'(x)$$

We find $h'(x)$ and $g'(x)$ by the chain rule, thus giving us

$$f'(x) = (3x^2 + 2)^2[3(x^2 - 5x)^2(2x - 5)] + (x^2 - 5x)^3[2(3x^2 + 2)(6x)]$$
$$= 3(3x^2 + 2)(x^2 - 5x)^2[(3x^2 + 2)(2x - 5) + 4x(x^2 - 5x)]$$
$$= 3(3x^2 + 2)(x^2 - 5x)^2[6x^3 - 15x^2 + 4x - 10 + 4x^3 - 20x^2]$$
$$= 3(3x^2 + 2)(x^2 - 5x)^2(10x^3 - 35x^2 + 4x - 10)$$

Exercises 3.6

In Exercises 1 through 20, find the derivative of the given function.

1. $F(x) = (x^2 + 4x - 5)^3$

2. $f(x) = (10 - 5x)^4$

3. $f(t) = (2t^4 - 7t^3 + 2t - 1)^2$

4. $g(r) = (2r^4 + 8r^2 + 1)^5$

5. $f(x) = (x + 4)^{-2}$

6. $H(z) = (z^3 - 3z^2 + 1)^{-3}$

7. $h(u) = (3u^2 + 5)^3(3u - 1)^2$

8. $f(x) = (4x^2 + 7)^2(2x^3 + 1)^4$

9. $g(x) = (2x - 5)^{-1}(4x + 3)^{-2}$

10. $f(x) = (x^2 - 4x^{-2})^2(x^2 + 1)^{-1}$

11. $f(y) = \left(\dfrac{y - 7}{y + 2}\right)^2$

12. $g(t) = \left(\dfrac{2t^2 + 1}{3t^3 + 1}\right)^2$

13. $f(x) = \dfrac{2}{7x^2 + 3x - 1}$

14. $h(x) = \left(\dfrac{x + 4}{2x^2 - 5x + 6}\right)^3$

15. $f(r) = (r^2 + 1)^3(2r + 5)^2$

16. $f(y) = (y + 3)^3(5y + 1)^2(3y^2 - 4)$

17. $f(z) = \dfrac{(z^2 - 5)^3}{(z^2 + 4)^2}$

18. $g(x) = (2x - 9)^2(x^3 + 4x - 5)^3$

19. $G(x) = \dfrac{(4x - 1)^3(x^2 + 2)^4}{(3x^2 + 5)^2}$

20. $F(x) = \dfrac{(5x - 8)^{-2}}{(x^2 + 3)^{-3}}$

21. A particle is moving along a straight line according to the equation of motion $s = [(t^2 - 1)/(t^2 + 1)]^2$, with $t \geq 0$, where s ft is the directed distance of the particle from the origin at t sec. (a) What is the instantaneous velocity of the particle at t_1 sec? (b) What is the instantaneous velocity of the particle at 1 sec? (c) What is the instantaneous velocity at $\frac{3}{2}$ sec?

22. Find an equation of the tangent line to the curve $y = 2/(4 - x)^2$ at each of the following points: $(0, \frac{1}{8})$, $(1, \frac{2}{9})$, $(2, \frac{1}{2})$, $(3, 2)$, $(5, 2)$, $(6, \frac{1}{2})$. Draw a sketch of the graph and segments of the tangent lines at the given points.

23. Find an equation of the normal line to the curve $y = 2/(x^2 - 2x - 4)^2$ at the point $(3, 2)$.

24. Find an equation of the tangent line to the curve $y = (x^2 - 4)^2/(3x - 5)^2$ at the point $(1, \frac{9}{4})$.

25. Given $f(x) = x^3$ and $g(x) = f(x^2)$. Find: (a) $f'(x^2)$; (b) $g'(x)$.

26. Given $f(u) = u^2 + 5u + 5$ and $g(x) = (x + 1)/(x - 1)$. Find the derivative of $f \circ g$ in two ways: (a) by first finding $(f \circ g)(x)$ and then finding $(f \circ g)'(x)$; (b) by using the chain rule.

27. Suppose that f and g are two functions such that (i) $g'(x_1)$ and $f'(g(x_1))$ exist and (ii) for all $x \neq x_1$ in some open interval containing x_1, $g(x) - g(x_1) \neq 0$. Then

$$\frac{(f \circ g)(x) - (f \circ g)(x_1)}{x - x_1} = \frac{(f \circ g)(x) - (f \circ g)(x_1)}{g(x) - g(x_1)} \cdot \frac{g(x) - g(x_1)}{x - x_1} \tag{6}$$

(a) Prove that as $x \to x_1$, $g(x) \to g(x_1)$ and hence that

$$(f \circ g)'(x_1) = f'(g(x_1))g'(x_1)$$

thus simplifying the proof of the chain rule under the additional hypothesis (ii); (b) Show that the proof of the chain rule given in part (a) applies if $f(u) = u^2$ and $g(x) = x^3$, but that it does not apply if $f(u) = u^2$ and $g(x) = \text{sgn } x$.

28. Use the chain rule to prove that (a) the derivative of an even function is an odd function, and (b) the derivative of an odd function is an even function, provided that these derivatives exist.

29. Use the result of Exercise 28(a) to prove that if g is an even function and $g'(x)$ exists, then if $h(x) = (f \circ g)(x)$ and f is differentiable everywhere, $h'(0) = 0$.

30. Suppose that f and g are functions such that $f'(x) = 1/x$ and $f(g(x)) = x$. Prove that if $g'(x)$ exists then $g'(x) = g(x)$.

31. Suppose that y is a function of v, v is a function of u, and u is a function of x, and that the derivatives $D_v y, D_u v$, and $D_x u$ all exist. Prove the chain rule for three functions:

$$D_x y = (D_v y)(D_u v)(D_x u)$$

3.7 THE DERIVATIVE OF THE POWER FUNCTION FOR RATIONAL EXPONENTS

The function f defined by

$$f(x) = x^r \tag{1}$$

is called the *power function*. In Sec. 3.5 we obtained the following formula for the derivative of this function when r is a positive or negative integer:

$$f'(x) = rx^{r-1} \tag{2}$$

We now show that this formula holds when r is a rational number, with certain stipulations when $x = 0$.

We first consider $x \neq 0$, and $r = 1/q$, where q is a positive integer. Equation (1) then can be written

$$f(x) = x^{1/q}$$

From Definition 3.3.1, we have

$$f'(x) = \lim_{\Delta x \to 0} \frac{(x + \Delta x)^{1/q} - x^{1/q}}{\Delta x} \tag{3}$$

To evaluate the limit in Eq. (3) we must rationalize the numerator. To do this, we use formula (2) in Sec. 2.10, which is

$$a^n - b^n = (a - b)(a^{n-1} + a^{n-2}b + a^{n-3}b^2 + \cdots + a^2 b^{n-3} + ab^{n-2} + b^{n-1}) \tag{4}$$

So we rationalize the numerator of the fraction in Eq. (3) by applying Eq. (4), where $a = (x + \Delta x)^{1/q}$, $b = x^{1/q}$, and $n = q$. So we multiply the numerator and denominator by

$$[(x + \Delta x)^{1/q}]^{(q-1)} + [(x + \Delta x)^{1/q}]^{(q-2)}x^{1/q} + \cdots$$
$$+ (x + \Delta x)^{1/q}(x^{1/q})^{(q-2)} + (x^{1/q})^{(q-1)}$$

We have, then, from Eq. (3), $f'(x)$ equals

$$\lim_{\Delta x \to 0} \frac{[(x + \Delta x)^{1/q} - x^{1/q}][(x + \Delta x)^{(q-1)/q} + (x + \Delta x)^{(q-2)/q}x^{1/q} + \cdots + x^{(q-1)/q}]}{\Delta x[(x + \Delta x)^{(q-1)/q} + (x + \Delta x)^{(q-2)/q}x^{1/q} + \cdots + x^{(q-1)/q}]} \tag{5}$$

and now applying Eq. (4) to the numerator we get $(x + \Delta x)^{q/q} - x^{q/q}$, which is Δx. So from (5) we obtain

$$f'(x) = \lim_{\Delta x \to 0} \frac{\Delta x}{\Delta x[(x + \Delta x)^{(q-1)/q} + (x + \Delta x)^{(q-2)/q}x^{1/q} + \cdots + x^{(q-1)/q}]}$$

$$= \lim_{\Delta x \to 0} \frac{1}{(x + \Delta x)^{(q-1)/q} + (x + \Delta x)^{(q-2)/q}x^{1/q} + \cdots + x^{(q-1)/q}}$$

$$= \frac{1}{x^{(q-1)/q} + x^{(q-1)/q} + \cdots + x^{(q-1)/q}}$$

Because there are exactly q terms in the denominator of the above fraction, we have

$$f'(x) = \frac{1}{qx^{1-(1/q)}}$$

or, equivalently,

$$f'(x) = \frac{1}{q} x^{1/q-1} \qquad (6)$$

which is formula (2) with $r = 1/q$.

Now, in Eq. (1) with $x \neq 0$, let $r = p/q$, where p is any nonzero integer, and q is any positive integer; that is, r is any rational number except zero. Then Eq. (1) is written as

$$f(x) = x^{p/q}$$

or, equivalently,

$$f(x) = (x^{1/q})^p$$

Because p is either a positive or negative integer, we have, from the chain rule and Theorems 3.5.2 and 3.5.8,

$$f'(x) = p(x^{1/q})^{p-1} \cdot D_x(x^{1/q})$$

Applying formula (6) for $D_x(x^{1/q})$, we get

$$f'(x) = p(x^{1/q})^{p-1} \cdot \frac{1}{q} x^{1/q-1}$$

$$f'(x) = \frac{p}{q} x^{p/q-1/q+1/q-1}$$

$$f'(x) = \frac{p}{q} x^{p/q-1} \qquad (7)$$

Formula (7) is the same as formula (2) with $r = p/q$.

If $r = 0$, and $x \neq 0$, Eq. (1) becomes $f(x) = x^0 = 1$. In this case $f'(x) = 0$, which can be written as $f'(x) = 0 \cdot x^{0-1}$. Therefore, formula (2) holds if $r = 0$ with $x \neq 0$. We have therefore shown that formula (2) holds when r is any rational number and $x \neq 0$.

Now 0 is in the domain of the power function f if and only if r is a positive number because when $r \leq 0$, $f(0)$ is not defined. Hence, we wish to determine for what positive values of r, $f'(0)$ will be given by formula (2). We must exclude the numbers in the interval (0, 1] because for those values of r, x^{r-1} is not a real number when $x = 0$. Suppose, then, that $r > 1$. By the definition of a derivative

$$f'(0) = \lim_{x \to 0} \frac{x^r - 0^r}{x - 0} = \lim_{x \to 0} x^{r-1}$$

When $r > 1$, $\lim_{x \to 0} x^{r-1}$ exists and equals 0 provided that r is a number such that x^{r-1} is defined on some open interval containing 0. For example, if $r = \frac{3}{2}$, $x^{r-1} = x^{3/2-1} = x^{1/2}$, which is not defined on any open interval containing 0 (since $x^{1/2}$ does not exist when $x < 0$). However, if $r = \frac{5}{3}$, $x^{r-1} = x^{5/3-1} = x^{2/3}$, which is defined on every open interval containing 0. Hence, we conclude that formula (2) gives the derivative of the power function when $x = 0$ provided that r is a number for which x^{r-1} is defined on some open interval containing 0. Thus, we have proved the following theorem.

3.7.1 Theorem   If f is the power function, where r is any rational number (i.e., $f(x) = x^r$), then

$$f'(x) = rx^{r-1}$$

For this formula to give $f'(0)$, r must be a number such that x^{r-1} is defined on some open interval containing 0.

An immediate consequence of Theorem 3.7.1 and the chain rule is the following theorem.

3.7.2 Theorem   If f and g are functions such that $f(x) = [g(x)]^r$, where r is any rational number, and if $g'(x)$ exists, then

$$f'(x) = r[g(x)]^{r-1}g'(x)$$

For this formula to give $f'(0)$, r must be a number such that $[g(x)]^{r-1}$ is defined on some open interval containing 0.

EXAMPLE 1:   Given

$$f(x) = 4\sqrt[3]{x^2}$$

find $f'(x)$.

SOLUTION: $f(x) = 4x^{2/3}$.

Applying Theorem 3.7.1, we find

$$f'(x) = 4 \cdot \frac{2}{3} [x^{2/3-1}]$$

$$= \frac{8}{3} x^{-1/3}$$

$$= \frac{8}{3x^{1/3}}$$

$$= \frac{8}{3\sqrt[3]{x}}$$

EXAMPLE 2: Given

$$h(x) = \sqrt{2x^3 - 4x + 5}$$

find $h'(x)$.

SOLUTION: $h(x) = (2x^3 - 4x + 5)^{1/2}$.
Applying Theorem 3.7.2, we have

$$h'(x) = \tfrac{1}{2}(2x^3 - 4x + 5)^{-1/2}(6x^2 - 4)$$

$$= \frac{3x^2 - 2}{\sqrt{2x^3 - 4x + 5}}$$

EXAMPLE 3:   Given

$$g(x) = \frac{x^3}{\sqrt[3]{3x^2 - 1}}$$

find $g'(x)$.

SOLUTION: Writing the given fraction as a product we have

$$g(x) = x^3(3x^2 - 1)^{-1/3}$$

Using Theorems 3.5.6 and 3.7.2, we have

$$g'(x) = 3x^2(3x^2 - 1)^{-1/3} - \tfrac{1}{3}(3x^2 - 1)^{-4/3}(6x)(x^3)$$

$$= x^2(3x^2 - 1)^{-4/3}[3(3x^2 - 1) - 2x^2]$$

$$= \frac{x^2(7x^2 - 3)}{(3x^2 - 1)^{4/3}}$$

Exercises 3.7

In Exercises 1 through 18 find the derivative of the given function.

1. $f(x) = (3x + 5)^{2/3}$

2. $f(s) = \sqrt{2 - 3s^2}$

3. $g(x) = \sqrt{\dfrac{2x - 5}{3x + 1}}$

4. $h(t) = \dfrac{\sqrt{t - 1}}{\sqrt{t + 1}}$

5. $f(x) = 4x^{1/2} + 5x^{-1/2}$

6. $g(y) = (y^2 + 3)^{1/3}(y^3 - 1)^{1/2}$

7. $F(x) = \sqrt[3]{2x^3 - 5x^2 + x}$

8. $g(x) = \sqrt[3]{(3x^2 + 5x - 1)^2}$

9. $g(t) = \sqrt{2t} + \sqrt{\dfrac{2}{t}}$

10. $f(x) = 3x^{2/3} - 6x^{1/3} + x^{-1/3}$

11. $F(x) = \dfrac{\sqrt{x^2 - 1}}{x}$

12. $G(x) = \dfrac{4x + 6}{\sqrt{x^2 + 3x + 4}}$

13. $h(x) = \dfrac{\sqrt{x - 1}}{\sqrt[3]{x + 1}}$

14. $f(s) = (s^4 + 3s^2 + 1)^{-2/3}$

15. $f(x) = \sqrt{x^2 - 5\sqrt[3]{x^2 + 3}}$

16. $G(t) = \sqrt{\dfrac{5t + 6}{5t - 4}}$

17. $f(x) = \sqrt{9 + \sqrt{9 - x}}$

18. $g(x) = \sqrt[4]{\dfrac{y^3 + 1}{y^3 - 1}}$

19. Find an equation of the tangent line to the curve $y = \sqrt{x^2 + 9}$ at the point (4, 5).

20. Find an equation of the tangent line to the curve $y = (6 - 2x)^{1/3}$ at each of the following points: $(-1, 2)$, $(1, \sqrt[3]{4})$, $(3, 0)$, $(5, -\sqrt[3]{4})$, $(7, -2)$. Draw a sketch of the graph and segments of the tangent lines at the given points.

21. Find an equation of the normal line to the curve $y = x\sqrt{16 + x^2}$ at the origin.

22. Find an equation of the tangent line to the curve $y = 1/\sqrt[3]{7x - 6}$ which is perpendicular to the line $12x - 7y + 2 = 0$.

23. An object is moving along a straight line according to the equation of motion $s = \sqrt{4t^2 + 3}$, with $t \geq 0$. Find the values of t for which the measure of the instantaneous velocity is (a) 0; (b) 1; (c) 2.

24. Given $f(u) = 1/u^2$ and $g(x) = \sqrt{x}/\sqrt{2x^3 - 6x + 1}$, find the derivative of $f \circ g$ in two ways: (a) by first finding $(f \circ g)(x)$ and then finding $(f \circ g)'(x)$; (b) by using the chain rule.

In Exercises 25 through 28, find the derivative of the given function. (HINT: $|a| = \sqrt{a^2}$.)

25. $f(x) = |x^2 - 4|$

26. $g(x) = x|x|$

27. $g(x) = |x|^3$

28. $h(x) = \sqrt[3]{|x| + x}$

29. Suppose $g(x) = |f(x)|$. Prove that if $f'(x)$ and $g'(x)$ exist, then $|g'(x)| = |f'(x)|$.

30. Suppose that $g(x) = \sqrt{9 - x^2}$ and $h(x) = f(g(x))$ where f is differentiable at 3. Prove that $h'(0) = 0$.

31. If g and h are functions and if f is the function defined by

$$f(x) = [g(x)]^r[h(x)]^s$$

where r and s are rational numbers, prove that if $g'(x)$ and $h'(x)$ exist

$$f'(x) = [g(x)]^{r-1}[h(x)]^{s-1}[r \cdot h(x)g'(x) + s \cdot g(x)h'(x)]$$

In Exercises 32 through 35, use the result of Exercise 31 to find the derivative of the given function.

32. $g(x) = (4x + 3)^{1/2}(4 - x^2)^{1/3}$

33. $f(x) = (3x + 2)^4(x^2 - 1)^{2/3}$

34. $f(r) = \left(\dfrac{r + 1}{r^2 + 1}\right)^3 (r^3 + 4)^{1/3}$

35. $F(t) = (t^3 - 2t + 1)^{3/2}(t^2 + t + 5)^{1/3}$

3.8 IMPLICIT DIFFERENTIATION

If y is a function of x defined by the equation

$$y = 3x^2 + 5x + 1 \tag{1}$$

then y is defined *explicitly* in terms of x, and we can write

$$y = f(x) \qquad \text{where } f(x) = 3x^2 + 5x + 1$$

However, not all functions are defined explicitly. For example, if we have the equation

$$x^6 - 2x = 3y^6 + y^5 - y^2 \tag{2}$$

we cannot solve for y explicitly as a function of x; however, there may exist one or more functions f such that if $y = f(x)$, Eq. (2) is satisfied, that is, such that the equation

$$x^6 - 2x = 3[f(x)]^6 + [f(x)]^5 - [f(x)]^2$$

is true for all values of x in the domain of f. In this case we state that y is defined *implicitly* as a function of x, or that the function f is defined *implicitly* by the given equation.

Using the assumption that Eq. (2) defines y as one or more differentiable functions of x, we can find the derivative of y with respect to x by the process called *implicit differentiation*, which we now do.

The left side of Eq. (2) is a function of x, and the right side is a function of y. Let F be the function defined by the left side of (2), and let G be the function defined by the right side of (2). Thus,

$$F(x) = x^6 - 2x \tag{3}$$

and

$$G(y) = 3y^6 + y^5 - y^2 \tag{4}$$

where y is a function of x, say,

$$y = f(x)$$

So we write Eq. (2) as

$$F(x) = G(f(x)) \tag{5}$$

Equation (5) is satisfied by all values of x in the domain of f for which $G[f(x)]$ exists.

Then for all values of x for which f is differentiable, we have

$$D_x[x^6 - 2x] = D_x[3y^6 + y^5 - y^2] \tag{6}$$

The derivative on the left side of Eq. (6) is easily found, and we have

$$D_x[x^6 - 2x] = 6x^5 - 2 \tag{7}$$

We find the derivative on the right side of Eq. (6) by the chain rule, giving us

$$D_x[3y^6 + y^5 - y^2] = 18y^5 \cdot D_x y + 5y^4 \cdot D_x y - 2y \cdot D_x y \tag{8}$$

Substituting the values from (7) and (8) into (6), we obtain

$$6x^5 - 2 = [18y^5 + 5y^4 - 2y] \cdot D_x y$$

Solving for $D_x y$, we get

$$D_x y = \frac{6x^5 - 2}{18y^5 + 5y^4 - 2y}$$

Equation (2) is a special type of equation involving x and y because it can be written so that all the terms involving x are on one side of the equation and all the terms involving y are on the other side. We use the method of implicit differentiation to find $D_x y$ from an equation such as

$$3x^4 y^2 - 7xy^3 = 4 - 8y \tag{9}$$

assuming that there exist one or more differentiable functions f such that if $y = f(x)$, Eq. (9) is satisfied. Differentiating on both sides of Eq. (9) (bearing in mind that y is one or more differentiable functions of x), and applying the theorems for the derivative of a product, the derivative of a power, and the chain rule, we obtain

$$12x^3y^2 + 3x^4[2y \cdot D_xy] - 7y^3 - 7x[3y^2 \cdot D_xy] = 0 - 8D_xy$$

Solving for D_xy, we have

$$D_xy[6x^4y - 21xy^2 + 8] = 7y^3 - 12x^3y^2$$

$$D_xy = \frac{7y^3 - 12x^3y^2}{6x^4y - 21xy^2 + 8}$$

Remember that we assumed that both Eqs. (2) and (9) define y as one or more differentiable functions of x. It may be that an equation in x and y does not imply the existence of any real-valued function, as is the case for the equation

$$x^2 + y^2 + 4 = 0$$

which is not satisfied by any real values of x and y. Furthermore, it is possible that an equation in x and y may be satisfied by many different functions, some of which are differentiable and some of which are not. A general discussion is beyond the scope of this book, but can be found in an advanced calculus text. In subsequent discussions, when we state that an equation in x and y defines y implicitly as a function of x, we assume that one or more of these functions is differentiable. Example 3, which follows, illustrates the fact that implicit differentiation gives the derivative of every differentiable function defined by the given equation.

EXAMPLE 1: Given

$$(x + y)^2 - (x - y)^2 = x^4 + y^4$$

find D_xy.

SOLUTION: Differentiating implicitly with respect to x, we have

$$2(x + y)(1 + D_xy) - 2(x - y)(1 - D_xy) = 4x^3 + 4y^3 \cdot D_xy$$

from which we obtain

$$2x + 2y + (2x + 2y)D_xy - 2x + 2y + (2x - 2y)D_xy = 4x^3 + 4y^3D_xy$$

$$D_xy(4x - 4y^3) = 4x^3 - 4y$$

$$D_xy = \frac{x^3 - y}{x - y^3}$$

EXAMPLE 2: Find an equation of the tangent line to the curve $x^3 + y^3 = 9$ at the point (1, 2).

SOLUTION: Differentiating implicitly with respect to x, we obtain

$$3x^2 + 3y^2 \cdot D_xy = 0$$

Hence,

$$D_xy = -\frac{x^2}{y^2}$$

Therefore, at the point (1, 2), $D_x y = -\frac{1}{4}$. An equation of the tangent line is then

$$y - 2 = -\tfrac{1}{4}(x - 1)$$

EXAMPLE 3:   Given the equation $x^2 + y^2 = 9$, find: (a) $D_x y$ by implicit differentiation; (b) two functions defined by the equation; (c) the derivative of each of the functions obtained in part (b) by explicit differentiation. (d) Verify that the result obtained in part (a) agrees with the results obtained in part (c).

SOLUTION: (a) Differentiating implicitly, we find

$$2x + 2y D_x y = 0 \quad \text{and so} \quad D_x y = -\frac{x}{y}$$

(b) Solving the given equation for y, we obtain

$$y = \sqrt{9 - x^2} \quad \text{and} \quad y = -\sqrt{9 - x^2}$$

Let f_1 be the function for which

$$f_1(x) = \sqrt{9 - x^2}$$

and f_2 be the function for which

$$f_2(x) = -\sqrt{9 - x^2}$$

(c) Because $f_1(x) = (9 - x^2)^{1/2}$, by using the chain rule we obtain

$$f_1'(x) = \tfrac{1}{2}(9 - x^2)^{-1/2}(-2x)$$

$$= -\frac{x}{\sqrt{9 - x^2}}$$

Similarly, we get

$$f_2'(x) = \frac{x}{\sqrt{9 - x^2}}$$

(d) For $y = f_1(x)$, where $f_1(x) = \sqrt{9 - x^2}$, we have from part (c)

$$f_1'(x) = -\frac{x}{\sqrt{9 - x^2}} = -\frac{x}{y}$$

which agrees with the answer in part (a). For $y = f_2(x)$, where $f_2(x) = -\sqrt{9 - x^2}$, we have from part (c)

$$f_2'(x) = \frac{x}{\sqrt{9 - x^2}}$$

$$= -\frac{x}{-\sqrt{9 - x^2}}$$

$$= -\frac{x}{y}$$

which also agrees with the answer in part (a).

Exercises 3.8

In Exercises 1 through 16, find $D_x y$ by implicit differentiation.

1. $x^2 + y^2 = 16$

2. $2x^3 y + 3xy^3 = 5$

3. $x^3 + y^3 = 8xy$

4. $x^2 = \dfrac{x + 2y}{x - 2y}$

5. $\dfrac{1}{x} + \dfrac{1}{y} = 1$

6. $\dfrac{x}{y} - 4y = x$

7. $\sqrt{x} + \sqrt{y} = 4$

8. $y + \sqrt{xy} = 3x^3$

9. $x^2 y^2 = x^2 + y^2$

10. $y\sqrt{2 + 3x} + x\sqrt{1 + y} = x$

11. $(x + y)^2 - (x - y)^2 = x^3 + y^3$

12. $(2x + 3)^4 = 3y^4$

13. $\dfrac{y}{x - y} = 2 + x^2$

14. $\sqrt{y} + \sqrt[3]{y} + \sqrt[4]{y} = x$

15. $\sqrt{xy} + 2x = \sqrt{y}$

16. $x^2 y^3 = x^4 - y^4$

In Exercises 17 through 20, consider y as the independent variable and find $D_y x$.

17. $x^4 + y^4 = 12x^2 y$

18. $y = 2x^3 - 5x$

19. $x^3 y + 2y^4 - x^4 = 0$

20. $y\sqrt{x} - x\sqrt{y} = 9$

21. Find an equation of the tangent line to the curve $16x^4 + y^4 = 32$ at the point $(1, 2)$.

22. There are two lines through the point $(-1, 3)$ which are tangent to the curve

$$x^2 + 4y^2 - 4x - 8y + 3 = 0$$

Find an equation of each of these lines.

23. Prove that the sum of the x and y intercepts of any tangent line to the curve $x^{1/2} + y^{1/2} = k^{1/2}$ is constant and equal to k.

24. If $x^n y^m = (x + y)^{n+m}$, prove that $x \cdot D_x y = y$.

In Exercises 25 through 30, an equation is given. Do the following in each of these problems: (a) Find two functions defined by the equation, and state their domains. (b) Draw a sketch of the graph of each of the functions obtained in part (a). (c) Draw a sketch of the graph of the equation. (d) Find the derivative of each of the functions obtained in part (a) and state the domains of the derivatives. (e) Find $D_x y$ by implicit differentiation from the given equation, and verify that the result so obtained agrees with the results in part (d). (f) Find an equation of each tangent line at the given value of x_1.

25. $y^2 = 4x - 8$; $x_1 = 3$

26. $x^2 + y^2 = 25$; $x_1 = 4$

27. $x^2 - y^2 = 9$; $x_1 = -5$

28. $y^2 - x^2 = 16$; $x_1 = -3$

29. $x^2 + y^2 - 2x - 4y - 4 = 0$; $x_1 = 1$

30. $x^2 + 4y^2 + 6x - 40y + 93 = 0$; $x_1 = -2$

Review Exercises (Chapter 3)

In Exercises 1 through 14, find $D_x y$.

1. $y = \dfrac{x^2}{x^3 + a^3}$

2. $y = \dfrac{2x}{\sqrt{x^2 - 9}}$

3. $4x^2 + 4y^2 - y^3 = 0$

4. $y = \sqrt{1 + x} + \sqrt{1 - x}$

5. $y = \left(\sqrt{x} + \dfrac{1}{\sqrt{x}}\right)^3$

6. $y = \dfrac{x^2}{(x + 2)^2 (4x - 5)}$

7. $y = \sqrt[3]{\dfrac{x}{x^3 + 1}}$

8. $xy^2 + 2y^3 = x - 2y$

9. $y = \dfrac{1}{x - \sqrt{x^2 - 1}}$

10. $x^{2/3} + y^{2/3} = a^{2/3}$

11. $y = (x^2 - 1)^{3/2}(x^2 - 4)^{1/2}$

12. $y = \dfrac{\sqrt{x^2 + 1} + \sqrt{x^2 - 1}}{\sqrt{x^2 + 1} - \sqrt{x^2 - 1}}$

13. $y = x^2 + [x^3 + (x^4 + x)^2]^3$

14. $y = \dfrac{x\sqrt{3 + 2x}}{4x - 1}$

15. A particle is moving in a straight line according to the equation of motion $s = t^3 - 11t^2 + 24t + 100$ where s ft is the directed distance of the particle from the starting point at t sec. (a) The particle is at the starting point when $t = 0$. For what other values of t is the particle at the starting point? (b) Determine the velocity of the particle at each instant that it is at the starting point, and interpet the sign of the velocity in each case.

16. Find equations of the tangent lines to the curve $y = 2x^3 + 4x^2 - x$ that have the slope $\frac{1}{2}$.

17. Find equations of the tangent line and normal line to the curve $2x^3 + 2y^3 - 9xy = 0$ at the point $(2, 1)$.

18. An object is sliding down an inclined plane according to the equation of motion $s = 12t^2 + 6t$ where s ft is the directed distance of the object from the top t sec after starting. (a) Find the velocity 3 sec after the start. (b) Find the initial velocity.

19. Using only the definition of a derivative find $f'(x)$ if $f(x) = \sqrt{4x - 3}$.

20. Using only the definition of a derivative find $f'(5)$ if $f(x) = \sqrt[3]{3x + 1}$.

21. Find $f'(x)$ if $f(x) = (|x + 1| - |x|)^2$.

22. Find $f'(x)$ if $f(x) = x - [\![x]\!]$.

23. Given $f(x) = |x|^3$. (a) Draw a sketch of the graph of f. (b) Find $\lim\limits_{x \to 0} f(x)$ if it exists. (c) Find $f'(0)$ if it exists.

24. Given $f(x) = x^2 \operatorname{sgn} x$. (a) Discuss the differentiability of f. (b) Is f' continuous on its domain?

25. Find $f'(-3)$ if $f(x) = [\![x + \frac{1}{2}]\!] \sqrt[3]{9x}$.

26. Find $f'(-3)$ if $f(x) = (|x| - x) \sqrt[3]{9x}$.

27. Prove that the line tangent to the curve $y = -x^4 + 2x^2 + x$ at the point $(1, 2)$ is also tangent to the curve at another point, and find this point.

28. Find an equation of the normal line to the curve $x - y = \sqrt{x + y}$ at the point $(3, 1)$.

29. A ball is thrown vertically upward from the top of a house 112 ft high. Its equation of motion is $s = -16t^2 + 96t$ where s ft is the directed distance of the ball from the starting point at t sec. Find: (a) the instantaneous velocity of the ball at 2 sec; (b) how high the ball will go; (c) how long it takes for the ball to reach the ground; (d) the instantaneous velocity of the ball when it reaches the ground.

30. Prove that the tangent lines to the curves $4y^3 - x^2y - x + 5y = 0$ and $x^4 - 4y^3 + 5x + y = 0$ at the origin are perpendicular.

31. Given

$$f(x) = \begin{cases} ax^2 + b & \text{if } x \le 1 \\ \dfrac{1}{|x|} & \text{if } x > 1 \end{cases}$$

Find the values of a and b so that $f'(1)$ exists.

32. If the two functions f and g are differentiable at the number x_1, is the composite function $f \circ g$ necessarily differentiable at x_1? If your answer is yes, prove it. If your answer is no, give a counterexample.

33. Suppose $f(x) = 3x + |x|$ and $g(x) = \frac{3}{4}x - \frac{1}{4}|x|$. Prove that neither $f'(0)$ nor $g'(0)$ exists but that $(f \circ g)'(0)$ does exist.

34. Give an example of two functions f and g for which f is differentiable at $g(0)$, g is not differentiable at 0, and $f \circ g$ is differentiable at 0.

35. Give an example of two functions f and g for which f is not differentiable at $g(0)$, g is differentiable at 0, and $f \circ g$ is differentiable at 0.

36. In Exercise 27 of Exercises 3.3, you are to prove that if f is differentiable at a, then

$$f'(a) = \lim_{\Delta x \to 0} \frac{f(a + \Delta x) - f(a - \Delta x)}{2 \Delta x}$$

Show by using the absolute value function that it is possible for the limit in the above equation to exist even though $f'(a)$ does not exist.

37. If $f'(x_1)$ exists, prove that

$$\lim_{x \to x_1} \frac{xf(x_1) - x_1 f(x)}{x - x_1} = f(x_1) - x_1 f'(x_1)$$

38. Let f and g be two functions whose domains are the set of all real numbers. Furthermore, suppose that (i) $g(x) = xf(x) + 1$; (ii) $g(a + b) = g(a) \cdot g(b)$ for all a and b; (iii) $\lim_{x \to 0} f(x) = 1$. Prove that $g'(x) = g(x)$.

39. The remainder theorem of elementary algebra states that if $P(x)$ is a polynomial in x and r is any real number, then there is a polynomial $Q(x)$ such that $P(x) = Q(x)(x - r) + P(r)$. What is $\lim_{x \to r} Q(x)$?

4

Applications of the Derivative

4.1 THE DERIVATIVE AS A RATE OF CHANGE

The concept of velocity in rectilinear motion corresponds to the more general concept of instantaneous rate of change. For example, if a particle is moving along a straight line according to the equation of motion $s = f(t)$, we have seen that the velocity of the particle at t units of time is determined by the derivative of s with respect to t. Because velocity can be interpreted as a rate of change of distance per unit change in time, we see that the derivative of s with respect to t is the rate of change of s per unit change in t.

In a similar way, if a quantity y is a function of a quantity x, we may express the rate of change of y per unit change in x. The discussion is analogous to the discussions of the slope of a tangent line to a graph and the instantaneous velocity of a particle moving along a straight line.

If the functional relationship between y and x is given by

$$y = f(x)$$

and if x changes from the value x_1 to $x_1 + \Delta x$, then y changes from $f(x_1)$ to $f(x_1 + \Delta x)$. So the change in y, which we may denote by Δy, is $f(x_1 + \Delta x) - f(x_1)$ when the change in x is Δx. The average rate of change of y, per unit change in x, as x changes from x_1 to $x_1 + \Delta x$ is then

$$\frac{f(x_1 + \Delta x) - f(x_1)}{\Delta x} = \frac{\Delta y}{\Delta x} \tag{1}$$

If the limit of this quotient exists as $\Delta x \to 0$, this limit is what we intuitively think of as the instantaneous rate of change of y per unit change in x at x_1. Accordingly, we have the following definition.

179

4.1.1 Definition

If $y = f(x)$, the *instantaneous rate of change of y per unit change in x at x_1* is $f'(x_1)$ or, equivalently, the derivative of y with respect to x at x_1, if it exists there.

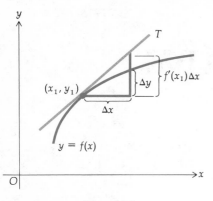

Figure 4.1.1

The instantaneous rate of change of y per unit change in x may be interpreted as the change in y caused by a change of one unit in x if the rate of change remains constant. To illustrate this geometrically, let $f'(x_1)$ be the instantaneous rate of change of y per unit change in x at x_1. Then if we multiply $f'(x_1)$ by Δx (the change in x) we have the change that would occur in y if the point (x, y) were to move along the tangent line at (x_1, y_1) of the graph of $y = f(x)$. See Fig. 4.1.1. The average rate of change of y per unit change in x is given by the fraction in Eq. (1), and if this is multiplied by Δx, we have

$$\frac{\Delta y}{\Delta x} \cdot \Delta x = \Delta y$$

which is the actual change in y caused by a change of Δx in x when the point (x, y) moves along the graph.

EXAMPLE 1: Let V cubic inches be the volume of a cube having an edge of length e inches. Find the average rate of change of the volume per inch change in the length of the edge as e changes from (a) 3 to 3.2; (b) 3 to 3.1; (c) 3 to 3.01. (d) What is the instantaneous rate of change of the volume per inch change in the length of the edge when $e = 3$?

SOLUTION: Because the formula for finding the volume of a cube is $V = e^3$, let f be the function defined by $f(e) = e^3$. Then the average rate of change of V per unit change in e as e changes from e_1 to $e_1 + \Delta e$ is

$$\frac{f(e_1 + \Delta e) - f(e_1)}{\Delta e}$$

(a) $e_1 = 3$, $\Delta e = 0.2$, and $\dfrac{f(3.2) - f(3)}{0.2} = \dfrac{(3.2)^3 - 3^3}{0.2} = \dfrac{5.768}{0.2} = 28.84$

(b) $e_1 = 3$, $\Delta e = 0.1$, and $\dfrac{f(3.1) - f(3)}{0.1} = \dfrac{(3.1)^3 - 3^3}{0.1} = \dfrac{2.791}{0.1} = 27.91$

(c) $e_1 = 3$, $\Delta e = 0.01$, and $\dfrac{f(3.01) - f(3)}{0.01} = \dfrac{(3.01)^3 - 3^3}{0.01} = \dfrac{0.2709}{0.01} = 27.09$

In part (a) we see that as the length of the edge of the cube changes from 3 inches to 3.2 inches, the change in the volume is 5.768 cubic inches and the average rate of change of the volume is 28.84 cubic inches per inch change in the length of the edge. There are similar interpretations of parts (b) and (c).

(d) The instantaneous rate of change of V per unit change in e at 3 is $f'(3)$.

$$f'(e) = 3e^2$$

Hence,

$$f'(3) = 27$$

Therefore, when the length of the edge of the cube is 3 inches, the instantaneous rate of change of the volume is 27 cubic inches per inch change in the length of the edge.

EXAMPLE 2: The annual gross earnings of a particular corporation t years after January 1, 1970, is p millions of dollars and

$$p = \tfrac{2}{5}t^2 + 2t + 10$$

Find: (a) the rate at which the gross earnings were growing January 1, 1972; (b) the rate at which the gross earnings should be growing January 1, 1976.

SOLUTION: (a) On January 1, 1972, $t = 2$; hence, we find $D_t p$ when $t = 2$.

$$D_t p = \tfrac{4}{5}t + 2 \qquad D_t p \bigg]_{t=2} = \tfrac{8}{5} + 2 = 3.6$$

So on January 1, 1972, the gross earnings were growing at the rate of 3.6 million dollars per year.

(b) On January 1, 1976, $t = 6$ and

$$D_t p \bigg]_{t=6} = \tfrac{24}{5} + 2 = 6.8$$

Therefore, on January 1, 1976, the gross earnings should be growing at the rate of 6.8 million dollars per year.

The results of Example 2 are meaningful only if they are compared to the actual earnings of the corporation. For example, if on January 1, 1971, it was found that the earnings of the corporation for the year 1970 had been 3 million dollars, then the rate of growth on January 1, 1972, of 3.4 million dollars annually would have been excellent. However, if the earnings in 1970 had been 300 million dollars, then the growth rate on January 1, 1972, would have been very poor. The measure used to compare the rate of change with the amount of the quantity which is being changed is called the *relative rate*.

4.1.2 Definition   If $y = f(x)$, the *relative rate of change of y per unit change in x* at x_1 is given by $f'(x_1)/f(x_1)$ or, equivalently, $D_x y/y$ evaluated at $x = x_1$.

If the relative rate is multiplied by 100, we have the percent rate of change.

EXAMPLE 3: Find the relative rate of growth of the gross earnings on January 1, 1972, and January 1, 1976, for the corporation of Example 2.

SOLUTION: (a) When $t = 2$, $p = \tfrac{2}{5}(4) + 2(2) + 10 = 15.6$. Hence, on January 1, 1972, the relative rate of growth of the corporation's annual gross earnings was

$$\frac{D_t p}{p}\bigg]_{t=2} = \frac{3.6}{15.6} = 0.231 = 23.1\%$$

(b) When $t = 6$, $p = \tfrac{2}{5}(36) + 2(6) + 10 = 36.4$. Therefore, on January 1, 1976, the relative rate of growth of the corporation's annual gross earnings should be

$$\frac{D_t p}{p}\bigg]_{t=6} = \frac{6.8}{36.4} = 0.187 = 18.7\%$$

Note that the growth rate of 6.8 million dollars for January 1, 1976, is greater than the 3.6 million dollars for January 1, 1972; however, the relative growth rate of 18.7% for January 1, 1976, is less than the relative growth rate of 23.1% for January 1, 1972.

Exercises 4.1

1. If A in.^{2} is the area of a square and s in. is the length of a side of the square, find the average rate of change of A with respect to s as s changes from (a) 4 to 4.6; (b) 4 to 4.3; (c) 4 to 4.1. (d) What is the instantaneous rate of change of A with respect to s when s is 4?

2. Suppose a right-circular cylinder has a constant height of 10 in. If V in.^{3} is the volume of the right-circular cylinder, and r in. is the radius of its base, find the average rate of change of V with respect to r as r changes from (a) 5 to 5.4; (b) 5 to 5.1; (c) 5 to 5.01. (d) Find the instantaneous rate of change of V with respect to r when r is 5.

3. Let r be the reciprocal of a number n. Find the instantaneous rate of change of r with respect to n and the relative rate of change of r per unit change in n when n is (a) 4 and (b) 10.

4. Let s be the principal square root of a number x. Find the instantaneous rate of change of s with respect to x and the relative rate of change of s per unit change in x when x is (a) 9 and (b) 4.

5. If water is being drained from a swimming pool and V gal is the volume of water in the pool t min after the draining starts, where $V = 250(40 - t)^2$, find (a) the average rate at which the water leaves the pool during the first 5 min, and (b) how fast the water is flowing out of the pool 5 min after the draining starts.

6. The supply equation for a certain kind of pencil is $x = 3p^2 + 2p$ where p cents is the price per pencil when $1000x$ pencils are supplied. (a) Find the average rate of change of the supply per 1 cent change in the price when the price is increased from 10 cents to 11 cents. (b) Find the instantaneous (or marginal) rate of change of the supply per 1 cent change in the price when the price is 10 cents.

7. The profit of a retail store is $100y$ dollars when x dollars are spent daily on advertising and $y = 2500 + 36x - 0.2x^2$. Use the derivative to determine if it would be profitable for the daily advertising budget to be increased if the current daily advertising budget is (a) \$60 and (b) \$100.

8. A balloon maintains the shape of a sphere as it is being inflated. Find the rate of change of the surface area with respect to the radius at the instant when the radius is 2 in.

9. In an electric circuit, if E volts is the electromotive force, R ohms is the resistance, and I amperes is the current, Ohm's law states that $IR = E$. Assuming that E is constant, show that R decreases at a rate that is proportional to the inverse square of I.

10. Boyle's law for the expansion of a gas is $PV = C$, where P is the number of pounds per square unit of pressure, V is the number of cubic units in the volume of the gas, and C is a constant. Find the instantaneous rate of change of the volume per change of one pound per square unit in the pressure when $P = 4$ and $V = 8$.

11. A bomber is flying parallel to the ground at an altitude of 2 mi and at a speed of $4\frac{1}{2}$ mi/min. If the bomber flies directly over a target, at what rate is the line-of-sight distance between the bomber and the target changing 20 sec later?

12. At 8 A.M. a ship sailing due north at 24 knots (nautical miles per hour) is at a point P. At 10 A.M. a second ship sailing due east at 32 knots is at P. At what rate is the distance between the two ships changing at (a) 9 A.M. and (b) 11 A.M.?

4.2 RELATED RATES

There are many problems concerned with the rate of change of two or more related variables with respect to time, in which it is not necessary to express each of these variables directly as functions of time. For example, suppose that we are given an equation involving the variables x and y, and that both x and y are functions of a third variable t, where t sec denotes time. Then, because the rate of change of x with respect to t and the rate of change of y with respect to t are given by $D_t x$ and $D_t y$, respectively, we differentiate on both sides of the given equation with respect to t by applying the chain rule and proceed as below.

EXAMPLE 1: A ladder 25 ft long is leaning against a vertical wall. If the bottom of the ladder is pulled horizontally away from the wall at 3 ft/sec, how fast is the top of the ladder sliding down the wall, when the bottom is 15 ft from the wall?

Figure 4.2.1

SOLUTION: Let $t =$ the number of seconds in the time that has elapsed since the ladder started to slide down the wall;
$y =$ the number of feet in the distance from the ground to the top of the ladder at t sec;
$x =$ the number of feet in the distance from the bottom of the ladder to the wall at t sec.

See Fig. 4.2.1. Because the bottom of the ladder is pulled horizontally away from the wall at 3 ft/sec, $D_t x = 3$. We wish to find $D_t y$ when $x = 15$. From the Pythagorean theorem, we have

$$y^2 = 625 - x^2 \qquad (1)$$

Because x and y are functions of t, we differentiate on both sides of Eq. (1) with respect to t and obtain

$$2y\, D_t y = -2x\, D_t x$$

giving us

$$D_t y = -\frac{x}{y}\, D_t x \qquad (2)$$

When $x = 15$, it follows from Eq. (1) that $y = 20$. Because $D_t x = 3$, we get from (2)

$$D_t y \Big]_{y=20} = -\tfrac{15}{20} \cdot 3 = -\tfrac{9}{4}$$

Therefore, the top of the ladder is sliding down the wall at the rate of $2\tfrac{1}{4}$ ft/sec when the bottom is 15 ft from the wall. (The significance of the minus sign is that y is decreasing as t is increasing.)

EXAMPLE 2: A tank is in the form of an inverted cone, having an altitude of 16 ft and a base radius of 4 ft. Water is flowing into the tank at the rate of 2 ft³/min. How fast is the water

SOLUTION: Let $t =$ the number of minutes in the time that has elapsed since water started to flow into the tank;
$h =$ the number of feet in the height of the water level at t min;
$r =$ the number of feet in the radius of the surface of the water at t min;
$V =$ the number of cubic feet in the volume of water in the tank at t min.

level rising when the water is 5 ft deep?

Figure 4.2.2

At any time, the volume of water in the tank may be expressed in terms of the volume of a cone (see Fig. 4.2.2).

$$V = \tfrac{1}{3}\pi r^2 h \qquad (3)$$

V, r, and h are all functions of t. Because water is flowing into the tank at the rate of 2 ft³/min, $D_t V = 2$. We wish to find $D_t h$ when $h = 5$. To express r in terms of h, we have from similar triangles

$$\frac{r}{h} = \frac{4}{16} \qquad r = \tfrac{1}{4}h$$

Substituting this value of r into formula (3), we obtain

$$V = \tfrac{1}{3}\pi(\tfrac{1}{4}h)^2(h) \quad \text{or} \quad V = \tfrac{1}{48}\pi h^3 \qquad (4)$$

Differentiating on both sides of Eq. (4) with respect to t, we get

$$D_t V = \tfrac{1}{16}\pi h^2 \, D_t h$$

Substituting 2 for $D_t V$ and solving for $D_t h$, we obtain

$$D_t h = \frac{32}{\pi h^2}$$

Therefore,

$$D_t h \Big]_{h=5} = \frac{32}{25\pi}$$

We conclude that the water level is rising at the rate of $32/25\pi$ ft/min when the water is 5 ft deep.

EXAMPLE 3: Two cars, one going due east at the rate of 37.5 mi/hr and the other going due south at the rate of 30 mi/hr, are traveling toward an intersection of the two roads. At what rate are the two cars approaching each other at the instant when the first car is 400 ft and the second car is 300 ft from the intersection?

SOLUTION: Refer to Fig. 4.2.3, where the point P is the intersection of the two roads.

Let $x =$ the number of feet in the distance of the first car from P at t sec;

$y =$ the number of feet in the distance of the second car from P at t sec;

$z =$ the number of feet in the distance between the two cars at t sec.

Because the first car is approaching P at the rate of 37.5 mi/hr = $37.5 \cdot \tfrac{22}{15}$ ft/sec = 55 ft/sec and because x is decreasing as t is increasing, it follows that $D_t x = -55$. Similarly, because 30 mi/hr = $30 \cdot \tfrac{22}{15}$ ft/sec = 44 ft/sec, $D_t y = -44$. We wish to find $D_t z$ when $x = 400$ and $y = 300$. From the Pythagorean theorem we have

$$z^2 = x^2 + y^2 \qquad (5)$$

Figure 4.2.3

Differentiating on both sides of Eq. (5) with respect to t, we obtain

$$2z \, D_t z = 2x \, D_t x + 2y \, D_t y$$

and so

$$D_t z = \frac{x \, D_t x + y \, D_t y}{z} \tag{6}$$

When $x = 400$ and $y = 300$, it follows from Eq. (5) that $z = 500$. In Eq. (6), substituting $D_t x = -55$, $D_t y = -44$, $x = 400$, $y = 300$, and $z = 500$, we get

$$D_t z \Big]_{z=500} = \frac{(400)(-55) + (300)(-44)}{500} = -70.4$$

Therefore, at the instant in question the cars are approaching each other at the rate of 70.4 ft/sec.

Exercises 4.2

1. A kite is flying at a height of 40 ft. A boy is flying it so that it is moving horizontally at a rate of 3 ft/sec. If the string is taut, at what rate is the string being paid out when the length of the string released is 50 ft?

2. A spherical balloon is being inflated so that its volume is increasing at the rate of 5 ft³/min. At what rate is the diameter increasing when the diameter is 12 ft?

3. A spherical snowball is being made so that its volume is increasing at the rate of 8 ft³/min. Find the rate at which the radius is increasing when the snowball is 4 ft in diameter.

4. Suppose that when the diameter is 6 ft the snowball in Exercise 3 stopped growing and started to melt at the rate of $\frac{1}{4}$ ft³/min. Find the rate at which the radius is changing when the radius is 2 ft.

5. Sand is being dropped at the rate of 10 ft³/min onto a conical pile. If the height of the pile is always twice the base radius, at what rate is the height increasing when the pile is 8 ft high?

6. A light is hung 15 ft above a straight horizontal path. If a man 6 ft tall is walking away from the light at the rate of 5 ft/sec, how fast is his shadow lengthening?

7. In Exercise 6 at what rate is the tip of the man's shadow moving?

8. A man 6 ft tall is walking toward a building at the rate of 5 ft/sec. If there is a light on the ground 50 ft from the building, how fast is the man's shadow on the building growing shorter when he is 30 ft from the building?

9. A water tank in the form of an inverted cone is being emptied at the rate of 6 ft³/min. The altitude of the cone is 24 ft, and the base radius is 12 ft. Find how fast the water level is lowering when the water is 10 ft deep.

10. A trough is 12 ft long and its ends are in the form of inverted isosceles triangles having an altitude of 3 ft and a base of 3 ft. Water is flowing into the trough at the rate of 2 ft³/min. How fast is the water level rising when the water is 1 ft deep?

11. Boyle's law for the expansion of gas is $PV = C$, where P is the number of pounds per square unit of pressure, V is the number of cubic units of volume of the gas, and C is a constant. At a certain instant the pressure is 3000 lb/ft², the volume is 5 ft³, and the volume is increasing at the rate of 3 ft³/min. Find the rate of change of the pressure at this instant.

12. The adiabatic law (no gain or loss of heat) for the expansion of air is $PV^{1.4} = C$, where P is the number of pounds per square unit of pressure, V is the number of cubic units of volume, and C is a constant. At a specific instant, the pressure is 40 lb/in.² and is increasing at the rate of 8 lb/in.² each second. What is the rate of change of volume at this instant?

13. An automobile traveling at a rate of 30 ft/sec is approaching an intersection. When the automobile is 120 ft from the intersection, a truck traveling at the rate of 40 ft/sec crosses the intersection. The automobile and the truck are on roads that are at right angles to each other. How fast are the automobile and the truck separating 2 sec after the truck leaves the intersection?

14. A man on a dock is pulling in a boat at the rate of 50 ft/min by means of a rope attached to the boat at water level. If the man's hands are 16 ft above the water level, how fast is the boat approaching the dock when the amount of rope out is 20 ft?

15. A ladder 20 ft long is leaning against an embankment inclined 60° to the horizontal. If the bottom of the ladder is being moved horizontally toward the embankment at 1 ft/sec, how fast is the top of the ladder moving when the bottom is 4 ft from the embankment?

16. A horizontal trough is 16 ft long, and its ends are isosceles trapezoids with an altitude of 4 ft, a lower base of 4 ft, and an upper base of 6 ft. Water is being poured into the trough at the rate of 10 ft³/min. How fast is the water level rising when the water is 2 ft deep?

17. In Exercise 16 if the water level is decreasing at the rate of $\frac{1}{4}$ ft/min when the water is 3 ft deep, at what rate is water being drawn from the trough?

18. Water is being poured at the rate of 8 ft³/min into a tank in the form of a cone. The cone is 20 ft deep and 10 ft in diameter at the top. If there is a leak in the bottom, and the water level is rising at the rate of 1 in./min, when the water is 16 ft deep, how fast is the water leaking?

4.3 MAXIMUM AND MINIMUM VALUES OF A FUNCTION

We have seen that the geometrical interpretation of the derivative of a function is the slope of the tangent line to the graph of a function at a point. This fact enables us to apply derivatives as an aid in sketching graphs. For example, the derivative may be used to determine at what points the tangent line is horizontal; these are the points where the derivative is zero. Also, the derivative may be used to find the intervals for which the graph of a function lies above the tangent line and the intervals for which the graph lies below the tangent line. Before applying the derivative to draw sketches of graphs, we need some definitions and theorems.

4.3.1 Definition

The function f is said to have a *relative maximum value* at c if there exists an open interval containing c, on which f is defined, such that $f(c) \geq f(x)$ for all x in this interval.

Figures 4.3.1 and 4.3.2 each show a sketch of a portion of the graph of a function having a relative maximum value at c.

Figure 4.3.1

Figure 4.3.2

4.3.2 Definition   The function f is said to have a *relative minimum value* at c if there exists an open interval containing c, on which f is defined, such that $f(c) \leq f(x)$ for all x in this interval.

Figures 4.3.3 and 4.3.4 each show a sketch of a portion of the graph of a function having a relative minimum value at c.

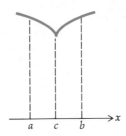

Figure 4.3.3   Figure 4.3.4

If the function f has either a relative maximum or a relative minimum value at c, then f is said to have a *relative extremum* at c. (The plurals of maximum and minimum are maxima and minima; the plural of extremum is extrema.)

The following theorem enables us to locate the possible values of c for which there is a relative extremum.

4.3.3 Theorem   If $f(x)$ exists for all values of x in the open interval (a, b) and if f has a relative extremum at c, where $a < c < b$, then if $f'(c)$ exists, $f'(c) = 0$.

PROOF: The proof will be given for the case when f has a relative minimum value at c.

If $f'(c)$ exists, from formula (5) of Sec. 3.3 we have

$$f'(c) = \lim_{x \to c} \frac{f(x) - f(c)}{x - c} \tag{1}$$

Because f has a relative minimum value at c, by Definition 4.3.2, if x is sufficiently close to c, it follows that

$$f(x) - f(c) \geq 0$$

If x is approaching c from the right, $x - c > 0$, and therefore

$$\frac{f(x) - f(c)}{x - c} \geq 0$$

By Theorem 2.10.7, if the limit exists,

$$\lim_{x \to c^+} \frac{f(x) - f(c)}{x - c} \geq 0 \tag{2}$$

Similarly, if x is approaching c from the left, $x - c < 0$, and therefore

$$\frac{f(x) - f(c)}{x - c} \leq 0$$

so that by Theorem 2.10.6, if the limit exists,

$$\lim_{x \to c^-} \frac{f(x) - f(c)}{x - c} \leq 0 \tag{3}$$

Because $f'(c)$ exists, the limits in inequalities (2) and (3) must be equal, and both must be equal to $f'(c)$. So from (2) we have

$$f'(c) \geq 0 \tag{4}$$

and from (3),

$$f'(c) \leq 0 \tag{5}$$

Because both (4) and (5) are taken to be true, we conclude that

$$f'(c) = 0$$

which was to be proved.

The proof for the case when f has a relative maximum value at c is similar and is left for the reader (see Exercise 37). ∎

The geometrical interpretation of Theorem 4.3.3 is that if f has a relative extremum at c and if $f'(c)$ exists, then the graph of $y = f(x)$ must have a horizontal tangent line at the point where $x = c$.

If f is a differentiable function, then the only possible values of x for which f can have a relative extremum are those for which $f'(x) = 0$. However, $f'(x)$ can be equal to zero for a specific value of x, and yet f may not have a relative extremum there. For example, consider the function f defined by

$$f(x) = (x - 1)^3$$

Figure 4.3.5

A sketch of the graph of this function is shown in Fig. 4.3.5. $f'(x) = 3(x - 1)^2$, and so $f'(1) = 0$. However, $f(x) < 0$, if $x < 1$, and $f(x) > 0$, if $x > 1$. So f does not have a relative extremum at 1.

Furthermore, f may have a relative extremum at a number, and f' may fail to exist there. This is illustrated by the function f defined as follows:

$$f(x) = \begin{cases} 2x - 1 & \text{if } x \leq 3 \\ 8 - x & \text{if } 3 < x \end{cases}$$

Figure 4.3.6

A sketch of the graph of this function is shown in Fig. 4.3.6. The function f has a relative maximum value at 3. The derivative from the left at 3 is given by $f'_-(3) = 2$, and the derivative from the right at 3 is given by $f'_+(3) = -1$. Therefore, we conclude that $f'(3)$ does not exist.

This example demonstrates why the condition "$f'(c)$ exists" must be included in the hypothesis of Theorem 4.3.3.

In summary, then, if a function f is defined at a number c, a necessary condition for f to have a relative extremum there is that either $f'(c) = 0$ or $f'(c)$ does not exist. But we have noted that this condition is not sufficient.

4.3.4 Definition   If c is a number in the domain of the function f and if either $f'(c) = 0$ or $f'(c)$ does not exist, then c is called a *critical number* of f.

Because of this definition and the previous discussion, we can conclude that a necessary condition for a function to have a relative extremum at a number c is for c to be a critical number.

EXAMPLE 1:   Find the critical numbers of the function f defined by $f(x) = x^{4/3} + 4x^{1/3}$.

SOLUTION: $f'(x) = \dfrac{4}{3} x^{1/3} + \dfrac{4}{3} x^{-2/3} = \dfrac{4}{3} x^{-2/3}(x + 1) = \dfrac{4(x + 1)}{3x^{2/3}}$

$f'(x) = 0$ when $x = -1$, and $f'(x)$ does not exist when $x = 0$. Both -1 and 0 are in the domain of f; therefore, the critical numbers of f are -1 and 0.

We are frequently concerned with a function which is defined on a given interval, and we wish to find the largest or smallest function value on the interval. These intervals can be either closed, open, or closed at one end and open at the other. The greatest function value on an interval is called the *absolute maximum value*, and the smallest function value on an interval is called the *absolute minimum value*. Following are the precise definitions.

4.3.5 Definition   The function f is said to have an *absolute maximum value on an interval* if there is some number c in the interval such that $f(c) \geq f(x)$ for all x in the interval. In such a case, $f(c)$ is the absolute maximum value of f on the interval.

4.3.6 Definition   The function f is said to have an *absolute minimum value on an interval* if there is some number c in the interval such that $f(c) \leq f(x)$ for all x in the interval. In such a case, $f(c)$ is the absolute minimum value of f on the interval.

An *absolute extremum* of a function on an interval is either an absolute maximum value or an absolute minimum value of the function on the interval. A function may or may not have an absolute extremum on a given interval. In each of the following examples a function and an interval are given, and we determine the absolute extrema of the function on the interval if there are any.

EXAMPLE 2: Given

$$f(x) = 2x$$

find the absolute extrema of f on the interval [1, 4) if there are any.

SOLUTION: A sketch of the graph of f on [1, 4) is shown in Fig. 4.3.7. The function f has an absolute minimum value of 2 on [1,4). There is no absolute maximum value of f on [1, 4), because $\lim\limits_{x \to 4^-} f(x) = 8$, but $f(x)$ is always less than 8 on the given interval.

Figure 4.3.7

EXAMPLE 3:   Given

$$f(x) = -x^2$$

find the absolute extrema of f on (−3, 2] if there are any.

SOLUTION: A sketch of the graph of f on (−3, 2] is shown in Fig. 4.3.8. The function f has an absolute maximum value of 0 on (−3, 2]. There is no absolute minimum value of f on (−3, 2] because $\lim\limits_{x \to -3^+} f(x) = -9$, but $f(x)$ is always greater than −9 on the given interval.

Figure 4.3.8

EXAMPLE 4:   Given

$$f(x) = \frac{x}{1 - x^2}$$

SOLUTION: A sketch of the graph of f on (−1, 1) is shown in Fig. 4.3.9. The function f has neither an absolute maximum value nor an absolute minimum value on (−1, 1).

find the absolute extrema of f on $(-1, 1)$ if there are any.

$$\lim_{x \to -1^+} f(x) = -\infty \quad \text{and} \quad \lim_{x \to 1^-} f(x) = +\infty$$

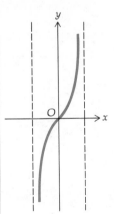

Figure 4.3.9

EXAMPLE 5: Given

$$f(x) = \begin{cases} x + 1 & \text{if } x < 1 \\ x^2 - 6x + 7 & \text{if } 1 \le x \end{cases}$$

find the absolute extrema of f on $[-5, 4]$ if there are any.

SOLUTION: A sketch of the graph of f on $[-5, 4]$ is shown in Fig. 4.3.10. The absolute maximum value of f on $[-5, 4]$ occurs at 1, and $f(1) = 2$; the absolute minimum value of f on $[-5, 4]$ occurs at -5, and $f(-5) = -4$. Note that f has a relative maximum value at 1 and a relative minimum value at 3. Also, note that 1 is a critical number of f because f' does not exist at 1, and 3 is a critical number of f because $f'(3) = 0$.

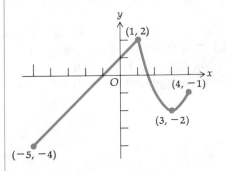

Figure 4.3.10

EXAMPLE 6: Given

$$f(x) = \frac{1}{x - 3}$$

find the absolute extrema of f on the interval $[1, 5]$ if there are any.

SOLUTION: A sketch of the graph is shown in Fig. 4.3.11. The function f has neither an absolute maximum value nor an absolute minimum value on $[1, 5]$. $\lim_{x \to 3^-} f(x) = -\infty$; so $f(x)$ can be made less than any negative number by taking $(3 - x) > 0$ and less than a suitable positive δ. Also, $\lim_{x \to 3^+} f(x) = +\infty$; so $f(x)$ can be made greater than any positive number by taking $(x - 3) > 0$ and less than a suitable positive δ.

Figure 4.3.11

We may speak of an absolute extremum of a function when no interval is specified. In such a case we are referring to an absolute extremum of the function on the entire domain of the function.

4.3.7 Definition $f(c)$ is said to be the *absolute maximum value* of the function f if c is in the domain of f and if $f(c) \geq f(x)$ for all values of x in the domain of f.

4.3.8 Definition $f(c)$ is said to be the *absolute minimum value* of the function f if c is in the domain of f and if $f(c) \leq f(x)$ for all values of x in the domain of f.

EXAMPLE 7:   Given

$$f(x) = x^2 - 4x + 8$$

determine the absolute extrema of f if there are any.

SOLUTION: The graph of f is a parabola, and a sketch is shown in Fig. 4.3.12. The vertex of the parabola is at the point (2, 4), and the parabola opens upward. The function has an absolute minimum value of 4 at 2. There is no absolute maximum value of f.

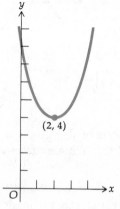

Figure 4.3.12

Referring back to Examples 2–7, we see that the only case in which there is both an absolute maximum function value and an absolute minimum function value is in Example 5, where the function is continuous on the closed interval [−5, 4]. In the other examples, either we do not have a closed interval or we do not have a continuous function. If a function is continuous on a closed interval, there is a theorem, called the *extreme-value theorem*, which assures us that the function has both an absolute maximum value and an absolute minimum value on the interval. The proof of this theorem is beyond the scope of this book, but we can state it without proof. The reader is referred to an advanced calculus text for the proof.

4.3.9 Theorem
Extreme-Value Theorem

If the function f is continuous on the closed interval $[a, b]$, then f has an absolute maximum value and an absolute minimum value on $[a, b]$.

An absolute extremum of a function continuous on a closed interval must be either a relative extremum or a function value at an endpoint of the interval. Because a necessary condition for a function to have a relative extremum at a number c is for c to be a critical number, we can determine the absolute maximum value and the absolute minimum value of a continuous function f on a closed interval $[a, b]$ by the following procedure:

(1) find the function values at the critical numbers of f on $[a, b]$;
(2) find the values of $f(a)$ and $f(b)$;
(3) the largest of the values from steps (1) and (2) is the absolute maximum value, and the smallest of the values from steps (1) and (2) is the absolute minimum value.

EXAMPLE 8: Given

$$f(x) = x^3 + x^2 - x + 1$$

find the absolute extrema of f on $[-2, \tfrac{1}{2}]$.

SOLUTION: Because f is continuous on $[-2, \tfrac{1}{2}]$, the extreme-value theorem applies. To find the critical numbers of f we first find f':

$$f'(x) = 3x^2 + 2x - 1$$

$f'(x)$ exists for all real numbers, and so the only critical numbers of f will be the values of x for which $f'(x) = 0$. Setting $f'(x) = 0$, we have

$$(3x - 1)(x + 1) = 0$$

from which we obtain

$$x = \tfrac{1}{3} \quad \text{and} \quad x = -1$$

The critical numbers of f are -1 and $\tfrac{1}{3}$, and each of these numbers is in the given closed interval $[-2, \tfrac{1}{2}]$. We find the function values at the critical numbers and at the endpoints of the interval, which are given in Table 4.3.1.

Table 4.3.1

x	-2	-1	$\tfrac{1}{3}$	$\tfrac{1}{2}$
$f(x)$	-1	2	$\tfrac{22}{27}$	$\tfrac{7}{8}$

Figure 4.3.13

The absolute maximum value of f on $[-2, \frac{1}{2}]$ is therefore 2, which occurs at -1, and the absolute minimum value of f on $[-2, \frac{1}{2}]$ is -1, which occurs at the left endpoint -2. A sketch of the graph of this function on $[-2, \frac{1}{2}]$ is shown in Fig. 4.3.13.

EXAMPLE 9:   Given

$$f(x) = (x - 2)^{2/3}$$

find the absolute extrema of f on $[1, 5]$.

Table 4.3.2

x	1	2	5
$f(x)$	1	0	$\sqrt[3]{9}$

Figure 4.3.14

SOLUTION: Because f is continuous on $[1, 5]$, the extreme-value theorem applies.

$$f'(x) = \frac{2}{3(x - 2)^{1/3}}$$

There is no value of x for which $f'(x) = 0$. However, because $f'(x)$ does not exist at 2, we conclude that 2 is a critical number of f, so that the absolute extrema occur either at 2 or at one of the endpoints of the interval. The function values at these numbers are given in Table 4.3.2. From the table we conclude that the absolute minimum value of f on $[1, 5]$ is 0, occurring at 2, and the absolute maximum value of f on $[1, 5]$ is $\sqrt[3]{9}$, occurring at 5. A sketch of the graph of this function on $[1, 5]$ is shown in Fig. 4.3.14.

Exercises 4.3

In Exercises 1 through 10, find the critical numbers of the given function.

1. $f(x) = x^3 + 7x^2 - 5x$

2. $f(x) = 2x^3 - 2x^2 - 16x + 1$

3. $f(x) = x^4 + 4x^3 - 2x^2 - 12x$

4. $f(x) = x^{7/3} + x^{4/3} - 3x^{1/3}$

5. $f(x) = x^{6/5} - 12x^{1/5}$

6. $f(x) = x^4 + 11x^3 + 34x^2 + 15x - 2$

7. $f(x) = (x^2 - 4)^{2/3}$

8. $f(x) = (x^3 - 3x^2 + 4)^{1/3}$

9. $f(x) = \dfrac{x}{x^2 - 9}$

10. $f(x) = \dfrac{x+1}{x^2 - 5x + 4}$

In Exercises 11 through 24, find the absolute extrema of the given function on the given interval, if there are any, and find the values of x at which the absolute extrema occur. Draw a sketch of the graph of the function on the interval.

11. $f(x) = 4 - 3x$; $(-1, 2]$

12. $f(x) = x^2 - 2x + 4$; $(-\infty, +\infty)$

13. $f(x) = \dfrac{1}{x}$; $[-2, 3]$

14. $f(x) = \dfrac{1}{x}$; $[2, 3)$

15. $f(x) = \sqrt{3 + x}$; $[-3, +\infty)$

16. $f(x) = \dfrac{3x}{9 - x^2}$; $(-3, 2)$

17. $f(x) = \dfrac{4}{(x-3)^2}$; $[2, 5]$

18. $f(x) = \sqrt{4 - x^2}$; $(-2, 2)$

19. $f(x) = |x - 4| + 1$; $(0, 6)$

20. $f(x) = |4 - x^2|$; $(-\infty, +\infty)$

21. $f(x) = \begin{cases} \dfrac{2}{x - 5} & \text{if } x \neq 5 \\ 2 & \text{if } x = 5 \end{cases}$; $[3, 5]$

22. $f(x) = \begin{cases} |x + 1| & \text{if } x \neq -1 \\ 3 & \text{if } x = -1 \end{cases}$; $[-2, 1]$

23. $f(x) = x - [\![x]\!]$; $(1, 3)$

24. $f(x) = U(x) - U(x - 1)$; $(-1, 1)$

In Exercises 25 through 36, find the absolute maximum value and the absolute minimum value of the given function on the indicated interval by the method used in Examples 8 and 9 of this section. Draw a sketch of the graph of the function on the interval.

25. $f(x) = x^3 + 5x - 4$; $[-3, -1]$

26. $f(x) = x^3 + 3x^2 - 9x$; $[-4, 4]$

27. $f(x) = x^4 - 8x^2 + 16$; $[-4, 0]$

28. $f(x) = x^4 - 8x^2 + 16$; $[-1, 4]$

29. $f(x) = x^4 - 8x^2 + 16$; $[0, 3]$

30. $f(x) = x^4 - 8x^2 + 16$; $[-3, 2]$

31. $f(x) = \dfrac{x}{x + 2}$; $[-1, 2]$

32. $f(x) = \dfrac{x + 5}{x - 3}$; $[-5, 2]$

33. $f(x) = (x + 1)^{2/3}$; $[-2, 1]$

34. $f(x) = 1 - (x - 3)^{2/3}$; $[-5, 4]$

35. $f(x) = \begin{cases} 3x - 4 & \text{if } -3 \leq x < 1 \\ x^2 - 2 & \text{if } 1 \leq x \leq 3 \end{cases}$; $[-3, 3]$

36. $f(x) = \begin{cases} 4 - (x + 5)^2 & \text{if } -6 \leq x \leq -4 \\ 12 - (x + 1)^2 & \text{if } -4 < x \leq 0 \end{cases}$; $[-6, 0]$

37. Prove Theorem 4.3.3 for the case when f has a relative maximum value at c.

4.4 APPLICATIONS INVOLVING AN ABSOLUTE EXTREMUM ON A CLOSED INTERVAL

We consider some problems in which the solution is an absolute extremum of a function on a closed interval. Use is made of the extreme-value theorem, which assures us that both an absolute maximum value and an absolute minimum value of a function exist on a closed interval if the function is continuous on that closed interval. The procedure is illustrated by some examples.

EXAMPLE 1: A cardboard box manufacturer wishes to make open boxes from pieces of cardboard 12 in. square by cutting equal squares from the four corners and turning up the sides.

SOLUTION: Let $x =$ the number of inches in the length of the side of the square to be cut out;
$V =$ the number of cubic inches in the volume of the box.
The number of inches in the dimensions of the box are then x, $(12 - 2x)$, and $(12 - 2x)$. Figure 4.4.1 represents a given piece of cardboard, and Fig. 4.4.2 represents the box.

Find the length of the side of the square to be cut out in order to obtain a box of the largest possible volume.

Figure 4.4.1

Figure 4.4.2

The volume of the box is the product of the three dimensions, and so V is a function of x, and we write

$$V(x) = x(12 - 2x)(12 - 2x) \qquad (1)$$

If $x = 0$, $V = 0$, and if $x = 6$, $V = 0$. The value of x that we wish to find is in the closed interval $[0, 6]$. Because V is continuous on the closed interval $[0, 6]$, it follows from the extreme-value theorem that V has an absolute maximum value on this interval. We also know that this absolute maximum value of V must occur either at a critical number or at an endpoint of the interval. To find the critical numbers of V, we find $V'(x)$, and then find the values of x for which either $V'(x) = 0$ or $V'(x)$ does not exist.

From Eq. (1), we obtain

$$V(x) = 144x - 48x^2 + 4x^3$$

Thus,

$$V'(x) = 144 - 96x + 12x^2$$

$V'(x)$ exists for all values of x. Setting $V'(x) = 0$, we have

$$12(x^2 - 8x + 12) = 0$$

from which we obtain

$$x = 6 \quad \text{and} \quad x = 2$$

The critical numbers of V are 2 and 6, both of which are in the closed interval $[0, 6]$. The absolute maximum value of V on $[0, 6]$ must occur at either a critical number or at an endpoint of the interval. Because $V(0) = 0$ and $V(6) = 0$, while $V(2) = 128$, we conclude that the absolute maximum value of V on $[0, 6]$ is 128, occurring at 2.

Therefore, the largest possible volume is 128 in.³, and this is obtained when the length of the side of the square cut out is 2 in.

We should emphasize that in Example 1 the existence of an absolute maximum value of V is guaranteed by the extreme-value theorem. In the following example, the existence of an absolute minimum value is guaranteed by the same theorem.

EXAMPLE 2: An island is at point A, 6 miles offshore from the nearest point B on a straight beach. A store is at point C, 7 miles down the beach from B. If a man can row at the rate of 4 mi/hr and walk at the rate of

SOLUTION: Refer to Fig. 4.4.3. Let P be the point on the beach where the man lands. Therefore, the man rows from A to P and walks from P to C.

Let $x =$ the number of miles in the distance from B to P.

$T =$ the number of hours in the time it takes the man to make the trip from A to C.

Then $T =$ the number of hours in the time to go from A to P plus the number of hours in the time to go from P to C. Because time is obtained

5 mi/hr, where should he land in order to go from the island to the store in the least possible time?

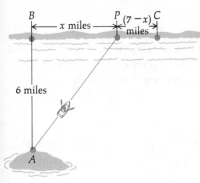

6 miles

Figure 4.4.3

by dividing distance by rate, we have

$$T = \frac{|\overline{AP}|}{4} + \frac{|\overline{PC}|}{5} \tag{2}$$

From Fig. 4.4.3, we see that $|\overline{AP}|$ is the length of the hypotenuse of right triangle ABP. Therefore,

$$|\overline{AP}| = \sqrt{x^2 + 36}$$

We also see from the figure that $|\overline{PC}| = 7 - x$. So from Eq. (2) T can be expressed as a function of x, and we have

$$T(x) = \frac{\sqrt{x^2 + 36}}{4} + \frac{7 - x}{5}$$

Because the distance from B to C is 7 miles and because P can be any point on the line segment BC, we know that x is in the closed interval $[0, 7]$.

We wish to find the value of x for which T has an absolute minimum value on $[0, 7]$. Because T is a continuous function of x on $[0, 7]$, we know that such a value exists. The critical numbers of T are found by first computing $T'(x)$:

$$T'(x) = \frac{x}{4\sqrt{x^2 + 36}} - \frac{1}{5}$$

$T'(x)$ exists for all values of x. Setting $T'(x) = 0$ and solving for x, we have

$$\frac{x}{4\sqrt{x^2 + 36}} - \frac{1}{5} = 0 \tag{3}$$

$$5x = 4\sqrt{x^2 + 36}$$

$$25x^2 = 16(x^2 + 36)$$

$$9x^2 = 16 \cdot 36$$

$$x^2 = 64$$

$$x = \pm 8$$

The number -8 is an extraneous root of Eq. (3), and 8 is not in the interval $[0, 7]$. Therefore, there are no critical numbers of T in $[0, 7]$. The absolute minimum value of T on $[0, 7]$ must therefore occur at an endpoint of the interval. Computing $T(0)$ and $T(7)$, we get

$$T(0) = \tfrac{29}{10} \quad \text{and} \quad T(7) = \tfrac{1}{4}\sqrt{85}$$

Since $\tfrac{1}{4}\sqrt{85} < \tfrac{29}{10}$, the absolute minimum value of T on $[0, 7]$ is $\tfrac{1}{4}\sqrt{85}$, occurring when $x = 7$. Therefore, in order for the man to go from the island to the store in the least possible time, he should row directly there and do no walking.

EXAMPLE 3: A rectangular field is to be fenced off along the bank of a river and no fence is required along the river. If the material for the fence costs $2 per running foot for the two ends and $3 per running foot for the side parallel to the river, find the dimensions of the field of largest possible area that can be enclosed with $900 worth of fence.

SOLUTION: Let x = the number of feet in the length of an end of the field;
y = the number of feet in the length of the side parallel to the river;
A = the number of square feet in the area of the field.

Hence,

$$A = xy \tag{4}$$

Since the cost of the material for each end is $2 per running foot and the length of an end is x ft, the total cost for the fence for each end is $2x$ dollars. Similarly, the total cost of the fence for the third side is $3y$ dollars. We have, then,

$$2x + 2x + 3y = 900 \tag{5}$$

To express A in terms of a single variable, we solve Eq. (5) for y in terms of x and substitute this value into Eq. (4), yielding A as a function of x, and

$$A(x) = x(300 - \tfrac{4}{3}x) \tag{6}$$

If $y = 0$, $x = 225$, and if $x = 0$, $y = 300$. Because both x and y must be non-negative, the value of x that will make A an absolute maximum is in the closed interval $[0, 225]$. Because A is continuous on the closed interval $[0, 225]$, we conclude from the extreme-value theorem that A has an absolute maximum value on this interval. From Eq. (6), we have

$$A(x) = 300x - \tfrac{4}{3}x^2$$

Hence,

$$A'(x) = 300 - \tfrac{8}{3}x$$

Because $A'(x)$ exists for all x, the critical values of A will be found by setting $A'(x) = 0$, which gives

$$x = 112\tfrac{1}{2}$$

The only critical number of A is $112\tfrac{1}{2}$, which is in the closed interval $[0, 225]$. Thus, the absolute maximum value of A must occur at either 0, $112\tfrac{1}{2}$, or 225. Because $A(0) = 0$ and $A(225) = 0$, while $A(112\tfrac{1}{2}) = 16{,}875$, we conclude that the absolute maximum value of A on $[0, 225]$ is 16,875 occurring when $x = 112\tfrac{1}{2}$ and $y = 150$ (obtained from Eq. (5) by substituting $112\tfrac{1}{2}$ for x).

Therefore, the largest possible area that can be enclosed for $900 is 16,875 square feet, and this is obtained when the side parallel to the river is 150 ft long and the ends are each $112\tfrac{1}{2}$ ft long.

EXAMPLE 4: In the planning of a coffee shop it is estimated that if

SOLUTION: Let x = the number of places in the seating capacity;
P = the number of dollars in the total weekly profit.

there are places for 40 to 80 people, the weekly profit will be $8 per place. However, if the seating capacity is above 80 places, the weekly profit on each place will be decreased by 4 cents times the number of places above 80. What should be the seating capacity in order to yield the greatest weekly profit?

The value of P depends upon x, and it is obtained by multiplying x by the number of dollars in the profit per place. When $40 \leq x \leq 80$, $8 is the profit per place, and so $P = 8x$. However, when $x > 80$, the number of dollars in the profit per place is $[8 - 0.04(x - 80)]$, thus giving $P = x[8 - 0.04(x - 80)] = 11.20x - 0.04x^2$. So we have

$$P(x) = \begin{cases} 8x & \text{if } 40 \leq x \leq 80 \\ 11.20x - 0.04x^2 & \text{if } 80 \leq x \leq 280 \end{cases}$$

The upper bound of 280 for x is obtained by noting that $11.20x - 0.04x^2 = 0$ when $x = 280$; and when $x > 280$, $11.20x - 0.04x^2$ is negative.

Even though x, by definition, is an integer, to have a continuous function we let x take on all real values in the interval $[40, 280]$. Note that there is continuity at 80 because

$$\lim_{x \to 80^-} P(x) = \lim_{x \to 80^-} 8x = 640$$

and

$$\lim_{x \to 80^+} P(x) = \lim_{x \to 80^+} (11.20x - 0.04x^2) = 640$$

from which it follows that the two-sided limit $\lim_{x \to 80} P(x) = 640 = P(80)$.

So P is continuous on the closed interval $[40, 280]$ and the extreme-value theorem guarantees an absolute maximum value of P on this interval.

When $40 < x < 80$, $P'(x) = 8$, and when $80 < x < 280$, $P'(x) = 11.20 - 0.08x$. $P'(80)$ does not exist since $P'_-(80) = 8$ and $P'_+(80) = 4.80$. Setting $P'(x) = 0$, we have

$$11.20 - 0.08x = 0$$

$$x = 140$$

The critical numbers of P are then 80 and 140. Evaluating $P(x)$ at the endpoints of the interval $[40, 280]$ and at the critical numbers, we have $P(40) = 320$, $P(80) = 640$, $P(140) = 784$, and $P(280) = 0$. The absolute maximum value of P, then, is 784 occurring when $x = 140$.

The seating capacity should be 140 places, which gives a total weekly profit of $784.

EXAMPLE 5: Find the dimensions of the right-circular cylinder of greatest volume which can be inscribed in a right-circular cone with a radius of 5 in. and a height of 12 in.

SOLUTION: Let $r =$ the number of inches in the radius of the cylinder;
$h =$ the number of inches in the height of the cylinder;
$V =$ the number of cubic inches in the volume of the cylinder.

Figure 4.4.4 illustrates the cylinder inscribed in the cone, and Fig. 4.4.5 illustrates a plane section through the axis of the cone.

If $r = 0$ and $h = 12$, we have a degenerate cylinder, which is the axis of the cone. If $r = 5$ and $h = 0$, we also have a degenerate cylinder, which

Figure 4.4.4

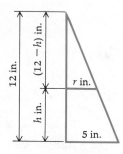

Figure 4.4.5

is a diameter of the base of the cone. We conclude that r is in the closed interval $[0, 5]$ and h is in the closed interval $[0, 12]$.

The following formula expresses V in terms of r and h:

$$V = \pi r^2 h \tag{7}$$

To express V in terms of a single variable we need another equation involving r and h. From Fig. 4.4.5, and using similar triangles, we have

$$\frac{12 - h}{r} = \frac{12}{5}$$

or

$$h = \frac{60 - 12r}{5} \tag{8}$$

Substituting from Eq. (8) into formula (7), we obtain V as a function of r and write

$$V(r) = \tfrac{12}{5} \pi (5r^2 - r^3) \qquad \text{with } r \text{ in } [0, 5] \tag{9}$$

Because V is continuous on the closed interval $[0, 5]$, it follows from the extreme-value theorem that V has an absolute maximum value on this interval. The values of r and h that give this absolute maximum value for V are the numbers we wish to find.

$$V'(r) = \tfrac{12}{5} \pi (10r - 3r^2)$$

To find the critical numbers of V, we set $V'(r) = 0$ and solve for r:

$$r(10 - 3r) = 0$$

from which we obtain

$$r = 0 \quad \text{and} \quad r = \tfrac{10}{3}$$

Because $V'(r)$ exists for all values of r, the only critical numbers of V are 0 and $\tfrac{10}{3}$, both of which are in the closed interval $[0, 5]$. The absolute maximum value of V on $[0, 5]$ must occur at either 0, $\tfrac{10}{3}$, or 5. From Eq. (9) we obtain $V(0) = 0$, $V(\tfrac{10}{3}) = \tfrac{400}{9}\pi$, and $V(5) = 0$. We therefore conclude that the absolute maximum value of V is $\tfrac{400}{9}\pi$, and this occurs when $r = \tfrac{10}{3}$. When $r = \tfrac{10}{3}$, we find from Eq. (8) that $h = 4$.

Thus, the greatest volume of an inscribed cylinder in the given cone is $\tfrac{400}{9}\pi$ in.^{3}, which occurs when the radius is $\tfrac{10}{3}$ in. and the height is 4 in.

Exercises 4.4

1. Find the area of the largest rectangle having a perimeter of 200 ft.

2. Find the area of the largest isosceles triangle having a perimeter of 18 in.

3. A manufacturer of tin boxes wishes to make use of pieces of tin with dimensions 8 in. by 15 in. by cutting equal squares from the four corners and turning up the sides. Find the length of the side of the square to be cut out if an open box having the largest possible volume is to be obtained from each piece of tin.

4. A rectangular plot of ground is to be enclosed by a fence and then divided down the middle by another fence. If the fence down the middle costs $1 per running foot and the other fence costs $2.50 per running foot, find the dimensions of the plot of largest possible area that can be enclosed with $480 worth of fence.

5. Points A and B are opposite each other on shores of a straight river that is 3 mi wide. Point C is on the same shore as B but 6 mi down the river from B. A telephone company wishes to lay a cable from A to C. If the cost per mile of the cable is 25% more under the water than it is on land, what line of cable would be least expensive for the company?

6. Solve Exercise 5 if point C is only 3 mi down the river from B.

7. Solve Example 2 of this section if the store is 9 mi down the beach from point B.

8. Example 2 and Exercises 5, 6, and 7 are special cases of the following more general problem. Let $f(x) = u\sqrt{a^2 + x^2} + v(b - x)$, where x is in $[0, b]$ and $u > v > 0$. Show that in order for the absolute minimum value of f to occur at a number in the open interval $(0, b)$ the following inequality must be satisfied: $av < b\sqrt{u^2 - v^2}$.

9. Find the dimensions of the right-circular cylinder of greatest lateral surface area that can be inscribed in a sphere with a radius of 6 in.

10. Find the dimensions of the right-circular cylinder of greatest volume that can be inscribed in a sphere with a radius of 6 in.

11. Given the circle having the equation $x^2 + y^2 = 9$, find (a) the shortest distance from the point $(4, 5)$ to a point on the circle, and (b) the longest distance from the point $(4, 5)$ to a point on the circle.

12. A manufacturer can make a profit of $20 on each item if not more than 800 items are produced each week. The profit decreases 2 cents per item over 800. How many items should the manufacturer produce each week in order to have the greatest profit?

13. A school-sponsored trip will cost each student $15 if not more than 150 students make the trip; however, the cost per student will be reduced 5 cents for each student in excess of 150. How many students should make the trip in order for the school to receive the largest gross income?

14. Solve Exercise 13 if the reduction per student in excess of 150 is 7 cents.

15. A private club charges annual membership dues of $100 per member less 50 cents for each member over 600 and plus 50 cents for each member less than 600. How many members would give the club the most revenue from annual dues?

16. Suppose a weight is to be held 10 ft below a horizontal line AB by a wire in the shape of a Y. If the points A and B are 8 ft apart, what is the shortest total length of wire that can be used?

17. A piece of wire 10 ft long is cut into two pieces. One piece is bent into the shape of a circle and the other into the shape of a square. How should the wire be cut so that (a) the combined area of the two figures is as small as possible and (b) the combined area of the two figures is as large as possible?

18. Solve Exercise 17 if one piece of wire is bent into the shape of an equilateral triangle and the other piece is bent into the shape of a square.

4.5 ROLLE'S THEOREM AND THE MEAN-VALUE THEOREM   Let f be a function which is continuous on the closed interval $[a, b]$, differentiable on the open interval (a, b), and let $f(a) = 0$ and $f(b) = 0$. The French mathematician Michel Rolle (1652–1719) proved that if a function

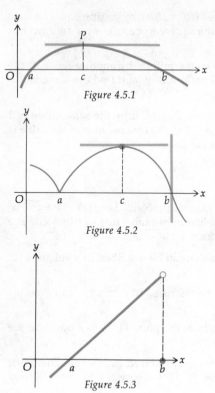

Figure 4.5.1

Figure 4.5.2

Figure 4.5.3

f satisfies these conditions, there is at least one number c between a and b for which $f'(c) = 0$.

Let us see what this means geometrically. Figure 4.5.1 shows a sketch of the graph of a function f that satisfies the conditions in the preceding paragraph. We intuitively see that there is at least one point on the curve between the points $(a, 0)$ and $(b, 0)$ where the tangent line is parallel to the x axis; that is, the slope of the tangent line is zero. This situation is illustrated in Fig. 4.5.1 at the point P. So the abscissa of P would be the c such that $f'(c) = 0$.

The function, whose graph is sketched in Fig. 4.5.1, not only is differentiable on the open interval (a, b) but also is differentiable at the end-points of the interval. However, the condition that f be differentiable at the endpoints is not necessary for the graph to have a horizontal tangent line at some point in the interval; Fig. 4.5.2 illustrates this. We see in Fig. 4.5.2 that the function is not differentiable at a and b; there is, however, a horizontal tangent line at the point where $x = c$, and c is between a and b.

It is necessary, however, that the function be continuous at the end-points of the interval to guarantee a horizontal tangent line at an interior point. Figure 4.5.3 shows a sketch of the graph of a function that is continuous on the interval $[a, b)$ but discontinuous at b; the function is differentiable on the open interval (a, b), and the function values are zero at both a and b. However, there is no point at which the graph has a horizontal tangent line.

We now state and prove Rolle's theorem.

4.5.1 Theorem
Rolle's Theorem

Let f be a function such that

    (i) it is continuous on the closed interval $[a, b]$;
    (ii) it is differentiable on the open interval (a, b);
    (iii) $f(a) = f(b) = 0$.

Then there is a number c in the open interval (a, b) such that

$$f'(c) = 0$$

PROOF: We consider two cases.

Case 1: $f(x) = 0$ for all x in $[a, b]$.

Then $f'(x) = 0$ for all x in (a, b); therefore, any number between a and b can be taken for c.

Case 2: $f(x)$ is not zero for some value of x in the open interval (a, b).

Because f is continuous on the closed interval $[a, b]$, we know by Theorem 4.3.9 that f has an absolute maximum value on $[a, b]$ and an absolute minimum value on $[a, b]$. Because $f(a) = f(b) = 0$ by hypothesis, and for this case $f(x)$ is not zero for some x in (a, b), we can conclude that f will have either a positive absolute maximum value at some c_1 in (a, b) or a negative absolute minimum value at some c_2 in (a, b), or both. Thus, for $c = c_1$, or $c = c_2$ as the case may be, we have an absolute extremum at an interior point of the interval $[a, b]$. Therefore, the absolute extremum $f(c)$ is also a relative extremum, and because $f'(c)$ exists by hypothesis, it follows from Theorem 4.3.3 that $f'(c) = 0$. This proves the theorem. ■

It should be noted that there may be more than one number in the open interval (a, b) for which the derivative of f is zero. This is illustrated geometrically in Fig. 4.5.4, where there is a horizontal tangent line at the point where $x = c_1$ and also at the point where $x = c_2$, so that both $f'(c_1) = 0$ and $f'(c_2) = 0$.

The converse of Rolle's theorem is not true. That is, we cannot conclude that if a function f is such that $f'(c) = 0$, with $a < c < b$, then the conditions (i), (ii), and (iii) must hold. (See Exercise 40.)

Figure 4.5.4

EXAMPLE 1:   Given

$$f(x) = 4x^3 - 9x$$

verify that conditions (i), (ii), and (iii) of the hypothesis of Rolle's theorem are satisfied for each of the following intervals: $[-\frac{3}{2}, 0]$, $[0, \frac{3}{2}]$, and $[-\frac{3}{2}, \frac{3}{2}]$. Then find a suitable value for c in each of these intervals for which $f'(c) = 0$.

SOLUTION: $f'(x) = 12x^2 - 9$; $f'(x)$ exists for all values of x, and so f is differentiable on $(-\infty, +\infty)$ and therefore continuous on $(-\infty, +\infty)$. Conditions (i) and (ii) of Rolle's theorem thus hold on any interval. To determine on which intervals condition (iii) holds, we find the values of x for which $f(x) = 0$. Setting $f(x) = 0$, we have

$$4x(x^2 - \tfrac{9}{4}) = 0$$

which gives us

$$x = -\tfrac{3}{2} \qquad x = 0 \qquad x = \tfrac{3}{2}$$

Taking $a = -\frac{3}{2}$ and $b = 0$, we see that Rolle's theorem holds on $[-\frac{3}{2}, 0]$. Similarly, Rolle's theorem holds on $[0, \frac{3}{2}]$ and $[-\frac{3}{2}, \frac{3}{2}]$.

To find the suitable values for c, we set $f'(x) = 0$ and get

$$12x^2 - 9 = 0$$

which gives us

$$x = -\tfrac{1}{2}\sqrt{3} \quad \text{and} \quad x = \tfrac{1}{2}\sqrt{3}$$

Therefore, in the interval $[-\frac{3}{2}, 0]$ a suitable choice for c is $-\frac{1}{2}\sqrt{3}$. In the interval $[0, \frac{3}{2}]$, we take $c = \frac{1}{2}\sqrt{3}$. In the interval $[-\frac{3}{2}, \frac{3}{2}]$ there are two possibilities for c: either $-\frac{1}{2}\sqrt{3}$ or $\frac{1}{2}\sqrt{3}$.

We apply Rolle's theorem to prove one of the most important theorems in calculus—that known as the *mean-value theorem* (or law of the mean). The mean-value theorem is used to prove many theorems of both differential and integral calculus. You should become thoroughly familiar with the content of this theorem.

4.5.2 Theorem
Mean-Value Theorem

Let f be a function such that

(i) it is continuous on the closed interval $[a, b]$;
(ii) it is differentiable on the open interval (a, b).

Then there is a number c in the open interval (a, b) such that

$$f'(c) = \frac{f(b) - f(a)}{b - a}$$

Before proving this theorem, we interpret it geometrically. If we draw a sketch of the graph of the function f, then $[f(b) - f(a)]/(b - a)$ is the slope of the line segment joining the points $A(a, f(a))$ and $B(b, f(b))$. The mean-value theorem states that there is some point on the curve between A and B where the tangent line is parallel to the secant line through A and B; that is, there is some number c in (a, b) such that

$$f'(c) = \frac{f(b) - f(a)}{b - a}$$

Refer to Fig. 4.5.5.

Notice that if the x axis were along the line segment AB, then the mean-value theorem is a generalization of Rolle's theorem, which is used in its proof.

Figure 4.5.5

PROOF: An equation of the line through A and B in Fig. 4.5.5 is

$$y - f(a) = \frac{f(b) - f(a)}{b - a} (x - a)$$

or

$$y = \frac{f(b) - f(a)}{b - a} (x - a) + f(a)$$

Now if $F(x)$ measures the vertical distance between a point $(x, f(x))$ on the graph of the function f and the corresponding point on the secant line through A and B, then

$$F(x) = f(x) - \frac{f(b) - f(a)}{b - a} (x - a) - f(a) \tag{1}$$

We show that this function F satisfies the three conditions of the hypothesis of Rolle's theorem.

The function F is continuous on the closed interval $[a, b]$ because it is the sum of f and a linear polynomial, both of which are continuous there. Therefore, condition (i) is satisfied by F. Condition (ii) is satisfied by F because f is differentiable on (a, b). From Eq. (1) we see that $F(a) = 0$ and $F(b) = 0$. Therefore, condition (iii) of Rolle's theorem is satisfied by F.

The conclusion of Rolle's theorem states that there is a c in the open interval (a, b) such that $F'(c) = 0$.

But

$$F'(x) = f'(x) - \frac{f(b) - f(a)}{b - a}$$

Thus

$$F'(c) = f'(c) - \frac{f(b) - f(a)}{b - a}$$

Therefore, there is a number c in (a, b) such that

$$0 = f'(c) - \frac{f(b) - f(a)}{b - a}$$

or, equivalently,

$$f'(c) = \frac{f(b) - f(a)}{b - a}$$

which was to be proved. ∎

EXAMPLE 2: Given

$$f(x) = x^3 - 5x^2 - 3x$$

verify that the hypothesis of the mean-value theorem is satisfied for $a = 1$ and $b = 3$. Then find all numbers c in the open interval $(1, 3)$ such that

$$f'(c) = \frac{f(3) - f(1)}{3 - 1}$$

SOLUTION: Because f is a polynomial function, f is continuous and differentiable for all values of x. Therefore, the hypothesis of the mean-value theorem is satisfied for any a and b.

$$f'(x) = 3x^2 - 10x - 3$$

$$f(1) = -7 \quad \text{and} \quad f(3) = -27$$

Hence,

$$\frac{f(3) - f(1)}{3 - 1} = \frac{-27 - (-7)}{2} = -10$$

Setting $f'(c) = -10$, we obtain

$$3c^2 - 10c - 3 = -10$$

or

$$3c^2 - 10c + 7 = 0$$

or

$$(3c - 7)(c - 1) = 0$$

which gives us

$$c = \tfrac{7}{3} \quad \text{and} \quad c = 1$$

Because 1 is not in the open interval $(1, 3)$, the only possible value for c is $\tfrac{7}{3}$.

EXAMPLE 3: Given

$$f(x) = x^{2/3}$$

draw a sketch of the graph of f. Show that there is no number c in the open interval $(-2, 2)$ such that

SOLUTION: A sketch of the graph of f is shown in Fig. 4.5.6.

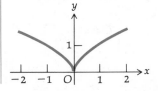

Figure 4.5.6

$$f'(c) = \frac{f(2) - f(-2)}{2 - (-2)}$$

Which condition of the hypothesis of the mean-value theorem fails to hold for f when $a = -2$ and $b = 2$?

So

$$f'(x) = \tfrac{2}{3}x^{-1/3}$$

$$f'(c) = \frac{2}{3c^{1/3}}$$

$$\frac{f(2) - f(-2)}{2 - (-2)} = \frac{4^{1/3} - 4^{1/3}}{4}$$

$$= 0$$

There is no number c for which $2/3c^{1/3} = 0$.

The function f is continuous on the closed interval $[-2, 2]$; however, f is not differentiable on the open interval $(-2, 2)$ because $f'(0)$ does not exist. Therefore, condition (ii) of the hypothesis of the mean-value theorem fails to hold for f when $a = -2$ and $b = 2$.

Exercises 4.5

In Exercises 1 through 4, verify that conditions (i), (ii), and (iii) of the hypothesis of Rolle's theorem are satisfied by the given function on the indicated interval. Then find a suitable value for c that satisfies the conclusion of Rolle's theorem.

1. $f(x) = x^2 - 4x + 3$; $[1, 3]$

2. $f(x) = x^3 - 2x^2 - x + 2$; $[1, 2]$

3. $f(x) = x^3 - 2x^2 - x + 2$; $[-1, 2]$

4. $f(x) = x^3 - 16x$; $[-4, 0]$

5. For the function f defined by $f(x) = 4x^3 + 12x^2 - x - 3$, determine three sets of values for a and b so that conditions (i), (ii), and (iii) of the hypothesis of Rolle's theorem are satisfied. Then find a suitable value for c in each of the three open intervals (a, b) for which $f'(c) = 0$.

In Exercises 6 through 13, verify that the hypothesis of the mean-value theorem is satisfied for the given function on the indicated interval. Then find a suitable value for c that satisfies the conclusion of the mean-value theorem.

6. $f(x) = x^3 + x^2 - x$; $[-2, 1]$

7. $f(x) = x^2 + 2x - 1$; $[0, 1]$

8. $f(x) = x - 1 + \frac{1}{x - 1}$; $[\tfrac{3}{2}, 3]$

9. $f(x) = x^{2/3}$; $[0, 1]$

10. $f(x) = \sqrt{100 - x^2}$; $[-6, 8]$

11. $f(x) = \sqrt{x + 2}$; $[4, 6]$

12. $f(x) = \frac{x^2 + 4x}{x - 7}$; $[2, 6]$

13. $f(x) = \frac{x^2 - 3x - 4}{x + 5}$; $[-1, 4]$

In Exercises 14 through 23, (a) draw a sketch of the graph of the given function on the indicated interval; (b) test the three conditions (i), (ii), and (iii) of the hypothesis of Rolle's theorem and determine which conditions are satisfied and which, if any, are not satisfied; and (c) if the three conditions in part (b) are satisfied, determine a point at which there is a horizontal tangent line.

14. $f(x) = x^{3/4} - 2x^{1/4}$; $[0, 4]$

15. $f(x) = x^{4/3} - 3x^{1/3}$; $[0, 3]$

16. $f(x) = \frac{2x^2 - 5x - 3}{x - 1}$; $[-\tfrac{1}{2}, 3]$

17. $f(x) = \begin{cases} x + 3 & \text{if } x \le 2 \\ 7 - x & \text{if } 2 < x \end{cases}$; $[-3, 7]$

18. $f(x) = \begin{cases} 3x + 6 & \text{if } x < 1 \\ x - 4 & \text{if } 1 \le x \end{cases}$; $[-2, 4]$

19. $f(x) = \frac{x^2 - x - 12}{x - 3}$; $[-3, 4]$

20. $f(x) = \begin{cases} \dfrac{x^2 - 5x + 4}{x - 1} & \text{if } x \neq 1 \\ 0 & \text{if } x = 1 \end{cases}$; $[1, 4]$

21. $f(x) = \begin{cases} x^2 - 4 & \text{if } x < 1 \\ 5x - 8 & \text{if } 1 \leq x \end{cases}$; $[-2, \frac{8}{5}]$

22. $f(x) = 1 - |x|$; $[-1, 1]$

23. $f(x) = |9 - 4x^2|$; $[-\frac{3}{2}, \frac{3}{2}]$

24. If $f(x) = (2x - 1)/(2x - 4)$ and if $a = 1$ and $b = 2$, show that there is no number c in the open interval (a, b) that satisfies the conclusion of the mean-value theorem. Which part of the hypothesis of the mean-value theorem fails to hold? Draw a sketch of the graph of f on $[1, 2]$.

The geometric interpretation of the mean-value theorem is that for a suitable c in the open interval (a, b), the tangent line to the curve $y = f(x)$ at the point $(c, f(c))$ is parallel to the secant line through the points $(a, f(a))$ and $(b, f(b))$. In Exercises 25 through 30, find a value of c satisfying the conclusion of the mean-value theorem, draw a sketch of the graph on the closed interval $[a, b]$, and show the tangent line and secant line.

25. $f(x) = x^2$; $a = 3$, $b = 5$

26. $f(x) = x^2$; $a = 2$, $b = 4$

27. $f(x) = \dfrac{2}{x - 3}$; $a = 3.1$, $b = 3.2$

28. $f(x) = x - 1$; $a = 10$, $b = 26$

29. $f(x) = x^3 - 9x + 1$; $a = -3$, $b = 4$

30. $f(x) = \dfrac{2}{x - 3}$; $a = 3.01$, $b = 3.02$

For each of the functions in Exercises 31 through 34, there is no number c in the open interval (a, b) that satisfies the conclusion of the mean-value theorem. In each exercise, determine which part of the hypothesis of the mean-value theorem fails to hold. Draw a sketch of the graph of $y = f(x)$ and the line through the points $(a, f(a))$ and $(b, f(b))$.

31. $f(x) = \dfrac{4}{(x - 3)^2}$; $a = 1$, $b = 6$

32. $f(x) = \dfrac{2x - 1}{3x - 4}$; $a = 1$, $b = 2$

33. $f(x) = 3(x - 4)^{2/3}$; $a = -4$, $b = 5$

34. $f(x) = \begin{cases} 2x + 3 & \text{if } x < 3 \\ 15 - 2x & \text{if } 3 \leq x \end{cases}$; $a = -1$, $b = 5$

35. If $f(x) = x^4 - 2x^3 + 2x^2 - x$, then $f'(x) = 4x^3 - 6x^2 + 4x - 1$. Prove by Rolle's theorem that the equation $4x^3 - 6x^2 + 4x - 1 = 0$ has at least one real root in the open interval $(0, 1)$.

36. Prove by Rolle's theorem that the equation $x^3 + 2x + c = 0$, where c is any constant, cannot have more than one real root.

37. Use Rolle's theorem to prove that the equation $4x^5 + 3x^3 + 3x - 2 = 0$ has exactly one root that lies in the interval $(0, 1)$. (HINT: First show that there is at least one number in $(0, 1)$ that is a root of the equation. Then assume that there is more than one root of the equation in $(0, 1)$ and show that this leads to a contradiction.)

38. Suppose $s = f(t)$ is an equation of motion of a particle moving in a straight line where f satisfies the hypothesis of the mean-value theorem. Show that the conclusion of the mean-value theorem assures us that there will be some instant during any time interval when the instantaneous velocity will equal the average velocity during that time interval.

39. Suppose that the function f is continuous on $[a, b]$ and $f'(x) = 1$ for all x in (a, b). Prove that $f(x) = x - a + f(a)$ for all x in $[a, b]$.

40. The converse of Rolle's theorem is not true. Make up an example of a function for which the conclusion of Rolle's theorem is true and for which (a) condition (i) is not satisfied but conditions (ii) and (iii) are satisfied; (b) condition (ii) is not satisfied but conditions (i) and (iii) are satisfied; (c) condition (iii) is not satisfied but conditions (i) and (ii) are satisfied. Draw a sketch of the graph showing the horizontal tangent line for each case.

41. Use Rolle's theorem to prove that if every polynomial of the fourth degree has at most four real roots, then every polynomial of the fifth degree has at most five real roots. (HINT: Assume a polynomial of the fifth degree has six real roots and show that this leads to a contradiction.)

42. Use the method of Exercise 41 and mathematical induction to prove that a polynomial of the nth degree has at most n real roots.

**4.6 INCREASING AND
DECREASING FUNCTIONS
AND THE
FIRST-DERIVATIVE TEST**

Suppose that Fig. 4.6.1 represents a sketch of the graph of a function f for all x in the closed interval $[x_1, x_7]$. In drawing this sketch, we have assumed that, for all values of x in this interval, f is defined and that the first and second derivatives of f exist. Then, because f is differentiable for all x in the interval, it follows that f is continuous on the interval. Because the second derivative of f exists for all values of x in the interval, f' is differentiable for all x in the interval, and so f' is continuous on the interval. Therefore, the slope of the tangent line to the curve is a continuous function of x; thus, as a point P moves along the curve so that its abscissa x increases, the tangent line to the curve at P turns continuously.

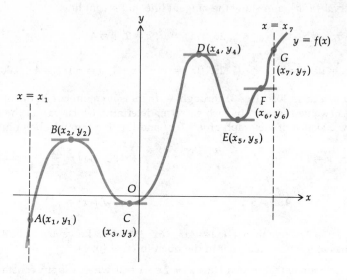

Figure 4.6.1

Figure 4.6.1 shows that as a point moves along the curve from A to B, the function values increase as the abscissa increases, and that as a point moves along the curve from B to C, the function values decrease as the abscissa increases. We say, then, that f is *increasing* on the closed interval $[x_1, x_2]$ and that f is *decreasing* on the closed interval $[x_2, x_3]$. Following are the precise definitions of a function increasing or decreasing on an interval.

4.6.1 Definition

A function f defined on an interval is said to be *increasing* on that interval if and only if

$$f(x_1) < f(x_2) \qquad \text{whenever } x_1 < x_2$$

where x_1 and x_2 are any numbers in the interval.

The function of Fig. 4.6.1 is increasing on the following closed intervals: $[x_1, x_2]$; $[x_3, x_4]$; $[x_5, x_6]$; $[x_6, x_7]$; $[x_5, x_7]$.

4.6.2 Definition   A function f defined on an interval is said to be *decreasing* on that interval if and only if

$$f(x_1) > f(x_2) \qquad \text{whenever } x_1 < x_2$$

where x_1 and x_2 are any numbers in the interval.

The function of Fig. 4.6.1 is decreasing on the following closed intervals: $[x_2, x_3]$; $[x_4, x_5]$.

If a function f is either increasing on an interval or decreasing on an interval, then f is said to be *monotonic* on the interval.

Before stating a theorem that gives a test for determining if a given function is monotonic on an interval, let us see what is happening geometrically. Referring to Fig. 4.6.1, we observe that when the slope of the tangent line is positive the function is increasing, and when the slope of the tangent line is negative the function is decreasing. Because $f'(x)$ is the slope of the tangent line to the curve $y = f(x)$, f is increasing when $f'(x) > 0$, and f is decreasing when $f'(x) < 0$. Also, because $f'(x)$ is the rate of change of the function values $f(x)$ with respect to x, when $f'(x) > 0$, the function values are increasing as x increases; and when $f'(x) < 0$, the function values are decreasing as x increases. We have the following theorem.

4.6.3 Theorem   Let the function f be continuous on the closed interval $[a, b]$ and differentiable on the open interval (a, b):

(i) if $f'(x) > 0$ for all x in (a, b), then f is increasing on $[a, b]$;
(ii) if $f'(x) < 0$ for all x in (a, b), then f is decreasing on $[a, b]$.

PROOF OF (i):   Let x_1 and x_2 be any two numbers in $[a, b]$ such that $x_1 < x_2$. Then f is continuous on $[x_1, x_2]$ and differentiable on (x_1, x_2). From the mean-value theorem it follows that there is some number c in (x_1, x_2) such that

$$f'(c) = \frac{f(x_2) - f(x_1)}{x_2 - x_1}$$

Because $x_1 < x_2$, then $x_2 - x_1 > 0$. Also, $f'(c) > 0$ by hypothesis. Therefore $f(x_2) - f(x_1) > 0$, and so $f(x_2) > f(x_1)$. We have shown, then, that $f(x_1) < f(x_2)$ whenever $x_1 < x_2$, where x_1 and x_2 are any numbers in the interval $[a, b]$. Therefore, by Definition 4.6.1, it follows that f is increasing on $[a, b]$.

The proof of part (ii) is similar and is left for the reader (see Exercise 34).   ∎

An immediate application of Theorem 4.6.3 is in the proof of what is known as the *first-derivative test for relative extrema* of a function.

4.6.4 Theorem
First-Derivative Test for Relative Extrema

Figure 4.6.2

Figure 4.6.3

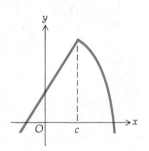

Figure 4.6.4

Let the function f be continuous at all points of the open interval (a, b) containing the number c, and suppose that f' exists at all points of (a, b) except possibly at c:

(i) if $f'(x) > 0$ for all values of x in some open interval having c as its right endpoint, and if $f'(x) < 0$ for all values of x in some open interval having c as its left endpoint, then f has a relative maximum value at c;

(ii) if $f'(x) < 0$ for all values of x in some open interval having c as its right endpoint, and if $f'(x) > 0$ for all values of x in some open interval having c as its left endpoint, then f has a relative minimum value at c.

PROOF OF (i): Let (d, c) be the interval having c as its right endpoint for which $f'(x) > 0$ for all x in the interval. It follows from Theorem 4.6.3(i) that f is increasing on $[d, c]$. Let (c, e) be the interval having c as its left endpoint for which $f'(x) < 0$ for all x in the interval. By Theorem 4.6.3(ii) f is decreasing on $[c, e]$. Because f is increasing on $[d, c]$, it follows from Definition 4.6.1 that if x_1 is in $[d, c]$ and $x_1 \neq c$, then $f(x_1) < f(c)$. Also, because f is decreasing on $[c, e]$, it follows from Definition 4.6.2 that if x_2 is in $[c, e]$ and $x_2 \neq c$, then $f(c) > f(x_2)$. Therefore, from Definition 4.3.1, f has a relative maximum value at c.

The proof of part (ii) is similar to the proof of part (i), and it is left for the reader (see Exercise 35). ■

The first-derivative test for relative extrema essentially states that if f is continuous at c and $f'(x)$ changes algebraic sign from positive to negative as x increases through the number c, then f has a relative maximum value at c; and if $f'(x)$ changes algebraic sign from negative to positive as x increases through c, then f has a relative minimum value at c.

Figures 4.6.2 and 4.6.3 illustrate parts (i) and (ii), respectively, of Theorem 4.6.4 when $f'(c)$ exists. Figure 4.6.4 shows a sketch of the graph of a function f that has a relative maximum value at a number c, but $f'(c)$ does not exist; however, $f'(x) > 0$ when $x < c$, and $f'(x) < 0$ when $x > c$. In Fig. 4.6.5, we show a sketch of the graph of a function f for which c is a critical number, and $f'(x) < 0$ when $x < c$, and $f'(x) < 0$ when $x > c$; f does not have a relative extremum at c.

Further illustrations of Theorem 4.6.4 occur in Fig. 4.6.1. At x_2 and x_4 the function has a relative maximum value, and at x_3 and x_5 the function has a relative minimum value; even though x_6 is a critical number for the function, there is no relative extremum at x_6.

In summary, to determine the relative extrema of a function f:

(1) Find $f'(x)$.
(2) Find the critical numbers of f, that is, the values of x for which

$f'(x) = 0$ or for which $f'(x)$ does not exist.
(3) Apply the first-derivative test (Theorem 4.6.4).

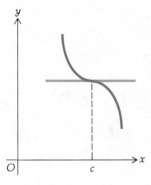

Figure 4.6.5

The following examples illustrate this procedure.

EXAMPLE 1:   Given

$$f(x) = x^3 - 6x^2 + 9x + 1$$

find the relative extrema of f by applying the first-derivative test. Determine the values of x at which the relative extrema occur, as well as the intervals on which f is increasing and the intervals on which f is decreasing. Draw a sketch of the graph.

SOLUTION: $f'(x) = 3x^2 - 12x + 9$.
    $f'(x)$ exists for all values of x. Setting $f'(x) = 0$, we have

$$3x^2 - 12x + 9 = 0$$

or

$$3(x - 3)(x - 1) = 0$$

which gives us

$$x = 3 \quad \text{and} \quad x = 1$$

Thus, the critical numbers of f are 1 and 3. To determine whether f has a relative extremum at either of these numbers, we apply the first-derivative test. The results are summarized in Table 4.6.1.
    We see from the table that 5 is a relative maximum value of f occur-

Table 4.6.1

	$f(x)$	$f'(x)$	Conclusion
$x < 1$		+	f is increasing
$x = 1$	5	0	f has a relative maximum value
$1 < x < 3$		−	f is decreasing
$x = 3$	1	0	f has a relative minimum value
$3 < x$		+	f is increasing

ring at 1, and 1 is a relative minimum value of f occurring at 3. A sketch of the graph is shown in Fig. 4.6.6.

Figure 4.6.6

EXAMPLE 2:   Given

$$f(x) = \begin{cases} x^2 - 4 & \text{if } x < 3 \\ 8 - x & \text{if } 3 \le x \end{cases}$$

find the relative extrema of f by applying the first-derivative test. Determine the values of x at which the relative extrema occur, as well as the intervals on which f is increasing and the intervals on which f is decreasing. Draw a sketch of the graph.

Figure 4.6.7

SOLUTION: If $x < 3$, $f'(x) = 2x$. If $x > 3$, $f'(x) = -1$. Because $f_-'(3) = 6$ and $f_+'(3) = -1$, we conclude that $f'(3)$ does not exist. Therefore, 3 is a critical number of f.

Because $f'(x) = 0$ when $x = 0$, it follows that 0 is a critical number of f. Applying the first-derivative test, we summarize the results in Table 4.6.2. A sketch of the graph is shown in Fig. 4.6.7.

Table 4.6.2

	$f(x)$	$f'(x)$	Conclusion
$x < 0$		$-$	f is decreasing
$x = 0$	-4	0	f has a relative minimum value
$0 < x < 3$		$+$	f is increasing
$x = 3$	5	does not exist	f has a relative maximum value
$3 < x$		$-$	f is decreasing

EXAMPLE 3:   Given

$$f(x) = x^{4/3} + 4x^{1/3}$$

find the relative extrema of f, determine the values of x at

SOLUTION: $f'(x) = \frac{4}{3}x^{1/3} + \frac{4}{3}x^{-2/3} = \frac{4}{3}x^{-2/3}(x + 1)$

Because $f'(x)$ does not exist when $x = 0$, and $f'(x) = 0$ when $x = -1$, the critical numbers of f are -1 and 0. We apply the first-derivative test and summarize the results in Table 4.6.3. A sketch of the graph is shown in Fig. 4.6.8.

which the relative extrema occur, and determine the intervals on which f is increasing and the intervals on which f is decreasing. Draw a sketch of the graph.

Figure 4.6.8

Table 4.6.3

	$f(x)$	$f'(x)$	Conclusion
$x < -1$		$-$	f is decreasing
$x = -1$	-3	0	f has a relative minimum value
$-1 < x < 0$		$+$	f is increasing
$x = 0$	0	does not exist	f does not have a relative extremum at $x = 0$
$0 < x$		$+$	f is increasing

Exercises 4.6

In Exercises 1 through 30, do each of the following: (a) find the relative extrema of f by applying the first-derivative test; (b) determine the values of x at which the relative extrema occur; (c) determine the intervals on which f is increasing; (d) determine the intervals on which f is decreasing; (e) draw a sketch of the graph.

1. $f(x) = x^2 - 4x - 1$

2. $f(x) = x^3 - 9x^2 + 15x - 5$

3. $f(x) = 2x^3 - x^2 + 3x - 1$

4. $f(x) = x^4 + 4x$

5. $f(x) = x^5 - 5x^3 - 20x - 2$

6. $f(x) = 2x + \dfrac{1}{2x}$

7. $f(x) = \sqrt{x} - \dfrac{1}{\sqrt{x}}$

8. $f(x) = \dfrac{x - 2}{x + 2}$

9. $f(x) = 2x\sqrt{3 - x}$

10. $f(x) = x\sqrt{5 - x^2}$

11. $f(x) = (1 - x)^2(1 + x)^3$

12. $f(x) = (x + 2)^2(x - 1)^2$

13. $f(x) = 2 - 3(x - 4)^{2/3}$

14. $f(x) = 2 - (x - 1)^{1/3}$

15. $f(x) = \begin{cases} 2x + 1 & \text{if } x \le 4 \\ 13 - x & \text{if } 4 < x \end{cases}$

16. $f(x) = \begin{cases} 5 - 2x & \text{if } x < 3 \\ 3x - 10 & \text{if } 3 \le x \end{cases}$

17. $f(x) = \begin{cases} 2x + 9 & \text{if } x \le -2 \\ x^2 + 1 & \text{if } -2 < x \end{cases}$

18. $f(x) = \begin{cases} 4 - (x + 5)^2 & \text{if } x < -4 \\ 12 - (x + 1)^2 & \text{if } -4 \le x \end{cases}$

19. $f(x) = \begin{cases} (x - 2)^2 - 3 & \text{if } x \le 5 \\ \frac{1}{2}(x + 7) & \text{if } 5 < x \end{cases}$

20. $f(x) = \begin{cases} \sqrt{25 - (x + 7)^2} & \text{if } x \le -3 \\ 12 - x^2 & \text{if } -3 < x \end{cases}$

21. $f(x) = \begin{cases} 3x + 5 & \text{if } x < -1 \\ x^2 + 1 & \text{if } -1 \le x < 2 \\ 7 - x & \text{if } 2 \le x \end{cases}$

22. $f(x) = \begin{cases} x - 6 & \text{if } x \le 6 \\ -\sqrt{4 - (x - 8)^2} & \text{if } 6 < x \le 10 \\ 20 - 2x & \text{if } 10 < x \end{cases}$

23. $f(x) = \begin{cases} (x + 9)^2 - 8 & \text{if } x < -7 \\ -\sqrt{25 - (x + 4)^2} & \text{if } -7 \le x \le 0 \\ (x - 2)^2 - 7 & \text{if } 0 < x \end{cases}$

24. $f(x) = \begin{cases} 12 - (x + 5)^2 & \text{if } x \le -3 \\ 5 - x & \text{if } -3 < x \le -1 \\ \sqrt{100 - (x - 7)^2} & \text{if } -1 < x \end{cases}$

25. $f(x) = x^{5/4} + 10x^{1/4}$

26. $f(x) = x^{5/3} - 10x^{2/3}$

27. $f(x) = (x + 1)^{2/3}(x - 2)^{1/3}$

28. $f(x) = (4x - a)^{1/3}(2x - a)^{2/3}$

29. $f(x) = x^{1/3}(x + 4)^{-2/3}$

30. $f(x) = (x - a)^{2/5} + 1$

31. Find a and b so that the function defined by $f(x) = x^3 + ax^2 + b$ will have a relative extremum at $(2, 3)$.

32. Find a, b, and c so that the function defined by $f(x) = ax^2 + bx + c$ will have a relative maximum value of 7 at 1 and the graph of $y = f(x)$ will go through the point $(2, -2)$.

33. Find a, b, c, and d so that the function defined by $f(x) = ax^3 + bx^2 + cx + d$ will have relative extrema at $(1, 2)$ and $(2, 3)$.

34. Prove Theorem 4.6.3(ii).   35. Prove Theorem 4.6.4(ii).

36. Given that the function f is continuous for all values of x, $f(3) = 2$, $f'(x) < 0$ if $x < 3$, and $f'(x) > 0$ if $x > 3$, draw a sketch of a possible graph of f in each of the following cases, where the additional condition is satisfied: (a) f' is continuous at 3; (b) $f'(x) = -1$ if $x < 3$, and $f'(x) = 1$ if $x > 3$; (c) $\lim_{x \to 3^-} f'(x) = -1$, $\lim_{x \to 3^+} f'(x) = 1$, and $f'(a) \ne f'(b)$ if $a \ne b$.

37. Given $f(x) = x^p(1 - x)^q$, where p and q are positive integers greater than 1, prove each of the following: (a) if p is even, f has a relative minimum value at 0; (b) if q is even, f has a relative minimum value at 1; (c) f has a relative maximum value at $p/(p + q)$ whether p and q are odd or even.

38. Prove that if f is increasing on $[a, b]$ and if g is increasing on $[f(a), f(b)]$, then if $f \circ g$ exists on $[a, b]$, $f \circ g$ is increasing on $[a, b]$.

39. The function f is increasing on the interval I. Prove: (a) if $g(x) = -f(x)$, then g is decreasing on I; (b) if $h(x) = 1/f(x)$ and $f(x) > 0$ on I, then h is decreasing on I.

40. The function f is differentiable at each number in the closed interval $[a, b]$. Prove that if $f'(a) \cdot f'(b) < 0$, there is a number c in the open interval (a, b) such that $f'(c) = 0$.

4.7 DERIVATIVES OF HIGHER ORDER

If f' is the derivative of the function f, then f' is also a function, and it is the *first derivative* of f. It is sometimes referred to as the *first derived function*. If the derivative of f' exists, it is called the *second derivative* of f, or the second derived function, and can be denoted by f'' (read as "f double prime"). Similarly, we define the *third derivative* of f, or the third derived function, as the first derivative of f'' if it exists. We denote the third derivative of f by f''' (read as "f triple prime").

The nth *derivative* of the function f, where n is a positive integer greater than 1, is the first derivative of the $(n - 1)$st derivative of f. We denote the nth derivative of f by $f^{(n)}$. Thus, if $f^{(n)}$ denotes the nth derived function, we can denote the function f itself by $f^{(0)}$. Another symbol for the nth derivative of f is $D_x^n f$. If the function f is defined by the equation $y = f(x)$, we can denote the nth derivative of f by $D_x^n y$.

EXAMPLE 1:   Find all the derivatives of the function f defined by

$$f(x) = 8x^4 + 5x^3 - x^2 + 7$$

SOLUTION:

$$f'(x) = 32x^3 + 15x^2 - 2x$$

$$f''(x) = 96x^2 + 30x - 2$$

$$f'''(x) = 192x + 30$$

$$f^{(4)}(x) = 192$$

$$f^{(5)}(x) = 0$$

$$f^{(n)}(x) = 0 \qquad n \geq 5$$

Because $f'(x)$ gives the rate of change of $f(x)$ per unit change in x, $f''(x)$, being the derivative of $f'(x)$, gives the rate of change of $f'(x)$ per unit change in x. The second derivative $f''(x)$ is expressed in units of $f'(x)$ per unit of x, which is units of $f(x)$ per unit of x, per unit of x. For example, in straight-line motion, if $f(t)$ feet is the distance of a particle from the origin at t seconds, then $f'(t)$ feet per second is the velocity of the particle at t seconds, and $f''(t)$ feet per second per second is the instantaneous rate of change of the velocity at t seconds. In physics, the instantaneous rate of change of the velocity is called the *instantaneous acceleration*. Therefore, if a particle is moving along a straight line according to the equation of motion $s = f(t)$, where the instantaneous velocity at t sec is given by v ft/sec and the instantaneous acceleration is given by a ft/sec^2, then a is the first derivative of v with respect to t or, equivalently, the second derivative of s with respect to t; that is,

$$v = D_t s \quad \text{and} \quad a = D_t v = D_t^2 s$$

EXAMPLE 2:   A particle is moving along a straight line according to the equation of motion

$$s = \frac{1}{2} t^2 + \frac{4t}{t + 1}$$

where s ft is the directed distance of the particle from the origin at t sec. If v ft/sec is the instantaneous velocity at t sec and a ft/sec^2 is the instantaneous acceleration at t sec, find t, s, and v when $a = 0$.

SOLUTION:

$$v = D_t s = t + \frac{4}{(t + 1)^2}$$

$$a = D_t v = D_t^2 s = 1 - \frac{8}{(t + 1)^3}$$

Setting $a = 0$, we have

$$\frac{(t + 1)^3 - 8}{(t + 1)^3} = 0$$

or

$$(t + 1)^3 = 8$$

from which the only real value of t is obtained from the principal cube root of 8, so that

$$t + 1 = 2 \quad \text{or} \quad t = 1$$

When $t = 1$

$$s = \frac{1}{2}(1)^2 + \frac{4 \cdot 1}{1 + 1} = 2\frac{1}{2}$$

and

$$v = 1 + \frac{4}{(1 + 1)^2} = 2$$

If (x, y) is any point on the graph of $y = f(x)$, then $D_x y$ gives the slope of the tangent line to the graph at the point (x, y). Then $D_x^2 y$ is the rate of change of the slope of the tangent line with respect to x at the point (x, y).

EXAMPLE 3: Let $m(x)$ be the slope of the tangent line to the curve $y = x^3 - 2x^2 + x$ at the point (x, y). Find the instantaneous rate of change of m per unit change in x at the point $(2, 2)$.

SOLUTION: $m = D_x y = 3x^2 - 4x + 1$.

The instantaneous rate of change of m per unit change in x is given by $D_x m$ or, equivalently, $D_x^2 y$.

$$D_x m = D_x^2 y = 6x - 4$$

At the point $(2, 2)$, $D_x^2 y = 8$. Hence, at the point $(2, 2)$, the change in m is 8 times the change in x.

Further applications of the second derivative are its uses in the second-derivative test for relative extrema (Sec. 4.8) and the sketching of the graph of a function (Secs. 4.10 and 4.11). An important application of other higher-ordered derivatives is to determine infinite series as shown in Chapter 14.

The following example illustrates how the second derivative is found for functions defined implicitly.

EXAMPLE 4: Given

$$4x^2 + 9y^2 = 36$$

find $D_x^2 y$ by implicit differentiation.

SOLUTION: Differentiating implicitly with respect to x, we have

$$8x + 18y \cdot D_x y = 0$$

so that

$$D_x y = -\frac{4x}{9y} \tag{1}$$

To find $D_x^2 y$, we find the derivative of a quotient and keep in mind that y is a function of x. So we have

$$D_x^2 y = \frac{9y(-4) - (-4x)(9\,D_x y)}{81y^2} \tag{2}$$

Substituting the value of $D_x y$ from Eq. (1) into Eq. (2), we get

$$D_x^2 y = \frac{-36y + (36x)\dfrac{-4x}{9y}}{81y^2} = \frac{-36y^2 - 16x^2}{81y^3}$$

or

$$D_x{}^2y = \frac{-4(9y^2 + 4x^2)}{81y^3} \tag{3}$$

Because any values of x and y satisfying Eq. (3) must also satisfy the original equation, we can replace $(9y^2 + 4x^2)$ by 36 and obtain

$$D_x{}^2y = \frac{-4(36)}{81y^3} = -\frac{16}{9y^3}$$

Exercises 4.7

In Exercises 1 through 10, find the first and second derivative of the function defined by the given equation.

1. $f(x) = x^5 - 2x^3 + x$

2. $F(x) = 7x^3 - 8x^2$

3. $g(s) = 2s^4 - 4s^3 + 7s - 1$

4. $G(t) = t^3 - t^2 + t$

5. $f(x) = \sqrt{x^2 + 1}$

6. $h(y) = \sqrt[3]{2y^3 + 5}$

7. $F(x) = x^2\sqrt{x} - 5x$

8. $g(r) = \sqrt{r} + \frac{1}{\sqrt{r}}$

9. $G(x) = \frac{1}{\sqrt{3 + 2x^2}}$

10. $f(x) = \frac{2 - \sqrt{x}}{2 + \sqrt{x}}$

11. Find $D_x{}^3y$ if $y = x^4 - 2x^2 + x - 5$.

12. Find $D_t{}^3s$ if $s = \sqrt{4t + 1}$.

13. Find $D_x{}^3f(x)$ if $f(x) = \frac{x}{(1 - x)^2}$.

14. Find $f^{(4)}(x)$ if $f(x) = \frac{2}{x - 1}$.

15. Find $D_x{}^4y$ if $y = x^{7/2} - 2x^{5/2} + x^{1/2}$.

16. Find $D_v{}^3u$ if $u = v\sqrt{v - 2}$.

17. Given $x^3 + y^3 = 1$, show that $D_x{}^2y = \frac{-2x}{y^5}$.

18. Given $x^{1/2} + y^{1/2} = 2$, show that $D_x{}^2y = 1/x^{3/2}$.

19. Given $x^4 + y^4 = a^4$ (a is a constant), find $D_x{}^2y$ in simplest form.

20. Given $b^2x^2 - a^2y^2 = a^2b^2$ (a and b are constants), find $D_x{}^2y$ in simplest form.

21. Find the slope of the tangent line at each point of the graph of $y = x^4 + x^3 - 3x^2$ where the rate of change of the slope is zero.

In Exercises 22 and 23, a particle is moving along a straight line according to the given equation of motion, where s ft is the directed distance of the particle from the origin at t sec. If v ft/sec is the velocity and a ft/sec² is the acceleration of the particle at t sec, find v and a in terms of t. Also find when the velocity is an absolute maximum and the intervals of time when the particle is moving toward the origin and when it is moving away from the origin.

22. $s = t^3 - 9t^2 + 15t$

23. $s = \frac{1}{4}t^4 - 2t^3 + 4t^2$

In Exercises 24 through 27, a particle is moving along a straight line according to the given equation of motion, where s ft is the directed distance of the particle from the origin at t sec. Find the time when the instantaneous acceleration is zero, and then find the directed distance of the particle from the origin and the instantaneous velocity at this instant.

24. $s = 2t^3 - 6t^2 + 3t - 4, t \geq 0$

25. $s = \dfrac{125}{16t + 32} - \dfrac{2}{5} t^5, t \geq 0$

26. $s = 9t^2 + 2\sqrt{2t + 1}, t \geq 0$

27. $s = \frac{4}{9}t^{3/2} + 2t^{1/2}, t \geq 0$

In Exercises 28 through 31, find formulas for $f'(x)$ and $f''(x)$ and state the domains of f' and f''.

28. $f(x) = \begin{cases} \dfrac{x^2}{|x|} & \text{if } x \neq 0 \\ 0 & \text{if } x = 0 \end{cases}$

29. $f(x) = \begin{cases} -x^2 & \text{if } x < 0 \\ x^2 & \text{if } x \geq 0 \end{cases}$

30. $f(x) = |x|^3$

31. $f(x) = \begin{cases} \dfrac{x^5}{|x|} & \text{if } x \neq 0 \\ 0 & \text{if } x = 0 \end{cases}$

32. For the function of Exercise 30 find $f'''(x)$ when it exists.

33. For the function of Exercise 31 find $f'''(x)$ when it exists.

34. Show that if $xy = 1$, then $D_x^2 y \cdot D_y^2 x = 4$.

35. If f', g', f'', and g'' exist and if $h = f \circ g$, express $h''(x)$ in terms of the derivatives of f and g.

36. If f and g are two functions such that their first and second derivatives exist and if h is the function defined by $h(x) = f(x) \cdot g(x)$, prove that

$$h''(x) = f(x) \cdot g''(x) + 2f'(x) \cdot g'(x) + f''(x) \cdot g(x)$$

37. If $y = x^n$, where n is any positive integer, prove by mathematical induction that $D_x^n y = n!$

38. If

$$y = \frac{1}{1 - 2x}$$

prove by mathematical induction that

$$D_x^n y = \frac{2^n n!}{(1 - 2x)^{n+1}}$$

4.8 THE SECOND-DERIVATIVE TEST FOR RELATIVE EXTREMA

In Sec. 4.6 we learned how to determine whether a function f has a relative maximum value or a relative minimum value at a critical number c by checking the algebraic sign of f' at numbers in intervals to the left and right of c. Another test for relative extrema is one that involves only the critical number c, and often it is the easier test to apply. It is called the *second-derivative test for relative extrema*, and it is stated in the following theorem.

4.8.1 Theorem
Second-Derivative Test for Relative Extrema

Let c be a critical number of a function f at which $f'(c) = 0$, and let f' exist for all values of x in some open interval containing c. Then if $f''(c)$ exists and

(i) if $f''(c) < 0$, f has a relative maximum value at c;

(ii) if $f''(c) > 0$, f has a relative minimum value at c.

Figure 4.8.1

PROOF OF (i):   By hypothesis, $f''(c)$ exists and is negative; so we have

$$f''(c) = \lim_{x \to c} \frac{f'(x) - f'(c)}{x - c} < 0$$

Therefore, by Theorem 2.10.4, there is an open interval I containing c such that

$$\frac{f'(x) - f'(c)}{x - c} < 0 \tag{1}$$

for every $x \neq c$ in the interval.

Let I' be the open interval containing all values of x in I for which $x < c$; therefore, c is the right endpoint of the open interval I'. Let I'' be the open interval containing all values of x in I for which $x > c$; so c is the left endpoint of the open interval I''.

Then if x is in I', $(x - c) < 0$, and it follows from inequality (1) that $[f'(x) - f'(c)] > 0$ or, equivalently, $f'(x) > f'(c)$. If x is in I'', $(x - c) > 0$, and it follows from (1) that $[f'(x) - f'(c)] < 0$ or, equivalently, $f'(x) < f'(c)$.

But because $f'(c) = 0$, we conclude that if x is in I', $f'(x) > 0$, and if x is in I'', $f'(x) < 0$. Therefore, $f'(x)$ changes algebraic sign from positive to negative as x increases through c, and so by Theorem 4.6.4, f has a relative maximum value at c.

The proof of part (ii) is similar and is left for the reader (see Exercise 18).   ∎

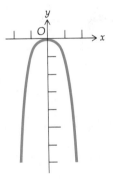

Figure 4.8.2

Note that if $f''(c) = 0$, as well as $f'(c) = 0$, nothing can be concluded regarding a relative extremum of f at c. For example, if $f(x) = x^4$, then $f'(x) = 4x^3$ and $f''(x) = 12x^2$; hence, $f(0)$, $f'(0)$, and $f''(0)$ all have the value zero. In this case, f has a relative minimum value at 0, as can be seen by applying the first-derivative test. If $g(x) = -x^4$, then $g'(x) = -4x^3$ and $g''(x) = -12x^2$; thus, $g(0) = g'(0) = g''(0) = 0$. By applying the first-derivative test, we see that g has a relative maximum value at 0. If $h(x) = x^3$, then $h'(x) = 3x^2$ and $h''(x) = 6x$; so $h(0) = h'(0) = h''(0) = 0$. The function does not have a relative extremum at 0 because if $x < 0$, $h(x) < h(0)$; and if $x > 0$, $h(x) > h(0)$. Here we have examples of three functions, each of which has zero for its second derivative at a number for which its first derivative is zero; yet one function has a relative minimum value at that number, another function has a relative maximum value at that number, and the third function has neither a relative maximum value nor a relative minimum value at that number. Sketches of the graphs of these functions f, g, and h are shown in Figs. 4.8.1, 4.8.2, and 4.8.3, respectively.

Figure 4.8.3

EXAMPLE 1: Given

$$f(x) = x^4 + \tfrac{4}{3}x^3 - 4x^2$$

find the relative maxima and the relative minima of f by applying the second-derivative test.

SOLUTION:

$$f'(x) = 4x^3 + 4x^2 - 8x$$
$$f''(x) = 12x^2 + 8x - 8$$

Setting $f'(x) = 0$, we have

$$4x(x+2)(x-1) = 0$$

which gives

$$x = 0 \qquad x = -2 \qquad x = 1$$

Thus, the critical numbers of f are $-2, 0$, and 1. We determine whether or not there is a relative extremum at any of these critical numbers by finding the sign of the second derivative there. The results are summarized in Table 4.8.1.

Table 4.8.1

	$f(x)$	$f'(x)$	$f''(x)$	Conclusion
$x = -2$	$-\tfrac{32}{3}$	0	$+$	f has a relative minimum value
$x = 0$	0	0	$-$	f has a relative maximum value
$x = 1$	$-\tfrac{5}{3}$	0	$+$	f has a relative minimum value

Exercises 4.8

In Exercises 1 through 14, find the relative extrema of the given function by using the second-derivative test, if it can be applied. If the second-derivative test cannot be applied, use the first-derivative test.

1. $f(x) = 3x^2 - 2x + 1$

2. $g(x) = x^3 - 5x + 6$

3. $f(x) = -4x^3 + 3x^2 + 18x$

4. $h(x) = 2x^3 - 9x^2 + 27$

5. $f(x) = (x-4)^2$

6. $G(x) = (x+2)^3$

7. $G(x) = (x-3)^4$

8. $f(x) = x(x-1)^3$

9. $h(x) = x\sqrt{x+3}$

10. $f(x) = x\sqrt{8-x^2}$

11. $f(x) = 4x^{1/2} + 4x^{-1/2}$

12. $g(x) = \dfrac{9}{x} + \dfrac{x^2}{9}$

13. $F(x) = 6x^{1/3} - x^{2/3}$

14. $G(x) = x^{2/3}(x-4)^2$

15. Given $f(x) = x^3 + 3rx + 5$, prove that (a) if $r > 0$, f has no relative extrema; (b) if $r < 0$, f has both a relative maximum value and a relative minimum value.

16. Given $f(x) = x^r - rx + k$, where $r > 0$ and $r \neq 1$, prove that (a) if $0 < r < 1$, f has a relative maximum value at 1; (b) if $r > 1$, f has a relative minimum value at 1.

17. Given $f(x) = x^2 + rx^{-1}$, prove that regardless of the value of r, f has a relative minimum value and no relative maximum value.

18. Prove Theorem 4.8.1(ii).

4.9 ADDITIONAL PROBLEMS INVOLVING ABSOLUTE EXTREMA

The extreme-value theorem (Theorem 4.3.9) guarantees an absolute maximum value and an absolute minimum value for a function which is continuous on a closed interval. We now consider some functions defined on intervals for which the extreme-value theorem does not apply and which may or may not have absolute extrema.

EXAMPLE 1:   Given

$$f(x) = \frac{x^2 - 27}{x - 6}$$

find the absolute extrema of f on the interval $[0, 6)$ if there are any.

SOLUTION: f is continuous on the interval $[0, 6)$ because the only discontinuity of f is at 6, which is not in the interval.

$$f'(x) = \frac{2x(x - 6) - (x^2 - 27)}{(x - 6)^2} = \frac{x^2 - 12x + 27}{(x - 6)^2} = \frac{(x - 3)(x - 9)}{(x - 6)^2}$$

$f'(x)$ exists for all values of x in $[0, 6)$, and $f'(x) = 0$ when $x = 3$ or 9; so the only critical number of f in the interval $[0, 6)$ is 3. The first-derivative test is applied to determine if f has a relative extremum at 3. The results are summarized in Table 4.9.1.

Table 4.9.1

	$f(x)$	$f'(x)$	Conclusion
$0 \leq x < 3$		$+$	f is increasing
$x = 3$	6	0	f has a relative maximum value
$3 < x < 6$		$-$	f is decreasing

Because f has a relative maximum value at 3, and f is increasing on the interval $[0, 3)$ and decreasing on the interval $(3, 6)$, we conclude that on $[0, 6)$ f has an absolute maximum value at 3, and it is $f(3)$ which is 6. Noting that $\lim_{x \to 6^-} f(x) = -\infty$, we conclude that there is no absolute minimum value of f on $[0, 6)$.

EXAMPLE 2:   Given

$$f(x) = \frac{-x}{(x^2 + 6)^2}$$

find the absolute extrema of f on $[0, +\infty)$ if there are any.

SOLUTION: f is continuous for all values of x.

$$f'(x) = \frac{-1(x^2 + 6)^2 + 4x^2(x^2 + 6)}{(x^2 + 6)^4} = \frac{-(x^2 + 6) + 4x^2}{(x^2 + 6)^3} = \frac{3x^2 - 6}{(x^2 + 6)^3}$$

$f'(x)$ exists for all values of x. Setting $f'(x) = 0$, we obtain $x = \pm\sqrt{2}$; so $\sqrt{2}$ is the only critical number of f in $[0, +\infty)$. The first-derivative test is applied at $\sqrt{2}$, and the results are summarized in Table 4.9.2.

Because f has a relative minimum value at $\sqrt{2}$ and because f is decreasing on $[0, \sqrt{2})$ and increasing on $(\sqrt{2}, +\infty)$, we conclude that f has an absolute minimum value at $\sqrt{2}$ on $[0, +\infty)$. The absolute minimum value is $-\frac{1}{64}\sqrt{2}$. There is no absolute maximum value of f on $[0, +\infty)$.

Table 4.9.2

	$f(x)$	$f'(x)$	Conclusion
$0 \le x < \sqrt{2}$		$-$	f is decreasing
$x = \sqrt{2}$	$-\frac{1}{64}\sqrt{2}$	0	f has a relative minimum value
$\sqrt{2} < x < +\infty$		$+$	f is increasing

EXAMPLE 3:   Find the shortest distance from the point $A(2, \frac{1}{2})$ to a point on the parabola $y = x^2$, and find the point on the parabola that is closest to A.

Figure 4.9.1

SOLUTION: Let $z =$ the number of units in the distance from the point $A(2, \frac{1}{2})$ to a point $P(x, y)$ on the parabola. Refer to Fig. 4.9.1.

$$z = \sqrt{(x-2)^2 + (y - \tfrac{1}{2})^2} \tag{1}$$

Because $P(x, y)$ is on the parabola, its coordinates satisfy the equation $y = x^2$. Substituting this value of y into Eq. (1), we obtain z as a function of x and write

$$z(x) = \sqrt{(x-2)^2 + (x^2 - \tfrac{1}{2})^2}$$

or

$$z(x) = \sqrt{x^4 - 4x + \tfrac{17}{4}} \tag{2}$$

Because P can be any point on the parabola, x is any real number. We wish to find the absolute minimum value of z on $(-\infty, +\infty)$.

$$z'(x) = \tfrac{1}{2}(4x^3 - 4)(x^4 - 4x + \tfrac{17}{4})^{-1/2} = \frac{2(x-1)(x^2 + x + 1)}{\sqrt{x^4 - 4x + \tfrac{17}{4}}}$$

$z'(x)$ exists for all values of x because the denominator is $z(x)$, which is never zero. Consequently, the critical numbers are obtained by setting $z'(x) = 0$. The only real solution is 1; thus, 1 is the only critical number of z. We apply the first-derivative test and summarize the results in Table 4.9.3.

Table 4.9.3

	$z(x)$	$z'(x)$	Conclusion
$-\infty < x < 1$		$-$	z is decreasing
$x = 1$	$\frac{1}{2}\sqrt{5}$	0	z has a relative minimum value
$1 < x < +\infty$		$+$	z is increasing

Because z has a relative minimum value at 1, and because z is decreasing on $(-\infty, 1)$ and increasing on $(1, +\infty)$, we conclude that z has an absolute minimum value of $\frac{1}{2}\sqrt{5}$ at 1. So the point on the parabola closest to A is (1, 1).

We can show that the point $A(2, \frac{1}{2})$ lies on the normal line at (1, 1) of the graph of the parabola. Because the slope of the tangent line at any point (x, y) of the parabola is $2x$, the slope of the tangent line at (1, 1) is 2. Therefore, the slope of the normal line at (1, 1) is $-\frac{1}{2}$, which is the same as the slope of the line through $A(2, \frac{1}{2})$ and (1, 1).

In the next two examples, where the second-derivative test is used to determine the relative extrema, we use the following theorem to determine the absolute extrema.

4.9.1 Theorem   Let the function f be continuous on the interval I containing the number c. If $f(c)$ is the one and only relative extremum of f on I, then $f(c)$ is an absolute extremum of f on I. Furthermore,

(i) if $f(c)$ is a relative maximum value of f on I, then $f(c)$ is an absolute maximum value of f on I;

(ii) if $f(c)$ is a relative minimum value of f on I, then $f(c)$ is an absolute minimum value of f on I.

The proof of this theorem is beyond the scope of this book and can be found in an advanced calculus text.

EXAMPLE 4:   A closed box with a square base is to have a volume of 2000 cubic inches. The material for the top and bottom of the box is to cost $3 per square inch, and the material for the sides is to cost $1.50 per square inch. If the cost of the material is to be the least, find the dimensions of the box.

SOLUTION: Let $x =$ the number of inches in the length of a side of the square base;

$y =$ the number of inches in the depth of the box;

$C =$ the number of dollars in the cost of the material.

The total number of square inches in the combined area of the top and bottom is $2x^2$, and for the sides it is $4xy$; so we have

$$C = 3(2x^2) + \tfrac{3}{2}(4xy) \qquad (3)$$

Because the volume of the box is the product of the area of the base and the depth, we have

$$x^2y = 2000 \qquad (4)$$

Solving Eq. (4) for y in terms of x and substituting into Eq. (3) we get

$$C = 6x^2 + \frac{12{,}000}{x} \qquad (5)$$

x is in the interval $(0, +\infty)$, and C is a function of x, which is continuous on $(0, +\infty)$. From Eq. (5) we obtain

$$D_xC = 12x - \frac{12{,}000}{x^2} \qquad (6)$$

D_xC does not exist when $x = 0$, but 0 is not in $(0, +\infty)$. Hence, the only critical numbers will be those obtained by setting $D_xC = 0$. The only real solution is 10; thus, 10 is the only critical number. To determine if $x = 10$ makes C a relative minimum we apply the second-derivative test. From Eq. (6) it follows that

$$D_x^2C = 12 + \frac{24{,}000}{x^3}$$

The results of the second-derivative test are summarized in Table 4.9.4.

Table 4.9.4

	D_xC	D_x^2C	Conclusion
$x = 10$	0	+	C has a relative minimum value

From Eq. (5) we see that C is a continuous function of x on $(0, +\infty)$. Because the one and only relative extremum of C on $(0, +\infty)$ is at $x = 10$, it follows from Theorem 4.9.1(ii) that this relative minimum value of C is the absolute minimum value of C. Hence, we conclude that the total cost of the material will be the least when the side of the square base is 10 in. and the depth is 20 in.

In the preceding examples and in the exercises of Sec. 4.4, the variable for which we wished to find an absolute extremum was expressed as a function of only one variable. Sometimes this procedure is either too difficult or too laborious, or occasionally even impossible. Often the given information enables us to obtain two equations involving three variables. Instead of eliminating one of the variables, it may be more advantageous to differentiate implicitly. The following example illustrates this method.

EXAMPLE 5: If a closed tin can of specific volume is to be in the form of a right-circular cylinder, find the ratio of the height to the base radius if the least amount of material is to be used in its manufacture.

SOLUTION: We wish to find a relationship between the height and the base radius of the right-circular cylinder in order for the total surface area to be an absolute minimum for a fixed volume. Therefore, we consider the volume of the cylinder a constant.

Let $V =$ the number of cubic units in the volume of a cylinder (a constant).

We now define the variables:

$r =$ the number of units in the base radius of the cylinder; $0 < r < +\infty$;

$h =$ the number of units in the height of the cylinder; $0 < h < +\infty$;

$S =$ the number of square units in the total surface area of the cylinder.

We have the following equations:

$$S = 2\pi r^2 + 2\pi rh \tag{7}$$

$$V = \pi r^2 h \tag{8}$$

Because V is a constant, we could solve Eq. (8) for either r or h in terms of the other and substitute into Eq. (7), which will give us S as a function of one variable. The alternative method is to consider S as a function of two variables r and h; however, r and h are not independent of each other. That is, if we choose r as the independent variable, then S depends on r; also, h depends on r.

Differentiating S and V with respect to r and bearing in mind that h is a function of r, we have

$$D_r S = 4\pi r + 2\pi h + 2\pi r \, D_r h \tag{9}$$

and

$$D_r V = 2\pi r h + \pi r^2 \, D_r h \tag{10}$$

Because V is a constant, $D_r V = 0$; therefore, from Eq. (10) we have

$$2\pi r h + \pi r^2 \, D_r h = 0$$

with $r \neq 0$, and we can divide by r and solve for $D_r h$, thus obtaining

$$D_r h = -\frac{2h}{r} \tag{11}$$

Substituting from Eq. (11) into Eq. (9), we obtain

$$D_r S = 2\pi \left[2r + h + r \left(-\frac{2h}{r} \right) \right]$$

or

$$D_r S = 2\pi (2r - h) \tag{12}$$

To find when S has a relative minimum value, we set $D_r S = 0$ and obtain $2r - h = 0$, which gives us

$$r = \tfrac{1}{2}h$$

To determine if this relationship between r and h makes S a relative minimum, we apply the second-derivative test. From Eq. (12) we find that

$$D_r^2 S = 2\pi (2 - D_r h) \tag{13}$$

Substituting from Eq. (11) into (13), we get

$$D_r^2 S = 2\pi \left[2 - \left(\frac{-2h}{r} \right) \right] = 2\pi \left(2 + \frac{2h}{r} \right)$$

The results of the second-derivative test are summarized in Table 4.9.5.

Table 4.9.5

	$D_r S$	$D_r^2 S$	Conclusion
$r = \tfrac{1}{2}h$	0	+	S has a relative minimum value

From Eqs. (7) and (8) we see that S is a continuous function of r on $(0, +\infty)$. Because the one and only relative extremum of S on $(0, +\infty)$ is at $r = \frac{1}{2}h$, we conclude from Theorem 4.9.1(ii) that S has an absolute minimum value at $r = \frac{1}{2}h$. Therefore, the total surface area of the tin can will be least for a specific volume when the ratio of the height to the base radius is 2.

Exercises 4.9

In Exercises 1 through 8 find the absolute extrema of the given function on the given interval if there are any.

1. $f(x) = x^2$; $(-3, 2]$

2. $g(x) = x^3 + 2x^2 - 4x + 1$; $(-3, 2)$

3. $F(x) = \dfrac{x+2}{x-2}$; $[-4, 4]$

4. $f(x) = \dfrac{x^2}{x+3}$; $[-4, -1]$

5. $g(x) = 4x^2 - 2x + 1$; $(-\infty, +\infty)$

6. $G(x) = (x-5)^{2/3}$; $(-\infty, +\infty)$

7. $f(x) = \dfrac{x}{(x^2+4)^{3/2}}$; $[0, +\infty)$

8. $f(x) = \dfrac{x^2 - 30}{x - 4}$; $(-\infty, 4)$

9. A rectangular field, having an area of 2700 yd², is to be enclosed by a fence, and an additional fence is to be used to divide the field down the middle. If the cost of the fence down the middle is $2 per running yard, and the fence along the sides costs $3 per running yard, find the dimensions of the field so that the cost of the fencing will be the least.

10. A rectangular open tank is to have a square base, and its volume is to be 125 yd³. The cost per square yard for the bottom is $8 and for the sides is $4. Find the dimensions of the tank in order for the cost of the material to be the least.

11. A box manufacturer is to produce a closed box of specific volume whose base is a rectangle having a length that is three times its width. Find the most economical dimensions.

12. Solve Exercise 11 if the box is to have an open top.

13. A funnel of specific volume is to be in the shape of a right-circular cone. Find the ratio of the height to the base radius if the least amount of material is to be used in its manufacture.

14. A Norman window consists of a rectangle surmounted by a semicircle. Find the shape of such a window that will admit the most light for a given perimeter.

15. Solve Exercise 14 if the window is such that the semicircle transmits only half as much light per square unit of area as the rectangle.

16. The strength of a rectangular beam is proportional to the breadth and the square of its depth. Find the dimensions of the strongest beam that can be cut from a log in the shape of a right-circular cylinder of radius a in.

17. The stiffness of a rectangular beam is proportional to the breadth and the cube of its depth. What is the shape of the stiffest beam that can be cut from a log in the shape of a right-circular cylinder?

18. A page of print is to contain 24 in.² of printed area, a margin of $1\frac{1}{2}$ in. at the top and bottom, and a margin of 1 in. at the sides. What are the dimensions of the smallest page that would fill these requirements?

19. A one-story building having a rectangular floor space of 13,200 ft² is to be constructed where a 22-ft easement is required in the front and back and a 15-ft easement is required on each side. Find the dimensions of the lot having the least area on which this building can be located.

20. Find the point on the curve $y^2 - x^2 = 1$ that is closest to the point $(2, 0)$.

21. A direct current generator has an electromotive force of E volts and an internal resistance of r ohms. E and r are constants. If R ohms is the external resistance, the total resistance is $(r + R)$ ohms and if P watts is the power, then

$$P = \frac{E^2 R}{(r + R)^2}$$

What external resistance will consume the most power?

22. A right-circular cone is to be inscribed in a sphere of given radius. Find the ratio of the altitude to the base radius of the cone of largest possible volume.

23. A right-circular cone is to be circumscribed about a sphere of given radius. Find the ratio of the altitude to the base radius of the cone of least possible volume.

24. Prove by the method of this section that the shortest distance from the point $P_1(x_1, y_1)$ to the line l, having the equation $Ax + By + C = 0$, is $|Ax_1 + By_1 + C|/\sqrt{A^2 + B^2}$. (HINT: If s is the number of units from P_1 to a point $P(x, y)$ on l, then s will be an absolute minimum when s^2 is an absolute minimum.)

4.10 CONCAVITY AND POINTS OF INFLECTION

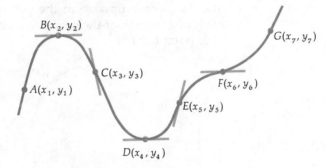

Figure 4.10.1

Figure 4.10.1 shows a sketch of the graph of a function f whose first and second derivatives exist on the closed interval $[x_1, x_7]$. Because both f and f' are differentiable there, f and f' are continuous on $[x_1, x_7]$.

If we consider a point P moving along the graph of Fig. 4.10.1 from A to G, then the position of P varies as we increase x from x_1 to x_7. As P moves along the graph from A to B, the slope of the tangent line to the graph is positive and is decreasing; that is, the tangent line is turning clockwise, and the graph lies below the tangent line. When the point P is at B, the slope of the tangent line is zero and is still decreasing. As P moves along the graph from B to C, the slope of the tangent line is negative and is still decreasing; the tangent line is still turning clockwise, and the graph is below its tangent line. We say that the graph is *concave downward* from A to C. As P moves along the graph from C to D, the slope of the tangent line is negative and is increasing; that is, the tangent line is turning counterclockwise, and the graph is above its tangent line. At D, the slope of the tangent line is zero and is still increasing. From D to E, the slope of the tangent line is positive and increasing; the tangent line is still turning counterclockwise, and the graph is above its tangent line.

We say that the graph is *concave upward* from C to E. At the point C, the graph changes from concave downward to concave upward. Point C is called a *point of inflection*. We have the following definitions.

4.10.1 Definition   The graph of a function f is said to be *concave upward* at the point $(c, f(c))$ if $f'(c)$ exists and if there is an open interval I containing c such that for all values of $x \neq c$ in I the point $(x, f(x))$ on the graph is above the tangent line to the graph at $(c, f(c))$.

4.10.2 Definition   The graph of a function f is said to be *concave downward* at the point $(c, f(c))$ if $f'(c)$ exists and if there is an open interval I containing c such that for all values of $x \neq c$ in I the point $(x, f(x))$ on the graph is below the tangent line to the graph at $(c, f(c))$.

Figure 4.10.2 shows a sketch of a portion of the graph of a function f that is concave upward at the point $(c, f(c))$, and Fig. 4.10.3 shows a sketch of a portion of the graph of a function f that is concave downward at the point $(c, f(c))$.

Figure 4.10.2   Figure 4.10.3

The graph of the function f of Fig. 4.10.1 is concave downward at all points $(x, f(x))$ for which x is in either of the following open intervals: (x_1, x_3) or (x_5, x_6). Similarly, the graph of the function f in Fig. 4.10.1 is concave upward at all points $(x, f(x))$ for which x is in either (x_3, x_5) or (x_6, x_7). The following theorem gives a test for concavity.

4.10.3 Theorem   Let f be a function which is differentiable on some open interval containing c. Then

(i) if $f''(c) > 0$, the graph of f is concave upward at $(c, f(c))$;
(ii) if $f''(c) < 0$, the graph of f is concave downward at $(c, f(c))$.

PROOF OF (i):

$$f''(c) = \lim_{x \to c} \frac{f'(x) - f'(c)}{x - c}$$

Because $f''(c) > 0$,

$$\lim_{x \to c} \frac{f'(x) - f'(c)}{x - c} > 0$$

Then, by Theorem 2.10.3, there is an open interval I containing c such that

$$\frac{f'(x) - f'(c)}{x - c} > 0 \qquad (1)$$

for every $x \neq c$ in I.

Now consider the tangent line to the graph of f at the point $(c, f(c))$. An equation of this tangent line is

$$y - f(c) = f'(c)(x - c)$$

or

$$y = f(c) + f'(c)(x - c) \qquad (2)$$

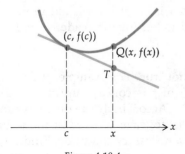

Let x be a number in the interval I such that $x \neq c$, and let Q be the point on the graph of f whose abscissa is x. Through Q draw a line parallel to the y axis, and let T be the point of intersection of this line with the tangent line (see Fig. 4.10.4).

Figure 4.10.4

To prove that the graph of f is concave upward at $(c, f(c))$, we must show that the point Q is above the point T or, equivalently, that the directed distance $\overline{TQ} > 0$ for all values of $x \neq c$ in I. $\overline{TQ}$ equals the ordinate of Q minus the ordinate of T. The ordinate of Q is $f(x)$, and the ordinate of T is obtained from Eq. (2); so we have

$$\overline{TQ} = f(x) - [f(c) + f'(c)(x - c)]$$

or

$$\overline{TQ} = [f(x) - f(c)] - f'(c)(x - c) \qquad (3)$$

From the mean-value theorem there exists some number d between x and c such that

$$f'(d) = \frac{f(x) - f(c)}{x - c}$$

or

$$f(x) - f(c) = f'(d)(x - c) \qquad \text{for some } d \text{ between } x \text{ and } c \qquad (4)$$

Substituting from Eq. (4) into (3), we have

$$\overline{TQ} = f'(d)(x - c) - f'(c)(x - c)$$

or

$$\overline{TQ} = (x - c)[f'(d) - f'(c)] \qquad (5)$$

Because d is between x and c, d is in the interval I, and so by taking $x = d$ in inequality (1), we obtain

$$\frac{f'(d) - f'(c)}{d - c} > 0 \qquad (6)$$

To prove that $\overline{TQ} > 0$, we show that both of the factors on the right side of Eq. (5) have the same sign. If $(x - c) > 0$, then $x > c$. And because d is between x and c, then $d > c$; therefore, from inequality (6), $[f'(d) - f'(c)] > 0$. If $(x - c) < 0$, then $x < c$, and so $d < c$; therefore, from (6), $[f'(d) - f'(c)] < 0$. We conclude that $(x - c)$ and $[f'(d) - f'(c)]$ have the same sign; therefore, $\overline{TQ}$ is a positive number. Thus, the graph of f is concave upward at $(c, f(c))$, which is what we wished to prove.

The proof of part (ii) is similar and is left for the reader (see Exercise 27). ∎

The converse of Theorem 4.10.3 is not true. For example, if f is the function defined by $f(x) = x^4$, the graph of f is concave upward at the point $(0, 0)$ but $f''(0) = 0$ (see Fig. 4.8.1). Accordingly, a sufficient condition for the graph of a function f to be concave upward at the point $(c, f(c))$ is that $f''(c) > 0$, but this is not a necessary condition. Similarly, a sufficient—but not a necessary—condition that the graph of a function f be concave downward at the point $(c, f(c))$ is that $f''(c) < 0$.

If there is a point on the graph of a function at which the sense of concavity changes, then the graph crosses its tangent line at this point, as shown in Figs. 4.10.5, 4.10.6, and 4.10.7. Such a point is called a *point of inflection*.

4.10.4 Definition The point $(c, f(c))$ is a *point of inflection* of the graph of the function f if the graph has a tangent line there, and if there exists an open interval I containing c such that if x is in I, then either

(i) $f''(x) < 0$ if $x < c$ and $f''(x) > 0$ if $x > c$; or
(ii) $f''(x) > 0$ if $x < c$ and $f''(x) < 0$ if $x > c$

Figure 4.10.5 illustrates a point of inflection where condition (i) of the above definition holds; in this case, the graph is concave downward at points immediately to the left of the point of inflection, and the graph is concave upward at points immediately to the right of the point of inflection. Condition (ii) is illustrated in Fig. 4.10.6, where the sense of concavity changes from upward to downward at the point of inflection. Figure 4.10.7 is another illustration of condition (i), where the sense of

Figure 4.10.5

Figure 4.10.6   *Figure 4.10.7*

concavity changes from downward to upward at the point of inflection. Note that in Fig. 4.10.7 there is a horizontal tangent line at the point of inflection. For the graph in Fig. 4.10.1 there are points of inflection at C, E, and F.

Definition 4.10.4 indicates nothing about the value of the second derivative of f at a point of inflection. The following theorem states that if the second derivative exists at a point of inflection, it must be zero there.

4.10.5 Theorem   If the function f is differentiable on some open interval containing c, and if $(c, f(c))$ is a point of inflection of the graph of f, then if $f''(c)$ exists, $f''(c) = 0$.

PROOF: Let g be the function such that $g(x) = f'(x)$; then $g'(x) = f''(x)$. Because $(c, f(c))$ is a point of inflection of the graph of f, then $f''(x)$ changes sign at c and so $g'(x)$ changes sign at c. Therefore, by the first-derivative test (Theorem 4.6.4), g has a relative extremum at c, and c is a critical number of g. Because $g'(c) = f''(c)$ and since by hypothesis $f''(c)$ exists, it follows that $g'(c)$ exists. Therefore, by Theorem 4.3.3 $g'(c) = 0$ and $f''(c) = 0$, which is what we wanted to prove.   ∎

The converse of Theorem 4.10.5 is not true. That is, if the second derivative of a function is zero at a number c, it is not necessarily true that the graph of the function has a point of inflection at the point where $x = c$. This can be shown by again considering the function f defined by $f(x) = x^4$. $f'(x) = 4x^3$ and $f''(x) = 12x^2$. Further, $f''(0) = 0$; but because $f''(x) > 0$ if $x < 0$ and $f''(x) > 0$ if $x > 0$, the graph is concave upward at points on the graph immediately to the left of $(0, 0)$ and at points immediately to the right of $(0, 0)$. Consequently, $(0, 0)$ is not a point of inflection. We showed previously that this function f has a relative minimum value at zero and that the graph is concave upward at the point $(0, 0)$ (see Fig. 4.8.1).

The graph of a function may have a point of inflection at a point, and the second derivative may fail to exist there. For example, if f is the function defined by $f(x) = x^{1/3}$, then

$$f'(x) = \tfrac{1}{3}x^{-2/3} \quad \text{and} \quad f''(x) = -\tfrac{2}{9}x^{-5/3}$$

$f''(0)$ does not exist; but if $x < 0$, $f''(x) > 0$, and if $x > 0$, $f''(x) < 0$. Hence, f has a point of inflection at $(0, 0)$. A sketch of the graph of this function is shown in Fig. 4.10.8. Note that for this function $f'(0)$ also fails to exist. The tangent line to the graph at $(0, 0)$ is the y axis.

In drawing a sketch of a graph having points of inflection, it is helpful to draw a segment of the tangent line at a point of inflection. Such a tangent line is called an *inflectional tangent*.

Figure 4.10.8

EXAMPLE 1:   For the function in Example 1 of Sec. 4.6, find the points of inflection of the graph of the function, and determine where the graph is concave upward and where it is concave downward.

SOLUTION:

$$f(x) = x^3 - 6x^2 + 9x + 1$$

$$f'(x) = 3x^2 - 12x + 9$$

$$f''(x) = 6x - 12$$

$f''(x)$ exists for all values of x; so the only possible point of inflection is where $f''(x) = 0$, which occurs at $x = 2$. To determine whether there is a point of inflection at $x = 2$, we must check to see if $f''(x)$ changes sign; at the same time, we determine the concavity of the graph for the respective intervals. The results are summarized in Table 4.10.1.

Table 4.10.1

	$f(x)$	$f'(x)$	$f''(x)$	Conclusion
$-\infty < x < 2$			$-$	graph is concave downward
$x = 2$	3	-3	0	graph has a point of inflection
$2 < x < +\infty$			$+$	graph is concave upward

In Example 1 of Sec. 4.6 we showed that f has a relative maximum value at 1 and a relative minimum value at 3. A sketch of the graph showing a segment of the inflectional tangent is shown in Fig. 4.10.9.

Figure 4.10.9

EXAMPLE 2:   If $f(x) = (1 - 2x)^3$, find the points of inflection of the graph of f and determine where the graph is concave upward and where it is concave downward.

SOLUTION:

$$f'(x) = -6(1 - 2x)^2$$

$$f''(x) = 24(1 - 2x)$$

Because $f''(x)$ exists for all values of x, the only possible point of inflection is where $f''(x) = 0$, that is, at $x = \frac{1}{2}$. By using the results summarized in Table 4.10.2, we see that $f''(x)$ changes sign from "+" to "−" at $x = \frac{1}{2}$, and so the graph has a point of inflection there. Note also that because $f'(\frac{1}{2}) = 0$, the graph has a horizontal tangent line at the point of inflection. A sketch of the graph is shown in Fig. 4.10.10.

Table 4.10.2

	$f(x)$	$f'(x)$	$f''(x)$	Conclusion
$-\infty < x < \frac{1}{2}$			$+$	graph is concave upward
$x = \frac{1}{2}$	0	0	0	graph has a point of inflection
$\frac{1}{2} < x < +\infty$			$-$	graph is concave downward

Figure 4.10.10

Exercises 4.10

In Exercises 1 through 10 determine where the graph of the given function is concave upward, where it is concave downward, and find the points of inflection if there are any.

1. $f(x) = x^3 + 9x$

2. $g(x) = x^3 + 3x^2 - 3x - 3$

3. $F(x) = x^4 - 8x^3 + 24x^2$

4. $f(x) = 16x^4 + 32x^3 + 24x^2 - 5x - 20$

5. $g(x) = \dfrac{x}{x^2 - 1}$

6. $G(x) = \dfrac{2x}{(x^2 + 4)^{3/2}}$

7. $f(x) = (x - 2)^{1/5}$

8. $F(x) = (2x - 6)^{3/2} + 1$

9. $f(x) = \begin{cases} x^2 & \text{if } x < 0 \\ -x^2 & \text{if } x \geq 0 \end{cases}$

10. $f(x) = \begin{cases} x^2 & \text{if } x < 1 \\ x^3 - 4x^2 + 7x - 3 & \text{if } x \geq 1 \end{cases}$

11. If $f(x) = ax^3 + bx^2$, determine a and b so that the graph of f will have a point of inflection at $(1, 2)$.

12. If $f(x) = ax^3 + bx^2 + cx$, determine a, b, and c so that the graph of f will have a point of inflection at $(1, 2)$ and so that the slope of the inflectional tangent there will be -2.

13. If $f(x) = ax^3 + bx^2 + cx + d$, determine a, b, c, and d so that f will have a relative extremum at $(0, 3)$ and so that the graph of f will have a point of inflection at $(1, -1)$.

14. If $f(x) = ax^4 + bx^3 + cx^2 + dx + e$, determine the values of a, b, c, d, and e so the graph of f will have a point of inflection at $(1, -1)$, have the origin on it, and be symmetric with respect to the y axis.

In Exercises 15 through 24, draw a sketch of a portion of the graph of the function f through the point where $x = c$ if the given conditions are satisfied. If the conditions are incomplete or inconsistent, explain. It is assumed that f is continuous on some open interval containing c.

15. $f'(x) > 0$ if $x < c$; $f'(x) < 0$ if $x > c$; $f''(x) > 0$ if $x < c$; $f''(x) > 0$ if $x > c$.

16. $f'(x) > 0$ if $x < c$; $f'(x) > 0$ if $x > c$; $f''(x) > 0$ if $x < c$; $f''(x) < 0$ if $x > c$.

17. $f''(c) = 0$; $f'(c) = 0$; $f''(x) > 0$ if $x < c$; $f''(x) > 0$ if $x > c$.

18. $f'(c) = 0$; $f'(x) > 0$ if $x < c$; $f''(x) > 0$ if $x > c$.

19. $f'(c) = 0$; $f'(x) < 0$ if $x < c$; $f''(x) > 0$ if $x > c$.

20. $f''(c) = 0$; $f'(c) = \frac{1}{2}$; $f''(x) > 0$ if $x < c$; $f''(x) < 0$ if $x > c$.

21. $f'(c)$ does not exist; $f''(x) > 0$ if $x < c$; $f''(x) > 0$ if $x > c$.

22. $f'(c)$ does not exist; $f''(c)$ does not exist; $f''(x) < 0$ if $x < c$; $f''(x) > 0$ if $x > c$.

23. $\lim\limits_{x \to c^-} f'(x) = +\infty$; $\lim\limits_{x \to c^+} f'(x) = 0$; $f''(x) > 0$ if $x < c$; $f''(x) < 0$ if $x > c$.

24. $\lim\limits_{x \to c^-} f'(x) = +\infty$; $\lim\limits_{x \to c^+} f'(x) = -\infty$; $f''(x) > 0$ if $x < c$; $f''(x) > 0$ if $x > c$.

25. Draw a sketch of the graph of a function f for which $f(x)$, $f'(x)$, and $f''(x)$ exist and are positive for all x.

26. If $f(x) = 3x^2 + x|x|$, prove that $f''(0)$ does not exist but the graph of f is concave upward everywhere.

27. Prove Theorem 4.10.3(ii).

28. Suppose that f is a function for which $f''(x)$ exists for all values of x in some open interval I and that at a number c in I, $f''(c) = 0$ and $f'''(c)$ exists and is not zero. Prove that the point $(c, f(c))$ is a point of inflection of the graph of f. (HINT: The proof is similar to the proof of the second-derivative test (Theorem 8.7.1).)

4.11 APPLICATIONS TO DRAWING A SKETCH OF THE GRAPH OF A FUNCTION

We now apply the discussions in Secs. 4.6, 4.8, and 4.10 to drawing a sketch of the graph of a function. If we are given $f(x)$ and wish to draw a sketch of the graph of f, we proceed as follows. First, find $f'(x)$ and $f''(x)$. Then the critical numbers of f are the values of x in the domain of f for which either $f'(x)$ does not exist or $f'(x) = 0$. Next, apply the first-derivative test (Theorem 4.6.4) or the second-derivative test (Theorem 4.8.1) to determine whether we have at a critical number a relative maximum value, a relative minimum value, or neither. To determine the intervals on which f is increasing, we find the values of x for which $f'(x)$ is positive; to determine the intervals on which f is decreasing, we find the values of x for which $f'(x)$ is negative. In determining the intervals on which f is monotonic, we also check the critical numbers at which f does not have a relative extremum. The values of x for which $f''(x) = 0$ or $f''(x)$ does not exist give us the possible points of inflection, and we check to see if $f''(x)$ changes sign at each of these values of x to determine whether we actually have a point of inflection. The values of x for which $f''(x)$ is positive and those for which $f''(x)$ is negative will give us points at which the graph is concave upward and points at which the graph is concave downward. It is also helpful to find the slope of each inflectional tangent. It is suggested that all the information so obtained be incorporated into a table, as illustrated in the following examples.

EXAMPLE 1:   Given

$$f(x) = x^3 - 3x^2 + 3$$

find: the relative extrema of f; the points of inflection of the graph of f; the intervals on which f is increasing; the intervals on which f is decreasing; where the graph is concave upward; where the graph is concave downward; and the slope of any inflectional tangent. Draw a sketch of the graph.

SOLUTION: $f'(x) = 3x^2 - 6x$; $f''(x) = 6x - 6$. Setting $f'(x) = 0$, we obtain $x = 0$ and $x = 2$. Setting $f''(x) = 0$, we obtain $x = 1$. In making the table, we consider the points at which $x = 0$, $x = 1$, and $x = 2$, and the intervals excluding these values of x:

$$-\infty < x < 0 \qquad 0 < x < 1 \qquad 1 < x < 2 \qquad 2 < x < +\infty$$

Using the information in Table 4.11.1 and plotting a few points, we obtain the sketch of the graph shown in Fig. 4.11.1.

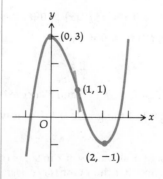

Figure 4.11.1

Table 4.11.1

	$f(x)$	$f'(x)$	$f''(x)$	Conclusion
$-\infty < x < 0$		+	−	f is increasing; graph is concave downward
$x = 0$	3	0	−	f has a relative maximum value; graph is concave downward
$0 < x < 1$		−	−	f is decreasing; graph is concave downward
$x = 1$	1	−3	0	f is decreasing; graph has a point of inflection
$1 < x < 2$		−	+	f is decreasing; graph is concave upward
$x = 2$	−1	0	+	f has a relative minimum value; graph is concave upward
$2 < x < +\infty$		+	+	f is increasing; graph is concave upward

EXAMPLE 2: Given

$$f(x) = 5x^{2/3} - x^{5/3}$$

find: the relative extrema of f; the points of inflection of the graph of f; the intervals on which f is increasing; the intervals on which f is decreasing; where the graph is concave upward; where the graph is concave downward; and the slope of any inflectional tangent. Draw a sketch of the graph.

SOLUTION:

$$f'(x) = \tfrac{10}{3}x^{-1/3} - \tfrac{5}{3}x^{2/3} \quad \text{and} \quad f''(x) = -\tfrac{10}{9}x^{-4/3} - \tfrac{10}{9}x^{-1/3}$$

$f'(x)$ does not exist when $x = 0$. Setting $f'(x) = 0$, we obtain $x = 2$. Therefore, the critical numbers of f are 0 and 2. $f''(x)$ does not exist when $x = 0$.

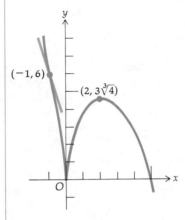

$(-1, 6)$

$(2, 3\sqrt[3]{4})$

Figure 4.11.2

Setting $f''(x) = 0$, we obtain $x = -1$. In making the table, we consider the points at which $x = -1$, $x = 0$, and $x = 2$, and the following intervals:

$$-\infty < x < -1 \quad -1 < x < 0 \quad 0 < x < 2 \quad 2 < x < +\infty$$

A sketch of the graph, drawn from the information in Table 4.11.2 and by plotting a few points, is shown in Fig. 4.11.2.

Table 4.11.2

	$f(x)$	$f'(x)$	$f''(x)$	Conclusion
$-\infty < x < -1$		$-$	$+$	f is decreasing; graph is concave upward
$x = -1$	6	-5	0	f is decreasing; graph has a point of inflection
$-1 < x < 0$		$-$	$-$	f is decreasing; graph is concave downward
$x = 0$	0	does not exist	does not exist	f has a relative minimum value
$0 < x < 2$		$+$	$-$	f is increasing; graph is concave downward
$x = 2$	$3\sqrt[3]{4} \approx 4.8$	0	$-$	f has a relative maximum value; graph is concave downward
$2 < x < +\infty$		$-$	$-$	f is decreasing; graph is concave downward

Exercises 4.11

For each of the following functions find: the relative extrema of f; the points of inflection of the graph of f; the intervals on which f is increasing; the intervals on which f is decreasing; where the graph is concave upward; where the graph is concave downward; the slope of any inflectional tangent. Draw a sketch of the graph.

1. $f(x) = 2x^3 - 6x + 1$

2. $f(x) = x^3 + x^2 - 5x$

3. $f(x) = x^4 - 2x^3$

4. $f(x) = 3x^4 + 2x^3$

5. $f(x) = x^3 + 5x^2 + 3x - 4$

6. $f(x) = 2x^3 - \frac{1}{2}x^2 - 12x + 1$

7. $f(x) = x^4 - 3x^3 + 3x^2 + 1$

8. $f(x) = x^4 - 4x^3 + 16x$

9. $f(x) = \frac{1}{4}x^4 - \frac{1}{3}x^3 - x^2 + 1$

10. $f(x) = 3x^4 + 4x^3 + 6x^2 - 4$

11. $f(x) = \begin{cases} x^2 & \text{if } x < 0 \\ 2x^2 & \text{if } x \geq 0 \end{cases}$

12. $f(x) = \begin{cases} -x^3 & \text{if } x < 0 \\ x^3 & \text{if } x \geq 0 \end{cases}$

13. $f(x) = \begin{cases} -x^4 & \text{if } x < 0 \\ x^4 & \text{if } x \geq 0 \end{cases}$

14. $f(x) = \begin{cases} 2(x-1)^3 & \text{if } x < 1 \\ (x-1)^4 & \text{if } x \geq 1 \end{cases}$

15. $f(x) = (x+1)^3(x-2)^2$

16. $f(x) = x^2(x+4)^3$

17. $f(x) = 3x^5 + 5x^4$

18. $f(x) = 3x^5 + 5x^3$

19. $f(x) = 3x^{2/3} - 2x$

20. $f(x) = 3x^{1/3} - x$

21. $f(x) = x^{1/3} + 2x^{4/3}$

22. $f(x) = 3x^{4/3} - 4x$

23. $f(x) = 2 + (x-3)^{1/3}$

24. $f(x) = 2 + (x-3)^{4/3}$

25. $f(x) = 2 + (x-3)^{5/3}$

26. $f(x) = 2 + (x-3)^{2/3}$

27. $f(x) = 3 + (x+1)^{6/5}$

28. $f(x) = 3 + (x+1)^{7/5}$

29. $f(x) = x^2\sqrt{4-x}$

30. $f(x) = x\sqrt{9-x^2}$

31. $f(x) = \dfrac{(x+1)^2}{x^2+1}$

32. $f(x) = \dfrac{9x}{x^2+9}$

33. $f(x) = (x+2)\sqrt{-x}$

34. $f(x) = \dfrac{x-1}{x^2-2x+2}$

4.12 AN APPLICATION OF THE DERIVATIVE IN ECONOMICS

In economics the variation of one quantity with respect to another can be described by either an *average* concept or a *marginal* concept. The average concept expresses the variation of one quantity over a specified range of values of a second quantity, whereas the marginal concept is the instantaneous change in the first quantity that results from a very small unit change in the second quantity. For example, in our discussion of rectilinear motion (Sec. 3.2) we considered both an average concept and a marginal concept. The average velocity in traveling a distance of s miles in t hours is s/t mi/hr, whereas the instantaneous velocity is a marginal concept as it gives the rate of change of s with respect to a small unit change in t at a particular instant of time. We begin our examples in economics with the definitions of average cost and marginal cost. It should be clear that to define a marginal concept precisely we must use the notion of a limit, and this will lead to the derivative.

Suppose that $C(x)$ dollars is the total cost of producing x units of a commodity. The function C is called a *total cost function*. In normal circumstances, x and $C(x)$ are nonnegative. If zero is in the domain of C, $C(0)$ is called the *overhead* cost of production. Note that since x represents the number of units of a commodity, x must be a nonnegative integer. However, to apply the calculus we assume that x is a nonnegative real number (and then round off any noninteger values of x to the nearest integer), thus giving us the continuity requirements for the function C.

The *average cost* of producing each unit of a commodity is obtained by dividing the total cost by the number of units produced. Letting $Q(x)$ be the number of dollars in the average cost, we have

$$Q(x) = \frac{C(x)}{x}$$

and Q is called an *average cost function*.

Now, let us suppose that the number of units in a particular output is x_1 and this is changed by Δx. Then the change in the total cost is given by $C(x_1 + \Delta x) - C(x_1)$, and the average change in the total cost with respect to the change in the number of units produced is given by

$$\frac{C(x_1 + \Delta x) - C(x_1)}{\Delta x} \tag{1}$$

Economists use the term *marginal cost* for the limit of the quotient in (1) as Δx approaches zero, provided the limit exists. Being the derivative of C at x_1, this limit gives us the following definition.

4.12.1 Definition   If $C(x)$ is the number of dollars in the total cost of producing x units of a commodity, then the *marginal cost*, when $x = x_1$, is given by $C'(x_1)$ if it exists. The function C' is called the *marginal cost function*.

In the above definition, $C'(x_1)$ can be interpreted as the rate of change of the total cost per unit change in the quantity produced, when x_1 units are produced.

EXAMPLE 1: Suppose that $C(x)$ is the number of dollars in the total cost of producing x picture frames $(x \geq 10)$ and

$$C(x) = 15 + 8x + \frac{50}{x}$$

Find: (a) the marginal cost function; (b) the marginal cost when $x = 50$; (c) the cost of producing the fifty-first frame.

SOLUTION: (a) $C'(x) = 8 - \dfrac{50}{x^2}$

(b) $C'(50) = 8 - \dfrac{50}{50^2} = 8 - 0.02 = 7.98$

(c) The number of dollars in the cost of producing the fifty-first frame is $C(51) - C(50) = 423.9804 - 416 = 7.9804$.

Note that the answers in parts (b) and (c) differ by 0.0004. This discrepancy occurs because the marginal cost is the instantaneous rate of change of $C(x)$ with respect to a unit change in x. Hence $C'(50)$ is the approximate number of dollars in the cost of producing the fifty-first frame.

Reasoning similar to that preceding Definition 4.12.1 leads to the following definition.

4.12.2 Definition   If $Q(x)$ is the number of dollars in the average cost of producing one unit of x units of a commodity, then the *marginal average cost*, when $x = x_1$, is given by $Q'(x_1)$ if it exists, and Q' is called the *marginal average cost function*.

The graphs of the total cost function, the marginal cost function, and the average cost function are called the *total cost curve* (labeled TC), the *marginal cost curve* (labeled MC), and the *average cost curve* (labeled AC), respectively. $Q'(x_1)$ gives the slope of the tangent line to the average cost curve at the point where $x = x_1$.

Consider now a linear total cost function.

$$C(x) = mx + b$$

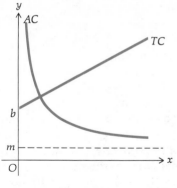

Figure 4.12.1

Note that b represents the overhead cost (the total cost when $x = 0$). The marginal cost is given by $C'(x) = m$. If Q is the average cost function, $Q(x) = m + b/x$, and the marginal average cost is given by $Q'(x) = -b/x^2$.

Refer to Fig. 4.12.1 for sketches of the total cost curve and the average cost curve. The total cost curve is a segment of a straight line in the first quadrant having slope m and y-intercept b. The average cost curve is a branch of an equilateral hyperbola in the first quadrant having as horizontal asymptote the line $y = m$. Because $Q'(x)$ is always negative, the average cost function is always decreasing, and as x increases, the value of $Q(x)$ gets closer and closer to m.

Now suppose that we have a quadratic total cost function

$$C(x) = ax^2 + bx + c$$

where a and c are positive. Here c is the number of dollars in the overhead cost. The total cost curve is a parabola opening upward. Because $C'(x) = 2ax + b$, a critical number of C is $-b/2a$. We distinguish two cases: $b \geq 0$ and $b < 0$.

Case 1: $b \geq 0$. $-b/2a$ is then either negative or zero, and the vertex of the parabola is either to the left of the y axis or on the y axis. Hence, the domain of C is the set of all nonnegative numbers. A sketch of TC for which $b > 0$ is shown in Fig. 4.12.2.

Case 2: $b < 0$. $-b/2a$ is positive; thus, the vertex of the parabola is to the right of the y axis, and the domain of C is restricted to numbers in the interval $[-b/2a, +\infty)$. A sketch of TC for which $b < 0$ is shown in Fig. 4.12.3.

Figure 4.12.2

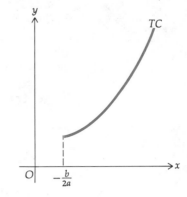

Figure 4.12.3

EXAMPLE 2: Suppose that $C(x)$ dollars is the total cost of producing $100x$ units of a commodity and $C(x) = \frac{1}{2}x^2 - 2x + 5$. Find the function giving (a) the average

SOLUTION:

(a) If Q is the average cost function,

$$Q(x) = \frac{1}{2}x - 2 + \frac{5}{x}$$

cost; (b) the marginal cost; (c) the marginal average cost. (d) Find the absolute minimum average unit cost. (e) Draw sketches of the total cost curve, the average cost curve, and the marginal cost curve on the same set of axes.

Figure 4.12.4

(b) The marginal cost function is C', and

$$C'(x) = x - 2$$

(c) Q' is the marginal average cost function, and

$$Q'(x) = \frac{1}{2} - \frac{5}{x^2}$$

(d) Setting $Q'(x) = 0$, we obtain $\sqrt{10}$ as a critical number of Q, and $Q(\sqrt{10}) = \sqrt{10} - 2 \approx 1.16$. Because $Q''(x) = 10/x^3$, $Q''(\sqrt{10}) > 0$, and so Q has a relative minimum value of approximately 1.16 at $x = \sqrt{10}$. From the equation defining $Q(x)$ we see that Q is continuous on $(0, +\infty)$. Because the only relative extremum of Q on $(0, +\infty)$ is at $x = \sqrt{10}$, it follows from Theorem 4.9.1(ii) that Q has an absolute minimum value there. When $x = \sqrt{10} \approx 3.16$, $100x = 316$, and so we conclude that the absolute minimum average unit cost is \$1.16 when 316 units are produced.

The sketches of the curves TC, AC, and MC are shown in Fig. 4.12.4.

In Fig. 4.12.4 note that the lowest point on curve AC occurs at the point of intersection of the curves AC and MC, and this is the point where the marginal average cost is zero. This is true in general and it follows from the fact that the value of x which causes the marginal average cost to be zero is a critical number of the function Q. That is, since $Q(x) = C(x)/x$,

$$Q'(x) = \frac{xC'(x) - C(x)}{x^2}$$

and so $Q'(x) = 0$ when $xC'(x) - C(x) = 0$ or, equivalently, when

$$C'(x) = \frac{C(x)}{x}$$

You should note the economic significance that when the marginal cost and the average cost are equal, the commodity is being produced at the very lowest average unit cost.

In normal circumstances, when the number of units of the commodity produced is large, the marginal cost will be eventually increasing or zero; hence, $C''(x) \geq 0$ for x greater than some positive number N. So unless $C''(x) = 0$, the graph of the total cost function is concave upward for $x > N$. However, the marginal cost may decrease for some values of x; hence, for these values of x, $C''(x) < 0$, and therefore the graph of the total cost function will be concave downward for these values of x. The following example involving a cubic cost function illustrates the case in which the concavity of the graph of the total cost function changes.

EXAMPLE 3: Draw a sketch of the graph of the total cost function C for which

$$C(x) = x^3 - 6x^2 + 13x + 1$$

Determine where the graph is concave upward and where it is concave downward. Find any points of inflection and an equation of any inflectional tangent. Draw a segment of the inflectional tangent.

Figure 4.12.5

SOLUTION:
$$C'(x) = 3x^2 - 12x + 13$$
$$C''(x) = 6x - 12$$
$C'(x)$ can be written as $3(x-2)^2 + 1$. Hence, $C'(x)$ is never zero. $C''(x) = 0$ when $x = 2$. To determine the concavity of the graph for the intervals $(0, 2)$ and $(2, +\infty)$ and if the graph has a point of inflection at $x = 2$, we use the results summarized in Table 4.12.1.

Table 4.12.1

	$C(x)$	$C'(x)$	$C''(x)$	Conclusion
$0 < x < 2$			$-$	graph is concave downward
$x = 2$	11	1	0	graph has a point of inflection
$2 < x < +\infty$			$+$	graph is concave upward

An equation of the inflectional tangent is $x - y + 9 = 0$. A sketch of the graph of the total cost function together with a segment of the inflectional tangent is shown in Fig. 4.12.5.

Consider now an economic situation in which the variables are the price and quantity of the commodity demanded. Let p dollars be the price of one unit of the commodity and x be the number of units of the commodity. Upon reflection, it should seem reasonable that the amount of the commodity demanded in the marketplace by consumers depends on the price of the commodity. As the price falls, consumers generally demand more of the commodity. Should the price rise, the opposite occurs. Consumers demand less. Thus, if p_1 and p_2 are the number of dollars in the prices of x_1 and x_2 units, respectively, of a commodity, then

$$p_1 > p_2 \quad \text{if and only if} \quad x_1 < x_2 \tag{1}$$

An equation giving the relationship between the amount, given by

x, of a commodity demanded and the price, given by p, is called a *demand equation*. If the equation is solved for p, we have

$$p = P(x)$$

The function P is called the *price function* and $P(x)$ is the number of dollars in the unit price for which x units of the commodity are demanded at that price. Because of statement (1), P is a decreasing function. In a normal economic situation, x and $P(x)$ are nonnegative numbers. Even though x should be an integer (because x is the number of units of a commodity) we assume only that x is a real number in order that P may be a continuous function so that we can apply the calculus.

Another function important in economics is the *total revenue function*, which we denote by R, and

$$R(x) = xP(x)$$

where $P(x)$ dollars is the price of each unit and x is the number of units sold. When $x \neq 0$, from the above equation we obtain

$$\frac{R(x)}{x} = P(x)$$

which shows that the revenue per unit (the average revenue) and the price per unit are equal.

4.12.3 Definition   If $R(x)$ is the number of dollars in the total revenue obtained when x units of a commodity are demanded, then the *marginal revenue*, when $x = x_1$, is given by $R'(x_1)$, if it exists. The function R' is called the *marginal revenue function*.

$R'(x_1)$ can be positive, negative, or zero, and it can be interpreted as the rate of change of the total revenue per unit change in the demand when x_1 units are demanded. The graphs of the functions R and R' are called the *total revenue curve* (labeled TR) and the *marginal revenue curve* (labeled MR), respectively. The graph of the demand equation is called the *demand curve*.

EXAMPLE 4:   The demand equation for a particular commodity is $p^2 + x - 12 = 0$. Find the price function, the total revenue function, and the marginal revenue function. Draw sketches of the demand curve, the total revenue curve, and the marginal revenue curve on the same set of axes.

SOLUTION: If the demand equation is solved for p, we find $p = \pm\sqrt{12 - x}$. Since $P(x) \geq 0$, we have

$$P(x) = \sqrt{12 - x}$$
$$R(x) = x\sqrt{12 - x}$$
$$R'(x) = \frac{24 - 3x}{2\sqrt{12 - x}}$$

Setting $R'(x) = 0$, we obtain $x = 8$. Using the information in Table 4.12.2, we see that the required sketches are drawn as shown in Fig. 4.12.6.

Table 4.12.2

x	$P(x)$	$R(x)$	$R'(x)$
0	$\sqrt{12}$	0	$\sqrt{12}$
3	3	9	$\frac{5}{2}$
8	2	16	0
11	1	11	$-\frac{9}{2}$
12	0	0	does not exist

Figure 4.12.6

We have seen that for a given demand equation the amount demanded by the consumer depends only on the price of the commodity. Under a *monopoly* (which means that there is only one producer of a certain commodity), price and, hence, demand can be controlled by regulating the quantity of the commodity produced. The producer under a monopoly is called a *monopolist*, and he wishes to control the quantity produced and, hence, the price per unit so that the profit will be as large as possible.

The *profit* earned by a business is the difference between the total revenue and the total cost. That is, if $S(x)$ dollars is the profit obtained by producing x units of a commodity, then

$$S(x) = R(x) - C(x) \qquad (2)$$

where $R(x)$ dollars is the total revenue and $C(x)$ dollars is the total cost. S is called the *profit function*. From Eq. (2), if we differentiate with respect to x, we obtain

$$S'(x) = R'(x) - C'(x) \qquad (3)$$

and

$$S''(x) = R''(x) - C''(x) \qquad (4)$$

It follows from Eq. (3) that $S'(x) > 0$ if and only if $R'(x) > C'(x)$; therefore, the profit is increasing if and only if the marginal revenue is greater than the marginal cost. Let us determine what level of production is necessary to obtain the greatest profit. S has a relative maximum function value at a number x for which $S'(x) = 0$ and $S''(x) < 0$. From Eqs. (3) and (4) we observe that this will occur at a value of x for which the marginal

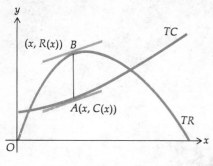

Figure 4.12.7

revenue equals the marginal cost and $R''(x) < C''(x)$. The values of x will be restricted to a closed interval, in which the left endpoint is 0 (since $x \geq 0$) and the right endpoint (the largest permissible value of x) is determined from the demand equation. At each of the endpoints there will be no profit, and so the absolute maximum value of S occurs at a value of x where S has a relative maximum value.

To illustrate this geometrically, refer to Fig. 4.12.7 where both the total revenue curve and the total cost curve are drawn on the same set of axes. The vertical distance between the two curves for a particular value of x is $S(x)$, which gives the profit corresponding to that value of x. When this vertical distance is largest, $S(x)$ is an absolute maximum. This is the distance $\overline{AB}$ in the figure where A and B are the points on the two curves where the tangent lines are parallel, and hence $C'(x) = R'(x)$.

EXAMPLE 5: Suppose that the demand equation for a certain commodity is $p = 4 - 0.0002x$, where x is the number of units produced each week and p dollars is the price of each unit. The number of dollars in the total cost of producing x units is $600 + 3x$. If the weekly profit is to be as large as possible, find: (a) the number of units that should be produced each week; (b) the price of each unit; (c) the weekly profit.

SOLUTION: The price function is given by $P(x) = 4 - 0.0002x$, and x is in the closed interval $[0, 20{,}000]$ because x and $P(x)$ must be nonnegative. $R(x) = xP(x)$, and so

$$R(x) = 4x - 0.0002x^2 \qquad x \text{ in } [0, 20{,}000] \tag{5}$$

The cost function is given by

$$C(x) = 600 + 3x \tag{6}$$

If $S(x)$ dollars is the profit, $S(x) = R(x) - C(x)$, and so

$$S(x) = x - 0.0002x^2 - 600 \qquad x \text{ in } [0, 20{,}000]$$

From Eqs. (5) and (6) we obtain

$$R'(x) = 4 - 0.0004x$$

and

$$C'(x) = 3$$

Also, $R''(x) = -0.004$ and $C''(x) = 0$. Equating $R'(x)$ and $C'(x)$ we get

$$4 - 0.0004x = 3$$

$$x = 2500$$

Because $R''(x)$ is always less than $C''(x)$, $S''(x) = R''(x) - C''(x) < 0$, and so we conclude that $S(2500)$ is an absolute maximum value. (Note that $S(x)$ is negative for $x = 0$ and $x = 20{,}000$.) $P(2500) = 3.50$ and $S(2500) = 650$.

Therefore, to have the greatest weekly profit, 2500 units should be produced each week to be sold at \$3.50 each for a total profit of \$650.

EXAMPLE 6: Solve Example 5 if a tax of 20 cents is levied by the

SOLUTION: With the added tax, the total cost function is now given by

$$C(x) = (600 + 3x) + 0.20x$$

government on the monopolist for each unit produced.

and so the marginal cost function is given by

$$C'(x) = 3.20$$

Equating $R'(x)$ and $C'(x)$, we get

$$4 - 0.0004x = 3.20$$

$$x = 2000$$

As in Example 5 it follows that when $x = 2000$, S has an absolute maximum value on $[0, 20,000]$. From $P(x) = 4 - 0.0002x$ and $S(x) = 0.8x - 0.0002x^2 - 600$, we have $P(2000) = 3.60$ and $S(2000) = 200$.

Therefore, if the tax of 20 cents per unit is levied, only 2000 units should be produced each week to be sold at $3.60 in order to attain a maximum total weekly profit of $200.

It is interesting to note that in comparing the results of Examples 5 and 6, the entire 20 cents rise should not be passed on to the consumer to achieve the greatest weekly profit. That is, it is most profitable to raise the unit price by only 10 cents. The economic significance of this result is that consumers are sensitive to price changes, which prohibits the monopolist from passing on the tax completely to the consumer.

A further note of interest in the two examples is how the fixed costs of a company do not affect the determination of the number of units to be produced or the unit price such that maximum profit is obtained. The *fixed cost* of a company is the cost that does not change as the company's output changes. Regardless of whether anything is produced, the fixed cost must be met. In Examples 5 and 6, because $C(x) = 600 + 3x$ and $600 + 3.2x$, respectively, the fixed cost is $600. If the 600 in the expressions for $C(x)$ is replaced by any constant k, $C'(x)$ is not affected; hence, the value of x for which the marginal cost equals the marginal revenue is not affected by any such change. Of course, a change in fixed cost affects the unit cost and hence the actual profit; however, if a company is to have the greatest profit possible, a change in its fixed cost will not affect the number of units to be produced nor the price per unit.

Exercises 4.12

1. The number of dollars in the total cost of manufacturing x watches in a certain plant is given by $C(x) = 1500 + 30x + 20/x$. Find (a) the marginal cost function, (b) the marginal cost when $x = 40$, and (c) the cost of manufacturing the forty-first watch.

2. If $C(x)$ dollars is the total cost of manufacturing x toys and $C(x) = 110 + 4x + 0.02x^2$, find (a) the marginal cost function, (b) the marginal cost when $x = 10$, and (c) the cost of manufacturing the eleventh toy.

3. Suppose a liquid is produced by a certain chemical process and the total cost function C is given by $C(x) = 6 + 4\sqrt{x}$, where $C(x)$ dollars is the total cost of producing x gallons of the liquid. Find (a) the marginal cost when 16 gal are produced and (b) the number of gallons produced when the marginal cost is 40 cents per gal.

4. The number of dollars in the total cost of producing x units of a certain commodity is $C(x) = 40 + 3x + 9\sqrt{2x}$. Find (a) the marginal cost when 50 units are produced and (b) the number of units produced when the marginal cost is $4.50.

5. The number of dollars in the total cost of producing x units of a commodity is $C(x) = x^2 + 4x + 8$. Find the function giving (a) the average cost, (b) the marginal cost, and (c) the marginal average cost. (d) Find the absolute minimum average unit cost. (e) Draw sketches of the total cost, average cost, and marginal cost curves on the same set of axes. Verify that the average cost and marginal cost are equal when the average cost has its least value.

6. If $C(x)$ dollars is the total cost of producing x units of a commodity and $C(x) = 3x^2 - 6x + 4$, find (a) the average cost function, (b) the marginal cost function, and (c) the marginal average cost function. (d) What is the range of C? (e) Find the absolute minimum average unit cost. (f) Draw sketches of the total cost, average cost, and marginal cost curves on the same set of axes. Verify that the average cost and marginal cost are equal when the average cost has its least value.

7. The total cost function C is given by $C(x) = \frac{1}{3}x^3 - 2x^2 + 5x + 2$. (a) Determine the range of C. (b) Find the marginal cost function. (c) Find the interval on which the marginal cost function is decreasing and the interval on which it is increasing. (d) Draw a sketch of the graph of the total cost function; determine where the graph is concave upward and where it is concave downward, and find the points of inflection and an equation of any inflectional tangent.

8. If $C(x)$ dollars is the total cost of producing x units of a commodity and $C(x) = 2x^2 - 8x + 18$, find (a) the domain and range of C, (b) the average cost function, (c) the absolute minimum average unit cost, and (d) the marginal cost function. (e) Draw sketches of the total cost, average cost, and marginal cost curves on the same set of axes.

9. The fixed overhead expense of a manufacturer of children's toys is $400 per week, and other costs amount to $3 for each toy produced. Find (a) the total cost function, (b) the average cost function, and (c) the marginal cost function. (d) Show that there is no absolute minimum average unit cost. (e) What is the smallest number of toys that must be produced so that the average cost per toy is less than $3.42? (f) Draw sketches of the graphs of the functions in (a), (b), and (c) on the same set of axes.

10. The number of hundreds of dollars in the total cost of producing $100x$ radios per day in a certain factory is $C(x) = 4x + 5$. Find (a) the average cost function, (b) the marginal cost function, and (c) the marginal average cost function. (d) Show that there is no absolute minimum average unit cost. (e) What is the smallest number of radios that the factory must produce in a day so that the average cost per radio is less than $7? (f) Draw sketches of the total cost, average cost, and marginal cost curves on the same set of axes.

11. If the demand equation for a particular commodity is $3x + 4p = 12$, find (a) the price function, (b) the total revenue function, and (c) the marginal revenue function. Draw sketches of the demand, total revenue, and marginal revenue curves on the same set of axes. Verify that the marginal revenue curve intersects the x axis at the point whose abscissa is the value of x for which the total revenue is greatest and that the demand curve intersects the x axis at the point whose abscissa is twice that.

12. The demand equation for a particular commodity is $px^2 + 9p - 18 = 0$ where p dollars is the price per unit when $100x$ units are demanded. Find (a) the price function, (b) the total revenue function, and (c) the marginal revenue function. (d) Find the absolute maximum total revenue.

13. Follow the instructions of Exercise 12 if the demand equation is $x^2 + p^2 - 36 = 0$.

14. Let $R(x)$ dollars be the total revenue obtained when x units of a commodity are demanded and $R(x) = 2 + 3\sqrt{x - 1}$, where x is in the closed interval $[2, 17]$. Find (a) the demand equation, (b) the price function, and (c) the marginal revenue function. (d) Find the absolute maximum total revenue. (e) Draw sketches of the demand, total revenue, and marginal revenue curves on the same set of axes.

15. The demand equation for a certain commodity is $x + p = 14$, where x is the number of units produced daily and p is the number of hundreds of dollars in the price of each unit. The number of hundreds of dollars in the total cost of producing x units is given by $C(x) = x^2 - 2x + 2$, and x is in the closed interval $[1, 14]$. (a) Find the profit function and draw a sketch of its graph. (b) On a set of axes different from that in (a), draw sketches of the total revenue and total cost curves and show the geometrical interpretation of the profit function. (c) Find the maximum daily profit. (d) Find

the marginal revenue and marginal cost functions. (e) Draw sketches of the graphs of the marginal revenue and margi-nal cost functions on the same set of axes and show that they intersect at the point for which the value of x makes the profit a maximum.

16. Follow the instructions of Exercise 15 if the demand equation is $x^2 + p = 32$ and $C(x) = 5x$.

17. The demand equation for a certain commodity is $p = (x - 8)^2$, and the total cost function is given by $C(x) = 18x - x^2$, where $C(x)$ dollars is the total cost when x units are purchased. (a) Determine the permissible values of x. (b) Find the marginal revenue and marginal cost functions. (c) Find the value of x which yields the maximum profit. (d) Draw sketches of the marginal revenue and marginal cost functions on the same set of axes.

18. A monopolist determines that if $C(x)$ cents is the total cost of producing x units of a certain commodity, then $C(x) = 25x + 20,000$. The demand equation is $x + 50p = 5000$, where x units are demanded each week when the unit price is p cents. If the weekly profit is to be maximized, find (a) the number of units that should be produced each week, (b) the price of each unit, and (c) the weekly profit.

19. Solve Exercise 18 if the government levies a tax on the monopolist of 10 cents per unit produced.

20. Solve Exercise 18 if the government imposes a 10% tax based upon the consumer's price.

21. For the monopolist of Exercise 18, determine the amount of tax that should be levied by the government on each unit produced in order for the tax revenue received by the government to be maximized.

22. Find the maximum tax revenue that can be received by the government if an additive tax for each unit produced is levied on a monopolist for which the demand equation is $x + 3p = 75$, where x units are demanded when p dollars is the price of one unit, and $C(x) = 3x + 100$, where $C(x)$ dollars is the total cost of producing x units.

23. The demand equation for a certain commodity produced by a monopolist is $p = a - bx$, and the total cost, $C(x)$ dollars, of producing x units is determined by $C(x) = c + dx$, where $a, b, c,$ and d are positive constants. If the government levies a tax on the monopolist of t dollars per unit produced, show that in order for the monopolist to maximize his profits he should pass on to the consumer only one-half of the tax; that is, he should increase his unit price by $\frac{1}{2}t$ dollars.

Review Exercises (Chapter 4)

1. Given $f(x) = |9 - x^2|$. Find the absolute extrema of f on the interval $[-2, 3]$.

2. Given $f(x) = x^4 - 12x^2 + 36$. Find the absolute extrema of f on the interval (a) $[-2, 6]$ and (b) $[0, 5]$.

3. Two towns A and B are to get their water supply from the same pumping station to be located on the bank of a straight river that is 15 mi from town A and 10 mi from town B. If the points on the river nearest to A and B are 20 mi apart and A and B are on the same side of the river, where should the pumping station be located so that the least amount of piping is required?

4. Find the shortest distance from the point $(\frac{9}{2}, 0)$ to the curve $y = \sqrt{x}$.

5. A ship leaves a port at 12 noon and travels due west at 20 knots. At 12 noon the next day, a second ship leaves the same port and travels northwest at 15 knots. How fast are the two ships separating when the second ship has traveled 90 nautical miles?

6. The demand in a certain market for a particular kind of breakfast cereal is given by the demand equation $px + 25p - 2000 = 0$, where p cents is the price of one box and x thousands of boxes is the quantity demanded per week. If the current price of the cereal is 40 cents per box and the price per box is increasing at the rate of 0.2 cents each week, find the rate of change in the demand.

7. A particle is moving in a straight line according to the equation of motion $s = \sqrt{a + bt^2}$, where a and b are positive constants. Prove that the measure of the acceleration of the particle is inversely proportional to s^3 for any t.

8. As the last car of a train passes under a bridge, an automobile crosses the bridge on a roadway perpendicular to the track and 30 ft above it. The train is traveling at the rate of 80 ft/sec and the automobile is traveling at the rate of 40 ft/sec. How fast are the train and the automobile separating after 2 sec?

9. A manufacturer offers to deliver to a dealer 300 tables at $90 per table and to reduce the price per table on the entire order by 25 cents for each additional table over 300. Find the dollar total involved in the largest possible transaction between the manufacturer and the dealer under these circumstances.

10. A particle is moving along the curve $x^2 - y^2 = 9$, and the ordinate of the point of its position is increasing at the rate of 3 units per second. How fast is the abscissa changing at the point $(5, -4)$?

11. A funnel in the form of a cone is 10 in. across the top and 8 in. deep. Water is flowing into the funnel at the rate of 12 in.^{3}/sec, and out at the rate of 4 in.^{3}/sec. How fast is the surface of the water rising when it is 5 in. deep?

12. Prove that among all the rectangles having a given perimeter the square has the greatest area.

13. Prove that among all the rectangles of a given area, the square has the least perimeter.

14. If f is the function defined by $f(x) = |2x - 4| - 6$, then $f(-1) = f(5) = 0$. However, f' never has the value 0. Show why Rolle's theorem does not hold.

15. (a) If f is a polynomial function and $f(a) = f(b) = f'(a) = f'(b) = 0$ prove that there are at least two numbers in the open interval (a, b) that are roots of the equation $f''(x) = 0$. (b) Show that the function defined by the equation $f(x) = (x^2 - 4)^2$ satisfies part (a).

16. If f is a polynomial function, show that between any two consecutive roots of the equation $f'(x) = 0$ there is at most one root of the equation $f(x) = 0$.

17. Suppose that f and g are two functions that satisfy the hypothesis of the mean-value theorem on $[a, b]$. Furthermore, suppose that $f'(x) = g'(x)$ for all x in the open interval (a, b). Prove that $f(x) - g(x) = f(a) - g(a)$ for all x in the closed interval $[a, b]$.

18. Let f and g be two functions that are differentiable at every number in the closed interval $[a, b]$. Suppose further that $f(a) = g(a)$ and $f(b) = g(b)$. Prove that there exists a number c in the open interval (a, b) such that $f'(c) = g'(c)$. (HINT: Consider the function $f - g$.)

19. Find the dimensions of the right-circular cone of least volume that can be circumscribed about a right-circular cylinder of radius r in. and altitude h in.

20. A tent is to be in the shape of a cone. Find the ratio of the measure of the radius to the measure of the altitude for a tent of given volume to require the least material.

21. Two particles start their motion at the same time. One particle is moving along a horizontal line and its equation of motion is $x = t^2 - 2t$ where x ft is the directed distance of the particle from the origin at t sec. The other particle is moving along a vertical line that intersects the horizontal line at the origin and its equation of motion is $y = t^2 - 2$, where y ft is the directed distance of the particle from the origin at t sec. Find when the directed distance between the two particles is least, and their velocities at that time.

22. A property development company rents each apartment at p dollars per month when x apartments are rented and $p = 10\sqrt{300 - 2x}$. How many apartments must be rented before the marginal revenue is zero?

23. Using Boyle's law for the expansion of gas (Exercise 10 in Exercises 4.1) find the rate of change of the pressure of a certain gas at the instant when the pressure is 8 lb/in.^{2} and the volume is 700 ft^3 if the volume of the gas is increasing at the rate of 3 ft^3/min.

24. Suppose y is the number of workers in the labor force needed to produce x units of a certain commodity, and $x = 4y^2$. If the production of the commodity this year is 250,000 units and the production is increasing at the rate of 18,000 units per year, what is the current rate at which the labor force should be increased?

25. Suppose C is the number of millions of dollars in the capitalization of a certain corporation, P is the number of mil-

lions of dollars in the corporation's annual profit, and $P = 0.05C - 0.004C^2$. If its capitalization is increasing at the rate of $400,000 per year, find the rate of change of the corporation's annual profit if its current capitalization is (a) $3 million and (b) $6 million.

In Exercises 26 through 29 find: the relative extrema of f; the points of inflection of the graph of f; the intervals on which f is increasing; the intervals on which f is decreasing; where the graph is concave upward; where the graph is concave downward; the slope of any inflectional tangent. Draw a sketch of the graph.

26. $f(x) = (x + 2)^{4/3}$

27. $f(x) = (x - 4)^2 (x + 2)^3$

28. $f(x) = x\sqrt{25 - x^2}$

29. $f(x) = (x - 3)^{5/3} + 1$

30. If

$$f(x) = \frac{x + 1}{x^2 + 1}$$

prove that the graph of f has three points of inflection that are collinear. Draw a sketch of the graph.

31. If $f(x) = x|x|$, show that the graph of f has a point of inflection at the origin.

32. Let $f(x) = x^n$ where n is a positive integer. Prove that the graph of f has a point of inflection at the origin if and only if n is an odd integer and $n > 1$. Furthermore show that if n is even, f has a relative minimum value at 0.

33. If $f(x) = (x^2 + a^2)^p$, where p is a rational number and $p \neq 0$, prove that if $p < \frac{1}{2}$ the graph of f has two points of inflection and if $p \geq \frac{1}{2}$ the graph of f has no points of inflection. Assume $a \neq 0$.

34. Suppose the graph of a function has a point of inflection at $x = c$. What can you conclude, if anything, about (a) the continuity of f at c; (b) the continuity of f' at c; (c) the continuity of f'' at c?

35. The demand equation for a particular commodity is $(p + 4)(x + 3) = 48$ where p dollars is the price per unit when $100x$ units are demanded. Find (a) the price function, (b) the total revenue function, (c) the marginal revenue function. (d) Find the absolute maximum total revenue. (e) Draw sketches of the demand, total revenue, and marginal revenue curves on the same set of axes.

36. The demand equation for a certain commodity is $p + 2\sqrt{x - 1} = 6$ and the total cost function is given by $C(x) = 2x - 1$. (a) Determine the permissible values of x. (b) Find the marginal revenue and marginal cost functions. (c) Find the value of x which yields the maximum profit.

37. The demand equation for a certain commodity is

$$10^6 px = 10^9 - 2 \cdot 10^6 x + 18 \cdot 10^3 x^2 - 6x^3$$

where x is the number of units produced weekly and p dollars is the price of each unit, and $x \geq 100$. The number of dollars in the average cost of producing each unit is given by $Q(x) = \frac{1}{50}x - 24 + 11 \cdot 10^3 x^{-1}$. Find the number of units that should be produced each week and the price of each unit in order for the weekly profit to be maximized.

38. When $1000x$ boxes of a certain kind of material are produced, the number of dollars in the total cost of production is given by $C(x) = 135x^{1/3} + 450$. Find (a) the marginal cost when 8000 boxes are produced and (b) the number of boxes produced when the marginal cost (per thousand boxes) is $20.

39. A ladder is to reach over a fence h ft high to a wall w ft behind the fence. Find the length of the shortest ladder that may be used.

40. Draw a sketch of the graph of a function f on the interval I in each case: (a) I is the open interval $(0, 2)$ and f is continuous on I. At 1, f has a relative maximum value but $f'(1)$ does not exist. (b) I is the closed interval $[0, 2]$. The function f has a relative minimum value at 1, but the absolute minimum value of f is at 0. (c) I is the open interval $(0, 2)$, and f' has a relative maximum value at 1.

41. Suppose

$$f(x) = \begin{cases} x^3 & \text{if } x < 1 \\ ax^2 + bx + c & \text{if } x \geq 1 \end{cases}$$

Find the values of a, b, and c so that $f''(1)$ exists.

42. (a) If $f(x) = 3|x| + 4|x - 1|$, prove that f has an absolute minimum value of 3. (b) If $g(x) = 4|x| + 3|x - 1|$, prove that g has an absolute minimum value of 3. (c) If $h(x) = a|x| + b|x - 1|$, where $a > 0$ and $b > 0$ prove that h has an absolute minimum value that is the smaller of the two numbers a and b.

43. If $f(x) = |x|^a \cdot |x - 1|^b$, where a and b are positive rational numbers, prove that f has a relative maximum value of $a^a b^b / (a + b)^{a+b}$.

44. Suppose $g(x) = |f(x)|$. If $f^{(n)}(x)$ exists and $f(x) \neq 0$, prove that

$$g^{(n)}(x) = \frac{f(x)}{|f(x)|} f^{(n)}(x)$$

5

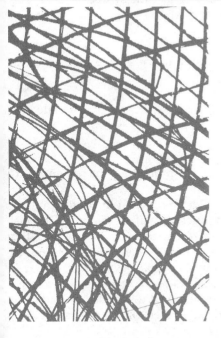

The Differential
and Antidifferentiation

Suppose that the function f is defined by

$$y = f(x)$$

Then, when $f'(x)$ exists

$$f'(x) = \lim_{\Delta x \to 0} \frac{\Delta y}{\Delta x}$$

where $\Delta y = f(x + \Delta x) - f(x)$. Because

$$\lim_{\Delta x \to 0} \left[\frac{\Delta y}{\Delta x} - f'(x) \right] = \lim_{\Delta x \to 0} \frac{\Delta y}{\Delta x} - \lim_{\Delta x \to 0} f'(x)$$

$$= f'(x) - f'(x)$$

$$= 0$$

it follows that for any $\epsilon > 0$ there exists a $\delta > 0$ such that

$$\left| \frac{\Delta y}{\Delta x} - f'(x) \right| < \epsilon \qquad \text{whenever } 0 < |\Delta x| < \delta$$

which is equivalent to

$$|\Delta y - f'(x)\,\Delta x| < \epsilon |\Delta x| \qquad \text{whenever } 0 < |\Delta x| < \delta$$

This means that $|\Delta y - f'(x)\,\Delta x|$ can be made as small as we please by taking $|\Delta x|$ sufficiently small. Hence, $f'(x)\,\Delta x$ is a good approximation to the value of Δy for a sufficiently small $|\Delta x|$. Using the symbol $\approx$, meaning "is approximately equal to," we say then that

$$\Delta y \approx f'(x)\, \Delta x$$

if $|\Delta x|$ is sufficiently small. The right side of the above expression is defined to be the *differential* of y.

5.1.1 Definition If the function f is defined by $y = f(x)$, then the *differential* of y, denoted by dy, is given by

$$dy = f'(x)\, \Delta x \tag{1}$$

where x is in the domain of f' and Δx is an arbitrary increment of x.

This concept of the differential involves a special type of function of two variables (a detailed study of such functions will be given in Chapter 17). The notation df may be used to represent this function, where the symbol df is regarded as a single entity. The variable x can be any number in the domain of f', and Δx can be any number whatsoever. To state that df is a function of the two independent variables x and Δx means that to each ordered pair $(x, \Delta x)$ in the domain of df there corresponds one and only one number in the range of df, and this number can be represented by $df(x, \Delta x)$, so that

$$df(x, \Delta x) = f'(x)\, \Delta x \tag{2}$$

Comparing Eqs. (1) and (2) we see that when $y = f(x)$, dy and $df(x, \Delta x)$ are two different notations for $f'(x)\, \Delta x$. We shall use the "dy" symbolism in subsequent discussions.

As a particular example, if $y = 4x^2 - x$, then $f(x) = 4x^2 - x$, and so $f'(x) = 8x - 1$. Therefore, from Definition 5.1.1, $dy = (8x - 1)\, \Delta x$. In particular, if $x = 2$, $dy = 15\, \Delta x$.

When $y = f(x)$, Definition 5.1.1 indicates what is meant by dy, the differential of the dependent variable. We also wish to define the differential of the independent variable, or dx. To arrive at a suitable definition for dx that is consistent with the definition of dy, we consider the identity function, which is the function f defined by $f(x) = x$. Then $f'(x) = 1$ and $y = x$; so $dy = 1 \cdot \Delta x = \Delta x$. Because $y = x$, we want dx to be equal to dy for this particular function; that is, for this function we want $dx = \Delta x$. It is this reasoning that leads us to the following definition.

5.1.2 Definition If the function f is defined by $y = f(x)$, then the *differential of x*, denoted by dx, is given by

$$dx = \Delta x \tag{3}$$

where Δx is an arbitrary increment of x, and x is any number in the domain of f'.

From Eqs. (1) and (3) we obtain

$$dy = f'(x)\ dx \tag{4}$$

Dividing on both sides of the above by dx, we have

$$\frac{dy}{dx} = f'(x) \qquad \text{if } dx \neq 0 \tag{5}$$

Equation (5) expresses the derivative as the quotient of two differentials. The notation dy/dx often denotes the derivative of y with respect to x—a symbolism we have avoided until now.

Because $\Delta y \approx f'(x)\ \Delta x$ when Δx is sufficiently small, we conclude that the differential of y, which is dy, and the increment of y, which is Δy, are approximately equal when dx is sufficiently close to zero.

We now interpret the differential geometrically. In Fig. 5.1.1 the equation of the curve is $y = f(x)$. The line PT is tangent to the curve at P; Δx and dx are equal and are represented by the directed distance $\overline{PM}$; $\overline{MQ}$ is Δy. The slope of PT is $f'(x) = dy/dx$. Also, the slope of PT is $\overline{MR}/\overline{PM}$, and because $\overline{PM} = dx$, we have $dy = \overline{MR}$ and $\overline{RQ} = \Delta y - dy$. Note that the smaller the value of dx (i.e., the closer the point Q is to the point P), then the smaller will be the value of $\Delta y - dy$ (i.e., the smaller will be the length of the line segment RQ).

Note that in Fig. 5.1.1 the graph is concave upward. In Exercise 30 you are asked to draw a similar figure if the graph is concave downward.

Figure 5.1.1

EXAMPLE 1:   Given

$$y = 4x^2 - 3x + 1$$

SOLUTION: (a) Because $y = 4x^2 - 3x + 1$, we have

$$y + \Delta y = 4(x + \Delta x)^2 - 3(x + \Delta x) + 1$$

find Δy and dy for (a) any x and Δx; (b) $x = 2, \Delta x = 0.1$; (c) $x = 2, \Delta x = 0.01$; (d) $x = 2, \Delta x = 0.001$.

$$(4x^2 - 3x + 1) + \Delta y = 4x^2 + 8x\,\Delta x + 4(\Delta x)^2 - 3x - 3\,\Delta x + 1$$
$$\Delta y = (8x - 3)\,\Delta x + 4(\Delta x)^2$$

Also,
$$dy = f'(x)\,dx$$

or
$$dy = (8x - 3)\,dx$$
$$= (8x - 3)\,\Delta x$$

The results for parts (b), (c), and (d) are given in Table 5.1.1, where $\Delta y = (8x - 3)\,\Delta x + 4(\Delta x)^2$ and $dy = (8x - 3)\,\Delta x$.

Table 5.1.1

x	Δx	Δy	dy	$\Delta y - dy$
2	0.1	1.34	1.3	0.04
2	0.01	0.1304	0.13	0.0004
2	0.001	0.013004	0.013	0.000004

Note from Table 5.1.1 that the closer Δx is to zero, the smaller is the difference between Δy and dy. Therefore, dy is an approximation of Δy when Δx is small. Or, if x is changed by a small amount Δx, the corresponding change in y is approximately dy.

EXAMPLE 2: Find an approximate value for $\sqrt[3]{28}$ without using tables.

SOLUTION: Consider the function f defined by $f(x) = \sqrt[3]{x}$ and let $y = f(x)$. Hence,
$$y = \sqrt[3]{x}$$
$$y + \Delta y = \sqrt[3]{x + \Delta x}$$
and
$$dy = f'(x)\,dx$$
$$= \frac{1}{3x^{2/3}}\,dx$$

Because the nearest perfect cube to 28 is 27, we take $x = 27$ and $\Delta x = 1$. Therefore, $x + \Delta x = 28$, $dx = \Delta x = 1$, and
$$dy = \frac{1}{3(27)^{2/3}}\,(1)$$
$$= \tfrac{1}{27}$$

Then,
$$\sqrt[3]{28} = \sqrt[3]{27 + 1}$$

$$= \sqrt[3]{x + \Delta x}$$

$$= y + \Delta y$$

Because $\Delta y \approx dy$, we have

$$\sqrt[3]{28} \approx y + dy$$

or

$$\sqrt[3]{28} \approx 3 + \tfrac{1}{27}$$

Hence, $\sqrt[3]{28} \approx 3.037$.

EXAMPLE 3:   Find the approximate volume of a spherical shell whose inner radius is 4 in. and whose thickness is $\tfrac{1}{16}$ in.

SOLUTION: We consider the volume of the spherical shell as an increment of the volume of a sphere.

Let $r =$ the number of inches in the radius of a sphere;

$V =$ the number of cubic inches in the volume of a sphere;

$\Delta V =$ the number of cubic inches in the volume of a spherical shell.

$V = \tfrac{4}{3}\pi r^3$ so that $dV = 4\pi r^2\, dr$

Substituting $r = 4$ and $dr = \tfrac{1}{16}$ into the above, we obtain

$$dV = 4\pi (4)^2\, \tfrac{1}{16}$$

$$= 4\pi$$

Therefore, $\Delta V \approx 4\pi$, and we conclude that the volume of the spherical shell is approximately 4π in.^{3}.

Exercises 5.1

In Exercises 1 through 6, find (a) Δy; (b) dy; (c) $\Delta y - dy$.

1. $y = x^3$

2. $y = 4x^2 - 3x + 1$

3. $y = \sqrt{x}$

4. $y = \dfrac{1}{x^2 + 1}$

5. $y = 2x^3 + 3x^2$

6. $y = \dfrac{1}{\sqrt[3]{x}}$

In Exercises 7 through 12, find for the given values: (a) Δy; (b) dy; (c) $\Delta y - dy$.

7. $y = x^2 - 3x$; $x = 2$; $\Delta x = 0.03$

8. $y = x^2 - 3x$; $x = -1$; $\Delta x = 0.02$

9. $y = x^3 + 1$; $x = 1$; $\Delta x = -0.5$

10. $y = x^3 + 1$; $x = -1$; $\Delta x = 0.1$

11. $y = \dfrac{1}{x^2}$; $x = 2$; $\Delta x = 0.01$

12. $y = \dfrac{1}{x^2}$; $x = -3$; $\Delta x = -0.1$

In Exercises 13 through 20, use differentials to find an approximate value for the given quantity. Express each answer to three significant digits.

13. $\sqrt{37.5}$

14. $\sqrt[3]{7.5}$

15. $\sqrt[4]{82}$

16. $\sqrt{82}$ 17. $\sqrt[3]{0.00098}$ 18. $\sqrt{0.042}$ 19. $\dfrac{1}{\sqrt[3]{120}}$ 20. $\dfrac{1}{\sqrt[4]{15}}$

21. The measurement of an edge of a cube is found to be 15 in. with a possible error of 0.01 in. Using differentials find the approximate error in computing from this measurement (a) the volume; (b) the area of one of the faces.

22. The altitude of a right-circular cone is twice the radius of the base. The altitude is measured as 12 in., with a possible error of 0.005 in. Find the approximate error in the calculated volume of the cone.

23. An open cylindrical tank is to have an outside coating of thickness $\frac{1}{8}$ in. If the inner radius is 6 ft and the altitude is 10 ft, find by differentials the approximate amount of coating material to be used.

24. A metal box in the form of a cube is to have an interior volume of 64 in.^{3}. The six sides are to be made of metal $\frac{1}{4}$ in. thick. If the cost of the metal to be used is 8 cents per cubic inch use differentials to find the approximate cost of the metal to be used in the manufacture of the box.

25. If the possible error in the measurement of the volume of a gas is 0.1 ft^3 and the allowable error in the pressure is $0.001C$ lb/ft^2, find the size of the smallest container for which Boyle's law (Exercise 10 in Exercises 4.1) holds.

26. A contractor agrees to paint on both sides of 1000 circular signs each of radius 3 ft. Upon receiving the signs, it is discovered that the radius is $\frac{1}{2}$ in. too large. Use differentials to find the approximate percent increase of paint that will be needed.

27. The measure of the electrical resistance of a wire is proportional to the measure of its length and inversely proportional to the square of the measure of its diameter. Suppose the resistance of a wire of given length is computed from a measurement of the diameter with a possible 2% error. Find the possible percent error in the computed value of the resistance.

28. If t sec is the time for one complete swing of a simple pendulum of length l ft, then $4\pi^2 l = gt^2$, where $g = 32.2$. A clock having a pendulum of length 1 ft gains 5 min each day. Find the approximate amount by which the pendulum should be lengthened in order to correct the inaccuracy.

29. For the adiabatic law for the expansion of air of Exercise 12 in Sec. 4.2, prove that $dP/P = -1.4\ dV/V$.

30. Draw a figure similar to Fig. 5.1.1, if the graph is concave downward. Indicate the line segments whose lengths represent the following quantities: $\Delta x, \Delta y, dx,$ and dy.

5.2 DIFFERENTIAL FORMULAS

Suppose that y is a function of x and that x, in turn, is a function of a third variable t; that is,

$$y = f(x) \quad \text{and} \quad x = g(t)$$

The two equations in (1) together define y as a function of t. For example, suppose that $y = x^3$ and $x = 2t - 1$. Combining these two equations, we get $y = (2t - 1)^3$. In general, if the two equations in (1) are combined, we obtain

$$y = f(g(t)) \tag{2}$$

The derivative of y with respect to t can be found by the chain rule, which yields

$$D_t y = D_x y\ D_t x \tag{3}$$

Equation (3) expresses $D_t y$ as a function of x and t because $D_x y$ is a function of x and $D_t x$ is a function of t.

Because Eq. (2) defines y as a function of the independent variable t, the differential of y is obtained from Definition 5.1.1:

$$dy = D_t y \ dt \tag{4}$$

Equation (4) expresses dy as a function of t and dt. Substituting from (3) into (4), we get

$$dy = D_x y \ D_t x \ dt \tag{5}$$

Now because x is a function of the independent variable t, Definition 5.1.1 can be applied to obtain the differential of x, and we have

$$dx = D_t x \ dt \tag{6}$$

Equation (6) expresses dx as a function of t and dt. From (5) and (6), we get

$$dy = D_x y \ dx \tag{7}$$

You should bear in mind that in Eq. (7) dy is a function of t and dt, and that dx is a function of t and dt. If $D_x y$ in Eq. (7) is replaced by $f'(x)$, we have

$$dy = f'(x) \ dx \tag{8}$$

Equation (8) resembles Eq. (4) of Sec. 5.1. However, in that equation x is the independent variable, and dy is expressed in terms of x and dx, whereas in Eq. (8) t is the independent variable, and both dy and dx are expressed in terms of t and dt. Thus, we have the following theorem.

5.2.1 Theorem   If $y = f(x)$, then when $f'(x)$ exists

$$dy = f'(x) \ dx$$

whether or not x is an independent variable.

If on both sides of Eq. (8) we divide by dx (provided $dx \neq 0$), we obtain

$$f'(x) = \frac{dy}{dx} \qquad dx \neq 0 \tag{9}$$

Equation (9) states that if $y = f(x)$, then $f'(x)$ is the quotient of the two differentials dy and dx, even though x may not be an independent variable.

We now proceed to write the chain rule for differentiation by expressing the derivatives as quotients of differentials. If $y = f(u)$ and $D_u y$ exists, and if $u = f(x)$ and $D_x u$ exists, then the chain rule gives

$$D_x y = D_u y \ D_x u \tag{10}$$

But $D_x y = dy/dx$ if $dx \neq 0$; $D_u y = dy/du$ if $du \neq 0$; and $D_x u = du/dx$ if $dx \neq 0$. From (10), therefore, we have

$$\frac{dy}{dx} = \left(\frac{dy}{du}\right) \cdot \left(\frac{du}{dx}\right) \qquad \text{if } du \neq 0 \text{ and } dx \neq 0$$

The German mathematician Gottfried Leibnitz (1646–1716) was the first to use the notation dy/dx for the derivative of y with respect to x. The concept of a derivative was introduced, in the seventeenth century, almost simultaneously by Leibnitz and Sir Isaac Newton (1642–1727), who were working independently. Leibnitz probably thought of dx and dy as small changes in the variables x and y and of the derivative of y with respect to x as the ratio of dy to dx as dy and dx become small. The concept of a limit as we know it today was not known to Leibnitz.

Corresponding to the Leibnitz notation dy/dx for the first derivative of y with respect to x, we have the symbol d^2y/dx^2 for the second derivative of y with respect to x. However, d^2y/dx^2 must not be thought of as a quotient because in this text the differential of a differential is not considered. Similarly, d^ny/dx^n is a notation for the nth derivative of y with respect to x. The symbolism f', f'', f''', and so on, for the successive derivatives of a function f was introduced by the French mathematician Joseph Lagrange in the eighteenth century.

Earlier in this chapter, we derived formulas for finding derivatives. These formulas are now stated by using the Leibnitz notation. Along with the formula for the derivative, we shall give a corresponding formula for the differential, which is obtained by multiplying on both sides of the first formula by dx. In these formulas, u and v are functions of x, and it is understood that the formulas hold if $D_x u$ and $D_x v$ exist. When c appears, it is a constant.

$$\text{I} \quad \frac{d(c)}{dx} = 0 \qquad\qquad \text{I'} \quad d(c) = 0$$

$$\text{II} \quad \frac{d(x^n)}{dx} = nx^{n-1} \qquad\qquad \text{II'} \quad d(x^n) = nx^{n-1}\, dx$$

$$\text{III} \quad \frac{d(cu)}{dx} = c\,\frac{du}{dx} \qquad\qquad \text{III'} \quad d(cu) = c\, du$$

$$\text{IV} \quad \frac{d(u+v)}{dx} = \frac{du}{dx} + \frac{dv}{dx} \qquad\qquad \text{IV'} \quad d(u+v) = du + dv$$

$$\text{V} \quad \frac{d(uv)}{dx} = u\,\frac{dv}{dx} + v\,\frac{du}{dx} \qquad\qquad \text{V'} \quad d(uv) = u\, dv + v\, du$$

$$\text{VI} \quad \frac{d\left(\dfrac{u}{v}\right)}{dx} = \frac{v\,\dfrac{du}{dx} - u\,\dfrac{dv}{dx}}{v^2} \qquad\qquad \text{VI'} \quad d\left(\frac{u}{v}\right) = \frac{v\, du - u\, dv}{v^2}$$

$$\text{VII} \quad \frac{d(u^n)}{dx} = nu^{n-1}\,\frac{du}{dx} \qquad\qquad \text{VII'} \quad d(u^n) = nu^{n-1}\, du$$

The operation of differentiation is extended to include the process of finding the differential as well as finding the derivative. If $y = f(x)$, dy can be found either by applying formulas I'–VII' or by finding $f'(x)$ and multiplying it by dx.

EXAMPLE 1: Given

$$y = \frac{\sqrt{x^2 + 1}}{2x + 1}$$

find dy.

SOLUTION: Applying formula VI', we obtain

$$dy = \frac{(2x + 1)\, d(\sqrt{x^2 + 1}) - \sqrt{x^2 + 1}\; d(2x + 1)}{(2x + 1)^2} \tag{11}$$

From formula VII',

$$d(\sqrt{x^2 + 1}) = \tfrac{1}{2}(x^2 + 1)^{-1/2}\, 2x\, dx = x(x^2 + 1)^{-1/2}\, dx \tag{12}$$

and

$$d(2x + 1) = 2\, dx \tag{13}$$

Substituting values from (12) and (13) into (11), we get

$$dy = \frac{x(2x + 1)(x^2 + 1)^{-1/2}\, dx - 2(x^2 + 1)^{1/2}\, dx}{(2x + 1)^2}$$

or

$$dy = \frac{(2x^2 + x)\, dx - 2(x^2 + 1)\, dx}{(2x + 1)^2(x^2 + 1)^{1/2}}$$

or

$$dy = \frac{x - 2}{(2x + 1)^2\sqrt{x^2 + 1}}\, dx$$

EXAMPLE 2: Given

$$2x^2y^2 - 3x^3 + 5y^3 + 6xy^2 = 5$$

where x and y are functions of a third variable t, find dy/dx by finding the differential term by term.

SOLUTION: This is a problem in implicit differentiation. Taking the differential term by term, we get

$$4xy^2\, dx + 4x^2y\, dy - 9x^2\, dx + 15y^2\, dy + 6y^2\, dx + 12xy\, dy = 0$$

Dividing by dx, if $dx \neq 0$, we have

$$(4x^2y + 15y^2 + 12xy)\frac{dy}{dx} = -4xy^2 + 9x^2 - 6y^2$$

$$\frac{dy}{dx} = \frac{9x^2 - 6y^2 - 4xy^2}{4x^2y + 15y^2 + 12xy}$$

Exercises 5.2

In Exercises 1 through 8, find dy.

1. $y = (3x^2 - 2x + 1)^3$

2. $y = \sqrt{4 - x^2}$

3. $y = x^2\sqrt[3]{2x + 3}$

4. $y = \dfrac{3x}{x^2 + 2}$

5. $y = \sqrt{\dfrac{x - 1}{x + 1}}$

6. $y = (x + 2)^{1/3}(x - 2)^{2/3}$

7. $y = \dfrac{2x}{\sqrt{x^2 + 1}}$

8. $y = \sqrt{3x + 4} \; \sqrt[3]{x^2 - 1}$

In Exercises 9 through 16, x and y are functions of a third variable t. Find dy/dx by finding the differential term by term (see Example 2).

9. $3x^3 + 4y^2 = 48$

10. $8x^2 - y^2 = 32$

11. $\sqrt{x} + \sqrt{y} = 4$

12. $2x^2y - 3xy^3 + 6y^2 = 1$

13. $x^4 - 3x^3y + 4xy^3 + y^4 = 2$

14. $x^{2/3} + y^{2/3} = a^{2/3}$

15. $3x^3 - x^2y + 2xy^2 - y^3 - 3x^2 + y^2 = 1$

16. $x^2 + y^2 = \sqrt[3]{x + y}$

In Exercises 17 through 24, find dy/dt.

17. $y = 3x^3 - 5x^2 + 1; \; x = t^2 - 1$

18. $y = \dfrac{5x - 2}{x^2 + 1}; \; x = (2t - 1)^2$

19. $y = x^2 - 3x + 1; \; x = \sqrt{t^2 - t + 4}$

20. $y = \sqrt[3]{5x - 1}; \; x = \sqrt{2t + 3}$

21. $y = x^2 - 5x + 1; \; x = s^3 - 2s + 1; \; s = \sqrt{t^2 + 1}$

22. $y = \dfrac{x^2 - 1}{x^2 + 1}; \; x = \dfrac{2s + 2}{\sqrt{s^2 + 2}}; \; s = t^2 - 4t + 5$

23. $x^3 - 3x^2y + y^3 = 5; \; x = 4t^2 + 1$

24. $3x^2y - 4xy^2 + 7y^3 = 0; \; 2x^3 - 3xt^2 + t^3 = 1$

5.3 THE INVERSE OF DIFFERENTIATION

The reader is already familiar with *inverse operations*. Addition and subtraction are inverse operations; multiplication and division are also inverse operations, as well as raising to powers and extracting roots. The inverse operation of differentiation is called *antidifferentiation*.

5.3.1 Definition

A function F is called an *antiderivative* of a function f on an interval I if $F'(x) = f(x)$ for every value of x in I.

For example, if F is defined by $F(x) = 4x^3 + x^2 + 5$, then $F'(x) = 12x^2 + 2x$. Thus, if f is the function defined by $f(x) = 12x^2 + 2x$, we state that f is the derivative of F and that F is an antiderivative of f. If G is the function defined by $G(x) = 4x^3 + x^2 - 17$, then G is also an antiderivative of f because $G'(x) = 12x^2 + 2x$. Actually any function whose function value is given by $4x^3 + x^2 + C$, where C is any constant, is an antiderivative of f.

In general, if a function F is an antiderivative of a function f on an interval I and if G is defined by

$$G(x) = F(x) + C$$

where C is an arbitrary constant, then

$$G'(x) = F'(x) = f(x)$$

and G is also an antiderivative of f on the interval I.

In the next chapter we state that if f is a continuous function on an interval I, then an antiderivative of f exists on I. We now proceed to prove that if F is any particular antiderivative of f on an interval I, then all possible antiderivatives of f on I are defined by $F(x) + C$, where C is an arbitrary constant. First, two preliminary theorems are needed.

5.3.2 Theorem   If f is a function such that $f'(x) = 0$ for all values of x in the interval I, then f is constant on I.

PROOF: Let us assume that f is not constant on the interval I. Then there exist two distinct numbers x_1 and x_2 in I where $x_1 < x_2$ such that $f(x_1) \neq f(x_2)$. Because, by hypothesis, $f'(x) = 0$ for all x in I, then $f'(x) = 0$ for all x in the closed interval $[x_1, x_2]$. Hence, f is differentiable at all x in $[x_1, x_2]$ and f is continuous on $[x_1, x_2]$. Therefore, the hypothesis of the mean-value theorem is satisfied, and we conclude that there is a number c, with $x_1 < c < x_2$, such that

$$f'(c) = \frac{f(x_1) - f(x_2)}{x_1 - x_2} \tag{1}$$

But because $f'(x) = 0$ for all x in the interval $[x_1, x_2]$, then $f'(c) = 0$, and from Eq. (1) it follows that $f(x_1) = f(x_2)$. Yet our assumption was that $f(x_1) \neq f(x_2)$. Hence, there is a contradiction, and so f is constant on I, which is what we wished to prove. ∎

5.3.3 Theorem   If f and g are two functions such that $f'(x) = g'(x)$ for all values of x in the interval I, then there is a constant K such that

$$f(x) = g(x) + K \qquad \text{for all } x \text{ in } I$$

PROOF: Let h be the function defined on I by

$$h(x) = f(x) - g(x)$$

so that for all values of x in I we have

$$h'(x) = f'(x) - g'(x)$$

But, by hypothesis, $f'(x) = g'(x)$ for all values of x in I. Therefore,

$$h'(x) = 0 \qquad \text{for all values of } x \text{ in } I$$

Thus, Theorem 5.3.2 applies to the function h, and there is a constant K such that

$$h(x) = K \qquad \text{for all values of } x \text{ in } I$$

Replacing $h(x)$ by $f(x) - g(x)$, we have

$$f(x) = g(x) + K \qquad \text{for all values of } x \text{ in } I$$

and the theorem is proved. ∎

The next theorem follows immediately from Theorem 5.3.3.

5.3.4 Theorem   If F is any particular antiderivative of f on an interval I, then the most general antiderivative of f on I is given by

$$F(x) + C \tag{2}$$

where C is an arbitrary constant, and all antiderivatives of f on I can be obtained from (2) by assigning particular values to C.

PROOF: Let G be any antiderivative of f on I; then

$$G'(x) = f(x) \qquad \text{on } I \tag{3}$$

Because F is a particular antiderivative of f on I, we have

$$F'(x) = f(x) \qquad \text{on } I \tag{4}$$

From Eqs. (3) and (4), it follows that

$$G'(x) = F'(x) \qquad \text{on } I$$

Therefore, from Theorem 5.3.3, there is a constant K such that

$$G(x) = F(x) + K \qquad \text{for all } x \text{ in } I$$

Because G is any antiderivative of f on I, it follows that all antiderivatives of f can be obtained from $F(x) + C$, where C is an arbitrary constant. Hence, the theorem is proved.   ∎

If F is an antiderivative of f, then $F'(x) = f(x)$, and so

$$d(F(x)) = f(x) \, dx$$

Antidifferentiation is the process of finding the most general antiderivative of a given function. The symbol

$$\int$$

denotes the operation of antidifferentiation, and we write

$$\int f(x) \, dx = F(x) + C \tag{5}$$

where

$$F'(x) = f(x)$$

or, equivalently,

$$d(F(x)) = f(x) \, dx \tag{6}$$

From Eqs. (5) and (6), we can write

$$\int d(F(x)) = F(x) + C \tag{7}$$

Equation (7) says that when we antidifferentiate the differential of a function we obtain that function plus an arbitrary constant. So we can think of the $\int$ symbol for antidifferentiation as meaning that operation which is the inverse of the operation denoted by d for finding the differential.

Because antidifferentiation is the inverse operation of differentiation, we can obtain antidifferentiation formulas from differentiation formulas. We use the following formulas that can be proved from the corresponding formulas for differentiation.

5.3.5 Formula 1 $\int dx = x + C.$

5.3.6 Formula 2 $\int af(x)\, dx = a\int f(x)\, dx$, where a is a constant.

Formula 2 states that to find an antiderivative of a constant times a function, first find an antiderivative of the function, and then multiply it by the constant.

5.3.7 Formula 3 $\int [f_1(x) + f_2(x)]\, dx = \int f_1(x)\, dx + \int f_2(x)\, dx.$

Formula 3 states that to find an antiderivative of the sum of two functions, find an antiderivative of each of the functions separately, and then add the results. It is understood that both functions must be defined on the same interval. Formula 3 can be extended to any finite number of functions. Combining Formula 3 with Formula 2, we have Formula 4.

5.3.8 Formula 4 $\int [c_1 f_1(x) + c_2 f_2(x) + \cdots + c_n f_n(x)]\, dx$
$$= c_1 \int f_1(x)\, dx + c_2 \int f_2(x)\, dx + \cdots + c_n \int f_n(x)\, dx.$$

5.3.9 Formula 5 $\int x^n\, dx = \dfrac{x^{n+1}}{(n+1)} + C \qquad \text{if } n \neq -1.$

As stated above, these formulas follow from the corresponding formulas for finding the differential. Following is the proof of Formula 5:

$$d\left(\frac{x^{n+1}}{n+1} + C\right) = \frac{(n+1)x^n}{n+1}\, dx$$

$$= x^n\, dx$$

Application of the above formulas is illustrated in the following examples.

EXAMPLE 1: **Evaluate**

$$\int (3x + 5)\, dx$$

SOLUTION:

$$\int (3x + 5)\, dx = 3\int x\, dx + 5\int dx \quad \text{(by Formula 4)}$$

$$= 3\left(\frac{x^2}{2} + C_1\right) + 5(x + C_2) \quad \text{(by Formulas 5 and 1)}$$

$$= \tfrac{3}{2}x^2 + 5x + 3C_1 + 5C_2$$

Because $3C_1 + 5C_2$ is an arbitrary constant, it may be denoted by C, and so our answer is

$$\tfrac{3}{2}x^2 + 5x + C$$

This answer may be checked by finding the derivative. Doing this, we have

$$D_x(\tfrac{3}{2}x^2 + 5x + C) = 3x + 5$$

EXAMPLE 2: Evaluate

$$\int \sqrt[3]{x^2}\, dx$$

SOLUTION:
$$\int \sqrt[3]{x^2}\, dx = \int x^{2/3}\, dx$$

$$= \frac{x^{2/3+1}}{\tfrac{2}{3}+1} + C \quad \text{(from Formula 5)}$$

$$= \tfrac{3}{5}x^{5/3} + C$$

EXAMPLE 3: Evaluate

$$\int \left(\frac{1}{x^4} + \frac{1}{\sqrt[4]{x}} \right) dx$$

SOLUTION:
$$\int \left(\frac{1}{x^4} + \frac{1}{\sqrt[4]{x}} \right) dx = \int (x^{-4} + x^{-1/4})\, dx$$

$$= \frac{x^{-4+1}}{-4+1} + \frac{x^{-1/4+1}}{-\tfrac{1}{4}+1} + C$$

$$= \frac{x^{-3}}{-3} + \frac{x^{3/4}}{\tfrac{3}{4}} + C$$

$$= -\frac{1}{3x^3} + \frac{4}{3}\, x^{3/4} + C$$

Many antiderivatives cannot be found directly by applying formulas. However, sometimes it is possible to find an antiderivative by the formulas after changing the variable. For example, suppose that we wish to find

$$\int 2x\sqrt{1+x^2}\, dx \qquad (8)$$

If we make the substitution $u = 1 + x^2$, then $du = 2x\, dx$, and (8) becomes

$$\int u^{1/2}\, du$$

which by Formula 5 gives

$$\tfrac{2}{3}u^{3/2} + C$$

Then, replacing u by $(1 + x^2)$, we have as our result

$$\tfrac{2}{3}(1 + x^2)^{3/2} + C$$

Justification of this procedure is provided by the following theorem, which is analogous to the chain rule for differentiation, and hence may be called the *chain rule for antidifferentiation*.

5.3.10 Theorem
Chain Rule for Antidifferentiation

Let g be a differentiable function of x, and let the range of g be an interval I. Suppose that f is a function defined on I and that F is an antiderivative of f on I. Then if $u = g(x)$,

$$\int f(g(x))g'(x)\ dx = \int f(u)\ du = F(u) + C = F(g(x)) + C$$

PROOF: Because $u = g(x)$, then u is in I; and because F is an antiderivative of f on I, it follows that

$$\frac{dF(u)}{du} = f(u) \tag{9}$$

and

$$\int f(u)\ du = F(u) + C \tag{10}$$

Also,

$$\frac{dF(g(x))}{dx} = \frac{dF(u)}{dx} \tag{11}$$

Applying the chain rule for differentiation to the right side of Eq. (11), we obtain

$$\frac{dF(g(x))}{dx} = \frac{dF(u)}{du} \cdot \frac{du}{dx} \tag{12}$$

Substituting from Eq. (9) into (12) gives

$$\frac{dF(g(x))}{dx} = f(u) \cdot \frac{du}{dx} \tag{13}$$

Because $u = g(x)$, from Eq. (13) we have

$$\frac{dF(g(x))}{dx} = f(g(x)) \cdot g'(x)$$

from which we conclude that

$$\int f(g(x)) \cdot g'(x)\ dx = F(g(x)) + C \tag{14}$$

Because $u = g(x)$, we have

$$F(g(x)) + C = F(u) + C \tag{15}$$

Therefore, from (10), (14), and (15), we have

$$\int f(g(x))g'(x)\ dx = \int f(u)\ du = F(u) + C = F(g(x)) + C$$

which is what we wished to prove.   ∎

As a particular case of Theorem 5.3.10, from Formula 5 we have the generalized power formula for antiderivatives, which we state as Formula 6.

5.3.11 Formula 6   If g is a differentiable function, then if $u = g(x)$,

$$\int [g(x)]^n g'(x)\ dx = \int u^n\ du = \frac{u^{n+1}}{n+1} + C = \frac{[g(x)]^{n+1}}{n+1} + C$$

where $n \neq -1$.

Examples 4, 5, and 6 illustrate the application of Formula 6.

EXAMPLE 4:   Evaluate

$$\int \sqrt{3x+4}\ dx$$

SOLUTION: To apply Formula 6, we make the substitution $u = 3x + 4$; then $du = 3\ dx$, or $\frac{1}{3}\ du = dx$. Hence,

$$\int \sqrt{3x+4}\ dx = \int u^{1/2} \cdot \frac{du}{3}$$

$$= \tfrac{1}{3} \int u^{1/2}\ du$$

$$= \frac{1}{3} \cdot \frac{u^{3/2}}{\frac{3}{2}} + C$$

$$= \tfrac{2}{9} u^{3/2} + C$$

$$= \tfrac{2}{9}(3x+4)^{3/2} + C$$

The details of the solution of Example 4 can be shortened by not explicitly stating the substitution of u. The solution then takes the following form.

$$\int \sqrt{3x+4}\ dx = \tfrac{1}{3} \int (3x+4)^{1/2} 3\ dx$$

$$= \frac{1}{3} \cdot \frac{(3x+4)^{3/2}}{\frac{3}{2}} + C$$

$$= \tfrac{2}{9}(3x+4)^{3/2} + C$$

EXAMPLE 5:   Evaluate

$$\int t(5+3t^2)^8\ dt$$

SOLUTION: Since $d(5+3t^2) = 6t\ dt$, we write

$$\int t(5+3t^2)^8\ dt = \tfrac{1}{6} \int (5+3t^2)^8 6t\ dt$$

$$= \frac{1}{6} \cdot \frac{(5+3t^2)^9}{9} + C$$

$$= \tfrac{1}{54}(5+3t^2)^9 + C$$

EXAMPLE 6:   Evaluate

$$\int x^2 \sqrt[5]{7 - 4x^3}\, dx$$

SOLUTION:

$$\int x^2 \sqrt[5]{7 - 4x^3}\, dx = -\tfrac{1}{12} \int (7 - 4x^3)^{1/5}(-12x^2)\, dx$$

$$= -\frac{1}{12} \cdot \frac{(7 - 4x^3)^{6/5}}{\frac{6}{5}} + C$$

$$= -\tfrac{5}{12}(7 - 4x^3)^{6/5} + C$$

EXAMPLE 7:   Evaluate

$$\int x^2 \sqrt{1 + x}\, dx$$

SOLUTION: Let $v = \sqrt{1 + x}$; then $v^2 = 1 + x$. Hence, $x = v^2 - 1$, and $dx = 2v\, dv$. Making these substitutions, we have

$$\int x^2 \sqrt{1 + x}\, dx = \int (v^2 - 1)^2 \cdot v \cdot (2v\, dv)$$

$$= 2 \int v^6\, dv - 4 \int v^4\, dv + 2 \int v^2\, dv$$

$$= \tfrac{2}{7}v^7 - \tfrac{4}{5}v^5 + \tfrac{2}{3}v^3 + C$$

$$= \tfrac{2}{7}(1 + x)^{7/2} - \tfrac{4}{5}(1 + x)^{5/2} + \tfrac{2}{3}(1 + x)^{3/2} + C$$

The answers to each of the above examples can be checked by finding the derivative (or the differential) of the answer. In particular, in Example 5, we have

$$\int t(5 + 3t^2)^8\, dt = \tfrac{1}{54}(5 + 3t^2)^9 + C$$

Checking by differentiation gives

$$D_t[\tfrac{1}{54}(5 + 3t^2)^9] = \tfrac{1}{54} \cdot 9(5 + 3t^2)^8 \cdot 6t$$
$$= t(5 + 3t^2)^8$$

In Example 7, we have

$$\int x^2 \sqrt{1 + x}\, dx = \tfrac{2}{7}(1 + x)^{7/2} - \tfrac{4}{5}(1 + x)^{5/2} + \tfrac{2}{3}(1 + x)^{3/2} + C$$

Checking by differentiation gives

$$D_x[\tfrac{2}{7}(1 + x)^{7/2} - \tfrac{4}{5}(1 + x)^{5/2} + \tfrac{2}{3}(1 + x)^{3/2}]$$
$$= (1 + x)^{5/2} - 2(1 + x)^{3/2} + (1 + x)^{1/2}$$
$$= (1 + x)^{1/2}[(1 + x)^2 - 2(1 + x) + 1]$$
$$= (1 + x)^{1/2}[1 + 2x + x^2 - 2 - 2x + 1]$$
$$= x^2 \sqrt{1 + x}$$

Exercises 5.3

In Exercises 1 through 26 find the most general antiderivative. In Exercises 1 through 10 check by finding the derivative of your answer.

1. $\int 3x^4 \, dx$

2. $\int (4x^3 - 3x^2 + 6x - 1) \, dx$

3. $\int (3 - 2t + t^2) \, dt$

4. $\int (ax^2 + bx + c) \, dx$

5. $\int \left(\frac{2}{x^3} + \frac{3}{x^2} + 5\right) dx$

6. $\int \frac{y^4 + 2y^2 - 1}{\sqrt{y}} \, dy$

7. $\int \left(\sqrt{2x} - \frac{1}{\sqrt{2x}}\right) dx$

8. $\int \frac{27t^3 - 1}{\sqrt[3]{t}} \, dt$

9. $\int x^2 \sqrt{x^3 - 1} \, dx$

10. $\int x\sqrt[3]{(4 - x^2)^2} \, dx$

11. $\int \frac{s \, ds}{\sqrt{3s^2 + 1}}$

12. $\int \sqrt{5r + 1} \, dr$

13. $\int \sqrt{1 + \frac{1}{2x}} \frac{dx}{x^3}$

14. $\int x^4 \sqrt{3x^5 - 5} \, dx$

15. $\int x^2 (4 - x^2)^3 \, dx$

16. $\int (x^2 - 4x + 4)^{4/3} \, dx$

17. $\int \frac{t \, dt}{\sqrt{t + 3}}$

18. $\int \frac{2r \, dr}{(1 - r)^{2/3}}$

19. $\int \sqrt{3 - x} \, x^2 \, dx$

20. $\int (x^3 + 3)^{1/4} x^5 \, dx$

21. $\int \frac{(x^2 + 2x) \, dx}{\sqrt{x^3 + 3x^2 + 1}}$

22. $\int \sqrt{3 + s}(s + 1)^2 \, ds$

23. $\int \frac{y + 3}{(3 - y)^{2/3}} \, dy$

24. $\int (2t^2 + 1)^{1/3} t^3 \, dt$

25. $\int \frac{(r^{1/3} + 2)^4}{\sqrt[3]{r^2}} \, dr$

26. $\int \left(t + \frac{1}{t}\right)^{3/2} \left(\frac{t^2 - 1}{t^2}\right) dt$

27. Evaluate $\int (2x + 1)^3 \, dx$ by two methods: (a) Expand $(2x + 1)^3$ by the binomial theorem, and apply Formulas 1, 4, and 5; (b) make the substitution $u = 2x + 1$. Explain the difference in appearance of the answers obtained in (a) and (b).

28. Evaluate $\int \sqrt{x - 1} \, x^2 \, dx$ by two methods: (a) Make the substitution $u = x - 1$; (b) make the substitution $v = \sqrt{x - 1}$. Compare the answers obtained in (a) and (b) and explain the difference in appearance of the answers.

29. Let $f(x) = 1$ for all x in $(-1, 1)$ and

$$g(x) = \begin{cases} -1 & \text{if } -1 < x \le 0 \\ 1 & \text{if } 0 < x < 1 \end{cases}$$

Then $f'(x) = 0$ for all x in $(-1, 1)$ and $g'(x) = 0$ whenever g' exists in $(-1, 1)$. However, $f(x) \ne g(x) + K$ for x in $(-1, 1)$. Why doesn't Theorem 5.3.3 hold?

30. Let $f(x) = \text{sgn } x$ and $F(x) = |x|$. Show that $F'(x) = f(x)$ if $x \ne 0$. Is F an antiderivative of f on $(-\infty, +\infty)$? Explain.

31. Let $f(x) = |x|$ and F be defined by

$$F(x) = \begin{cases} -\frac{1}{2}x^2 & \text{if } x < 0 \\ \frac{1}{2}x^2 & \text{if } x \ge 0 \end{cases}$$

Show that F is an antiderivative of f on $(-\infty, +\infty)$.

32. Show that the unit step function U (Exercise 1 in Exercises 2.3) does not have an antiderivative on $(-\infty, +\infty)$. (HINT: Assume that U has an antiderivative F on $(-\infty, +\infty)$, and a contradiction is obtained by showing that it follows from the mean-value theorem that there exists a number k such that $F(x) = x + k$ if $x > 0$, and $F(x) = k$ if $x < 0$.)

5.4 DIFFERENTIAL EQUATIONS WITH VARIABLES SEPARABLE

If F is a function defined by the equation

$$y = F(x) \tag{1}$$

and f is the derivative of F, then

$$\frac{dy}{dx} = f(x) \tag{2}$$

and F is an antiderivative of f.

Writing Eq. (2) using differentials, we have

$$dy = f(x)\ dx \tag{3}$$

Equations (2) and (3) are very simple types of *differential equations*. They are differential equations of the *first order* (because only derivatives of the first order are involved) for which the variables are separable. To solve Eq. (3) we must find all functions G for which $y = G(x)$ so that the equation is satisfied. So if F is an antiderivative of f, all functions G are defined by $G(x) = F(x) + C$, where C is an arbitrary constant. That is, if $d(G(x)) = d(F(x) + C) = f(x)\ dx$, then what is called the *complete solution* of Eq. (3) is given by

$$y = F(x) + C \tag{4}$$

Often in problems involving differential equations it is desired to find particular solutions which satisfy certain conditions called *boundary conditions* or *initial conditions*. For example, if differential equation (3) is given as well as the boundary condition that $y = y_1$ when $x = x_1$, then after the complete solution (4) is found, if x and y in (4) are replaced by x_1 and y_1, a particular value of C is determined. When this value of C is substituted back into Eq. (4), a particular solution is obtained.

Equation (4) represents a family of functions depending on an arbitrary constant C. This is called a *one-parameter family*. The graphs of these functions form a one-parameter family of curves in the plane, and through any particular point (x_1, y_1) there passes just one curve of the family.

EXAMPLE 1:   Find the complete solution of the differential equation

$$dy = 2x\ dx$$

and then find the particular solution satisfying the boundary condition that $y = 6$ when $x = 2$.

SOLUTION: The most general antiderivative for the left side of the given equation is $(y + C_1)$, and the most general antiderivative of $2x$ is $(x^2 + C_2)$. So we have

$$y + C_1 = x^2 + C_2$$

Because $(C_2 - C_1)$ is an arbitrary constant if C_2 and C_1 are arbitrary, we can replace $(C_2 - C_1)$ by C, thereby obtaining

$$y = x^2 + C \tag{5}$$

which is the complete solution of the given differential equation.

Equation (5) represents a one-parameter family of functions. Figure 5.4.1 shows sketches of the graphs of the functions corresponding to $C = -4$, $C = -1$, $C = 0$, $C = 1$, and $C = 2$.

C = 2
C = 1
C = 0
C = −1
C = −4

Figure 5.4.1

To find the particular solution for which $y = 6$, when $x = 2$, we substitute these values in Eq. (5) and solve for C, giving $6 = 4 + C$, or $C = 2$. Substituting this value of C in (5), we obtain

$$y = x^2 + 2$$

which is the particular solution desired.

Another type of differential equation is

$$\frac{d^2y}{dx^2} = f(x) \tag{6}$$

Equation (6) is a differential equation of the *second order*. Two successive antidifferentiations are necessary to solve Eq. (6), and two arbitrary constants occur in the complete solution. The complete solution of Eq. (6) therefore represents a *two-parameter family* of functions, and the graphs of these functions form a two-parameter family of curves in the plane.

EXAMPLE 2:   Find the complete solution of the differential equation

$$\frac{d^2y}{dx^2} = 4x + 3$$

SOLUTION: Because $d^2y/dx^2 = dy'/dx$, the given equation can be written as

$$\frac{dy'}{dx} = 4x + 3$$

Writing this in differential form, we have

$$dy' = (4x + 3) \, dx$$

Antidifferentiating, we have

$$\int dy' = \int (4x + 3) \, dx$$

from which we get

$$y' = 2x^2 + 3x + C_1$$

Because $y' = dy/dx$, we make this substitution in the above equation and get

$$\frac{dy}{dx} = 2x^2 + 3x + C_1$$

Using differentials, we have

$$dy = (2x^2 + 3x + C_1) \, dx$$

Antidifferentiating, we obtain

$$\int dy = \int (2x^2 + 3x + C_1) \, dx$$

from which we get

$$y = \tfrac{2}{3}x^3 + \tfrac{3}{2}x^2 + C_1 x + C_2$$

which is the complete solution.

EXAMPLE 3:   Find the particular solution of the differential equation in Example 2 for which $y = 2$ and $y' = -3$ when $x = 1$.

SOLUTION: Because $y' = 2x^2 + 3x + C_1$, we substitute -3 for y' and 1 for x, giving $-3 = 2 + 3 + C_1$, or $C_1 = -8$. Substituting this value of C_1 into the complete solution gives

$$y = \tfrac{2}{3}x^3 + \tfrac{3}{2}x^2 - 8x + C_2$$

Because $y = 2$ when $x = 1$, we substitute these values in the above equation and get $2 = \tfrac{2}{3} + \tfrac{3}{2} - 8 + C_2$, from which we obtain $C_2 = \tfrac{47}{6}$. The particular solution desired, then, is

$$y = \tfrac{2}{3}x^3 + \tfrac{3}{2}x^2 - 8x + \tfrac{47}{6}$$

A more general type of differential equation of the first order is of the form

$$\frac{dy}{dx} = \frac{f(x)}{g(y)} \tag{7}$$

For such equations, the variables can be separated by multiplying on both sides of the equation by $g(y) \, dx$; thus, Eq. (7) can be written as

$$g(y) \, dy = f(x) \, dx$$

The following example gives us an equation of this type.

EXAMPLE 4:   The slope of the tangent line to a curve at any point (x, y) on the curve is equal to $3x^2y^2$. Find an equation of the curve if it contains the point $(2, 1)$.

SOLUTION: Because the slope of the tangent line to a curve at any point (x, y) is the value of the derivative at that point, we have

$$\frac{dy}{dx} = 3x^2y^2$$

This is a first-order differential equation, in which the variables can be separated, and we have

$$\frac{dy}{y^2} = 3x^2 \, dx$$

Antidifferentiating, we have

$$\int y^{-2} \, dy = \int 3x^2 \, dx$$

from which we obtain

$$-\frac{1}{y} = x^3 + C$$

This is an equation of a one-parameter family of curves. To find the particular curve of this family which contains the point $(2, 1)$, we substitute 2 for x and 1 for y, which gives us $-1 = 8 + C$, from which we obtain $C = -9$. Therefore, the required curve has the equation

$$-\frac{1}{y} = x^3 - 9$$

Exercises 5.4

In Exercises 1 through 8, find the complete solution of the given differential equation.

1. $\dfrac{dy}{dx} = 3x^2 + 2x - 7$

2. $\dfrac{dy}{dx} = (3x + 1)^3$

3. $\dfrac{dy}{dx} = 3xy^2$

4. $\dfrac{ds}{dt} = 5\sqrt{s}$

5. $\dfrac{dy}{dx} = \dfrac{3x\sqrt{1 + y^2}}{y}$

6. $\dfrac{dy}{dx} = \dfrac{\sqrt{x} + x}{\sqrt{y} - y}$

7. $\dfrac{d^2y}{dx^2} = 5x^2 + 1$

8. $\dfrac{d^2y}{dx^2} = \sqrt{2x - 3}$

In Exercises 9 through 14, for each of the differential equations find the particular solution determined by the given boundary conditions.

9. $\dfrac{dy}{dx} = x^2 - 2x - 4$; $y = -6$ when $x = 3$

10. $\dfrac{dy}{dx} = (x + 1)(x + 2)$; $y = -\frac{3}{2}$ when $x = -3$

11. $\dfrac{dx}{y} = \dfrac{4 \, dy}{x}$; $y = -2$ when $x = 4$

12. $\dfrac{dy}{dx} = \dfrac{x}{4\sqrt{(1 + x^2)^3}}$; $y = 0$ when $x = 1$

13. $\dfrac{d^2y}{dx^2} = 4(1 + 3x)^2$; $y = -1$ and $y' = -2$ when $x = -1$

14. $\dfrac{d^2y}{dx^2} = \sqrt[3]{3x - 1}$; $y = 2$ and $y' = 5$ when $x = 3$

15. The point $(3, 2)$ is on a curve, and at any point (x, y) on the curve the tangent line has a slope equal to $2x - 3$. Find an equation of the curve.

16. The slope of the tangent line at any point (x, y) on a curve is $3\sqrt{x}$. If the point $(9, 4)$ is on the curve, find an equation of the curve.

17. The points $(-1, 3)$ and $(0, 2)$ are on a curve, and at any point (x, y) on the curve $D_x^2 y = 2 - 4x$. Find an equation of the curve.

18. An equation of the tangent line to a curve at the point $(1, 3)$ is $y = x + 2$. If at any point (x, y) on the curve, $D_x^2 y = 6x$, find an equation of the curve.

19. At any point (x, y) on a curve, $D_x^2 y = 1 - x^2$, and an equation of the tangent line to the curve at the point $(1, 1)$ is $y = 2 - x$. Find an equation of the curve.

20. At any point (x, y) on a curve, $D_x^3 y = 2$, and $(1, 3)$ is a point of inflection at which the slope of the inflectional tangent is -2. Find an equation of the curve.

21. The equation $x^2 = 4ay$ represents a one-parameter family of parabolas. Find an equation of another one-parameter family of curves such that at any point (x, y) there is a curve of each family through it and the tangent lines to the two curves at this point are perpendicular. (HINT: First show that the slope of the tangent line at any point (x, y), not on the y axis, of the parabola of the given family through that point is $2y/x$.)

22. Solve Exercise 21 if the given one-parameter family of curves has the equation $x^3 + y^3 = a^3$.

5.5 ANTIDIFFERENTIATION AND RECTILINEAR MOTION

We learned in Secs. 3.2 and 4.7 that in considering the motion of a particle along a straight line, when an equation of motion, $s = f(t)$, is given, then the instantaneous velocity and the instantaneous acceleration can be determined from the equations

$$v = D_t s = f'(t)$$

and

$$a = D_t^2 s = D_t v = f''(t)$$

Hence, if we are given v or a as a function of t, as well as some boundary conditions, it is possible to determine the equation of motion by antidifferentiation. This is illustrated in the following example.

EXAMPLE 1: A particle is moving on a straight line; s is the number of feet in the directed distance of the particle from the origin at t sec of time, v is the number of ft/sec in the velocity of the particle at t sec, and a is the number of ft/sec² in the acceleration of the particle at t sec. If $a = 2t - 1$ and $v = 3$, and $s = 4$ when $t = 1$, express v and s as functions of t.

SOLUTION: Because $a = D_t v$, we have

$$\frac{dv}{dt} = 2t - 1$$

which, expressed in differential form, gives

$$dv = (2t - 1) \, dt$$

Antidifferentiating, we have

$$\int dv = \int (2t - 1) \, dt$$

from which we get

$$v = t^2 - t + C_1 \tag{1}$$

Substituting $v = 3$ and $t = 1$, we have

$$3 = 1 - 1 + C_1$$

and hence $C_1 = 3$. Therefore, substituting this value of C_1 into Eq. (1), we obtain

$$v = t^2 - t + 3 \qquad (2)$$

which expresses v as a function of t.

Now, letting $v = D_t s$ in Eq. (2), we have

$$\frac{ds}{dt} = t^2 - t + 3$$

and writing this in differential form gives

$$ds = (t^2 - t + 3)\, dt$$

Antidifferentiating, we get

$$s = \tfrac{1}{3}t^3 - \tfrac{1}{2}t^2 + 3t + C_2 \qquad (3)$$

Letting $s = 4$ and $t = 1$ in the above equation and solving for C_2, we obtain $C_2 = \tfrac{7}{6}$. Therefore, by substituting $\tfrac{7}{6}$ for C_2 in Eq. (3) we have s expressed as a function of t, which is

$$s = \tfrac{1}{3}t^3 - \tfrac{1}{2}t^2 + 3t + \tfrac{7}{6}$$

If an object is moving freely in a vertical line and is being pulled toward the earth by a force of gravity, the acceleration of *gravity*, denoted by g ft/sec^2, varies with the distance of the object from the center of the earth. However, for small changes of distances the acceleration of gravity is almost constant, and an approximate value of g if the object is near sea level is 32.

EXAMPLE 2:   A stone is thrown vertically upward from the ground with an initial velocity of 128 ft/sec. If the only force considered is that attributed to the acceleration of gravity, find how high the stone will rise and the speed with which it will strike the ground. Also, find how long it will take for the stone to strike the ground.

SOLUTION: The motion of the stone is illustrated in Fig. 5.5.1. The positive direction is taken as upward.

Let t = the number of seconds in the time that has elapsed since the stone was thrown;

s = the number of feet in the distance of the stone from the ground at t sec of time;

v = the number of feet per second in the velocity of the stone at t sec of time;

$|v|$ = the number of feet per second in the speed of the stone at t sec of time.

The stone will be at its highest point when the velocity is zero. Let $\bar{s}$ be the particular value of s when $v = 0$. When the stone strikes the ground, $s = 0$. Let $\bar{t}$ and $\bar{v}$ be the particular values of t and v when $s = 0$, and $t \neq 0$. Table 5.5.1 is a table of boundary conditions for this problem.

The positive direction of the stone from the starting point is taken as upward. Because the only acceleration is due to gravity, which is in the downward direction, the acceleration has a constant value of -32 ft/sec^2.

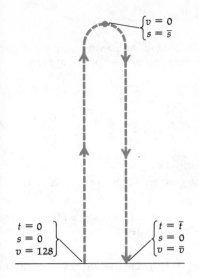

$$\begin{cases} v = 0 \\ s = \bar{s} \end{cases}$$

$$\begin{cases} t = 0 \\ s = 0 \\ v = 128 \end{cases}$$

$$\begin{cases} t = \bar{t} \\ s = 0 \\ v = \bar{v} \end{cases}$$

Figure 5.5.1

Table 5.5.1

t	0		$\bar{t}$
s	0	$\bar{s}$	0
v	128	0	$\bar{v}$

Because a is the derivative of v with respect to t, we have

$$\frac{dv}{dt} = -32$$

Writing this in differential form, we have

$$dv = -32 \, dt$$

Antidifferentiating, we have

$$\int dv = \int -32 \, dt$$

from which we obtain

$$v = -32t + C_1$$

Because $v = 128$ when $t = 0$, we substitute these values in the above and get $C_1 = 128$. Therefore, we have

$$v = -32t + 128 \tag{4}$$

Because v is the derivative of s with respect to t, then $v = ds/dt$, and so

$$\frac{ds}{dt} = -32t + 128$$

which in differential form is

$$ds = (-32t + 128) \, dt$$

Antidifferentiating gives

$$\int ds = \int (-32t + 128) \, dt$$

from which we obtain

$$s = -16t^2 + 128t + C_2$$

Because $s = 0$ when $t = 0$, we get $C_2 = 0$, and substituting 0 for C_2 in the above equation gives

$$s = -16t^2 + 128t$$

Substituting $\bar{t}$ for t and 0 for s, we get

$$0 = -16\bar{t}(\bar{t} - 8)$$

from which we obtain $\bar{t} = 0$ and $\bar{t} = 8$. However, the value 0 occurs when the stone is thrown; so we conclude that it takes 8 sec for the stone to strike the ground.

To obtain $\bar{v}$, substitute 8 for t and $\bar{v}$ for v in Eq. (4), which gives $\bar{v} = (-32)(8) + 128$, from which we obtain $\bar{v} = -128$. So $|\bar{v}| = 128$. Therefore, the stone strikes the ground with a speed of 128 ft/sec.

Exercises 5.5

In Exercises 1 through 4, a particle is moving on a straight line, s ft is the directed distance of the particle from the origin at t sec of time, v ft/sec is the velocity of the particle at t sec, and a ft/sec^2 is the acceleration of the particle at t sec.

1. $a = 5 - 2t$; $v = 2$ and $s = 0$ when $t = 0$. Express v and s in terms of t.

2. $a = 3t - t^2$; $v = \frac{7}{6}$ and $s = 1$ when $t = 1$. Express v and s in terms of t.

3. $a = 800$; $v = 20$ when $s = 1$. Find an equation involving v and s. $\left(\text{HINT: } a = \dfrac{dv}{dt} = \dfrac{dv}{ds} \dfrac{ds}{dt} = v \dfrac{dv}{ds} \right)$

4. $a = 2s + 1$; $v = 2$ when $s = 1$. (HINT: See Hint for Exercise 3.)

In Exercises 5 through 10, the only force considered is that due to the acceleration of gravity, which we take as 32 ft/sec^2 in the downward direction.

5. A stone is thrown vertically upward from the ground with an initial velocity of 20 ft/sec. How long will it take the stone to strike the ground, and with what speed will it strike? How long will the stone be going upward, and how high will it go?

6. A ball is dropped from the top of the Washington monument, which is 555 ft high. How long will it take the ball to reach the ground, and with what speed will it strike the ground?

7. A man in a balloon drops his binoculars when it is 150 ft above the ground and rising at the rate of 10 ft/sec. How long will it take the binoculars to strike the ground, and what is their speed on impact?

8. A stone is thrown vertically upward from the top of a house 60 ft above the ground with an initial velocity of 40 ft/sec. At what time will the stone reach its greatest height, and what is its greatest height? How long will it take the stone to pass the top of the house on its way down, and what is its velocity at that instant? How long will it take the stone to strike the ground, and with what velocity does it strike the ground?

9. A ball is thrown vertically upward with an initial velocity of 40 ft/sec from a point 20 ft above the ground. If v ft/sec is the velocity of the ball when it is s ft from the starting point, express v in terms of s. What is the velocity of the ball when it is 36 ft from the ground and rising? (HINT: See Hint for Exercise 3.)

10. If a ball is rolled across level ground with an initial velocity of 20 ft/sec and if the speed of the ball is decreasing at the rate of 6 ft/sec^2 due to friction, how far will the ball roll?

11. If the driver of an automobile wishes to increase his speed from 20 mi/hr to 50 mi/hr while traveling a distance of 528 ft, what constant acceleration should he maintain?

12. What constant acceleration (negative) will enable a driver to decrease his speed from 60 mi/hr to 20 mi/hr while traveling a distance of 300 ft?

13. If the brakes are applied on a car traveling 50 mi/hr and the brakes can give the car a constant negative acceleration of 20 ft/sec^2, how long will it take the car to come to a stop? How far will the car travel before stopping?

14. A ball started upward from the bottom of an inclined plane with an initial velocity of 6 ft/sec. If there is a downward acceleration of 4 ft/sec^2, how far up the plane will the ball go before rolling down?

15. If the brakes on a car can give the car a constant negative acceleration of 20 ft/sec^2, what is the greatest speed it may be going if it is necessary to be able to stop the car within 80 ft after the brake is applied?

5.6 APPLICATIONS OF ANTIDIFFERENTIATION IN ECONOMICS In Sec. 4.12 we learned that the marginal cost function and the marginal revenue function are the first derivatives of the total cost function and the total revenue function, respectively. Hence, if the marginal cost function and the marginal revenue function are known, the total cost function and the total revenue function are obtained from them by antidifferentiation.

In finding the total cost function from the marginal cost function, the arbitrary constant can be evaluated if we know either the fixed cost (i.e., the cost when no units are produced) or the cost of production of a specific number of units of the commodity. Because it is generally true that the total revenue is zero when the number of units produced is zero, this fact may be used to evaluate the arbitrary constant when finding the total revenue function from the marginal revenue function.

EXAMPLE 1: If the marginal revenue is given by $27 - 12x + x^2$, find the total revenue function and the demand equation. Also determine the permissible values of x. Draw sketches of the demand curve, the total revenue curve, and the marginal revenue curve on the same set of axes.

Figure 5.6.1

SOLUTION: If R is the total revenue function, the marginal revenue function is R', and

$$R'(x) = 27 - 12x + x^2$$

Antidifferentiating, we get

$$R(x) = 27x - 6x^2 + \tfrac{1}{3}x^3 + C$$

Because $R(0) = 0$, we get $C = 0$. Hence,

$$R(x) = 27x - 6x^2 + \tfrac{1}{3}x^3$$

If P is the price function, $R(x) = xP(x)$, and so

$$P(x) = 27 - 6x + \tfrac{1}{3}x^2$$

If we let p dollars be the price of one unit of the commodity when x units are demanded, and because $p = P(x)$, the demand equation is

$$3p = 81 - 18x + x^2$$

To determine the permissible values of x, we use the facts that $x \geq 0$, $p \geq 0$, and P is a decreasing function. Because

$$P'(x) = -6 + \tfrac{2}{3}x$$

P is decreasing when $x < 9$ (i.e., when $P'(x) < 0$). Also, when $x = 9$, $p = 0$, and so the permissible values of x are the numbers in the closed interval $[0, 9]$. The required sketches are shown in Fig. 5.6.1.

EXAMPLE 2: The marginal cost function C' is given by $C'(x) = 4x - 8$. If the cost of producing 5 units is $20, find the total cost

SOLUTION: The marginal cost must be nonnegative. Hence, $4x - 8 \geq 0$, and therefore the permissible values of x are $x \geq 2$.

$$C'(x) = 4x - 8$$

function. Determine the permissible values of x and draw sketches of the total cost curve and the marginal cost curve on the same set of axes.

Figure 5.6.2

Therefore,

$$C(x) = \int (4x - 8) \, dx$$

$$= 2x^2 - 8x + k$$

Because $C(5) = 20$, we get $k = 10$. Hence,

$$C(x) = 2x^2 - 8x + 10 \qquad (x \geq 2)$$

The required sketches are shown in Fig. 5.6.2.

EXAMPLE 3: After experimentation, a certain manufacturer determined that if x units of a particular commodity are produced per week, the marginal cost is given by $0.3x - 11$, where the production cost is in dollars. If the selling price of the commodity is fixed at $19 per unit, and the fixed cost is $100 per week, find the maximum weekly profit that can be obtained.

SOLUTION: Let $C(x) =$ the number of dollars in the total production cost of x units;

$P(x) =$ the number of dollars in the selling price of one unit if x units are produced;

$R(x) =$ the number of dollars in the total revenue obtained by selling x units;

$S(x) =$ the number of dollars in the profit obtained by selling x units.

Because $R(x) = xP(x)$, we have

$$R(x) = 19x$$

The marginal revenue then is given by

$$R'(x) = 19$$

C' is the marginal cost function, and we are given that

$$C'(x) = 0.3x - 11$$

The profit will be a maximum when marginal revenue equals marginal cost (see Sec. 4.12). Equating $R'(x)$ and $C'(x)$, we get $x = 100$. So 100 units should be produced each week for maximum profit.

$$C(x) = \int (0.3x - 11) \, dx$$

$$= 0.15x^2 - 11x + k$$

Because the fixed cost is \$100, $C(0) = 100$, and hence $k = 100$. Therefore,

$$C(x) = 0.15x^2 - 11x + 100$$

Setting $S(x) = R(x) - C(x)$, we have

$$S(x) = 19x - (0.15x^2 - 11x + 100)$$

$$= -0.15x^2 + 30x - 100$$

Hence, $S(100) = 1400$. Therefore, the maximum weekly profit is \$1400, which is obtained if 100 units are produced weekly.

EXAMPLE 4: A business firm has made an analysis of its production facilities and its personnel. With the present equipment and number of workers, the firm can produce 3000 units per day. It was estimated that without any change in investment, the rate of change of the number of units produced per day with respect to a change in the number of additional workers is $80 - 6x^{1/2}$, where x is the number of additional workers. Find the daily production if 25 workers are added to the labor force.

SOLUTION: Let $y = $ the number of units produced per day. Then

$$\frac{dy}{dx} = 80 - 6x^{1/2}$$

from which we get

$$dy = (80 - 6x^{1/2}) \, dx$$

Antidifferentiating gives us

$$y = 80x - 4x^{3/2} + C$$

Because $y = 3000$ when $x = 0$, we get $C = 3000$. Hence,

$$y = 80x - 4x^{3/2} + 3000$$

Letting y_{25} be the value of y when $x = 25$, we have

$$y_{25} = 2000 - 500 + 3000$$

$$= 4500$$

Therefore, 4500 units are produced per day if the labor force is increased by 25 workers.

Exercises 5.6

1. Find an equation of the total revenue curve of a company if its slope at any point is given by $12 - 3x$ and $P(4) = 6$, where P is the price function. Draw sketches of the total revenue curve and the demand curve on the same set of axes.

2. The rate of change of the slope of the total cost curve of a particular company is the constant 2, and the total cost curve contains the points (2, 12) and (3, 18). Find the total cost function.

3. Find the demand equation for a commodity for which the marginal revenue function is given by $10/(x + 5)^2 - 4$.

4. The marginal cost function is given by $3/\sqrt{2x + 4}$. If the fixed cost is zero, find the total cost function.

5. The marginal revenue function is given by $16 - 3x^2$. Find the permissible values of x, the total revenue function, and

the demand equation. Draw sketches of the demand curve, the total revenue curve, and the marginal revenue curve on the same set of axes.

6. Find the total revenue function, the demand equation, and the permissible values of x if the marginal revenue function is given by $\frac{3}{4}x^2 - 10x + 12$. Also draw sketches of the demand curve, the total revenue curve, and the marginal revenue curve on the same set of axes.

7. The marginal cost function is given by $3x^2 + 8x + 4$, and the fixed cost is $6. If $C(x)$ dollars is the total cost of x units, find the total cost function, and draw sketches of the total cost curve and the marginal cost curve on the same set of axes.

8. The marginal cost function C' is defined by $C'(x) = 6x$, where $C(x)$ is the number of hundreds of dollars in the total cost of x hundred units of a certain commodity. If the cost of 200 units is $2000, find the total cost function and the fixed cost. Draw sketches of the total cost curve and the marginal cost curve on the same set of axes.

9. The cost of a certain piece of machinery is $700 and its value depreciates with time according to the formula $D_t V = -500(t + 1)^{-2}$ where V dollars is its value t years after its purchase. What is its value three years after its purchase?

10. Suppose that a particular company estimates its growth in income from sales by the formula $D_t S = 2(t - 1)^{2/3}$, where S millions of dollars is the gross income from sales t years hence. If the gross income from the current year's sales is $8 million, what should be the expected gross income from sales two years from now?

Review Exercises (Chapter 5)

In Exercises 1 through 6, find the most general antiderivative.

1. $\int \dfrac{\sqrt[4]{x^3}}{3x^2} \, dx$

2. $\int \left(\sqrt[3]{t} - \dfrac{1}{\sqrt[3]{t}} \right) dt$

3. $\int 5x \sqrt{2 + 3x^2} \, dx$

4. $\int (x^3 + x) \sqrt{x^2 + 3} \, dx$

5. $\int \sqrt{4x + 3}(x^2 + 1) \, dx$

6. $\int \left(\dfrac{x^3 + 2}{x^3} \right) \sqrt{x - \dfrac{1}{x^2}} \, dx$

In Exercises 7 through 10, find the complete solution of the given differential equation.

7. $x^2 y \dfrac{dy}{dx} = (y^2 - 1)^2$

8. $\dfrac{dy}{dx} = \dfrac{x + 1}{\sqrt{x}}$

9. $y^2 \, dx + y^2 \, dy = dy$

10. $\dfrac{d^2 y}{dx^2} = 12x^2 - 30x$

11. If $y = 80x - 16x^2$, find the difference $\Delta y - dy$ if (a) $x = 2$, $\Delta x = 0.1$; (b) $x = 4$, $\Delta x = -0.2$.

12. Use differentials to find an approximate value of $\sqrt[3]{126}$.

13. The slope of the tangent line at any point (x, y) on a curve is $10 - 4x$ and the point $(1, -1)$ is on the curve. Find an equation of the curve.

14. At any point (x, y) on a curve $D_x^2 y = 4 - x^2$ and an equation of the tangent line to the curve at the point $(1, -1)$ is $2x - 3y = 3$. Find an equation of the curve.

15. If $x^3 + y^3 - 3xy^2 + 1 = 0$, find dy at the point $(1, 1)$ if $dx = 0.1$.

16. Find dy/dt if $y = x^3 - 2x + 1$ and $x^3 + t^3 - 3t = 0$.

17. Find dy/dt if $8x^3 + 27y^3 - 4xy = 0$ and $t^3 + t^2 x - x^3 = 4$.

18. Evaluate $\int (x^4)^6 4x^3 \, dx$ as $\int u^6 \, du$ and as $\int 4x^{27} \, dx$ and compare the results.

19. Evaluate $\int (x^3 + 1)^2 x^2 \, dx$ by two methods: (a) Make the substitution $u = x^3 + 1$; (b) first expand $(x^3 + 1)^2$. Compare the results and explain the difference in the appearance of the answers obtained in (a) and (b).

20. Find the particular solution of the differential equation $x^2 \, dy = y^3 \, dx$ for which $y = 1$ when $x = 4$.

21. Find the particular solution of the differential equation $D_x{}^2 y = \sqrt{x+4}$ for which $y = 3$ and $y' = 2$ when $x = 4$.

22. A ball is thrown vertically upward from the top of a house 64 ft above the ground, and the initial velocity is 48 ft/sec. How long will it take the ball to reach its greatest height, and what is its greatest height? How long will it take the ball to strike the ground and with what velocity does it strike the ground?

23. Suppose the ball in Exercise 22 is thrown downward with an initial velocity of 48 ft/sec. How long will it take the ball to strike the ground and with what velocity does it strike the ground?

24. Suppose the ball in Exercise 22 is dropped from the top of the house. Determine how long it takes for the ball to strike the ground and the velocity when it strikes the ground.

25. Neglecting air resistance, if an object is dropped from an airplane at a height of 30,000 ft above the ocean, how long would it take the object to strike the water?

26. Suppose a bullet is fired directly downward from the airplane in Exercise 25 with a muzzle velocity of 2500 ft/sec. If air resistance is neglected, how long would it take the bullet to reach the ocean?

27. A container in the form of a cube having a volume of 1000 in.³ is to be made by using 6 equal squares of material costing 2 cents per square inch. How accurately must the side of each square be made so that the total cost of the material shall be correct to within 50 cents?

28. The measure of the radius of a right-circular cone is $\frac{3}{4}$ times the measure of the altitude. How accurately must the altitude be measured if the error in the computed volume is not to exceed 3%?

29. If t sec is the time for one complete swing of a simple pendulum of length l ft, then $4\pi^2 l = gt^2$, where $g = 32.2$. What is the effect upon the time if an error of 0.01 ft is made in measuring the length of the pendulum?

30. An automobile traveling at a constant speed of 60 mi/hr along a straight highway fails to stop at a stop sign. If 3 sec later a highway patrol car starts from rest from the stop sign and maintains a constant acceleration of 8 ft/sec², how long will it take the patrol car to overtake the automobile, and how far from the stop sign will this occur? Also determine the speed of the patrol car when it overtakes the automobile.

31. If $f(x) = x + |x - 1|$, and

$$F(x) = \begin{cases} x & \text{if } x < 1 \\ x^2 - x + 1 & \text{if } x \geq 1 \end{cases}$$

show that F is an antiderivative of f on $(-\infty, +\infty)$.

32. Let f and g be two functions such that for all x in $(-\infty, +\infty)$, $f'(x) = g(x)$ and $g'(x) = -f(x)$. Furthermore, suppose that $f(0) = 0$ and $g(0) = 1$. Prove that $[f(x)]^2 + [g(x)]^2 = 1$. (HINT: Consider the functions F and G where $F(x) = [f(x)]^2$ and $G(x) = -[g(x)]^2$ and show that $F'(x) = G'(x)$ for all x.)

33. The marginal revenue function is given by $ab/(x+b)^2 - c$. Find the total revenue function and the demand equation.

6

The Definite Integral

6.1 THE SIGMA NOTATION

In this chapter we are concerned with the sums of many terms, and so a notation called the sigma notation is introduced to facilitate writing these sums. This notation involves the use of the symbol Σ, the capital sigma of the Greek alphabet, which corresponds to our letter S. Here are some examples of the sigma notation:

$$\sum_{i=1}^{5} i^2 = 1^2 + 2^2 + 3^2 + 4^2 + 5^2$$

$$\sum_{i=-2}^{2} (3i + 2) = [3(-2) + 2] + [3(-1) + 2] + [3 \cdot 0 + 2]$$
$$+ [3 \cdot 1 + 2] + [3 \cdot 2 + 2]$$
$$= (-4) + (-1) + 2 + 5 + 8$$

$$\sum_{j=1}^{n} j^3 = 1^3 + 2^3 + 3^3 + \cdots + n^3$$

$$\sum_{k=3}^{8} \frac{1}{k} = \frac{1}{3} + \frac{1}{4} + \frac{1}{5} + \frac{1}{6} + \frac{1}{7} + \frac{1}{8}$$

We have, in general,

$$\sum_{i=m}^{n} F(i) = F(m) + F(m+1) + F(m+2) + \cdots + F(n) \qquad (1)$$

where m and n are integers, and $m \le n$.

The right side of formula (1) consists of the sum of $(n - m + 1)$ terms, the first of which is obtained by replacing i by m in $F(i)$, the second by replacing i by $(m + 1)$ in $F(i)$, and so on, until the last term is obtained by replacing i by n in $F(i)$.

The number m is called the *lower limit* of the sum, and n is called the *upper limit*. The symbol i is called the *index of summation*. It is a "dummy" symbol because any other letter can be used. For example,

$$\sum_{i=3}^{5} i^2 = 3^2 + 4^2 + 5^2$$

is the same as

$$\sum_{k=3}^{5} k^2 = 3^2 + 4^2 + 5^2$$

We give an example of formula (1):

$$\sum_{i=3}^{6} \frac{i^2}{i+1} = \frac{3^2}{3+1} + \frac{4^2}{4+1} + \frac{5^2}{5+1} + \frac{6^2}{6+1}$$

Sometimes the terms of the sum involve subscripts, as illustrated here:

$$\sum_{i=1}^{n} A_i = A_1 + A_2 + \cdots + A_n$$

$$\sum_{k=4}^{9} kb_k = 4b_4 + 5b_5 + 6b_6 + 7b_7 + 8b_8 + 9b_9$$

$$\sum_{i=1}^{5} f(x_i) \, \Delta x = f(x_1) \, \Delta x + f(x_2) \, \Delta x + f(x_3) \, \Delta x + f(x_4) \, \Delta x + f(x_5) \, \Delta x$$

The following properties of the sigma notation are useful, and they are easily proved.

6.1.1 Property 1 $\displaystyle\sum_{i=1}^{n} c = cn$ where c is any constant.

The proof is left for the reader (see Exercise 9).

6.1.2 Property 2 $\displaystyle\sum_{i=1}^{n} c \cdot F(i) = c \sum_{i=1}^{n} F(i)$ where c is any constant.

PROOF:

$$\sum_{i=1}^{n} c \cdot F(i) = c \cdot F(1) + c \cdot F(2) + c \cdot F(3) + \cdots + c \cdot F(n)$$

$$= c[F(1) + F(2) + F(3) + \cdots + F(n)]$$

$$= c \sum_{i=1}^{n} F(i)$$

6.1.3 Property 3 $\sum_{i=1}^{n} [F(i) + G(i)] = \sum_{i=1}^{n} F(i) + \sum_{i=1}^{n} G(i).$

The proof is left for the reader (see Exercise 10). Property 3 can be extended to the sum of any number of functions.

6.1.4 Property 4 $\sum_{i=1}^{n} [F(i) - F(i-1)] = F(n) - F(0).$

$$\sum_{i=1}^{n} [F(i) - F(i-1)] = [F(1) - F(0)] + [F(2) - F(1)] + [F(3) - F(2)] + \cdots$$

$$+ [F(n-1) - F(n-2)] + [F(n) - F(n-1)]$$

$$= -F(0) + [F(1) - F(1)] + [F(2) - F(2)]$$

$$+ \cdots + [F(n-1) - F(n-1)] + F(n)$$

$$= -F(0) + 0 + 0 + \cdots + 0 + F(n)$$

$$= F(n) - F(0)$$

The following formulas, which are numbered for future reference, are also useful.

6.1.5 Formula 1 $\sum_{i=1}^{n} i = \dfrac{n(n+1)}{2}.$

6.1.6 Formula 2 $\sum_{i=1}^{n} i^2 = \dfrac{n(n+1)(2n+1)}{6}.$

6.1.7 Formula 3 $\sum_{i=1}^{n} i^3 = \dfrac{n^2(n+1)^2}{4}.$

6.1.8 Formula 4 $\sum_{i=1}^{n} i^4 = \dfrac{n(n+1)(6n^3 + 9n^2 + n - 1)}{30}.$

These formulas can be proved with or without using mathematical induction.

EXAMPLE 1: Prove Formula 1 without using mathematical induction.

SOLUTION:

$$\sum_{i=1}^{n} i = 1 + 2 + 3 + \cdots + (n-1) + n$$

and

$$\sum_{i=1}^{n} i = n + (n-1) + (n-2) + \cdots + 2 + 1$$

If we add these two equations term by term, the left side is

$$2 \sum_{i=1}^{n} i$$

and on the right side there are n terms, each having the value $(n+1)$. Hence,

$$2 \sum_{i=1}^{n} i = (n+1) + (n+1) + (n+1) + \cdots + (n+1) \qquad n \text{ terms}$$

$$= n(n+1)$$

Therefore,

$$\sum_{i=1}^{n} i = \frac{n(n+1)}{2}$$

The proof of Formula 1 by mathematical induction is left for the reader (see Exercise 11).

EXAMPLE 2: Prove Formula 2 by mathematical induction.

SOLUTION: We wish to prove that

$$\sum_{i=1}^{n} i^2 = \frac{n(n+1)(2n+1)}{6}$$

First the formula is verified for $n = 1$. The left side is then $\sum_{i=1}^{1} i^2 = 1$. When $n = 1$, the right side is $[1(1+1)(2+1)]/6 = (1 \cdot 2 \cdot 3)/6 = 1$. Therefore, the formula is true when $n = 1$. Now we assume that the formula is true for $n = k$, where k is any positive integer; and with this assumption we wish to prove that the formula is also true for $n = k + 1$. If the formula is true for $n = k$, we have

$$\sum_{i=1}^{k} i^2 = \frac{k(k+1)(2k+1)}{6} \tag{2}$$

When $n = k + 1$, we have

$$\sum_{i=1}^{k+1} i^2 = 1^2 + 2^2 + 3^2 + \cdots + k^2 + (k+1)^2$$

$$= \sum_{i=1}^{k} i^2 + (k+1)^2$$

$$= \frac{k(k+1)(2k+1)}{6} + (k+1)^2 \quad \text{(by applying Eq. (2))}$$

$$= \frac{k(k+1)(2k+1) + 6(k+1)^2}{6}$$

$$= \frac{(k+1)[k(2k+1) + 6(k+1)]}{6}$$

$$= \frac{(k+1)(2k^2 + 7k + 6)}{6}$$

$$= \frac{(k+1)(k+2)(2k+3)}{6}$$

$$= \frac{(k+1)[(k+1) + 1][2(k+1) + 1]}{6}$$

Therefore, the formula is true for $n = k + 1$. We have proved that the formula holds for $n = 1$, and we have also proved that when the formula holds for $n = k$, the formula also holds for $n = k + 1$. Therefore, it follows that the formula holds when n is any positive integer.

A proof of Formula 2, analogous to the proof of Formula 1, without using mathematical induction is left for the reader. The proofs of Formulas 3 and 4 are also left to the reader (see Exercises 12 to 16).

EXAMPLE 3: Evaluate

$$\sum_{i=1}^{n} (4^i - 4^{i-1})$$

SOLUTION: From Property 4, where $F(i) = 4^i$, it follows that

$$\sum_{i=1}^{n} (4^i - 4^{i-1}) = 4^n - 4^0$$

$$= 4^n - 1$$

EXAMPLE 4: Evaluate

$$\sum_{i=1}^{n} i(3i - 2)$$

by using Properties 1–4 and Formulas 1–4.

SOLUTION:

$$\sum_{i=1}^{n} i(3i - 2) = \sum_{i=1}^{n} (3i^2 - 2i)$$

$$= \sum_{i=1}^{n} (3i^2) + \sum_{i=1}^{n} (-2i) \quad \text{(by Property 3)}$$

$$= 3 \sum_{i=1}^{n} i^2 - 2 \sum_{i=1}^{n} i \quad \text{(by Property 2)}$$

$$= 3 \cdot \frac{n(n+1)(2n+1)}{6} - 2 \cdot \frac{n(n+1)}{2} \quad \text{(by Formulas 2 and 1)}$$

$$= \frac{2n^3 + 3n^2 + n - 2n^2 - 2n}{2}$$

$$= \frac{2n^3 + n^2 - n}{2}$$

Exercises 6.1

In Exercises 1 through 8, find the given sum.

1. $\displaystyle\sum_{i=1}^{6} (3i - 2)$

2. $\displaystyle\sum_{i=1}^{7} (i + 1)^2$

3. $\displaystyle\sum_{i=2}^{5} \frac{i}{i - 1}$

4. $\displaystyle\sum_{j=3}^{6} \frac{2}{j(j - 2)}$

5. $\displaystyle\sum_{i=-2}^{3} 2^i$

6. $\displaystyle\sum_{i=0}^{3} \frac{1}{1 + i^2}$

7. $\displaystyle\sum_{k=1}^{4} \frac{(-1)^{k+1}}{k}$

8. $\displaystyle\sum_{k=-2}^{3} \frac{k}{k + 3}$

9. Prove Property 1 (6.1.1).

10. Prove Property 3 (6.1.3).

11. Prove Formula 1 (6.1.5) by mathematical induction.

12. Prove Formula 2 (6.1.6) without using mathematical induction. (HINT: $i^3 - (i - 1)^3 = 3i^2 - 3i + 1$, so that

$$\sum_{i=1}^{n} [i^3 - (i - 1)^3] = \sum_{i=1}^{n} (3i^2 - 3i + 1)$$

On the left side of the above equation, use Property 4; on the right side, use Properties 1, 2, and 3 and Formula 1.)

13. Prove Formula 3 (6.1.7) without using mathematical induction. (HINT: $i^4 - (i - 1)^4 = 4i^3 - 6i^2 + 4i - 1$, and use a method similar to the one for Exercise 12.)

14. Prove Formula 4 (6.1.8) without using mathematical induction (see hints for Exercises 12 and 13 above).

15. Prove Formula 3 (6.1.7) by mathematical induction.

16. Prove Formula 4 (6.1.8) by mathematical induction.

In Exercises 17 through 25, evaluate the indicated sum by using Properties 1 through 4 and formulas 1 through 4.

17. $\displaystyle\sum_{i=1}^{25} 2i(i - 1)$

18. $\displaystyle\sum_{i=1}^{20} 3i(i^2 + 2)$

19. $\displaystyle\sum_{i=1}^{n} (10^{i+1} - 10^i)$

20. $\displaystyle\sum_{k=1}^{n} (2^{k-1} - 2^k)$

21. $\displaystyle\sum_{k=1}^{100} \left[\frac{1}{k} - \frac{1}{k + 1} \right]$

22. $\displaystyle\sum_{i=1}^{40} [\sqrt{2i + 1} - \sqrt{2i - 1}]$

23. $\displaystyle\sum_{i=1}^{n} 4i^2(i-2)$

24. $\displaystyle\sum_{i=1}^{n} 2i(1+i^2)$

25. $\displaystyle\sum_{k=1}^{n} [(3^{-k}-3^k)^2 - (3^{k-1}+3^{-k-1})^2]$

26. Prove: $\displaystyle\sum_{i=-n}^{n} \left[1-\left(\frac{i}{n}\right)^2\right]^{1/2} = 2\sum_{i=1}^{n} \left[1-\left(\frac{i}{n}\right)^2\right]^{1/2} + 1$

27. (a) Use Property 4 to show that

$$\sum_{i=1}^{n} [F(i+1) - F(i-1)] = F(n+1) + F(n) - F(1) - F(0)$$

(b) Prove that

$$\sum_{i=1}^{n} [(i+1)^3 - (i-1)^3] = (n+1)^3 + n^3 - 1$$

(c) Prove that

$$\sum_{i=1}^{n} [(i+1)^3 - (i-1)^3] = \sum_{i=1}^{n} (6i^2+2) = 2n + 6\sum_{i=1}^{n} i^2$$

(d) Using the results of parts (b) and (c), prove Formula 2.

28. Use the method of Exercise 27 to prove Formula 3.

29. If $\displaystyle \bar{x} = \frac{\displaystyle\sum_{i=1}^{n} x_i}{n}$, prove that $\displaystyle\sum_{i=1}^{n} (x_i - \bar{x})^2 = \sum_{i=1}^{n} x_i^2 - \bar{x}\sum_{i=1}^{n} x_i$

Figure 6.2.1

Figure 6.2.2

6.2 AREA

We use the word *measure* extensively throughout the book. A measure refers to a number (no units are included). For example, if the area of a triangle is 10 in.², we say that the measure of the area of the triangle is 10. You probably have an intuitive idea of what is meant by the measure of the area of certain geometrical figures; it is a number that in some way gives the size of the region enclosed by the figure. The area of a rectangle is the product of its length and width, and the area of a triangle is half the product of the lengths of the base and the altitude.

The area of a polygon can be defined as the sum of the areas of triangles into which it is decomposed, and it can be proved that the area thus obtained is independent of how the polygon is decomposed into triangles (see Fig. 6.2.1). However, how do we define the measure of the area of a region in a plane if the region is bounded by a curve? Are we even certain that such a region has an area?

Let us consider a region R in the plane as shown in Fig. 6.2.2. The region R is bounded by the x axis, the lines $x = a$ and $x = b$, and the curve having the equation $y = f(x)$, where f is a function continuous on the closed interval $[a, b]$. For simplicity, we take $f(x) \geq 0$ for all x in $[a, b]$. We wish to assign a number A to be the measure of the area of R. We use a limiting process similar to the one used in defining the area of a circle: The area of a circle is defined as the limit of the areas of inscribed regular polygons as the number of sides increases without bound. We realize intuitively that, whatever number is chosen to represent A, that number must be at least as great as the measure of the area of any polygonal region contained in R, and must be no greater than the measure of the area of any polygonal region containing R.

We first define a polygonal region contained in R. Divide the closed interval $[a, b]$ into n subintervals. For simplicity, we shall now take each of these subintervals as being of equal length, for instance, Δx. Therefore, $\Delta x = (b - a)/n$. Denote the endpoints of these subintervals by x_0, x_1, x_2, . . . , x_{n-1}, x_n, where $x_0 = a$, $x_1 = a + \Delta x$, . . . , $x_i = a + i\,\Delta x$, . . . , $x_{n-1} = a + (n-1)\,\Delta x$, $x_n = b$. Let the ith subinterval be denoted by $[x_{i-1}, x_i]$. Because f is continuous on the closed interval $[a, b]$, it is continuous on each closed subinterval. By the extreme-value theorem (4.3.9), there is a number in each subinterval for which f has an absolute minimum value. In the ith subinterval, let this number be c_i, so that $f(c_i)$ is the absolute minimum value of f on the subinterval $[x_{i-1}, x_i]$. Consider n rectangles, each having a width Δx units and an altitude $f(c_i)$ units (see Fig. 6.2.3). Let the sum of the areas of these n rectangles be given by S_n square units; then

$$S_n = f(c_1)\,\Delta x + f(c_2)\,\Delta x + \cdots + f(c_i)\,\Delta x + \cdots + f(c_n)\,\Delta x$$

or, with the sigma notation,

$$S_n = \sum_{i=1}^{n} f(c_i)\,\Delta x \tag{1}$$

Figure 6.2.3

The summation on the right side of Eq. (1) gives the sum of the measures of the areas of n inscribed rectangles. Thus, however we define A, it must be such that

$$A \geq S_n$$

In Fig. 6.2.3 the shaded region has an area of S_n square units. Now, let n increase. Specifically, multiply n by 2; then the number of rectangles is doubled, and the width of each rectangle is halved. This is illustrated in Fig. 6.2.4, showing twice as many rectangles as Fig. 6.2.3. By comparing the two figures, notice that the shaded region in Fig. 6.2.4 appears to approximate the region R more nearly than that of Fig. 6.2.3. So the sum of the measures of the areas of the rectangles in Fig. 6.2.4 is closer to the number we wish to represent the measure of the area of R.

Figure 6.2.4

As n increases, the values of S_n found from Eq. (1) increase, and successive values of S_n differ from each other by amounts that become arbitrarily small. This is proved in advanced calculus by a theorem which states that if f is continuous on $[a, b]$, then as n increases without bound, the value of S_n given by (1) approaches a limit. It is this limit that we take as the definition of the measure of the area of region R.

6.2.1 Definition   Suppose that the function f is continuous on the closed interval $[a, b]$, with $f(x) \geq 0$ for all x in $[a, b]$, and that R is the region bounded by the curve $y = f(x)$, the x axis, and the lines $x = a$ and $x = b$. Divide the interval $[a, b]$

into n subintervals, each of length $\Delta x = (b-a)/n$, and denote the ith subinterval by $[x_{i-1}, x_i]$. Then if $f(c_i)$ is the absolute minimum function value on the ith subinterval, the measure of the area of region R is given by

$$A = \lim_{n \to +\infty} \sum_{i=1}^{n} f(c_i)\, \Delta x \tag{2}$$

Equation (2) means that, for any $\epsilon > 0$, there is a number $N > 0$ such that

$$\left| \sum_{i=1}^{n} f(c_i)\, \Delta x - A \right| < \epsilon \qquad \text{whenever } n > N$$

and n is a positive integer.

We could take circumscribed rectangles instead of inscribed rectangles. In this case, we take as the measures of the altitudes of the rectangles the absolute maximum value of f on each subinterval. The existence of an absolute maximum value of f on each subinterval is guaranteed by the extreme-value theorem (4.3.9). The corresponding sums of the measures of the areas of the circumscribed rectangles are at least as great as the measure of the area of the region R, and it can be shown that the limit of these sums as n increases without bound is exactly the same as the limit of the sum of the measures of the areas of the inscribed rectangles. This is also proved in advanced calculus. Thus, we could define the measure of the area of the region R by

$$A = \lim_{n \to +\infty} \sum_{i=1}^{n} f(d_i)\, \Delta x \tag{3}$$

where $f(d_i)$ is the absolute maximum value of f on $[x_{i-1}, x^i]$.

The measure of the altitude of the rectangle in the ith subinterval actually can be taken as the function value of any number in that subinterval, and the limit of the sum of the measures of the areas of the rectangles is the same no matter what numbers are selected. This is also proved in advanced calculus, and later in this chapter we extend the definition of the measure of the area of a region to be the limit of such a sum.

EXAMPLE 1:   Find the area of the region bounded by the curve $y = x^2$, the x axis, and the line $x = 3$ by taking inscribed rectangles.

SOLUTION: Figure 6.2.5 shows the region and the ith inscribed rectangle. We apply Definition 6.2.1. Divide the closed interval $[0, 3]$ into n subintervals, each of length Δx: $x_0 = 0$, $x_1 = \Delta x$, $x_2 = 2\,\Delta x$, . . . , $x_i = i\,\Delta x$, . . . , $x_{n-1} = (n-1)\,\Delta x$, $x_n = 3$.

$$\Delta x = \frac{3-0}{n} = \frac{3}{n}$$

The function value $f(x) = x^2$ and because f is increasing on $[0, 3]$, the absolute minimum value of f on the ith subinterval $[x_{i-1}, x_i]$ is $f(x_{i-1})$.

Figure 6.2.5

Therefore, from Eq. (2)

$$A = \lim_{n \to +\infty} \sum_{i=1}^{n} f(x_{i-1}) \, \Delta x \tag{4}$$

Because $x_{i-1} = (i-1) \, \Delta x$ and $f(x) = x^2$, we have

$$f(x_{i-1}) = [(i-1) \, \Delta x]^2$$

Therefore,

$$\sum_{i=1}^{n} f(x_{i-1}) \, \Delta x = \sum_{i=1}^{n} (i-1)^2 (\Delta x)^3$$

But $\Delta x = 3/n$, so that

$$\sum_{i=1}^{n} f(x_{i-1}) \, \Delta x = \sum_{i=1}^{n} (i-1)^2 \frac{27}{n^3} = \frac{27}{n^3} \sum_{i=1}^{n} (i-1)^2$$

$$= \frac{27}{n^3} \left[\sum_{i=1}^{n} i^2 - 2 \sum_{i=1}^{n} i + \sum_{i=1}^{n} 1 \right]$$

and using Formulas 2 and 1 and Property 1 from Sec. 6.1, we get

$$\sum_{i=1}^{n} f(x_{i-1}) \, \Delta x = \frac{27}{n^3} \left[\frac{n(n+1)(2n+1)}{6} - 2 \cdot \frac{n(n+1)}{2} + n \right]$$

$$= \frac{27}{n^3} \cdot \frac{2n^3 + 3n^2 + n - 6n^2 - 6n + 6n}{6}$$

$$= \frac{9}{2} \cdot \frac{2n^2 - 3n + 1}{n^2}$$

Then, from Eq. (4), we have

$$A = \lim_{n \to +\infty} \left[\frac{9}{2} \cdot \frac{2n^2 - 3n + 1}{n^2} \right]$$

$$= \frac{9}{2} \cdot \lim_{n \to +\infty} \left(2 - \frac{3}{n} + \frac{1}{n^2} \right)$$

$$= \tfrac{9}{2} (2 - 0 + 0)$$

$$= 9$$

Therefore, the area of the region is 9 square units.

EXAMPLE 2:   Find the area of the region in Example 1 by taking circumscribed rectangles.

SOLUTION: We take as the measure of the altitude of the ith rectangle the absolute maximum value of f on the ith subinterval $[x_{i-1}, x_i]$ which is $f(x_i)$. From Eq. (3), we have

$$A = \lim_{n \to +\infty} \sum_{i=1}^{n} f(x_i) \, \Delta x \tag{5}$$

Because $x_i = i \, \Delta x$, then $f(x_i) = (i \, \Delta x)^2$, and so

$$\sum_{i=1}^{n} f(x_i) \, \Delta x = \sum_{i=1}^{n} i^2 (\Delta x)^3 = \frac{27}{n^3} \sum_{i=1}^{n} i^2$$

$$= \frac{27}{n^3} \left[\frac{n(n+1)(2n+1)}{6} \right]$$

$$= \frac{9}{2} \cdot \frac{2n^2 + 3n + 1}{n^2}$$

Therefore, from Eq. (5), we obtain

$$A = \lim_{n \to +\infty} \frac{9}{2} \cdot \left(2 + \frac{3}{n} + \frac{1}{n^2} \right)$$

$$= 9 \quad \text{(as in Example 1)}$$

EXAMPLE 3:   Find the area of the trapezoid which is the region bounded by the line $2x + y = 8$, the x axis, and the lines $x = 1$ and $x = 3$. Take inscribed rectangles.

Figure 6.2.6

SOLUTION: The region and the ith inscribed rectangle are shown in Fig. 6.2.6. The closed interval $[1, 3]$ is divided into n subintervals, each of length Δx; $x_0 = 1$, $x_1 = 1 + \Delta x$, $x_2 = 1 + 2 \, \Delta x$, . . . , $x_i = 1 + i \, \Delta x$, . . . , $x_{n-1} = 1 + (n-1) \, \Delta x$, $x_n = 3$.

$$\Delta x = \frac{3-1}{n} = \frac{2}{n}$$

Solving the equation of the line for y, we obtain $y = -2x + 8$. Therefore, $f(x) = -2x + 8$, and because f is decreasing on $[1, 3]$, the absolute minimum value of f on the ith subinterval $[x_{i-1}, x_i]$ is $f(x_i)$. Because $x_i = 1 + i \, \Delta x$, and $f(x) = -2x + 8$, $f(x_i) = -2(1 + i \, \Delta x) + 8 = 6 - 2i \, \Delta x$. From Eq. (2), we have

$$A = \lim_{n \to +\infty} \sum_{i=1}^{n} f(x_i) \, \Delta x$$

$$= \lim_{n \to +\infty} \sum_{i=1}^{n} (6 - 2i \, \Delta x) \, \Delta x$$

$$= \lim_{n \to +\infty} \sum_{i=1}^{n} [6 \, \Delta x - 2i (\Delta x)^2]$$

$$= \lim_{n \to +\infty} \sum_{i=1}^{n} \left[6 \left(\frac{2}{n} \right) - 2i \left(\frac{2}{n} \right)^2 \right]$$

$$= \lim_{n \to +\infty} \left[\frac{12}{n} \sum_{i=1}^{n} 1 - \frac{8}{n^2} \sum_{i=1}^{n} i \right]$$

Using Property 1 (6.1.1) and Formula 1 (6.1.5), we have

$$A = \lim_{n \to +\infty} \left[\frac{12}{n} \cdot n - \frac{8}{n^2} \cdot \frac{n(n+1)}{2} \right]$$

$$= \lim_{n \to +\infty} \left(8 - \frac{4}{n} \right)$$

$$= 8$$

Therefore, the area is 8 square units. Using the formula from plane geometry for the area of a trapezoid, $A = \frac{1}{2}h(b_1 + b_2)$, where h, b_1, and b_2 are, respectively, the number of units in the lengths of the altitude and the two bases, we get $A = \frac{1}{2}(2)(6 + 2) = 8$, which agrees with our result.

Exercises 6.2

In Exercises 1 through 14, use the method of this section to find the area of the given region; use inscribed or circumscribed rectangles as indicated. For each exercise, draw a figure showing the region and the ith rectangle.

1. The region bounded by $y = x^2$, the x axis, and the line $x = 2$; inscribed rectangles.

2. The region of Exercise 1; circumscribed rectangles.

3. The region bounded by $y = 2x$, the x axis, and the lines $x = 1$ and $x = 4$; circumscribed rectangles.

4. The region of Exercise 3; inscribed rectangles.

5. The region above the x axis and to the right of the line $x = 1$ bounded by the x axis, the line $x = 1$, and the curve $y = 4 - x^2$; inscribed rectangles.

6. The region of Exercise 5; circumscribed rectangles.

7. The region lying to the left of the line $x = 1$ bounded by the curve and lines of Exercise 5; circumscribed rectangles.

8. The region of Exercise 7; inscribed rectangles.

9. The region bounded by $y = 3x^4$, the x axis, and the line $x = 1$; inscribed rectangles.

10. The region of Exercise 9; circumscribed rectangles.

11. The region bounded by $y = x^3$, the x axis, and the lines $x = -1$ and $x = 2$; inscribed rectangles.

12. The region of Exercise 11; circumscribed rectangles.

13. The region bounded by $y = mx$, with $m > 0$, the x axis, and the lines $x = a$ and $x = b$, with $b > a > 0$; circumscribed rectangles.

14. The region of Exercise 13; inscribed rectangles.

15. Use the method of this section to find the area of an isosceles trapezoid whose bases have measures b_1 and b_2 and whose altitude has measure h.

16. The graph of $y = 4 - |x|$ and the x axis from $x = -4$ to $x = 4$ form a triangle. Use the method of this section to find the area of this triangle.

In Exercises 17 through 22, find the area of the region by taking as the measure of the altitude of the ith rectangle $f(m_i)$, where m_i is the midpoint of the ith subinterval. (HINT: $m_i = \frac{1}{2}(x_i + x_{i-1})$.)

17. The region of Example 1.   18. The region of Exercise 1.   19. The region of Exercise 3.

20. The region of Exercise 5.   21. The region of Exercise 7.   22. The region of Exercise 9.

6.3 THE DEFINITE INTEGRAL

In the preceding section, the measure of the area of a region was defined as the following limit:

$$\lim_{n \to +\infty} \sum_{i=1}^{n} f(c_i)\, \Delta x \tag{1}$$

To lead up to this definition, we divided the closed interval $[a, b]$ into subintervals of equal length and then took c_i as the point in the ith subinterval for which f has an absolute minimum value. We also restricted the function values $f(x)$ to be nonnegative on $[a, b]$ and further required f to be continuous on $[a, b]$.

To define the definite integral, we need to consider a new kind of limiting process, of which the limit given in (1) is a special case. Let f be a function defined on the closed interval $[a, b]$. Divide this interval into n subintervals by choosing any $(n - 1)$ intermediate points between a and b. Let $x_0 = a$ and $x_n = b$, and $x_1, x_2, \ldots, x_{n-1}$ be the intermediate points so that

$$x_0 < x_1 < x_2 < \cdots < x_{n-1} < x_n$$

The points $x_0, x_1, x_2, \ldots, x_{n-1}, x_n$ are not necessarily equidistant. Let $\Delta_1 x$ be the length of the first subinterval so that $\Delta_1 x = x_1 - x_0$; let $\Delta_2 x$ be the length of the second subinterval so that $\Delta_2 x = x_2 - x_1$; and so forth, so that the length of the ith subinterval is $\Delta_i x$, and

$$\Delta_i x = x_i - x_{i-1}$$

A set of all such subintervals of the interval $[a, b]$ is called a *partition* of the interval $[a, b]$. Let Δ be such a partition. Figure 6.3.1 illustrates one such partition Δ of $[a, b]$.

Figure 6.3.1

The partition Δ contains n subintervals. One of these subintervals is longest; however, there may be more than one such subinterval. The length of the longest subinterval of the partition Δ, called the *norm* of the partition, is denoted by $\|\Delta\|$.

Choose a point in each subinterval of the partition Δ: Let ξ_1 be the point chosen in $[x_0, x_1]$ so that $x_0 \leq \xi_1 \leq x_1$. Let ξ_2 be the point chosen in $[x_1, x_2]$ so that $x_1 \leq \xi_2 \leq x_2$, and so forth, so that ξ_i is the point chosen in $[x_{i-1}, x_1]$, and $x_{i-1} \leq \xi_i \leq x_i$. Form the sum

$$f(\xi_1)\, \Delta_1 x + f(\xi_2)\, \Delta_2 x + \cdots + f(\xi_i)\, \Delta_i x + \cdots + f(\xi_n)\, \Delta_n x$$

or

$$\sum_{i=1}^{n} f(\xi_i)\, \Delta_i x$$

Such a sum is called a *Riemann sum*.

EXAMPLE 1:   Given $f(x) = 10 - x^2$, with $\frac{1}{4} \le x \le 3$, find the Riemann sum for the function f on $[\frac{1}{4}, 3]$ for the partition Δ: $x_0 = \frac{1}{4}$, $x_1 = 1$, $x_2 = 1\frac{1}{2}$, $x_3 = 1\frac{3}{4}$, $x_4 = 2\frac{1}{4}$, $x_5 = 3$, and $\xi_1 = \frac{1}{2}$, $\xi_2 = 1\frac{1}{4}$, $\xi_3 = 1\frac{3}{4}$, $\xi_4 = 2$, $\xi_5 = 2\frac{3}{4}$. Draw a sketch of the graph of the function on $[\frac{1}{4}, 3]$, and show the rectangles, the measures of whose areas are the terms of the Riemann sum. What is the norm of the partition?

SOLUTION: Figure 6.3.2 shows a sketch of the graph and the five rectangles.

$$\sum_{i=1}^{5} f(\xi_i)\ \Delta_i x = f(\xi_1)\ \Delta_1 x + f(\xi_2)\ \Delta_2 x + f(\xi_3)\ \Delta_3 x + f(\xi_4)\ \Delta_4 x + f(\xi_5)\ \Delta_5 x$$

$$= f(\tfrac{1}{2})(1 - \tfrac{1}{4}) + f(\tfrac{5}{4})(1\tfrac{1}{2} - 1) + f(\tfrac{7}{4})(1\tfrac{3}{4} - 1\tfrac{1}{2})$$

$$+ f(2)(2\tfrac{1}{4} - 1\tfrac{3}{4}) + f(\tfrac{11}{4})(3 - 2\tfrac{1}{4})$$

$$= (9\tfrac{3}{4})(\tfrac{3}{4}) + (8\tfrac{7}{16})(\tfrac{1}{2}) + (6\tfrac{15}{16})(\tfrac{1}{4}) + (6)(\tfrac{1}{2}) + (2\tfrac{7}{16})(\tfrac{3}{4})$$

$$= 18\tfrac{3}{32}$$

The norm of Δ is the length of the longest subinterval. Hence, $\|\Delta\| = \frac{3}{4}$.

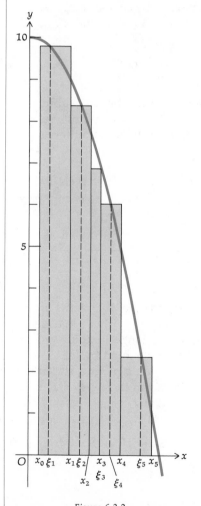

Figure 6.3.2

Because the function values $f(x)$ are not restricted to nonnegative values, some of the $f(\xi_i)$ could be negative. In such a case, the geometric interpretation of the Riemann sum would be the sum of the measures of the areas of the rectangles lying above the x axis plus the negatives of the measures of the areas of the rectangles lying below the x axis. This situation is illustrated in Fig. 6.3.3. Here

$$\sum_{i=1}^{10} f(\xi_i)\,\Delta_i x = A_1 + A_2 - A_3 - A_4 - A_5 + A_6 + A_7 - A_8 - A_9 - A_{10}$$

because $f(\xi_3)$, $f(\xi_4)$, $f(\xi_5)$, $f(\xi_8)$, $f(\xi_9)$, and $f(\xi_{10})$ are negative numbers.

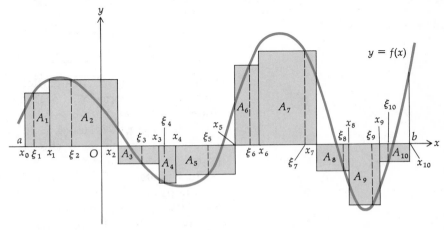

Figure 6.3.3

We are now in a position to define what is meant by a function f being *integrable* on the closed interval $[a, b]$.

6.3.1 Definition   Let f be a function whose domain includes the closed interval $[a, b]$. Then f is said to be *integrable* on $[a, b]$ if there is a number L satisfying the condition that, for every $\epsilon > 0$, there exists a $\delta > 0$ such that

$$\left| \sum_{i=1}^{n} f(\xi_i)\,\Delta_i x - L \right| < \epsilon$$

for every partition Δ for which $\|\Delta\| < \delta$, and for any ξ_i in the closed interval $[x_{i-1}, x_i]$, $i = 1, 2, \ldots, n$.

In words, Definition 6.3.1 states that, for a given function f defined on the closed interval $[a, b]$, we can make the values of the Riemann sums as close to L as we please by taking the norms $\|\Delta\|$ of all partitions Δ of $[a, b]$ sufficiently small for all possible choices of the numbers ξ_i for which $x_{i-1} \le \xi_i \le x_i$. If Definition 6.3.1 holds, we write

$$\lim_{\|\Delta\| \to 0} \sum_{i=1}^{n} f(\xi_i)\,\Delta_i x = L \tag{2}$$

The above limiting process is different from that discussed in Chapter 2. From Definition 6.3.1, the number L in (2) exists if for every $\epsilon > 0$ there exists a $\delta > 0$ such that

$$\left| \sum_{i=1}^{n} f(\xi_i) \, \Delta_i x - L \right| < \epsilon$$

for every partition Δ for which $\|\Delta\| < \delta$, and for any ξ_i in the closed interval $[x_{i-1}, x_i]$, $i = 1, 2, \ldots, n$.

In Definition 2.4.1 we had the following:

$$\lim_{x \to a} f(x) = L \tag{3}$$

if for every $\epsilon > 0$ there exists a $\delta > 0$ such that

$$|f(x) - L| < \epsilon \qquad \text{whenever } 0 < |x - a| < \delta$$

In limiting process (2), for a particular $\delta > 0$ there are infinitely many partitions Δ having norm $\|\Delta\| < \delta$. This is analogous to the fact that in limiting process (3), for a given $\delta > 0$ there are infinitely many values of x for which $0 < |x - a| < \delta$. However, in limiting process (2), for each partition Δ there are infinitely many choices of ξ_i. It is in this respect that the two limiting processes differ.

In Chapter 2 (Theorem 2.4.2) we showed that if the number L in limiting process (3) exists, it is unique. In a similar manner we can show that if there is a number L satisfying Definition 6.3.1, then it is unique. Now we can define the *definite integral*.

6.3.2 Definition   If f is a function defined on the closed interval $[a, b]$, then the *definite integral* of f from a to b, denoted by $\int_a^b f(x) \, dx$, is given by

$$\int_a^b f(x) \, dx = \lim_{\|\Delta\| \to 0} \sum_{i=1}^{n} f(\xi_i) \, \Delta_i x \tag{4}$$

if the limit exists.

Note that the statement, "the function f is integrable on the closed interval $[a, b]$," is synonymous with the statement, "the definite integral of f from a to b exists."

In the notation for the definite integral $\int_a^b f(x) \, dx$, $f(x)$ is called the *integrand*, a is called the *lower limit*, and b is called the *upper limit*. The symbol

$$\int$$

is called an *integral sign*. The integral sign resembles a capital S, which is appropriate because the definite integral is the limit of a sum. It is the same symbol we used in Chapter 5 to indicate the operation of antidifferentiation. The reason for the common symbol is that a theorem (6.6.2), called the fundamental theorem of the calculus, enables us to evaluate a definite integral by finding an antiderivative (also called an *indefinite integral*).

A question that now arises is as follows: Under what conditions does a number L satisfying Definition 6.3.1 exist; that is, under what conditions is a function f integrable? An answer to this question is given by the following theorem.

6.3.3 Theorem   If a function f is continuous on the closed interval $[a, b]$ then f is integrable on $[a, b]$.

The proof of this theorem is beyond the scope of this book and is given in advanced calculus texts. The condition that f is continuous on $[a, b]$, while being sufficient to guarantee that f is integrable on $[a, b]$, is not a necessary condition for the existence of $\int_a^b f(x)\, dx$. That is, if f is continuous on $[a, b]$, then Theorem 6.3.3 assures us that $\int_a^b f(x)\, dx$ exists; however, it is possible for the integral to exist even if the function is discontinuous at some numbers in $[a, b]$. The following example gives a function which is discontinuous and yet integrable on a closed interval.

EXAMPLE 2:   Let f be the function defined by

$$f(x) = \begin{cases} 0 & \text{if } x \neq 0 \\ 1 & \text{if } x = 0 \end{cases}$$

Let $[a, b]$ be any interval such that $a < 0 < b$. Show that f is discontinuous on $[a, b]$ and yet integrable on $[a, b]$.

SOLUTION: Because $\lim\limits_{x \to 0} f(x) = 0 \neq f(0)$, f is discontinuous at 0 and hence discontinuous on $[a, b]$.

To prove that f is integrable on $[a, b]$ we show that Definition 6.3.1 is satisfied. Consider the Riemann sum

$$\sum_{i=1}^{n} f(\xi_i)\, \Delta_i x$$

If none of the numbers $\xi_1, \xi_2, \ldots, \xi_n$ is zero, then the Riemann sum is zero. Suppose that $\xi_j = 0$. Then

$$\sum_{i=1}^{n} f(\xi_i)\, \Delta_i x = 1 \cdot \Delta_j x$$

In either case

$$\left| \sum_{i=1}^{n} f(\xi_i)\, \Delta_i x \right| \leq \|\Delta\|$$

Hence,

$$\left| \sum_{i=1}^{n} f(\xi_i)\, \Delta_i x - 0 \right| < \epsilon \qquad \text{whenever } \|\Delta\| < \epsilon$$

Comparing the above with Definition 6.3.1 where $\delta = \epsilon$ and $L = 0$, we see that f is integrable on $[a, b]$.

In Definition 6.3.2, the closed interval $[a, b]$ is given, and so we assume that $a < b$. To consider the definite integral of a function f from a to b when $a > b$, or when $a = b$, we have the following definitions.

6.3.4 Definition   If $a > b$, then

$$\int_a^b f(x) \, dx = - \int_b^a f(x) \, dx$$

if $\int_b^a f(x) \, dx$ exists.

6.3.5 Definition $\int_a^a f(x) \, dx = 0$ if $f(a)$ exists.

At the beginning of this section, we stated that the limit used in Definition 6.2.1 to define the measure of the area of a region is a special case of the limit used in Definition 6.3.2 to define the definite integral. In the discussion of area, the interval $[a, b]$ was divided into n subintervals of equal length. Such a partition of the interval $[a, b]$ is called a *regular partition*. If Δx is the length of each subinterval in a regular partition, then each $\Delta_i x = \Delta x$, and the norm of the partition is Δx. Making these substitutions in Eq. (4), we have

$$\int_a^b f(x) \, dx = \lim_{\Delta x \to 0} \sum_{i=1}^{n} f(\xi_i) \, \Delta x \tag{5}$$

Furthermore,

$$\Delta x = \frac{b - a}{n} \tag{6}$$

and

$$n = \frac{b - a}{\Delta x} \tag{7}$$

So from Eq. (6)

$$\lim_{n \to +\infty} \Delta x = 0 \tag{8}$$

and from (7), because $b > a$ and Δx approaches zero through positive values (because $\Delta x > 0$),

$$\lim_{\Delta x \to 0} n = +\infty \tag{9}$$

From limits (8) and (9), we conclude that

$$\Delta x \to 0 \quad \text{is equivalent to} \quad n \to +\infty \tag{10}$$

Thus, we have from Eq. (5) and statement (10),

$$\int_a^b f(x)\ dx = \lim_{n \to +\infty} \sum_{i=1}^{n} f(\xi_i)\ \Delta x \tag{11}$$

It should be remembered that ξ_i can be any point in the ith subinterval $[x_{i-1}, x_i]$.

In applications of the definite integral regular partitions are often used; therefore, formulas (5) and (11) are especially important.

Comparing the limit used in Definition 6.2.1, which gives the measure of the area of a region, with the limit on the right side of Eq. (11), we have in the first case:

$$\lim_{n \to +\infty} \sum_{i=1}^{n} f(c_i)\ \Delta x \tag{12}$$

where $f(c_i)$ is the absolute minimum function value on $[x_{i-1}, x_i]$. In the second case, we have

$$\lim_{n \to +\infty} \sum_{i=1}^{n} f(\xi_i)\ \Delta x \tag{13}$$

where ξ_i is any number in $[x_{i-1}, x_i]$.

Because the function f is continuous on $[a, b]$, by Theorem 6.3.3, $\int_a^b f(x)\ dx$ exists; therefore, this definite integral is the limit of all Riemann sums of f on $[a, b]$ including those in (12) and (13). Because of this, we redefine the area of a region in a more general way.

6.3.6 Definition   Let the function f be continuous on $[a, b]$ and $f(x) \geq 0$ for all x in $[a, b]$. Let R be the region bounded by the curve $y = f(x)$, the x axis, and the lines $x = a$ and $x = b$. Then the measure of the area of region R is given by

$$A = \lim_{||\Delta|| \to 0} \sum_{i=1}^{n} f(\xi_i)\ \Delta_i x = \int_a^b f(x)\ dx$$

The above definition states that if $f(x) \geq 0$ for all x in $[a, b]$, the definite integral $\int_a^b f(x)\ dx$ can be interpreted geometrically as the measure of the area of the region R shown in Fig. 6.3.4.

Equation (11) can be used to find the exact value of a definite integral as illustrated in the following example.

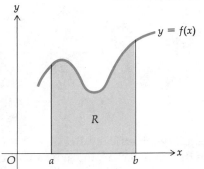

Figure 6.3.4

EXAMPLE 3:   Find the exact value of the definite integral

$$\int_1^3 x^2\,dx$$

SOLUTION: Consider a regular partition of the closed interval $[1, 3]$ into n subintervals. Then $\Delta x = 2/n$.

If we choose ξ_i as the right endpoint of each subinterval, we have

$$\xi_1 = 1 + \frac{2}{n},\ \xi_2 = 1 + 2\left(\frac{2}{n}\right),\ \xi_3 = 1 + 3\left(\frac{2}{n}\right),\ \dots,\ \xi_i = 1 + i\left(\frac{2}{n}\right),$$

$$\dots,\ \xi_n = 1 + n\left(\frac{2}{n}\right)$$

Because $f(x) = x^2$,

$$f(\xi_i) = \left(1 + \frac{2i}{n}\right)^2 = \left(\frac{n + 2i}{n}\right)^2$$

Therefore, by using Eq. (11) and applying properties and formulas from Sec. 6.1, we get

$$\int_1^3 x^2\,dx = \lim_{n \to +\infty} \sum_{i=1}^{n} \left(\frac{n + 2i}{n}\right)^2 \frac{2}{n}$$

$$= \lim_{n \to +\infty} \frac{2}{n^3} \sum_{i=1}^{n} (n^2 + 4ni + 4i^2)$$

$$= \lim_{n \to +\infty} \frac{2}{n^3} \left[n^2 \sum_{i=1}^{n} 1 + 4n \sum_{i=1}^{n} i + 4 \sum_{i=1}^{n} i^2\right]$$

$$= \lim_{n \to +\infty} \frac{2}{n^3} \left[n^2 n + 4n \cdot \frac{n(n + 1)}{2} + \frac{4n(n + 1)(2n + 1)}{6}\right]$$

$$= \lim_{n \to +\infty} \frac{2}{n^3} \left[n^3 + 2n^3 + 2n^2 + \frac{2n(2n^2 + 3n + 1)}{3}\right]$$

$$= \lim_{n \to +\infty} \left[6 + \frac{4}{n} + \frac{8n^2 + 12n + 4}{3n^2}\right]$$

$$= \lim_{n \to +\infty} \left[6 + \frac{4}{n} + \frac{8}{3} + \frac{4}{n} + \frac{4}{3n^2}\right]$$

$$= 6 + 0 + \tfrac{8}{3} + 0 + 0$$

$$= 8\tfrac{2}{3}$$

Let us interpret the result of this example geometrically. Because $x^2 \geq 0$ for all x in $[1, 3]$, the region bounded by the curve $y = x^2$, the axis, and the lines $x = 1$ and $x = 3$ has an area of $8\tfrac{2}{3}$ square units. The region is shown in Fig. 6.3.5.

Figure 6.3.5

Exercises 6.3

In Exercises 1 through 6, find the Riemann sum for the function on the interval, using the given partition Δ and the given values of ξ_i. Draw a sketch of the graph of the function on the given interval, and show the rectangles the measure of whose areas are the terms of the Riemann sum. (See Example 1 and Fig. 6.3.2.)

1. $f(x) = x^2$, $0 \le x \le 3$; for Δ: $x_0 = 0$, $x_1 = \frac{1}{2}$, $x_2 = 1\frac{1}{4}$, $x_3 = 2\frac{1}{4}$, $x_4 = 3$; $\xi_1 = \frac{1}{4}$, $\xi_2 = 1$, $\xi_3 = 1\frac{1}{2}$, $\xi_4 = 2\frac{1}{2}$

2. $f(x) = x^2$, $0 \le x \le 3$; for Δ: $x_0 = 0$, $x_1 = \frac{3}{4}$, $x_2 = 1\frac{1}{4}$, $x_3 = 2$, $x_4 = 2\frac{3}{4}$, $x_5 = 3$; $\xi_1 = \frac{1}{2}$, $\xi_2 = 1$, $\xi_3 = 1\frac{3}{4}$, $\xi_4 = 2\frac{1}{4}$, $\xi_5 = 2\frac{3}{4}$

3. $f(x) = 1/x$, $1 \le x \le 3$; for Δ: $x_0 = 1$, $x_1 = 1\frac{2}{3}$, $x_2 = 2\frac{1}{4}$, $x_3 = 2\frac{2}{3}$, $x_4 = 3$; $\xi_1 = 1\frac{1}{4}$, $\xi_2 = 2$, $\xi_3 = 2\frac{1}{2}$, $\xi_4 = 2\frac{3}{4}$

4. $f(x) = x^3$, $-1 \le x \le 2$; for Δ: $x_0 = -1$, $x_1 = -\frac{1}{3}$, $x_2 = \frac{1}{2}$, $x_3 = 1$, $x_4 = 1\frac{1}{4}$, $x_5 = 2$; $\xi_1 = -\frac{1}{2}$, $\xi_2 = 0$, $\xi_3 = \frac{2}{3}$, $\xi_4 = 1$, $\xi_5 = 1\frac{1}{2}$

5. $f(x) = x^2 - x + 1$, $0 \le x \le 1$; for Δ: $x_0 = 0$, $x_1 = 0.2$, $x_2 = 0.5$, $x_3 = 0.7$, $x_4 = 1$; $\xi_1 = 0.1$, $\xi_2 = 0.4$, $\xi_3 = 0.6$, $\xi_4 = 0.9$

6. $f(x) = 1/(x + 2)$, $-1 \le x \le 3$; for Δ: $x_0 = -1$, $x_1 = -\frac{1}{4}$, $x_2 = 0$, $x_3 = \frac{1}{2}$, $x_4 = 1\frac{1}{4}$, $x_5 = 2$, $x_6 = 2\frac{1}{4}$, $x_7 = 2\frac{3}{4}$, $x_8 = 3$; $\xi_1 = -\frac{3}{4}$, $\xi_2 = 0$, $\xi_3 = \frac{1}{4}$, $\xi_4 = 1$, $\xi_5 = 1\frac{1}{2}$, $\xi_6 = 2$, $\xi_7 = 2\frac{1}{2}$, $\xi_8 = 3$

In Exercises 7 through 14, find the exact value of the definite integral. Use the method of Example 3 of this section.

7. $\int_0^2 x^2 \, dx$

8. $\int_2^4 x^2 \, dx$

9. $\int_1^2 x^3 \, dx$

10. $\int_{-2}^1 x^4 \, dx$

11. $\int_1^4 (x^2 + 4x + 5) \, dx$

12. $\int_0^4 (x^2 + x - 6) \, dx$

13. $\int_{-2}^2 (x^3 + 1) \, dx$

14. $\int_{-1}^2 (4x^3 - 3x^2) \, dx$

In Exercises 15 through 20, find the exact area of the region in the following way: (a) Express the measure of the area as the limit of a Riemann sum with regular partitions; (b) express this limit as a definite integral; (c) evaluate the definite integral by the method of this section and a suitable choice of ξ_i. Draw a figure showing the region.

15. Bounded by the line $y = 2x - 1$, the x axis, and the lines $x = 1$ and $x = 5$.

16. Bounded by the line $y = 2x - 6$, the x axis, and the lines $x = 4$ and $x = 7$.

17. Bounded by the curve $y = 4 - x^2$, the x axis, and the lines $x = 1$ and $x = 2$.

18. Bounded by the curve $y = (x + 3)^2$, the x axis, and the lines $x = -3$ and $x = 0$.

19. Bounded by the curve $y = 12 - x - x^2$, the x axis, and the lines $x = -3$, and $x = 2$.

20. Bounded by the curve $y = 6x + x^2 - x^3$, the x axis, and the lines $x = -1$ and $x = 3$.

21. Express as a definite integral: $\lim_{n \to +\infty} \sum_{i=1}^n (8i^2/n^3)$. (HINT: Consider the function f for which $f(x) = x^2$.)

22. Express as a definite integral: $\lim_{n \to +\infty} \sum_{i=1}^n 1/(n + i)$. (HINT: Consider the function f for which $f(x) = 1/x$ on $[1, 2]$.)

23. Express as a definite integral: $\lim_{n \to +\infty} \sum_{i=1}^n (n/i^2)$. (HINT: Consider the function f for which $f(x) = 1/x^2$.)

24. Let $[a, b]$ be any interval such that $a < 0 < b$. Prove that even though the unit step function (Exercise 1 in Exercises 2.3) is discontinuous on $[a, b]$, it is integrable on $[a, b]$ and $\int_a^b U(x) \, dx = b$.

25. Prove that the signum function is discontinuous on $[-1, 1]$ and yet integrable on $[-1, 1]$. Furthermore show that $\int_{-1}^1 \operatorname{sgn} x \, dx = 0$.

26. Prove that the greatest integer function is discontinuous on $[0, \frac{3}{2}]$ and yet integrable on $[0, \frac{3}{2}]$. Furthermore, show that $\int_0^{3/2} [\![x]\!] \, dx = \frac{1}{2}$.

6.4 PROPERTIES OF THE DEFINITE INTEGRAL

Evaluating a definite integral from the definition, by actually finding the limit of a sum as we did in Sec. 6.3, is usually quite tedious and frequently almost impossible. To establish a much simpler method we first need to develop some properties of the definite integral. First the following two theorems about Riemann sums are needed.

6.4.1 Theorem   If Δ is any partition of the closed interval $[a, b]$, then

$$\lim_{||\Delta|| \to 0} \sum_{i=1}^{n} \Delta_i x = b - a$$

PROOF:

$$\sum_{i=1}^{n} \Delta_i x - (b - a) = (b - a) - (b - a) = 0$$

Hence, for any $\epsilon > 0$ any choice of $\delta > 0$ guarantees the inequality

$$\left| \sum_{i=1}^{n} \Delta_i x - (b - a) \right| < \epsilon \qquad \text{whenever } ||\Delta|| < \delta$$

and so by Definition 6.3.1

$$\lim_{||\Delta|| \to 0} \sum_{i=1}^{n} \Delta_i x = b - a$$ ∎

6.4.2 Theorem   If f is defined on the closed interval $[a, b]$ and if

$$\lim_{||\Delta|| \to 0} \sum_{i=1}^{n} f(\xi_i) \, \Delta_i x$$

exists, where Δ is any partition of $[a, b]$, then if k is any constant,

$$\lim_{||\Delta|| \to 0} \sum_{i=1}^{n} k f(\xi_i) \, \Delta_i x = k \lim_{||\Delta|| \to 0} \sum_{i=1}^{n} f(\xi_i) \, \Delta_i x$$

The proof of this theorem is left for the reader (see Exercise 1).

We now state and prove some theorems that give important properties of the definite integral.

6.4.3 Theorem   If the function f is integrable on the closed interval $[a, b]$ and if k is any constant, then

$$\int_a^b k f(x) \, dx = k \int_a^b f(x) \, dx$$

PROOF: Because f is integrable on $[a, b]$, $\lim\limits_{||\Delta||\to 0} \sum\limits_{i=1}^{n} f(\xi_i)\, \Delta_i x$ exists and so by Theorem 6.4.2

$$\lim_{||\Delta||\to 0} \sum_{i=1}^{n} kf(\xi_i)\, \Delta_i x = k \lim_{||\Delta||\to 0} \sum_{i=1}^{n} f(\xi_i)\, \Delta_i x$$

Therefore,

$$\int_a^b kf(x)\, dx = k \int_a^b f(x)\, dx \qquad \blacksquare$$

6.4.4 Theorem   If the functions f and g are integrable on $[a, b]$, then $f + g$ is integrable on $[a, b]$ and

$$\int_a^b [f(x) + g(x)]\, dx = \int_a^b f(x)\, dx + \int_a^b g(x)\, dx$$

PROOF: The functions f and g are integrable on $[a, b]$; thus, let

$$\int_a^b f(x)\, dx = M \quad \text{and} \quad \int_a^b g(x)\, dx = N$$

To prove that $f + g$ is integrable on $[a, b]$ and that $\int_a^b [f(x) + g(x)]\, dx = M + N$, we must show that for any $\epsilon > 0$ there exists a $\delta > 0$ such that

$$\left| \sum_{i=1}^{n} [f(\xi_i) + g(\xi_i)]\, \Delta_i x - (M + N) \right| < \epsilon$$

for all partitions Δ for which $||\Delta|| < \delta$ and for any ξ_i in $[x_{i-1}, x_i]$. Because

$$M = \lim_{||\Delta||\to 0} \sum_{i=1}^{n} f(\xi_i)\, \Delta_i x \quad \text{and} \quad N = \lim_{||\Delta||\to 0} \sum_{i=1}^{n} g(\xi_i)\, \Delta_i x$$

it follows that for any $\epsilon > 0$ there exist a $\delta_1 > 0$ and a $\delta_2 > 0$ such that

$$\left| \sum_{i=1}^{n} f(\xi_i)\, \Delta_i x - M \right| < \frac{\epsilon}{2} \quad \text{and} \quad \left| \sum_{i=1}^{n} g(\xi_i)\, \Delta_i x - N \right| < \frac{\epsilon}{2}$$

for all partitions Δ for which $||\Delta|| < \delta_1$ and $||\Delta|| < \delta_2$, and for any ξ_i in $[x_{i-1}, x_i]$. Therefore, if $\delta = \min(\delta_1, \delta_2)$, then for any $\epsilon > 0$

$$\left| \sum_{i=1}^{n} f(\xi_i)\, \Delta_i x - M \right| + \left| \sum_{i=1}^{n} g(\xi_i)\, \Delta_i x - N \right| < \frac{\epsilon}{2} + \frac{\epsilon}{2} = \epsilon \qquad (1)$$

for all partitions Δ for which $||\Delta|| < \delta$ and for any ξ_i in $[x_{i-1}, x_i]$.

By the triangle inequality, we have

$$\left| \left(\sum_{i=1}^{n} f(\xi_i)\, \Delta_i x - M \right) + \left(\sum_{i=1}^{n} g(\xi_i)\, \Delta_i x - N \right) \right|$$
$$\leq \left| \sum_{i=1}^{n} f(\xi_i)\, \Delta_i x - M \right| + \left| \sum_{i=1}^{n} g(\xi_i)\, \Delta_i x - N \right| \qquad (2)$$

From inequalities (1) and (2), we have

$$\left| \left(\sum_{i=1}^{n} f(\xi_i) \ \Delta_i x + \sum_{i=1}^{n} g(\xi_i) \ \Delta_i x \right) - (M + N) \right| < \epsilon \tag{3}$$

From Property 3 (6.1.3) of the sigma notation, we have

$$\sum_{i=1}^{n} f(\xi_i) \ \Delta_i x + \sum_{i=1}^{n} g(\xi_i) \ \Delta_i x = \sum_{i=1}^{n} [f(\xi_i) + g(\xi_i)] \ \Delta_i x \tag{4}$$

So by substituting from (4) into (3) we can conclude that for any $\epsilon > 0$

$$\left| \sum_{i=1}^{n} [f(\xi_i) + g(\xi_i)] \ \Delta_i x - (M + N) \right| < \epsilon$$

for all partitions Δ for which $\|\Delta\| < \delta$, where $\delta = \min(\delta_1, \delta_2)$ and for any ξ_i in $[x_{i-1}, x_i]$. This proves that $f + g$ is integrable on $[a, b]$ and that

$$\int_a^b [f(x) + g(x)] \ dx = \int_a^b f(x) \ dx + \int_a^b g(x) \ dx \qquad \blacksquare$$

Theorem 6.4.4 can be extended to any number of functions. That is, if the functions $f_1, f_2, \ldots, f_n$ are all integrable on $[a, b]$, then $(f_1 + f_2 + \cdots + f_n)$ is integrable on $[a, b]$ and

$$\int_a^b [f_1(x) + f_2(x) + \cdots + f_n(x)] \ dx$$
$$= \int_a^b f_1(x) \ dx + \int_a^b f_2(x) \ dx + \cdots + \int_a^b f_n(x) \ dx$$

The plus sign in the statement of Theorem 6.4.4 can be replaced by a minus sign as a result of applying Theorem 6.4.3, where $k = -1$.

6.4.5 Theorem   If the function f is integrable on the closed intervals $[a, b]$, $[a, c]$, and $[c, b]$,

$$\int_a^b f(x) \ dx = \int_a^c f(x) \ dx + \int_c^b f(x) \ dx$$

where $a < c < b$.

PROOF: Let Δ be a partition of $[a, b]$. Form the partition Δ' of $[a, b]$ in the following way. If c is one of the partitioning points of Δ (i.e., $c = x_i$ for some i), then Δ' is exactly the same as Δ. If c is not one of the partitioning points of Δ but is contained in the subinterval $[x_{i-1}, x_i]$, then the partition Δ' has as its partitioning points all the partitioning points of Δ and, in addition, the point c. Therefore, the subintervals of the partition Δ' are the same as the subintervals of Δ, with the exception that the subinterval $[x_{i-1}, x_i]$ of Δ is divided into the two subintervals $[x_{i-1}, c]$ and $[c, x_i]$. If $\|\Delta'\|$ is the norm of Δ' and if $\|\Delta\|$ is the norm of Δ, then

$$\|\Delta'\| \leq \|\Delta\|$$

If in the partition Δ' the interval $[a, c]$ is divided into r subintervals and the interval $[c, b]$ is divided into $(n - r)$ subintervals, then the part of the partition Δ' from a to c gives a Riemann sum of the form

$$\sum_{i=1}^{r} f(\xi_i) \, \Delta_i x$$

and the other part of the partition Δ', from c to b, gives a Riemann sum of the form

$$\sum_{i=r+1}^{n} f(\xi_i) \, \Delta_i x$$

Using the definition of the definite integral and properties of the sigma notation, we have

$$\int_{a}^{b} f(x) \, dx = \lim_{||\Delta|| \to 0} \sum_{i=1}^{n} f(\xi_i) \, \Delta_i x$$

$$= \lim_{||\Delta|| \to 0} \left[\sum_{i=1}^{r} f(\xi_i) \, \Delta_i x + \sum_{i=r+1}^{n} f(\xi_i) \, \Delta_i x \right]$$

$$= \lim_{||\Delta|| \to 0} \sum_{i=1}^{r} f(\xi_i) \, \Delta_i x + \lim_{||\Delta|| \to 0} \sum_{i=r+1}^{n} f(\xi_i) \, \Delta_i x$$

Since $0 < ||\Delta'|| \le ||\Delta||$, we can replace $||\Delta|| \to 0$ by $||\Delta'|| \to 0$, giving us

$$\int_{a}^{b} f(x) \, dx = \lim_{||\Delta'|| \to 0} \sum_{i=1}^{r} f(\xi_i) \, \Delta_i x + \lim_{||\Delta'|| \to 0} \sum_{i=r+1}^{n} f(\xi_i) \, \Delta_i x$$

Applying the definition of the definite integral to the right side of the above equation, we have

$$\int_{a}^{b} f(x) \, dx = \int_{a}^{c} f(x) \, dx + \int_{c}^{b} f(x) \, dx \qquad \blacksquare$$

Figure 6.4.1

We now interpret Theorem 6.4.5 geometrically. If $f(x) \ge 0$ for all x in $[a, b]$, then Theorem 6.4.5 states that the measure of the area of the region bounded by the curve $y = f(x)$ and the x axis from a to b is equal to the sum of the measures of the areas of the regions from a to c and from c to b (see Fig. 6.4.1).

The result of Theorem 6.4.5 is true for any ordering of the numbers a, b, and c. This is stated as another theorem.

6.4.6 Theorem   If f is integrable on a closed interval containing the three numbers a, b, and c, then

$$\int_{a}^{b} f(x) \, dx = \int_{a}^{c} f(x) \, dx + \int_{c}^{b} f(x) \, dx \qquad (5)$$

regardless of the order of a, b, and c.

PROOF: If a, b, and c are distinct, there are six possible orderings of these three numbers: $a < b < c$, $a < c < b$, $b < a < c$, $b < c < a$, $c < a < b$, and $c < b < a$. The second ordering, $a < c < b$, is Theorem 6.4.5. We make use of Theorem 6.4.5 in proving that Eq. (5) holds for the other orderings.

Suppose that $a < b < c$; then from Theorem 6.4.5 we have

$$\int_a^b f(x)\ dx + \int_b^c f(x)\ dx = \int_a^c f(x)\ dx \tag{6}$$

From Definition 6.3.4

$$\int_b^c f(x)\ dx = -\int_c^b f(x)\ dx \tag{7}$$

Substituting from (7) into (6), we obtain

$$\int_a^b f(x)\ dx - \int_c^b f(x)\ dx = \int_a^c f(x)\ dx$$

or

$$\int_a^b f(x)\ dx = \int_a^c f(x)\ dx + \int_c^b f(x)\ dx$$

which is the desired result.

The proofs for the other four orderings are similar and are left for the reader (see Exercises 2 to 5).

There is also the possibility that two of the three numbers are equal; for example, $a = c < b$. Then

$$\int_a^c f(x)\ dx = \int_a^a f(x)\ dx = 0 \quad \text{(by Definition 6.3.5)}$$

Also, because $a = c$,

$$\int_c^b f(x)\ dx = \int_a^b f(x)\ dx$$

Therefore,

$$\int_a^c f(x)\ dx + \int_c^b f(x)\ dx = 0 + \int_a^b f(x)\ dx$$

which is the desired result. ∎

6.4.7 Theorem If k is any constant and if f is a function such that $f(x) = k$ for all x in $[a, b]$, then

$$\int_a^b f(x)\ dx = \int_a^b k\ dx = k(b - a)$$

PROOF: From Definition 6.3.2,

$$\int_a^b f(x)\ dx = \lim_{||\Delta||\to 0} \sum_{i=1}^n f(\xi_i)\ \Delta_i x$$

$$= \lim_{||\Delta||\to 0} \sum_{i=1}^n k\ \Delta_i x$$

$$= k \lim_{||\Delta||\to 0} \sum_{i=1}^n \Delta_i x \quad \text{(by Theorem 6.4.2)}$$

$$= k(b-a) \quad \text{(by Theorem 6.4.1)} \qquad \blacksquare$$

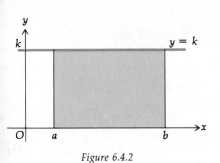

Figure 6.4.2

A geometric interpretation of Theorem 6.4.7 when $k > 0$ is given by Fig. 6.4.2. The definite integral $\int_a^b k\ dx$ gives the measure of the area of the shaded region, which is a rectangle whose dimensions are k units and $(b-a)$ units.

6.4.8 Theorem   If the functions f and g are integrable on the closed interval $[a, b]$ and if $f(x) \geq g(x)$ for all x in $[a, b]$, then

$$\int_a^b f(x)\ dx \geq \int_a^b g(x)\ dx$$

PROOF: Because f and g are integrable on $[a, b]$, $\int_a^b f(x)\ dx$ and $\int_a^b g(x)\ dx$ both exist. Therefore (by Theorem 6.4.3),

$$\int_a^b f(x)\ dx - \int_a^b g(x)\ dx = \int_a^b f(x)\ dx + \int_a^b [-g(x)]\ dx$$

$$= \int_a^b [f(x) - g(x)]\ dx \quad \text{(by Theorem 6.4.4)}$$

Let h be the function defined by

$$h(x) = f(x) - g(x)$$

Then $h(x) \geq 0$ for all x in $[a, b]$ because $f(x) \geq g(x)$ for all x in $[a, b]$. We wish to prove that $\int_a^b [f(x) - g(x)]\ dx \geq 0$.

$$\int_a^b [f(x) - g(x)]\ dx = \int_a^b h(x)\ dx = \lim_{||\Delta||\to 0} \sum_{i=1}^n h(\xi_i)\ \Delta_i x \qquad (8)$$

Assume that

$$\lim_{||\Delta||\to 0} \sum_{i=1}^n h(\xi_i)\ \Delta_i x = L < 0 \qquad (9)$$

Then by Definition 6.3.1, with $\epsilon = -L$, there exists a $\delta > 0$ such that

$$\left| \sum_{i=1}^{n} h(\xi_i) \, \Delta_i x - L \right| < -L \qquad \text{whenever } \|\Delta\| < \delta \tag{10}$$

But because

$$\sum_{i=1}^{n} h(\xi_i) \, \Delta_i x - L \le \left| \sum_{i=1}^{n} h(\xi_i) \, \Delta_i x - L \right|$$

from inequality (10) we have

$$\sum_{i=1}^{n} h(\xi_i) \, \Delta_i x - L < -L \qquad \text{whenever } \|\Delta\| < \delta$$

or

$$\sum_{i=1}^{n} h(\xi_i) \, \Delta_i x < 0 \qquad \text{whenever } \|\Delta\| < \delta \tag{11}$$

But statement (11) is impossible because every $h(\xi_i)$ is nonnegative and every $\Delta_i x > 0$; thus, we have a contradiction to our assumption (9). Therefore, (9) is false, and

$$\lim_{\|\Delta\| \to 0} \sum_{i=1}^{n} h(\xi_i) \, \Delta_i x \ge 0 \tag{12}$$

From (8) and (12), we have

$$\int_{a}^{b} [f(x) - g(x)] \, dx \ge 0$$

Hence,

$$\int_{a}^{b} f(x) \, dx - \int_{a}^{b} g(x) \, dx \ge 0$$

and so

$$\int_{a}^{b} f(x) \, dx \ge \int_{a}^{b} g(x) \, dx$$

Figure 6.4.3

Figure 6.4.3 gives a geometric interpretation of Theorem 6.4.8 when $f(x) \ge g(x) \ge 0$ for all x in $[a, b]$. $\int_{a}^{b} f(x) \, dx$ gives the measure of the area of the region bounded by the curve $y = f(x)$, the x axis, and the lines $x = a$ and $x = b$. $\int_{a}^{b} g(x) \, dx$ gives the measure of the area of the region bounded by the curve $y = g(x)$, the x axis, and the lines $x = a$ and $x = b$. In the figure we see that the first area is greater than the second area.

6.4.9 Theorem   Suppose that the function f is continuous on the closed interval $[a, b]$. If m and M are, respectively, the absolute minimum and absolute maximum function values of f on $[a, b]$ so that

$$m \leq f(x) \leq M \qquad \text{for } a \leq x \leq b$$

then

$$m(b-a) \leq \int_a^b f(x) \, dx \leq M(b-a)$$

PROOF: Because f is continuous on $[a, b]$, the extreme-value theorem (4.3.9) guarantees the existence of m and M.

By Theorem 6.4.7

$$\int_a^b m \, dx = m(b-a) \tag{13}$$

and

$$\int_a^b M \, dx = M(b-a) \tag{14}$$

Because f is continuous on $[a, b]$, it follows from Theorem 6.3.3 that f is integrable on $[a, b]$. Then because $f(x) \geq m$ for all x in $[a, b]$, we have from Theorem 6.4.8

$$\int_a^b f(x) \, dx \geq \int_a^b m \, dx$$

which from (13) gives

$$\int_a^b f(x) \, dx \geq m(b-a) \tag{15}$$

Similarly, because $M \geq f(x)$ for all x in $[a, b]$, it follows from Theorem 6.4.8 that

$$\int_a^b M \, dx \geq \int_a^b f(x) \, dx$$

which from (14) gives

$$M(b-a) \geq \int_a^b f(x) \, dx \tag{16}$$

Combining inequalities (15) and (16) we have

$$m(b-a) \leq \int_a^b f(x) \, dx \leq M(b-a) \qquad \blacksquare$$

Figure 6.4.4

A geometric interpretation of Theorem 6.4.9 is given in Fig. 6.4.4, where $f(x) \geq 0$ for all x in $[a, b]$. The integral $\int_a^b f(x) \, dx$ gives the measure of the area of the region bounded by the curve $y = f(x)$, the x axis, and the lines $x = a$ and $x = b$. This area is greater than that of the rectangle whose dimensions are m and $(b-a)$ and less than that of the rectangle whose dimensions are M and $(b-a)$.

EXAMPLE 1:   Apply Theorem 6.4.9 to find the smallest and largest possible values of

$$\int_{1/2}^{4} (x^3 - 6x^2 + 9x + 1) \, dx$$

Use the results of Example 1, Sec. 4.6.

SOLUTION: Referring to Example 1, Sec. 4.6, we see that f has a relative minimum value of 1 at $x = 3$ and a relative maximum value of 5 at $x = 1$. $f(\frac{1}{2}) = \frac{33}{8}$ and $f(4) = 5$. Hence, the absolute minimum value of f on $[\frac{1}{2}, 4]$ is 1, and the absolute maximum value is 5. Taking $m = 1$ and $M = 5$ in Theorem 6.4.9, we have

$$1(4 - \tfrac{1}{2}) \le \int_{1/2}^{4} (x^3 - 6x^2 + 9x + 1) \, dx \le 5(4 - \tfrac{1}{2})$$

and so

$$\tfrac{7}{2} \le \int_{1/2}^{4} (x^3 - 6x^2 + 9x + 1) \, dx \le \tfrac{35}{2}$$

In Example 2, Sec. 6.6, the exact value of the definite integral is shown to be $10\frac{39}{64}$.

EXAMPLE 2:   Apply Theorem 6.4.9 to find the smallest and largest possible values of

$$\int_{-1}^{1} (x^{4/3} + 4x^{1/3}) \, dx$$

Use the results of Example 3, Sec. 4.6.

SOLUTION: From Example 3, Sec. 4.6, we see that f has a relative minimum value of -3 at $x = -1$. Furthermore, $f(1) = 5$. Hence, on $[-1, 1]$ the absolute minimum value of f is -1 and the absolute maximum value is 5. So, taking $m = -1$ and $M = 5$ in Theorem 6.4.9, we have

$$(-1)[1 - (-1)] \le \int_{-1}^{1} (x^{4/3} + 4x^{1/3}) \, dx \le 5[1 - (-1)]$$

Therefore,

$$-2 \le \int_{-1}^{1} (x^{4/3} + 4x^{1/3}) \, dx \le 10$$

The exact value of the definite integral is $\frac{6}{7}$ as shown in Example 3, Sec. 6.6.

Exercises 6.4

1. Prove Theorem 6.4.2.

In Exercises 2 through 7, prove that Theorem 6.4.6 is valid in each case using the result of Theorem 6.4.5.

2. $b < a < c$

3. $b < c < a$

4. $c < a < b$

5. $c < b < a$

6. $a < c = b$

7. $a = b < c$

In Exercises 8 through 17, apply Theorem 6.4.9 to find a smallest and a largest possible value of the given integral.

8. $\displaystyle\int_{2}^{5} 3x \, dx$

9. $\displaystyle\int_{0}^{4} x^2 \, dx$

10. $\displaystyle\int_{-2}^{1} (x + 1)^{2/3} \, dx$

11. $\displaystyle\int_{-3}^{6} \sqrt{3 + x} \, dx$

12. $\displaystyle\int_{-1}^{4} (x^4 - 8x^2 + 16) \, dx$

13. $\displaystyle\int_{-4}^{0} (x^4 - 8x^2 + 16) \, dx$

14. $\displaystyle\int_{-5}^{2} \frac{x + 5}{x - 3} \, dx$

15. $\displaystyle\int_{-1}^{2} \frac{x}{x + 2} \, dx$

16. $\displaystyle\int_{-1}^{2} \sqrt{x^2 + 5} \, dx$

17. $\displaystyle\int_1^4 |x - 2| \, dx$

18. Show that if f is continuous on $[-1, 2]$ then

$$\int_{-1}^2 f(x) \, dx + \int_2^0 f(x) \, dx + \int_0^1 f(x) \, dx + \int_1^{-1} f(x) \, dx = 0$$

19. Show that $\displaystyle\int_0^1 x \, dx \geq \int_0^1 x^2 \, dx$ but $\displaystyle\int_1^2 x \, dx \leq \int_1^2 x^2 \, dx$

20. If f is continuous on $[a, b]$, prove that

$$\left| \int_a^b f(x) \, dx \right| \leq \int_a^b |f(x)| \, dx$$

(HINT: $-|f(x)| \leq f(x) \leq |f(x)|$.)

6.5 THE MEAN-VALUE THEOREM FOR INTEGRALS

Before stating and proving the mean-value theorem for integrals, we discuss an important theorem about a function that is continuous on a closed interval. It is called the *intermediate-value theorem,* and we need to use it to prove the mean-value theorem for integrals.

6.5.1 Theorem
Intermediate-Value Theorem

If the function f is continuous on the closed interval $[a, b]$ and if $f(a) \neq f(b)$, then for any number k between $f(a)$ and $f(b)$ there exists a number c between a and b such that $f(c) = k$.

Figure 6.5.1

Figure 6.5.2

The proof of this theorem is beyond the scope of this book; it can be found in an advanced calculus text. However, we discuss the geometric interpretation of the theorem. In Fig. 6.5.1, $(0, k)$ is any point on the y axis between the points $(0, f(a))$ and $(0, f(b))$. Theorem 6.5.1 states that the line $y = k$ must intersect the curve whose equation is $y = f(x)$ at the point (c, k), where c lies between a and b. Figure 6.5.1 shows this intersection.

Note that for some values of k there may be more than one possible value for c. The theorem states that there is always at least one value of c, but that it is not necessarily unique. Figure 6.5.2 shows three possible values of c (c_1, c_2, and c_3) for a particular k. Theorem 6.5.1 states that if the function f is continuous on a closed interval $[a, b]$, then f assumes every value between $f(a)$ and $f(b)$ as x assumes all values between a and b. The importance of the continuity of f on $[a, b]$ should be pointed out. For example, consider the function f, defined by

$$f(x) = \begin{cases} x - 1 & \text{if } 0 \leq x \leq 2 \\ x^2 & \text{if } 2 < x \leq 3 \end{cases}$$

A sketch of the graph of this function is shown in Fig. 6.5.3.

The function f is discontinuous at 2, which is in the closed interval $[0, 3]$; $f(0) = -1$ and $f(3) = 9$. If k is any number between 1 and 4, there is no value of c such that $f(c) = k$ because there are no function values between 1 and 4.

Let us consider an example of another function for which Theorem 6.5.1 does not hold. Let g be defined by

$$g(x) = \frac{2}{x-4}$$

A sketch of the graph of this function is shown in Fig. 6.5.4.

Figure 6.5.3   Figure 6.5.4

The function g is discontinuous at 4, which is in the closed interval $[2, 5]$; $g(2) = -1$ and $g(5) = 2$. If k is any number between -1 and 2, there is no value of c between 2 and 5 such that $g(c) = k$. In particular, if $k = 1$, then $g(6) = 1$, but 6 is not in the interval $[2, 5]$.

EXAMPLE 1:   Given the function f defined by

$$f(x) = 4 + 3x - x^2 \quad 2 \leq x \leq 5$$

verify the intermediate-value theorem if $k = 1$.

SOLUTION: $f(2) = 6$, $f(5) = -6$.
   To find c, set $f(c) = k = 1$, or

$$4 + 3c - c^2 = 1$$

$$c^2 - 3c - 3 = 0$$

This gives

$$c = \frac{3 \pm \sqrt{21}}{2}$$

We reject $\frac{1}{2}(3 - \sqrt{21})$ because this number is outside the interval $[2, 5]$. The number $\frac{1}{2}(3 + \sqrt{21})$ is in the interval $[2, 5]$, and

$$f\left(\frac{3 + \sqrt{21}}{2}\right) = 1$$

We are now ready to state and prove the mean-value theorem for integrals.

6.5.2 Theorem
Mean-Value Theorem
for Integrals

If the function f is continuous on the closed interval $[a, b]$, then there exists a number X such that $a \leq X \leq b$, and

$$\int_a^b f(x) \, dx = f(X) (b - a)$$

PROOF: Because f is continuous on $[a, b]$, from the extreme-value theorem (4.3.9) f has an absolute maximum value and an absolute minimum value on $[a, b]$.

Let m be the absolute minimum value occurring at $x = x_m$. Thus,

$$f(x_m) = m \qquad a \leq x_m \leq b \tag{1}$$

Let M be the absolute maximum value, occurring at $x = x_M$. Thus,

$$f(x_M) = M \qquad a \leq x_M \leq b \tag{2}$$

We have, then,

$$m \leq f(x) \leq M \qquad \text{for all } x \text{ in } [a, b]$$

From Theorem 6.4.9 it follows that

$$m(b - a) \leq \int_a^b f(x) \, dx \leq M(b - a)$$

Dividing by $(b - a)$ and noting that $(b - a)$ is positive because $b > a$, we get

$$m \leq \frac{\int_a^b f(x) \, dx}{b - a} \leq M$$

But from Eqs. (1) and (2), $m = f(x_m)$ and $M = f(x_M)$, and so we have

$$f(x_m) \leq \frac{\int_a^b f(x) \, dx}{b - a} \leq f(x_M) \tag{3}$$

From inequalities (3) and the intermediate-value theorem (6.5.1), there is some number X in a closed interval containing x_m and x_M such that

$$f(X) = \frac{\int_a^b f(x) \, dx}{b - a}$$

or

$$\int_a^b f(x) \, dx = f(X) (b - a) \qquad a \leq X \leq b \qquad \blacksquare$$

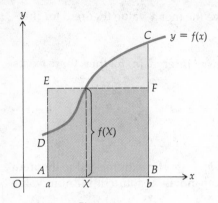

Figure 6.5.5

To interpret Theorem 6.5.2 geometrically, we consider $f(x) \geq 0$ for all values of x in $[a, b]$. Then $\int_a^b f(x)\, dx$ is the measure of the area of the region bounded by the curve whose equation is $y = f(x)$, the x axis, and the lines $x = a$ and $x = b$ (see Fig. 6.5.5). Theorem 6.5.2 states that there is a number X in $[a, b]$ such that the area of the rectangle AEFB of height $f(X)$ units and width $(b - a)$ units is equal to the area of the region ADCB.

The value of X is not necessarily unique. The theorem does not provide a method for finding X, but it states that a value of X exists, and this is used to prove other theorems. In some particular cases we can find the value of X, as is illustrated in the following example.

EXAMPLE 2:   Find the value of X such that

$$\int_1^3 f(x)\, dx = f(X)(3 - 1)$$

if $f(x) = x^2$. Use the result of Example 3 in Sec. 6.3.

SOLUTION: In Example 3 of Sec. 6.3, we obtained

$$\int_1^3 x^2\, dx = 8\tfrac{2}{3}$$

Therefore, we wish to find X such that

$$f(X) \cdot (2) = \tfrac{26}{3}$$

or

$$X^2 = \tfrac{13}{3}$$

Therefore,

$$X = \pm \tfrac{1}{3}\sqrt{39}$$

We reject $-\tfrac{1}{3}\sqrt{39}$ since it is not in the interval $[1, 3]$, and we have

$$\int_1^3 f(x)\, dx = f(\tfrac{1}{3}\sqrt{39})(3 - 1)$$

The value $f(X)$ given by Theorem 6.5.2 is called the *mean value* (or *average value*) of f on the interval $[a, b]$. It is a generalization of the arithmetic mean of a finite set of numbers. That is, if $f(x_1), f(x_2), \ldots, f(x_n)$ is a set of n numbers, then the arithmetic mean is given by

$$\frac{\sum\limits_{i=1}^{n} f(x_i)}{n}$$

To generalize this definition, consider a regular partition of the closed interval $[a, b]$, which is divided into n subintervals of equal length $\Delta x = (b - a)/n$. Let ξ_i be any point in the ith subinterval. Form the sum:

$$\frac{\sum\limits_{i=1}^{n} f(\xi_i)}{n} \tag{4}$$

The quotient (4) corresponds to the arithmetic mean of n numbers. Because $\Delta x = (b - a)/n$, we have

$$n = \frac{b - a}{\Delta x} \tag{5}$$

Substituting from (5) into (4), we obtain

$$\frac{\sum\limits_{i=1}^{n} f(\xi_i)}{\dfrac{(b - a)}{\Delta x}}$$

or

$$\frac{\sum\limits_{i=1}^{n} f(\xi_i) \cdot \Delta x}{b - a}$$

Taking the limit as $n \to +\infty$ (or $\Delta x \to 0$), we have, if the limit exists,

$$\lim_{n \to +\infty} \frac{\sum\limits_{i=1}^{n} f(\xi_i)\, \Delta x}{b - a} = \frac{\int_{a}^{b} f(x)\, dx}{b - a}$$

This leads to the following definition.

6.5.3 Definition   If the function f is integrable on the closed interval $[a, b]$, the *average value* of f on $[a, b]$ is

$$\frac{\int_{a}^{b} f(x)\, dx}{b - a}$$

EXAMPLE 3:   Find the average value of the function f defined by $f(x) = x^2$ on the interval $[1, 3]$.

SOLUTION: In Example 3, Sec. 6.3, we obtained

$$\int_{1}^{3} x^2\, dx = \tfrac{26}{3}$$

So if A.V. = the average value of f on $[1, 3]$, we have

$$\text{A.V.} = \frac{\tfrac{26}{3}}{3 - 1} = \frac{13}{3}$$

An important application of the average value of a function occurs in physics and engineering in connection with the concept of center of mass. This is discussed in the next chapter.

In economics, Definition 6.5.3 can be used to find an average total cost or an average total revenue. For example, if the total cost function C is given by $C(x) = x^2$, where $C(x)$ thousands of dollars is the total cost of producing $100x$ units of a certain commodity, then the number of thousands of dollars in the average total cost, when the number of units produced takes on all values from 100 to 300, is given by the average value of C on $[1, 3]$. From Example 3, this is $\frac{13}{3} = 4.33$. Hence, the average total cost is $4333.

Exercises 6.5

In Exercises 1 through 8, a function f and a closed interval $[a, b]$ are given. Determine if the intermediate-value theorem holds for the given value of k. If the theorem holds, find a number c such that $f(c) = k$. If the theorem does not hold, give the reason. Draw a sketch of the curve and the line $y = k$.

1. $f(x) = 2 + x - x^2$; $[a, b] = [0, 3]$; $k = 1$

2. $f(x) = x^2 + 5x - 6$; $[a, b] = [-1, 2]$; $k = 4$

3. $f(x) = \sqrt{25 - x^2}$; $[a, b] = [-4.5, 3]$; $k = 3$

4. $f(x) = -\sqrt{100 - x^2}$; $[a, b] = [0, 8]$; $k = -8$

5. $f(x) = \dfrac{4}{x + 2}$; $[a, b] = [-3, 1]$; $k = \frac{1}{2}$

6. $f(x) = \begin{cases} 1 + x & \text{if } -4 \le x \le -2 \\ 2 - x & \text{if } -2 < x \le 1 \end{cases}$; $[a, b] = [-4, 1]$; $k = \frac{1}{2}$

7. $f(x) = \begin{cases} x^2 - 4 & \text{if } -2 \le x < 1 \\ x^2 - 1 & \text{if } 1 \le x \le 3 \end{cases}$; $[a, b] = [-2, 3]$; $k = -1$

8. $f(x) = \dfrac{5}{2x - 1}$; $[a, b] = [0, 1]$; $k = 2$

In Exercises 9 through 13, find the value of X satisfying the mean-value theorem for integrals. For the value of the definite integral, use the results of the corresponding Exercises 9 through 13 in Exercises 6.3. Draw a figure illustrating the application of the theorem.

9. $\displaystyle\int_1^2 x^3 \, dx$

10. $\displaystyle\int_{-2}^1 x^4 \, dx$

11. $\displaystyle\int_1^4 (x^2 + 4x + 5) \, dx$

12. $\displaystyle\int_0^4 (x^2 + x - 6) \, dx$

13. $\displaystyle\int_{-2}^2 (x^3 + 1) \, dx$

14. Find the average value of the function f defined by $f(x) = x^2$ on the interval $[2, 4]$, and find the value of x at which it occurs. Make a sketch. Use the result of Exercise 8 of Exercises 6.3 for the value of the definite integral.

15. Suppose a ball is dropped from rest and after t sec its velocity is v ft/sec. Neglecting air resistance, express v in terms of t as $v = f(t)$ and find the average value of f on $[0, 2]$.

16. Suppose $C(x)$ hundreds of dollars is the total cost of producing $10x$ units of a certain commodity, and $C(x) = x^2$. Find the average total cost when the number of units produced takes on all values from 0 to 20. Use the result of Exercise 7 in Exercises 6.3 for the value of the definite integral.

17. Find the average value of the function f defined by $f(x) = \sqrt{16 - x^2}$ on the interval $[-4, 4]$. Draw a figure. (HINT: Find the value of the definite integral by interpreting it as the measure of the area of a region enclosed by a semicircle.)

18. Find the average value of the function f defined by $f(x) = \sqrt{49 - x^2}$ on the interval $[0, 7]$. Draw a figure. (HINT: Find the value of the definite integral by interpreting it as the measure of the area of a region enclosed by a quarter-circle.)

19. Show that the intermediate-value theorem guarantees that the equation $x^3 - 4x^2 + x + 3 = 0$ has a root between 1 and 2.

20. Suppose f is a function for which $0 \leq f(x) \leq 1$ if $0 \leq x \leq 1$. Prove that there is at least one number c in $[0, 1]$ such that $f(c) = c$. (HINT: If neither 0 nor 1 qualifies as c, then $f(0) > 0$ and $f(1) < 1$. Consider the function g for which $g(x) = f(x) - x$ and apply the intermediate-value theorem to g on $[0, 1]$.)

21. If f is continuous on $[a, b]$ and $\int_a^b f(x)\, dx = 0$, prove that there is at least one number c in $[a, b]$ such that $f(c) = 0$.

6.6 THE FUNDAMENTAL THEOREM OF THE CALCULUS

Historically the basic concepts of the definite integral were used by the ancient Greeks many years before the differential calculus was discovered. In the seventeenth century, almost simultaneously but working independently, Newton and Leibnitz showed how the calculus could be used to find the area of a region bounded by a curve or a set of curves, by evaluating a definite integral by antidifferentiation. The procedure involves what is known as the *fundamental theorem of the calculus.* Before we state and prove this important theorem, we discuss definite integrals having a variable upper limit, and a preliminary theorem.

Let f be a function continuous on the closed interval $[a, b]$. Then the value of the definite integral $\int_a^b f(x)\, dx$ depends only on the function f and the numbers a and b, and not on the letter x, which is used here as the independent variable. In Example 3, Sec. 6.3, we found the value of $\int_1^3 x^2\, dx$ to be $8\frac{2}{3}$. Any other letter instead of x could have been used; for example,

$$\int_1^3 t^2\, dt = \int_1^3 u^2\, du = \int_1^3 r^2\, dr = 8\tfrac{2}{3}$$

If f is continuous on the closed interval $[a, b]$, then by Theorem 6.3.3 and the definition of the definite integral, $\int_a^b f(t)\, dt$ exists. We previously stated that if the definite integral exists, it is a unique number. If x is a number in $[a, b]$, then f is continuous on $[a, x]$ because it is continuous on $[a, b]$. Consequently, $\int_a^x f(t)\, dt$ exists and is a unique number whose value depends on x. Therefore, $\int_a^x f(t)\, dt$ defines a function F having as its domain all numbers in the closed interval $[a, b]$ and whose function value at any number x in $[a, b]$ is given by

$$F(x) = \int_a^x f(t)\, dt \tag{1}$$

As a notational observation, if the limits of the definite integral are

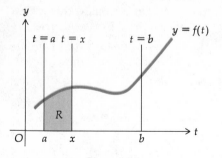

Figure 6.6.1

variables, different letters are used for these limits and for the independent variable in the integrand. Hence, in Eq. (1), because x is the upper limit, we use the letter t as the independent variable in the integrand.

If, in Eq. (1), $f(t) \geq 0$ for all values of t in $[a, b]$, then the function value $F(x)$ can be interpreted geometrically as the measure of the area of the region bounded by the curve whose equation is $y = f(t)$, the t axis, and the lines $t = a$ and $t = x$. (See Fig. 6.6.1.) Note that $F(a) = \int_a^a f(t) \, dt$, which by Definition 6.3.5 equals 0.

We now state and prove an important theorem giving the derivative of a function F defined as a definite integral having a variable upper limit.

6.6.1 Theorem   Let the function f be continuous on the closed interval $[a, b]$ and x be any number in $[a, b]$. If F is the function defined by

$$F(x) = \int_a^x f(t) \, dt$$

then

$$F'(x) = f(x) \tag{2}$$

(If $x = a$, the derivative in (2) may be a derivative from the right, and if $x = b$, the derivative in (2) may be a derivative from the left.)

PROOF: Consider two numbers x_1 and $(x_1 + \Delta x)$ in $[a, b]$. Then

$$F(x_1) = \int_a^{x_1} f(t) \, dt$$

and

$$F(x_1 + \Delta x) = \int_a^{x_1 + \Delta x} f(t) \, dt$$

so that

$$F(x_1 + \Delta x) - F(x_1) = \int_a^{x_1 + \Delta x} f(t) \, dt - \int_a^{x_1} f(t) \, dt \tag{3}$$

By Theorem 6.4.6,

$$\int_a^{x_1} f(t) \, dt + \int_{x_1}^{x_1 + \Delta x} f(t) \, dt = \int_a^{x_1 + \Delta x} f(t) \, dt$$

or, equivalently,

$$\int_a^{x_1 + \Delta x} f(t) \, dt - \int_a^{x_1} f(t) \, dt = \int_{x_1}^{x_1 + \Delta x} f(t) \, dt \tag{4}$$

Substituting from Eq. (4) into (3), we get

$$F(x_1 + \Delta x) - F(x_1) = \int_{x_1}^{x_1 + \Delta x} f(t) \, dt \tag{5}$$

By the mean-value theorem for integrals (6.5.2), there is some number X in the closed interval bounded by x_1 and $(x_1 + \Delta x)$ such that

$$\int_{x_1}^{x_1 + \Delta x} f(t)\ dt = f(X)\ \Delta x \tag{6}$$

From Eqs. (5) and (6), we obtain

$$F(x_1 + \Delta x) - F(x_1) = f(X)\ \Delta x$$

or, if we divide by Δx,

$$\frac{F(x_1 + \Delta x) - F(x_1)}{\Delta x} = f(X)$$

Taking the limit as Δx approaches zero, we have

$$\lim_{\Delta x \to 0} \frac{F(x_1 + \Delta x) - F(x_1)}{\Delta x} = \lim_{\Delta x \to 0} f(X) \tag{7}$$

The left side of Eq. (7) is $F'(x_1)$. To determine $\lim_{\Delta x \to 0} f(X)$, recall that X is in the closed interval bounded by x_1 and $x_1 + \Delta x$, and because

$$\lim_{\Delta x \to 0} x_1 = x_1 \quad \text{and} \quad \lim_{\Delta x \to 0} (x_1 + \Delta x) = x_1,$$

it follows from the squeeze theorem (2.10.5) that $\lim_{\Delta x \to 0} X = x_1$. Because f is continuous at x_1, we have $\lim_{\Delta x \to 0} f(X) = \lim_{X \to x_1} f(X) = f(x_1)$; thus, from Eq. (7) we get

$$F'(x_1) = f(x_1) \tag{8}$$

If the function f is not defined for values of x less than a but is continuous from the right at a, then in the above argument, if $x_1 = a$ in Eq. (7), Δx must approach 0 from the right. Hence, the left side of Eq. (8) will be $F'_+(x_1)$. Similarly, if f is not defined for values of x greater than b but is continuous from the left at b, then if $x_1 = b$ in Eq. (7), Δx must approach 0 from the left. Hence, we have $F'_-(x_1)$ on the left side of Eq. (8).

Because x_1 is any number in $[a, b]$, Eq. (8) states what we wished to prove. ■

Theorem 6.6.1 states that the definite integral $\int_a^x f(t)\ dt$, with variable upper limit x, is an antiderivative of f.

6.6.2 Theorem
Fundamental Theorem of the Calculus

Let the function f be continuous on the closed interval $[a, b]$ and g be a function such that

$$g'(x) = f(x) \tag{9}$$

for all x in $[a, b]$. Then

$$\int_a^b f(t) \; dt = g(b) - g(a)$$

(If $x = a$, the derivative in (9) may be a derivative from the right, and if $x = b$, the derivative in (9) may be a derivative from the left).

PROOF: If f is continuous at all numbers in $[a, b]$, we know from Theorem 6.6.1 that the definite integral $\int_a^x f(t) \; dt$, with variable upper limit x, defines a function F whose derivative on $[a, b]$ is f. Because by hypothesis $g'(x) = f(x)$, it follows from Theorem 5.3.3 that

$$g(x) = \int_a^x f(t) \; dt + k \tag{10}$$

where k is some constant.

Letting $x = b$ and $x = a$, successively, in Eq. (10), we get

$$g(b) = \int_a^b f(t) \; dt + k \tag{11}$$

and

$$g(a) = \int_a^a f(t) \; dt + k \tag{12}$$

From Eqs. (11) and (12), we obtain

$$g(b) - g(a) = \int_a^b f(t) \; dt - \int_a^a f(t) \; dt$$

But, by Definition 6.3.5, $\int_a^a f(t) \; dt = 0$, and so we have

$$g(b) - g(a) = \int_a^b f(t) \; dt$$

which is what we wished we prove.

If f is not defined for values of x greater than b but is continuous from the left at b, the derivative in (9) is a derivative from the left, and we have $g'_-(b) = F'_-(b)$ from which (11) follows. Similarly, if f is not defined for values of x less than a but is continuous from the right at a, then the derivative in (9) is a derivative from the right, and we have $g'_+(a) = F'_+(a)$ from which (12) follows. ∎

We are now in a position to find the exact value of a definite integral by applying Theorem 6.6.2. In applying the theorem, we denote

$$[g(b) - g(a)] \quad \text{by} \quad g(x) \, \Big]_a^b$$

EXAMPLE 1: Evaluate

$$\int_1^3 x^2 \, dx$$

by the fundamental theorem of the calculus.

SOLUTION: In this example, $f(x) = x^2$.

An antiderivative of x^2 is $\frac{1}{3}x^3$. From this we choose

$$g(x) = \frac{x^3}{3}$$

Therefore, from Theorem 6.6.2, we get

$$\int_1^3 x^2 \, dx = \frac{x^3}{3} \Big]_1^3 = 9 - \frac{1}{3}$$

$$= 8\tfrac{2}{3}$$

Compare this result with that of Example 3, Sec. 6.3.

Because of the connection between definite integrals and antiderivatives, we used the integral sign $\int$ for the notation $\int f(x) \, dx$ for an antiderivative. We now dispense with the terminology of antiderivatives and antidifferentiation and begin to call $\int f(x) \, dx$ the *indefinite integral* of "f of x, dx." The process of evaluating an indefinite integral or a definite integral is called *integration*.

The difference between an indefinite integral and a definite integral should be emphasized. The indefinite integral $\int f(x) \, dx$ is defined as a function g such that its derivative $D_x[g(x)] = f(x)$. However, the definite integral $\int_a^b f(x) \, dx$ is a number whose value depends on the function f and the numbers a and b, and it is defined as the limit of a Riemann sum. The definition of the definite integral makes no reference to differentiation.

The general indefinite integral involves an arbitrary constant; for instance,

$$\int x^2 \, dx = \frac{x^3}{3} + C$$

This arbitrary constant C is called a *constant of integration*. In applying the fundamental theorem to evaluate a definite integral, we do not need to include the arbitrary constant C in the expression for $g(x)$ because the fundamental theorem permits us to select *any* antiderivative, including the one for which $C = 0$.

EXAMPLE 2: Evaluate

$$\int_{1/2}^4 (x^3 - 6x^2 + 9x + 1) \, dx$$

SOLUTION:

$$\int_{1/2}^4 (x^3 - 6x^2 + 9x + 1) \, dx = \int_{1/2}^4 x^3 \, dx - 6 \int_{1/2}^4 x^2 \, dx$$

$$+ 9 \int_{1/2}^4 x \, dx + \int_{1/2}^4 dx$$

$$= \frac{x^4}{4} - 6 \cdot \frac{x^3}{3} + 9 \cdot \frac{x^2}{2} + x \Big]_{1/2}^4$$

$$= (64 - 128 + 72 + 4) - (\tfrac{1}{64} - \tfrac{1}{4} + \tfrac{9}{8} + \tfrac{1}{2})$$

$$= \tfrac{679}{64}$$

EXAMPLE 3:   Evaluate

$$\int_{-1}^{1} (x^{4/3} + 4x^{1/3}) \ dx$$

SOLUTION: $\int_{-1}^{1} (x^{4/3} + 4x^{1/3}) \ dx = \tfrac{3}{7}x^{7/3} + 4 \cdot \tfrac{3}{4}x^{4/3} \ \Big]_{-1}^{1}$

$$= \tfrac{3}{7} + 3 - (-\tfrac{3}{7} + 3)$$

$$= \tfrac{6}{7}$$

EXAMPLE 4:   Evaluate

$$\int_{0}^{2} 2x^2 \sqrt{x^3 + 1} \ dx$$

SOLUTION: $\int_{0}^{2} 2x^2 \sqrt{x^3 + 1} \ dx = \tfrac{2}{3} \int_{0}^{2} \sqrt{x^3 + 1} \ (3x^2) \ dx$

$$= \frac{2}{3} \frac{(x^3 + 1)^{3/2}}{\tfrac{3}{2}} \ \Big]_{0}^{2}$$

$$= \tfrac{4}{9}(8 + 1)^{3/2} - \tfrac{4}{9}(0 + 1)^{3/2}$$

$$= \tfrac{4}{9}(27 - 1)$$

$$= \tfrac{104}{9}$$

EXAMPLE 5:   Evaluate

$$\int_{0}^{3} x\sqrt{1 + x} \ dx$$

SOLUTION: To evaluate the indefinite integral $\int x\sqrt{1 + x} \ dx$ we let

$$u = \sqrt{1 + x} \qquad u^2 = 1 + x \qquad x = u^2 - 1 \qquad dx = 2u \ du$$

Substituting, we have

$$\int x\sqrt{1 + x} \ dx = \int (u^2 - 1)u(2u \ du)$$

$$= 2 \int (u^4 - u^2) \ du$$

$$= \tfrac{2}{5}u^5 - \tfrac{2}{3}u^3 + C$$

$$= \tfrac{2}{5}(1 + x)^{5/2} - \tfrac{2}{3}(1 + x)^{3/2} + C$$

Therefore, the definite integral

$$\int_{0}^{3} x\sqrt{1 + x} \ dx = \tfrac{2}{5}(1 + x)^{5/2} - \tfrac{2}{3}(1 + x)^{3/2} \ \Big]_{0}^{3}$$

$$= \tfrac{2}{5}(4)^{5/2} - \tfrac{2}{3}(4)^{3/2} - \tfrac{2}{5}(1)^{5/2} + \tfrac{2}{3}(1)^{3/2}$$

$$= \tfrac{64}{5} - \tfrac{16}{3} - \tfrac{2}{5} + \tfrac{2}{3}$$

$$= \tfrac{116}{15}$$

Another method for evaluating the definite integral in Example 5 involves changing the limits of the definite integral to values of u. Because

$u = \sqrt{1 + x}$, we see that when $x = 0$, $u = 1$; and when $x = 3$, $u = 2$. Thus, we have

$$\int_0^3 x\sqrt{1+x}\ dx = 2\int_1^2 (u^4 - u^2)\ du$$

$$= \tfrac{2}{5}u^5 - \tfrac{2}{3}u^3 \ \Big]_1^2$$

$$= \tfrac{64}{5} - \tfrac{16}{3} - \tfrac{2}{5} + \tfrac{2}{3}$$

$$= \tfrac{116}{15}$$

Often this second method is shorter, and its justification follows immediately from Theorems 5.3.10 and 6.6.2.

EXAMPLE 6: Evaluate

$$\int_{-3}^4 |x + 2|\ dx$$

SOLUTION: If we let $f(x) = |x + 2|$, instead of finding an antiderivative of f directly, we write $f(x)$ as

$$f(x) = \begin{cases} x + 2 & \text{if } x \geq -2 \\ -x - 2 & \text{if } x \leq -2 \end{cases}$$

Applying Theorem 6.4.6, we have

$$\int_{-3}^4 |x + 2|\ dx = \int_{-3}^{-2} (-x - 2)\ dx + \int_{-2}^4 (x + 2)\ dx$$

$$= \left[-\frac{x^2}{2} - 2x \right]_{-3}^{-2} + \left[\frac{x^2}{2} + 2x \right]_{-2}^4$$

$$= \tfrac{1}{2} + 18$$

$$= \tfrac{37}{2}$$

EXAMPLE 7: Find the area of the region in the first quadrant bounded by the curve whose equation is $y = x\sqrt{x^2 + 5}$, the x axis, and the line $x = 2$. Make a sketch.

SOLUTION: See Fig. 6.6.2: The region is shown together with one of the rectangular elements of area.

We take a regular partition of the interval $[0, 2]$. The width of each rectangle is Δx units, and the altitude of the ith rectangle is $\xi_i \sqrt{\xi_i^2 + 5}$ units, where ξ_i is any number in the ith subinterval. Therefore, the measure of the area of the rectangular element is $\xi_i \sqrt{\xi_i^2 + 5}\ \Delta x$. The sum of the measures of the areas of n such rectangles is

$$\sum_{i=1}^n \xi_i \sqrt{\xi_i^2 + 5}\ \Delta x$$

which is a Riemann sum. The limit of this sum as Δx approaches zero (or $n \to +\infty$) gives the measure of the desired area. The limit of the Riemann sum is a definite integral which we evaluate by the fundamental theorem of the calculus.

Figure 6.6.2

Let $A =$ the number of square units in the area of the region. Then,

$$A = \lim_{\Delta x \to 0} \sum_{i=1}^{n} \xi_i \sqrt{\xi_i^2 + 5} \; \Delta x$$

$$= \int_0^2 x\sqrt{x^2 + 5} \; dx$$

$$= \tfrac{1}{2} \int_0^2 \sqrt{x^2 + 5} \; (2x \; dx)$$

$$= \tfrac{1}{2} \cdot \tfrac{2}{3} (x^2 + 5)^{3/2} \Big]_0^2$$

$$= \tfrac{1}{3} [(9)^{3/2} - (5)^{3/2}]$$

$$= \tfrac{1}{3} (27 - 5\sqrt{5})$$

Hence, the area is $\tfrac{1}{3}(27 - 5\sqrt{5})$ square units.

EXAMPLE 8:   Given

$$f(x) = x\sqrt{x - 4}$$

find the average value of f on the interval $[5, 8]$.

SOLUTION: Let A.V. $=$ the average value of f on $[5, 8]$. We have, from Definition 6.5.3,

$$\text{A.V.} = \frac{1}{8 - 5} \int_5^8 x\sqrt{x - 4} \; dx$$

Let $u = \sqrt{x - 4}$; then $u^2 = x - 4$; $x = u^2 + 4$; $dx = 2u \; du$. When $x = 5, u = 1$; when $x = 8, u = 2$. Therefore,

$$\text{A.V.} = \tfrac{1}{3} \int_1^2 (u^2 + 4)u(2u \; du)$$

$$= \tfrac{2}{3} \int_1^2 (u^4 + 4u^2) \; du$$

$$= \tfrac{2}{3} \left[\tfrac{1}{5}u^5 + \tfrac{4}{3}u^3 \right]_1^2$$

$$= \tfrac{2}{3} [\tfrac{32}{5} + \tfrac{32}{3} - \tfrac{1}{5} - \tfrac{4}{3}]$$

$$= \tfrac{466}{45}$$

Exercises 6.6

In Exercises 1 through 18, evaluate the definite integral by using the fundamental theorem of the calculus.

1. $\displaystyle\int_2^7 (x^2 - 2x) \; dx$

2. $\displaystyle\int_{-1}^3 (3x^2 + 5x - 1) \; dx$

3. $\displaystyle\int_0^4 (y^3 - y^2 + 1) \; dy$

4. $\displaystyle\int_{-1}^3 \frac{dy}{(y + 2)^3}$

5. $\int_{-2}^{0} 3w \sqrt{4 - w^2} \, dw$

6. $\int_{1}^{3} \dfrac{x \, dx}{(3x^2 - 1)^3}$

7. $\int_{0}^{1} \dfrac{(y^2 + 2y) \, dy}{\sqrt[3]{y^3 + 3y^2 + 4}}$

8. $\int_{4}^{5} x^2 \sqrt{x - 4} \, dx$

9. $\int_{0}^{15} \dfrac{w \, dw}{(1 + w)^{3/4}}$

10. $\int_{-2}^{1} (x + 1) \sqrt{x + 3} \, dx$

11. $\int_{-2}^{5} |x - 3| \, dx$

12. $\int_{-3}^{3} \sqrt{3 + |x|} \, dx$

13. $\int_{-1}^{1} \sqrt{|x| - x} \, dx$

14. $\int_{1}^{4} \dfrac{x^5 - x}{3x^3} \, dx$

15. $\int_{1}^{2} \dfrac{x^3 + 2x^2 + x + 2}{(x + 1)^2} \, dx$

16. $\int_{-3}^{2} \dfrac{3x^3 - 24x^2 + 48x + 5}{x^2 - 8x + 16} \, dx$

(HINT: Divide the numerator by the denominator.)

17. $\int_{1}^{64} \left(\sqrt{t} - \dfrac{1}{\sqrt{t}} + \sqrt[3]{t} \right) dt$

18. $\int_{0}^{1} \sqrt{x} \, \sqrt{1 + x\sqrt{x}} \, dx$

In Exercises 19 through 22, use Theorem 6.6.1 to find the indicated derivative.

19. $D_x \displaystyle\int_{0}^{x} \sqrt{4 + t^6} \, dt$

20. $D_x \displaystyle\int_{x}^{5} \sqrt{1 + t^4} \, dt$

21. $D_x \displaystyle\int_{-x}^{x} \dfrac{dt}{3 + t^2}$

22. $D_x \displaystyle\int_{1}^{x^2} \sqrt{1 + t^4} \, dt$

In Exercises 23 through 28, find the area of the region bounded by the given curve and lines. Draw a figure showing the region and a rectangular element of area. Express the measure of the area as the limit of a Riemann sum and then as a definite integral. Evaluate the definite integral by the fundamental theorem of the calculus.

23. $y = 4x - x^2$; x axis; $x = 1$, $x = 3$

24. $y = x^2 - 2x + 3$; x axis; $x = -2$, $x = 1$

25. $y = \sqrt{x + 1}$; x axis, y axis; $x = 8$

26. $y = x\sqrt{x^2 + 9}$; x axis, y axis; $x = 4$

27. $y = x\sqrt{x + 5}$; x axis; $x = -1$, $x = 4$

28. $y = \dfrac{1}{x^2} - x$; x axis; $x = 2$, $x = 3$

In Exercises 29 through 32, find the average value of the function f on the given interval $[a, b]$. In Exercises 29 and 30, find the value of x at which the average value of f occurs and make a sketch.

29. $f(x) = 8x - x^2$; $[a, b] = [0, 4]$

30. $f(x) = 9 - x^2$; $[a, b] = [0, 3]$

31. $f(x) = x^2 \sqrt{x - 3}$; $[a, b] = [7, 12]$

32. $f(x) = 3x\sqrt{x^2 - 16}$; $[a, b] = [4, 5]$

33. A ball is dropped from rest and after t sec its velocity is v ft/sec. Neglecting air resistance show that the average velocity during the first $\frac{1}{2}T$ sec is one-third of the average velocity during the next $\frac{1}{2}T$ sec.

34. A stone is thrown downward with an initial velocity of v_0 ft/sec. Neglect air resistance. (a) Show that if v ft/sec is the velocity of the stone after falling s ft, then $v = \sqrt{v_0^2 + 2gs}$. (b) Find the average velocity during the first 100 ft of fall if the initial velocity is 60 ft/sec. (Take $g = 32$ and downward as the positive direction.)

35. The demand equation for a certain commodity is $x^2 + p^2 = 100$, where p dollars is the price of one unit when $100x$ units of the commodity are demanded. Find the average total revenue when the number of units demanded takes on all values from 600 to 800.

36. Let f be a function whose derivative f' is continuous on $[a, b]$. Find the average value of the slope of the tangent line of the graph of f on $[a, b]$ and give a geometric interpretation of the result.

Review Exercises (Chapter 6)

In Exercises 1 and 2, find the exact value of the definite integral by using the definition of the definite integral; do not use the fundamental theorem of the calculus.

1. $\displaystyle\int_{-2}^{1} (x^3 + 2x)\, dx$

2. $\displaystyle\int_{-1}^{3} (x^2 - 1)^2\, dx$

In Exercises 3 and 4 find the sum.

3. $\displaystyle\sum_{i=1}^{100} 2i(i^3 - 1)$

4. $\displaystyle\sum_{i=1}^{41} (\sqrt[3]{3i - 1} - \sqrt[3]{3i + 2})$

5. Prove that $\displaystyle\sum_{i=1}^{n} i^3 = \left(\sum_{i=1}^{n} i\right)^2$ and verify the formula for $n = 1, 2$, and 3.

6. Express as a definite integral and evaluate the definite integral: $\displaystyle\lim_{n \to +\infty} \sum_{i=1}^{n} (8\sqrt{i}\,/n^{3/2})$ (HINT: Consider the function f for which $f(x) = \sqrt{x}$.)

In Exercises 7 through 16, evaluate the definite integral by using the fundamental theorem of the calculus.

7. $\displaystyle\int_{-3}^{3} (t^6 - 3t)\, dt$

8. $\displaystyle\int_{2}^{4} \frac{4\, dx}{5x^4}$

9. $\displaystyle\int_{1}^{5} \frac{dx}{\sqrt{3x - 1}}$

10. $\displaystyle\int_{-5}^{5} 2x \sqrt[3]{x^2 + 2}\, dx$

11. $\displaystyle\int_{0}^{2} x\sqrt{3x + 4}\, dx$

12. $\displaystyle\int_{1}^{2} \frac{x\, dx}{\sqrt{5 - x}}$

13. $\displaystyle\int_{-1}^{7} \frac{x^2\, dx}{\sqrt{x + 2}}$

14. $\displaystyle\int_{0}^{1} (x^2 + 4x)\sqrt{x^3 + 6x^2 + 1}\, dx$

15. $\displaystyle\int_{-3}^{3} |x - 2|^3\, dx$

16. $\displaystyle\int_{-2}^{2} x|x - 3|\, dx$

17. Show that each of the following inequalities holds:

(a) $\displaystyle\int_{-2}^{-1} \frac{dx}{x - 3} \geq \int_{-2}^{-1} \frac{dx}{x}$; (b) $\displaystyle\int_{1}^{2} \frac{dx}{x} \geq \int_{1}^{2} \frac{dx}{x - 3}$; (c) $\displaystyle\int_{4}^{5} \frac{dx}{x - 3} \geq \int_{4}^{5} \frac{dx}{x}$

18. If

$$f(x) = \begin{cases} 0 & \text{if } a \leq x < c \\ k & \text{if } x = c \\ 1 & \text{if } c < x \leq b \end{cases}$$

prove that f is integrable on $[a, b]$ and $\displaystyle\int_{a}^{b} f(x)\, dx = b - c$ regardless of the value of k.

In Exercises 19 and 20 find a smallest and a largest possible value of the given integral.

19. $\displaystyle\int_{1}^{4} \sqrt{5 + 4x - x^2}\, dx$

20. $\displaystyle\int_{-2}^{1} \sqrt[3]{2x^3 - 3x^2 + 1}\, dx$

In Exercises 21 through 24, find the area of the region bounded by the given curve and lines. Draw a figure showing the region and a rectangular element of area. Express the measure of the area as the limit of a Riemann sum and then as a definite integral. Evaluate the definite integral by the fundamental theorem of the calculus.

21. $y = 9 - x^2$; x axis; y axis; $x = 3$

22. $y = 16 - x^2$; x axis; $x = -4$, $x = 4$

23. $y = 2\sqrt{x-1}$; x axis; $x = 5$, $x = 17$

24. $y = \dfrac{4}{x^2} - x$; x axis; $x = -2$, $x = -1$

25. If $f(x) = x^2\sqrt{x-3}$, find the average value of f on $[7, 12]$.

26. Interpret the mean-value theorem for integrals (6.5.2) in terms of an average function value.

27. A body falls from rest and travels a distance of s ft before striking the ground. If the only force acting is that of gravity, which gives the body an acceleration of g ft/sec^2 toward the ground, show that the average value of the velocity, expressed as a function of distance, while traveling this distance is $\tfrac{2}{3}\sqrt{2gs}$ ft/sec, and that this average velocity is two-thirds of the final velocity.

28. Suppose a ball is dropped from rest and after t sec its directed distance from the starting point is s ft and its velocity is v ft/sec. Neglect air resistance. When $t = t_1$, $s = s_1$, and $v = v_1$. (a) Express v as a function of t as $v = f(t)$ and find the average value of f on $[0, t_1]$. (b) Express v as a function of s as $v = g(s)$ and find the average velocity of g on $[0, s_1]$. (c) Write the results of parts (a) and (b) in terms of t_1, and determine which average velocity is larger.

29. The demand equation of a certain commodity is $p^2 + x - 10 = 0$, where p dollars is the price of one unit when $100x$ units of the commodity are demanded. Find the average total revenue when the number of units demanded takes on all values from 600 to 800.

30. (a) Find the average value of the function f defined by $f(x) = 1/x^2$ on the interval $[1, r]$. (b) If A is the average value found in part (a), find $\lim\limits_{r \to +\infty} A$.

31. Given $F(x) = \displaystyle\int_x^{2x} \frac{1}{t}\, dt$ and $x > 0$. Prove that F is a constant function by showing that $F'(x) = 0$. (HINT: Use Theorem 6.6.1 after writing the given integral as the difference of two integrals.)

32. Make up an example of a discontinuous function for which the mean-value theorem for integrals (a) does not hold, and (b) does hold.

33. Let f be continuous on $[a, b]$ and $\displaystyle\int_a^b f(t)\, dt \neq 0$. Show that for any number k in $(0, 1)$ there is a number c in (a, b) such that

$$\int_a^c f(t)\, dt = k \int_a^b f(t)\, dt$$

(HINT: Consider the function F for which $F(x) = \displaystyle\int_a^x f(t)\, dt \Big/ \int_a^b f(t)\, dt$ and apply the intermediate-value theorem.)

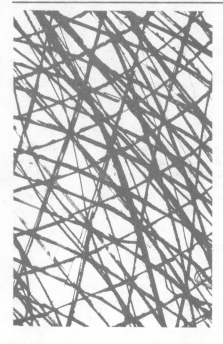

7

Applications of the Definite Integral

7.1 AREA OF A REGION IN A PLANE

If f is a function continuous on the closed interval $[a, b]$ and if $f(x) \geq 0$ for all x in $[a, b]$, then the number of square units in the area of the region bounded by the curve $y = f(x)$, the x axis, and the lines $x = a$ and $x = b$ was defined in Chapter 6 to be

$$\lim_{\Delta x \to 0} \sum_{i=1}^{n} f(\xi_i) \, \Delta x$$

which is equal to the definite integral $\int_a^b f(x) \, dx$.

Suppose that $f(x) < 0$ for all x in $[a, b]$. Then each $f(\xi_i)$ is a negative number, and so we define the number of square units in the area of the region bounded by $y = f(x)$, the x axis, and the lines $x = a$ and $x = b$ to be

$$\lim_{\Delta x \to 0} \sum_{i=1}^{n} [-f(\xi_i)] \, \Delta x$$

which equals

$$-\int_a^b f(x) \, dx$$

EXAMPLE 1: Find the area of the region bounded by the curve $y = x^2 - 4x$, the x axis, and the lines $x = 1$ and $x = 3$.

SOLUTION: The region, together with a rectangular element of area, is shown in Fig. 7.1.1.

If one takes a regular partition of the interval $[1, 3]$, the width of each rectangle is Δx. Because $x^2 - 4x < 0$ on $[1, 3]$, the altitude of the ith

330

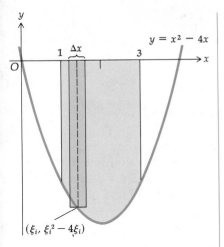

$y = x^2 - 4x$

Figure 7.1.1

$(\xi_i, \xi_i^2 - 4\xi_i)$

rectangle is $-(\xi_i^2 - 4\xi_i) = 4\xi_i - \xi_i^2$. Hence, the sum of the measures of the areas of n rectangles is given by

$$\sum_{i=1}^{n} (4\xi_i - \xi_i^2) \, \Delta x$$

The measure of the desired area is given by the limit of this sum as Δx approaches 0; so if A square units is the area of the region, we have

$$A = \lim_{\Delta x \to 0} \sum_{i=1}^{n} (4\xi_i - \xi_i^2) \, \Delta x$$

$$= \int_{1}^{3} (4x - x^2) \, dx$$

$$= 2x^2 - \tfrac{1}{3}x^3 \Big]_{1}^{3}$$

$$= \tfrac{22}{3}$$

Thus, the area of the region is $\tfrac{22}{3}$ square units.

EXAMPLE 2: Find the area of the region bounded by the curve $y = x^3 - 2x^2 - 5x + 6$, the x axis, and the lines $x = -1$ and $x = 2$.

$(\xi_i, f(\xi_i))$

$y = f(x)$

$(\xi_i, f(\xi_i))$

Figure 7.1.2

SOLUTION: The region is shown in Fig. 7.1.2. Let $f(x) = x^3 - 2x^2 - 5x + 6$. Because $f(x) \geq 0$ when x is in the closed interval $[-1, 1]$ and $f(x) \leq 0$ when x is in the closed interval $[1, 2]$, we separate the region into two parts. Let A_1 be the number of square units in the area of the region when x is in $[-1, 1]$, and let A_2 be the number of square units in the area of the region when x is in $[1, 2]$. Then

$$A_1 = \lim_{\Delta x \to 0} \sum_{i=1}^{n} f(\xi_i) \, \Delta x$$

$$= \int_{-1}^{1} f(x) \, dx$$

$$= \int_{-1}^{1} (x^3 - 2x^2 - 5x + 6) \, dx$$

and

$$A_2 = \lim_{\Delta x \to 0} \sum_{i=1}^{n} [-f(\xi_i)] \, \Delta x = \int_{1}^{2} -(x^3 - 2x^2 - 5x + 6) \, dx$$

If A square units is the area of the entire region, then

$$A = A_1 + A_2$$

$$= \int_{-1}^{1} (x^3 - 2x^2 - 5x + 6) \, dx - \int_{1}^{2} (x^3 - 2x^2 - 5x + 6) \, dx$$

$$= \left[\tfrac{1}{4}x^4 - \tfrac{2}{3}x^3 - \tfrac{5}{2}x^2 + 6x \right]_{-1}^{1} - \left[\tfrac{1}{4}x^4 - \tfrac{2}{3}x^3 - \tfrac{5}{2}x^2 + 6x \right]_{1}^{2}$$

$$= [(\tfrac{1}{4} - \tfrac{2}{3} - \tfrac{5}{2} + 6) - (\tfrac{1}{4} + \tfrac{2}{3} - \tfrac{5}{2} - 6)]$$

$$- [(4 - \tfrac{16}{3} - 10 + 12) - (\tfrac{1}{4} - \tfrac{2}{3} - \tfrac{5}{2} + 6)]$$

$$= \tfrac{32}{3} - (-\tfrac{29}{12})$$

$$= \tfrac{157}{12}$$

The area of the region is therefore $\tfrac{157}{12}$ square units.

Now consider two functions f and g continuous on the closed interval $[a, b]$ and such that $f(x) \geq g(x)$ for all x in $[a, b]$. We wish to find the area of the region bounded by the two curves $y = f(x)$ and $y = g(x)$ and the two lines $x = a$ and $x = b$. Such a situation is shown in Fig. 7.1.3.

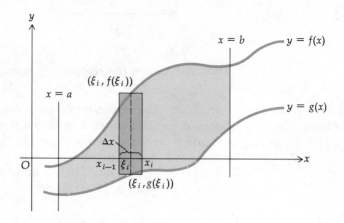

Figure 7.1.3

Take a regular partition of the interval $[a, b]$, with each subinterval having a length of Δx. In each subinterval choose a point ξ_i. Consider the rectangle having altitude $[f(\xi_i) - g(\xi_i)]$ units and width Δx units. Such a rectangle is shown in Fig. 7.1.3. There are n such rectangles, one associated with each subinterval. The sum of the measures of the areas of these n rectangles is given by the following Riemann sum:

$$\sum_{i=1}^{n} [f(\xi_i) - g(\xi_i)] \, \Delta x$$

This Riemann sum is an approximation to what we intuitively think of as the number representing the "measure of the area" of the region. The larger the value of n—or, equivalently, the smaller the value of Δx—the closer is this approximation. If A square units is the area of the region, we define

$$A = \lim_{\Delta x \to 0} \sum_{i=1}^{n} [f(\xi_i) - g(\xi_i)] \, \Delta x \tag{1}$$

Because f and g are continuous on $[a, b]$, so also is $(f - g)$; therefore, the limit in Eq. (1) exists and is equal to the definite integral

$$\int_a^b [f(x) - g(x)] \, dx$$

EXAMPLE 3: Find the area of the region bounded by the curves $y = x^2$ and $y = -x^2 + 4x$.

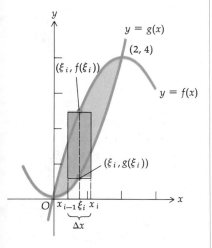

Figure 7.1.4

SOLUTION: To find the points of intersection of the two curves, we solve the equations simultaneously and obtain the points $(0, 0)$ and $(2, 4)$. The region is shown in Fig. 7.1.4.

Let $f(x) = -x^2 + 4x$, and $g(x) = x^2$. Therefore, in the interval $[0, 2]$ the curve $y = f(x)$ is above the curve $y = g(x)$. We draw a vertical rectangular element of area, having altitude $[f(\xi_i) - g(\xi_i)]$ units and width Δx units. The measure of the area of this rectangle then is given by $[f(\xi_i) - g(\xi_i)] \, \Delta x$. The sum of the measures of the areas of n such rectangles is given by the Riemann sum

$$\sum_{i=1}^{n} [f(\xi_i) - g(\xi_i)] \, \Delta x$$

If A square units is the area of the region, then

$$A = \lim_{\Delta x \to 0} \sum_{i=1}^{n} [f(\xi_i) - g(\xi_i)] \, \Delta x$$

and the limit of the Riemann sum is a definite integral. Hence,

$$A = \int_0^2 [f(x) - g(x)] \, dx$$

$$= \int_0^2 [(-x^2 + 4x) - x^2] \, dx$$

$$= \int_0^2 (-2x^2 + 4x) \, dx$$

$$= \left[-\tfrac{2}{3}x^3 + 2x^2 \right]_0^2$$

$$= -\tfrac{16}{3} + 8 - 0$$

$$= \tfrac{8}{3}$$

The area of the region is $\tfrac{8}{3}$ square units.

EXAMPLE 4: Find the area of the region bounded by the parabola $y^2 = 2x - 2$ and the line $y = x - 5$.

SOLUTION: The two curves intersect at the points $(3, -2)$ and $(9, 4)$. The region is shown in Fig. 7.1.5.

The equation $y^2 = 2x - 2$ is equivalent to the two equations

$$y = \sqrt{2x - 2} \quad \text{and} \quad y = -\sqrt{2x - 2}$$

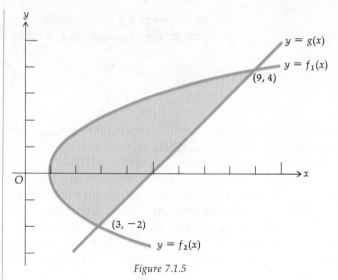

Figure 7.1.5

with the first equation giving the upper half of the parabola and the second equation giving the bottom half. If we let $f_1(x) = \sqrt{2x-2}$ and $f_2(x) = -\sqrt{2x-2}$, the equation of the top half of the parabola is $y = f_1(x)$, and the equation of the bottom half of the parabola is $y = f_2(x)$. If we let $g(x) = x - 5$, the equation of the line is $y = g(x)$.

In Fig. 7.1.6 we see two vertical rectangular elements of area. Each rectangle has the upper base on the curve $y = f_1(x)$. Because the base of the first rectangle is on the curve $y = f_2(x)$, the altitude is $[f_1(\xi_i) - f_2(\xi_i)]$ units. Because the base of the second rectangle is on the curve $y = g(x)$, its

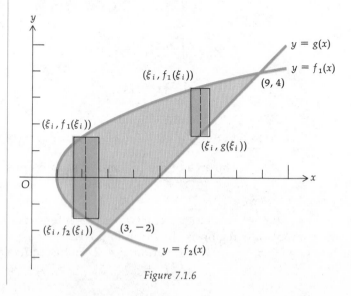

Figure 7.1.6

altitude is $[f_1(\xi_i) - g(\xi_i)]$ units. If we wish to solve this problem by using vertical rectangular elements of area, we must divide the region into two separate regions, for instance R_1 and R_2, where R_1 is the region bounded by the curves $y = f_1(x)$ and $y = f_2(x)$ and the line $x = 3$, and where R_2 is the region bounded by the curves $y = f_1(x)$ and $y = g(x)$ and the line $x = 3$ (see Fig. 7.1.7).

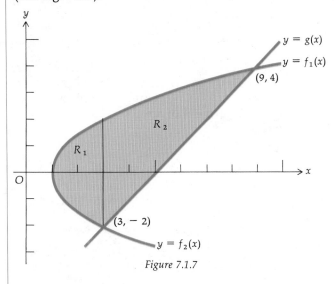

Figure 7.1.7

If A_1 is the number of square units in the area of region R_1, we have

$$A_1 = \lim_{\Delta x \to 0} \sum_{i=1}^{n} [f_1(\xi_i) - f_2(\xi_i)] \, \Delta x$$

$$= \int_1^3 [f_1(x) - f_2(x)] \, dx$$

$$= \int_1^3 [\sqrt{2x - 2} + \sqrt{2x - 2}] \, dx$$

$$= 2 \int_1^3 \sqrt{2x - 2} \, dx$$

$$= \tfrac{2}{3}(2x - 2)^{3/2} \, \Big]_1^3$$

$$= \tfrac{16}{3}$$

If A_2 is the number of square units in the area of region R_2, we have

$$A_2 = \lim_{\Delta x \to 0} \sum_{i=1}^{n} [f_1(\xi_i) - g(\xi_i)] \, \Delta x$$

$$= \int_3^9 [f_1(x) - g(x)] \, dx$$

$$= \int_3^9 \left[\sqrt{2x-2} - (x-5) \right] dx$$

$$= \left[\tfrac{1}{3}(2x-2)^{3/2} - \tfrac{1}{2}x^2 + 5x \right]_3^9$$

$$= \left[\tfrac{64}{3} - \tfrac{81}{2} + 45 \right] - \left[\tfrac{8}{3} - \tfrac{9}{2} + 15 \right]$$

$$= \tfrac{38}{3}$$

Hence $A_1 + A_2 = \tfrac{16}{3} + \tfrac{38}{3} = 18$. Therefore, the area of the entire region is 18 square units.

EXAMPLE 5: Find the area of the region in Example 4 by taking horizontal rectangular elements of area.

SOLUTION: Figure 7.1.8 illustrates the region with a horizontal rectangular element of area.

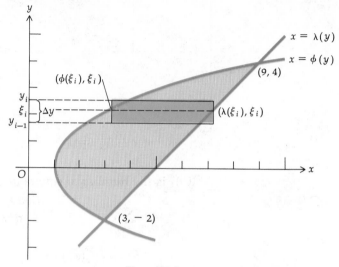

Figure 7.1.8

If in the equations of the parabola and the line we solve for x, we have

$$x = \tfrac{1}{2}(y^2 + 2) \quad \text{and} \quad x = y + 5$$

Letting $\phi(y) = \tfrac{1}{2}(y^2 + 2)$ and $\lambda(y) = y + 5$, the equation of the parabola may be written as $x = \phi(y)$ and the equation of the line as $x = \lambda(y)$. If we consider the closed interval $[-2, 4]$ on the y axis and take a regular partition of this interval, each subinterval will have a length of Δy. In the ith subinterval $[y_{i-1}, y_i]$, choose a point ξ_i. Then the length of the ith rectangular element is $[\lambda(\xi_i) - \phi(\xi_i)]$ units and the width is Δy units. The measure of the area of the region can be approximated by the Riemann sum:

$$\sum_{i=1}^{n} [\lambda(\xi_i) - \phi(\xi_i)] \, \Delta y$$

If A square units is the area of the region, then

$$A = \lim_{\Delta y \to 0} \sum_{i=1}^{n} [\lambda(\xi_i) - \phi(\xi_i)] \, \Delta y$$

Because λ and ϕ are continuous on $[-2, 4]$, so also is $(\lambda - \phi)$, and the limit of the Riemann sum is a definite integral:

$$A = \int_{-2}^{4} [\lambda(y) - \phi(y)] \, dy$$

$$= \int_{-2}^{4} [(y + 5) - \tfrac{1}{2}(y^2 + 2)] \, dy$$

$$= \tfrac{1}{2} \int_{-2}^{4} (-y^2 + 2y + 8) \, dy$$

$$= \tfrac{1}{2} \left[-\tfrac{1}{3}y^3 + y^2 + 8y \right]_{-2}^{4}$$

$$= \tfrac{1}{2} [-\tfrac{64}{3} + 16 + 32) - (\tfrac{8}{3} + 4 - 16)]$$

$$= 18$$

Comparing the solutions in Examples 4 and 5, we see that in the first case we have two definite integrals to evaluate, whereas in the second case we have only one. In general, if possible, the rectangular elements of area should be constructed so that a single definite integral is obtained. The following example illustrates a situation where two definite integrals are necessary.

EXAMPLE 6:   Find the area of the region bounded by the two curves $y = x^3 - 6x^2 + 8x$ and $y = x^2 - 4x$.

SOLUTION: The points of intersection of the two curves are $(0, 0)$, $(3, -3)$, and $(4, 0)$. The region is shown in Fig. 7.1.9.

Let $f(x) = x^3 - 6x^2 + 8x$ and $g(x) = x^2 - 4x$. In the interval $[0, 3]$ the curve $y = f(x)$ is above the curve $y = g(x)$, and in the interval $[3, 4]$ the curve $y = g(x)$ is above the curve $y = f(x)$. So the region must be divided into two separate regions R_1 and R_2, where R_1 is the region bounded by the two curves in the interval $[0, 3]$ and R_2 is the region bounded by the two curves in the interval $[3, 4]$. Letting A_1 square units be the area of R_1 and A_2 square units be the area of R_2, we have

$$A_1 = \lim_{\Delta x \to 0} \sum_{i=1}^{n} [f(\xi_i) - g(\xi_i)] \, \Delta x$$

and

$$A_2 = \lim_{\Delta x \to 0} \sum_{i=1}^{n} [g(\xi_i) - f(\xi_i)] \, \Delta x$$

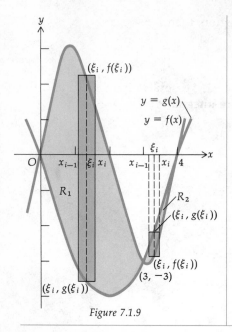

Figure 7.1.9

so that

$$A_1 + A_2 = \int_0^3 \left[(x^3 - 6x^2 + 8x) - (x^2 - 4x) \right] dx$$

$$+ \int_3^4 \left[(x^2 - 4x) - (x^3 - 6x^2 + 8x) \right] dx$$

$$= \int_0^3 (x^3 - 7x^2 + 12x) \, dx + \int_3^4 (-x^3 + 7x^2 - 12x) \, dx$$

$$= \left[\tfrac{1}{4}x^4 - \tfrac{7}{3}x^3 + 6x^2 \right]_0^3 + \left[-\tfrac{1}{4}x^4 + \tfrac{7}{3}x^3 - 6x^2 \right]_3^4$$

$$= \tfrac{45}{4} + \tfrac{7}{12}$$

$$= \tfrac{71}{6}$$

Therefore, the required area is $\tfrac{71}{6}$ square units.

Exercises 7.1

In Exercises 1 through 20, find the area of the region bounded by the given curves. In each problem do the following: (a) Draw a figure showing the region and a rectangular element of area; (b) express the area of the region as the limit of a Riemann sum; (c) find the limit in part (b) by evaluating a definite integral by the fundamental theorem of the calculus.

1. $x^2 = -y$; $y = -4$

2. $y^2 = -x$; $x = -2$; $x = -4$

3. $x^2 + y + 4 = 0$; $y = -8$. Take the elements of area perpendicular to the y axis.

4. The same region as in Exercise 3. Take the elements of area parallel to the y axis.

5. $x^3 = 2y^2$; $x = 0$, $y = -2$ 6. $y^3 = 4x$; $x = 0$; $y = -2$ 7. $y = 2 - x^2$; $y = -x$

8. $y = x^2$; $y = x^4$ 9. $y^2 = x - 1$; $x = 3$ 10. $y = x^2$; $x^2 = 18 - y$

11. $y = \sqrt{x}$; $y = x^3$ 12. $x = 4 - y^2$; $x = 4 - 4y$ 13. $y^3 = x^2$; $x - 3y + 4 = 0$

14. $xy^2 = y^2 - 1$; $x = 1$; $y = 1$; $y = 4$ 15. $x = y^2 - 2$; $x = 6 - y^2$ 16. $x = y^2 - y$; $x = y - y^2$

17. $y = 2x^3 - 3x^2 - 9x$; $y = x^3 - 2x^2 - 3x$ 18. $3y = x^3 - 2x^2 - 15x$; $y = x^3 - 4x^2 - 11x + 30$

19. $y = |x|$, $y = x^2 - 1$, $x = -1$, $x = 1$ 20. $y = |x + 1| + |x|$, $y = 0$, $x = -2$, $x = 3$

21. Find by integration the area of the triangle having vertices at $(5, 1)$, $(1, 3)$, and $(-1, -2)$.

22. Find by integration the area of the triangle having vertices at $(3, 4)$, $(2, 0)$, and $(0, 1)$.

23. Find the area of the region bounded by the curve $x^3 - x^2 + 2xy - y^2 = 0$ and the line $x = 4$. (HINT: Solve the cubic equation for y in terms of x, and express y as two functions of x.)

24. Find the area of the region bounded by the three curves $y = x^2$, $x = y^3$, and $x + y = 2$.

25. Find the area of the region bounded by the three curves $y = x^2$, $y = 8 - x^2$, and $4x - y + 12 = 0$.

26. Find the area of the region above the parabola $x^2 = 4py$ and inside the triangle formed by the x axis and the lines $y = x + 8p$ and $y = -x + 8p$.

27. (a) Find the area of the region bounded by the curves $y^2 = 4px$ and $x^2 = 4py$. (b) Find the rate of change of the measure of the area in part (a) with respect to p when $p = 3$.

28. Find the rate of change of the measure of the area of Exercise 26 with respect to p when $p = \frac{3}{8}$.

29. If A square units is the area of the region bounded by the parabola $y^2 = 4x$ and the line $y = mx$ $(m > 0)$, find the rate of change of A with respect to m.

30. Determine m so that the region above the line $y = mx$ and below the parabola $y = 2x - x^2$ has an area of 36 square units.

7.2 VOLUME OF A SOLID OF REVOLUTION: CIRCULAR-DISK AND CIRCULAR-RING METHODS

We have developed a method for finding the area of a plane region. Now this process is extended to find the volume of a *solid of revolution*, which is a solid obtained by revolving a region in a plane about a line in the plane, called the *axis of revolution*, which either touches the boundary of the region or does not intersect the region at all. For example, if the region bounded by a semicircle and its diameter is revolved about the diameter, a sphere is generated (see Fig. 7.2.1). A right-circular cone is generated if the region bounded by a right triangle is revolved about one of its legs (see Fig. 7.2.2).

We must first define what is meant by the "volume" of a solid of revolution; that is, we wish to assign a number, for example V, to what we intuitively think of as the measure of the volume of such a solid. We define the measure of the volume of a right-circular cylinder by $\pi r^2 h$, where r and h are, respectively, the number of units in the base radius and altitude.

Consider first the case where the axis of revolution is a boundary of the region that is revolved. Let the function f be continuous on the closed interval $[a, b]$ and assume that $f(x) \geq 0$ for all x in $[a, b]$. Let R be the region bounded by the curve $y = f(x)$, the x axis, and the lines $x = a$ and $x = b$. Let S be the solid of revolution obtained by revolving the region R about the x axis. We proceed to find a suitable definition for the number V which gives the measure of the volume of S.

Let Δ be a partition of the closed interval $[a, b]$ given by

$$a = x_0 < x_1 < x_2 < \cdots < x_{n-1} < x_n = b$$

Then we have n subintervals of the form $[x_{i-1}, x_i]$, where $i = 1, 2, \ldots, n$, with the length of the ith subinterval being $\Delta_i x = x_i - x_{i-1}$. Choose any point ξ_i, with $x_{i-1} \leq \xi_i \leq x_i$, in each subinterval and draw the rectangles having widths $\Delta_i x$ units and altitudes $f(\xi_i)$ units. Figure 7.2.3 shows the region R together with the ith rectangle.

When the ith rectangle is revolved about the x axis, we obtain a circular disk in the form of a right-circular cylinder whose base radius is given by $f(\xi_i)$ units and whose altitude is given by $\Delta_i x$ units, as shown in Fig. 7.2.4. The measure of the volume of this circular disk, which we denote by $\Delta_i V$, is given by

$$\Delta_i V = \pi [f(\xi_i)]^2 \, \Delta_i x \tag{1}$$

Figure 7.2.1

Figure 7.2.2

Figure 7.2.3

Figure 7.2.4

Because there are n rectangles, n circular disks are obtained in this way, and the sum of the measures of the volumes of these n circular disks is given by

$$\sum_{i=1}^{n} \Delta_i V = \sum_{i=1}^{n} \pi [f(\xi_i)]^2 \, \Delta_i x \tag{2}$$

which is a Riemann sum.

The Riemann sum given in Eq. (2) is an approximation to what we intuitively think of as the number of cubic units in the volume of the solid of revolution. The smaller we take the norm $\|\Delta\|$ of the partition, the larger will be n, and the closer this approximation will be to the number V we wish to assign to the measure of the volume. We therefore define V to be the limit of the Riemann sum in Eq. (2) as $\|\Delta\|$ approaches zero. This limit exists because f^2 is continuous on $[a, b]$, which is true because f is continuous there. We have, then, the following definition.

7.2.1 Definition   Let the function f be continuous on the closed interval $[a, b]$, and assume that $f(x) \geq 0$ for all x in $[a, b]$. If S is the solid of revolution obtained by revolving about the x axis the region bounded by the curve $y = f(x)$, the x axis, and the lines $x = a$ and $x = b$, and if V is the number of cubic units in the volume of S, then

$$V = \lim_{\|\Delta\| \to 0} \sum_{i=1}^{n} \pi [f(\xi_i)]^2 \, \Delta_i x = \pi \int_a^b [f(x)]^2 \, dx \tag{3}$$

A similar definition applies when both the axis of revolution and a boundary of the revolved region is the y axis or any line parallel to either the x axis or the y axis.

EXAMPLE 1:   The region bounded by the curve $y = x^2$, the x axis, and the lines $x = 1$ and $x = 2$ is revolved about the x axis. Find the volume of the solid of revolution generated.

SOLUTION: Refer to Fig. 7.2.5, showing the region and a rectangular element of area. Figure 7.2.6 shows an element of volume and the solid of revolution. The measure of the volume of the circular disk is given by

$$\Delta_i V = \pi (\xi_i^2)^2 \, \Delta_i x = \pi \xi_i^4 \, \Delta_i x$$

Then

$$V = \lim_{\|\Delta\| \to 0} \sum_{i=1}^{n} \pi \xi_i^4 \, \Delta_i x$$

$$= \pi \int_1^2 x^4 \, dx$$

$$= \pi \left(\tfrac{1}{5} x^5 \right) \Big]_1^2$$

$$= \tfrac{31}{5} \pi$$

Therefore, the volume of the solid of revolution is $\tfrac{31}{5} \pi$ cubic units.

Figure 7.2.5

Figure 7.2.6

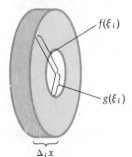

Figure 7.2.9

Now suppose that the axis of revolution is not a boundary of the region being revolved. Let f and g be two continuous functions on the closed interval $[a, b]$, and assume that $f(x) \geq g(x) \geq 0$ for all x in $[a, b]$. Let R be the region bounded by the curves $y = f(x)$ and $y = g(x)$ and the lines $x = a$ and $x = b$. Let S be the solid of revolution generated by revolving the region R about the x axis. If V cubic units is the volume of S, we wish to find a value for V.

Let Δ be a partition of the interval $[a, b]$, given by

$$a = x_0 < x_1 < x_2 < \cdots < x_{n-1} < x_n = b$$

and the ith subinterval $[x_{i-1}, x_i]$ has length $\Delta_i x = x_i - x_{i-1}$. In the ith subinterval, choose any ξ_i, with $x_{i-1} \leq \xi_i \leq x_i$. Consider the n rectangular elements of area for the region R. See Fig. 7.2.7 illustrating the region and the ith rectangle, and Fig. 7.2.8 showing the solid of revolution.

Figure 7.2.7

Figure 7.2.8

When the ith rectangle is revolved about the x axis, a circular ring (or "washer"), as shown in Fig. 7.2.9, is obtained. The number giving the difference of the measures of the areas of the two circular regions is $(\pi[f(\xi_i)]^2 - \pi[g(\xi_i)]^2)$ and the thickness is $\Delta_i x$ units. Therefore, the measure of the volume of the circular ring is given by

$$\Delta_i V = \pi([f(\xi_i)]^2 - [g(\xi_i)]^2) \Delta_i x$$

The sum of the measures of the volumes of the n circular rings formed by revolving the n rectangular elements of area about the x axis is

$$\sum_{i=1}^{n} \Delta_i V = \sum_{i=1}^{n} \pi([f(\xi_i)]^2 - [g(\xi_i)]^2) \Delta_i x \tag{4}$$

The number of cubic units in the volume, then, is defined to be the limit of the Riemann sum in Eq. (4) as $\|\Delta\|$ approaches zero. The limit exists since f^2 and g^2 are continuous on $[a, b]$ because f and g are continuous there.

7.2.2 Definition   Let the functions f and g be continuous on the closed interval $[a, b]$, and assume that $f(x) \geq g(x) \geq 0$ for all x in $[a, b]$. Then if V cubic units is the volume of the solid of revolution generated by revolving about the x axis the region bounded by the curves $y = f(x)$ and $y = g(x)$ and the lines $x = a$ and $x = b$,

$$V = \lim_{||\Delta|| \to 0} \sum_{i=1}^{n} \pi([f(\xi_i)]^2 - [g(\xi_i)]^2) \, \Delta_i x = \pi \int_a^b ([f(x)]^2 - [g(x)]^2) \, dx \quad (5)$$

As before, a similar definition applies when the axis of revolution is the y axis or any line parallel to either the x axis or the y axis.

EXAMPLE 2:   Find the volume of the solid generated by revolving about the x axis the region bounded by the parabola $y = x^2 + 1$ and the line $y = x + 3$.

SOLUTION: The points of intersection are $(-1, 2)$ and $(2, 5)$. Figure 7.2.10 shows the region and a rectangular element of area. An element of volume and the solid of revolution are shown in Fig. 7.2.11.

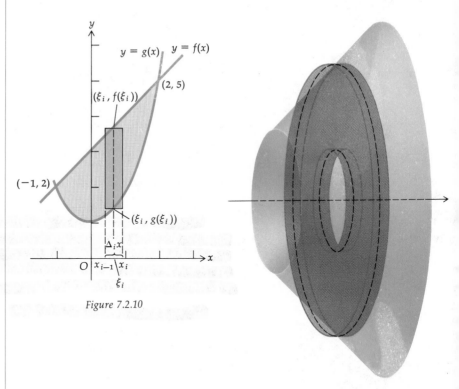

Figure 7.2.10

Figure 7.2.11

Taking $f(x) = x + 3$ and $g(x) = x^2 + 1$, we find that the measure of the volume of the circular ring is

$$\Delta_i V = \pi([f(\xi_i)]^2 - [g(\xi_i)]^2) \, \Delta_i x$$

If V cubic units is the volume of the solid, then

$$V = \lim_{||\Delta|| \to 0} \sum_{i=1}^{n} \pi([f(\xi_i)]^2 - [g(\xi_i)]^2)\, \Delta_i x$$

$$= \pi \int_{-1}^{2} ([f(x)]^2 - [g(x)]^2)\, dx$$

$$= \pi \int_{-1}^{2} [(x+3)^2 - (x^2+1)^2]\, dx$$

$$= \pi \int_{-1}^{2} [-x^4 - x^2 + 6x + 8]\, dx$$

$$= \pi \left[-\tfrac{1}{5}x^5 - \tfrac{1}{3}x^3 + 3x^2 + 8x \right]_{-1}^{2}$$

$$= \pi[(-\tfrac{32}{5} - \tfrac{8}{3} + 12 + 16) - (\tfrac{1}{5} + \tfrac{1}{3} + 3 - 8)]$$

$$= \tfrac{117}{5}\pi$$

Therefore, the volume of the solid of revolution is $\tfrac{117}{5}\pi$ cubic units.

EXAMPLE 3:   Find the volume of the solid generated by revolving about the line $x = -4$ the region bounded by the two parabolas $x = y - y^2$ and $x = y^2 - 3$.

SOLUTION: The curves intersect at the points $(-2, -1)$ and $(-\tfrac{3}{4}, \tfrac{3}{2})$. The region and a rectangular element of area are shown in Fig. 7.2.12. Figure 7.2.13 shows the solid of revolution as well as an element of volume, which is a circular ring.

Figure 7.2.13

Let $F(y) = y - y^2$ and $G(y) = y^2 - 3$. The number of cubic units in the volume of the circular ring is

$$\Delta_i V = \pi([4 + F(\xi_i)]^2 - [4 + G(\xi_i)]^2)\, \Delta_i y$$

Thus,

$$V = \lim_{||\Delta|| \to 0} \sum_{i=1}^{n} \pi([4 + F(\xi_i)]^2 - [4 + G(\xi_i)]^2)\, \Delta_i y$$

$$= \pi \int_{-1}^{3/2} [(4 + y - y^2)^2 - (4 + y^2 - 3)^2]\, dy$$

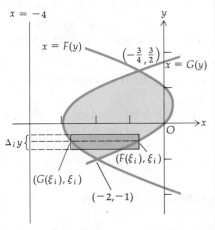

Figure 7.2.12

$$= \pi \int_{-1}^{3/2} (-2y^3 - 9y^2 + 8y + 15)\, dy$$

$$= \pi \left[-\tfrac{1}{2}y^4 - 3y^3 + 4y^2 + 15y \right]_{-1}^{3/2}$$

$$= \tfrac{875}{32}\pi$$

The volume of the solid of revolution is then $\tfrac{875}{32}\pi$ cubic units.

Exercises 7.2

In Exercises 1 through 8, find the volume of the solid of revolution when the given region of Fig. 7.2.14 is revolved about the indicated line. An equation of the curve in the figure is $y^2 = x^3$.

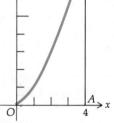

Figure 7.2.14

1. *OAC* about the x axis
2. *OAC* about the line *AC*
3. *OAC* about the line *BC*
4. *OAC* about the y axis
5. *OBC* about the y axis
6. *OBC* about the line *BC*
7. *OBC* about the line *AC*
8. *OBC* about the x axis

9. Find the volume of the sphere generated by revolving the circle whose equation is $x^2 + y^2 = r^2$ about a diameter.

10. Find by integration the volume of a right-circular cone of altitude h units and base radius a units.

11. Find the volume of the solid generated by revolving about the x axis the region bounded by the curve $y = x^3$ and the lines $y = 0$ and $x = 2$.

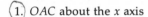 12. Find the volume of the solid generated by revolving the region in Exercise 11 about the y axis.

13. Find the volume of the solid generated by revolving about the line $x = -4$ the region bounded by that line and the parabola $x = 4 + 6y - 2y^2$.

14. Find the volume of the solid generated by revolving the region bounded by the curves $y^2 = 4x$ and $y = x$ about the x axis.

15. Find the volume of the solid generated by revolving the region of Exercise 14 about the line $x = 4$.

16. An oil tank in the shape of a sphere has a diameter of 60 ft. How much oil does the tank contain if the depth of the oil is 25 ft?

17. A paraboloid of revolution is obtained by revolving a parabola about its axis. Find the volume bounded by a paraboloid of revolution and a plane perpendicular to its axis if the plane is 10 in. from the vertex, and if the plane section of intersection is a circle having a radius of 6 in.

18. Find the volume of the solid generated by revolving about the x axis the region bounded by the loop of the curve whose equation is $2y^2 = x(x^2 - 4)$.

19. Find the volume of the solid generated when the region bounded by one loop of the curve whose equation is $x^2y^2 = (x^2 - 9)(1 - x^2)$ is revolved about the x axis.

20. The region bounded by a pentagon having vertices at $(-4, 4)$, $(-2, 0)$, $(0, 8)$, $(2, 0)$, and $(4, 4)$ is revolved about the x axis. Find the volume of the solid generated.

7.3 VOLUME OF A SOLID OF REVOLUTION: CYLINDRICAL-SHELL METHOD

Figure 7.3.1

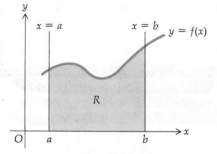

Figure 7.3.2

In the preceding section we found the volume of a solid of revolution by taking the rectangular elements of area perpendicular to the axis of revolution, and the element of volume was either a circular disk or a circular ring. If a rectangular element of area is parallel to the axis of revolution, then when this element of area is revolved about the axis of revolution, a *cylindrical shell* is obtained. A cylindrical shell is a solid contained between two cylinders having the same center and axis. Such a cylindrical shell is shown in Fig. 7.3.1.

If the cylindrical shell has an inner radius r_1 units, outer radius r_2 units, and altitude h units, then its volume V cubic units is given by

$$V = \pi r_2^2 h - \pi r_1^2 h \tag{1}$$

Let R be the region bounded by the curve $y = f(x)$, the x axis, and the lines $x = a$ and $x = b$, where f is continuous on the closed interval $[a, b]$ and $f(x) \geq 0$ for all x in $[a, b]$; furthermore, assume that $a \geq 0$. Such a region is shown in Fig. 7.3.2. If R is revolved about the y axis, a solid of revolution S is generated. Such a solid is shown in Fig. 7.3.3. To find the volume of S when the rectangular elements of area are taken parallel to the y axis, we proceed in the following manner.

Let Δ be a partition of the closed interval $[a, b]$ given by

$$a = x_0 < x_1 < x_2 < \cdots < x_{n-1} < x_n = b$$

Figure 7.3.3

Let m_i be the midpoint of the ith subinterval $[x_{i-1}, x_i]$. Then $m_i = \frac{1}{2}(x_{i-1} + x_i)$. Consider the rectangle having altitude $f(m_i)$ units and width $\Delta_i x$ units. If this rectangle is revolved about the y axis, a cylindrical shell is obtained. Figure 7.3.3 shows the cylindrical shell generated by the rectangular element of area.

If $\Delta_i V$ gives the measure of the volume of this cylindrical shell, we have, from formula (1), where $r_1 = x_{i-1}$, $r_2 = x_i$, and $h = f(m_i)$,

$$\Delta_i V = \pi x_i^2 f(m_i) - \pi x_{i-1}^2 f(m_i)$$

$$= \pi(x_i^2 - x_{i-1}^2) f(m_i)$$

$$\Delta_i V = \pi(x_i - x_{i-1})(x_i + x_{i-1}) f(m_i) \tag{2}$$

Because $x_i - x_{i-1} = \Delta_i x$ and because $x_i + x_{i-1} = 2m_i$, we have from Eq. (2)

$$\Delta_i V = 2\pi m_i f(m_i) \; \Delta_i x \tag{3}$$

If n rectangular elements of area are revolved about the y axis, n cylindrical shells are obtained. The sum of the measures of their volumes is given by

$$\sum_{i=1}^{n} \Delta_i V = \sum_{i=1}^{n} 2\pi m_i f(m_i) \; \Delta_i x \tag{4}$$

which is a Riemann sum.

Then we define the measure of the volume of the solid of revolution to be the limit of the Riemann sum in Eq. (4) as $\|\Delta\|$ approaches zero. The limit exists because if f is continuous on $[a, b]$, so is the function having function values $2\pi x f(x)$.

7.3.1 Definition   Let the function f be continuous on the closed interval $[a, b]$ where $a \geq 0$. Assume that $f(x) \geq 0$ for all x in $[a, b]$. If R is the region bounded by the curve $y = f(x)$, the x axis, and the lines $x = a$ and $x = b$, if S is the solid of revolution obtained by revolving R about the y axis, and if V cubic units is the volume of S, then

$$V = \lim_{\|\Delta\| \to 0} \sum_{i=1}^{n} 2\pi m_i f(m_i) \; \Delta_i x = 2\pi \int_a^b x f(x) \; dx \tag{5}$$

Definition 7.3.1 is consistent with Definitions 7.2.1 and 7.2.2 for the measure of the volume of a solid of revolution for which the definitions apply.

The formula for the measure of the volume of the shell is easily remembered by noticing that $2\pi m_i$, $f(m_i)$, and $\Delta_i x$ are, respectively, the numbers giving the circumference of the circle having as radius the mean of the inner and outer radii of the shell, the altitude of the shell, and the thickness.

EXAMPLE 1:   The region bounded by the curve $y = x^2$, the x axis, and the line $x = 2$ is revolved about the y axis. Find the volume of the solid generated. Take the elements of area parallel to the axis of revolution.

SOLUTION: Figure 7.3.4 shows the region and a rectangular element of area. Figure 7.3.5 shows the solid of revolution and the cylindrical shell obtained by revolving the rectangular element of area about the y axis.

The element of volume is a cylindrical shell the measure of whose volume is given by

$$\Delta_i V = 2\pi m_i (m_i^2) \Delta_i x = 2\pi m_i^3 \; \Delta_i x$$

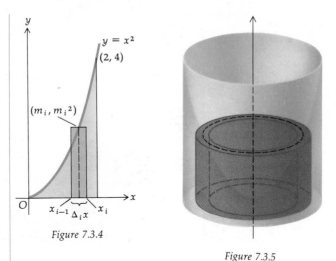

Figure 7.3.4

Figure 7.3.5

Thus,

$$V = \lim_{||\Delta|| \to 0} \sum_{i=1}^{n} 2\pi m_i^3 \, \Delta_i x$$

$$= 2\pi \int_0^2 x^3 \, dx$$

$$= 2\pi (\tfrac{1}{4}x^4) \Big]_0^2$$

$$= 8\pi$$

Therefore, the volume of the solid of revolution is 8π cubic units.

EXAMPLE 2: The region bounded by the curve $y = x^2$ and the lines $y = 1$ and $x = 2$ is revolved about the line $y = -3$. Find the volume of the solid generated by taking the rectangular elements of area parallel to the axis of revolution.

SOLUTION: The region and a rectangular element of area are shown in Fig. 7.3.6.

The equation of the curve is $y = x^2$. Solving for x, we obtain $x = \pm\sqrt{y}$. Because $x > 0$ for the given region, we have $x = \sqrt{y}$.

The solid of revolution as well as a cylindrical shell element of volume is shown in Fig. 7.3.7. The outer radius of the cylindrical shell is $(y_i + 3)$ units and the inner radius is $(y_{i-1} + 3)$ units. Hence, the mean of the inner and outer radii is $(m_i + 3)$ units. Because the altitude and thickness of the cylindrical shell are, respectively, $(2 - \sqrt{m_i})$ units and $\Delta_i y$ units,

$$\Delta_i V = 2\pi (m_i + 3)(2 - \sqrt{m_i}) \, \Delta_i y$$

Hence, if V cubic units is the volume of the solid of revolution,

$$V = \lim_{||\Delta|| \to 0} \sum_{i=1}^{n} 2\pi (m_i + 3)(2 - \sqrt{m_i}) \, \Delta_i y$$

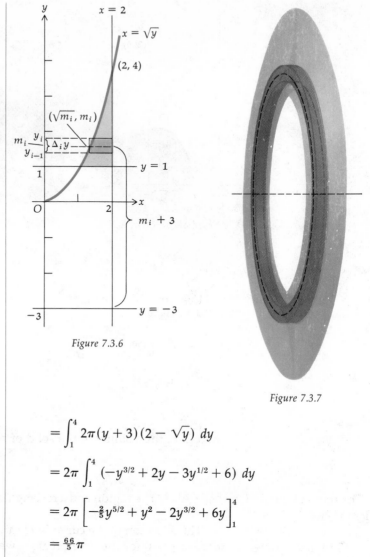

Figure 7.3.6

Figure 7.3.7

$$= \int_1^4 2\pi(y+3)(2-\sqrt{y})\, dy$$

$$= 2\pi \int_1^4 (-y^{3/2} + 2y - 3y^{1/2} + 6)\, dy$$

$$= 2\pi \left[-\tfrac{2}{5}y^{5/2} + y^2 - 2y^{3/2} + 6y \right]_1^4$$

$$= \tfrac{66}{5}\pi$$

Therefore, the volume is $\tfrac{66}{5}\pi$ cubic units.

Exercises 7.3

1–8. Solve Exercises 1 through 8 in Sec. 7.2 by taking the rectangular elements parallel to the axis of revolution.

In Fig. 7.3.8 the region bounded by the x axis, the line $x = 1$, and the curve $y = x^2$ is denoted by R_1; the region bounded by the two curves $y = x^2$ and $y^2 = x$ is denoted by R_2; the region bounded by the y axis, the line $y = 1$, and the curve $y^2 = x$ is denoted by R_3. In Exercises 9 through 16, find the volume of the solid generated when the indicated region is revolved about the given line.

9. R_1 is resolved about the y axis; the rectangular elements are parallel to the axis of revolution.

10. Same as Exercise 9; but the rectangular elements are perpendicular to the axis of revolution.

11. R_2 is revolved about the x axis; the rectangular elements are parallel to the axis of revolution.

12. Same as Exercise 11; but the rectangular elements are perpendicular to the axis of revolution.

13. R_3 is revolved about the line $y = 2$; the rectangular elements are parallel to the axis of revolution.

14. Same as Exercise 13; but the rectangular elements are perpendicular to the axis of revolution.

15. R_2 is revolved about the line $x = -2$; the rectangular elements are parallel to the axis of revolution.

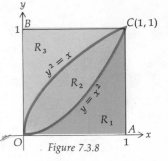

Figure 7.3.8

16. Same as Exercise 15; but the rectangular elements are perpendicular to the axis of revolution.

17. Find the volume of the solid generated if the region bounded by the parabola $y^2 = 4ax$ $(a > 0)$ and the line $x = a$ is revolved about $x = a$.

18. Find the volume of the solid generated by revolving the region bounded by the curve $x^{2/3} + y^{2/3} = a^{2/3}$ about the y axis.

19. Find the volume of the solid generated by revolving about the y axis the region outside the curve $y = x^2$ and between the lines $y = 2x - 1$ and $y = x + 2$.

20. Through a spherical shaped solid of radius 6 in., a hole of radius 2 in. is bored, and the axis of the hole is a diameter of the sphere. Find the volume of the part of the solid that remains.

21. A hole of radius $2\sqrt{3}$ in. is bored through the center of a spherical shaped solid of radius 4 in. Find the volume of the portion of the solid cut out.

22. Find the volume of the solid generated if the region bounded by a parabola and its latus rectum is revolved about a line through its vertex and perpendicular to its axis.

7.4 VOLUME OF A SOLID HAVING KNOWN PARALLEL PLANE SECTIONS

Let S be a solid. By a *plane section* of S is meant a plane region formed by the intersection of a plane with S. In Sec. 7.2 we learned how to find the volume of a solid of revolution for which all plane sections perpendicular to the axis of revolution are circular. We now generalize this method to find the volume of a solid for which it is possible to express the area of any plane section perpendicular to a fixed line in terms of the perpendicular distance of the plane section from a fixed point. We first define what we mean when we say that a solid is a *cylinder*.

7.4.1 Definition   A solid is a *right cylinder* if it is bounded by two congruent plane regions R_1 and R_2 lying in parallel planes and by a lateral surface generated by a line segment, having its endpoints on the boundaries of R_1 and R_2, which moves so that it is always perpendicular to the planes of R_1 and R_2.

Figure 7.4.1 illustrates a right cylinder. The *height* of the cylinder is the perpendicular distance between the planes of R_1 and R_2, and the base is

| Figure 7.4.1 | Figure 7.4.2 | Figure 7.4.3 |

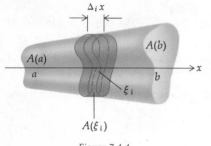

Figure 7.4.4

either R_1 or R_2. If the base of the right cylinder is a region enclosed by a circle, we have a *right-circular cylinder* (see Fig. 7.4.2); if the base is a region enclosed by a rectangle, we have a *rectangular parallelpiped* (see Fig. 7.4.3).

If the area of the base of a right cylinder is A square units and the height is h units, then by definition we let the volume of the right cylinder be measured by the product of A and h. As stated above, we are considering solids for which the area of any plane section that is perpendicular to a fixed line is a function of the perpendicular distance of the plane section from a fixed point. The solid S of Fig. 7.4.4 is such a solid, and it lies between the planes perpendicular to the x axis at a and b. We represent the number of square units in the area of the plane section of S in the plane perpendicular to the x axis at x by $A(x)$, where A is continuous on $[a, b]$.

Let Δ be a partition of the closed interval $[a, b]$ given by

$$a = x_0 < x_1 < x_2 < \cdots < x_n = b$$

We have, then, n subintervals of the form $[x_{i-1}, x_i]$, where $i = 1, 2, \ldots, n$, with the length of the ith subinterval being $\Delta_i x = x_i - x_{i-1}$. Choose any number ξ_i, with $x_{i-1} \le \xi_i \le x_i$, in each subinterval and construct the right cylinders of heights $\Delta_i x$ units and plane section areas $A(\xi_i)$ square units. The volume of the ith cylinder is $A(\xi_i) \, \Delta_i x$ cubic units. We obtain n right cylinders, and the sum of the measures of the volumes of these n cylinders is given by the Riemann sum

$$\sum_{i=1}^{n} A(\xi_i) \, \Delta_i x \qquad (1)$$

This Riemann sum is an approximation of what we intuitively think of as the measure of the volume of S, and the smaller we take the norm $\|\Delta\|$ of the partition Δ, the larger will be n, and the closer this approximation will be to the number we wish to assign to the measure of the volume. We have, then, the following definition.

7.4.2 Definition   Let S be a solid such that S lies between planes drawn perpendicular to the x axis at a and b. If the measure of the area of the plane section of S drawn perpendicular to the x axis at x is given by $A(x)$, where A is continuous on $[a, b]$, then the measure of the volume of S is given by

$$V = \lim_{||\Delta|| \to 0} \sum_{i=1}^{n} A(\xi_i)\, \Delta_i x = \int_a^b A(x)\ dx \qquad (2)$$

Note that Definitions 7.2.1 and 7.2.2 are special cases of Definition 7.4.2. If in Eq. (2) we take $A(x) = \pi[f(x)]^2$, we have Eq. (3) of Sec. 7.2. If we take $A(x) = \pi([f(x)]^2 - [g(x)]^2)$, we have Eq. (5) of Sec. 7.2.

EXAMPLE 1:   If the base of a solid is a circle with a radius of r units and if all plane sections perpendicular to a fixed diameter of the base are squares, find the volume of the solid.

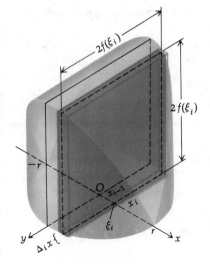

Figure 7.4.5

SOLUTION: Take the circle in the xy plane, the center at the origin, and the fixed diameter along the x axis. Therefore, an equation of the circle is $x^2 + y^2 = r^2$. Figure 7.4.5 shows the solid and an element of volume, which is a right cylinder of altitude $\Delta_i x$ units and with an area of the base given by $[2f(\xi_i)]^2$ square units, where $f(x)$ is obtained by solving the equation of the circle for y and setting $y = f(x)$. This computation gives $f(x) = \sqrt{r^2 - x^2}$. Therefore, if V cubic units is the volume of the solid, we have

$$V = \lim_{||\Delta|| \to 0} \sum_{i=1}^{n} [2f(\xi_i)]^2\, \Delta_i x$$

$$= 4\int_{-r}^{r} (r^2 - x^2)\ dx$$

$$= \tfrac{16}{3} r^3$$

EXAMPLE 2:   A wedge is cut from a right-circular cylinder with a radius of r in. by two planes, one perpendicular to the axis of the cylinder and the other intersecting the first at an angle of measurement 60° along a diameter of the circular plane section.

SOLUTION: The wedge is shown in Fig. 7.4.6. The xy plane is taken as the plane perpendicular to the axis of the cylinder, and the origin is at the point of perpendicularity. An equation of the circular plane section is then $x^2 + y^2 = r^2$. Every plane section of the wedge perpendicular to the x axis is a right triangle. An element of volume is a right cylinder having altitude $\Delta_i x$ in., and area of the base given by $\tfrac{1}{2}\sqrt{3}\,[f(\xi_i)]^2$ in.², where $f(x)$ is obtained by solving the equation of the circle for y and setting $y = f(x)$, thereby giving $f(x) = \sqrt{r^2 - x^2}$. Therefore, if V in.³ is the volume of the wedge,

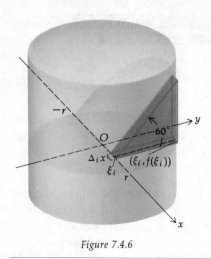

Figure 7.4.6

$$V = \lim_{\|\Delta\| \to 0} \sum_{i=1}^{n} \tfrac{1}{2} \sqrt{3} \, (r^2 - \xi_i^2) \, \Delta_i x$$

$$= \tfrac{1}{2} \sqrt{3} \int_{-r}^{r} (r^2 - x^2) \, dx$$

$$= \tfrac{1}{2} \sqrt{3} \left[r^2 x - \tfrac{1}{3} x^3 \right]_{-r}^{r}$$

$$= \tfrac{2}{3} \sqrt{3} \, r^3$$

Hence, the volume of the wedge is $\tfrac{2}{3} \sqrt{3} \, r^3$ in.^{3}

Exercises 7.4

1. The base of a solid is a circle having a radius of r units. Find the volume of the solid if all plane sections perpendicular to a fixed diameter of the base are equilateral triangles.

2. The base of a solid is a circle with a radius of r units, and all plane sections perpendicular to a fixed diameter of the base are isosceles right triangles having the hypotenuse in the plane of the base. Find the volume of the solid.

3. Solve Exercise 2 if the isosceles right triangles have one leg in the plane of the base.

4. Find the volume of a right pyramid having a height of h units and a square base of side a units.

5. Find the volume of the tetrahedron having 3 mutually perpendicular faces and three mutually perpendicular edges whose lengths have measures a, b, and c.

6. The base of a solid is a circle with a radius of 4 in., and each plane section perpendicular to a fixed diameter of the base is an isosceles triangle having an altitude of 10 in. and a chord of the circle as a base. Find the volume of the solid.

7. The base of a solid is a circle with a radius of 9 in., and each plane section perpendicular to a fixed diameter of the base is a square having a chord of the circle as a diagonal. Find the volume of the solid.

8. Two right-circular cylinders, each having a radius of r units, have axes that intersect at right angles. Find the volume of the solid common to the two cylinders.

9. A wedge is cut from a solid in the shape of a right-circular cylinder with a radius of r in. by a plane through a diameter of the base and inclined to the plane of the base at an angle of measurement 45°. Find the volume of the wedge.

10. A wedge is cut from a solid in the shape of a right-circular cone having a base radius of 5 ft and an altitude of 20 ft by two half planes through the axis of the cone. The angle between the two planes has a measurement of 30°. Find the volume of the wedge cut out.

7.5 WORK   The "work" done by a force acting on an object is defined in physics as "force times displacement." For example, suppose that an object is moving to the right along the x axis from a point a to a point b, and a constant force of F lb is acting on the object in the direction of motion. Then if the displacement is measured in feet, $(b - a)$ is the number of feet in the displacement. And if W is the number of foot-pounds of work done by the force, W is defined by

$$W = F(b - a) \tag{1}$$

EXAMPLE 1: Find the work necessary to lift a 70-lb weight to a height of 3 ft.	SOLUTION: Let W = the number of foot-pounds in the work done. Then $$W = 70 \cdot 3 = 210$$ Hence, the work required is 210 ft-lb.

In this section we consider the work done by a variable force, which is a function of the position of the object on which the force is acting. We wish to define what is meant by the term "work" in such a case.

Suppose that $f(x)$, where f is continuous on $[a, b]$, is the number of units in the force acting in the direction of motion on an object as it moves to the right along the x axis from point a to point b. Let Δ be a partition of the closed interval $[a, b]$:

$$a = x_0 < x_1 < x_2 < \cdots < x_{n-1} < x_n = b$$

The ith subinterval is $[x_{i-1}, x_i]$; and if x_{i-1} is close to x_i, the force is almost constant in this subinterval. If we assume that the force is constant in the ith subinterval and if ξ_i is any point such that $x_{i-1} \le \xi_i \le x_i$, then if $\Delta_i W$ is the number of units of work done on the object as it moves from the point x_{i-1} to the point x_i, from formula (1) we have

$$\Delta_i W = f(\xi_i)(x_i - x_{i-1})$$

Replacing $x_i - x_{i-1}$ by $\Delta_i x$, we have

$$\Delta_i W = f(\xi_i)\, \Delta_i x$$

and

$$\sum_{i=1}^{n} \Delta_i W = \sum_{i=1}^{n} f(\xi_i)\, \Delta_i x \tag{2}$$

The smaller we take the norm of the partition Δ, the larger n will be and the closer the Riemann sum in Eq. (2) will be to what we intuitively think of as the measure of the total work done. We therefore define the measure of the total work as the limit of the Riemann sum in Eq. (2).

7.5.1 Definition   Let the function f be continuous on the closed interval $[a, b]$ and $f(x)$ be the number of units in the force acting on an object at the point x on the x axis. Then if W units is the *work* done by the force as the object moves from a to b, W is given by

$$W = \lim_{\|\Delta\| \to 0} \sum_{i=1}^{n} f(\xi_i)\, \Delta_i x = \int_{a}^{b} f(x)\, dx \tag{3}$$

In the following example we use *Hooke's law,* which states that if a spring is stretched x in. beyond its natural length, it is pulled back with a force equal to kx lb, where k is a constant depending on the wire used.

EXAMPLE 2:   A spring has a natural length of 14 in. If a force of 5 lb is required to keep the spring stretched 2 in., how much work is done in stretching the spring from its natural length to a length of 18 in.?

SOLUTION: Place the spring along the x axis with the origin at the point where the stretching starts (see Fig. 7.5.1).

Figure 7.5.1

Let $x =$ the number of inches the spring is stretched;
$f(x) =$ the number of pounds in the force acting on the spring x in. beyond its natural length.

Then, by Hooke's law, $f(x) = kx$. Because $f(2) = 5$, we have

$$5 = k \cdot 2$$

$$k = \tfrac{5}{2}$$

Therefore,

$$f(x) = \tfrac{5}{2}x$$

If $W =$ the number of inch-pounds of work done in stretching the spring from its natural length of 14 in. to a length of 18 in., we have

$$W = \lim_{||\Delta|| \to 0} \sum_{i=1}^{n} f(\xi_i)\, \Delta_i x$$

$$= \int_0^4 f(x)\, dx$$

$$= \int_0^4 \tfrac{5}{2}x\, dx$$

$$= \tfrac{5}{4}x^2 \Big]_0^4$$

$$= 20$$

Therefore, the work done in stretching the spring is 20 in.-lb.

EXAMPLE 3:   A water tank in the form of an inverted right-circular cone is 20 ft across the top and 15 ft deep. If the surface of the water is 5 ft below the top of the tank, find the work done in pumping the water to the top of the tank.

SOLUTION: Refer to Fig. 7.5.2. The positive x axis is chosen in the downward direction because the motion is vertical. Take the origin at the top of the tank. We consider a partition of the closed interval $[5, 15]$ on the x axis and let ξ_i be any point in the ith subinterval $[x_{i-1}, x_i]$. An element of volume is a circular disk having thickness $\Delta_i x$ ft and radius $f(\xi_i)$ ft, where the function f is determined by an equation of the line through the points $(0, 10)$ and $(15, 0)$ in the form $y = f(x)$. The number of cubic feet in the volume of this element is given by $\Delta_i V = \pi [f(\xi_i)]^2\, \Delta_i x$. If w is the number

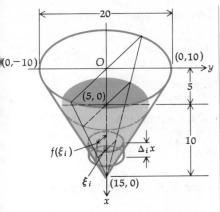

Figure 7.5.2

of pounds in the weight of 1 ft³ of water, then the number of pounds in the weight of this element is $w\pi[f(\xi_i)]^2\,\Delta_i x$, which is the force required to pump the element to the top of the tank. If x_{i-1} is close to x_i, then the distance through which this element moves is approximately ξ_i ft. Thus, if $\Delta_i W$ ft-lb is the work done in pumping the element to the top of the tank, $\Delta_i W$ is approximately $(w\pi[f(\xi_i)]^2\,\Delta_i x)\cdot\xi_i$; so if W is the number of foot-pounds of work done,

$$W = \lim_{||\Delta||\to 0}\sum_{i=1}^{n} w\pi[f(\xi_i)]^2\cdot\xi_i\,\Delta_i x$$

$$= w\pi\int_{5}^{15}[f(x)]^2 x\,dx$$

To determine $f(x)$, we find an equation of the line through the points $(15,0)$ and $(0,10)$ by using the intercept form:

$$\frac{x}{15}+\frac{y}{10}=1 \quad\text{or}\quad y=-\tfrac{2}{3}x+10$$

Therefore, $f(x) = -\tfrac{2}{3}x+10$, and

$$W = w\pi\int_{5}^{15}(-\tfrac{2}{3}x+10)^2 x\,dx$$

$$= w\pi\int_{5}^{15}(\tfrac{4}{9}x^3-\tfrac{40}{3}x^2+100x)\,dx$$

$$= w\pi\left[\tfrac{1}{9}x^4-\tfrac{40}{9}x^3+50x^2\right]_{5}^{15}$$

$$= \tfrac{1}{9}(10{,}000\pi w)$$

Therefore, the work done is $10{,}000\pi w/9$ ft-lb.

Exercises 7.5

1. A spring has a natural length of 8 in. If a force of 20 lb stretches the spring $\tfrac{1}{2}$ in., find the work done in stretching the spring from 8 in. to 11 in.

2. A spring has a natural length of 10 in., and a 30-lb force stretches it to $11\tfrac{1}{2}$ in. Find the work done in stretching the spring from 10 in. to 12 in. Then find the work done in stretching the spring from 12 in. to 14 in.

3. A spring has a natural length of 6 in. A 12,000-lb force compresses the spring to $5\tfrac{1}{2}$ in. Find the work done in compressing it from 6 in. to 5 in. Hooke's law holds for compression as well as for extension.

4. A spring has a natural length of 6 in. A 1200-lb force compresses it to $5\tfrac{1}{2}$ in. Find the work done in compressing it from 6 in. to $4\tfrac{1}{2}$ in.

5. A swimming pool full of water is in the form of a rectangular parallelepiped 5 ft deep, 15 ft wide, and 25 ft long. Find the work required to pump the water in the pool up to a level 1 ft above the surface of the pool.

6. A trough full of water is 10 ft long, and its cross section is in the shape of an isosceles triangle 2 ft wide across the top and 2 ft high. How much work is done in pumping all the water out of the trough over the top?

7. A hemispherical tank with a radius of 6 ft is filled with water to a depth of 4 ft. Find the work done in pumping the water to the top of the tank.

8. A right-circular cylindrical tank with a depth of 12 ft and a radius of 4 ft is half full of oil weighing 60 lb/ft³. Find the work done in pumping the oil to a height 6 ft above the tank.

9. A cable 200 ft long and weighing 4 lb/ft is hanging vertically down a well. If a weight of 100 lb is suspended from the lower end of the cable, find the work done in pulling the cable and weight to the top of the well.

10. A bucket weighing 20 lb containing 60 lb of sand is attached to the lower end of a 100 ft long chain that weighs 10 lb and is hanging in a deep well. Find the work done in raising the bucket to the top of the well.

11. Solve Exercise 10 if the sand is leaking out of the bucket at a constant rate and has all leaked out just as soon as the bucket is at the top of the well.

12. As a water tank is being raised water spills out at a constant rate of 2 ft³ per foot of rise. If the tank originally contained 1000 ft³ of water, find the work done in raising the tank 20 ft.

13. A tank in the form of a rectangular parallelepiped 6 ft deep, 4 ft wide, and 12 ft long is full of oil weighing 50 lb/ft³. When one-third of the work necessary to pump the oil to the top of the tank has been done, find by how much the surface of the oil is lowered.

14. A cylindrical tank 10 ft high and 5 ft in radius is standing on a platform 50 ft high. Find the depth of the water when one-half of the work required to fill the tank from the ground level through a pipe in the bottom has been done.

15. A one horsepower motor can do 550 ft-lb of work per second. If a 0.1 hp motor is used to pump water from a full tank in the shape of a rectangular parallelepiped 2 ft deep, 2 ft wide, and 6 ft long to a point 5 ft above the top of the tank, how long will it take?

16. A meteorite is a miles from the center of the earth and falls to the surface of the earth. The force of gravity is inversely proportional to the square of the distance of a body from the center of the earth. Find the work done by gravity if the weight of the meteorite is w lb at the surface of the earth. Let R miles be the radius of the earth.

7.6 LIQUID PRESSURE

Another application of the definite integral in physics is to find the force caused by liquid pressure on a plate submerged in the liquid or on a side of a container holding the liquid. First of all, suppose that a flat plate is inserted horizontally into a liquid in a container. The weight of the liquid exerts a force on the plate. The force per square unit of area exerted by the liquid on the plate is called the *pressure* of the liquid.

Let w be the number of pounds in the weight of one cubic foot of the liquid and h be the number of feet in the depth of a point below the surface of the liquid. If p is the number of pounds per square foot of pressure exerted by the liquid at the point, then

$$p = wh \tag{1}$$

If A is the number of square feet in the area of a flat plate that is submerged horizontally in the liquid, and F is the number of pounds in the force caused by liquid pressure acting on the upper face of the plate, then

$$F = pA \tag{2}$$

Substituting from formula (1) into (2) gives us

$$F = whA \tag{3}$$

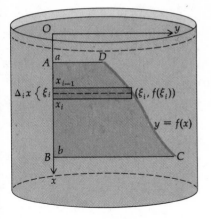

Figure 7.6.1

Note that formula (1) states that the size of the container is immaterial so far as liquid pressure is concerned. For example, at a depth of 5 ft in a swimming pool filled with salt water the pressure is the same as at a depth of 5 ft in the Pacific Ocean, assuming the density of the water is the same.

Now suppose that the plate is submerged vertically in the liquid. Then at points on the plate at different depths the pressure, computed from formula (1), will be different and will be greater at the bottom of the plate than at the top. We now proceed to define the force caused by liquid pressure when the plate is submerged vertically in the liquid. We use Pascal's principle: At any point in a liquid, the pressure is the same in all directions.

In Fig. 7.6.1 let $ABCD$ be the region bounded by the x axis, the lines $x = a$ and $x = b$, and the curve $y = f(x)$, where the function f is continuous and $f(x) \geq 0$ on the closed interval $[a, b]$. Choose the coordinate axes so the y axis lies along the line of the surface of the liquid. Take the x axis vertical with the positive direction downward. The length of the plate at a depth x ft is given by $f(x)$ ft.

Let Δ be a partition of the closed interval $[a, b]$ which divides the interval into n subintervals. Choose a point ξ_i in the ith subinterval, with $x_{i-1} \leq \xi_i \leq x_i$. Draw n horizontal rectangles. The ith rectangle has a length of $f(\xi_i)$ ft and a width of $\Delta_i x$ ft (see Fig. 7.6.1).

If we rotate each rectangular element through an angle of 90°, each element becomes a plate submerged in the liquid at a depth of ξ_i ft below the surface of the liquid and perpendicular to the region $ABCD$. Then the force on the ith rectangular element is given by $w\xi_i f(\xi_i) \Delta_i x$ lb. An approximation to F, the number of pounds in the total force on the vertical plate, is given by

$$\sum_{i=1}^{n} w\xi_i f(\xi_i) \Delta_i x \tag{4}$$

which is a Riemann sum.

The smaller we take $\|\Delta\|$, the larger n will be and the closer the approximation given by (4) will be to what we wish to be the measure of the total force. We have, then, the following definition.

7.6.1 Definition   Suppose that a flat plate is submerged vertically in a liquid of weight w pounds per cubic unit. The length of the plate at a depth of x units below the surface of the liquid is $f(x)$ units, where f is continuous on the closed interval $[a, b]$ and $f(x) \geq 0$ on $[a, b]$. Then F, the number of pounds of *force caused by liquid pressure* on the plate, is given by

$$F = \lim_{\|\Delta\| \to 0} \sum_{i=1}^{n} w\xi_i f(\xi_i) \Delta_i x = \int_a^b wxf(x) \, dx \tag{5}$$

EXAMPLE 1:   A trough having a trapezoidal cross section is full of water. If the trapezoid is 3 ft wide at the top, 2 ft wide at the bottom, and 2 ft deep, find the total force owing to liquid pressure on one end of the trough.

SOLUTION: Figure 7.6.2 illustrates one end of the trough together with a rectangular element of area. An equation of line AB is $y = \frac{3}{2} - \frac{1}{4}x$. Let $f(x) = \frac{3}{2} - \frac{1}{4}x$. If we rotate the rectangular element through 90°, the force on the element is given by $2w\xi_i f(\xi_i)\ \Delta_i x$ lb. If F is the number of pounds in the total force on the side of the trough,

$$F = \lim_{\|\Delta\| \to 0} \sum_{i=1}^{n} 2w\xi_i f(\xi_i)\ \Delta_i x$$

$$= 2w \int_0^2 xf(x)\ dx$$

$$= 2w \int_0^2 x(\tfrac{3}{2} - \tfrac{1}{4}x)\ dx$$

$$= 2w \left[\tfrac{3}{4}x^2 - \tfrac{1}{12}x^3 \right]_0^2$$

$$= \tfrac{14}{3}w$$

Taking $w = 62.5$, we find that the total force is 291.2 lb.

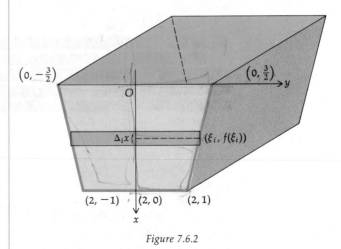

$(0, -\tfrac{3}{2})$ $(0, \tfrac{3}{2})$

O

$\Delta_i x$ $(\xi_i, f(\xi_i))$

$(2, -1)$ $(2, 0)$ $(2, 1)$

x

Figure 7.6.2

EXAMPLE 2:   The ends of a trough are semicircular regions, each with a radius of 2 ft. Find the force caused by liquid pressure on one end if the trough is full of water.

SOLUTION: Figure 7.6.3 shows one end of the trough together with a rectangular element of area. An equation of the semicircle is $x^2 + y^2 = 4$. Solving for y gives $y = \sqrt{4 - x^2}$, and so let $f(x) = \sqrt{4 - x^2}$. The force on the rectangular element is given by $2w\xi_i f(\xi_i)\ \Delta_i x$. So if F pounds is the total force on the side of the trough,

$$F = \lim_{\|\Delta\| \to 0} \sum_{i=1}^{n} 2w\xi_i f(\xi_i)\ \Delta_i x$$

$$= 2w \int_0^2 xf(x)\ dx$$

$$= 2w \int_0^2 x\sqrt{4 - x^2} \; dx$$

$$= -\tfrac{2}{3}w(4 - x^2)^{3/2} \Big]_0^2$$

$$= \tfrac{16}{3}w$$

Therefore, the total force is $\tfrac{16}{3}w$ lb.

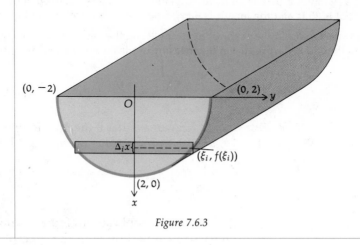

Figure 7.6.3

Exercises 7.6

1. A plate in the shape of a rectangle is submerged vertically in a tank of water, with the upper edge lying in the surface. If the width of the plate is 10 ft and the depth is 8 ft, find the force due to liquid pressure on one side of the plate.

2. A square plate of side 4 ft is submerged vertically in a tank of water and its center is 2 ft below the surface. Find the force due to liquid pressure on one side of the plate.

3. Solve Exercise 2 if the center of the plate is 4 ft below the surface.

4. A plate in the shape of an isosceles right triangle is submerged vertically in a tank of water, with one leg lying in the surface. The legs are each 6 ft long. Find the force due to liquid pressure on one side of the plate.

5. A rectangular tank full of water is 2 ft wide and 18 in. deep. Find the force due to liquid pressure on one end of the tank.

6. The ends of a trough are equilateral triangles having sides with lengths of 2 ft. If the water in the trough is 1 ft deep, find the force due to liquid pressure on one end.

7. The face of a dam adjacent to the water is vertical, and its shape is in the form of an isosceles triangle 250 ft wide across the top and 100 ft high in the center. If the water is 10 ft deep in the center, find the total force on the dam due to liquid pressure.

8. An oil tank is in the shape of a right-circular cylinder 4 ft in diameter, and its axis is horizontal. If the tank is half full of oil weighing 50 lb/ft³, find the total force on one end due to liquid pressure.

9. The face of the gate of a dam is in the shape of an isosceles triangle 4 ft wide at the top and 3 ft high. If the upper edge of the face of the gate is 15 ft below the surface of the water, find the total force due to liquid pressure on the gate.

10. The face of a gate of a dam is vertical and in the shape of an isosceles trapezoid 3 ft wide at the top, 4 ft wide at the bottom, and 3 ft high. If the upper base is 20 ft below the surface of the water, find the total force due to liquid pressure on the gate.

11. The face of a dam adjacent to the water is inclined at an angle of 30° from the vertical. The shape of the face is a rectangle of width 50 ft and slant height 30 ft. If the dam is full of water, find the total force due to liquid pressure on the face.

12. Solve Exercise 11 if the face of the dam is an isosceles trapezoid 120 ft wide at the top, 80 ft wide at the bottom, and with a slant height of 40 ft.

13. The bottom of a swimming pool is an inclined plane. The pool is 2 ft deep at one end and 8 ft deep at the other. If the width of the pool is 25 ft and the length is 40 ft, find the total force due to liquid pressure on the bottom.

14. If the end of a water tank is in the shape of a rectangle and the tank is full, show that the measure of the force due to liquid pressure on the end is the product of the measure of the area of the end and the measure of the force at the geometrical center.

7.7 CENTER OF MASS OF A ROD

In Sec. 6.5 we saw that if the function f is continuous on the closed interval $[a, b]$, the average value of f on $[a, b]$ is given by

$$\frac{\int_a^b f(x)\ dx}{b - a}$$

An important application of the average value of a function occurs in physics in connection with the concept of *center of mass.*

To arrive at a definition of "mass" consider a particle that is set into motion along an axis by a force of F lb exerted on the particle. So long as the force is acting on the particle, the velocity of the particle is increasing; that is, the particle has an acceleration. The ratio of the force to the acceleration is constant regardless of the magnitude of the force, and this constant ratio is called the *mass* of the particle. In particular, if the acceleration of a certain particle is 10 ft/sec² when the force is 30 lb, the mass of the particle is

$$\frac{30\text{ lb}}{10\text{ ft/sec}^2} = \frac{3\text{ lb}}{1\text{ ft/sec}^2}$$

Thus, for every 1 ft/sec² of acceleration, a force of 3 lb must be exerted on the particle. When the unit of force is 1 lb and the unit of acceleration is 1 ft/sec², the unit of mass is called *one slug*. That is, 1 slug is the mass of a particle whose acceleration is 1 ft/sec² when the magnitude of the force on the particle is 1 lb. Hence, the particle having an acceleration of 10 ft/sec² when the force is 30 lb has a mass of 3 slugs.

From physics, if W lb is the weight of an object having a mass of m slugs, and g ft/sec² is the constant of acceleration due to gravity, then

$$W = mg$$

Consider now a horizontal rod, of negligible weight and thickness, placed on the x axis. On the rod is a system of n particles located at points

Figure 7.7.1

$x_1, x_2, \ldots, x_n$. The ith particle $(i = 1, 2, \ldots, n)$ is at a directed distance x_i ft from the origin and its mass is m_i slugs. See Fig. 7.7.1. The number of slugs in the total mass of the system is $\sum_{i=1}^{n} m_i$. We define the *moment of mass* of the ith particle with respect to the origin as $m_i x_i$ slug-ft. The moment of mass for the system is defined as the sum of the moments of mass of all the particles. Hence, if M_0 slug-ft is the moment of mass of the system with respect to the origin, then

$$M_O = \sum_{i=1}^{n} m_i x_i$$

Now we wish to find a point $\bar{x}$ such that if the total mass of the system were concentrated there, its moment of mass with respect to the origin would be equal to the moment of mass of the system with respect to the origin. Then $\bar{x}$ must satisfy the equation

$$\bar{x} \sum_{i=1}^{n} m_1 = \sum_{i=1}^{n} m_i x_i$$

and so

$$\bar{x} = \frac{\sum_{i=1}^{n} m_i x_i}{\sum_{i=1}^{n} m_i} \tag{1}$$

The point $\bar{x}$ is called the *center of mass* of the system, and it is the point where the system will balance. The position of the center of mass is independent of the position of the origin; that is, the location of the center of mass relative to the positions of the particles does not change when the origin is changed.

EXAMPLE 1: Given four particles of masses 2, 3, 1, and 5 slugs located on the x axis at the points having coordinates $5, 2, -3,$ and -4, respectively, where distance measurement is in feet, find the center of mass of this system.

SOLUTION: If $\bar{x}$ is the coordinate of the center of mass, we have from formula (1)

$$\bar{x} = \frac{2(5) + 3(2) + (1)(-3) + 5(-4)}{2 + 3 + 1 + 5} = -\frac{7}{11}$$

Thus, the center of mass is $\frac{7}{11}$ ft to the left of the origin.

The preceding discussion is now extended to a rigid horizontal rod having a continuously distributed mass. The rod is said to be *homogeneous* if its mass is directly proportional to its length. In other words, if the segment of the rod whose length is $\Delta_i x$ ft has a mass of $\Delta_i m$ slugs, and $\Delta_i m = k \, \Delta_i x$, then the rod is homogeneous. The number k is a constant and k slugs/ft is called the *linear density* of the rod.

Figure 7.7.2

Suppose that we have a nonhomogeneous rod, in which case the linear density varies along the rod. Let L ft be the length of the rod, and place the rod on the x axis so the left endpoint of the rod is at the origin and the right endpoint is at L. See Fig. 7.7.2. The linear density at any point x on the rod is $\rho(x)$ slugs/ft, where ρ is continuous on $[0, L]$. To find the total mass of the rod we consider a partition Δ of the closed interval $[0, L]$ into n subintervals. The ith subinterval is $[x_{i-1}, x_i]$, and its length is $\Delta_i x$ ft. If ξ_i is any point in $[x_{i-1}, x_i]$, an approximation to the mass of the part of the rod contained in the ith subinterval is $\Delta_i m$ slugs, where

$$\Delta_i m = \rho(\xi_i) \, \Delta_i x$$

The number of slugs in the total mass of the rod is approximated by

$$\sum_{i=1}^{n} \Delta_i m = \sum_{i=1}^{n} \rho(\xi_i) \, \Delta_i x \tag{2}$$

The smaller we take the norm of the partition Δ, the closer the Riemann sum in Eq. (2) will be to what we intuitively think of as the measure of the mass of the rod, and so we define the measure of the mass as the limit of the Riemann sum in Eq. (2).

7.7.1 Definition   A rod of length L ft has its left endpoint at the origin. If the number of slugs per foot in the linear density at a point x ft from the origin is $\rho(x)$, where ρ is continuous on $[0, L]$, then the total *mass* of the rod is M slugs, where

$$M = \lim_{\|\Delta\| \to 0} \sum_{i=1}^{n} \rho(\xi_i) \, \Delta_i x = \int_0^L \rho(x) \, dx \tag{3}$$

EXAMPLE 2:   The density at any point of a rod 4 ft long varies directly as the distance from the

SOLUTION: Figure 7.7.3 shows the rod placed on the x axis. If $\rho(x)$ is the number of slugs per foot in the density of the rod at the point x,

$$\rho(x) = c(6 - x)$$

point to an external point in the line of the rod and 2 ft from an end, where the density is 5 slugs/ft. Find the total mass of the rod.

Figure 7.7.3

where c is the constant of proportionality. Because $\rho(4) = 5$, we have $5 = 2c$ or $c = \frac{5}{2}$. Hence, $\rho(x) = \frac{5}{2}(6 - x)$. Therefore, if M slugs is the total mass of the rod, we have from Definition 7.7.1

$$M = \lim_{\|\Delta\| \to 0} \sum_{i=1}^{n} \tfrac{5}{2}(6 - \xi_i)\, \Delta_i x$$

$$= \int_0^4 \tfrac{5}{2}(6 - x)\, dx$$

$$= \tfrac{5}{2}\left[6x - \tfrac{1}{2}x^2\right]_0^4$$

$$= 40$$

The total mass of the rod is therefore 40 slugs.

We now proceed to define the center of mass of the rod of Definition 7.7.1. However, first we must define the moment of mass of the rod with respect to the origin.

Figure 7.7.4

As before, place the rod on the x axis with the left endpoint at the origin and the right endpoint at L. See Fig. 7.7.4. Let Δ be a partition of $[0, L]$ into n subintervals, with the ith subinterval $[x_{i-1}, x_i]$ having length $\Delta_i x$ ft. If ξ_i is any point in $[x_{i-1}, x_i]$, an approximation to the moment of mass with respect to the origin of the part of the rod contained in the ith subinterval is $\xi_i \Delta_i m$ slug-ft, where $\Delta_i m = \rho(\xi_i)\, \Delta_i x$. The number of slug-feet in the moment of mass of the entire rod is approximated by

$$\sum_{i=1}^{n} \xi_i \Delta_i m = \sum_{i=1}^{n} \xi_i\, \rho(\xi_i)\, \Delta_i x \tag{4}$$

The smaller we take the norm of the partition Δ, the closer the Riemann sum in Eq. (4) will be to what we intuitively think of as the measure of the moment of mass of the rod with respect to the origin. We have, then, the following definition.

7.7.2 Definition   A rod of length L ft has its left endpoint at the origin and the number of slugs per foot in the linear density at a point x ft from the origin is $\rho(x)$, where ρ is continuous on $[0, L]$. The *moment of mass* of the rod with respect to the origin is M_0 slug-ft, where

$$M_0 = \lim_{||\Delta|| \to 0} \sum_{i=1}^{n} \xi_i \rho(\xi_i) \, \Delta_i x = \int_0^L x\rho(x) \, dx \tag{5}$$

The center of mass of the rod is at the point $\bar{x}$ such that if M slugs is the total mass of the rod, $\bar{x}M = M_0$. Therefore, from Eqs. (3) and (5) we get

$$\bar{x} = \frac{\displaystyle\int_0^L x\rho(x) \, dx}{\displaystyle\int_0^L \rho(x) \, dx} \tag{6}$$

EXAMPLE 3:   Find the center of mass for the rod in Example 2.

SOLUTION: In Example 2, we found $M = 40$. Using Eq. (6) with $\rho(x) = \frac{5}{2}(6 - x)$, we have

$$\bar{x} = \frac{\displaystyle\int_0^4 \frac{5}{2}x(6 - x) \, dx}{40} = \frac{1}{16}\left[3x^2 - \frac{1}{3}x^3\right]_0^4 = \frac{5}{3}$$

Therefore, the center of mass is at $\frac{5}{3}$.

Note that if a rod is of uniform density k slugs/ft, where k is a constant, then from formula (6) we have

$$\bar{x} = \frac{\displaystyle\int_0^L xk \, dx}{\displaystyle\int_0^L k \, dx} = \frac{\dfrac{kx^2}{2}\Big]_0^L}{kx\Big]_0^L} = \frac{\dfrac{kL^2}{2}}{kL} = \frac{L}{2}$$

Thus, the center of mass is at the center of the rod, which is to be expected.

Exercises 7.7

In Exercises 1 through 4 a system of particles is located on the x axis. The number of slugs in the mass of each particle and the coordinate of its position are given. Distance is measured in feet. Find the center of mass of each system.

1. $m_1 = 5$ at 2; $m_2 = 6$ at 3; $m_3 = 4$ at 5; $m_4 = 3$ at 8.

2. $m_1 = 2$ at -4; $m_2 = 8$ at -1; $m_3 = 4$ at 2; $m_4 = 2$ at 3.

3. $m_1 = 2$ at -3; $m_2 = 4$ at -2; $m_3 = 20$ at 4; $m_4 = 10$ at 6; $m_5 = 30$ at 9.

4. $m_1 = 5$ at -7; $m_2 = 3$ at -2; $m_3 = 5$ at 0; $m_4 = 1$ at 2; $m_5 = 8$ at 10.

In Exercises 5 through 9, find the total mass of the given rod and the center of mass.

5. The length of a rod is 9 in. and the linear density of the rod at a point x in. from one end is $(4x + 1)$ slugs/in.

6. The length of a rod is 3 ft, and the linear density of the rod at a point x ft from one end is $(5 + 2x)$ slugs/ft.

7. The length of a rod is 10 ft and the measure of the linear density at a point is a linear function of the measure of the distance of the point from the left end of the rod. The linear density at the left end is 2 slugs/ft and at the right end is 3 slugs/ft.

8. A rod is 10 ft long, and the measure of the linear density at a point is a linear function of the measure of the distance from the center of the rod. The linear density at each end of the rod is 5 slugs/ft and at the center the linear density is $3\frac{1}{2}$ slugs/ft.

9. The measure of the linear density at a point of a rod varies directly as the third power of the measure of the distance of the point from one end. The length of the rod is 4 ft and the linear density is 2 slugs/ft at the center.

10. A rod is 6 ft long and its mass is 24 slugs. If the measure of the linear density at any point of the rod varies directly as the square of the distance of the point from one end, find the largest value of the linear density.

11. The length of a rod is L ft and the center of mass of the rod is at the point $\frac{3}{4}L$ ft from the left end. If the measure of the linear density at a point is proportional to a power of the measure of the distance of the point from the left end and the linear density at the right end is 20 slugs/ft find the linear density at a point x ft from the left end. Assume the mass is measured in slugs.

12. The total mass of a rod of length L ft is M slugs and the measure of the linear density at a point x ft from the left end is proportional to the measure of the distance of the point from the right end. Show that the linear density at a point on the rod x ft from the left end is $2M(L - x)/L^2$ slugs/ft.

7.8 CENTER OF MASS OF A PLANE REGION

Let the masses of n particles located at the points (x_1, y_1), (x_2, y_2) , . . . , (x_n, y_n) in the xy plane be measured in slugs by $m_1, m_2, \ldots , m_n$, and consider the problem of finding the center of mass of this system. We may imagine the particles being supported by a sheet of negligible weight and negligible thickness and may assume that each particle has its position at exactly one point. The center of mass is the point where the sheet will balance. To determine the center of mass, we must find two averages: $\bar{x}$, which is the average value for the abscissas of the n points, and $\bar{y}$, the average value for the ordinates of the n points. We first define the moment of mass of a system of particles with respect to an axis.

If a particle at a distance d ft from an axis has a mass of m slugs, then if M_1 slug-ft is the moment of mass of the particle with respect to the axis,

$$M_1 = md \tag{1}$$

If the ith particle, having mass m_i slugs, is located at the point (x_i, y_i), its distance from the y axis is x_i ft; thus, from formula (1), the moment of mass of this particle with respect to the y axis is $m_i x_i$ slug-ft. Similarly, the moment of mass of the particle with respect to the x axis is $m_i y_i$ slug-ft. The moment of the system of n particles with respect to the y axis is M_y slug-ft, where

$$M_y = \sum_{i=1}^{n} m_i x_i \tag{2}$$

and the moment of the system with respect to the x axis is M_x slug-ft, where

$$M_x = \sum_{i=1}^{n} m_i y_i \tag{3}$$

The total mass of the system is M slugs, where

$$M = \sum_{i=1}^{n} m_i \tag{4}$$

The center of mass of the system is at the point $(\bar{x}, \bar{y})$, where

$$\bar{x} = \frac{M_y}{M} \tag{5}$$

and

$$\bar{y} = \frac{M_x}{M} \tag{6}$$

The point $(\bar{x}, \bar{y})$ can be interpreted as the point such that, if the total mass M slugs of the system were concentrated there, its moment of mass with respect to the y axis, M_y slug-ft, would be determined by $M_y = M\bar{x}$, and its moment of mass with respect to the x axis, M_x slug-ft, would be determined by $M_x = M\bar{y}$.

EXAMPLE 1:   Find the center of mass of the four particles having masses $2, 6, 4$, and 1 slugs located at the points $(5, -2)$, $(-2, 1)$, $(0, 3)$, and $(4, -1)$, respectively.

SOLUTION:

$$M_y = \sum_{i=1}^{4} m_i x_i = 2(5) + 6(-2) + 4(0) + 1(4) = 2$$

$$M_x = \sum_{i=1}^{4} m_i y_i = 2(-2) + 6(1) + 4(3) + 1(-1) = 13$$

$$M = \sum_{i=1}^{4} m_i = 2 + 6 + 4 + 1 = 13$$

Therefore,

$$\bar{x} = \frac{M_y}{M} = \frac{2}{13} \quad \text{and} \quad \bar{y} = \frac{M_x}{M} = \frac{13}{13} = 1$$

The center of mass is at $(\frac{2}{13}, 1)$.

Consider now a thin sheet of continuously distributed mass, for example, a piece of paper or a flat strip of tin. We regard such sheets as being two dimensional and call such a plane region a *lamina*. In this section we confine our discussion to homogeneous laminae, that is, laminae having constant area density. Laminae of variable area density are considered in Chapter 18 in connection with applications of multiple integrals.

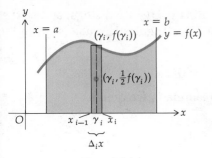

Figure 7.8.1

Let a homogeneous lamina of area A ft² have a mass of M slugs. Then if the constant area density is k slugs/ft², $M = kA$. If the homogeneous lamina is a rectangle, its center of mass is defined to be at the center of the rectangle. We use this definition to define the center of mass of a more general homogeneous lamina.

Let L be the homogeneous lamina whose constant area density is k slugs/ft², and which is bounded by the curve $y = f(x)$, the x axis, and the lines $x = a$ and $x = b$. The function f is continuous on the closed interval $[a, b]$, and $f(x) \geq 0$ for all x in $[a, b]$. See Fig. 7.8.1. Let Δ be a partition of the interval $[a, b]$ into n subintervals. The ith subinterval is $[x_{i-1}, x_i]$ and $\Delta_i x = x_i - x_{i-1}$. The midpoint of $[x_{i-1}, x_i]$ is γ_i. Associated with each subinterval is a rectangular lamina whose width, altitude, and area density are given by $\Delta_i x$ ft, $f(\gamma_i)$ ft, and k slugs/ft², respectively, and whose center of mass is at the point $(\gamma_i, \frac{1}{2}f(\gamma_i))$. The area of the rectangular lamina is $f(\gamma_i) \Delta_i x$ ft²; hence, $kf(\gamma_i) \Delta_i x$ slugs is its mass. Consequently, if $\Delta_i M_y$ slug-ft is the moment of mass of this rectangular element with respect to the y axis,

$$\Delta_i M_y = \gamma_i k f(\gamma_i) \; \Delta_i x$$

The sum of the measures of the moments of mass of n such rectangular laminae with respect to the y axis is given by the Riemann sum

$$\sum_{i=1}^{n} k\gamma_i f(\gamma_i) \; \Delta_i x$$

If M_y slug-ft is the moment of mass of the lamina L with respect to the y axis, we define

$$M_y = \lim_{||\Delta|| \to 0} \sum_{i=1}^{n} k\gamma_i f(\gamma_i) \; \Delta_i x = k \int_a^b x f(x) \; dx \tag{7}$$

Similarly, if $\Delta_i M_x$ slug-ft is the moment of mass of the ith rectangular lamina with respect to the x axis,

$$\Delta_i M_x = \tfrac{1}{2} f(\gamma_i) k f(\gamma_i) \; \Delta_i x$$

and the sum of the measures of the moments of mass of n such rectangular laminae with respect to the x axis is given by the Riemann sum

$$\sum_{i=1}^{n} \tfrac{1}{2} k [f(\gamma_i)]^2 \; \Delta_i x \tag{8}$$

Thus, if M_x slug-ft is the moment of mass of the lamina L with respect to the x axis, we define

$$M_x = \lim_{||\Delta|| \to 0} \sum_{i=1}^{n} \tfrac{1}{2} k [f(\gamma_i)]^2 \; \Delta_i x = \tfrac{1}{2} k \int_a^b [f(x)]^2 \; dx \tag{9}$$

The mass of the ith rectangular lamina is $kf(\gamma_i)\ \Delta_i x$ slugs, and so the sum of the measures of the masses of n rectangular laminae is given by

$$\sum_{i=1}^{n} kf(\gamma_i)\ \Delta_i x$$

So, if M slugs is the total mass of the lamina L, we define

$$M = \lim_{||\Delta|| \to 0} \sum_{i=1}^{n} kf(\gamma_i)\ \Delta_i x = k \int_{a}^{b} f(x)\ dx \qquad (10)$$

Denoting the center of mass of the lamina L by the point $(\bar{x}, \bar{y})$, we define

$$\bar{x} = \frac{M_y}{M} \quad \text{and} \quad \bar{y} = \frac{M_x}{M}$$

which by using formulas (7), (9), and (10) gives

$$\bar{x} = \frac{k \int_{a}^{b} xf(x)\ dx}{k \int_{a}^{b} f(x)\ dx} \quad \text{and} \quad \bar{y} = \frac{\frac{1}{2}k \int_{a}^{b} [f(x)]^2\ dx}{k \int_{a}^{b} f(x)\ dx}$$

Dividing both the numerator and denominator by k, we get

$$\bar{x} = \frac{\int_{a}^{b} xf(x)\ dx}{\int_{a}^{b} f(x)\ dx} \qquad (11)$$

and

$$\bar{y} = \frac{\frac{1}{2} \int_{a}^{b} [f(x)]^2\ dx}{\int_{a}^{b} f(x)\ dx} \qquad (12)$$

In formulas (11) and (12) the denominator is the number of square units in the area of the region, and so we have expressed a physical problem in terms of a geometric one. That is, $\bar{x}$ and $\bar{y}$ can be considered as the average abscissa and the average ordinate, respectively, of a geometric region. In such a case, $\bar{x}$ and $\bar{y}$ depend only on the region, not on the mass of the lamina. So we refer to the center of mass of a plane region instead of to the center of mass of a homogeneous lamina. In such a case, we call the center of mass the *centroid* of the region. Instead of moments of mass, we consider moments of the region. We define the moments of the plane region in the above discussion with respect to the x axis and the y axis by the following:

$$M_x = \lim_{||\Delta|| \to 0} \sum_{i=1}^{n} \tfrac{1}{2}[f(\gamma_i)]^2 \, \Delta_i x = \tfrac{1}{2} \int_a^b [f(x)]^2 \, dx$$

$$M_y = \lim_{||\Delta|| \to 0} \sum_{i=1}^{n} \gamma_i f(\gamma_i) \, \Delta_i x = \int_a^b x f(x) \, dx$$

If $(\bar{x}, \bar{y})$ is the centroid of the plane region and if M_x and M_y are defined as above,

$$\bar{x} = \frac{M_y}{A} \quad \text{and} \quad \bar{y} = \frac{M_x}{A}$$

EXAMPLE 2:   Find the centroid of the first quadrant region bounded by the curve $y^2 = 4x$, the x axis, and the lines $x = 1$ and $x = 4$.

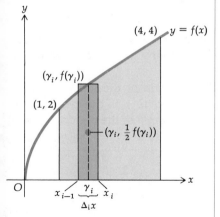

Figure 7.8.2

SOLUTION: Let $f(x) = 2x^{1/2}$. The equation of the curve is then $y = f(x)$. In Fig. 7.8.2, the region is shown together with the ith rectangular element. The centroid of the rectangle is at $(\gamma_i, \tfrac{1}{2}f(\gamma_i))$. The area A square units of the region is given by

$$A = \lim_{||\Delta|| \to 0} \sum_{i=1}^{n} f(\gamma_i) \, \Delta_i x$$

$$= \int_1^4 f(x) \, dx$$

$$= \int_1^4 2x^{1/2} \, dx$$

$$= \tfrac{4}{3} x^{3/2} \Big]_1^4$$

$$= \tfrac{28}{3}$$

We now compute M_y and M_x.

$$M_y = \lim_{||\Delta|| \to 0} \sum_{i=1}^{n} \gamma_i f(\gamma_i) \, \Delta_i x$$

$$= \int_1^4 x f(x) \, dx$$

$$= \int_1^4 x(2x^{1/2}) \, dx$$

$$= 2 \int_1^4 x^{3/2} \, dx$$

$$= \tfrac{4}{5} x^{5/2} \Big]_1^4$$

$$= \tfrac{124}{5}$$

$$M_x = \lim_{||\Delta|| \to 0} \sum_{i=1}^{n} \tfrac{1}{2} f(\gamma_i) \cdot f(\gamma_i) \, \Delta_i x$$

$$= \tfrac{1}{2} \int_1^4 [f(x)]^2 \, dx$$

$$= \tfrac{1}{2} \int_1^4 4x \, dx$$

$$= x^2 \Big]_1^4$$

$$= 15$$

Hence,

$$\bar{x} = \frac{M_y}{A} = \frac{\frac{124}{5}}{\frac{28}{3}} = \frac{93}{35}$$

and

$$\bar{y} = \frac{M_x}{A} = \frac{15}{\frac{28}{3}} = \frac{45}{28}$$

Therefore, the centroid is at the point $(\frac{93}{35}, \frac{45}{28})$.

EXAMPLE 3: Find the centroid of the region bounded by the curves $y = x^2$ and $y = 2x + 3$.

SOLUTION: The points of intersection of the two curves are $(-1, 1)$ and $(3, 9)$. The region is shown in Fig. 7.8.3, together with the ith rectangular element.

Let $f(x) = x^2$ and $g(x) = 2x + 3$. The centroid of the ith rectangular element is at the point $(\gamma_i, \tfrac{1}{2}[f(\gamma_i) + g(\gamma_i)])$ where γ_i is the midpoint of the ith subinterval $[x_{i-1}, x_i]$. The measure of the area of the region is given by

$$A = \lim_{||\Delta|| \to 0} \sum_{i=1}^n [g(\gamma_i) - f(\gamma_i)] \, \Delta_i x$$

$$= \int_{-1}^3 [g(x) - f(x)] \, dx$$

$$= \int_{-1}^3 [2x + 3 - x^2] \, dx$$

$$= \tfrac{32}{3}$$

We now compute M_y and M_x.

$$M_y = \lim_{||\Delta|| \to 0} \sum_{i=1}^n \gamma_i [g(\gamma_i) - f(\gamma_i)] \, \Delta_i x$$

$$= \int_{-1}^3 x[g(x) - f(x)] \, dx$$

$$= \int_{-1}^3 x[2x + 3 - x^2] \, dx$$

$$= \tfrac{32}{3}$$

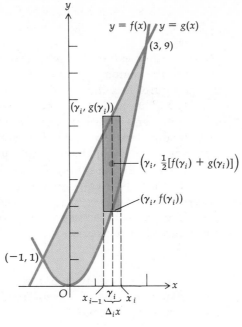

$y = f(x)$ $y = g(x)$

$(3, 9)$

$(\gamma_i, g(\gamma_i))$

$\left(\gamma_i, \frac{1}{2}[f(\gamma_i) + g(\gamma_i)]\right)$

$(\gamma_i, f(\gamma_i))$

$(-1, 1)$

O x_{i-1} γ_i x_i

$\Delta_i x$

Figure 7.8.3

$$M_x = \lim_{||\Delta|| \to 0} \sum_{i=1}^{n} \tfrac{1}{2}[g(\gamma_i) + f(\gamma_i)][g(\gamma_i) - f(\gamma_i)]\,\Delta_i x$$

$$= \tfrac{1}{2} \int_{-1}^{3} [g(x) + f(x)][g(x) - f(x)]\,dx$$

$$= \tfrac{1}{2} \int_{-1}^{3} [2x + 3 + x^2][2x + 3 - x^2]\,dx$$

$$= \tfrac{1}{2} \int_{-1}^{3} [4x^2 + 12x + 9 - x^4]\,dx$$

$$= \tfrac{544}{15}$$

Therefore,

$$\bar{x} = \frac{M_y}{A} = \frac{\frac{32}{3}}{\frac{32}{3}} = 1 \quad \text{and} \quad \bar{y} = \frac{M_x}{A} = \frac{\frac{544}{15}}{\frac{32}{3}} = \frac{17}{5}$$

Hence, the centroid is at the point $(1, \frac{17}{5})$.

If a plane region has an axis of symmetry, the centroid of the region lies on the axis of symmetry. This is now stated and proved as a theorem.

7.8.1 Theorem   If the plane region R has the line L as an axis of symmetry, the centroid of R lies on L.

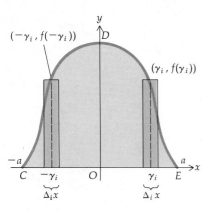

Figure 7.8.4

PROOF: Choose the coordinate axes so that L is on the y axis and the origin is in the region R. Figure 7.8.4 illustrates an example of this situation. In the figure, R is the region CDE, C is the point $(-a, 0)$, E is the point $(a, 0)$, and an equation of the curve CDE is $y = f(x)$.

Consider a partition of the interval $[0, a]$. Let γ_i be the midpoint of the ith subinterval $[x_{i-1}, x_i]$. The moment with respect to the y axis of the rectangular element having an altitude $f(\gamma_i)$ and a width $\Delta_i x$ is $\gamma_i[f(\gamma_i) \Delta_i x]$. Because of symmetry, for a similar partition of the interval $[-a, 0]$ there is a corresponding element having as its moment with respect to the y axis $-\gamma_i f(\gamma_i) \Delta_i x$. The sum of these two moments is zero; therefore, $M_y = 0$. Because $\bar{x} = M_y / A$, we conclude that $\bar{x} = 0$. Therefore, the centroid of the region R lies on the y axis, which is what was to be proved.   ◾

By applying the preceding theorem, we can simplify the problem of finding the centroid of a plane region that can be divided into regions having axes of symmetry.

EXAMPLE 4:   Find the centroid of the region bounded by the semicircle $y = \sqrt{4 - x^2}$ and the x axis.

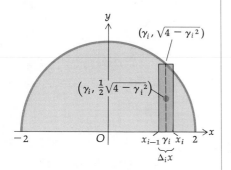

Figure 7.8.5

SOLUTION: The region is shown in Fig. 7.8.5.

Because the y axis is an axis of symmetry, we conclude that the centroid lies on the y axis; so $\bar{x} = 0$.

The moment of the region with respect to the x axis is given by

$$M_x = \lim_{\|\Delta\| \to 0} \sum_{i=1}^{n} \tfrac{1}{2}[\sqrt{4 - \gamma_i^2}]^2 \, \Delta_i x$$

$$= 2 \cdot \tfrac{1}{2} \int_0^2 (4 - x^2) \, dx$$

$$= 4x - \tfrac{1}{3}x^3 \Big]_0^2$$

$$= \tfrac{16}{3}$$

The area of the region is 2π square units; so

$$\bar{y} = \frac{\frac{16}{3}}{2\pi} = \frac{8}{3\pi}$$

There is a useful relation between the force caused by liquid pressure on a plane region and the location of the centroid of the region. As in Sec. 7.6, let $ABCD$ be the region bounded by the x axis, the lines $x = a$ and $x = b$, and the curve $y = f(x)$, where f is continuous and $f(x) \geq 0$ on the closed interval $[a, b]$. The region $ABCD$ can be considered as a vertical plate immersed in a liquid having weight w pounds per cubic unit of the

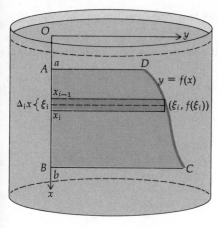

Figure 7.8.6

liquid (see Fig. 7.8.6). If F lb is the force owing to liquid pressure on the vertical plate,

$$F = \lim_{\|\Delta\| \to 0} \sum_{i=1}^{n} w\xi_i f(\xi_i)\,\Delta_i x$$

or, equivalently,

$$F = w \int_a^b xf(x)\,dx \tag{13}$$

If $\bar{x}$ is the abscissa of the centroid of the region $ABCD$, then $\bar{x} = M_y / A$. Because $M_y = \int_a^b xf(x)\,dx$, we have

$$\bar{x} = \frac{\displaystyle\int_a^b xf(x)\,dx}{A}$$

and so

$$\int_a^b xf(x)\,dx = \bar{x}A \tag{14}$$

Substituting from Eq. (14) into (13), we obtain

$$F = w\bar{x}A \tag{15}$$

Formula (15) states that the total force owing to liquid pressure against a vertical plane region is the same as it would be if the region were horizontal at a depth $\bar{x}$ units below the surface of a liquid.

For example, consider a trough full of water having as ends semicircular regions each with a radius of 2 ft. Using the result of Example 4, we find that the centroid of the region is at a depth of $8/3\pi$ ft. Therefore, using formula (15), we see that if F lb is the force on one end of the trough,

$$F = w \cdot \frac{8}{3\pi} \cdot 2\pi = \frac{16}{3}\,w$$

This agrees with the result found in Example 2 of Sec. 7.6.

For various simple plane regions, the centroid may be found in a table. When both the area of the region and the centroid of the region may be obtained directly, formula (15) is easy to apply and is used in such cases by engineers to find the force caused by liquid pressure.

Exercises 7.8

1. Find the center of mass of the three particles having masses of 1, 2, and 3 slugs and located at the points $(-1, 3)$, $(2, 1)$, and $(3, -1)$, respectively.

2. Find the center of mass of the four particles having masses of 2, 3, 3, and 4 slugs and located at the points $(-1, -2)$, $(1, 3)$, $(0, 5)$, and $(2, 1)$, respectively.

3. Prove that the centroid of three particles, having equal masses, in a plane lies at the point of intersection of the medians of the triangle having as vertices the points at which the particles are located.

In Exercises 4 through 11, find the centroid of the region with the indicated boundaries.

4. The parabola $x = 2y - y^2$ and the y axis.

5. The parabola $y = 4 - x^2$ and the x axis.

6. The parabola $y^2 = 4x$, the y axis, and the line $y = 4$.

7. The parabola $y = x^2$ and the line $y = 4$.

8. The lines $y = 2x + 1$, $x + y = 7$, and $x = 8$.

9. The curves $y = x^3$ and $y = 4x$ in the first quadrant.

10. The curves $y = x^2$ and $y = x^3$.

11. The curves $y = x^2 - 4$ and $y = 2x - x^2$.

12. Prove that the distance from the centroid of a triangle to any side of the triangle is equal to one-third the length of the altitude to that side.

13. If the centroid of the region bounded by the parabola $y^2 = 4px$ and the line $x = a$ is to be the focus of the parabola, find the value of a.

14. Solve Exercise 4 of Sec. 7.6 by using formula (15) of this section.

15. Solve Exercise 5 of Sec. 7.6 by using formula (15) of this section.

16. The face of a dam adjacent to the water is vertical and is in the shape of an isosceles trapezoid 90 ft wide at the top, 60 ft wide at the bottom, and 20 ft high. Use formula (15) of this section to find the total force due to liquid pressure on the face of the dam.

17. Find the moment about the lower base of the trapezoid of the force in Exercise 16.

18. Solve Exercise 6 of Sec. 7.6 by using formula (15) of this section.

19. Find the center of mass of the lamina bounded by the parabola $2y^2 = 18 - 3x$ and the y axis if the area density at any point (x, y) is $\sqrt{6 - x}$ slugs/ft^2.

20. Solve Exercise 19 if the area density at any point (x, y) is x slugs/ft^2.

21. Let R be the region bounded by the curves $y = f_1(x)$ and $y = f_2(x)$ (see Fig. 7.8.7). If A is the measure of the area of R and if $\bar{y}$ is the ordinate of the centroid of R, prove that the measure of the volume, V, of the solid of revolution obtained by revolving R about the x axis is given by

$$V = 2\pi \bar{y} A$$

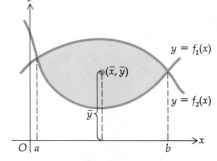

Figure 7.8.7

Stating this formula in words we have:

If a plane region is revolved about a line in its plane that does not cut the region, then the measure of the volume of the solid of revolution generated is equal to the product of the measure of the area of the region and the measure of the distance traveled by the centroid of the region.

The above statement is known as the *theorem of Pappus* for volumes of solids of revolution.

22. Use the theorem of Pappus to find the volume of the torus (doughnut-shaped) generated by revolving a circle with a radius of r units about a line in its plane at a distance of b units from its center, where $b > r$.

23. Use the theorem of Pappus to find the centroid of the region bounded by a semicircle and its diameter.

24. Use the theorem of Pappus to find the volume of a sphere with a radius of r units.

25. Let R be the region bounded by the semicircle $y = \sqrt{r^2 - x^2}$ and the x axis. Use the theorem of Pappus to find the moment of R with respect to the line $y = -4$.

26. If R is the region of Exercise 25, use the theorem of Pappus to find the volume of the solid of revolution generated by revolving R about the line $x - y = r$. (HINT: Use the result of Exercise 24 in Sec. 4.9.)

7.9 CENTER OF MASS OF A SOLID OF REVOLUTION

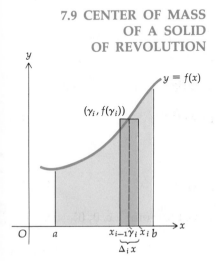

$y = f(x)$

$(\gamma_i, f(\gamma_i))$

a $x_{i-1}\gamma_i\,x_i$ b

$\Delta_i x$

Figure 7.9.1

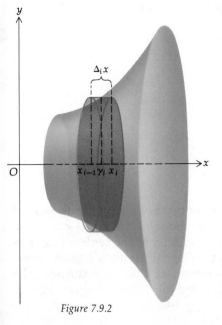

$\Delta_i x$

$x_{i-1}\gamma_i\,x_i$

Figure 7.9.2

To find the center of mass of a solid, in general we must make use of multiple integration. This procedure is taken up in Chapter 18 as an application of multiple integrals. However, if the shape of the solid is that of a solid of revolution, and its volume density is constant, we find the center of mass by a method similar to the one used to obtain the center of mass of a homogeneous lamina. Following is the procedure for finding the center of mass of a homogeneous solid of revolution, with the assumption that the center of mass is on the axis of revolution.

We first set up a three-dimensional coordinate system. The x and y axes are taken as in two dimensions, and the third axis, the z axis, is taken perpendicular to them at the origin. A point in three dimensions is then given by (x, y, z). The plane containing the x and y axes is called the xy plane, and the xz plane and the yz plane are defined similarly.

Suppose that the x axis is the axis of revolution. Then under the assumption that the center of mass lies on the axis of revolution, the y and z coordinates of the center of mass are each zero, and so it is only necessary to find the x coordinate, which we call $\bar{x}$. To find $\bar{x}$ we make use of the moment of the solid of revolution with respect to the yz plane.

Let f be a function that is continuous on the closed interval $[a, b]$, and assume that $f(x) \geq 0$ for all x in $[a, b]$. R is the region bounded by the curve $y = f(x)$, the x axis, and the lines $x = a$ and $x = b$; S is the homogeneous solid of revolution whose volume density is k slugs/ft³, where k is a constant, and which is generated by revolving the region R about the x axis. Take a partition Δ of the closed interval $[a, b]$, and denote the ith subinterval by $[x_{i-1}, x_i]$ (with $i = 1, 2, \ldots, n$). Let γ_i be the midpoint of $[x_{i-1}, x_i]$. Form n rectangles having altitudes of $f(\gamma_i)$ ft and bases whose width is $\Delta_i x$ ft. Refer to Fig. 7.9.1, showing the region R and the ith rectangle. If each of the n rectangles is revolved about the x axis, n circular disks are generated. The ith rectangle generates a circular disk having a radius of $f(\gamma_i)$ ft and a thickness of $\Delta_i x$ ft; its volume is $\pi[f(\gamma_i)]^2\,\Delta_i x$ ft³, and its mass is $k\pi[f(\gamma_i)]^2\,\Delta_i x$ slugs. Figure 7.9.2 shows the solid of revolution S and the ith circular disk.

The center of mass of the circular disk lies on the axis of revolution at the center of the disk: $(\gamma_i, 0, 0)$. The moment of mass of the disk with respect to the yz plane is then $\Delta_i M_{yz}$ slug-ft where

$$\Delta_i M_{yz} = \gamma_i(k\pi[f(\gamma_i)]^2\,\Delta_i x)$$

The sum of the measures of the moments of mass of the n circular disks with respect to the yz plane is given by the Riemann sum

$$\sum_{i=1}^{n} \gamma_i k\pi [f(\gamma_i)]^2 \, \Delta_i x \tag{1}$$

The number of slugs-feet in the moment of mass of S with respect to the yz plane, denoted by M_{yz}, is then defined to be the limit of the Riemann sum in (1) as $\|\Delta\|$ approaches zero; so we have

$$M_{yz} = \lim_{\|\Delta\| \to 0} \sum_{i=1}^{n} \gamma_i k\pi [f(\gamma_i)]^2 \, \Delta_i x = k\pi \int_a^b x[f(x)]^2 \, dx \tag{2}$$

The volume, V ft^3, of S was defined in Sec. 7.2 by

$$V = \lim_{\|\Delta\| \to 0} \sum_{i=1}^{n} \pi [f(\gamma_i)]^2 \, \Delta_i x = \pi \int_a^b [f(x)]^2 \, dx \tag{3}$$

The mass, M slugs, of solid S is defined by

$$M = \lim_{\|\Delta\| \to 0} \sum_{i=1}^{n} k\pi [f(\gamma_i)]^2 \, \Delta_i x = k\pi \int_a^b [f(x)]^2 \, dx \tag{4}$$

We define the center of mass of S as the point $(\bar{x}, 0, 0)$ such that

$$\bar{x} = \frac{M_{yz}}{M} \tag{5}$$

Substituting from Eqs. (2) and (4) into (5), we get

$$\bar{x} = \frac{k\pi \int_a^b x[f(x)]^2 \, dx}{k\pi \int_a^b [f(x)]^2 \, dx}$$

or, equivalently,

$$\bar{x} = \frac{\int_a^b x[f(x)]^2 \, dx}{\int_a^b [f(x)]^2 \, dx} \tag{6}$$

From Eq. (6), we see that the center of mass of a homogeneous solid of revolution depends only on the shape of the solid, not on its substance. Therefore, as for a homogeneous lamina, we refer to the center of mass as the centroid of the solid of revolution. When we have a homogeneous solid of revolution, instead of the moment of mass we consider the moment of the solid. The moment, M_{yz}, of the solid S with respect to the yz plane is given by

$$M_{yz} = \lim_{||\Delta|| \to 0} \sum_{i=1}^{n} \gamma_i \pi [f(\gamma_i)]^2 \, \Delta_i x = \pi \int_a^b x[f(x)]^2 \, dx \qquad (7)$$

Thus, if $(\bar{x}, 0, 0)$ is the centroid of S, from Eqs. (3), (6), and (7) we have

$$x = \frac{M_{yz}}{V}$$

EXAMPLE 1:   Find the centroid of the solid of revolution generated by revolving about the x axis the region bounded by the curve $y = x^2$, the x axis, and the line $x = 3$.

SOLUTION: The region and a rectangular element are shown in Fig. 7.9.3. The solid of revolution and an element of volume are shown in Fig. 7.9.4.

$$f(x) = x^2$$

$$M_{yz} = \lim_{||\Delta|| \to 0} \sum_{i=1}^{n} \gamma_i \pi [f(\gamma_i)]^2 \, \Delta_i x$$

$$= \pi \int_0^3 x[f(x)]^2 \, dx$$

$$= \pi \int_0^3 x^5 \, dx$$

$$= \tfrac{243}{2} \pi$$

$$V = \lim_{||\Delta|| \to 0} \sum_{i=1}^{n} \pi [f(\gamma_i)]^2 \, \Delta_i x$$

$$= \pi \int_0^3 [f(x)]^2 \, dx$$

$$= \pi \int_0^3 x^4 \, dx$$

$$= \tfrac{243}{5} \pi$$

Therefore,

$$\bar{x} = \frac{M_{yz}}{V} = \frac{\tfrac{243}{2}\pi}{\tfrac{243}{5}\pi} = \frac{5}{2}$$

Therefore, the centroid is at the point $(\tfrac{5}{2}, 0, 0)$.

Figure 7.9.3

Figure 7.9.4

Figure 7.9.5

Figure 7.9.6

The centroid of a solid of revolution also can be found by the cylindrical-shell method. Let R be the region bounded by the curve $y = f(x)$, where f is continuous and $f(x) \geq 0$ on $[a, b]$, the x axis, and the lines $x = a$ and $x = b$. Let S be the solid of revolution generated by revolving R about the y axis. The centroid of S is then at the point $(0, \bar{y}, 0)$. If the rectangular elements are taken parallel to the y axis, then the element of volume is a cylindrical shell. Let the ith rectangle have a width of $\Delta_i x = x_i - x_{i-1}$, and let γ_i be the midpoint of the interval $[x_{i-1}, x_i]$. The centroid of the cylindrical shell obtained by revolving this rectangle about the y axis is at the center of the cylindrical shell, which is the point $(0, \frac{1}{2}f(\gamma_i), 0)$. Figure 7.9.5 shows the region R and a rectangular element of area, and Fig. 7.9.6 shows the cylindrical shell. The moment, M_{xz}, of S with respect to the xz plane is given by

$$M_{xz} = \lim_{||\Delta|| \to 0} \sum_{i=1}^{n} \tfrac{1}{2}f(\gamma_i)2\pi\gamma_i f(\gamma_i)\ \Delta_i x = \pi \int_a^b x[f(x)]^2\ dx$$

If V cubic units is the volume of S,

$$V = \lim_{||\Delta|| \to 0} \sum_{i=1}^{n} 2\pi\gamma_i f(\gamma_i)\ \Delta_i x$$

$$= 2\pi \int_a^b xf(x)\ dx$$

Then,

$$\bar{y} = \frac{M_{xz}}{V}$$

EXAMPLE 2:   Use the cylindrical-shell method to find the centroid of the solid of revolution generated by revolving the region in Example 1 about the y axis.

SOLUTION: Figure 7.9.7 shows the region and a rectangular element of area. The solid of revolution and a cylindrical-shell element of volume are shown in Fig. 7.9.8.

$$M_{xz} = \lim_{||\Delta|| \to 0} \sum_{i=1}^{n} \tfrac{1}{2}f(\gamma_i)2\pi\gamma_i f(\gamma_i)\ \Delta_i x$$

$$= \pi \int_0^3 x[f(x)]^2\ dx$$

$$= \pi \int_0^3 x^5\ dx$$

$$= \tfrac{243}{2}\pi$$

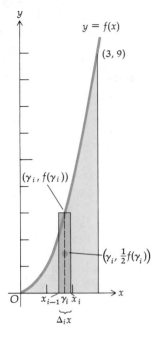

$$y = f(x)$$

$(3, 9)$

$(\gamma_i, f(\gamma_i))$

$(\gamma_i, \tfrac{1}{2}f(\gamma_i))$

$x_{i-1}\, \gamma_i\, \bar{x}_i$

$\Delta_i x$

Figure 7.9.7

$$V = \lim_{||\Delta|| \to 0} \sum_{i=1}^{n} 2\pi \gamma_i f(\gamma_i)\, \Delta_i x$$

$$= 2\pi \int_0^3 x f(x)\, dx$$

$$= 2\pi \int_0^3 x^3\, dx$$

$$= \tfrac{81}{2}\pi$$

Therefore,

$$\bar{y} = \frac{M_{xz}}{V} = \frac{\frac{243}{2}\pi}{\frac{81}{2}\pi} = 3$$

Hence, the centroid is at the point $(0, 3, 0)$.

Figure 7.9.8

EXAMPLE 3:   Solve Example 1 by the cylindrical-shell method.

SOLUTION: Figure 7.9.9 shows the region and a rectangular element of area, and Fig. 7.9.10 shows the cylindrical-shell element of volume obtained by revolving the rectangle about the x axis. The centroid of the cylindrical shell is at its center, which is the point $(\tfrac{1}{2}(3 + \sqrt{\gamma_i}), 0, 0)$. The centroid of the solid of revolution is at $(\bar{x}, 0, 0)$.

$$M_{yz} = \lim_{||\Delta|| \to 0} \sum_{i=1}^{n} \tfrac{1}{2}(3 + \sqrt{\gamma_i})\, 2\pi \gamma_i (3 - \sqrt{\gamma_i})\, \Delta_i y$$

$$= \pi \int_0^9 y(3 + \sqrt{y})(3 - \sqrt{y})\, dy$$

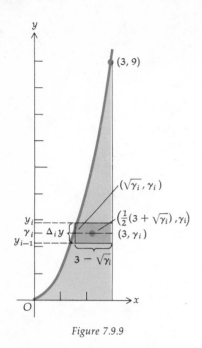

Figure 7.9.9

$$= \pi \int_0^9 (9y - y^2)\, dy$$

$$= \tfrac{243}{2}\pi$$

Finding V by the cylindrical-shell method, we have

$$V = \lim_{||\Delta|| \to 0} \sum_{i=1}^n 2\pi\gamma_i(3 - \sqrt{\gamma_i})\, \Delta_i y$$

$$= 2\pi \int_0^9 y(3 - y^{1/2})\, dy$$

$$= \tfrac{243}{5}\pi$$

Thus,

$$\bar{x} = \frac{M_{yz}}{V} = \frac{5}{2}$$

and the centroid is at $(\tfrac{5}{2}, 0, 0)$. The result agrees with that of Example 1.

Figure 7.9.10

Exercises 7.9

In Exercises 1 through 16 find the centroid of the solid of revolution generated by revolving the given region about the indicated line.

1. The region bounded by $y = 4x - x^2$ and the x axis, about the y axis. Take the rectangular elements perpendicular to the axis of revolution.

2. Same as Exercise 1, but take the rectangular elements parallel to the axis of revolution.

3. The region bounded by $x + 2y = 2$, the x axis, and the y axis, about the x axis. Take the rectangular elements perpendicular to the axis of revolution.

4. Same as Exercise 3, but take the rectangular elements parallel to the axis of revolution.

5. The region bounded by $y^2 = x^3$ and $x = 4$, about the x axis. Take the rectangular elements perpendicular to the axis of revolution.

6. Same as Exercise 5, but take the rectangular elements parallel to the axis of revolution.

7. The region bounded by $y = x^3$, $x = 2$, and the x axis, about the line $x = 2$. Take the rectangular elements perpendicular to the axis of revolution.

8. Same as Exercise 7, but take the rectangular elements parallel to the axis of revolution.

9. The region bounded by $x^4y = 1$, $y = 1$, and $y = 4$, about the y axis.

10. The region in Exercise 9, about the x axis.

11. The region bounded by the lines $y = x$, $y = 2x$, and $x + y = 6$, about the y axis.

12. The region bounded by the portion of the circle $x^2 + y^2 = 4$ in the first quadrant, the portion of the line $2x - y = 4$ in the fourth quadrant, and the y axis, about the y axis.

13. The region bounded by $y = x^2$ and $y = x + 2$, about the line $y = 4$.

14. The region bounded by $y^2 = 4x$ and $y^2 = 16 - 4x$, about the x axis.

15. The region bounded by $y = \sqrt{4px}$, the x axis, and the line $x = p$, about the line $x = p$.

16. The region of Exercise 15, about the line $y = 2p$.

17. Find the centroid of the right-circular cone of altitude h units and radius r units.

18. Find the center of mass of the solid of revolution of Exercise 3 if the measure of the volume density of the solid at any point is equal to a constant k times the measure of the distance of the point from the yz plane.

19. Find the center of mass of the solid of revolution of Exercise 5 if the measure of the volume density of the solid at any point is equal to a constant k times the measure of the distance of the point from the yz plane.

20. Suppose that a cylindrical hole with a radius of r units is bored through a solid wooden hemisphere of radius $2r$ units, so that the axis of the cylinder is the same as the axis of the hemisphere. Find the centroid of the solid remaining.

7.10 LENGTH OF ARC OF A PLANE CURVE

Let the function f be continuous on the closed interval $[a, b]$. Consider the graph of the equation $y = f(x)$ of which a sketch is shown in Fig. 7.10.1.

Figure 7.10.1

The portion of the curve from the point $A(a, f(a))$ to the point $B(b, f(b))$ is called an arc. We wish to assign a number to what we intuitively think of as the length of such an arc. If the arc is a line segment from the point (x_1, y_1) to the point (x_2, y_2), we know from the formula for the distance between two points that its length is given by $\sqrt{(x_1 - x_2)^2 + (y_1 - y_2)^2}$. We use this formula for defining the length of an arc in general. Recall from geometry that the circumference of a circle is defined as the limit of the perimeters of regular polygons inscribed in the circle. For other curves we proceed in a similar way.

Let Δ be a partition of the closed interval $[a, b]$ formed by dividing the interval into n subintervals by choosing any $(n-1)$ intermediate numbers between a and b. Let $x_0 = a$, and $x_n = b$, and let $x_1, x_2, x_3 \ldots,$ x_{n-1} be the intermediate numbers so that $x_0 < x_1 < x_2 < \cdots < x_{n-1} < x_n$. Then the ith subinterval is $[x_{i-1}, x_i]$; and its length, denoted by $\Delta_i x$, is $x_i - x_{i-1}$, where $i = 1, 2, 3, \ldots, n$. Then if $\|\Delta\|$ is the norm of the partition Δ, each $\Delta_i x \leq \|\Delta\|$.

Figure 7.10.2

Associated with each point $(x_i, 0)$ on the x axis is a point $P_i(x_i, f(x_i))$ on the curve. Draw a line segment from each point P_{i-1} to the next point P_i as shown in Fig. 7.10.2. The length of the line segment from P_{i-1} to P_i is denoted by $|\overline{P_{i-1}P_i}|$ and is given by the distance formula

$$|\overline{P_{i-1}P_i}| = \sqrt{(x_i - x_{i-1})^2 + (y_i - y_{i-1})^2} \tag{1}$$

The sum of the lengths of the line segments is

$$|\overline{P_0P_1}| + |\overline{P_1P_2}| + |\overline{P_2P_3}| + \cdots + |\overline{P_{i-1}P_i}| + \cdots + |\overline{P_{n-1}P_n}|$$

which can be written in sigma notation as

$$\sum_{i=1}^{n} |\overline{P_{i=1}P_i}| \tag{2}$$

It seems plausible that if n is sufficiently large, the sum in (2) will be "close to" what we would intuitively think of as the length of the arc AB. So we define the length of the arc as the limit of the sum in (2) as the norm of Δ approaches zero, in which case n increases without bound. We have, then, the following definition.

7.10.1 Definition   If the function f is continuous on the closed interval $[a, b]$ and if there exists a number L having the following property: for any $\epsilon > 0$ there is a $\delta > 0$ such that

$$\left| \sum_{i=1}^{n} |\overline{P_{i=1}P_i}| - L \right| < \epsilon$$

for every partition Δ of the interval $[a, b]$ for which $\|\Delta\| < \delta$, then we write

$$L = \lim_{||\Delta|| \to 0} \sum_{i=1}^{n} |\overline{P_{i-1}P_i}| \tag{3}$$

and L is called the *length of the arc* of the curve $y = f(x)$ from the point $A(a, f(a))$ to the point $B(b, f(b))$.

If the limit in Eq. (3) exists, the arc is said to be *rectifiable*.

We now derive a formula for finding the length L of an arc that is rectifiable. The derivation requires that the derivative of f be continuous on $[a, b]$. See Fig. 7.10.3.

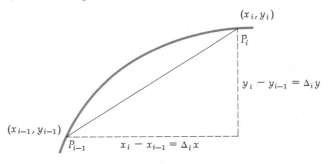

Figure 7.10.3

If P_{i-1} has coordinates (x_{i-1}, y_{i-1}) and P_i has coordinates (x_i, y_i), then the length of the chord $P_{i-1}P_i$ is given by formula (1).

Letting $x_i - x_{i-1} = \Delta_i x$ and $y_i - y_{i-1} = \Delta_i y$, we have

$$|\overline{P_{i-1}P_i}| = \sqrt{(\Delta_i x)^2 + (\Delta_i y)^2} \tag{4}$$

or, equivalently, because $\Delta_i x \neq 0$,

$$|\overline{P_{i-1}P_i}| = \sqrt{1 + \left(\frac{\Delta_i y}{\Delta_i x}\right)^2} \, (\Delta_i x) \tag{5}$$

Because we required that f' be continuous on $[a, b]$, the hypothesis of the mean-value theorem (4.5.2) is satisfied by f, and so there is a number z_i in the open interval (x_{i-1}, x_i) such that

$$f(x_i) - f(x_{i-1}) = f'(z_i)(x_i - x_{i-1}) \tag{6}$$

Because $\Delta_i y = f(x_i) - f(x_{i-1})$ and $\Delta_i x = x_i - x_{i-1}$, from Eq. (6) we have

$$\frac{\Delta_i y}{\Delta_i x} = f'(z_i) \tag{7}$$

Substituting from Eq. (7) into (5), we get

$$|\overline{P_{i-1}P_i}| = \sqrt{1 + [f'(z_i)]^2} \, \Delta_i x \tag{8}$$

where $x_{i-1} < z_i < x_i$.

For each i from 1 to n there is an equation of the form (8).

$$\sum_{i=1}^{n} |\overline{P_{i-1}P_i}| = \sum_{i=1}^{n} \sqrt{1 + [f'(z_i)]^2} \, \Delta_i x \tag{9}$$

Taking the limit on both sides of Eq. (9) as $\|\Delta\|$ approaches zero, we obtain

$$\lim_{\|\Delta\|\to 0} \sum_{i=1}^{n} |\overline{P_{i-1}P_i}| = \lim_{\|\Delta\|\to 0} \sum_{i=1}^{n} \sqrt{1 + [f'(z_i)]^2} \, \Delta_i x \tag{10}$$

if this limit exists.

To show that the limit on the right side of Eq. (10) exists, let g be the function defined by

$$g(x) = \sqrt{1 + [f'(x)]^2}$$

Because f' is continuous on $[a, b]$, g is continuous on $[a, b]$. Therefore, because $x_{i-1} < z_i < x_i$, for $i = 1, 2, \ldots, n$,

$$\lim_{\|\Delta\|\to 0} \sum_{i=1}^{n} \sqrt{1 + [f'(z_i)]^2} \, \Delta_i x = \lim_{\|\Delta\|\to 0} \sum_{i=1}^{n} g(z_i) \, \Delta_i x$$

or, equivalently,

$$\lim_{\|\Delta\|\to 0} \sum_{i=1}^{n} \sqrt{1 + [f'(z_i)]^2} \, \Delta_i x = \int_{a}^{b} g(x) \, dx \tag{11}$$

Because $g(x) = \sqrt{1 + [f'(x)]^2}$, from Eq. (11) we have

$$\lim_{\|\Delta\|\to 0} \sum_{i=1}^{n} \sqrt{1 + [f'(z_i)]^2} \, \Delta_i x = \int_{a}^{b} \sqrt{1 + [f'(x)]^2} \, dx \tag{12}$$

Substituting from Eq. (12) into (10), we get

$$\lim_{\|\Delta\|\to 0} \sum_{i=1}^{n} |\overline{P_{i-1}P_i}| = \int_{a}^{b} \sqrt{1 + [f'(x)]^2} \, dx \tag{13}$$

Then from Eqs. (3) and (13) we obtain

$$L = \int_{a}^{b} \sqrt{1 + [f'(x)]^2} \, dx \tag{14}$$

In this way, we have proved the following theorem.

7.10.2 Theorem If the function f and its derivative f' are continuous on the closed interval $[a, b]$, then the length of arc of the curve $y = f(x)$ from the point $(a, f(a))$ to the point $(b, f(b))$ is given by

$$L = \int_{a}^{b} \sqrt{1 + [f'(x)]^2} \, dx$$

We also have the following theorem, which gives the length of the arc of a curve when x is expressed as a function of y.

7.10.3 Theorem   If the function F and its derivative F' are continuous on the closed interval $[c, d]$, then the length of arc of the curve $x = F(y)$ from the point $(F(c), c)$ to the point $(F(d), d)$ is given by

$$L = \int_c^d \sqrt{1 + [F'(y)]^2} \, dy$$

The proof of Theorem 7.10.3 is identical with the proof of Theorem 7.10.2; here we interchange x and y as well as the function f and the function F.

The definite integral obtained when applying Theorem 7.10.2 or Theorem 7.10.3 is often difficult to evaluate. Because our techniques of integration have so far been limited to integration of powers, we are further restricted in finding equations of curves for which we can evaluate the resulting definite integrals to find the length of an arc.

EXAMPLE 1: Find the length of the arc of the curve $y = x^{2/3}$ from the point $(1, 1)$ to $(8, 4)$ by using Theorem 7.10.2.

Figure 7.10.4

SOLUTION: See Fig. 7.10.4. Because $f(x) = x^{2/3}$, $f'(x) = \frac{2}{3}x^{-1/3}$. From Theorem 7.10.2 we have

$$L = \int_1^8 \sqrt{1 + \frac{4}{9x^{2/3}}} \, dx$$

$$= \frac{1}{3} \int_1^8 \frac{\sqrt{9x^{2/3} + 4}}{x^{1/3}} \, dx$$

To evaluate this definite integral, let $u = 9x^{2/3} + 4$; then $du = 6x^{-1/3} \, dx$. When $x = 1$, $u = 13$; when $x = 8$, $u = 40$. Therefore,

$$L = \frac{1}{18} \int_{13}^{40} u^{1/2} \, du$$

$$= \frac{1}{18} \left[\frac{2}{3} u^{3/2} \right]_{13}^{40}$$

$$= \frac{1}{27} (40^{3/2} - 13^{3/2})$$

$$\approx 7.6$$

EXAMPLE 2: Find the length of the arc in Example 1 by using Theorem 7.10.3.

SOLUTION: Because $y = x^{2/3}$, we solve for x and obtain $x = y^{3/2}$. Letting $F(y) = y^{3/2}$, we have

$$F'(y) = \frac{3}{2} y^{1/2}$$

Then, from Theorem 7.10.3, we have

$$L = \int_1^4 \sqrt{1 + \frac{9}{4}y} \, dy$$

$$= \tfrac{1}{2} \int_1^4 \sqrt{4 + 9y} \; dy$$

$$= \tfrac{1}{18} \left[\tfrac{2}{3}(4 + 9y)^{3/2} \right]_1^4$$

$$= \tfrac{1}{27}(40^{3/2} - 13^{3/2})$$

$$\approx 7.6$$

If f' is continuous on $[a, b]$, then the definite integral $\int_a^x \sqrt{1 + [f'(t)]^2} \; dt$ is a function of x; and it gives the length of the arc of the curve $y = f(x)$ from the point $(a, f(a))$ to the point $(x, f(x))$, where x is any number in the closed interval $[a, b]$. Let s denote the length of this arc; thus, s is a function of x, and we have

$$s(x) = \int_a^x \sqrt{1 + [f'(t)]^2} \; dt$$

From Theorem 6.6.1, we have

$$s'(x) = \sqrt{1 + [f'(x)]^2}$$

or because $s'(x) = ds/dx$ and $f'(x) = dy/dx$,

$$\frac{ds}{dx} = \sqrt{1 + \left(\frac{dy}{dx} \right)^2}$$

Multiplying by dx, we obtain

$$ds = \sqrt{1 + \left(\frac{dy}{dx} \right)^2} \; dx \tag{15}$$

Similarly, if we are talking about the length of arc of the curve $x = g(y)$ from $(g(c), c)$ to $(g(y), y)$, we have

$$ds = \sqrt{\left(\frac{dx}{dy} \right)^2 + 1} \; dy \tag{16}$$

Squaring on both sides of Eq. (15) gives

$$(ds)^2 = (dx)^2 + (dy)^2 \tag{17}$$

From Eq. (17) we get the geometric interpretation of ds, which is shown in Fig. 7.10.5.

In Fig. 7.10.5, line T is tangent to the curve $y = f(x)$ at the point P. $|\overline{PM}| = \Delta x = dx$; $|\overline{MQ}| = \Delta y$; $|\overline{MR}| = dy$; $|\overline{PR}| = ds$; the length of arc $PQ = \Delta s$.

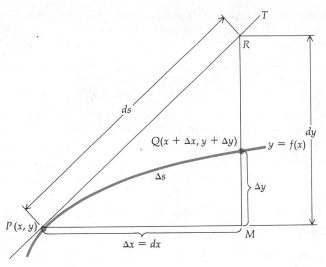

Figure 7.10.5

Exercises 7.10

1. Find the length of the arc of the curve $9y^2 = 4x^3$ from the origin to the point $(3, 2\sqrt{3})$.

2. Find the length of the arc of the curve $x^2 = (2y + 3)^3$ from $(1, -1)$ to $(7\sqrt{7}, 2)$.

3. Find the length of the arc of the curve $8y = x^4 + 2x^{-2}$ from the point where $x = 1$ to the point where $x = 2$.

4. Use Theorem 7.10.2 to find the length of the arc of the curve $y^3 = 8x^2$ from the point $(1, 2)$ to the point $(27, 18)$.

5. Solve Exercise 4 by using Theorem 7.10.3.

6. Find the entire length of the curve $x^{2/3} + y^{2/3} = 1$.

7. Find the length of the arc of the curve $y = \frac{1}{3}(x^2 + 2)^{3/2}$ from the point where $x = 0$ to the point where $x = 3$.

8. Find the length of the curve $6xy = y^4 + 3$ from the point where $y = 1$ to the point where $y = 2$.

9. Find the length of the curve $(x/a)^{2/3} + (y/b)^{2/3} = 1$ in the first quadrant from $x = \frac{1}{8}a$ to $x = a$.

10. Find the length of the curve $9y^2 = 4(1 + x^2)^3$ in the first quadrant from $x = 0$ to $x = 2\sqrt{2}$.

11. Find the length of the loop of the curve $9y^2 = x(x - 3)^2$.

12. Find the length of the loop of the curve $9y^2 = x^2(2x + 3)$.

Review Exercises (Chapter 7)

1. Find the area of the region bounded by the loop of the curve $y^2 = x^2(4 - x)$.

2. The region in the first quadrant bounded by the curves $x = y^2$ and $x = y^4$ is revolved about the y axis. Find the volume of the solid generated.

3. The base of a solid is a region bounded by a parabola and a line perpendicular to the axis of the parabola. If the segment of the line between its points of intersection with the parabola has a length of 16 in. and is 8 in. from the vertex of the parabola, find the volume of the solid if every plane section perpendicular to the axis of the base is a square.

4. A container has the same shape and dimensions as a solid of revolution formed by revolving about the y axis the region in the first quadrant bounded by the parabola $x^2 = 4py$, the y axis, and the line $y = p$. If the container is full of water, find the work done in pumping all the water up to a point $3p$ ft above the top of the container.

5. The surface of a tank is the same as that of a paraboloid of revolution which is obtained by revolving a parabola about its axis. The vertex of the parabola is at the bottom of the tank, the tank is 36 ft high, and the diameter at the top is 12 ft. If the tank is filled with water to a depth of 20 ft, find the work done in pumping all of the water out over the top.

6. A plate in the shape of a region bounded by a parabola and its latus rectum of length 6 ft is placed in a water tank with its vertex downward and the latus rectum in the surface of the water. Find the force due to liquid pressure on one side of the plate.

7. Find the area of the region bounded by the curves $y = |x - 1|$, $y = x^2 - 2x$, the y axis, and the line $x = 2$.

8. Find the area of the region bounded by the curves $y = |x| + |x - 1|$ and $y = x + 1$.

9. Find the volume of the solid generated by revolving the region bounded by the curve $y = |x - 2|$, the x axis, and the lines $x = 1$ and $x = 4$ about the x axis.

10. Find the length of arc of the curve $ay^2 = x^3$ from the origin to $(4a, 8a)$.

11. Find the length of the curve $6y^2 = x(x - 2)^2$ from $(2, 0)$ to $(8, 4\sqrt{3})$.

12. Find the center of mass of the four particles having equal masses located at the points $(3, 0)$, $(2, 2)$, $(2, 4)$, and $(-1, 2)$.

13. Three particles having masses 5, 2, and 8 slugs are located, respectively, at the points $(-1, 3)$, $(2, -1)$, and $(5, 2)$. Find the center of mass.

14. The length of a rod is 8 in. and the linear density of the rod at a point x in. from the left end is $2\sqrt{x + 1}$ slugs/in. Find the total mass of the rod and the center of mass.

15. Find the centroid of the region bounded by the parabola $y^2 = x$ and the line $y = x - 2$.

16. Find the centroid of the region bounded by the loop of the curve $y^2 = x^2 - x^3$.

17. The length of a rod is 4 ft and the linear density of the rod at a point x ft from the left end is $(3x + 1)$ slugs/ft. Find the total mass of the rod and the center of mass.

18. Give an example to show that the centroid of a plane region is not necessarily a point within the region.

19. Find the volume of the solid generated by revolving about the line $y = -1$ the region bounded by the line $2y = x + 3$ and outside the curves $y^2 + x = 0$ and $y^2 - 4x = 0$.

20. Use integration to find the volume of a segment of a sphere if the sphere has a radius of r units and the altitude of the segment is h units.

21. A church steeple is 30 ft high and every horizontal plane section is a square having sides of length one-tenth of the distance of the plane section from the top of the steeple. Find the volume of the steeple.

22. A trough full of water is 6 ft long, and its cross section is in the shape of a semicircle with a diameter of 2 ft at the top. How much work is required to pump the water out over the top?

23. A water tank is in the shape of a hemisphere surmounted by a right-circular cylinder. The radius of both the hemisphere and the cylinder is 4 ft and the altitude of the cylinder is 8 ft. If the tank is full of water find the work necessary to empty the tank by pumping it through an outlet at the top of the tank.

24. A force of 500 lb is required to compress a spring whose natural length is 10 in. to a length of 9 in. Find the work done to compress the spring to a length of 8 in.

25. A cable is 20 ft long and weighs 2 lb/ft, and is hanging vertically from the top of a pole. Find the work done in raising the entire cable to the top of the pole.

26. The work necessary to stretch a spring from 9 in. to 10 in. is $\frac{3}{2}$ times the work necessary to stretch it from 8 in. to 9 in. What is the natural length of the spring?

27. Find the length of the curve $9x^{2/3} + 4y^{2/3} = 36$ in the second quadrant from $x = -1$ to $x = -\frac{1}{8}$.

28. A semicircular plate with a radius of 3 ft is submerged vertically in a tank of water, with its diameter lying in the surface. Use formula (15) of Sec. 7.8 to find the force due to liquid pressure on one side of the plate.

29. A cylindrical tank is half full of gasoline weighing 42 lb/ft^3. If the axis is horizontal and the diameter is 6 ft, find the force on an end due to liquid pressure.

30. Find the centroid of the region bounded above by the parabola $4x^2 = 36 - 9y$ and below by the x axis.

31. Use the theorem of Pappus to find the volume of a right-circular cone with a base radius of r units and an altitude of h units.

32. The region bounded by the parabola $x^2 = 4y$, the x axis, and the line $x = 4$ is revolved about the y axis. Find the centroid of the solid of revolution formed.

33. Find the center of mass of the region of Exercise 30 if the measure of the area density at any point (x, y) is $\sqrt{4 - y}$.

34. Find the center of mass of the solid of revolution of Exercise 32 if the measure of the volume density of the solid at any point is equal to the measure of the distance of the point from the xz plane.

8

Logarithmic and Exponential Functions

8.1 THE NATURAL LOGARITHMIC FUNCTION

The definition of the logarithmic function that the reader has encountered in algebra is based on exponents. The laws of logarithms are then proved from corresponding laws of exponents. One such law of exponents is

$$a^x \cdot a^y = a^{x+y} \tag{1}$$

If the exponents, x and y, are positive integers and a is any real number, (1) follows from the definition of a positive integer exponent and mathematical induction. If the exponents are allowed to be any integers, either positive, negative, or zero, and $a \neq 0$, then (1) will hold if a zero exponent and a negative integer exponent are defined by

$$a^0 = 1$$

and

$$a^{-n} = \frac{1}{a^n} \qquad n > 0$$

If the exponents are rational numbers and $a \geq 0$, then Eq. (1) holds when $a^{m/n}$ is defined by

$$a^{m/n} = (\sqrt[n]{a})^m$$

It is not quite so simple to define a^x when x is an irrational number. For example, what is meant by $4^{\sqrt{3}}$? The definition of the logarithmic function, as given in elementary algebra, is based on the assumption that a^x exists if a is any positive number and x is any real number.

This definition states that the equation

$$a^x = N$$

where a is any positive number except 1 and N is any positive number, can be solved for x, and x is uniquely determined by

$$x = \log_a N$$

In elementary algebra, logarithms are used mainly as an aid to computation, and for such purposes the number a (called the *base*) is taken as 10. The following laws of logarithms are proved from the laws of exponents:

MAIN THINGS

Law 1 $\log_a MN = \log_a M + \log_a N$

Law 2 $\log_a \dfrac{M}{N} = \log_a M - \log_a N$

Law 3 $\log_a 1 = 0$

Law 4 $\log_a M^n = n \log_a M$

Law 5 $\log_a a = 1$

In this chapter we define the logarithmic function by using calculus and prove the laws of logarithms by means of this definition. Then the exponential function is defined in terms of the logarithmic function. This definition enables us to define a^x when x is any real number and $a \neq 0$. The laws of exponents will then be proved if the exponent is any real number.

Let us recall the formula

$$\int t^n \, dt = \frac{t^{n+1}}{n+1} + C \qquad n \neq -1$$

This formula does not hold when $n = -1$. Consider the function defined by the equation $y = t^{-1}$, where t is positive. A sketch of the graph of this equation is shown in Fig. 8.1.1.

Let R be the region bounded above by the curve $y = 1/t$, below by the t axis, on the left by the line $t = 1$, and on the right by the line $t = x$, where x is greater than 1. This region R is shown in Fig. 8.1.1. The measure of the area of R is a function of x; call it $A(x)$ and define it as a definite integral by

$$A(x) = \int_1^x \frac{1}{t} \, dt \tag{2}$$

Now consider the integral in (2) if $0 < x < 1$. From Definition 6.3.4, we have

$$\int_1^x \frac{1}{t} \, dt = - \int_x^1 \frac{1}{t} \, dt$$

Then the integral $\int_x^1 (1/t) \, dt$ represents the measure of the area of the

Figure 8.1.1

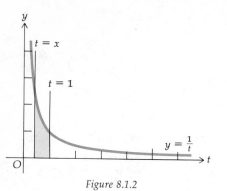

Figure 8.1.2

region bounded above by the curve $y = 1/t$, below by the t axis, on the left by the line $t = x$, and on the right by the line $t = 1$. So the integral $\int_1^x (1/t)\, dt$ is then the negative of the measure of the area of the region shown in Fig. 8.1.2.

If $x = 1$, the integral $\int_1^x (1/t)\, dt$ becomes $\int_1^1 (1/t)\, dt$, which equals 0 by Definition 6.3.5. In this case the left and right boundaries of the region are the same and the measure of the area is 0.

Thus, we see that the integral $\int_1^x (1/t)\, dt$ for $x > 0$ can be interpreted in terms of the measure of the area of a region. Its value depends on x and is therefore a function of x. This integral is used to define the *natural logarithmic function*.

8.1.1 Definition   The *natural logarithmic function* is the function defined by

$$\ln x = \int_1^x \frac{1}{t}\, dt \qquad x > 0$$

The domain of the natural logarithmic function is the set of all positive numbers. We read $\ln x$ as "the natural logarithm of x."

The natural logarithmic function is differentiable because by applying Theorem 6.6.1 we have

$$D_x(\ln x) = D_x \left(\int_1^x \frac{1}{t}\, dt \right) = \frac{1}{x}$$

Therefore,

$$D_x(\ln x) = \frac{1}{x} \tag{3}$$

From formula (3) and the chain rule, if u is a differentiable function of x, and $u(x) > 0$, then

$$D_x(\ln u) = \frac{1}{u} \cdot D_x u \tag{4}$$

EXAMPLE 1:   Given

$$y = \ln(3x^2 - 6x + 8)$$

find $D_x y$.

SOLUTION: Applying formula (4), we get

$$D_x y = \frac{1}{3x^2 - 6x + 8} \cdot (6x - 6) = \frac{6x - 6}{3x^2 - 6x + 8}$$

EXAMPLE 2:   Given

$$y = \ln[(4x^2 + 3)(2x - 1)]$$

find $D_x y$.

SOLUTION: Applying formula (4), we get

$$D_x y = \frac{1}{(4x^2 + 3)(2x - 1)} \cdot [8x(2x - 1) + 2(4x^2 + 3)]$$

$$= \frac{24x^2 - 8x + 6}{(4x^2 + 3)(2x - 1)} \tag{5}$$

EXAMPLE 3:   Given

$$y = \ln \left(\frac{x}{x+1} \right)$$

find $D_x y$.

SOLUTION: From formula (4), we have

$$D_x y = \frac{1}{\dfrac{x}{x+1}} \cdot \frac{(x+1) - x}{(x+1)^2}$$

$$= \frac{x+1}{x} \cdot \frac{1}{(x+1)^2}$$

$$= \frac{1}{x(x+1)}$$

It should be emphasized that when using formula (4), $u(x)$ must be positive; that is, a number in the domain of the derivative must be in the domain of the given natural logarithmic function. In particular, in Example 1, the domain of the given natural logarithmic function is the set of all real numbers because $3x^2 - 6x + 8 > 0$ for all x. This can be seen from the fact that the parabola having equation $y = 3x^2 - 6x + 8$ has its vertex at $(1, 5)$ and opens upward. Hence, $(6x - 6)/(3x^2 - 6x + 8)$ is the derivative for all values of x.

In Example 2, because $(4x^2 + 3)(2x - 1) > 0$ only when $x > \frac{1}{2}$, the domain of the given natural logarithmic function is the interval $(\frac{1}{2}, +\infty)$. Therefore, it is understood that fraction (5) is the derivative only if $x > \frac{1}{2}$.

Because $x/(x+1) > 0$ when either $x < -1$ or $x > 0$, the domain of the natural logarithmic function in Example 3 consists of the two intervals $(-\infty, -1)$ and $(0, +\infty)$, and so $1/x(x+1)$ is the derivative if either $x < -1$ or $x > 0$.

We show that the natural logarithmic function obeys the laws of logarithms as stated earlier. However, first we need a preliminary theorem, which we state and prove.

8.1.2 Theorem   If a and b are any positive numbers, then

$$\int_a^{ab} \frac{1}{t}\, dt = \int_1^b \frac{1}{t}\, dt$$

PROOF: In the integral $\int_a^{ab} (1/t)\, dt$, make the substitution $t = au$; then $dt = a\, du$. When $t = a$, $u = 1$, and when $t = ab$, $u = b$. Therefore, we have

$$\int_a^{ab} \frac{1}{t}\, dt = \int_1^b \frac{1}{au}\, (a\, du)$$

$$= \int_1^b \frac{1}{u} \, du$$

$$= \int_1^b \frac{1}{t} \, dt$$

In terms of geometry, Theorem 8.1.2 states that the measure of the area of the region shown in Fig. 8.1.3 is the same as the measure of the area of the region shown in Fig. 8.1.4.

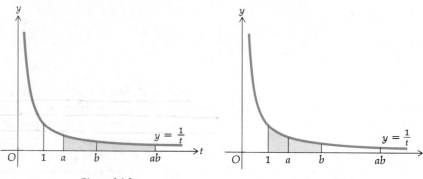

Figure 8.1.3   Figure 8.1.4

If we take $x = 1$ in Definition 8.1.1, we have

$$\ln 1 = \int_1^1 \frac{1}{t} \, dt$$

The right side of the above is zero by Definition 6.3.5. So we have

$$\boxed{\ln 1 = 0}$$ (6)

Equation (6) corresponds to Law 3 of logarithms, given earlier.

The following three theorems give some properties of the natural logarithmic function.

8.1.3 Theorem   If a and b are any positive numbers, then

$$\boxed{\ln (ab) = \ln a + \ln b}$$

PROOF: From Definition 8.1.1,

$$\ln(ab) = \int_1^{ab} \frac{1}{t} \, dt$$

which, from Theorem 6.4.6, gives

$$\ln(ab) = \int_1^a \frac{1}{t} \, dt + \int_a^{ab} \frac{1}{t} \, dt$$

Applying Theorem 8.1.2 to the second integral on the right side of the above, we obtain

$$\ln(ab) = \int_1^a \frac{1}{t}\,dt + \int_1^b \frac{1}{t}\,dt$$

and so from Definition 8.1.1 we have

$$\ln(ab) = \ln a + \ln b$$ ∎

8.1.4 Theorem   If a and b are any positive numbers, then

$$\ln \frac{a}{b} = \ln a - \ln b$$

PROOF: Because $a = (a/b) \cdot b$, we have

$$\ln a = \ln \left(\frac{a}{b} \cdot b \right)$$

Applying Theorem 8.1.3 to the right side of the above equation, we get

$$\ln a = \ln \frac{a}{b} + \ln b$$

Subtracting $\ln b$ on both sides of the above equation, we obtain

$$\ln \frac{a}{b} = \ln a - \ln b$$ ∎

8.1.5 Theorem   If a is any positive number and r is any rational number, then

$$\ln a^r = r \ln a$$

PROOF: From formula (4), if r is any rational number and $x > 0$, we have

$$D_x(\ln x^r) = \frac{1}{x^r} \cdot rx^{r-1} = \frac{r}{x}$$

and

$$D_x(r \ln x) = \frac{r}{x}$$

Therefore,

$$D_x(\ln x^r) = D_x(r \ln x)$$

From the above equation the derivatives of $\ln x^r$ and $r \ln x$ are equal, and so it follows from Theorem 5.3.3 that there is a constant K such that

$$\ln x^r = r \ln x + K \qquad \text{for all } x > 0 \tag{7}$$

To determine K, substitute 1 for x in Eq. (7) and we have

$$\ln 1^r = r \ln 1 + K$$

But, by Eq. (6), $\ln 1 = 0$; hence, $K = 0$. Replacing K by 0 in Eq. (7), we get

$$\ln x^r = r \ln x \qquad \text{for all } x > 0$$

from which it follows that if $x = a$, where a is any positive number, then

$$\ln a^r = r \ln a \qquad \blacksquare$$

Note that Theorems 8.1.3, 8.1.4, and 8.1.5 are the same properties as the laws of logarithms 1, 2, and 4, respectively, given earlier.

In Example 2, if Theorem 8.1.3 is applied before finding the derivative, we have

$$y = \ln(4x^2 + 3) + \ln(2x - 1) \tag{8}$$

Now the domain of the function defined by the above equation is the interval $(\frac{1}{2}, +\infty)$, which is the same as the domain of the given function. From Eq. (8) we get

$$D_x y = \frac{8x}{4x^2 + 3} + \frac{2}{2x - 1}$$

and combining the fractions gives

$$D_x y = \frac{8x(2x - 1) + 2(4x^2 + 3)}{(4x^2 + 3)(2x - 1)}$$

which is the same as the first line of the solution of Example 2.

If we apply Theorem 8.1.4 before finding the derivative in Example 3, we have

$$\ln y = \ln x - \ln(x + 1) \tag{9}$$

$\ln x$ is defined only when $x > 0$, and $\ln(x + 1)$ is defined only when $x > -1$. Therefore, the domain of the function defined by Eq. (9) is the interval $(0, +\infty)$. But the domain of the function given in Example 3 consists of the two intervals $(-\infty, -1)$ and $(0, +\infty)$. Finding $D_x y$ from Eq. (9), we have

$$D_x y = \frac{1}{x} - \frac{1}{x + 1} = \frac{1}{x(x + 1)}$$

but remember here that x must be greater than 0, whereas in the solution of Example 3 values of x less than -1 are also included. This illustrates the care that must be taken when applying Theorems 8.1.3, 8.1.4, and 8.1.5 to natural logarithmic functions.

EXAMPLE 4: Given

$$y = \ln(2x - 1)^3$$

find $D_x y$.

SOLUTION: From Theorem 8.1.5 we have

$$y = \ln(2x - 1)^3 = 3 \ln(2x - 1)$$

Note that $\ln(2x - 1)^3$ and $3 \ln(2x - 1)$ both have the same domain, $x > \frac{1}{2}$. Applying formula (4) gives

$$D_x y = 3 \cdot \frac{1}{2x - 1} \cdot 2 = \frac{6}{2x - 1}$$

In the discussion that follows we need to make use of $D_x(\ln |x|)$. To find this by using formula (4), $\sqrt{x^2}$ is substituted for $|x|$, and so we have

$$D_x(\ln |x|) = D_x(\ln \sqrt{x^2})$$

$$= \frac{1}{\sqrt{x^2}} \cdot D_x(\sqrt{x^2})$$

$$= \frac{1}{\sqrt{x^2}} \cdot \frac{x}{\sqrt{x^2}}$$

$$= \frac{x}{x^2}$$

Hence,

$$D_x(\ln |x|) = \frac{1}{x} \tag{10}$$

From formula (10) and the chain rule, if u is a differentiable function of x, we get

$$D_x(\ln |u|) = \frac{1}{u} \cdot D_x u \tag{11}$$

The following example illustrates how the properties of the natural logarithmic function, given in Theorems 8.1.3, 8.1.4, and 8.1.5, can simplify the work involved in differentiating complicated expressions involving products, quotients, and powers.

EXAMPLE 5: Given

$$y = \frac{\sqrt[3]{x+1}}{(x+2)\sqrt{x+3}},$$

find $D_x y$.

SOLUTION: From the given equation

$$|y| = \left| \frac{\sqrt[3]{x+1}}{(x+2)\sqrt{x+3}} \right| = \frac{|\sqrt[3]{x+1}|}{|x+2||\sqrt{x+3}|}$$

WHEN THE DENOMINATOR AND NUMERATOR CAN'T BE PUT IN ~~THE~~ FORM TO INTEGRATE.

Taking the natural logarithm and applying the properties of logarithms, we obtain

$$\ln |y| = \tfrac{1}{3} \ln |x+1| - \ln |x+2| - \tfrac{1}{2} \ln |x+3|$$

Differentiating on both sides implicitly with respect to x and applying formula (11), we get

$$\frac{1}{y} D_x y = \frac{1}{3(x+1)} - \frac{1}{x+2} - \frac{1}{2(x+3)}$$

Multiplying on both sides by y, we obtain

$$D_x y = y \cdot \frac{2(x+2)(x+3) - 6(x+1)(x+3) - 3(x+1)(x+2)}{6(x+1)(x+2)(x+3)}$$

Replacing y by its given value, we obtain $D_x y$ equal to

$$\frac{(x+1)^{1/3}}{(x+2)(x+3)^{1/2}} \cdot \frac{2x^2 + 10x + 12 - 6x^2 - 24x - 18 - 3x^2 - 9x - 6}{6(x+1)(x+2)(x+3)}$$

and so

$$D_x y = \frac{-7x^2 - 23x - 12}{6(x+1)^{2/3}(x+2)^2(x+3)^{3/2}}$$

The process illustrated in Example 5 is called *logarithmic differentiation*.

From formula (11) we obtain the following formula for indefinite integration:

$$\int \frac{1}{u}\, du = \ln |u| + C \tag{12}$$

Combining (12) with Formula 5.3.9 we have, for n any real number,

$$\int u^n\, du = \begin{cases} \dfrac{u^{n+1}}{n+1} + C & \text{if } n \neq -1 \\ \ln |u| + C & \text{if } n = -1 \end{cases} \tag{13}$$

EXAMPLE 6:   Evaluate

$$\int \frac{x^2\, dx}{x^3 + 1}$$

SOLUTION:

$$\int \frac{x^2\, dx}{x^3 + 1} = \frac{1}{3} \int \frac{3x^2\, dx}{x^3 + 1} = \frac{1}{3} \ln |x^3 + 1| + C$$

EXAMPLE 7:   Evaluate

$$\int_0^2 \frac{x^2 + 2}{x + 1}\, dx$$

SOLUTION: Because $(x^2 + 2)/(x + 1)$ is an improper fraction, we divide the numerator by the denominator and obtain

$$\frac{x^2 + 2}{x + 1} = x - 1 + \frac{3}{x + 1}$$

Therefore,

$$\int_0^2 \frac{x^2 + 2}{x + 1}\, dx = \int_0^2 \left(x - 1 + \frac{3}{x + 1} \right) dx$$

$$= \tfrac{1}{2} x^2 - x + 3 \ln |x + 1| \; \Big]_0^2$$

$$= 2 - 2 + 3 \ln 3 - 3 \ln 1$$

$$= 3 \ln 3 - 3 \cdot 0$$

$$= 3 \ln 3$$

The answer in the above example also can be written as $\ln 27$, because by Theorem 8.1.5, $3 \ln 3 = \ln 3^3$.

EXAMPLE 8:   Evaluate

$$\int \frac{\ln x}{x}\, dx$$

SOLUTION: Let $u = \ln x$; then $du = dx/x$; so we have

$$\int \frac{\ln x}{x}\, dx = \int u\, du = \frac{1}{2} u^2 + C = \frac{1}{2} (\ln x)^2 + C$$

Exercises 8.1

In Exercises 1 through 10, differentiate the given function and simplify the result.

1. $f(x) = \ln(1 + 4x^2)$

2. $f(x) = \ln \sqrt{1 + 4x^2}$

3. $f(x) = \ln \sqrt{4 - x^2}$

4. $g(x) = \ln(\ln x)$

5. $h(x) = \ln(x^2 \ln x)$

6. $f(x) = \ln \sqrt[4]{\dfrac{x^2 - 1}{x^2 + 1}}$

7. $f(x) = \ln |x^3 + 1|$

8. $f(x) = \sqrt[3]{\ln x^3}$

9. $F(x) = \sqrt{x+1} - \ln(1 + \sqrt{x+1})$

10. $G(x) = x \ln(x + \sqrt{1 + x^2}) - \sqrt{1 + x^2}$

In Exercises 11 through 16, find $D_x y$ by logarithmic differentiation.

11. $y = \dfrac{x^3 + 2x}{\sqrt[5]{x^7 + 1}}$

12. $y = \dfrac{x\sqrt{x+1}}{\sqrt[3]{x-1}}$

13. $y = \dfrac{3x}{\sqrt{(x+1)(x+2)}}$

14. $y = \dfrac{\sqrt{1 - x^2}}{(x+1)^{2/3}}$

15. $y = \sqrt{x^2 + 1} \, \ln(x^2 - 1)$

16. $y = (5x - 4)(x^2 + 3)(3x^3 - 5)$

In Exercises 17 and 18, find $D_x y$ by implicit differentiation.

17. $\ln xy + x + y = 2$

18. $\ln \dfrac{y}{x} + xy = 1$

In Exercises 19 through 26, evaluate the indefinite integral.

19. $\displaystyle \int \frac{dx}{3 - 2x}$

20. $\displaystyle \int \frac{3x \, dx}{5x^2 - 1}$

21. $\displaystyle \int \frac{dx}{x \ln x}$

22. $\displaystyle \int \frac{dx}{\sqrt{x} \, (1 + \sqrt{x})}$

23. $\displaystyle \int \frac{\ln^2 3x}{x} \, dx$

24. $\displaystyle \int \frac{5 - 4x^2}{3 + 2x} \, dx$

25. $\displaystyle \int \frac{2x^3 \, dx}{x^2 - 4}$

26. $\displaystyle \int \frac{(2 + \ln^2 x) \, dx}{x(1 - \ln x)}$

In Exercises 27 through 30, evaluate the definite integral.

27. $\displaystyle \int_3^5 \frac{2x \, dx}{x^2 - 5}$

28. $\displaystyle \int_1^3 \frac{2x + 3}{x + 1} \, dx$

29. $\displaystyle \int_4^5 \frac{x \, dx}{4 - x^2}$

30. $\displaystyle \int_1^5 \frac{4x^3 - 1}{2x - 1} \, dx$

31. Find $\displaystyle \int_0^t e^{-|x|} \, dx$ if t is any real number.

32. Prove that $\ln x^n = n \cdot \ln x$ by first showing that $\ln x^n$ and $n \cdot \ln x$ differ by a constant and then find the constant by taking $x = 1$.

33. Prove that $x - 1 - \ln x > 0$ and $1 - \ln x - 1/x < 0$ for all $x > 0$ and $x \neq 1$, thus establishing the inequality

$$1 - \frac{1}{x} < \ln x < x - 1$$

for all $x > 0$ and $x \neq 1$. (HINT: Let $f(x) = x - 1 - \ln x$ and $g(x) = 1 - \ln x - 1/x$ and determine the signs of $f'(x)$ and $g'(x)$ on the intervals $(0, 1)$ and $(1, +\infty)$.)

34. Use the result of Exercise 33 to prove

$$\lim_{x \to 0} \frac{\ln(1 + x)}{x} = 1$$

35. Establish the limit of Exercise 34 by using the definition of the derivative to find $F'(0)$ for the function F for which $F(x) = \ln(1 + x)$.

36. Prove $\lim\limits_{x \to +\infty} (\ln x)/x = 0$. (HINT: First prove that $\int_1^x (1/\sqrt{t}) \, dt \geq \int_1^x (1/t) \, dt$ by using Theorem 6.4.8.)

8.2 THE GRAPH OF THE NATURAL LOGARITHMIC FUNCTION

To draw a sketch of the graph of the natural logarithmic function, we must first consider some properties of this function.

Let f be the function defined by

$$f(x) = \ln x = \int_1^x \frac{1}{t} \, dt \qquad x > 0$$

The domain of f is the set of all positive numbers. The function f is differentiable for all x in its domain, and

$$f'(x) = \frac{1}{x} \tag{1}$$

Because f is differentiable for all $x > 0$, f is continuous for all $x > 0$. From (1) we conclude that $f'(x) > 0$ for all $x > 0$, and therefore f is an increasing function.

$$f''(x) = -\frac{1}{x^2} \tag{2}$$

From (2) it follows that $f''(x) < 0$ when $x > 0$. Therefore, the graph of $y = f(x)$ is concave downward at every point. Because $f(1) = \ln 1 = 0$, the x intercept of the graph is 1.

$$f(2) = \ln 2 = \int_1^2 \frac{1}{t} \, dt$$

To determine an approximate numerical value for $\ln 2$, the definite integral $\int_1^2 (1/t) \, dt$ is interpreted as the number of square units in the area of the region shown in Fig. 8.2.1.

From Fig. 8.2.1 we see that $\ln 2$ is between the measures of the areas of the rectangles, each having a base of length 1 unit and altitudes of lengths $\frac{1}{2}$ unit and 1 unit; that is,

$$0.5 < \ln 2 < 1 \tag{3}$$

An inequality can be obtained analytically, using Theorem 6.4.8, by proceeding as follows. Let $f(t) = 1/t$ and $g(t) = \frac{1}{2}$. Then $f(t) \geq g(t)$ for all t

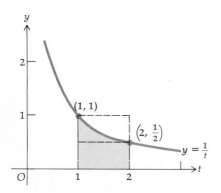

Figure 8.2.1

in $[1, 2]$. Because f and g are continuous on $[1, 2]$, they are integrable on $[1, 2]$, and we have from Theorem 6.4.8

$$\int_1^2 \frac{1}{t}\, dt \geq \int_1^2 \frac{1}{2}\, dt$$

or, equivalently,

$$\ln 2 \geq \tfrac{1}{2} \tag{4}$$

Similarly, if $f(t) = 1/t$ and $h(t) = 1$, then $h(t) \geq f(t)$ for all t in $[1, 2]$. Because h and f are continuous on $[1, 2]$, they are integrable there; and again using Theorem 6.4.8, we obtain

$$\int_1^2 1\, dt \geq \int_1^2 \frac{1}{t}\, dt$$

or, equivalently,

$$1 \geq \ln 2 \tag{5}$$

Combining (4) and (5), we get

$$0.5 \leq \ln 2 \leq 1 \tag{6}$$

The number 0.5 is a lower bound of $\ln 2$ and 1 is an upper bound of $\ln 2$. In a similar manner we obtain a lower and upper bound for the natural logarithm of any positive real number. Later we learn, by applying infinite series, how to compute the natural logarithm of any positive real number to any desired number of decimal places.

The value of $\ln 2$ to five decimal places is given by

$$\ln 2 \approx 0.69315$$

Using this value of $\ln 2$ and applying Theorem 8.1.5, we can find an approximate value for the natural logarithm of any power of 2. In particular, we have

$$\ln 4 = \ln 2^2 \;\; = \;\; 2 \ln 2 \approx \;\; 1.38630$$

$$\ln 8 = \ln 2^3 \;\; = \;\; 3 \ln 2 \approx \;\; 2.07945$$

$$\ln \tfrac{1}{2} = \ln 2^{-1} = -1 \ln 2 \approx -0.69315$$

$$\ln \tfrac{1}{4} = \ln 2^{-2} = -2 \ln 2 \approx -1.38630$$

In the appendix there is a table of natural logarithms, giving the values to four decimal places.

We now determine the behavior of the natural logarithmic function for large values of x by considering $\lim\limits_{x \to +\infty} \ln x$.

Because the natural logarithmic function is an increasing function, if we take p as any positive number,

$$\ln x > \ln 2^p \qquad \text{whenever } x > 2^p \tag{7}$$

From Theorem 8.1.5 we have

$$\ln 2^p = p \ln 2 \tag{8}$$

Substituting from (8) into (7), we get

$$\ln x > p \ln 2 \qquad \text{whenever } x > 2^p$$

Because from (6), $\ln 2 \geq \frac{1}{2}$, we have from the above

$$\ln x > \tfrac{1}{2}p \qquad \text{whenever } x > 2^p$$

Letting $p = 2n$, where $n > 0$, we have

$$\ln x > n \qquad \text{whenever } x > 2^{2n} \tag{9}$$

It follows from (9), by taking $N = 2^{2n}$, that for any $n > 0$

$$\ln x > n \qquad \text{whenever } x > N$$

So we may conclude that

$$\lim_{x \to +\infty} \ln x = +\infty \tag{10}$$

To determine the behavior of the natural logarithmic function for positive values of x near zero, we investigate $\lim_{x \to 0^+} \ln x$.

Because $\ln x = \ln(x^{-1})^{-1}$, we have

$$\ln x = -\ln \frac{1}{x} \tag{11}$$

The expression "$x \to 0^+$" is equivalent to "$1/x \to +\infty$," and so from (11) we write

$$\lim_{x \to 0^+} \ln x = - \lim_{1/x \to +\infty} \ln \frac{1}{x} \tag{12}$$

From (10) we have

$$\lim_{1/x \to +\infty} \ln \frac{1}{x} = +\infty \tag{13}$$

Therefore, from (12) and (13) we get

$$\lim_{x \to 0^+} \ln x = -\infty \tag{14}$$

From (14) and (10) and the intermediate-value theorem (6.5.1) we conclude that the range of the natural logarithmic function is the set of all real numbers. From (14) we conclude that the graph of the natural logarithmic function is asymptotic to the negative side of the y axis through the fourth quadrant. The properties of the natural logarithmic function are summarized as follows:

(i) The domain is the set of all positive numbers.
(ii) The range is the set of all real numbers.
(iii) The function is increasing on its entire domain.
(iv) The function is continuous at all numbers in its domain.
(v) The graph of the function is concave downward at all points.
(vi) The graph of the function is asymptotic to the negative side of the y axis through the fourth quadrant.

By using these properties and plotting a few points with a piece of the tangent line at the points, we can draw a sketch of the graph of the natural logarithmic function. In Fig. 8.2.2 we have plotted the points having abscissas of $\frac{1}{4}$, $\frac{1}{2}$, 1, 2, 4, and 8. The slope of the tangent line is found from $D_x(\ln x) = 1/x$.

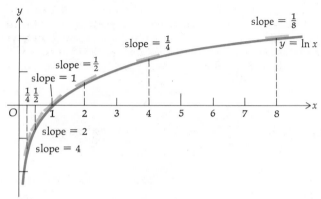

Figure 8.2.2

Exercises 8.2

1. Draw a sketch of the graph of $y = \ln x$ by plotting the points having the abscissas $\frac{1}{9}$, $\frac{1}{3}$, 1, 3, and 9, and use $\ln 3 \approx 1.09861$. At each of the five points, find the slope of the tangent line and draw a piece of the tangent line.

In Exercises 2 through 9, draw a sketch of the graph of the curve having the given equation.

2. $x = \ln y$

3. $y = \ln(-x)$

4. $y = \ln |x|$

5. $y = \ln(x + 1)$

6. $y = \ln(x - 1)$

7. $y = x - \ln x$

8. $y = x \ln x$

9. $y = \ln \dfrac{1}{x}$

10. Show the geometric interpretation of the inequality in Exercise 33 of Exercises 8.1 by drawing on the same pair of axes sketches of the graphs of the functions f, g, and h defined by the equations $f(x) = 1 - 1/x$, $g(x) = \ln x$, and $h(x) = x - 1$.

11. Find an equation of the tangent line to the curve $y = \ln x$ at the point whose abscissa is 2.

12. Find an equation of the normal line to the curve $y = \ln x$ that is parallel to the line $x + 2y - 1 = 0$.

In Exercises 13 through 20, find the exact value of the number to be found and then give an approximation of this number to three decimal places by using the table of natural logarithms in the appendix.

13. Find the area of the region bounded by the curve $y = 2/(x - 3)$, the x axis, and the lines $x = 4$ and $x = 5$.

14. If $f(x) = 1/x$, find the average value of f on the interval $[1, 5]$.

15. Using Boyle's law for the expansion of a gas (see Exercise 10 in Exercises 4.1) find the average pressure with respect to the volume as the volume increases from 4 ft³ to 8 ft³ and the pressure is 2000 lb/ft² when the volume is 4 ft³.

16. Find the volume of the solid of revolution generated when the region bounded by the curve $y = 1 - 3/x$, the x axis, and the line $x = 1$ is revolved about the x axis.

17. In a telegraph cable, the measure of the speed of the signal is proportional to $x^2 \ln(1/x)$, where x is the ratio of the measure of the radius of the core of the cable to the measure of the thickness of the cable's winding. Find the value of x for which the speed of the signal is greatest.

18. A particle is moving on a straight line according to the equation of motion $s = (t + 1)^2 \ln(t + 1)$ where s ft is the directed distance of the particle from the starting point at t sec. Find the velocity and acceleration when $t = 3$.

19. The linear density of a rod at a point x ft from one end is $2/(1 + x)$ slugs/ft. If the rod is 3 ft long, find the mass and center of mass of the rod.

20. A manufacturer of electric generators began operations on Jan. 1, 1962. During the first year there were no sales because the company concentrated on product development and research. After the first year, the sales have increased steadily according to the equation $y = x \ln x$, where x is the number of years during which the company has been operating and y is the number of millions of dollars in the sales volume. (a) Draw a sketch of the graph of the equation. Determine the rate at which the sales were increasing (b) on Jan. 1, 1966, and (c) on Jan. 1, 1972.

8.3 THE INVERSE OF A FUNCTION

Let us consider the equation

$$x^2 - y^2 = 4 \tag{1}$$

If this equation is solved for y in terms of x we obtain

$$y = \pm\sqrt{x^2 - 4}$$

Therefore, Eq. (1) does not define y as a function of x because for each value of x greater than 2 or less than −2 there are two values of y, and to have a functional relationship, there must be a unique value of the dependent variable for a value of the independent variable. If Eq. (1) is solved for x in terms of y, we obtain

$$x = \pm\sqrt{y^2 + 4}$$

and so x is not a function of y. Therefore, Eq. (1) neither defines y as a function of x nor x as a function of y. The equation

$$\boxed{y = x^2 - 1} \tag{2}$$

expresses y as a function of x because for each value of x a unique value of y is determined. As stated in Sec. 2.1, no vertical line can intersect the graph of a function in more than one point. In Fig. 8.3.1 we have a sketch of the graph of Eq. (1). We see that if $a > 2$ or $a < -2$, the straight line $x = a$ intersects the graph in two points. In Fig. 8.3.2 we have a sketch of the graph of Eq. (2). Here we see that any vertical line intersects the graph in only one point. Equation (2) does not define x as a function of y

Figure 8.3.1

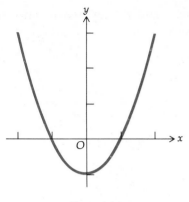

Figure 8.3.2

because for each value of y greater than -1, two values of x are determined.

In some cases, an equation involving x and y will define both y as a function of x and x as a function of y. For example, consider the equation

$$y = x^3 + 1 \tag{3}$$

If we let f be the function defined by

$$f(x) = x^3 + 1 \tag{4}$$

then Eq. (3) can be written as $y = f(x)$, and y is a function of x. If we solve Eq. (3) for x, we obtain

$$x = \sqrt[3]{y - 1} \tag{5}$$

and if we let g be the function defined by

$$g(y) = \sqrt[3]{y - 1} \tag{6}$$

then Eq. (5) may be written as $x = g(y)$, and x is a function of y.

The functions f and g defined by Eqs. (4) and (6) are called *inverse functions*. We also say that the function g is the *inverse* of the function f and that f is the *inverse* of g. The notation f^{-1} denotes the inverse of function f. Note that in using -1 to denote the inverse of a function, it should not be confused with the exponent -1. We have the following formal definition of the inverse of a function.

8.3.1 Definition   If the function f is the set of ordered pairs (x, y), and if there is a function f^{-1} such that

$$x = f^{-1}(y) \quad \text{if and only if} \quad y = f(x) \tag{7}$$

then f^{-1}, which is the set of ordered pairs (y, x), is called the *inverse of the function* f, and f and f^{-1} are called *inverse functions*. The domain of f^{-1} is the range of f, and the range of f^{-1} is the domain of f.

Eliminating y between the equations in (7), we obtain

$$x = f^{-1}(f(x)), \tag{8}$$

and eliminating x between the same pair of equations, we get

$$y = f(f^{-1}(y)) \tag{9}$$

So from Eqs. (8) and (9) we see that if the inverse of the function f is the function f^{-1}, then the inverse of the function f^{-1} is the function f.

Because the functions f and g defined by Eqs. (4) and (6) are inverse functions, f^{-1} can be written in place of g. We have from (4) and (6)

$$f(x) = x^3 + 1 \quad \text{and} \quad f^{-1}(x) = \sqrt[3]{x - 1} \tag{10}$$

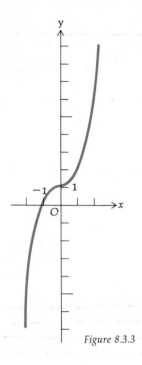

Figure 8.3.3

Sketches of the graphs of functions f and f^{-1} defined in (10) are shown in Figs. 8.3.3 and 8.3.4, respectively.

Figure 8.3.4

We observe that in Fig. 8.3.3 the function f is continuous and increasing on its entire domain. The definition of an increasing function (Definition 4.6.1) is satisfied by f for all values of x in its domain. We also observe in Fig. 8.3.3 that a horizontal line intersects the graph of f in only one point. We intuitively suspect that if a function is continuous and increasing, then a horizontal line will intersect the graph of the function in only one point, and so the function will have an inverse. The following theorem verifies this fact.

8.3.2 Theorem   Suppose that the function f is continuous and increasing on the closed interval $[a, b]$. Then

  (i) f has an inverse f^{-1}, which is defined on $[f(a), f(b)]$;
  (ii) f^{-1} is increasing on $[f(a), f(b)]$;
  (iii) f^{-1} is continuous on $[f(a), f(b)]$.

PROOF OF (i):   Since f is continuous on $[a, b]$, then if k is any number such that $f(a) < k < f(b)$, by the intermediate-value theorem (6.5.1), there exists a number c in (a, b) such that $f(c) = k$. So if y is any number in the closed interval $[f(a), f(b)]$, there is at least one number x in $[a, b]$ such that $y = f(x)$. We wish to show that for each number y there corresponds only one number x. Suppose to a number y_1 in $[f(a), f(b)]$ there correspond two numbers x_1 and x_2 $(x_1 \neq x_2)$ in $[a, b]$ such that $y_1 = f(x_1)$ and $y_1 = f(x_2)$. Then, we must have

$$f(x_1) = f(x_2) \tag{11}$$

Because we have assumed $x_1 \neq x_2$, either $x_1 < x_2$ or $x_2 < x_1$. If $x_1 < x_2$, because f is increasing on $[a, b]$, it follows that $f(x_1) < f(x_2)$; this contradicts (11). If $x_2 < x_1$, then $f(x_2) < f(x_1)$, and this also contradicts (11). Therefore, our assumption that $x_1 \neq x_2$ is false, and so to each value of y in $[f(a), f(b)]$ there corresponds exactly one number x in $[a, b]$ such that $y = f(x)$. Therefore, f has an inverse f^{-1}, which is defined for all numbers in $[f(a), f(b)]$.

PROOF OF (ii):   To prove that f^{-1} is increasing on $[f(a), f(b)]$, we must show that if y_1 and y_2 are two numbers in $[f(a), f(b)]$ such that $y_1 < y_2$ then $f^{-1}(y_1) < f^{-1}(y_2)$. Because f^{-1} is defined on $[f(a), f(b)]$, there exist numbers x_1 and x_2 in $[a, b]$ such that $y_1 = f(x_1)$ and $y_2 = f(x_2)$. Therefore,

$$f^{-1}(y_1) = f^{-1}(f(x_1)) = x_1 \tag{12}$$

and

$$f^{-1}(y_2) = f^{-1}(f(x_2)) = x_2 \tag{13}$$

If $x_2 < x_1$ then because f is increasing on $[a,b]$, $f(x_2) < f(x_1)$ or, equivalently, $y_2 < y_1$. But $y_1 < y_2$; therefore, x_2 cannot be less than x_1.

If $x_2 = x_1$, then because f is a function, $f(x_1) = f(x_2)$ or, equivalently, $y_1 = y_2$, but this also contradicts the fact that $y_1 < y_2$. Therefore, $x_2 \neq x_1$.

So if x_2 is not less than x_1 and $x_2 \neq x_1$, it follows that $x_1 < x_2$; hence, from (12) and (13), $f^{-1}(y_1) < f^{-1}(y_2)$. Thus, we have proved that f^{-1} is increasing on $[f(a), f(b)]$.

PROOF OF (iii):   To prove that f^{-1} is continuous on the closed interval $[f(a), f(b)]$ we must show that if r is any number in the open interval $(f(a), f(b))$, then f^{-1} is continuous at r, and f^{-1} is continuous from the right at $f(a)$, and f^{-1} is continuous from the left at $f(b)$.

We prove that f^{-1} is continuous at any r in the open interval $(f(a), f(b))$ by showing that Definition 2.12.4 holds at r. We wish to show that, for any $\epsilon > 0$ small enough so that $f^{-1}(r) - \epsilon$ and $f^{-1}(r) + \epsilon$ are both in $[a, b]$, there exists a $\delta > 0$ such that

$$|f^{-1}(y) - f^{-1}(r)| < \epsilon \qquad \text{whenever } |y - r| < \delta$$

Let $f^{-1}(r) = s$. Then $f(s) = r$. Because from (ii), f^{-1} is increasing on $[f(a), f(b)]$, we conclude that $a < s < b$. Therefore,

$$a \leq s - \epsilon < s < s + \epsilon \leq b$$

Because f is increasing on $[a, b]$,

$$f(a) \leq f(s - \epsilon) < r < f(s + \epsilon) \leq f(b) \tag{14}$$

Let δ be the smaller of the two numbers $r - f(s - \epsilon)$ and $f(s + \epsilon) - r$; so $\delta \leq r - f(s - \epsilon)$ and $\delta \leq f(s + \epsilon) - r$ or, equivalently,

$$f(s - \epsilon) \leq r - \delta \tag{15}$$

and

$$r + \delta \leq f(s + \epsilon) \tag{16}$$

Whenever $|y - r| < \delta$, we have $-\delta < y - r < \delta$ or, equivalently,

$$r - \delta < y < r + \delta \tag{17}$$

From (14), (15), (16), and (17), we have, whenever $|y - r| < \delta$,

$$f(a) \leq f(s - \epsilon) < y < f(s + \epsilon) \leq f(b)$$

Because f^{-1} is increasing on $[f(a), f(b)]$, it follows from the above that

$$f^{-1}(f(s - \epsilon)) < f^{-1}(y) < f^{-1}(f(s + \epsilon)) \qquad \text{whenever } |y - r| < \delta$$

or, equivalently,

$$s - \epsilon < f^{-1}(y) < s + \epsilon \qquad \text{whenever } |y - r| < \delta$$

or, equivalently,

$$-\epsilon < f^{-1}(y) - s < \epsilon \qquad \text{whenever } |y - r| < \delta$$

or, equivalently,

$$|f^{-1}(y) - f^{-1}(r)| < \epsilon \qquad \text{whenever } |y - r| < \delta$$

So f^{-1} is continuous on the open interval $(f(a), f(b))$.

The proofs that f^{-1} is continuous from the right at $f(a)$ and continuous from the left at $f(b)$ are left for the reader (see Exercise 24). ∎

A theorem analogous to the above theorem is obtained if the function f is continuous and *decreasing* (instead of increasing) on the closed interval $[a, b]$.

8.3.3 Theorem   Suppose that the function f is continuous and decreasing on the closed interval $[a, b]$. Then

(i) f has an inverse f^{-1}, which is defined on $[f(b), f(a)]$;
(ii) f^{-1} is decreasing on $[f(b), f(a)]$;
(iii) f^{-1} is continuous on $[f(b), f(a)]$.

The proof is similar to the proof of Theorem 8.3.2 and is left for the reader (see Exercises 25 to 27).

Let us now reconsider Eq. (2): $y = x^2 - 1$. As stated earlier in this section, this equation does not define x as a function of y because if we solve for x we obtain

$$x = \sqrt{y + 1} \quad \text{and} \quad x = -\sqrt{y + 1} \tag{18}$$

So actually Eq. (2) defines x as two distinct functions of y. If in Eq. (2) we restrict x to the closed interval $[0, c]$ and let $y = f_1(x)$ if x is in $[0, c]$, we have

$$f_1(x) = x^2 - 1 \qquad \text{and } x \text{ in } [0, c] \tag{19}$$

If in Eq. (2) we restrict x to the closed interval $[-c, 0]$ and let $y = f_2(x)$ if x is in $[-c, 0]$, we have

$$f_2(x) = x^2 - 1 \qquad \text{and } x \text{ in } [-c, 0] \tag{20}$$

The functions f_1 and f_2 defined by (19) and (20) are distinct functions because their domains are different. If we find the derivatives of f_1 and f_2, we obtain

$$f_1'(x) = 2x \quad \text{and } x \text{ in } [0, c]$$

and

$$f_2'(x) = 2x \quad \text{and } x \text{ in } [-c, 0]$$

Because f_1 is continuous on $[0, c]$ and $f_1'(x) > 0$ for all x in $(0, c)$, by Theorem 4.6.3(i), f is increasing on $[0, c]$; and so by Theorem 8.3.2, f_1 has an inverse on $[-1, c^2 - 1]$. The inverse function is given by

$$f_1^{-1}(y) = \sqrt{y + 1} \tag{21}$$

Similarly, because f_2 is continuous on $[-c, 0]$ and because $f_2'(x) < 0$ for all x in $(-c, 0)$, by Theorem 4.6.3(ii), f_2 is decreasing on $[-c, 0]$. Hence, by Theorem 8.3.3, f_2 has an inverse on $[-1, c^2 - 1]$, and the inverse function is given by

$$f_2^{-1}(y) = -\sqrt{y + 1} \tag{22}$$

Because the letter used to represent the independent variable is irrelevant as far as the function is concerned, x could be used instead of y in (21) and (22), and we write

$$f_1^{-1}(x) = \sqrt{x + 1} \quad \text{and } x \text{ in } [-1, c^2 - 1] \tag{23}$$

and

$$f_2^{-1}(x) = -\sqrt{x + 1} \quad \text{and } x \text{ in } [-1, c^2 - 1] \tag{24}$$

Figure 8.3.5

In Fig. 8.3.5 there are sketches of the graphs of f_1 and its inverse f_1^{-1}, as defined in (19) and (23), plotted on the same set of axes. In Fig. 8.3.6 there are sketches of the graphs of f_2 and its inverse f_2^{-1}, as defined in (20) and (24), plotted on the same set of axes. It appears intuitively true from Fig. 8.3.5 that if the point $Q(u, v)$ is on the graph of f_1, then the point $R(v, u)$ is on the graph of f_1^{-1}. From Fig. 8.3.6 it appears to be true that if the point $Q(u, v)$ is on the graph of f_2, then the point $R(v, u)$ is on the graph of f_2^{-1}.

In general, if Q is the point (u, v) and R is the point (v, u), the line segment QR is perpendicular to the line $y = x$ and is bisected by it. We state that the point Q is a *reflection* of the point R with respect to the line $y = x$, and the point R is a *reflection* of the point Q with respect to the line $y = x$. If x and y are interchanged in the equation $y = f(x)$, we obtain the equation $x = f(y)$, and the graph of the equation $x = f(y)$ is said to be a *reflection of the graph* of the equation $y = f(x)$ with respect to the line $y = x$. Because the equation $x = f(y)$ is equivalent to the equation $y = f^{-1}(x)$, we conclude that the graph of the equation $y = f^{-1}(x)$ is a reflection of the graph of the equation $y = f(x)$ with respect to the line $y = x$. Therefore, if a function f has an inverse f^{-1}, their graphs are reflections of each other with respect to the line $y = x$.

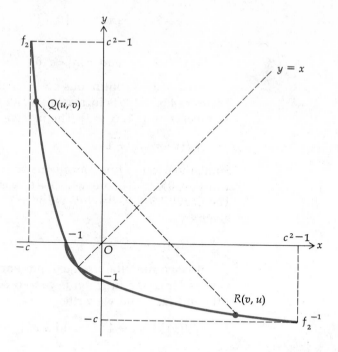

Figure 8.3.6

EXAMPLE 1: Given the function f is defined by

$$f(x) = \frac{2x + 3}{x - 1}$$

find the inverse f^{-1} if it exists. Draw a sketch of the graph of f, and if f^{-1} exists, draw a sketch of the graph of f^{-1} on the same set of axes as the graph of f.

SOLUTION: $f'(x) = -5/(x - 1)^2$. Because f is continuous for all values of x except 1, and $f'(x) < 0$ if $x \neq 1$, it follows from Theorem 8.3.3 that f has an inverse if x is any real number except 1. To find f^{-1}, let $y = f(x)$, and solve for x, thus giving $x = f^{-1}(y)$. So we have

$$y = \frac{2x + 3}{x - 1}$$

$$xy - y = 2x + 3$$

$$x(y - 2) = y + 3$$

$$x = \frac{y + 3}{y - 2}$$

Thus,

$$f^{-1}(y) = \frac{y + 3}{y - 2}$$

or, equivalently,

$$f^{-1}(x) = \frac{x + 3}{x - 2}$$

The domain of f^{-1} is the set of all real numbers except 2. Sketches of the graphs of f and f^{-1} are shown in Fig. 8.3.7.

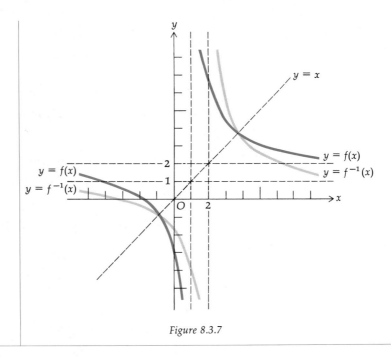

Figure 8.3.7

The following theorem expresses a relationship between the derivative of a function and the derivative of the inverse of the function if the function has an inverse.

8.3.4 Theorem   Suppose that the function f is continuous and monotonic on the closed interval $[a, b]$, and let $y = f(x)$. If f is differentiable on $[a, b]$ and $f'(x) \neq 0$ for any x in $[a, b]$, then the derivative of the inverse function f^{-1}, defined by $x = f^{-1}(y)$, is given by

$$D_y x = \frac{1}{D_x y}$$

PROOF: Because f is continuous and monotonic on $[a, b]$, then by Theorems 8.3.2 and 8.3.3, f has an inverse which is continuous and monotonic on $[f(a), f(b)]$ (or $[f(b), f(a)]$ if $f(b) < f(a)$).

If x is a number in $[a, b]$, let Δx be an increment of x, $\Delta x \neq 0$, such that $x + \Delta x$ is also in $[a, b]$. Then the corresponding increment of y is given by

$$\Delta y = f(x + \Delta x) - f(x) \tag{25}$$

$\Delta y \neq$ since $\Delta x \neq 0$ and f is monotonic on $[a, b]$; that is, either

$$f(x + \Delta x) < f(x) \quad \text{or} \quad f(x + \Delta x) > f(x) \qquad \text{on } [a, b]$$

If x is in $[a, b]$ and $y = f(x)$, then y is in $[f(a), f(b)]$ (or $[f(b), f(a)]$). Also, if $x + \Delta x$ is in $[a, b]$, then $y + \Delta y$ is in $[f(a), f(b)]$ (or $[f(b), f(a)]$) because $y + \Delta y = f(x + \Delta x)$ by (25). So

$$x = f^{-1}(y) \tag{26}$$

and

$$x + \Delta x = f^{-1}(y + \Delta y) \tag{27}$$

It follows from (26) and (27) that

$$\Delta x = f^{-1}(y + \Delta y) - f^{-1}(y) \tag{28}$$

From the definition of a derivative,

$$D_y x = \lim_{\Delta y \to 0} \frac{f^{-1}(y + \Delta y) - f^{-1}(y)}{\Delta y}$$

Substituting from (25) and (28) into the above equation, we get

$$D_y x = \lim_{\Delta y \to 0} \frac{\Delta x}{f(x + \Delta x) - f(x)}$$

and because $\Delta x \neq 0$,

$$D_y x = \lim_{\Delta y \to 0} \frac{1}{\dfrac{f(x + \Delta x) - f(x)}{\Delta x}} \tag{29}$$

Before we find the limit in (29) we show that under the hypothesis of this theorem "$\Delta x \to 0$" is equivalent to "$\Delta y \to 0$." First we show that $\lim_{\Delta y \to 0} \Delta x = 0$. From (28) we have

$$\lim_{\Delta y \to 0} \Delta x = \lim_{\Delta y \to 0} [f^{-1}(y + \Delta y) - f^{-1}(y)]$$

Because f^{-1} is continuous on $[f(a), f(b)]$ (or $[f(b), f(a)]$), the limit on the right side of the above equation is zero. So

$$\lim_{\Delta y \to 0} \Delta x = 0 \tag{30}$$

Now we demonstrate that $\lim_{\Delta x \to 0} \Delta y = 0$. From (25) we have

$$\lim_{\Delta x \to 0} \Delta y = \lim_{\Delta x \to 0} [f(x + \Delta x) - f(x)]$$

Because f is continuous on $[a, b]$, the limit on the right side of the above equation is zero, and therefore we have

$$\lim_{\Delta x \to 0} \Delta y = 0 \tag{31}$$

From (30) and (31) it follows that

$$\Delta x \to 0 \quad \text{if and only if} \quad \Delta y \to 0 \tag{32}$$

Thus, applying the limit theorem (regarding the limit of a quotient) to (29) and using (32), we have

$$D_y x = \cfrac{1}{\lim_{\Delta x \to 0} \cfrac{f(x + \Delta x) - f(x)}{\Delta x}}$$

Because f is differentiable on $[a, b]$, the limit in the denominator of the above is $f'(x)$ or, equivalently, $D_x y$, and so we have

$$D_y x = \frac{1}{D_x y} \qquad \blacksquare$$

EXAMPLE 2:   Show that Theorem 8.3.4 holds for the function of Example 1.

SOLUTION: If $y = f(x) = (2x + 3)/(x - 1)$, then

$$D_x y = f'(x) = -\frac{5}{(x - 1)^2}$$

Because $f'(x)$ exists if $x \neq 1$, f is differentiable and hence continuous at all $x \neq 1$. Furthermore, $f'(x) < 0$ if $x \neq 1$, and so f is decreasing for all $x \neq 1$. Therefore, the hypothesis of Theorem 8.3.4 holds for any interval $[a, b]$ which does not contain the number 1.

In the solution of Example 1 we showed that

$$x = f^{-1}(y) = \frac{y + 3}{y - 2}$$

Computing $D_y x$ from this equation, we get

$$D_y x = (f^{-1})'(y) = -\frac{5}{(y - 2)^2}$$

If in the above equation we let $y = (2x + 3)/(x - 1)$, we obtain

$$D_y x = -\frac{5}{\left(\dfrac{2x + 3}{x - 1} - 2\right)^2}$$

$$= -\frac{5(x - 1)^2}{(2x + 3 - 2x + 2)^2}$$

$$= -\tfrac{5}{25}(x - 1)^2$$

$$= -\tfrac{1}{5}(x - 1)^2$$

$$= \frac{1}{D_x y}$$

EXAMPLE 3:   Given f is the function defined by $f(x) = x^3 + x$, determine if f has an inverse. If it

SOLUTION: Because $f(x) = x^3 + x$, $f'(x) = 3x^2 + 1$. Therefore, $f'(x) > 0$ for all real numbers, and so f is increasing on its entire domain. Because f is also continuous on its entire domain, it follows from Theorem 8.3.2 that f

does, find the derivative of the inverse function.

has an inverse f^{-1}.

Let $y = f(x)$ and then $x = f^{-1}(y)$. So by Theorem 8.3.4

$$D_y x = \frac{1}{D_x y} = \frac{1}{3x^2 + 1}$$

Exercises 8.3

In Exercises 1 through 8, find the inverse of the given function, if it exists, and determine its domain. Draw a sketch of the graph of the given function and if the given function does not have an inverse, show that a horizontal line intersects the graph in more than one point. If the given function has an inverse, draw a sketch of the graph of the inverse function on the same set of axes as the graph of the given function.

1. $f(x) = x^3$

2. $f(x) = x^2 + 5$

3. $f(x) = \dfrac{1}{x^2}$

4. $f(x) = (x+2)^3$

5. $f(x) = \dfrac{2x-1}{x}$

6. $f(x) = \dfrac{8}{x^3+1}$

7. $f(x) = 2|x| + x$

8. $f(x) = \dfrac{3}{1+|x|}$

In Exercises 9 through 14 perform each of the following steps: (a) Solve the equation for y in terms of x and express y as one or more functions of x; (b) for each of the functions obtained in (a) determine if the function has an inverse, and if it does, determine the domain of the inverse function; (c) use implicit differentiation to find $D_x y$ and $D_y x$ and determine the values of x and y for which $D_x y$ and $D_y x$ are reciprocals.

9. $x^2 + y^2 = 9$

10. $x^2 - 4y^2 = 16$

11. $xy = 4$

12. $9y^2 - 8x^3 = 0$

13. $2x^2 - 3xy + 1 = 0$

14. $2x^2 + 2y + 1 = 0$

In Exercises 15 through 20 determine if the given function has an inverse, and if it does, determine the domain and range of the inverse function.

15. $f(x) = \sqrt{x-4}$

16. $f(x) = (x+3)^3$

17. $f(x) = x^2 - \dfrac{1}{x}, \; x > 0$

18. $f(x) = \dfrac{1}{x^2+4}, \; x \le 0$

19. $f(x) = x^5 + x^3$

20. $f(x) = x^3 + x$

21. Let the function f be defined by $f(x) = \displaystyle\int_0^x \sqrt{1-t^4}\, dt$. Determine if f has an inverse, and if it does, find the derivative of the inverse function.

22. Determine the value of the constant k so that the function defined by $f(x) = (x+5)/(x+k)$ will be its own inverse.

23. Given $f(x) = \begin{cases} x & \text{if } x < 1 \\ x^2 & \text{if } 1 \le x \le 9 \\ 27\sqrt{x} & \text{if } x > 9 \end{cases}$

    Prove that f has an inverse function and find $f^{-1}(x)$.

24. Given that the function f is continuous and increasing on the closed interval $[a, b]$. Assuming Theorem 8.3.1(i) and (ii), prove f^{-1} is continuous from the right at $f(a)$ and continuous from the left at $f(b)$.

25. Prove Theorem 8.3.3(i).

26. Prove Theorem 8.3.3(ii).

27. Prove Theorem 8.3.3(iii).

28. Show that the formula of Theorem 8.3.4 can be written as

$$(f^{-1})'(x) = \frac{1}{f'(f^{-1}(x))}$$

29. Use the formula of Exercise 28 to show that

$$(f^{-1})''(x) = -\frac{f''(f^{-1}(x))}{[f'(f^{-1}(x))]^3}$$

8.4 THE EXPONENTIAL FUNCTION

Because the natural logarithmic function is increasing on its entire domain, then by Theorem 8.3.2 it has an inverse which is also an increasing function. The inverse of the natural logarithmic function is called the *exponential function*, which we now define.

8.4.1 Definition

The *exponential function* is the inverse of the natural logarithmic function, and it is defined by

$$\exp(x) = y \quad \text{if and only if} \quad x = \ln y \tag{1}$$

The exponential function "$\exp(x)$" is read as "the value of the exponential function at x."

Because the range of the natural logarithmic function is the set of all real numbers, the domain of the exponential function is the set of all real numbers. The range of the exponential function is the set of positive numbers because this is the domain of the natural logarithmic function.

Because the natural logarithmic function and the exponential function are inverses of each other, it follows from Eqs. (8) and (9) of Sec. 8.3 that

$$\ln(\exp(x)) = x \tag{2}$$

and

$$\exp(\ln x) = x \tag{3}$$

Because $0 = \ln 1$, we have

$$\exp 0 = \exp(\ln 1)$$

which from (3) gives us

$$\exp 0 = 1 \tag{4}$$

We now state some properties of the exponential function as theorems.

8.4.2 Theorem

If a and b are any real numbers, then

$$\exp(a + b) = \exp(a) \cdot \exp(b)$$

PROOF: Let $A = \exp(a)$, and so from Definition 8.4.1 we have

$$a = \ln A \tag{5}$$

Let $B = \exp(b)$, and from Definition 8.4.1 it follows that

$$b = \ln B \tag{6}$$

From Theorem 8.1.3 we have

$$\ln A + \ln B = \ln AB \tag{7}$$

Substituting from (5) and (6) into (7), we obtain

$$a + b = \ln AB$$

So

$$\exp(a + b) = \exp(\ln AB) \tag{8}$$

From Eq. (3) it follows that the right side of Eq. (8) is AB, and so we have

$$\exp(a + b) = AB$$

Replacing A and B by their values, we get

$$\exp(a + b) = \exp(a) \cdot \exp(b)$$ ∎

8.4.3 Theorem   If a and b are any real numbers,

$$\exp(a - b) = \exp(a) \div \exp(b)$$

The proof is analogous to the proof of Theorem 8.4.2, where Theorem 8.1.3 is replaced by Theorem 8.1.4. It is left for the reader (see Exercise 1).

8.4.4 Theorem   If a is any real number and r is any rational number, then

$$\exp(ra) = [\exp(a)]^r$$

PROOF: If in Eq. (3) $x = [\exp(a)]^r$, we have

$$[\exp(a)]^r = \exp\{\ln[\exp(a)]^r\}$$

Applying Theorem 8.1.5 to the right side of the above equation, we obtain

$$[\exp(a)]^r = \exp\{r \ln[\exp(a)]\}$$

But from Eq. (2), $\ln[\exp(a)] = a$, and therefore

$$[\exp(a)]^r = \exp(ra)$$ ∎

We now wish to define what is meant by a^x, where a is a positive number and x is an irrational number. To arrive at a reasonable definition, consider the case a^r, where $a > 0$ and r is a rational number. We have from Eq. (3)

$$a^r = \exp[\ln (a^r)] \tag{9}$$

But by Theorem 8.1.5, $\ln a^r = r \ln a$; so from Eq. (9)

$$a^r = \exp(r \ln a) \tag{10}$$

Because the right side of Eq. (10) has a meaning if r is any real number, we use it for our definition.

8.4.5 Definition   If a is any positive number and x is any real number, we define

$$a^x = \exp(x \ln a)$$

8.4.6 Theorem   If a is any positive number and x is any real number,

$$\ln a^x = x \ln a$$

PROOF: From Definition 8.4.5,

$$a^x = \exp(x \ln a)$$

Hence, from Definition 8.4.1, we have

$$\ln a^x = x \ln a \qquad\blacksquare$$

Following is the definition of one of the most important numbers in mathematics.

8.4.7 Definition   The number e is defined by the formula

$$e = \exp 1$$

The letter "e" was chosen because of the Swiss mathematician and physicist Leonhard Euler (1707–1783).

The number e is a *transcendental* number; that is, it cannot be expressed as the root of any polynomial with integer coefficients. The number π is another example of a transcendental number. The proof that e is transcendental was first given in 1873, by Charles Hermite, and its value can be expressed to any required degree of accuracy. In Chapter 14 we learn an easy method for doing this. The value of e to seven decimal places is 2.7182818.

8.4.8 Theorem $\ln e = 1$.

PROOF: By Definition 8.4.7,

$$e = \exp 1$$

Hence,

$$\ln e = \ln(\exp 1) \tag{11}$$

Because the natural logarithmic function and the exponential function are inverse functions, it follows that

$$\ln(\exp 1) = 1 \tag{12}$$

Substituting from (12) into (11), we have

$$\ln e = 1 \qquad \blacksquare$$

8.4.9 Theorem $\exp(x) = e^x$, for all values of x.

PROOF: By Definition 8.4.5,

$$e^x = \exp(x \ln e) \tag{13}$$

But by Theorem 8.4.8, $\ln e = 1$. Substituting this in (13), we obtain

$$e^x = \exp(x) \qquad \blacksquare$$

From now on, we write e^x in place of $\exp(x)$, and so from Definition 8.4.1 we have

$$e^x = y \quad \text{if and only if} \quad x = \ln y \tag{14}$$

We now derive the formula for the derivative of the exponential function. Let

$$y = e^x$$

Then from (14) we have

$$x = \ln y \tag{15}$$

Differentiating on both sides of (15) implicitly with respect to x, we get

$$1 = \frac{1}{y} \cdot D_x y$$

So,

$$D_x y = y$$

Replacing y by e^x, we obtain

$$D_x(e^x) = e^x \tag{16}$$

If u is a differentiable function of x, it follows from (16) and the chain rule that

$$D_x(e^u) = e^u \, D_x u \tag{17}$$

It follows that the derivative of the function defined by $f(x) = ke^x$, where k is a constant, is itself. The only other function we have previously encountered that has this property is the constant function zero; actually, this is the special case of $f(x) = ke^x$ when $k = 0$. It can be proved that the most general function which is its own derivative is given by $f(x) = ke^x$ (see Exercise 36).

EXAMPLE 1:   Given $y = e^{1/x^2}$, find $D_x y$.

SOLUTION: From (17)

$$D_x y = e^{1/x^2}\left(-\frac{2}{x^3}\right) = -\frac{2e^{1/x^2}}{x^3}$$

From (17) we obtain the following indefinite integration formula:

$$\int e^u \, du = e^u + C \tag{18}$$

EXAMPLE 2:   Find

$$\int \frac{e^{\sqrt{x}}}{\sqrt{x}} \, dx.$$

SOLUTION: Let $u = \sqrt{x}$; then $du = \frac{1}{2}x^{-1/2} \, dx$; so

$$\int \frac{e^{\sqrt{x}}}{\sqrt{x}} \, dx = 2 \int e^u \, du$$

$$= 2e^u + C$$

$$= 2e^{\sqrt{x}} + C$$

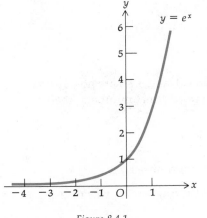

Figure 8.4.1

Because from (14), $e^x = y$ if and only if $x = \ln y$, the graph of $y = e^x$ is identical with the graph of $x = \ln y$. So we can obtain the graph of $y = e^x$ by interchanging the x and y axis in Fig. 8.2.2 (see Fig. 8.4.1).

The graph of $y = e^x$ can be obtained without referring to the graph of the natural logarithmic function. Because the range of the exponential function is the set of all positive numbers, it follows that $e^x > 0$ for all values of x. So the graph lies entirely above the x axis. $D_x y = e^x > 0$ for all x; so the function is increasing for all x. $D_x^2 y = e^x > 0$ for all x; so the graph is concave upward at all points.

We have the following two limits:

$$\lim_{x \to +\infty} e^x = +\infty \tag{19}$$

and

$$\lim_{x \to -\infty} e^x = 0 \tag{20}$$

The proofs of (19) and (20) are left for the reader (see Exercises 44 and 45). To plot some specific points use the table in the Appendix giving powers of e.

EXAMPLE 3: Find the area of the region bounded by the curve $y = e^x$, the coordinate axes, and the line $x = 2$.

Figure 8.4.2

SOLUTION: The region is shown in Fig. 8.4.2.

$$A = \lim_{||\Delta|| \to 0} \sum_{i=1}^{n} e^{\xi^i} \Delta_i x$$

$$= \int_0^2 e^x \, dx$$

$$= e^x \Big]_0^2$$

$$= e^2 - e^0$$

$$= e^2 - 1$$

From a table of powers of e, we see that the value of e^2 to two decimal places is 7.39. Therefore, the area of the region is approximately 6.39 square units.

The conclusions of Theorems 8.4.2, 8.4.3, and 8.4.4 are now restated by using e^x in place of $\exp(x)$. If a and b are any real numbers, then

$$e^{a+b} = e^a \cdot e^b$$

$$e^{a-b} = e^a \div e^b$$

$$e^{ra} = (e^a)^r \qquad \text{where } r \text{ is any rational number.}$$

Writing Eqs. (2), (3), and (4) by substituting e^x in place of $\exp(x)$, we have

$$\ln(e^x) = x$$

$$e^{\ln x} = x$$

and

$$e^0 = 1$$

EXAMPLE 4: Given

$$y = e^{2x + \ln x}$$

find $D_x y$.

SOLUTION: $e^{2x + \ln x} = e^{2x} e^{\ln x} = e^{2x}(x)$. So

$$y = xe^{2x}$$

Therefore,

$$D_x y = e^{2x} + 2xe^{2x}$$

In Definition 8.4.7, the number e was defined as the value of the exponential function at 1; that is, $e = \exp 1$. To arrive at another way of defining e, we consider the natural logarithmic function

$$f(x) = \ln x$$

We know that the derivative of f is given by $f'(x) = 1/x$; hence, $f'(1) = 1$. However, let us apply the definition of the derivative to find $f'(1)$. We have

$$f'(1) = \lim_{\Delta x \to 0} \frac{f(1 + \Delta x) - f(1)}{\Delta x}$$

$$= \lim_{\Delta x \to 0} \frac{\ln(1 + \Delta x) - \ln 1}{\Delta x}$$

$$= \lim_{\Delta x \to 0} \frac{1}{\Delta x} \ln(1 + \Delta x)$$

Therefore,

$$\lim_{\Delta x \to 0} \frac{1}{\Delta x} \ln(1 + \Delta x) = 1$$

Replacing Δx by h, we have from the above equation and Theorem 8.4.6

$$\lim_{h \to 0} \ln(1 + h)^{1/h} = 1 \tag{21}$$

Now, because the exponential function and the natural logarithmic function are inverse functions, we have

$$\lim_{h \to 0} (1 + h)^{1/h} = \lim_{h \to 0} \exp[\ln(1 + h)^{1/h}] \tag{22}$$

Because the exponential function is continuous and $\lim_{h \to 0} \ln(1 + h)^{1/h}$ exists and equals 1 as shown in Eq. (21), we can apply Theorem 2.12.5 to the right side of Eq. (22) and get

$$\lim_{h \to 0} (1 + h)^{1/h} = \exp\left[\lim_{h \to 0} \ln(1 + h)^{1/h}\right] = \exp 1$$

Hence,

$$\lim_{h \to 0} (1 + h)^{1/h} = e \tag{23}$$

Equation (23) is sometimes used to define e; however, to use this as a definition it is necessary to prove that the limit exists.

Let us consider the function F defined by

$$F(h) = (1+h)^{1/h} \qquad (24)$$

and determine the function values for some values of h close to zero. These values are given in Table 8.4.1.

Table 8.4.1

h	1	0.5	0.05	0.01	0.001	−0.001	−0.01	−0.05	−0.5
$F(h) = (1+h)^{1/h}$	2	2.25	2.65	2.70	2.7169	2.7196	2.73	2.79	4

Table 8.4.1 leads us to suspect that $\lim\limits_{h\to 0} (1+h)^{1/h}$ is probably a number that lies between 2.7169 and 2.7196. As previously mentioned, in Chapter 14 we learn a method for finding the value of e to any desired number of decimal places.

Exercises 8.4

1. Prove Theorem 8.4.3.

2. Draw a sketch of the graph of $y = e^{-x}$.

3. Draw a sketch of the graph of $y = e^{|x|}$.

In Exercises 4 through 14, find $D_x y$.

4. $y = e^{5x}$

5. $y = e^{-3x^2}$

6. $y = \dfrac{e^x}{x}$

7. $y = \dfrac{e^{2x}}{x^2}$

8. $y = e^{e^x}$

9. $y = \dfrac{e^x - e^{-x}}{e^x + e^{-x}}$

10. $y = \ln \dfrac{e^{4x} - 1}{e^{4x} + 1}$

11. $y = x^5 e^{-3\ln x}$

12. $y = \ln(e^x + e^{-x})$

13. $y = e^{x \ln x}$

14. $y = e^{x/\sqrt{4+x^2}}$

In Exercises 15 through 18, find $D_x y$ by implicit differentiation.

15. $e^x + e^y = e^{x+y}$

16. $ye^{2x} + xe^{2y} = 1$

17. $y^2 e^{2x} + xy^3 = 1$

18. $e^y = \ln(x^3 + 3y)$

In Exercises 19 through 26, evaluate the indefinite integral.

19. $\displaystyle\int e^{2-5x}\, dx$

20. $\displaystyle\int e^{2x+1}\, dx$

21. $\displaystyle\int \dfrac{1 + e^{2x}}{e^x}\, dx$

22. $\displaystyle\int e^{3x} e^{2x}\, dx$

23. $\displaystyle\int \dfrac{e^{3x}}{(1 - 2e^{3x})^2}\, dx$

24. $\displaystyle\int x^2 e^{2x^3}\, dx$

25. $\displaystyle\int \dfrac{e^{2x}}{e^x + 3}\, dx$

26. $\displaystyle\int \dfrac{dx}{1 + e^x}$

In Exercises 27 through 30, evaluate the definite integral.

27. $\displaystyle\int_0^1 e^2\, dx$

28. $\displaystyle\int_1^2 \frac{e^x}{e^x + e}\, dx$

29. $\displaystyle\int_0^2 xe^{4-x^2}\, dx$

30. $\displaystyle\int_0^3 \frac{e^x + e^{-x}}{2}\, dx$

In Exercises 31 and 32, find the relative extrema of f, the points of inflection of the graph of f, the intervals on which f is increasing, the intervals on which f is decreasing, where the graph is concave upward, where the graph is concave downward, and the slope of any inflectional tangent. Draw a sketch of the graph of f.

31. $f(x) = xe^{-x}$

32. $f(x) = e^{-x^2}$

33. Find an equation of the tangent line to the curve $y = e^{-x}$ that is perpendicular to the line $2x - y = 5$.

34. Find the area of the region bounded by the curve $y = e^x$ and the line through the points $(0, 1)$ and $(1, e)$.

35. A solid has as its base the region bounded by the curves $y = e^x$ and $y = e^{-x}$ and the line $x = 1$. If every plane section perpendicular to the x axis is a square find the volume of the solid.

36. Prove that the most general function that is equal to its derivative is given by $f(x) = ke^x$. (HINT: Let $y = f(x)$ and solve the differential equation $dy/dx = y$.)

37. If p lb/ft^2 is the atmospheric pressure at a height of h ft above sea level, then $p = 2116e^{-0.0000318h}$. Find the time rate of change of the atmospheric pressure outside of an airplane that is 5000 ft high and rising at the rate of 160 ft/sec.

38. At a certain height the gauge on an airplane indicates that the atmospheric pressure is 1500 lb/ft^2. Applying the formula of Exercise 37, approximate by differentials how much higher the airplane must rise so that the pressure will be 1480 lb/ft^2.

39. If l ft is the length of an iron rod when t degrees is its temperature, then $l = 60e^{0.00001t}$. Use differentials to find the approximate increase in l when t increases from 0 to 10.

40. A simple electric circuit containing no condensers, a resistance of R ohms, and an inductance of L henrys has the electromotive force cut off when the current is I_0 amperes. The current dies down so that at t sec the current is i amperes and

$$i = I_0 e^{-(R/L)t}$$

Show that the rate of change of the current is proportional to the current.

41. A body is moving along a straight line and at t sec the velocity is v ft/sec where $v = e^3 - e^{2t}$. Find the distance traveled by the particle while $v > 0$ after $t = 0$.

42. An advertising agency determined statistically that if a breakfast food manufacturer increases its budget for television commercials by x thousand dollars there will be an increase in the total profit of $25x^2e^{-0.2x}$ hundred dollars. What should be the advertising budget increase in order for the manufacturer to have the greatest profit? What will be the corresponding increase in the company's profit?

43. A tank is in the shape of the solid of revolution formed by rotating about the x axis the region bounded by the curve $y^2x = e^{-2x}$ and the lines $x = 1$ and $x = 4$. If the tank is full of water, find the work done in pumping all the water to a point 1 ft above the top of the tank. Distance is measured in feet.

44. Prove: $\displaystyle\lim_{x \to +\infty} e^x = +\infty$, by showing that for any $N > 0$ there exists an $M > 0$ such that $e^x > N$ whenever $x > M$.

45. Prove: $\displaystyle\lim_{x \to -\infty} e^x = 0$, by showing that for any $\epsilon > 0$ there exists an $N < 0$ such that $e^x < \epsilon$ whenever $x < N$.

46. Draw a sketch of the graph of F if $F(h) = (1 + h)^{1/h}$.

8.5 OTHER EXPONENTIAL AND LOGARITHMIC FUNCTIONS
8.5.1 Definition

If a is any positive number and x is any real number, then the function f defined by

$$f(x) = a^x$$

is called the *exponential function to the base a.*

From Definition 8.4.5, we have

$$a^x = e^{x \ln a} \tag{1}$$

The exponential function to the base a satisfies the same properties as the exponential function to the base e. For example, if x and y are any real numbers and a is positive, then

$$a^x a^y = a^{x+y} \tag{2}$$

The proof of (2) follows. From (1) we have

$$a^x a^y = e^{x \ln a} e^{y \ln a}$$

$$= e^{x \ln a + y \ln a}$$

$$= e^{(x+y) \ln a}$$

$$= a^{x+y} \qquad \blacksquare$$

We also have the following properties:

$$a^x \div a^y = a^{x-y} \tag{3}$$

$$(a^x)^y = a^{xy} \tag{4}$$

$$(ab)^x = a^x b^x \tag{5}$$

$$a^0 = 1 \tag{6}$$

The proofs of (3) through (6) are left for the reader (see Exercises 1 to 4).

To find the derivative of the exponential function to the base a, we set $a^x = e^{x \ln a}$ and apply the chain rule. We have

$$a^x = e^{x \ln a}$$

$$D_x(a^x) = e^{x \ln a} D_x(x \ln a)$$

$$= e^{x \ln a}(\ln a)$$

$$= a^x \ln a$$

Hence, if u is a differentiable function of x,

$$D_x(a^u) = a^u \ln a \, D_x u \tag{7}$$

EXAMPLE 1:   Given $y = 3^{x^2}$, find $D_x y$.

SOLUTION: Applying formula (7), we have

$$D_x y = 3^{x^2} \ln 3 (2x) = 2 (\ln 3) x 3^{x^2}$$

From (7) we obtain the following indefinite integration formula:

$$\int a^u \, du = \frac{a^u}{\ln a} + C \tag{8}$$

EXAMPLE 2:   Find

$$\int \sqrt{10^{3x}} \, dx$$

SOLUTION: $\int \sqrt{10^{3x}} \, dx = \int 10^{3x/2} \, dx$. Let $u = \frac{3}{2}x$; then $du = \frac{3}{2} \, dx$; thus $\frac{2}{3} \, du = dx$. We have then

$$\int 10^{3x/2} \, dx = \int 10^u \, \tfrac{2}{3} \, du$$

$$= \frac{2}{3} \cdot \frac{10^u}{\ln 10} + C$$

$$= \frac{2 \cdot 10^{3x/2}}{3 \ln 10} + C$$

EXAMPLE 3:   Draw sketches of the graphs of $y = 2^x$ and $y = 2^{-x}$ on the same set of axes. Find the area of the region bounded by these two graphs and the line $x = 2$.

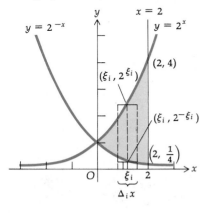

Figure 8.5.1

SOLUTION: The required sketches are shown in Fig. 8.5.1. The region is shaded in the figure. If A square units is the desired area, we have

$$A = \lim_{||\Delta|| \to 0} \sum_{i=1}^{n} [2^{\xi_i} - 2^{-\xi_i}] \, \Delta_i x$$

$$= \int_0^2 (2^x - 2^{-x}) \, dx$$

$$= \frac{2^x}{\ln 2} + \frac{2^{-x}}{\ln 2} \Big]_0^2$$

$$= \frac{4}{\ln 2} + \frac{\frac{1}{4}}{\ln 2} - \frac{1}{\ln 2} - \frac{1}{\ln 2}$$

$$= \frac{9}{4 \ln 2}$$

$$\approx 3.25$$

We can now define the *logarithmic function to the base a* if a is any positive number other than one.

8.5.2 Definition   If a is any positive number except 1, the *logarithmic function to the base a* is the inverse of the exponential function to the base a; and we write

$$y = \log_a x \quad \text{if and only if} \quad a^y = x \tag{9}$$

The above is the definition of the logarithmic function to the base a usually given in elementary algebra; however, (9) has meaning for y any real number because a^y has been precisely defined. It should be noted that if $a = e$, we have the logarithmic function to the base e, which is the natural logarithmic function.

$\log_a x$ is read as "the logarithm of x to the base a."

The logarithmic function to the base a obeys the same laws as the natural logarithmic function. We list them.

$$\log_a(xy) = \log_a x + \log_a y \tag{10}$$

$$\log_a(x \div y) = \log_a x - \log_a y \tag{11}$$

$$\log_a 1 = 0 \tag{12}$$

$$\log_a x^y = y \log_a x \tag{13}$$

The proofs of (10) through (13) are left for the reader (see Exercises 5 to 8).

A relationship between logarithms to the base a and natural logarithms follows easily. Let

$$y = \log_a x$$

Then

$$a^y = x$$

$$\ln a^y = \ln x$$

$$y \ln a = \ln x$$

$$y = \frac{\ln x}{\ln a}$$

Replacing y by $\log_a x$, we obtain

$$\log_a x = \frac{\ln x}{\ln a} \tag{14}$$

Equation (14) sometimes is used as the definition of the logarithmic function to the base a. Because the natural logarithmic function is continuous at all $x > 0$, it follows from (14) that the logarithmic function to the base a is continuous at all $x > 0$.

If in (14) we take $x = e$, we have

$$\log_a e = \frac{\ln e}{\ln a}$$

or, equivalently,

$$\log_a e = \frac{1}{\ln a} \tag{15}$$

We now find the derivative of the logarithmic function to the base a. We differentiate on both sides of Eq. (14) with respect to x, and we obtain

$$D_x(\log_a x) = \frac{1}{\ln a} D_x(\ln x)$$

or

$$D_x(\log_a x) = \frac{1}{\ln a} \cdot \frac{1}{x} \tag{16}$$

Substituting from (15) into (16), we get

$$D_x(\log_a x) = \frac{\log_a e}{x} \tag{17}$$

If u is a differentiable function of x, we have

$$D_x(\log_a u) = \frac{\log_a e}{u} D_x u \tag{18}$$

Note that if in (18) we take $a = e$, we get

$$D_x(\log_e u) = \frac{\log_e e}{u} D_x u$$

or, equivalently,

$$D_x(\ln u) = \frac{1}{u} D_x u$$

which is the formula we had previously for the derivative of the natural logarithmic function.

EXAMPLE 4:   Given

$$y = \log_{10} \frac{x+1}{x^2+1}$$

find $D_x y$.

SOLUTION: Using (11), we write

$$y = \log_{10}(x+1) - \log_{10}(x^2+1)$$

From (18) we have

$$D_x y = \frac{\log_{10} e}{x+1} - \frac{\log_{10} e}{x^2+1} \cdot 2x$$

$$= \log_{10} e \left(\frac{1}{x+1} - \frac{2x}{x^2+1} \right)$$

$$= \frac{\log_{10} e(1 - 2x - x^2)}{(x+1)(x^2+1)}$$

Because x^n has been defined for any real number n, we can now prove the formula for finding the derivative of the power function if the exponent is any real number.

8.5.3 Theorem   If n is any real number and the function f is defined by

$$f(x) = x^n \qquad \text{where } x > 0$$

then

$$f'(x) = nx^{n-1}$$

PROOF: Let $y = x^n$. Then from (1)

$$y = e^{n \ln x}$$

Thus,

$$D_x y = e^{n \ln x} D_x(n \ln x)$$

$$= e^{n \ln x} \left(\frac{n}{x}\right)$$

$$= x^n \cdot \frac{n}{x}$$

$$= nx^{n-1} \qquad\blacksquare$$

Theorem 8.5.3 enables us to find the derivative of a variable to a constant power. Previously in this section we learned how to differentiate a constant to a variable power. We now consider the derivative of a function whose function value is a variable to a variable power. The method of *logarithmic differentiation* is used and is illustrated in the following example.

EXAMPLE 5:   Given $y = x^x$, find $D_x y$.

SOLUTION: Because $y = x^x$, then $|y| = |x^x|$. We take the natural logarithm on both sides of the equation, and we have

$$\ln |y| = \ln |x^x|$$

or, equivalently,

$$\ln |y| = x \ln |x|$$

Differentiating on both sides of the above equation with respect to x, we obtain

$$\frac{1}{y} D_x y = \ln |x| + x \frac{1}{x}$$

So

$$D_x y = y(\ln |x| + 1)$$

$$= x^x(\ln |x| + 1) \cdot$$

Exercises 8.5

In Exercises 1 through 4, prove the given property if a is any positive number and x and y are any real numbers.

1. $a^x \div a^y = a^{x-y}$

2. $(a^x)^y = a^{xy}$

3. $(ab)^x = a^x b^x$

4. $a^0 = 1$

In Exercises 5 through 8, prove the given property if a is any positive number and x and y are any positive numbers.

5. $\log_a(xy) = \log_a x + \log_a y$

6. $\log_a(x \div y) = \log_a x - \log_a y$

7. $\log_a x^y = y \log_a x$

8. $\log_a 1 = 0$

In Exercises 9 through 24, find $f'(x)$.

9. $f(x) = 3^{5x}$

10. $f(x) = 6^{-3x}$

11. $f(x) = 2^{5x} 3^{4x^2}$

12. $f(x) = (x^3 + 3)2^{-7x}$

13. $f(x) = \dfrac{\log_{10} x}{x}$

14. $f(x) = \log_{10} \dfrac{x}{x+1}$

15. $f(x) = \sqrt{\log_a x}$

16. $f(x) = \log_a[\log_a(\log_a x)]$

17. $f(x) = \log_{10}[\log_{10}(x+1)]$

18. $f(x) = x^{\ln x}$

19. $f(x) = x^{\sqrt{x}}$

20. $f(x) = x^{x^2}$

21. $f(x) = x^{e^x}$

22. $f(x) = (x)^{x^x}$

23. $f(x) = (4e^x)^{3x}$

24. $f(x) = (\ln x)^{\ln x}$

In Exercises 25 through 32, evaluate the indefinite integral.

25. $\displaystyle\int 3^{2x} \, dx$

26. $\displaystyle\int a^{nx} \, dx$

27. $\displaystyle\int a^x e^x \, dx$

28. $\displaystyle\int 5^{x^4+2x}(2x^3 + 1) \, dx$

29. $\displaystyle\int x^2 10^{x^3} \, dx$

30. $\displaystyle\int a^{x \ln x}(\ln x + 1) \, dx$

31. $\displaystyle\int e^x 2^{e^x} 3^{e^x} \, dx$

32. $\displaystyle\int \dfrac{4^{\ln(1/x)}}{x} \, dx$

33. Find an equation of the tangent line to the curve $y^2 4^y = x2^x$ at $(4, 2)$.

34. A particle is moving along a straight line according to the equation of motion $s = A2^{kt} + B2^{-kt}$, where s ft is the directed distance of the particle from the starting point at t sec. Prove that if a ft/sec² is the acceleration at t sec, then a is proportional to s.

35. A company has learned that when it initiates a new sales campaign the number of sales per day increases. However, the number of extra daily sales per day decreases as the impact of the campaign wears off. For a specific campaign the company has determined that if S is the number of extra daily sales as a result of the campaign and x is the number of days that have elapsed since the campaign ended, then

$$S = 1000 \cdot 3^{-x/2}$$

Find the rate at which the extra daily sales is decreasing when (a) $x = 4$ and (b) $x = 10$.

In Exercises 36 and 37 use differentials to find an approximate value of the given logarithm and express the answer to three decimal places.

36. $\log_{10} 1.015$

37. $\log_{10} 997$

38. Draw sketches of the graphs of $y = \log_{10} x$ and $y = \ln x$ on the same set of axes.

39. Given: $f(x) = \frac{1}{2}(a^x + a^{-x})$. Prove that $f(b + c) + f(b - c) = 2f(b)f(c)$.

40. A particle moves along a straight line according to the equation of motion $s = t^{1/t}$ where s ft is the directed distance of the particle from the starting point at t sec. Find the velocity and acceleration at 2 sec.

8.6 LAWS OF GROWTH AND DECAY

The laws of growth and decay provide applications of the exponential function in chemistry, physics, biology, and business. Such a situation would arise when the rate of change of the amount of a substance with respect to time is proportional to the amount of the substance present at a given instant. This would occur in biology, where under certain circumstances the rate of growth of a culture of bacteria is proportional to the amount of bacteria present at any given instant. In a chemical reaction, it is often the case that the rate of the reaction is proportional to the quantity of the substance present; for instance, it is known from experiments that the rate of decay of radium is proportional to the amount of radium present at a given instant. An application in business occurs when interest is compounded continuously.

In such cases, if the time is represented by t units, and A units represents the amount of the substance present at any time, then

$$\frac{dA}{dt} = kA$$

where k is a constant. If A increases as t increases, then $k > 0$, and we have the *law of natural growth*. If A decreases as t increases, then $k < 0$, and we have the *law of natural decay*. In problems involving the law of natural decay, the *half life* of a substance is the time required for half of it to decay.

EXAMPLE 1: The rate of decay of radium is proportional to the amount present at any time. If 60 mg of radium are present now, and its half life is 1690 years, how much radium will be present 100 years from now?

Table 8.6.1

t	0	1690	100
A	60	30	A_{100}

SOLUTION: Let $t =$ the number of years in the time from now;
$A =$ the number of milligrams of radium present at t years.

We have the initial conditions given in Table 8.6.1. The differential equation is

$$\frac{dA}{dt} = kA$$

Separating the variables, we obtain

$$\frac{dA}{A} = k\,dt$$

Integrating, we have

$$\int \frac{dA}{A} = k \int dt$$

$$\ln |A| = kt + \bar{c}$$

$$|A| = e^{kt+\bar{c}} = e^{\bar{c}} \cdot e^{kt}$$

Letting $e^{\bar{c}} = C$, we have $|A| = Ce^{kt}$, and because A is nonnegative we can omit the absolute-value bars around A, thereby giving us

$$A = Ce^{kt}$$

Because $A = 60$ when $t = 0$, we obtain $60 = C$. So

$$A = 60e^{kt} \tag{1}$$

Because $A = 30$ when $t = 1690$, we get $30 = 60e^{1690k}$ or

$$0.5 = e^{1690k}$$

So

$$\ln 0.5 = 1690k$$

and

$$k = \frac{\ln 0.5}{1690} = \frac{-0.6931}{1690} = -0.000411$$

Substituting this value of k into Eq. (1), we obtain

$$A = 60e^{-0.000411t}$$

When $t = 100$, $A = A_{100}$, and we have

$$A_{100} = 60e^{-0.0411} = 58$$

Therefore, there will be 58 mg of radium present 100 years from now.

EXAMPLE 2: In a certain culture, the rate of growth of bacteria is proportional to the amount present. If there are 1000 bacteria present initially, and the amount doubles in 12 min, how long will it take before there will be 1,000,000 bacteria present?

Table 8.6.2

t	0	12	T
A	1,000	2,000	1,000,000

SOLUTION: Let $t =$ the number of minutes in the time from now;
$A =$ the number of bacteria present at t min.
Even though by definition A is a nonnegative integer, we assume that A can be any nonnegative number in order for A to be a continuous function of t. Table 8.6.2 gives the initial conditions. The differential equation is

$$\frac{dA}{dt} = kA$$

The differential equation is the same as we had in Example 1; hence, as above, the general solution is

$$A = Ce^{kt}$$

When $t = 0$, $A = 1000$; hence, $C = 1000$, which gives

$$A = 1000e^{kt}$$

From the condition that $A = 2000$ when $t = 12$, we obtain

$$e^{12k} = 2$$

and so

$$k = \tfrac{1}{12} \ln 2 = 0.05776$$

Hence, we have

$$A = 1000e^{0.05776t}$$

Replacing t by T and A by 1,000,000, we get

$$1,000,000 = 1000e^{0.05776T}$$

$$e^{0.05776T} = 1000$$

$$0.05776T = \ln 1000$$

$$T = \frac{\ln 1000}{0.05776} = 119.6$$

Therefore, there will be 1,000,000 bacteria present in 1 hr, 59 min, 36 sec.

EXAMPLE 3:   Newton's law of cooling states that the rate at which a body changes temperature is proportional to the difference between its temperature and that of the surrounding medium. If a body is in air of temperature 35° and the body cools from 120° to 60° in 40 min, find the temperature of the body after 100 min.

Table 8.6.3

t	0	40	100
x	120	60	x_{100}

SOLUTION: Let $t =$ the number of minutes in the time that has elapsed since the body started to cool;

$x =$ the number of degrees in the temperature of the body at t minutes.

Table 8.6.3 gives the initial conditions. From Newton's law of cooling, we have

$$\frac{dx}{dt} = k(x - 35)$$

Separating the variables, we obtain

$$\frac{dx}{x - 35} = k\,dt$$

So

$$\int \frac{dx}{x - 35} = k \int dt$$

$$\ln |x - 35| = kt + \bar{c}$$

$$x - 35 = Ce^{kt}$$

$$x = Ce^{kt} + 35$$

When $t = 0$, $x = 120$; so $C = 85$. Therefore,

$$x = 85e^{kt} + 35$$

When $t = 40$, $x = 60$; and we obtain

$$60 = 85e^{40k} + 35$$

$$40k = \ln \tfrac{5}{17}$$

$$k = \tfrac{1}{40} (\ln 5 - \ln 17)$$

$$= \tfrac{1}{40}\,(1.6094 - 2.8332)$$

$$= -0.0306$$

So

$$x = 85e^{-0.0306t} + 35$$

Then

$$x_{100} = 85e^{-3.06} + 35 = 39$$

Therefore, the temperature of the body is 39° after 100 min.

EXAMPLE 4: There are 100 gal of brine in a tank and the brine contains 70 lb of dissolved salt. Fresh water runs into the tank at the rate of 3 gal/min, and the mixture, kept uniform by stirring, runs out at the same rate. How many pounds of salt are there in the tank at the end of 1 hr?

Table 8.6.4

t	0	60
x	70	x_{60}

SOLUTION: Let $t =$ the number of minutes that have elapsed since the water started flowing into the tank;

$x =$ the number of pounds of salt in the tank at t min.

Because 100 gal of brine are in the tank at all times, at t minutes the number of pounds of salt per gallon is $x/100$. Three gallons of the mixture run out of the tank each minute, and so the tank loses $3(x/100)$ pounds of salt per minute. Because $D_t x$ is the rate of change of x with respect to t, and x is decreasing as t increases, we have the differential equation

$$\frac{dx}{dt} = -\frac{3x}{100}$$

We also have the initial conditions given in Table 8.6.4. Separating the variables and integrating, we have

$$\int \frac{dx}{x} = -0.03 \int dt$$

$$\ln |x| = -0.03t + \bar{c}$$

$$x = Ce^{-0.03t}$$

When $t = 0$, $x = 70$, and so $C = 70$. Letting $t = 60$ and $x = x_{60}$, we have

$$x_{60} = 70e^{-1.8}$$

$$= 70(0.1653)$$

$$= 11.57$$

So there are 11.57 lb of salt in the tank after 1 hr.

The calculus is often very useful to the economist for evaluating certain business decisions. However, to use the calculus we must be concerned with continuous functions. Consider, for example, the following formula which gives A, the number of dollars in the amount after t years, if P dollars is invested at a rate of $100i$ percent, compounded m times per year:

$$A = P \left(1 + \frac{i}{m}\right)^{mt} \tag{2}$$

Let us conceive of a situation in which the interest is continuously compounding; that is, consider formula (2), where we let the number of interest periods per year increase without bound. Then going to the limit in formula (2), we have

$$A = P \lim_{m \to +\infty} \left(1 + \frac{i}{m}\right)^{mt}$$

which can be written as

$$A = P \lim_{m \to +\infty} \left[\left(1 + \frac{i}{m}\right)^{m/i}\right]^{it} \tag{3}$$

Now consider

$$\lim_{m \to +\infty} \left(1 + \frac{i}{m}\right)^{m/i}$$

Letting $h = i/m$, we have $m/i = 1/h$; and because "$m \to +\infty$" is equivalent to "$h \to 0^+$," we have

$$\lim_{m \to +\infty} \left(1 + \frac{i}{m}\right)^{m/i} = \lim_{h \to 0^+} (1 + h)^{1/h} = e$$

Hence, using Theorem 2.12.5, we have

$$\lim_{m \to +\infty} \left[\left(1 + \frac{i}{m}\right)^{m/i}\right]^{it} = \left[\lim_{m \to +\infty} \left(1 + \frac{i}{m}\right)^{m/i}\right]^{it} = e^{it}$$

and so Eq. (3) becomes

$$A = Pe^{it} \tag{4}$$

By letting t vary through the set of nonnegative real numbers, we see that Eq. (4) expresses A as a continuous function of t.

Another way of looking at the same situation is to consider an investment of P dollars, which increases at a rate proportional to its size. This is the law of natural growth. Then if A dollars is the amount at t years, we have

$$\frac{dA}{dt} = kA$$

$$\int \frac{dA}{A} = k \int dt$$

$$\ln |A| = kt + \bar{c}$$

$$A = Ce^{kt}$$

When $t = 0$, $A = P$, and so $C = P$. Therefore, we have

$$A = Pe^{kt} \qquad (5)$$

Comparing Eq. (5) with Eq. (4), we see that they are the same if $k = i$. So if an investment increases at a rate proportional to its size, we say that the interest is *compounded continuously*, and the interest rate is the constant of proportionality. In particular, if P dollars is invested at a rate of 8% per year compounded continuously, and A dollars is the amount of the investment at t years,

$$\frac{dA}{dt} = 0.08A$$

and

$$A = Pe^{0.08t}$$

If in Eq. (4) we take $P = 1$, $i = 1$, and $t = 1$, we get $A = e$, which gives a justification for the economist's interpretation of the number "e" as the yield on an investment of one dollar for a year at an interest rate of 100% compounded continuously.

EXAMPLE 5: If $5000 is borrowed at an interest rate of 12% per year, compounded continuously, and the loan is to be repaid in one payment at the end of a year, how much must the borrower repay? Also, find the effective rate of interest which is the rate that gives the same amount of interest compounded once a year.

SOLUTION: Letting A dollars be the amount to be repaid, and because $P = 5000$, $i = 0.12$, and $t = 1$, we have from equation (4)

$$A = 5000e^{0.12}$$
$$= 5000(1.1275)$$
$$= 5637.50$$

Hence, the borrower must repay $5637.50. Letting j be the effective rate of interest, we have

$$5000(1 + j) = 5000e^{0.12}$$
$$1 + j = e^{0.12}$$
$$j = 1.1275 - 1$$
$$= 0.1275$$
$$= 12.75\%$$

Exercises 8.6

1. Bacteria grown in a certain culture increase at a rate proportional to the amount present. If there are 1000 bacteria present initially and the amount doubles in 1 hr, how many bacteria will there be in $3\frac{1}{2}$ hr?

2. In a certain culture where the rate of growth of bacteria is proportional to the amount present, the number triples in 3 hr, and at the end of 12 hr there were 10 million bacteria. How many bacteria were present initially?

3. In a certain chemical reaction the rate of conversion of a substance is proportional to the amount of the substance still untransformed at that time. After 10 min one-third of the original amount of the substance has been converted, and 20 g has been converted after 15 min. What was the original amount of the substance?

4. Sugar decomposes in water at a rate proportional to the amount still unchanged. If there were 50 lb of sugar present initially and at the end of 5 hr this is reduced to 20 lb, how long will it take until 90% of the sugar is decomposed?

5. The rate of natural increase of the population of a certain city is proportional to the population. If the population increases from 40,000 to 60,000 in 40 years, when will the population be 80,000?

6. Using Newton's law of cooling (see Example 3), if a body in air at a temperature of 0° cools from 200° to 100° in 40 min, how many more minutes will it take for the body to cool to 50°?

7. Under the conditions of Example 3, after how many minutes will the temperature of the body be 45°?

8. When a simple electric circuit, containing no condensers but having inductance and resistance, has the electromotive force removed, the rate of decrease of the current is proportional to the current. The current is i amperes t sec after the cutoff, and $i = 40$ when $t = 0$. If the current dies down to 15 amperes in 0.01 sec, find i in terms of t.

9. If a thermometer is taken from a room in which the temperature is 75° into the open, where the temperature is 35°, and the reading of the thermometer is 65° after 30 sec, (a) how long after the removal will the reading be 50°? (b) What is the thermometer reading 3 min after the removal? Use Newton's law of cooling (see Example 3).

10. Thirty percent of a radioactive substance disappears in 15 years. Find the half life of the substance.

11. If the half life of radium is 1690 years, what percent of the amount present now will be remaining after (a) 100 years and (b) 1000 years?

12. A tank contains 200 gal of brine in which there are 3 lb of salt per gallon. It is desired to dilute this solution by adding brine containing 1 lb of salt per gallon, which flows into the tank at the rate of 4 gal/min and runs out at the same rate. When will the tank contain $1\frac{1}{2}$ lb of salt per gallon?

13. A tank contains 100 gal of fresh water and brine containing 2 lb of salt per gallon flows into the tank at the rate of 3 gal/min. If the mixture, kept uniform by stirring, flows out at the same rate, how many pounds of salt are there in the tank at the end of 30 min?

14. A loan of $100 is repaid in one payment at the end of a year. If the interest rate is 8% compounded continuously, determine (a) the total amount repaid and (b) the effective rate of interest.

15. If an amount of money invested doubles itself in 10 years at interest compounded continuously, how long will it take for the original amount to triple itself?

16. If the purchasing power of a dollar is decreasing at the rate of 2% annually, compounded continuously, how long will it take for the purchasing power to be 50 cents?

17. In order to determine the date of death of a once-living object, use is made of the fact that the tissue of a living organism is composed of two kinds of carbons, a radioactive carbon A and a stable carbon B, in which the ratio of the amount of A to the amount of B is approximately constant. When the organism dies, the law of natural decay applies to A. If it is determined that the amount of A in a piece of charcoal is only 15% of its original amount and the half life of A is 5500 years, when did the tree from which the charcoal came die?

Review Exercises (Chapter 8)

In Exercises 1 through 8, differentiate the given function.

1. $f(x) = (\ln x^2)^2$

2. $f(x) = \dfrac{e^x}{(e^x + e^{-x})^2}$

3. $f(x) = \sqrt{\log_{10}\dfrac{1+x}{1-x}}$

4. $f(x) = 10^{-5x^2}$

5. $f(x) = x^{3/\ln x}$

6. $f(x) = e^{x/(4+x^2)}$

7. $f(x) = (x)^{x^{e^x}}$

8. $f(x) = 3^{x^{x^n}}$

In Exercises 9 through 14, evaluate the indefinite integral.

9. $\displaystyle\int \frac{3e^{2x}}{1+e^{2x}}\, dx$

10. $\displaystyle\int e^{2x^2-4x}(x-1)\, dx$

11. $\displaystyle\int (e^{3x} + a^{3x})\, dx$

12. $\displaystyle\int \frac{10^{\ln x^2}}{x}\, dx$

13. $\displaystyle\int \frac{2^x\, dx}{\sqrt{3}\cdot 2^x + 4}$

14. $\displaystyle\int \frac{10^x + 1}{10^x - 1}\, dx$

In Exercises 15 through 18, evaluate the definite integral.

15. $\displaystyle\int_0^2 x^2 e^{x^3}\, dx$

16. $\displaystyle\int_0^1 (e^{2x} + 1)^2\, dx$

17. $\displaystyle\int_1^8 \frac{x^{1/3}}{x^{4/3} + 4}\, dx$

18. $\displaystyle\int_{1/3}^{1/2} \frac{4x^{-3} + 2}{x^{-2} - x}\, dx$

19. Find $D_x y$ if $ye^x + xe^y + x + y = 0$.

20. If $f(x) = \log_{(e^x)}(x + 1)$, find $f'(x)$.

21. The linear density of a rod at a point x ft from one end is $1/(x + 1)$ slugs/ft. If the rod is 4 ft long, find the mass and center of mass of the rod.

22. Find an equation of the tangent line to the curve $y = x^{x-1}$ at $(2, 2)$.

23. A particle is moving on a straight line where s ft is the directed distance of the particle from the origin, v ft/sec is the velocity of the particle, and a ft/sec^2 is the acceleration of the particle at t sec. If $a = e^t + e^{-t}$ and $v = 1$ and $s = 2$ when $t = 0$, find v and s in terms of t.

24. The area of the region, bounded by the curve $y = e^{-x}$, the coordinate axes, and the line $x = b$ $(b > 0)$, is a function of b. If f is this function, find $f(b)$. Also find $\displaystyle\lim_{b \to +\infty} f(b)$.

25. The volume of the solid of revolution obtained by revolving the region in Exercise 24 about the x axis is a function of b. If g is this function, find $g(b)$. Also find $\displaystyle\lim_{b \to +\infty} g(b)$.

26. The rate of natural increase of the population of a certain city is proportional to the population. If the population doubles in 60 years and if the population in 1950 was 60,000, estimate the population in the year 2000.

27. The rate of decay of a radioactive substance is proportional to the amount present. If half of a given deposit of the substance disappears in 1900 years, how long will it take for 95% of the deposit to disappear?

28. Prove that if a rectangle is to have its base on the x axis and two of its vertices on the curve $y = e^{-x^2}$, then the rectangle will have the largest possible area if the two vertices are at the points of inflection of the graph.

29. Given $f(x) = \ln |x|$ and $x < 0$. Show that f has an inverse function. If g is the inverse function, find $g(x)$ and the domain of g.

In Exercises 30 and 31 find the inverse of the given function if there is one, and determine its domain. Draw a sketch of the given function, and if the given function has an inverse, draw a sketch of the graph of the inverse function on the same set of axes.

30. $f(x) = \dfrac{x + 4}{2x - 3}$

31. $f(x) = \dfrac{2}{8x^3 - 1}$

32. Prove that if $x < 1$, $\ln x < x$. (HINT: Let $f(x) = x - \ln x$ and show that f is decreasing on $(0, 1)$ and find $f(1)$.)

33. When a gas undergoes an adiabatic (no gain or loss of heat) expansion or compression then the rate of change of the pressure with respect to the volume varies directly as the pressure and inversely as the volume. If the pressure is p lb/in.^{2} when the volume is v in.^{3}, and the initial pressure and volume are p_0 lb/in.^{2} and v_0 in.^{3}, show that $pv^k = p_0 v_0^k$.

34. If W in.-lb is the work done by a gas expanding against a piston in a cylinder and P lb in.^{2} is the pressure of the gas when the volume of the gas is V in.^{3}, show that if V_1 in.^{3} and V_2 in.^{3} are the initial and final volumes, respectively, then

$$W = \int_{V_1}^{V_2} P\, dV$$

35. Suppose a piston compresses a gas in a cylinder from an initial volume of 60 in.^{3} to a volume of 40 in.^{3}. If Boyle's law (Exercise 10 in Exercises 4.1) holds, and the initial pressure is 50 lb/in.^{2}, find the work done by the piston. (Use the result of Exercise 34.)

36. The charge of electricity on a spherical surface leaks off at a rate proportional to the charge. Initially, the charge of electricity was 8 coulombs and one-fourth leaks off in 15 min. When will there be only 2 coulombs remaining?

37. How long will it take for an investment to double itself if interest is paid at the rate of 8% compounded continuously?

38. A tank contains 60 gal of salt water with 120 lb of dissolved salt. Salt water with 3 lb of salt per gallon flows into the tank at the rate of 2 gal/min and the mixture, kept uniform by stirring, flows out at the same rate. How long will it be before there are 200 lb of salt in the tank?

39. Prove that if $x > 0$, and $\int_1^x t^{h-1}\, dt = 1$, then $\lim_{h \to 0} x = \lim_{h \to 0} (1 + h)^{1/h}$.

40. Prove that
$$\lim_{x \to 0} \frac{\log_a(1 + x)}{x} = \log_a e.$$

(NOTE: Compare with Exercise 34 in Exercises 8.1.)

41. Prove that
$$\lim_{x \to 0} \frac{a^x - 1}{x} = \ln a$$

(HINT: Let $y = a^x - 1$ and express $(a^x - 1)/x$ as a function of y, say $g(y)$. Then show that $y \to 0$ as $x \to 0$, and find $\lim_{y \to 0} g(y)$.)

42. Use the results of Exercises 40 and 41 to prove that
$$\lim_{x \to 1} \frac{x^b - 1}{x - 1} = b$$

(HINT: Write
$$\frac{x^b - 1}{x - 1} = \frac{e^{b \ln x} - 1}{b \ln x} \cdot \frac{b \ln x}{x - 1}$$
Then let $s = b \ln x$ and $t = x - 1$.)

43. Prove that
$$\lim_{x \to 0} \frac{e^{ax} - 1}{x} = a$$

(HINT: Let $f(x) = e^{ax}$ and find $f'(0)$ by two methods.)

44. If the domain of f is the set of all real numbers and $f'(x) = cf(x)$ for all x where c is a constant, prove that there is a constant k for which $f(x) = ke^{cx}$ for all x. (HINT: Consider the function g for which $g(x) = f(x)e^{-cx}$ and find $g'(x)$.)

45. Prove that
$$D_x{}^n(\ln x) = (-1)^{n-1} \frac{(n - 1)!}{x^n}$$

(HINT: Use mathematical induction.)

46. Do Exercise 17 in the Review Exercises of Chapter 6 by evaluating each integral.

9

Trigonometric and Hyperbolic Functions

9.1 THE SINE AND COSINE FUNCTIONS

In geometry an *angle* is defined as the union of two rays called the *sides*, having a common endpoint called the *vertex*. Any angle is congruent to some angle having its vertex at the origin and one side, called the *initial side*, lying on the positive side of the *x* axis. Such an angle is said to be in *standard position*. Figure 9.1.1 shows an angle *AOB* in standard position with *AO* as the initial side. The other side *OB* is called the *terminal side*. The angle *AOB* can be formed by rotating the side *OA* to the side *OB*, and under such a rotation the point *A* moves along the circumference of a circle, having its center at *O* and radius $|\overline{OA}|$ to the point *B*.

In the study of trigonometry dealing with problems involving angles of triangles, the measurement of an angle is usually given in degrees. However, in the calculus we are concerned with trigonometric functions of real numbers, and we use *radian measure* to define these functions.

To define the radian measure of an angle we use the length of an arc of a circle. If such an arc is smaller than a semicircle, it can be considered the graph of a function having a continuous derivative; and so by Theorem 7.10.2 it has length. If the arc is a semicircle or larger, it has a length that is the sum of the lengths of arcs which are smaller than semicircles.

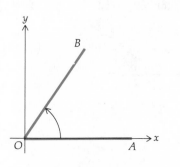

Figure 9.1.1

9.1.1 Definition

Let *AOB* be an angle in standard position and $|\overline{OA}| = 1$. If *s* units is the length of the arc of the circle traveled by point *A* as the initial side *OA* is rotated to the terminal side *OB*, the *radian measure*, *t*, of angle *AOB* is given by

$$t = s \qquad \text{if the rotation is counterclockwise}$$

and

$$t = -s \quad \text{if the rotation is clockwise}$$

By using the fact that the measure of the length of the unit circle's circumference is 2π, we determine the radian measures of the angles in Fig. 9.1.2a, b, c, d, e, and f. They are $\frac{1}{2}\pi, \frac{1}{4}\pi, -\frac{1}{2}\pi, \frac{3}{2}\pi, -\frac{3}{4}\pi$, and $\frac{7}{4}\pi$, respectively.

Figure 9.1.2

In Definition 9.1.1 it is possible that there may be more than one complete revolution in the rotation of OA. Figure 9.1.3a shows such an angle whose radian measure is $\frac{5}{2}\pi$, and Fig. 9.1.3b shows one whose radian measure is $-\frac{13}{4}\pi$.

An angle formed by one complete revolution so that OA is coincident with OB has degree measure of 360 and radian measure of 2π. Hence, there is the following correspondence between degree measure and radian measure (where the symbol $\sim$ indicates that the given measurements are for the same or congruent angles).

Figure 9.1.3

$$360° \sim 2\pi \text{ rad}$$

or, equivalently,

$$180° \sim \pi \text{ rad}$$

From this it follows that

$$1° \sim \tfrac{1}{180}\pi \text{ rad}$$

and

$$1 \text{ rad} \sim \frac{180°}{\pi} \approx 57°18'$$

From this correspondence the measurement of an angle can be converted from one system of units to the other. For example,

$$162° \sim 162 \cdot \tfrac{1}{180}\pi \text{ rad} = \tfrac{9}{10}\pi \text{ rad}$$

and

$$\frac{5}{12}\pi \text{ rad} \sim \frac{5}{12}\pi \cdot \frac{180°}{\pi} = 75°$$

Table 9.1.1 gives the corresponding degree and radian measures of certain angles.

Table 9.1.1

degree measure	30	45	60	90	120	135	150	180	270	360
radian measure	$\tfrac{1}{6}\pi$	$\tfrac{1}{4}\pi$	$\tfrac{1}{3}\pi$	$\tfrac{1}{2}\pi$	$\tfrac{2}{3}\pi$	$\tfrac{3}{4}\pi$	$\tfrac{5}{6}\pi$	π	$\tfrac{3}{2}\pi$	2π

We now define the sine and cosine functions of any real number.

9.1.2 Definition Suppose that t is a real number. Place an angle, having radian measure t, in standard position and let point P be at the intersection of the terminal side of the angle with the unit circle having its center at the origin. If P is the point (x, y), then the *cosine function* is defined by

$$\cos t = x$$

and the *sine function* is defined by

$$\sin t = y$$

From the above definition it is seen that $\sin t$ and $\cos t$ are defined for any value of t. Hence, the domain of the sine and cosine functions is the set of all real numbers. The largest value either function may have is 1, and the smallest value is -1. It will be shown later that the sine and cosine functions are continuous everywhere, and from this it follows that the range of the two functions is $[-1, 1]$.

For certain values of t, the cosine and sine are easily obtained from a figure. From Fig. 9.1.4 we see that $\cos 0 = 1$ and $\sin 0 = 0$, $\cos \tfrac{1}{4}\pi = \tfrac{1}{2}\sqrt{2}$

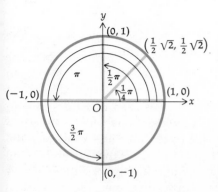

Figure 9.1.4

and $\sin \frac{1}{4}\pi = \frac{1}{2}\sqrt{2}$, $\cos \frac{1}{2}\pi = 0$ and $\sin \frac{1}{2}\pi = 1$, $\cos \pi = -1$ and $\sin \pi = 0$, $\cos \frac{3}{2}\pi = 0$ and $\sin \frac{3}{2}\pi = -1$. Table 9.1.2 gives these values and some others that are frequently used.

Table 9.1.2

x	0	$\frac{1}{6}\pi$	$\frac{1}{4}\pi$	$\frac{1}{3}\pi$	$\frac{1}{2}\pi$	$\frac{2}{3}\pi$	$\frac{3}{4}\pi$	$\frac{5}{6}\pi$	π	$\frac{3}{2}\pi$	2π
$\sin x$	0	$\frac{1}{2}$	$\frac{1}{2}\sqrt{2}$	$\frac{1}{2}\sqrt{3}$	1	$\frac{1}{2}\sqrt{3}$	$\frac{1}{2}\sqrt{2}$	$\frac{1}{2}$	0	-1	0
$\cos x$	1	$\frac{1}{2}\sqrt{3}$	$\frac{1}{2}\sqrt{2}$	$\frac{1}{2}$	0	$-\frac{1}{2}$	$-\frac{1}{2}\sqrt{2}$	$-\frac{1}{2}\sqrt{3}$	-1	0	1

Figure 9.1.5

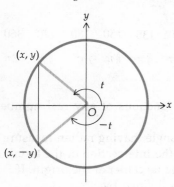

Figure 9.1.6

An equation of the unit circle having its center at the origin is $x^2 + y^2 = 1$. Because $x = \cos t$ and $y = \sin t$, it follows that

$$\cos^2 t + \sin^2 t = 1 \tag{1}$$

Note that $\cos^2 t$ and $\sin^2 t$ stand for $(\cos t)^2$ and $(\sin t)^2$. Equation (1) is called an *identity* because it is valid for any real number t.

Figures 9.1.5 and 9.1.6 show angles having a negative radian measure of $-t$ and corresponding angles having a positive radian measure of t. From these figures we see that

$$\cos(-t) = \cos t \quad \text{and} \quad \sin(-t) = -\sin t \tag{2}$$

These equations hold for any real number t because the points where the terminal sides of the angles (having radian measures t and $-t$) intersect the unit circle have equal abscissas and ordinates that differ only in sign. Hence, Eqs. (2) are identities. From these equations it follows that the cosine function is even and the sine function is odd.

From Definition 9.1.2 the following identities are obtained.

$$\cos(t + 2\pi) = \cos t \quad \text{and} \quad \sin(t + 2\pi) = \sin t \tag{3}$$

The property of cosine and sine stated by Eqs. (3) is called *periodicity*, which is now defined.

9.1.3 Definition A function f is said to be *periodic* with *period* $p \neq 0$ if whenever x is in the domain of f, then $x + p$ is also in the domain of f and

$$f(x + p) = f(x)$$

From the above definition and Eqs. (3) it is seen that the sine and cosine functions are periodic with period 2π; that is, whenever the value of the independent variable t is increased by 2π, the value of each of the functions is repeated. It is because of the periodicity of the sine and cosine that these functions have important applications in physics and engineering in connection with periodically repetitive phenomena such as wave motion and vibrations.

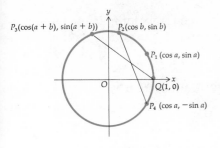

Figure 9.1.7

We now proceed to derive a useful formula because other important identities can be obtained from it. The formula we derive is as follows:

$$\cos(a + b) = \cos a \cos b - \sin a \sin b \qquad (4)$$

where a and b are any real numbers.

Refer to Fig. 9.1.7 showing a unit circle with the points $Q(1,0)$, $P_1(\cos a, \sin a)$, $P_2(\cos b, \sin b)$, $P_3(\cos(a+b), \sin(a+b))$, and $P_4(\cos a, -\sin a)$. Using the notation $\overparen{RS}$ to denote the measure of the length of arc from R to S, we have $\overparen{QP_1} = a$, $\overparen{QP_2} = b$, $\overparen{P_2P_3} = a$, and $\overparen{P_4Q} = |-a| = a$. Because $\overparen{QP_3} = \overparen{QP_2} + \overparen{P_2P_3}$, we have

$$\overparen{QP_3} = b + a \qquad (5)$$

and because $\overparen{P_4P_2} = \overparen{P_4Q} + \overparen{QP_2}$, it follows that

$$\overparen{P_4P_2} = a + b \qquad (6)$$

From Eqs. (5) and (6) we see that $\overparen{QP_3} = \overparen{P_4P_2}$; therefore, the length of the chord joining the points Q and P_3 is the same as the length of the chord joining the points P_4 and P_2. Squaring the measures of these lengths, we have

$$|\overline{QP_3}|^2 = |\overline{P_4P_2}|^2 \qquad (7)$$

Using the distance formula, we get

$$|\overline{QP_3}|^2 = [\cos(a + b) - 1]^2 + [\sin(a + b) - 0]^2$$
$$= \cos^2(a + b) - 2\cos(a + b) + 1 + \sin^2(a + b)$$

and because $\cos^2(a + b) + \sin^2(a + b) = 1$, the above may be written as

$$|\overline{QP_3}|^2 = 2 - 2\cos(a + b) \qquad (8)$$

Again applying the distance formula, we have

$$|\overline{P_4P_2}|^2 = (\cos b - \cos a)^2 + (\sin b + \sin a)^2$$
$$= \cos^2 b - 2\cos a \cos b + \cos^2 a$$
$$\qquad\qquad + \sin^2 b + 2\sin a \sin b + \sin^2 a$$

and because $\cos^2 b + \sin^2 b = 1$ and $\cos^2 a + \sin^2 a = 1$, the above becomes

$$|\overline{P_4P_2}|^2 = 2 - 2\cos a \cos b + 2\sin a \sin b \qquad (9)$$

Substituting from Eqs. (8) and (9) into (7), we obtain

$$2 - 2\cos(a + b) = 2 - 2\cos a \cos b + 2\sin a \sin b$$

from which follows

$$\cos(a + b) = \cos a \cos b - \sin a \sin b$$

which is formula (4).

A formula for $\cos(a - b)$ can be obtained from formula (4) by substituting $-b$ for b. Doing this, we have

$$\cos(a + (-b)) = \cos a \cos(-b) - \sin a \sin(-b)$$

Because $\cos(-b) = \cos b$ and $\sin(-b) = -\sin b$, we get

$$\cos(a - b) = \cos a \cos b + \sin a \sin b \tag{10}$$

for all real numbers a and b.

Letting $a = \frac{1}{2}\pi$ in formula (10), we have the equation $\cos(\frac{1}{2}\pi - b) = \cos \frac{1}{2}\pi \cos b + \sin \frac{1}{2}\pi \sin b$; and because $\cos \frac{1}{2}\pi = 0$ and $\sin \frac{1}{2}\pi = 1$, it becomes $\cos(\frac{1}{2}\pi - b) = \sin b$. Now if in this equation we let $\frac{1}{2}\pi - b = c$, then $b = \frac{1}{2}\pi - c$ and we obtain $\cos c = \sin(\frac{1}{2}\pi - c)$. We have therefore proved the following two identities.

$$\cos(\tfrac{1}{2}\pi - t) = \sin t \quad \text{and} \quad \sin(\tfrac{1}{2}\pi - t) = \cos t \tag{11}$$

Formulas similar to (4) and (10) for the sine of the sum and difference of two numbers follow easily from those we have. A formula for the sine of the sum of two numbers follows from (10) and (11). We have from (11)

$$\sin(a + b) = \cos(\tfrac{1}{2}\pi - (a + b)) = \cos((\tfrac{1}{2}\pi - a) - b)$$

With (10) it follows that

$$\sin(a + b) = \cos(\tfrac{1}{2}\pi - a) \cos b + \sin(\tfrac{1}{2}\pi - a) \sin b$$

and from (11) we get

$$\sin(a + b) = \sin a \cos b + \cos a \sin b \tag{12}$$

for all real numbers a and b.

To obtain a formula for the sine of the difference of two numbers we write $a - b$ as $a + (-b)$ and apply formula (12). Doing this, we have

$$\sin(a + (-b)) = \sin a \cos(-b) + \cos a \sin(-b)$$

and because $\cos(-b) = \cos b$ and $\sin(-b) = -\sin b$, we obtain

$$\sin(a - b) = \sin a \cos b - \cos a \sin b \tag{13}$$

which is valid for all real numbers a and b.

By letting $a = b = t$ in formulas (12) and (4), respectively, we get the formulas

$$\sin 2t = 2 \sin t \cos t \tag{14}$$

and

$$\cos 2t = \cos^2 t - \sin^2 t \tag{15}$$

Using the identity $\sin^2 t + \cos^2 t = 1$ we may rewrite formula (15) as

$$\cos 2t = 2 \cos^2 t - 1 \tag{16}$$

or

$$\cos 2t = 1 - 2 \sin^2 t \tag{17}$$

Replacing t by $\frac{1}{2}t$ in formulas (16) and (17) and performing some algebraic manipulations, we get, respectively,

$$\cos^2 \frac{1}{2} t = \frac{1 + \cos t}{2} \tag{18}$$

and

$$\sin^2 \frac{1}{2} t = \frac{1 - \cos t}{2} \tag{19}$$

Formulas (14) through (19) are identities because they hold for all real numbers t.

By subtracting the terms of formula (4) from the corresponding terms of formula (10) the following is obtained.

$$\sin a \sin b = \tfrac{1}{2}[-\cos(a + b) + \cos(a - b)] \tag{20}$$

By adding corresponding terms of formulas (4) and (10) we get

$$\cos a \cos b = \tfrac{1}{2}[\cos(a + b) + \cos(a - b)] \tag{21}$$

and by adding corresponding terms of formulas (12) and (13) we have

$$\sin a \cos b = \tfrac{1}{2}[\sin(a + b) + \sin(a - b)] \tag{22}$$

By letting $c = a + b$ and $d = a - b$ in formulas (22), (21), and (20), we obtain, respectively,

$$\sin c + \sin d = 2 \sin \frac{c + d}{2} \cos \frac{c - d}{2} \tag{23}$$

$$\cos c + \cos d = 2 \cos \frac{c + d}{2} \cos \frac{c - d}{2} \tag{24}$$

and

$$\cos c - \cos d = -2 \sin \frac{c + d}{2} \sin \frac{c - d}{2} \tag{25}$$

If the terms of formula (13) are subtracted from the corresponding terms of formula (12) and $a + b$ and $a - b$ are replaced by c and d, respectively, we have

$$\sin c - \sin d = 2 \cos \frac{c + d}{2} \sin \frac{c - d}{2} \tag{26}$$

You are asked to perform the indicated operations in the derivation of some of the above formulas in Exercises 1 to 6.

When referring to the trigonometric functions with a domain of angle measurements we use the notation $\theta°$ to denote the measurement of an angle if its degree measure is θ. For example, $45°$ is the measurement of an angle whose degree measure is 45 or, equivalently, radian measure is $\frac{1}{4}\pi$.

Figure 9.1.8

Consider an angle of $\theta°$ in standard position on a rectangular cartesian-coordinate system. Choose any point P, excluding the vertex, on the terminal side of the angle and let its abscissa be x, its ordinate be y, and $|\overline{OP}| = r$. Refer to Fig. 9.1.8. The ratios x/y and y/r are independent of the choice of P because if the point P_1 is chosen instead of P, we see by Fig. 9.1.8 that $x/r = x_1/r_1$ and $y/r = y_1/r_1$. Because the position of the terminal side depends on the angle, these two ratios are functions of the measurement of the angle, and we define

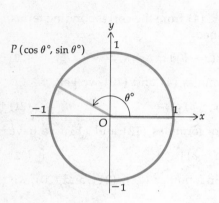

Figure 9.1.9

$$\cos \theta° = \frac{x}{r} \quad \text{and} \quad \sin \theta° = \frac{y}{r} \tag{27}$$

Because any point P (other than the origin) may be chosen on the terminal side, we could choose the point for which $r = 1$, and this is the point where the terminal side intersects the unit circle $x^2 + y^2 = 1$ (see Fig. 9.1.9). Then $\cos \theta°$ is the abscissa of the point and $\sin \theta°$ is the ordinate of the point. This gives the analogy between the sine and cosine of real numbers and those of angle measurements. We have the next definition.

9.1.4 Definition   If α degrees and x radians are measurements for the same angle, then

$$\sin \alpha° = \sin x \quad \text{and} \quad \cos \alpha° = \cos x$$

Exercises 9.1

1. Derive formula (20) by subtracting the terms of formula (4) from the corresponding terms of formula (10).

2. Derive formula (21) by a method similar to that suggested in Exercise 1.

3. Derive formula (22) by a method similar to that suggested in Exercise 1.

4. Derive formula (23) by using formula (22).   5. Derive formula (24) by using formula (21).

6. Derive formula (25) by using formula (20).

7. Derive a formula for $\sin 3t$ in terms of $\sin t$ by using formulas (12), (14), (15), and (1).

8. Derive a formula for $\cos 3t$ in terms of $\cos t$. Use a method similar to that suggested in Exercise 7.

9. Without using tables, find the value of (a) $\sin \frac{1}{12}\pi$ and (b) $\cos \frac{1}{12}\pi$.

10. Without using tables, find the value of (a) $\sin \frac{1}{8}\pi$ and (b) $\cos \frac{1}{8}\pi$.

11. Without using tables, find the value of (a) $\sin \frac{5}{12}\pi$ and (b) $\cos \frac{5}{12}\pi$.

12. Express each of the following in terms of $\sin t$ or $\sin(\frac{1}{2}\pi - t)$: (a) $\sin(\frac{3}{2}\pi - t)$; (b) $\cos(\frac{3}{2}\pi - t)$; (c) $\sin(\frac{3}{2}\pi + t)$; (d) $\cos(\frac{3}{2}\pi + t)$.

13. Express the function values of Exercise 12 in terms of $\cos t$ or $\cos(\frac{1}{2}\pi - t)$.

14. Express each of the following in terms of $\sin t$ or $\sin(\frac{1}{2}\pi - t)$: (a) $\sin(\pi - t)$; (b) $\cos(\pi - t)$; (c) $\sin(\pi + t)$; (d) $\cos(\pi + t)$.

15. Express the function values of Exercise 14 in terms of $\cos t$ or $\cos(\frac{1}{2}\pi - t)$.

16. Find all values of t for which (a) $\sin t = 0$, and (b) $\cos t = 0$.

17. Find all values of t for which (a) $\sin t = 1$, and (b) $\cos t = 1$.

18. Find all values of t for which (a) $\sin t = -1$, and (b) $\cos t = -1$.

19. Find all values of t for which (a) $\sin t = \frac{1}{2}$, and (b) $\cos t = \frac{1}{2}$.

20. Find all values of t for which (a) $\sin t = -\frac{1}{2}\sqrt{2}$, and (b) $\cos t = -\frac{1}{2}\sqrt{2}$.

21. Suppose f is a function which is periodic with period 2π, and whose domain is the set of all real numbers. Prove that f is also periodic with period -2π.

22. Prove that the function of Exercise 21 is periodic with period $2\pi n$ for every integer n. (HINT: Use mathematical induction.)

23. Prove that if f is defined by $f(x) = x - [\![x]\!]$, then f is periodic. What is the smallest positive period of f?

9.2 DERIVATIVES OF THE SINE AND COSINE FUNCTIONS

Before the formula for the derivative of the sine function can be derived we need to know the value of

$$\lim_{t \to 0} \frac{\sin t}{t}$$

Letting $f(t) = (\sin t)/t$, we see that $f(0)$ is not defined. However, we prove that $\lim_{t \to 0} f(t)$ exists and is equal to 1.

9.2.1 Theorem $$\lim_{t \to 0} \frac{\sin t}{t} = 1$$

PROOF: We first assume that $0 < t < \frac{1}{2}\pi$.

Refer to Fig. 9.2.1 which shows the unit circle $x^2 + y^2 = 1$ and the shaded sector BOP, where B is the point $(1, 0)$ and P is the point $(\cos t, \sin t)$. The area of a circular sector of radius r and central angle of radian measure t is determined by $\frac{1}{2}r^2 t$; and so if S square units is the area of sector BOP,

$$S = \tfrac{1}{2}t \tag{1}$$

Consider now the triangle BOP, and let K_1 square units be the area of this triangle. Hence,

$$K_1 = \tfrac{1}{2}|\overline{AP}| \cdot |\overline{OB}| = \tfrac{1}{2}(\sin t) \cdot (1) = \tfrac{1}{2}\sin t \tag{2}$$

The line through the points $O(0,0)$ and $P(\cos t, \sin t)$ has slope

Figure 9.2.1

$\sin t/\cos t$; therefore, its equation is

$$y = \frac{\sin t}{\cos t} x$$

This line intersects the line $x = 1$ at the point $(1, \sin t/\cos t)$, which is the point T in the figure.

Letting K_2 square units be the area of right triangle BOT, we have

$$K_2 = \frac{1}{2} |\overline{BT}| \cdot |\overline{OB}| = \frac{1}{2} \cdot \frac{\sin t}{\cos t} \cdot 1 = \frac{1}{2} \cdot \frac{\sin t}{\cos t} \tag{3}$$

From Fig. 9.2.1 we see that

$$K_1 < S < K_2 \tag{4}$$

Substituting from Eqs. (1), (2), and (3) in inequality (4), we get

$$\frac{1}{2} \sin t < \frac{1}{2} t < \frac{1}{2} \cdot \frac{\sin t}{\cos t}$$

Multiplying each member of the above inequality by $2/\sin t$, which is positive because $0 < t < \frac{1}{2}\pi$, we obtain

$$1 < \frac{t}{\sin t} < \frac{1}{\cos t}$$

Taking the reciprocal of each member of the above inequality and reversing the direction of the inequality signs, we get

$$\cos t < \frac{\sin t}{t} < 1 \tag{5}$$

From the right-hand inequality in the above we have

$$\sin t < t \tag{6}$$

and from formula (19) in Sec. 9.1 we have

$$\frac{1 - \cos t}{2} = \sin^2 \frac{1}{2} t \tag{7}$$

Replacing t by $\frac{1}{2}t$ in inequality (6) and squaring, we obtain

$$\sin^2 \tfrac{1}{2} t < \tfrac{1}{4} t^2 \tag{8}$$

Thus, from (7) and (8) it follows that

$$\frac{1 - \cos t}{2} < \frac{t^2}{4}$$

which is equivalent to

$$1 - \tfrac{1}{2} t^2 < \cos t \tag{9}$$

From (5) and (9) and because $0 < t < \frac{1}{2}\pi$, we have

$$1 - \frac{1}{2} t^2 < \frac{\sin t}{t} < 1 \qquad \text{if } 0 < t < \frac{1}{2} \pi \tag{10}$$

If $-\frac{1}{2}\pi < t < 0$, then $0 < -t < \frac{1}{2}\pi$; and so from (10) we have

$$1 - \frac{1}{2} (-t)^2 < \frac{\sin (-t)}{-t} < 1 \qquad \text{if } -\frac{1}{2} \pi < t < 0$$

But $\sin(-t) = -\sin t$; thus, the above can be written as

$$1 - \frac{1}{2} t^2 < \frac{\sin t}{t} < 1 \qquad \text{if } -\frac{1}{2} \pi < t < 0 \tag{11}$$

From (10) and (11) we conclude that

$$1 - \frac{1}{2} t^2 < \frac{\sin t}{t} < 1 \qquad \text{if } -\frac{1}{2} \pi < t < \frac{1}{2} \pi \text{ and } t \neq 0 \tag{12}$$

Because $\lim_{t \to 0} (1 - \frac{1}{2}t^2) = 1$ and $\lim_{t \to 0} 1 = 1$, it follows from (12) and the squeeze theorem (2.10.5) that

$$\lim_{t \to 0} \frac{\sin t}{t} = 1$$

∎

From the above theorem, we can prove that the sine function and the cosine function are continuous at 0.

9.2.2 Theorem   The sine function is continuous at 0.

PROOF: We show that the three conditions necessary for continuity at a number are satisfied.

(i) $\sin 0 = 0$.

(ii) $\displaystyle \lim_{t \to 0} \sin t = \lim_{t \to 0} \frac{\sin t}{t} \cdot t = \lim_{t \to 0} \frac{\sin t}{t} \cdot \lim_{t \to 0} t = 1 \cdot 0 = 0$.

(iii) $\displaystyle \lim_{t \to 0} \sin t = \sin 0$.

Therefore, the sine function is continuous at 0.

∎

9.2.3 Theorem   The cosine function is continuous at 0.

PROOF:

(i) $\cos 0 = 1$.

(ii) $\displaystyle \lim_{t \to 0} \cos t = \lim_{t \to 0} \sqrt{1 - \sin^2 t}$

$$= \sqrt{\lim_{t \to 0} (1 - \sin^2 t)} = \sqrt{1 - 0} = 1.$$

NOTE: We can replace $\cos t$ by $\sqrt{1 - \sin^2 t}$ since $\cos t > 0$ when $0 < t < \frac{1}{2}\pi$ and when $-\frac{1}{2}\pi < t < 0$.

(iii) $\lim\limits_{t \to 0} \cos t = \cos 0$.

Therefore, the cosine function is continuous at 0.   ■

The limit in the following theorem is also important. It follows from the previous three theorems and limit theorems.

9.2.4 Theorem $\lim\limits_{t \to 0} \dfrac{1 - \cos t}{t} = 0$

PROOF:

$$\lim_{t \to 0} \frac{1 - \cos t}{t} = \lim_{t \to 0} \frac{(1 - \cos t)(1 + \cos t)}{t(1 + \cos t)}$$

$$= \lim_{t \to 0} \frac{(1 - \cos^2 t)}{t(1 + \cos t)}$$

$$= \lim_{t \to 0} \frac{\sin^2 t}{t(1 + \cos t)}$$

$$= \lim_{t \to 0} \frac{\sin t}{t} \cdot \lim_{t \to 0} \frac{\sin t}{1 + \cos t}$$

By Theorem 9.2.1, $\lim\limits_{t \to 0} (\sin t/t) = 1$, and because the sine and cosine functions are continuous at 0, it follows that $\lim\limits_{t \to 0} [\sin t/(1 + \cos t)] = 0/(1 + 1) = 0$. Therefore,

$$\lim_{t \to 0} \frac{1 - \cos t}{t} = 0$$ ■

EXAMPLE 1:   Find

$$\lim_{x \to 0} \frac{\sin 3x}{\sin 5x}$$

if it exists.

SOLUTION: We wish to write the quotient $\sin 3x/\sin 5x$ in such a way that we can apply Theorem 9.2.1. We have, if $x \neq 0$,

$$\frac{\sin 3x}{\sin 5x} = \frac{3\left(\dfrac{\sin 3x}{3x}\right)}{5\left(\dfrac{\sin 5x}{5x}\right)}$$

As x approaches zero, so do $3x$ and $5x$. Hence, we have

$$\lim_{x \to 0} \frac{\sin 3x}{3x} = \lim_{3x \to 0} \frac{\sin 3x}{3x} = 1$$

and

$$\lim_{x \to 0} \frac{\sin 5x}{5x} = \lim_{5x \to 0} \frac{\sin 5x}{5x} = 1$$

Therefore,

$$\lim_{x \to 0} \frac{\sin 3x}{\sin 5x} = \frac{3 \lim\limits_{x \to 0} \left(\dfrac{\sin 3x}{3x} \right)}{5 \lim\limits_{x \to 0} \left(\dfrac{\sin 5x}{5x} \right)} = \frac{3 \cdot 1}{5 \cdot 1} = \frac{3}{5}$$

We now show that the sine function has a derivative. Let f be the function defined by

$$f(x) = \sin x$$

From the definition of a derivative, we have

$$f'(x) = \lim_{\Delta x \to 0} \frac{f(x + \Delta x) - f(x)}{\Delta x}$$

$$= \lim_{\Delta x \to 0} \frac{\sin(x + \Delta x) - \sin x}{\Delta x}$$

$$= \lim_{\Delta x \to 0} \frac{\sin x \cos(\Delta x) + \cos x \sin(\Delta x) - \sin x}{\Delta x}$$

$$= \lim_{\Delta x \to 0} \frac{\sin x [\cos(\Delta x) - 1]}{\Delta x} + \lim_{\Delta x \to 0} \frac{\cos x \sin(\Delta x)}{\Delta x}$$

$$= - \lim_{\Delta x \to 0} \frac{1 - \cos(\Delta x)}{\Delta x} \left(\lim_{\Delta x \to 0} \sin x \right) + \left(\lim_{\Delta x \to 0} \cos x \right) \lim_{\Delta x \to 0} \frac{\sin(\Delta x)}{\Delta x}$$

$$= -0 \cdot \sin x + \cos x \cdot 1 \quad \text{(by Theorems 9.2.4 and 9.2.1)}$$

$$= \cos x$$

IT is OBTAINED FOR THE PROCESS MADE ABOVE

Therefore, we have the formula

$$\boxed{D_x(\sin x) = \cos x} \tag{13}$$

If u is a differentiable function of x, we have from (13) and the chain rule

$$D_x(\sin u) = \cos u \, D_x u \tag{14}$$

The derivative of the cosine function is obtained by making use of (13) and the following identities:

$$\cos x = \sin(\tfrac{1}{2}\pi - x) \quad \text{and} \quad \sin x = \cos(\tfrac{1}{2}\pi - x)$$

$$D_x(\cos x) = D_x[\sin(\tfrac{1}{2}\pi - x)]$$

$$= \cos(\tfrac{1}{2}\pi - x) \cdot D_x(\tfrac{1}{2}\pi - x) = \sin x(-1)$$

Therefore,

$$D_x(\cos x) = -\sin x \tag{15}$$

So if u is a differentiable function of x, it follows from (15) and the chain rule that

$$D_x(\cos u) = -\sin u\, D_x u \qquad (16)$$

EXAMPLE 2:   Given

$$f(x) = \frac{\sin x}{1 - 2\cos x}$$

find $f'(x)$.

SOLUTION:

$$f'(x) = \frac{(1 - 2\cos x)\, D_x(\sin x) - \sin x \cdot D_x(1 - 2\cos x)}{(1 - 2\cos x)^2}$$

$$= \frac{(1 - 2\cos x)(\cos x) - \sin x(2\sin x)}{(1 - 2\cos x)^2}$$

$$= \frac{\cos x - 2(\cos^2 x + \sin^2 x)}{(1 - 2\cos x)^2}$$

$$= \frac{\cos x - 2}{(1 - 2\cos x)^2}$$

EXAMPLE 3:   Given

$$y = (1 + \cos 3x^2)^4$$

find $D_x y$.

SOLUTION:

$$D_x y = 4(1 + \cos 3x^2)^3(-\sin 3x^2)(6x)$$

$$= -24x \sin 3x^2 (1 + \cos 3x^2)^3$$

EXAMPLE 4:   Given

$$x \cos y + y \cos x = 1$$

find $D_x y$.

SOLUTION: Differentiating implicitly with respect to x, we get

$$1 \cdot \cos y + x(-\sin y)\, D_x y + D_x y(\cos x) + y(-\sin x) = 0$$

$$D_x y(\cos x - x \sin y) = y \sin x - \cos y$$

$$D_x y = \frac{y \sin x - \cos y}{\cos x - x \sin y}$$

Geometric problems involving absolute extrema occasionally are more easily solved by using trigonometric functions. The following example illustrates this fact.

EXAMPLE 5:   A right-circular cylinder is to be inscribed in a sphere of given radius. Find the ratio of the altitude to the base radius of the cylinder having the largest lateral surface area.

SOLUTION: Refer to Fig. 9.2.2. The measure of the constant radius of the sphere is taken as a.

Let θ = the number of radians in the angle at the center of the sphere subtended by the radius of the cylinder;

r = the number of inches in the radius of the cylinder;

h = the number of inches in the altitude of the cylinder;

S = the number of square inches in the lateral surface area of the cylinder.

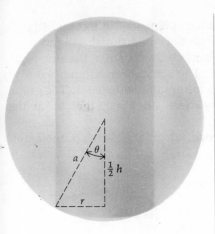

Figure 9.2.2

From Fig. 9.2.2, we see that

$$r = a \sin \theta \quad \text{and} \quad h = 2a \cos \theta$$

Because $S = 2\pi rh$, we have

$$S = 2\pi (a \sin \theta)(2a \cos \theta) = 2\pi a^2 (2 \sin \theta \cos \theta) = 2\pi a^2 \sin 2\theta$$

So

$$D_\theta S = 4\pi a^2 \cos 2\theta \quad \text{and} \quad D_\theta^2 S = -8\pi a^2 \sin 2\theta$$

Setting $D_\theta S = 0$, we get

$$\cos 2\theta = 0$$

Because $0 < \theta < \frac{1}{2}\pi$,

$$\theta = \frac{1}{4}\pi$$

We apply the second derivative test for relative extrema and summarize the results in Table 9.2.1.

Table 9.2.1

	$D_\theta S$	$D_\theta^2 S$	conclusion
$\theta = \frac{1}{4}\pi$	0	—	S has a relative maximum value

Because the domain of θ is the open interval $(0, \frac{1}{2}\pi)$, the relative maximum value of S is the absolute maximum value of S.

When $\theta = \frac{1}{4}\pi$, $r = \frac{1}{2}\sqrt{2}a$, and $h = \sqrt{2}a$. So for the cylinder having the largest lateral surface area, $h/r = 2$.

Because $D_x(\sin x) = \cos x$ and $\cos x$ exists for all values of x, the sine function is differentiable everywhere and therefore continuous everywhere. Similarly, the cosine function is differentiable and continuous everywhere.

We now discuss the graph of the sine function. Let

$$f(x) = \sin x$$

Then $f'(x) = \cos x$ and $f''(x) = -\sin x$. To determine the relative extrema, we set $f'(x) = 0$ and get $x = \frac{1}{2}\pi + n\pi$, where $n = 0, \pm 1, \pm 2, \ldots$. If n is an even integer, then $f''(\frac{1}{2}\pi + n\pi) = -\sin(\frac{1}{2}\pi + n\pi) = -\sin \frac{1}{2}\pi = -1$; and if n is an odd integer, $f''(\frac{1}{2}\pi + n\pi) = -\sin(\frac{1}{2}\pi + n\pi) = -\sin \frac{3}{2}\pi = 1$. Therefore, f has relative extrema when $x = \frac{1}{2}\pi + n\pi$; and if n is an even integer, f has a relative maximum value; and if n is an odd integer, f has a relative minimum value.

To determine the points of inflection of the graph, we set $f''(x) = 0$ and obtain $x = n\pi$, where $n = 0, \pm 1, \pm 2, \ldots$. Because $f''(x)$ changes sign at each of these values of x, the graph has a point of inflection at each point having these abscissas. At each point of inflection $f'(x) = \cos n\pi = \pm 1$. Therefore, the slopes of the inflectional tangents are either $+1$ or -1. Furthermore, because $\sin(x + 2\pi) = \sin x$, the sine function is periodic and has the period 2π. The absolute maximum value of the sine function is 1, and the absolute minimum value is -1. The graph intersects the x axis at those points where $\sin x = 0$, that is, at the points where $x = n\pi$ (n is any integer).

From the information obtained above, we draw a sketch of the graph of the sine function; it is shown in Fig. 9.2.3.

$y = \sin x$

Figure 9.2.3

To obtain the graph of the cosine function, we use the identity

$$\cos x = \sin(\tfrac{1}{2}\pi + x)$$

which follows from formula (12) of Sec. 9.1. Hence, the graph of the cosine function is obtained from the graph of the sine function by translating the y axis $\tfrac{1}{2}\pi$ units to the right (see Fig. 9.2.4).

$y = \cos x$

Figure 9.2.4

Exercises 9.2

In Exercises 1 through 8 evaluate the limit, if it exists.

1. $\lim\limits_{x \to 0} \dfrac{\sin 4x}{x}$

2. $\lim\limits_{x \to 0} \dfrac{x}{\cos x}$

3. $\lim\limits_{x \to 0} \dfrac{\sin 9x}{\sin 7x}$

4. $\lim\limits_{x \to \pi/2} \dfrac{\tfrac{1}{2}\pi - x}{\cos x}$

5. $\lim\limits_{x \to 0} \dfrac{1 - \cos x}{x^2}$

6. $\lim\limits_{x \to 0} \dfrac{1 - \cos x}{\sin x}$

7. $\lim\limits_{x \to 0} \dfrac{3x^2}{1 - \cos^2 \tfrac{1}{2}x}$

8. $\lim\limits_{x \to 0} \dfrac{1 - \cos^2 x}{2x^2}$

In Exercises 9 through 24 find the derivative of the given function.

9. $f(x) = 3 \sin 2x$

10. $f(x) = \cos(3x^2 + 1)$

11. $g(x) = \sin 3x \cos 3x$

12. $f(t) = \cos t^2$

13. $h(t) = 2 \cos \sqrt{t}$

14. $g(x) = \sqrt{\sin x}$

15. $f(x) = \ln \sin 5x$

16. $F(x) = \sin(\ln x)$

17. $h(x) = \dfrac{\sin x}{2 + \cos x}$

18. $g(t) = \sin(\cos t)$

19. $g(x) = 2 \cos x \sin 2x - \sin x \cos 2x$

20. $h(y) = y^3 - y^2 \cos y + 2y \sin y + 2 \cos y$

21. $f(x) = (\sin x^2)^{4x}$

22. $g(x) = x^{\sin x}$

23. $h(x) = (\cos x)^{\sin x}$

24. $f(x) = (\ln \sin x)^{e^x}$

In Exercises 25 and 26, use logarithmic differentiation to find $D_x y$.

25. $y = \dfrac{\sin x \sqrt{1 + \cos^2 x}}{\cos^3 x}$

26. $y = \dfrac{\sin^3 x}{\sqrt{1 - 3 \cos x}}$

In Exercises 27 and 28, find $D_x y$ by implicit differentiation.

27. $y = \cos(x - y)$

28. $\cos(x + y) = y \sin x$

In Exercises 29 through 34, draw a sketch of the graph of the function defined by the given equations.

29. $f(x) = \sin 2x$

30. $f(x) = 2 \sin 3x$

31. $f(x) = |\cos 3x|$

32. $f(x) = \frac{1}{2}(1 - \cos x)$

33. $f(x) = \begin{cases} \sin x & \text{if } 0 \leq x < \frac{1}{2}\pi \\ \sin(x - \frac{1}{2}\pi) & \text{if } \frac{1}{2}\pi \leq x \leq \pi \end{cases}$

34. $f(x) = \begin{cases} \cos x & \text{if } -\pi \leq x \leq 0 \\ \cos(\pi - x) & \text{if } 0 < x \leq \pi \end{cases}$

35. If a ladder of length 30 ft, which is leaning against a wall, has its upper end sliding down the wall at the rate of $\frac{1}{2}$ ft/sec, what is the rate of change of the measure of the acute angle made by the ladder with the ground when the upper end is 18 ft above the ground?

36. The cross section of a trough has the shape of an inverted isosceles triangle. If the lengths of the equal sides are 15 in., find the size of the vertex angle that will give maximum capacity for the trough.

37. If a body of weight W lb is dragged along a horizontal floor by means of a force of magnitude F lb and directed at an angle of θ radians with the plane of the floor, then F is given by the equation

$$F = \frac{kW}{k \sin \theta + \cos \theta}$$

where k is a constant and is called the coefficient of friction. Find $\cos \theta$ when F is least.

38. Find the altitude of the right-circular cone of largest possible volume that can be inscribed in a sphere of radius a units. Let 2θ be the radian measure of the vertical angle of the cone.

39. A particle moving in a straight line is said to have *simple harmonic motion* if the measure of its acceleration is always proportional to the measure of its displacement from a fixed point on the line and its acceleration and displacement are oppositely directed. Show that the straight-line motion of a particle described by $s = A \sin 2\pi kt + B \cos 2\pi kt$, where s ft is the directed distance of the particle from the origin at t sec, and A, B, and k are constants, is a simple harmonic motion.

40. Show that if a particle is moving along a straight line according to the equation of motion $s = a \cos(kt + \theta)$ (where a, k, and θ are constants) and s ft is the directed distance of the particle from the origin at t sec, then the motion is simple harmonic. (See Exercise 39.)

41. Given $f(x) = x \sin(\pi/x)$, prove that f has an infinite number of relative extrema.

42. If the domain of the function of Exercise 41 is the interval $(0, 1]$, how should $f(0)$ be defined so that f is continuous on the closed interval $[0, 1]$?

9.3 INTEGRALS INVOLVING POWERS OF SINE AND COSINE

The formulas for the indefinite integral of the sine and cosine functions follow immediately from the corresponding formulas for differentiation.

$$\int \sin u \, du = -\cos u + C \tag{1}$$

$$D_u(-\cos u) = \sin u.$$

$$\int \cos u \, du = \sin u + C \tag{2}$$

PROOF: $D_u(\sin u) = \cos u.$

EXAMPLE 1: Find

$$\int \frac{\cos(\ln x)}{x} \, dx$$

SOLUTION: Let $u = \ln x$. Then $du = dx/x$; so we have

$$\int \frac{\cos(\ln x)}{x} \, dx = \int \cos u \, du$$
$$= \sin u + C$$
$$= \sin(\ln x) + C$$

EXAMPLE 2: Find

$$\int \frac{\sin x}{1 - \cos x} \, dx$$

SOLUTION: Let $u = 1 - \cos x$. Then $du = \sin x \, dx$; so

$$\int \frac{\sin x \, dx}{1 - \cos x} = \int \frac{du}{u}$$
$$= \ln |u| + C$$
$$= \ln |1 - \cos x| + C$$

EXAMPLE 3: Find

$$\int_0^\pi (1 + \sin x) \, dx$$

SOLUTION:

$$\int_0^\pi (1 + \sin x) \, dx = x - \cos x \Big]_0^\pi$$
$$= \pi - \cos \pi - (0 - \cos 0)$$
$$= \pi + 1 - (0 - 1)$$
$$= \pi + 2$$

We now consider four cases of integrals involving powers of sine and cosine. The method used in each case is illustrated by some examples.

Case 1: $\int \sin^n u \, du$ or $\int \cos^n u \, du$, where n is an odd integer.

EXAMPLE 4: Find

$$\int \cos^3 x \, dx$$

SOLUTION:

$$\int \cos^3 x \, dx = \int \cos^2 x \,(\cos x \, dx)$$
$$= \int (1 - \sin^2 x)(\cos x \, dx)$$

So

$$\int \cos^3 x \, dx = \int \cos x \, dx - \int \sin^2 x \cos x \, dx \tag{3}$$

To evaluate the second integral on the right side of (3), we let $u = \sin x$; then $du = \cos x\, dx$. This gives

$$\int \sin^2 x \,(\cos x\, dx) = \int u^2\, du$$

$$= \tfrac{1}{3}u^3 + C_1$$

$$= \tfrac{1}{3}\sin^3 x + C_1$$

Because the first integral on the right side of (3) is $\sin x + C_2$, we have

$$\int \cos^3 x\, dx = \sin x - \tfrac{1}{3}\sin^3 x + C$$

EXAMPLE 5: **Find**

$$\int \sin^5 x\, dx$$

SOLUTION:

$$\int \sin^5 x\, dx = \int (\sin^2 x)^2 \sin x\, dx$$

$$= \int (1 - \cos^2 x)^2 \sin x\, dx$$

$$= \int (1 - 2\cos^2 x + \cos^4 x) \sin x\, dx$$

Therefore,

$$\int \sin^5 x\, dx = \int \sin x\, dx - 2\int \cos^2 x \sin x\, dx + \int \cos^4 x(\sin x\, dx) \quad (4)$$

To evaluate the second and third integrals in (4), we let $u = \cos x$ and $du = -\sin x\, dx$; and we obtain

$$\int \sin^5 x\, dx = -\cos x + 2\int u^2\, du - \int u^4\, du$$

$$= -\cos x + \tfrac{2}{3}u^3 - \tfrac{1}{5}u^5 + C$$

$$= -\cos x + \tfrac{2}{3}\cos^3 x - \tfrac{1}{5}\cos^5 x + C$$

Case 2: $\int \sin^n u\, du$ and $\int \cos^n u\, du$, where n is an even integer.

The method used in Case 1 does not work in this case. We use the following formulas which are obtained from formulas (19) and (18) of Sec. 9.1 by substituting $2x$ for t.

$$\sin^2 x = \frac{1 - \cos 2x}{2}$$

$$\cos^2 x = \frac{1 + \cos 2x}{2}$$

EXAMPLE 6: **Find**

$$\int \sin^2 x\, dx$$

SOLUTION:

$$\int \sin^2 x\, dx = \int \frac{1 - \cos 2x}{2}\, dx$$

$$= \tfrac{1}{2}x - \tfrac{1}{4}\sin 2x + C$$

EXAMPLE 7: Find

$$\int \cos^4 x \, dx$$

SOLUTION:

$$\int \cos^4 x \, dx = \int (\cos^2 x)^2 \, dx = \int \left(\frac{1 + \cos 2x}{2}\right)^2 dx$$

$$= \frac{1}{4}\int dx + \frac{1}{2}\int \cos 2x \, dx + \frac{1}{4}\int \cos^2 2x \, dx$$

$$= \frac{1}{4}x + \frac{1}{4}\sin 2x + \frac{1}{4}\int \frac{1 + \cos 4x}{2} \, dx$$

$$= \tfrac{1}{4}x + \tfrac{1}{4}\sin 2x + \tfrac{1}{8}x + \tfrac{1}{32}\sin 4x + C$$

$$= \tfrac{3}{8}x + \tfrac{1}{4}\sin 2x + \tfrac{1}{32}\sin 4x + C$$

Case 3: $\int \sin^n x \cos^m x \, dx$, where at least one of the exponents is odd. The solution of this case is similar to the method used for Case 1.

EXAMPLE 8: Find

$$\int \sin^3 x \cos^4 x \, dx$$

SOLUTION:

$$\int \sin^3 x \cos^4 x \, dx = \int \sin^2 x \cos^4 x (\sin x \, dx)$$

$$= \int (1 - \cos^2 x) \cos^4 x (\sin x \, dx)$$

$$= \int \cos^4 x \sin x \, dx - \int \cos^6 x \sin x \, dx$$

$$= -\tfrac{1}{5}\cos^5 x + \tfrac{1}{7}\cos^7 x + C$$

Case 4: $\int \sin^n x \cos^m x \, dx$, where both m and n are even. The solution of this case is similar to the method used in Case 2.

EXAMPLE 9: Find

$$\int \sin^2 x \cos^4 x \, dx$$

SOLUTION:

$$\int \sin^2 x \cos^4 x \, dx = \int \left(\frac{1 - \cos 2x}{2}\right)\left(\frac{1 + \cos 2x}{2}\right)^2 dx$$

$$= \frac{1}{8}\int dx + \frac{1}{8}\int \cos 2x \, dx$$

$$\quad - \frac{1}{8}\int \cos^2 2x \, dx - \frac{1}{8}\int \cos^3 2x \, dx$$

$$= \frac{1}{8}x + \frac{1}{16}\sin 2x - \frac{1}{8}\int \frac{1 + \cos 4x}{2} \, dx$$

$$\quad - \frac{1}{8}\int (1 - \sin^2 2x) \cos 2x \, dx.$$

$$= \frac{x}{8} + \frac{\sin 2x}{16} - \frac{x}{16} - \frac{\sin 4x}{64}$$

$$\quad - \frac{1}{8}\int \cos 2x \, dx + \frac{1}{8}\int \sin^2 2x \cos 2x \, dx$$

$$= \frac{x}{16} + \frac{\sin 2x}{16} - \frac{\sin 4x}{64} - \frac{\sin 2x}{16} + \frac{\sin^3 2x}{48} + C$$

$$= \frac{x}{16} + \frac{\sin^3 2x}{48} - \frac{\sin 4x}{64} + C$$

EXAMPLE 10: Find

$$\int \sin^4 x \cos^4 x \, dx$$

SOLUTION: If we make use of the formula $\sin x \cos x = \frac{1}{2} \sin 2x$ we have

$$\int \sin^4 x \cos^4 x \, dx = \frac{1}{16} \int \sin^4 2x \, dx$$

$$= \frac{1}{16} \int \left(\frac{1 - \cos 4x}{2} \right)^2 dx$$

$$= \frac{1}{64} \int dx - \frac{1}{32} \int \cos 4x \, dx + \frac{1}{64} \int \cos^2 4x \, dx$$

$$= \frac{x}{64} - \frac{\sin 4x}{128} + \frac{1}{64} \int \frac{1 + \cos 8x}{2} \, dx$$

$$= \frac{x}{64} - \frac{\sin 4x}{128} + \frac{x}{128} + \frac{\sin 8x}{1024} + C$$

$$= \frac{3x}{128} - \frac{\sin 4x}{128} + \frac{\sin 8x}{1024} + C$$

The following example illustrates another type of integral involving a product of a sine and a cosine.

EXAMPLE 11: Find

$$\int \sin 3x \cos 2x \, dx$$

SOLUTION: We use formula (22) of Sec. 9.1, which is

$$\sin a \cos b = \frac{1}{2} \sin(a - b) + \frac{1}{2} \sin(a + b)$$

So

$$\int \sin 3x \cos 2x \, dx = \int \left[\frac{1}{2} \sin x + \frac{1}{2} \sin 5x \right] dx$$

$$= \frac{1}{2} \int \sin x \, dx + \frac{1}{2} \int \sin 5x \, dx$$

$$= -\frac{1}{2} \cos x - \frac{1}{10} \cos 5x + C$$

Exercises 9.3

In Exercises 1 through 22, evaluate the indefinite integral.

1. $\int (3 \sin x + 2 \cos x) \, dx$

2. $\int (\sin 3x + \cos 2x) \, dx$

3. $\int \sin x \, e^{\cos x} \, dx$

4. $\int \frac{\cos x}{2 + \sin x} \, dx$

5. $\int \sin x \cdot \sin(\cos x) \, dx$

6. $\int \frac{\cos 3\sqrt{x}}{\sqrt{x}} \, dx$

7. $\int \sin^3 x \, dx$

8. $\int \cos^5 x \, dx$

9. $\int \sin^4 x \, dx$

10. $\int \cos^6 x \, dx$

11. $\int \cos^2 \frac{1}{2} x \, dx$

12. $\int \sin^3 x \cos^3 x \, dx$

13. $\displaystyle\int \sin^5 x \cos^2 x \, dx$ 14. $\displaystyle\int \sin^2 2t \cos^4 2t \, dt$ 15. $\displaystyle\int \sin^2 3t \cos^2 3t \, dt$ 16. $\displaystyle\int \sqrt{\cos z} \, \sin^3 z$

17. $\displaystyle\int \frac{\cos^3 3x}{\sqrt[3]{\sin 3x}} \, dx$ 18. $\displaystyle\int \sin 2x \cos 4x \, dx$ 19. $\displaystyle\int \cos 4x \cos 3x \, dx$ 20. $\displaystyle\int \sin 3x \sin 2x \, dx$

21. $\displaystyle\int (\sin 3x - \sin 2x)^2 \, dx$ 22. $\displaystyle\int \sin x \sin 3x \sin 5x \, dx$

In Exercises 23 through 28, evaluate the definite integral.

23. $\displaystyle\int_0^{\pi/2} \sin 2x \, dx$ 24. $\displaystyle\int_{\ln \pi}^2 e^x \sin e^x \, dx$ 25. $\displaystyle\int_0^{\pi/2} \cos^3 x \, dx$

26. $\displaystyle\int_0^1 \sin^4 \tfrac{1}{2}\pi x \, dx$ 27. $\displaystyle\int_0^1 \sin^2 \pi x \cos^2 \pi x \, dx$ 28. $\displaystyle\int_0^{\pi/6} \sin 2x \cos 4x \, dx$

29. If n is any positive integer prove that $\displaystyle\int_0^{\pi} \sin^2 nx \, dx = \tfrac{1}{2}\pi$.

30. If n is a positive odd integer prove that $\displaystyle\int_0^{\pi} \cos^n x \, dx = 0$.

In Exercises 31 through 33, m and n are any integers except zero; show that the given formula is true.

31. $\displaystyle\int_{-1}^1 \cos n\pi x \cos m\pi x \, dx = \begin{cases} 0 & \text{if } m \neq n \\ 1 & \text{if } m = n \end{cases}$ 32. $\displaystyle\int_{-1}^1 \cos n\pi x \sin m\pi x \, dx = 0$

33. $\displaystyle\int_{-1}^1 \sin n\pi x \sin m\pi x \, dx = \begin{cases} 0 & \text{if } m \neq n \\ 1 & \text{if } m = n \end{cases}$

34. If q coulombs is the charge of electricity received by a condenser from an electric circuit of i amperes at t sec, then $i = D_t q$. Suppose $i = 5 \sin 60t$ and $q = 0$ when $t = \tfrac{1}{2}\pi$, find the greatest positive charge on the condenser.

35. In an electric circuit suppose that E volts is the electromotive force at t sec and $E = 2 \sin 3t$. Find the average value of E from $t = 0$ to $t = \tfrac{1}{3}\pi$.

36. For the electric circuit of Exercise 35, find the square root of the average value of E^2 from $t = 0$ to $t = \tfrac{1}{3}\pi$.

37. Find the area of the region bounded by one arch of the sine curve.

38. Find the volume of the solid of revolution generated if the region of Exercise 37 is revolved about the x axis.

39. Find the volume of the solid generated if the region bounded by the curve $y = \sin^2 x$ and the x axis from $x = 0$ to $x = \pi$ is revolved about the line $y = 1$.

40. Find the area of the region bounded by the two curves $y = \sin x$ and $y = \cos x$ between two consecutive points of inter-section.

9.4 THE TANGENT, COTANGENT, SECANT, AND COSECANT FUNCTIONS

The other trigonometric functions, tangent, cotangent, secant, and cosecant, are defined in terms of the sine and cosine.

9.4.1 Definition   The *tangent* and *secant* functions are defined by

$$\tan x = \frac{\sin x}{\cos x} \qquad \sec x = \frac{1}{\cos x}$$

for all real numbers x for which $\cos x \neq 0$.

The *cotangent* and *cosecant* functions are defined by

$$\cot x = \frac{\cos x}{\sin x} \qquad \csc x = \frac{1}{\sin x}$$

for all real numbers x for which $\sin x \neq 0$.

The tangent and secant functions are not defined when $\cos x = 0$, which occurs when x is $\frac{1}{2}\pi, \frac{3}{2}\pi$, or $\frac{1}{2}\pi + n\pi$, where n is any positive or negative integer, or zero. Therefore, the domain of the tangent and secant functions is the set of all real numbers except numbers of the form $\frac{1}{2}\pi + n\pi$, where n is any integer. Similarly, because $\cot x$ and $\csc x$ are not defined when $\sin x = 0$, the domain of the cotangent and cosecant functions is the set of all real numbers except numbers of the form $n\pi$, where n is any integer.

By Theorem 2.12.1(iv), if the functions f and g are continuous at the number a, then f/g is continuous at a, provided that $g(a) \neq 0$. Because the sine and cosine functions are continuous at all real numbers, it follows that the tangent, cotangent, secant, and cosecant functions are continuous at all numbers in their domain.

By using the identity

$$\cos^2 x + \sin^2 x = 1 \tag{1}$$

and Definition 9.4.1, we obtain two other important identities. If on both sides of (1) we divide by $\cos^2 x$, when $\cos x \neq 0$, we get

$$\frac{\cos^2 x}{\cos^2 x} + \frac{\sin^2 x}{\cos^2 x} = \frac{1}{\cos^2 x}$$

and because $\sin x / \cos x = \tan x$ and $1/\cos x = \sec x$, we have the identity

$$1 + \tan^2 x = \sec^2 x \tag{2}$$

By dividing on both sides of (1) by $\sin^2 x$ when $\sin x \neq 0$, we obtain in a similar way the identity

$$\cot^2 x + 1 = \csc^2 x \tag{3}$$

Three other important formulas follow immediately from Definition 9.4.1. They are

$$\sin x \csc x = 1 \tag{4}$$

$$\cos x \sec x = 1 \tag{5}$$

and

$$\tan x \cot x = 1 \tag{6}$$

Formulas (4), (5), and (6) are valid for all values of x for which the functions are defined, and therefore they are identities.

Another formula that we need is one that expresses the tangent of the difference of two numbers in terms of the tangents of the two numbers. By using formulas 13 and 10 from Sec. 9.1, we have

$$\tan(a - b) = \frac{\sin(a - b)}{\cos(a - b)} = \frac{\sin a \cos b - \cos a \sin b}{\cos a \cos b + \sin a \sin b}$$

Dividing both the numerator and denominator by $\cos a \cos b$, we get

$$\tan(a - b) = \frac{\dfrac{\sin a \cos b}{\cos a \cos b} - \dfrac{\cos a \sin b}{\cos a \cos b}}{\dfrac{\cos a \cos b}{\cos a \cos b} + \dfrac{\sin a \sin b}{\cos a \cos b}} = \frac{\dfrac{\sin a}{\cos a} - \dfrac{\sin b}{\cos b}}{1 + \dfrac{\sin a}{\cos a}\dfrac{\sin b}{\cos b}}$$

Therefore, we have the identity

$$\tan(a - b) = \frac{\tan a - \tan b}{1 + \tan a \tan b} \tag{7}$$

Taking $a = 0$ in formula (7) gives

$$\tan(0 - b) = \frac{\tan 0 - \tan b}{1 + \tan 0 \tan b}$$

Because $\tan 0 = 0$, we have from the above equation

$$\tan(-b) = -\tan b \tag{8}$$

Therefore, the tangent is an odd function.

Taking $b = -b$ in formula (7) gives

$$\tan(a - (-b)) = \frac{\tan a - \tan(-b)}{1 + \tan a \tan(-b)}$$

and replacing $\tan(-b)$ by $-\tan b$, we get the identity

$$\tan(a + b) = \frac{\tan a + \tan b}{1 - \tan a \tan b} \tag{9}$$

The derivatives of the tangent, cotangent, secant, and cosecant functions are obtained from those of the sine and cosine functions and differentiation formulas.

$$D_x(\tan x) = D_x\left(\frac{\sin x}{\cos x}\right) = \frac{\cos x \cdot D_x(\sin x) - \sin x \cdot D_x(\cos x)}{\cos^2 x}$$

$$= \frac{(\cos x)(\cos x) - (\sin x)(-\sin x)}{\cos^2 x}$$

$$= \frac{\cos^2 x + \sin^2 x}{\cos^2 x}$$

$$= \frac{1}{\cos^2 x}$$

$$= \sec^2 x$$

So we have

$$D_x(\tan x) = \sec^2 x \tag{10}$$

If u is a differentiable function of x, then from (10) and the chain rule we obtain

$$D_x(\tan u) = \sec^2 u \, D_x u \tag{11}$$

The formula for the derivative of the cotangent function is obtained in an analogous manner. The result is

$$D_x(\cot x) = -\csc^2 x \tag{12}$$

The derivation of (12) is left for the reader (see Exercise 1).

From (12) and the chain rule, if u is a differentiable function of x, we have

$$D_x(\cot u) = -\csc^2 u \, D_x u \tag{13}$$

$$D_x(\sec x) = D_x[(\cos x)^{-1}]$$

$$= -1(\cos x)^{-2}(-\sin x)$$

$$= \frac{1}{\cos^2 x} \cdot \sin x$$

$$= \frac{1}{\cos x} \cdot \frac{\sin x}{\cos x}$$

$$= \sec x \tan x$$

We have, then, the following formula:

$$D_x(\sec x) = \sec x \tan x \tag{14}$$

If u is a differentiable function of x, then from (14) and the chain rule we get

$$D_x(\sec u) = \sec u \tan u \, D_x u \tag{15}$$

In a similar manner the formula for the derivative of the cosecant function may be derived, and we obtain

$$D_x(\csc x) = -\csc x \cot x \tag{16}$$

So by applying (16) and the chain rule, if u is a differentiable function of x, we have

$$D_x(\csc u) = -\csc u \cot u \, D_x u \tag{17}$$

The derivation of (16) is left for the reader (see Exercise 2).

The following examples illustrate the use of the above formulas.

EXAMPLE 1:   Find $f'(x)$ if

$$f(x) = 2 \tan \tfrac{1}{2}x - x$$

SOLUTION: $f'(x) = 2 \sec^2 \tfrac{1}{2}x(\tfrac{1}{2}) - 1 = \sec^2 \tfrac{1}{2}x - 1$.

If we use identity (2), this simplifies to

$$f'(x) = \tan^2 \tfrac{1}{2}x$$

EXAMPLE 2:   Find $f'(x)$ if

$$f(x) = \sec^4 3x$$

SOLUTION:

$$f'(x) = 4 \sec^3 3x \cdot D_x(\sec 3x)$$

$$= 4 \sec^3 3x(\sec 3x \tan 3x)(3)$$

$$= 12 \sec^4 3x \tan 3x$$

EXAMPLE 3:   Find $f'(x)$ if

$$f(x) = \cot x \csc x$$

SOLUTION:

$$f'(x) = \cot x \cdot D_x(\csc x) + \csc x \cdot D_x(\cot x)$$

$$= \cot x(-\csc x \cot x) + \csc x(-\csc^2 x)$$

$$= -\csc x \cot^2 x - \csc^3 x$$

In Definition 9.1.4 we gave the analogy between the sine and cosine of real numbers and those of angle measurements. The following definition gives a similar analogy for the other four trigonometric functions.

9.4.2 Definition   If α degrees and x radians are measurements for the same angle, then

$$\tan \alpha^\circ = \tan x \qquad \cot \alpha^\circ = \cot x \qquad \sec \alpha^\circ = \sec x \qquad \csc \alpha^\circ = \csc x$$

EXAMPLE 4:   An airplane is flying west at 500 ft/sec at an altitude of 4000 ft. The airplane is in a vertical plane with a searchlight on the ground. If the light is to be kept on the plane, how fast is the searchlight revolving when the airplane is due east of the searchlight at an airline distance of 2000 ft?

SOLUTION: Refer to Fig. 9.4.1. The searchlight is at point L, and at a particular instant of time the airplane is at point P.

Let $t =$ the number of seconds in the time;

   $x =$ the number of feet due east in the airline distance of the airplane from the searchlight at time t sec;

   $\theta =$ the number of radians in the angle of elevation of the airplane at the searchlight at time t sec.

We are given $D_t x = -500$. We wish to find $D_t \theta$ when $x = 2000$.

$$\tan \theta = \frac{4000}{x} \tag{18}$$

4000 ft

θ

L x ft

Figure 9.4.1

Differentiating on both sides of Eq. (18) with respect to t, we obtain

$$\sec^2 \theta \, D_t\theta = -\frac{4000}{x^2} D_t x$$

Substituting $D_t x = -500$ in the above and dividing by $\sec^2 \theta$ gives

$$D_t\theta = \frac{2{,}000{,}000}{x^2 \sec^2 \theta} \tag{19}$$

When $x = 2000$, $\tan \theta = 2$. Therefore, $\sec^2 \theta = 1 + \tan^2 \theta = 5$. Substituting these values into Eq. (19), we have, when $x = 2000$,

$$D_t\theta = \frac{2{,}000{,}000}{4{,}000{,}000(5)} = \frac{1}{10}$$

We conclude that at the given instant the measurement of the angle is increasing at the rate of $\frac{1}{10}$ rad/sec, and this is how fast the searchlight is revolving.

We now consider the graph of the tangent function. Because from Eq. (8) $\tan(-x) = -\tan x$, the graph is symmetric with respect to the origin. Furthermore,

$$\tan(x + \pi) = \frac{\sin(x + \pi)}{\cos(x + \pi)}$$

$$= \frac{\sin x \cos \pi + \cos x \sin \pi}{\cos x \cos \pi - \sin x \sin \pi}$$

$$= \frac{\sin x(-1) + \cos x(0)}{\cos x(-1) - \sin x(0)}$$

$$= \frac{-\sin x}{-\cos x}$$

$$= \tan x$$

and so by Definition 9.1.3, the tangent function is periodic with period π.

The tangent function is continuous at all numbers in its domain which is the set of all real numbers except those of the form $\frac{1}{2}\pi + n\pi$, where n is any integer. However, $\lim\limits_{x \to (\pi/2 + n\pi)} \tan x = \infty$, and so the lines having equations $x = \frac{1}{2}\pi + n\pi$ are vertical asymptotes of the graph.

If n is any integer, $\sin n\pi = 0$ and $\cos n\pi$ is either $+1$ or -1, and so $\tan n\pi = 0$. Therefore, the graph intersects the x axis at the points $(n\pi, 0)$.

To find the relative extrema of the tangent function and the points of inflection of its graph, we consider the first and second derivatives. So if $f(x) = \tan x$, then $f'(x) = \sec^2 x$ and $f''(x) = 2\sec^2 x \tan x$.

Setting $f'(x) = 0$ gives $\sec^2 x = 0$. Because $\sec^2 x \geq 1$ for all x, we conclude that there are no relative extrema. Setting $f''(x) = 0$, we obtain $2\sec^2 x \tan x = 0$, from which we get $\tan x = 0$ because $\sec^2 x \neq 0$. Therefore, $f''(x) = 0$ if $x = n\pi$, where n is any integer. At these values of x, $f''(x)$ changes sign, and so the points of inflection are the points $(n\pi, 0)$, which are the points where the graph intersects the x axis. Because $f'(n\pi) = \sec^2 n\pi = 1$, the slopes of the inflectional tangents are 1.

Consider now the open interval $(-\tfrac{1}{2}\pi, \tfrac{1}{2}\pi)$ on which the tangent function is defined everywhere. Because $f'(x) = \sec^2 x > 0$ for all values of x, it follows that the tangent is an increasing function on this interval. When $-\tfrac{1}{2}\pi < x < 0$, $f''(x) = 2\sec^2 x \tan x < 0$; hence, the graph is concave downward on the open interval $(-\tfrac{1}{2}\pi, 0)$. When $0 < x < \tfrac{1}{2}\pi$, $f''(x) > 0$, from which it follows that the graph is concave upward on the open interval $(0, \tfrac{1}{2}\pi)$.

Table 9.4.1

x	0	$\tfrac{1}{6}\pi$	$\tfrac{1}{4}\pi$	$\tfrac{1}{3}\pi$
$\tan x$	0	$\tfrac{1}{3}\sqrt{3} \approx 0.58$	1	$\sqrt{3} \approx 1.73$

In Table 9.4.1 there are some corresponding values of x and y satisfying the equation $y = \tan x$. By plotting the points having as coordinates the number pairs (x, y) and using the above information, a sketch of the graph of the tangent function may be drawn, and it is shown in Fig. 9.4.2.

The graph of the cotangent function can be obtained from the graph of the tangent function by using an identity which will now be proved.

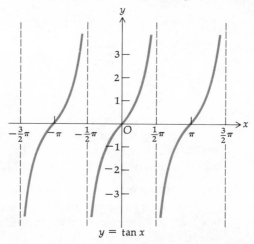

$y = \tan x$

Figure 9.4.2

$$\tan(\tfrac{1}{2}\pi + x) = \frac{\sin(\tfrac{1}{2}\pi + x)}{\cos(\tfrac{1}{2}\pi + x)}$$

$$= \frac{\sin\tfrac{1}{2}\pi \cos x + \cos\tfrac{1}{2}\pi \sin x}{\cos\tfrac{1}{2}\pi \cos x - \sin\tfrac{1}{2}\pi \sin x}$$

$$= \frac{(1)\cos x + (0)\sin x}{(0)\cos x - (1)\sin x}$$

$$= \frac{\cos x}{-\sin x}$$

$$= -\cot x$$

Therefore,

$$\cot x = -\tan(\tfrac{1}{2}\pi + x)$$

From the above identity it follows that the graph of the cotangent function is obtained from the graph of the tangent function by translating the y axis $\tfrac{1}{2}\pi$ units to the right and then taking a reflection of the graph with respect to the x axis. A sketch of the graph of the cotangent function is in Fig. 9.4.3.

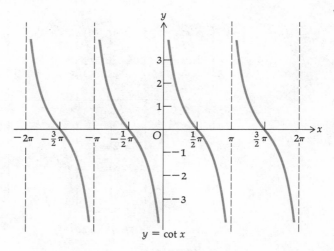

$$y = \cot x$$

Figure 9.4.3

The secant function is periodic with period 2π because

$$\sec(x + 2\pi) = \frac{1}{\cos(x + 2\pi)} = \frac{1}{\cos x} = \sec x$$

The domain of the secant function is the set of all real numbers except those of the form $\tfrac{1}{2}\pi + n\pi$, and the function is continuous on its domain. Because $\lim\limits_{x \to \pi/2 + n\pi} \sec x = \infty$, the graph of the secant function has the lines $x = \tfrac{1}{2}\pi + n\pi$ as vertical asymptotes. There is no intersection of the graph with the x axis because sec x is never zero. The secant function is even because

$$\sec(-x) = \frac{1}{\cos(-x)} = \frac{1}{\cos x} = \sec x$$

and so the graph of the secant function is symmetric with respect to the y axis.

If $f(x) = \sec x$, it follows that $f'(x) = \sec x \tan x$ and $f''(x) = \sec x(2 \tan^2 x + 1)$. Setting $f'(x) = 0$ gives sec $x \tan x = 0$. Because sec $x \neq 0$, $f'(x) = 0$ when $\tan x = 0$, which is when $x = n\pi$, where n is any integer. Also, $f''(n\pi) = \sec n\pi[2 \tan^2 n\pi + 1]$. If n is an even integer, $f''(n\pi) = 1 \cdot (0 + 1) = 1$; and if n is an odd integer, $f''(n\pi) = (-1)(0 + 1) = -1$. Therefore, when $x = n\pi$ and n is an even integer, f has a relative minimum value; and when $x = n\pi$ and n is an odd integer, f has a relative maximum value. There are no points of inflection because for all x, $f''(x) \neq 0$.

Using the above information and plotting a few points, we get a sketch of the graph of the secant function shown in Fig. 9.4.4.

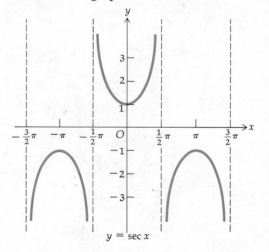

$$y = \sec x$$

Figure 9.4.4

Because

$$\sec(x + \tfrac{1}{2}\pi) = \frac{1}{\cos(x + \tfrac{1}{2}\pi)} = \frac{1}{-\sin x} = -\csc x$$

then

$$\csc x = -\sec(x + \tfrac{1}{2}\pi)$$

and so the graph of the cosecant function is obtained from that of the secant function by translating the y axis $\tfrac{1}{2}\pi$ units to the right and taking a reflection of the graph with respect to the x axis. A sketch of the graph of the cosecant function is in Fig. 9.4.5.

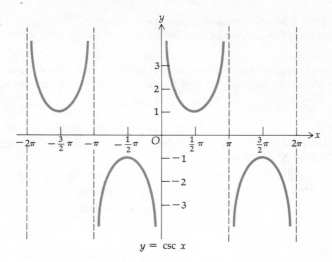

$y = \csc x$

Figure 9.4.5

Exercises 9.4

1. Derive: $D_x(\cot x) = -\csc^2 x$.

2. Derive: $D_x(\csc x) = -\csc x \cot x$.

In Exercises 3 through 20, find the derivative of the given function.

3. $f(x) = \sec x^2$

4. $g(x) = \ln \csc^2 x$

5. $F(x) = \ln |\sec 2x|$

6. $h(x) = \ln |\cot \tfrac{1}{2}x|$

7. $G(r) = \sqrt{\cot 3r}$

8. $h(t) = \sec^2 2t - \tan^2 2t$

9. $g(x) = \sec x \tan x$

10. $f(x) = \sin x \tan x$

11. $f(t) = \csc(t^3 + 1)$

12. $g(t) = 2 \sec \sqrt{t}$

13. $H(t) = \cot^4 t - \csc^4 t$

14. $F(x) = \dfrac{\cot^2 2x}{1 + x^2}$

15. $f(x) = \ln |\sec 5x + \tan 5x|$

16. $f(x) = \tfrac{1}{3} \sec^3 2x - \sec 2x$

17. $g(x) = 3^x \sec x$

18. $G(z) = \log_{10} |\csc x - \cot x|$

19. $F(x) = (\sin x)^{\tan x}$

20. $G(x) = (\tan x)^x$

In Exercises 21 and 22, use logarithmic differentiation to find $D_x y$.

21. $y = \dfrac{\sec x \sqrt{1 - \cot^2 x}}{\csc^3 x}$

22. $y = \dfrac{\tan^2 x}{\sqrt{1 + \sec^2 x}}$

In Exercises 23 through 26, find $D_x y$ by implicit differentiation.

23. $y = \tan(x + y)$

24. $\cot xy + xy = 0$

25. $\sec^2 x + \csc^2 y = 4$

26. $\csc(x - y) + \sec(x + y) = x$

In Exercises 27 through 30, draw a sketch of the graph of the given function.

27. $f(x) = \tan 2x$

28. $f(x) = \tfrac{1}{2} \sec 2x$

29. $f(x) = \tfrac{1}{2} |\cot x|$

30. $f(x) = |\csc \tfrac{1}{2}x|$

31. Find an equation of the tangent line to the curve $y = \sec x$ at the point $(\tfrac{1}{4}\pi, \sqrt{2})$.

32. A radar antenna is located on a ship that is 4 miles from a straight shore and it is rotating at 32 rpm. How fast is the radar beam moving along the shore line when the beam makes an angle of 45° with the shore?

33. A steel girder 27 ft long is moved horizontally along a passageway 8 ft wide and into a corridor at right angles to the passageway. How wide must the corridor be in order for the girder to go around the corner? Neglect the horizontal width of the girder.

34. If two corridors at right angles to each other are 10 ft and 15 ft wide, respectively, what is the length of the longest steel girder that can be moved horizontally around the corner? Neglect the horizontal width of the girder.

9.5 AN APPLICATION OF THE TANGENT FUNCTION TO THE SLOPE OF A LINE

The tangent function can be used in connection with the slope of a straight line. We first define the *angle of inclination* of a line.

9.5.1 Definition

The *angle of inclination* of a line not parallel to the x axis is the smallest angle measured counterclockwise from the positive direction of the x axis to the line. The inclination of a line parallel to the x axis is defined to have measure zero.

If α is the degree measure of the angle of inclination of a line, α may be any number in the interval $0 \leq \alpha < 180$. Figure 9.5.1 shows a line L for which $0 < \alpha < 90$, and Fig. 9.5.2 shows one for which $90 < \alpha < 180$.

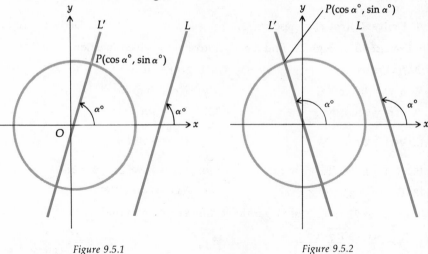

Figure 9.5.1   Figure 9.5.2

9.5.2 Theorem

If α is the degree measure of the angle of inclination of line L, not parallel to the y axis, then the slope m of L is given by

$$m = \tan \alpha°$$

PROOF: Refer to Figs. 9.5.1 and 9.5.2, which show the given line L whose angle of inclination has degree measure α and whose slope is m. The line L' that passes through the origin and is parallel to L also has slope m and an angle of inclination whose degree measure is α. The point $P(\cos \alpha°, \sin \alpha°)$, at the intersection of L and the unit circle $x^2 + y^2 = 1$, lies on L'. And because the point $(0, 0)$ also lies on L', it follows from Definition 1.5.1 that

$$m = \frac{\sin \alpha^\circ - 0}{\cos \alpha^\circ - 0} = \frac{\sin \alpha^\circ}{\cos \alpha^\circ} = \tan \alpha^\circ$$ ∎

If the line L is parallel to the y axis, the degree measure of the angle of inclination of L is 90 and tan 90° does not exist. This is consistent with the fact that a vertical line has no slope.

Theorem 9.5.2 is used to obtain a formula for finding the angle between two nonvertical intersecting lines. If two lines intersect, two supplementary angles are formed at their point of intersection. To distinguish these two angles, let L_2 be the line with the greater angle of inclination of degree measure α_2 and let L_1 be the other line for which the degree measure of its angle of inclination is α_1. If θ is the degree measure of the angle between the two lines, then we define

$$\theta = \alpha_2 - \alpha_1 \tag{1}$$

If L_1 and L_2 are parallel, then $\alpha_1 = \alpha_2$ and the angle between the two lines has degree measure 0. Thus, if L_1 and L_2 are two distinct lines, $0 \leq \theta < 180$. Refer to Figs. 9.5.3 and 9.5.4.

Figure 9.5.3   Figure 9.5.4

The following theorem enables us to find θ when the slopes of L_1 and L_2 are known.

9.5.3 Theorem   Let L_1 and L_2 be two nonvertical lines, which intersect and are not perpendicular, and let L_2 be the line having the greater angle of inclination. Then if m_1 is the slope of L_1, m_2 is the slope of L_2, and θ is the degree measure of the angle between L_1 and L_2,

$$\tan \theta^\circ = \frac{m_2 - m_1}{1 + m_1 m_2} \tag{2}$$

PROOF: If α_1 and α_2 are degree measures of the angles of inclination of L_1 and L_2, respectively, from Eq. (1) we have

$$\theta = \alpha_2 - \alpha_1$$

and so

$$\tan \theta° = \tan(\alpha_2° - \alpha_1°)$$

Applying formula (7) of Sec. 9.4 to the right side of the above, we get

$$\tan \theta° = \frac{\tan \alpha_2° - \tan \alpha_1°}{1 + \tan \alpha_2° \tan \alpha_1°}$$

$$= \frac{m_2 - m_1}{1 + m_1 m_2}$$

∎

EXAMPLE 1:   Find to the nearest degree the measurements of the interior angles of the triangle having vertices $B(-2, 1), C(2, 2), D(-3, 4)$.

Figure 9.5.5

SOLUTION: Let β, γ, and δ be the degree measures of the interior angles of the triangle at the vertices B, C, and D, respectively. Let u denote the line through B and C, v the line through C and D, w the line through B and D, and m_u, m_v, and m_w their respective slopes. Refer to Fig. 9.5.5.

Using the formula for the slope of a line through two given points, we get

$$m_u = \tfrac{1}{4} \qquad m_v = -\tfrac{2}{5} \qquad m_w = -3$$

To determine β, we observe that line w has a greater angle of inclination than line u; so in formula (2), $m_2 = m_w = -3$ and $m_1 = m_u = \tfrac{1}{4}$. The degree measure of the angle between lines u and v is β. Thus, from formula (2) we have

$$\tan \beta° = \frac{-3 - \tfrac{1}{4}}{1 + \tfrac{1}{4}(-3)} = -13$$

Therefore,

$$\beta = 94$$

To determine γ, because line v has a greater angle of inclination than line u, $m_2 = m_v = -\tfrac{2}{5}$ and $m_1 = m_u = \tfrac{1}{4}$. The degree measure of the angle between lines u and v is, by definition, $180 - \gamma$. Applying formula (2), then, we get

$$\tan(180° - \gamma°) = \frac{-\tfrac{2}{5} - \tfrac{1}{4}}{1 + \tfrac{1}{4}(-\tfrac{2}{5})} = -\tfrac{13}{18}$$

Hence,

$$180 - \gamma = 144$$

so that

$$\gamma = 36$$

To determine δ, because line v has a greater angle of inclination than line w, $m_2 = m_v = -\frac{2}{5}$ and $m_1 = m_w = -3$. The degree measure of the angle between lines v and w is then δ. Applying formula (2), we obtain

$$\tan \delta° = \frac{-\frac{2}{5} - (-3)}{1 + (-\frac{2}{5})(-3)} = \frac{13}{11}$$

Therefore,

$$\delta = 50$$

The sum of the degree measures of the angles of a triangle must be 180. We use this to check the results, and we have

$$\beta + \gamma + \delta = 94 + 36 + 50 = 180$$

9.5.4 Definition   The *angle between two curves* at a point of intersection is the angle between the tangent lines to the curves at the point.

EXAMPLE 2:   Find to the nearest degree the measurement of the angle between the curves $y = x^2 - 2$ and $y = -2x^2 + 10$ at their points of intersection.

Figure 9.5.6

SOLUTION: Solving the two equations simultaneously, we obtain $(2, 2)$ and $(-2, 2)$ as the points of intersection. In Fig. 9.5.6 sketches of the two curves are shown together with the tangent lines at each point of intersection. Because of the symmetry of the two curves with respect to the y axis, the angle between the curves at $(2, 2)$ has the same measure as the angle between them at $(-2, 2)$. Let P be the point $(2, 2)$, T_1 be the tangent line to $y = x^2 - 2$ at P, and T_2 be the tangent line to $y = -2x^2 + 10$ at P. The line T_2 has a greater angle of inclination than T_1. So if θ is the degree measure of the angle between T_1 and T_2,

$$\tan \theta° = \frac{m_2 - m_1}{1 + m_1 m_2}$$

where m_2 is the slope of T_2 and m_1 is the slope of T_1. From the equation $y = x^2 - 2$, we get $D_x y = 2x$, and so $m_1 = 4$. From the equation $y = -2x^2 + 10$, we get $D_x y = -4x$; thus, $m_2 = -8$. Hence,

$$\tan \theta° = \frac{-8 - 4}{1 + (4)(-8)} = \frac{12}{31} \approx 0.387$$

Therefore, to the nearest degree, $\theta° = 21°$.

Exercises 9.5

1. Find $\tan \theta°$ if $\theta°$ is the measurement of the angle between the lines whose slopes are (a) 1 and $\frac{1}{3}$; (b) 5 and $-\frac{5}{3}$; (c) $-\frac{2}{3}$ and $\frac{1}{2}$; (d) $-\frac{1}{3}$ and $-\frac{1}{10}$; (e) $-\frac{4}{3}$ and $-\frac{5}{2}$.

2. Find, to the nearest degree, the measurement of the angle between the lines whose slopes are (a) 5 and $-\frac{7}{9}$; (b) -3 and 2; (c) $\frac{3}{2}$ and $\frac{1}{4}$; (d) $-\frac{3}{2}$ and $-\frac{1}{4}$.

3. Find, to the nearest degree, the measurements of the interior angles of the triangle formed by the lines that have equations $2x + y - 6 = 0$, $3x - y - 4 = 0$, and $3x + 4y + 8 = 0$.

4. Find, to the nearest degree, the measurements of the interior angles of the triangle having vertices at $(1, 0)$, $(-3, 2)$, and $(2, 3)$.

5. Find an equation of a line through the point $(-1, 4)$ making an angle of radian measure $\frac{1}{4}\pi$ with the line having equation $2x + y - 5 = 0$ (two solutions).

6. Find an equation of a line through the point $(-3, -2)$ making an angle of radian measure $\frac{1}{3}\pi$ with the line having equation $3x - 2y - 7 = 0$.

7. Using Theorem 9.5.3, prove that the triangle having vertices at $(2, 3)$, $(6, 2)$, and $(3, -1)$ is isosceles.

8. Using Theorem 9.5.3, prove that the triangle having vertices at $(-3, 0)$, $(-1, 0)$, and $(-2, \sqrt{3})$ is equilateral.

9. Find the slope of the bisector of the angle at A in the triangle having the vertices: $A(4, 1)$; $B(6, 5)$; and $C(-1, 8)$.

10. Find the slope of the bisector of the angle at A in the triangle having the vertices: $A(-3, 5)$; $B(2, -4)$; and $C(-1, 7)$.

11. Let A, B, and C be the vertices of an oblique triangle (no right angle), and let α, β, and γ be the radian measures of the interior angles at vertices A, B, and C, respectively. Prove that $\tan \alpha + \tan \beta + \tan \gamma = \tan \alpha \tan \beta \tan \gamma$. (HINT: First show that $\tan(\alpha + \beta) = -\tan \gamma$.)

12. Find the tangents of the measurements of the interior angles of the triangle having vertices at $(-3, -2)$, $(-6, 3)$, and $(5, 1)$ and check by applying the result of Exercise 11.

13. Find the points of intersection of the graphs of the sine and cosine functions and find the measurement of the angle between their tangent lines at their points of intersection.

14. Find, to the nearest 10 minutes, the measurement of the angle between the curves $y = 2x^2 - 11$ and $y = x^2 - 2$ at their points of intersection.

9.6 INTEGRALS INVOLVING THE TANGENT, COTANGENT, SECANT, AND COSECANT

A formula for the indefinite integral of the tangent function is derived as follows. Because

$$\int \tan u \, du = \int \frac{\sin u}{\cos u} \, du$$

THE FUNCTION IS BROKEN IN THE TWO COMPONENTS

we let $v = \cos u$, $dv = -\sin u \, du$, and obtain

$$\int \tan u \, du = -\int \frac{dv}{v} = -\ln |v| + C$$

Hence,

$$\int \tan u \, du = -\ln |\cos u| + C \tag{1}$$

Because $-\ln |\cos u| = \ln |(\cos u)^{-1}| = \ln |\sec u|$, we can also write

$$\int \tan u \, du = \ln |\sec u| + C \tag{2}$$

The following formula is derived in a way similar to the derivation of (1). (See Exercise 29.)

$$\int \cot u \, du = \ln |\sin u| + C \tag{3}$$

To integrate $\int \sec u \, du$, we multiply the numerator and denominator of the integrand by $(\sec u + \tan u)$, and we have

THE DERIVATIVES ARE TAKEN $\cdot \longrightarrow$

$$\int \sec u \, du = \int \frac{\sec u(\sec u + \tan u)}{\sec u + \tan u} \, du = \int \frac{(\sec^2 u + \sec u \tan u)}{\sec u + \tan u} \, du$$

Let $v = \sec u + \tan u$. Then $dv = (\sec u \tan u + \sec^2 u) \, du$; and so we have

$$\int \sec u \, du = \int \frac{dv}{v} = \ln |v| + C$$

Therefore,

$$\int \sec u \, du = \ln |\sec u + \tan u| + C \tag{4}$$

The formula for $\int \csc u \, du$ is derived by multiplying the numerator and denominator of the integrand by $(\csc u - \cot u)$ and proceeding as above. This derivation is left for the reader (see Exercise 30). The formula is

$$\int \csc u \, du = \ln |\csc u - \cot u| + C \tag{5}$$

The application of these formulas to the evaluation of other integrals is illustrated in the following examples.

EXAMPLE 1:   Find

$$\int \tan 3x \, dx$$

SOLUTION:

$$\int \tan 3x \, dx = \frac{1}{3} \int \tan 3x \, (3 \, dx)$$

$$= \tfrac{1}{3} \ln |\sec 3x| + C$$

EXAMPLE 2:   Find

$$\int \frac{dx}{\sin 2x}$$

SOLUTION:

$$\int \frac{dx}{\sin 2x} = \int \csc 2x \, dx = \frac{1}{2} \int \csc 2x \, (2dx)$$

$$= \tfrac{1}{2} \ln |\csc 2x - \cot 2x| + C$$

The following two indefinite integral formulas follow immediately from the corresponding differentiation formulas.

$$\int \sec^2 u \, du = \tan u + C \tag{6}$$

$$\int \sec u \tan u \, du = \sec u + C \tag{7}$$

Many integrals involving powers of tangent and secant can be evaluated by applying these two formulas and the identity given by formula (2) in Sec. 9.4, which is

$$1 + \tan^2 u = \sec^2 u \tag{8}$$

There are similar formulas involving the cotangent and cosecant.

$$\int \csc^2 u \, du = -\cot u + C \tag{9}$$

PROOF: $D_u(-\cot u) = -(-\csc^2 u) = \csc^2 u.$

$$\int \csc u \cot u \, du = -\csc u + C \tag{10}$$

PROOF: $D_u(-\csc u) = -(-\csc u \cot u) = \csc u \cot u.$

EXAMPLE 3:   Find

$$\int \frac{2 + 3 \cos u}{\sin^2 u} \, du$$

SOLUTION:

$$\int \frac{2 + 3 \cos u}{\sin^2 u} \, du = 2 \int \frac{1}{\sin^2 u} \, du + 3 \int \frac{1}{\sin u} \cdot \frac{\cos u}{\sin u} \, du$$

$$= 2 \int \csc^2 u \, du + 3 \int \csc u \cot u \, du$$

$$= -2 \cot u - 3 \csc u + C$$

From formula (3) in Sec. 9.4 we have the identity

$$1 + \cot^2 u = \csc^2 u \tag{11}$$

Formulas (6), (7), and (8) are used to evaluate integrals of the form

$$\int \tan^m u \sec^n u \, du$$

and formulas (9), (10), and (11) are used to evaluate integrals of the form

$$\int \cot^m u \csc^n u \, du$$

where m and n are positive integers.

We distinguish various cases.

Case 1: $\int \tan^n u \, du$ or $\int \cot^n u \, du$, where n is a positive integer. We write

$$\tan^n u = \tan^{n-2} u \tan^2 u$$

$$= \tan^{n-2} u (\sec^2 u - 1)$$

and

$$\cot^n u = \cot^{n-2} u \cot^2 u$$

$$= \cot^{n-2} u (\csc^2 u - 1)$$

EXAMPLE 4:   Find

$$\int \tan^3 x \, dx$$

SOLUTION:

$$\int \tan^3 x \, dx = \int \tan x (\sec^2 x - 1) \, dx = \int \tan x \sec^2 x \, dx - \int \tan x \, dx$$

$$= \tfrac{1}{2} \tan^2 x + \ln |\cos x| + C$$

EXAMPLE 5: **Find**

$$\int \cot^4 3x \, dx$$

SOLUTION:

$$\int \cot^4 3x \, dx = \int \cot^2 3x (\csc^2 3x - 1) \, dx$$

$$= \int \cot^2 3x \csc^2 3x \, dx - \int \cot^2 3x \, dx$$

$$= \tfrac{1}{9} (-\cot^3 3x) - \int (\csc^2 3x - 1) \, dx$$

$$= -\tfrac{1}{9} \cot^3 3x + \tfrac{1}{3} \cot 3x + x + C$$

Case 2: $\int \sec^n u \, du$ or $\int \csc^n u \, du$, where n is a positive even integer.
We write $\sec^n u = \sec^{n-2} u \sec^2 u = (\tan^2 u + 1)^{(n-2)/2} \sec^2 u$
and
$$\csc^n u = \csc^{n-2} u \csc^2 u = (\cot^2 u + 1)^{(n-2)/2} \csc^2 u$$

EXAMPLE 6: **Find**

$$\int \csc^6 x \, dx$$

SOLUTION:

$$\int \csc^6 x \, dx = \int (\cot^2 x + 1)^2 \csc^2 x \, dx$$

$$= \int \cot^4 x \csc^2 x \, dx + 2 \int \cot^2 x \csc^2 x \, dx + \int \csc^2 x \, dx$$

$$= -\tfrac{1}{5} \cot^5 x - \tfrac{2}{3} \cot^3 x - \cot x + C$$

To integrate $\int \sec^n u \, du$ or $\int \csc^n u \, du$ when n is a positive odd integer,
we must use integration by parts, which is discussed in Sec. 10.2.

Case 3: $\int \tan^m u \sec^n u \, du$ or $\int \cot^m u \csc^n u \, du$, where n is a positive even
integer.
This case is illustrated by the following example.

EXAMPLE 7: **Find**

$$\int \tan^5 x \sec^4 x \, dx$$

SOLUTION:

$$\int \tan^5 x \sec^4 x \, dx = \int \tan^5 x (\tan^2 x + 1) \sec^2 x \, dx$$

$$= \int \tan^7 x \sec^2 x \, dx + \int \tan^5 x \sec^2 x \, dx$$

$$= \tfrac{1}{8} \tan^8 x + \tfrac{1}{6} \tan^6 x + C$$

Case 4: $\int \tan^m u \sec^n u \, du$ or $\int \cot^m u \csc^n u \, du$, where m is a positive odd
integer.
The following example illustrates this case.

EXAMPLE 8: **Find**

$$\int \tan^5 x \sec^7 x \, dx$$

SOLUTION:

$$\int \tan^5 x \sec^7 x \, dx = \int \tan^4 x \sec^6 x \sec x \tan x \, dx$$

$$= \int (\sec^2 x - 1)^2 \sec^6 x \, (\sec x \tan x \, dx)$$

$$= \int \sec^{10} x \, (\sec x \tan x \, dx)$$

$$- 2 \int \sec^8 x \, (\sec x \tan x \, dx) + \int \sec^6 x \, (\sec x \tan x \, dx)$$

$$= \tfrac{1}{11} \sec^{11} x - \tfrac{2}{9} \sec^9 x + \tfrac{1}{7} \sec^7 x + C$$

Integration by parts (Sec. 10.2) is used to integrate $\int \tan^m u \sec^n u \, du$ and $\int \cot^m u \csc^n u \, du$ when m is a positive even integer and n is a positive odd integer.

Exercises 9.6

In Exercises 1 through 22, evaluate the indefinite integral.

1. $\int \tan 2x \, dx$

2. $\int \cot(3x + 1) \, dx$

3. $\int x \csc 5x^2 \, dx$

4. $\int \sec x \tan x \tan(\sec x) \, dx$

5. $\int \cot^3 x \, dx$

6. $\int \csc^4 x \, dx$

7. $\int \csc^2 6x \, dx$

8. $\int x^2 \sec^2 x^3 \, dx$

9. $\int \tan^6 x \sec^4 x \, dx$

10. $\int \tan^5 x \sec^3 x \, dx$

11. $\int \cot^2 3x \csc^4 3x \, dx$

12. $\int (\sec 5x + \csc 5x)^2 \, dx$

13. $\int (\tan 3x + \cot 3x)^2 \, dx$

14. $\int \dfrac{dx}{1 + \cos x}$

15. $\int \tan^4 \tfrac{1}{2} x \, dx$

16. $\int \tan^5 3x \, dx$

17. $\int \cot^6 2t \, dt$

18. $\int \dfrac{\tan^4 y}{\sec^5 y} \, dy$

19. $\int \dfrac{du}{1 + \sec \tfrac{1}{2} u}$

20. $\int \dfrac{\csc^4 x}{\cot^2 x} \, dx$

21. $\int \dfrac{\sec^3 x}{\tan^4 x} \, dx$

22. $\int \dfrac{\sin^2 \pi x}{\cos^6 \pi x} \, dx$

In Exercises 23 through 28, evaluate the definite integral.

23. $\displaystyle\int_{\pi/16}^{\pi/12} \tan 4x \, dx$

24. $\displaystyle\int_{\pi/8}^{\pi/4} 3 \csc 2x \, dx$

25. $\displaystyle\int_{-\pi/4}^{\pi/4} \sec^6 x \, dx$

26. $\displaystyle\int_{\pi/6}^{\pi/4} \cot^3 w \, dw$

27. $\displaystyle\int_{\pi/4}^{\pi/2} \dfrac{\cos^4 t}{\sin^6 t} \, dt$

28. $\displaystyle\int_{0}^{\pi/3} \dfrac{\tan^3 x}{\sec x} \, dx$

29. Derive the formula $\int \cot u \, du = \ln |\sin u| + C$.

30. Derive the formula $\int \csc u \, du = \ln |\csc u - \cot u| + C$.

31. Find the length of the arc of the curve $y = \ln \csc x$ from $x = \tfrac{1}{6}\pi$ to $x = \tfrac{1}{2}\pi$.

32. Find the area of the region bounded by the curve $y = \tan^2 x$, the x axis, and the line $x = \tfrac{1}{4}\pi$.

33. Find the volume of the solid of revolution generated if the region bounded by the curve $y = \sec^2 x$, the axes, and the line $x = \tfrac{1}{4}\pi$ is revolved about the x axis.

34. Prove: $\displaystyle\int \cot x \csc^n x \, dx = -\dfrac{\csc^n x}{n} + C$, if $n \neq 0$

35. Prove: $\displaystyle\int \tan^n x \, dx = \dfrac{\tan^{n-1} x}{n - 1} - \int \tan^{n-2} x \, dx$ if n is a positive integer greater than 1.

36. Derive a formula similar to that in Exercise 34 for $\int \tan x \sec^n x \, dx$ if $n \neq 0$.

37. Derive a formula similar to that in Exercise 35 for $\int \cot^n x \, dx$, if n is a positive integer greater than 1.

38. We can integrate $\int \sec^2 x \tan x \, dx$ in two ways as follows: $\int \sec^2 x \tan x \, dx = \int \tan x (\sec^2 x \, dx) = \frac{1}{2} \tan^2 x + C$ and $\int \sec^2 x \tan x \, dx = \int \sec x (\sec x \tan x \, dx) = \frac{1}{2} \sec^2 x + C$. Explain the difference in the appearance of the two answers.

39. Prove that $\int \csc u \, du = -\ln |\csc u + \cot u| + C$.

9.7 INVERSE TRIGONOMETRIC FUNCTIONS

Figure 9.7.1

Consider the equation $x = \sin y$. A sketch of the graph of this equation is in Fig. 9.7.1. In the figure, the vertical line $x = \frac{1}{2}$ is shown; this line intersects the graph at the points for which $y = \frac{1}{6}\pi, \frac{5}{6}\pi, -\frac{7}{6}\pi, -\frac{11}{6}\pi$, and so on. We see, then, that the equation $x = \sin y$ does not define y as a function of x because every vertical line must intersect the graph of a function in at most one point. Hence, we conclude that the sine function does not have an inverse function.

Refer now to the graph of the sine function (Fig. 9.2.3). We see from the figure that the sine is an increasing function on the interval $[-\frac{1}{2}\pi, \frac{1}{2}\pi]$. This follows from Theorem 4.6.3 because if $f(x) = \sin x$, then $f'(x) = \cos x > 0$ for all x in $(-\frac{1}{2}\pi, \frac{1}{2}\pi)$. Thus, even though the sine function does not have an inverse function, it follows from Theorem 8.3.2 that the function F for which

$$F(x) = \sin x \quad \text{and} \quad -\tfrac{1}{2}\pi \leq x \leq \tfrac{1}{2}\pi \tag{1}$$

does have an inverse function. The domain of F is $[-\frac{1}{2}\pi, \frac{1}{2}\pi]$ and its range is $[-1, 1]$. A sketch of the graph of F is shown in Fig. 9.7.2. The inverse of the function defined by (1) is called the *inverse sine function* and is denoted by the symbol $\sin^{-1}$. Following is the formal definition.

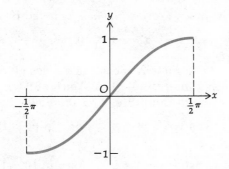

Figure 9.7.2

9.7.1 Definition   The *inverse sine function*, denoted by $\sin^{-1}$, is defined as follows:

$$y = \sin^{-1} x \quad \text{if and only if} \quad x = \sin y \text{ and } -\tfrac{1}{2}\pi \leq y \leq \tfrac{1}{2}\pi$$

The domain of $\sin^{-1}$ is the closed interval $[-1, 1]$, and the range is the closed interval $[-\frac{1}{2}\pi, \frac{1}{2}\pi]$. A sketch of the graph is shown in Fig. 9.7.3.

Figure 9.7.3

Figure 9.7.4

$y = \cos^{-1} x$

Figure 9.7.5

It follows from Definition 9.7.1 that

$$\sin(\sin^{-1} x) = x \qquad \text{for } x \text{ in } [-1, 1] \tag{2}$$

and

$$\sin^{-1}(\sin y) = y \qquad \text{for } y \text{ in } [-\tfrac{1}{2}\pi, \tfrac{1}{2}\pi] \tag{3}$$

In (1) the domain of F was restricted to the closed interval $[-\tfrac{1}{2}\pi, \tfrac{1}{2}\pi]$ so the function would be monotonic on its domain and therefore have an inverse function. However, the sine function has period 2π and is increasing on other intervals, for instance, $[-\tfrac{5}{2}\pi, -\tfrac{3}{2}\pi]$ and $[\tfrac{3}{2}\pi, \tfrac{5}{2}\pi]$. Also, the function is decreasing on certain closed intervals, in particular the intervals $[-\tfrac{3}{2}\pi, -\tfrac{1}{2}\pi]$ and $[\tfrac{1}{2}\pi, \tfrac{3}{2}\pi]$. Any one of these intervals could just as well have been chosen for the domain of the inverse sine function. The choice of the interval $[-\tfrac{1}{2}\pi, \tfrac{1}{2}\pi]$, however, is customary because it is the largest interval containing the number 0 on which the function is monotonic.

The cosine function does not have an inverse function for the same reason that the sine function doesn't. To define the inverse cosine function, we restrict the cosine to an interval on which the function is monotonic. We choose the interval $[0, \pi]$ on which the cosine is decreasing. So consider the function G defined by

$$G(x) = \cos x \quad \text{and} \quad 0 \le x \le \pi \tag{4}$$

The range of this function G is the closed interval $[-1, 1]$, and its domain is the closed interval $[0, \pi]$. A sketch of the graph of G is shown in Fig. 9.7.4. Because this function is continuous and decreasing on its domain, it has an inverse function which is called the *inverse cosine function* and is denoted by $\cos^{-1}$.

9.7.2 Definition   The *inverse cosine function*, denoted by $\cos^{-1}$, is defined as follows:

$$y = \cos^{-1} x \quad \text{if and only if} \quad x = \cos y \quad \text{and} \quad 0 \le y \le \pi$$

The domain of $\cos^{-1}$ is the closed interval $[-1, 1]$, and the range is the closed interval $[0, \pi]$. A sketch of its graph is shown in Fig. 9.7.5.

From Definition 9.7.2 it follows that

$$\cos(\cos^{-1} x) = x \qquad \text{for } x \text{ in } [-1, 1] \tag{5}$$

and

$$\cos^{-1}(\cos y) = y \qquad \text{for } y \text{ in } [0, \pi] \tag{6}$$

There is an interesting equation relating $\sin^{-1}$ and $\cos^{-1}$ that is given in the following example.

EXAMPLE 1:   Prove

$$\cos^{-1} x = \tfrac{1}{2}\pi - \sin^{-1} x$$

for $|x| \le 1$.

SOLUTION: Let x be in $[-1, 1]$ and $w = \tfrac{1}{2}\pi - \sin^{-1} x$. Then

$$\sin^{-1} x = \tfrac{1}{2}\pi - w$$

and so

$$\sin(\sin^{-1} x) = \sin(\tfrac{1}{2}\pi - w)$$

and using (2), we get

$$x = \sin(\tfrac{1}{2}\pi - w)$$

Applying (11) in Sec. 9.1 to the right side of the above equation, we get

$$x = \cos w \tag{7}$$

Because $-\tfrac{1}{2}\pi \leq \sin^{-1} x \leq \tfrac{1}{2}\pi$, by adding $-\tfrac{1}{2}\pi$ to each member we have

$$-\pi \leq -\tfrac{1}{2}\pi + \sin^{-1} x \leq 0$$

Multiplying each member of the above inequality by -1 and reversing the direction of the inequality signs, we have

$$0 \leq \tfrac{1}{2}\pi - \sin^{-1} x \leq \pi$$

Replacing $\tfrac{1}{2}\pi - \sin^{-1} x$ by w, we obtain

$$0 \leq w \leq \pi \tag{8}$$

From (7), (8), and Definition 9.7.2 it follows that

$$w = \cos^{-1} x \qquad \text{for } |x| \leq 1$$

and replacing w by $\tfrac{1}{2}\pi - \sin^{-1} x$, we get

$$\tfrac{1}{2}\pi - \sin^{-1} x = \cos^{-1} x \qquad \text{for } |x| \leq 1 \tag{9}$$

which is what we wished to prove.

Figure 9.7.6

Note in the above solution that the relation given by (9) depends on choosing the range of the inverse cosine function to be $[0, \pi]$.

To obtain the inverse tangent function we first restrict the tangent function to the open interval $(-\tfrac{1}{2}\pi, \tfrac{1}{2}\pi)$ on which the function is continuous and increasing. We let H be the function defined by

$$H(x) = \tan x \quad \text{and} \quad -\tfrac{1}{2}\pi < x < \tfrac{1}{2}\pi \tag{10}$$

The domain of H is the open interval $(-\tfrac{1}{2}\pi, \tfrac{1}{2}\pi)$, and the range is the set of all real numbers. A sketch of its graph is shown in Fig. 9.7.6. Because the function H is continuous and increasing on its domain, it has an inverse function, which is called the *inverse tangent function* and is denoted by $\tan^{-1}$.

9.7.3 Definition   The *inverse tangent function*, denoted by $\tan^{-1}$, is defined as follows:

$$y = \tan^{-1} x \quad \text{if and only if} \quad x = \tan y \quad \text{and} \quad -\tfrac{1}{2}\pi < y < \tfrac{1}{2}\pi$$

The domain of $\tan^{-1}$ is the set of all real numbers, and the range is the open interval $(-\tfrac{1}{2}\pi, \tfrac{1}{2}\pi)$. A sketch of its graph is shown in Fig. 9.7.7.

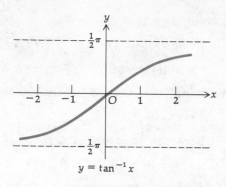

Figure 9.7.7

Before defining the inverse cotangent function, we refer back to Example 1, in which we proved the relationship between $\cos^{-1}$ and $\sin^{-1}$ given by Eq. (9). This equation can be used to define the inverse cosine function, and then it can be proved that the range of $\cos^{-1}$ is $[0, \pi]$. We use this kind of procedure in discussing the inverse cotangent function.

9.7.4 Definition   The *inverse cotangent function*, denoted by $\cot^{-1}$, is defined by

$$\cot^{-1} x = \tfrac{1}{2}\pi - \tan^{-1} x \qquad \text{where } x \text{ is any real number} \tag{11}$$

It follows from the definition that the domain of $\cot^{-1}$ is the set of all real numbers. To obtain the range we write Eq. (11) as

$$\tan^{-1} x = \tfrac{1}{2}\pi - \cot^{-1} x \tag{12}$$

Because

$$-\tfrac{1}{2}\pi < \tan^{-1} x < \tfrac{1}{2}\pi$$

by substituting from Eq. (12) into this inequality, we get

$$-\tfrac{1}{2}\pi < \tfrac{1}{2}\pi - \cot^{-1} x < \tfrac{1}{2}\pi$$

Subtracting $\tfrac{1}{2}\pi$ from each member, we get

$$-\pi < -\cot^{-1} x < 0$$

and now multiplying each member by -1 and reversing the direction of the inequality signs, we obtain

$$0 < \cot^{-1} x < \pi$$

$y = \cot^{-1} x$

Figure 9.7.8

Therefore, the range of the inverse cotangent function is the open interval $(0, \pi)$. A sketch of its graph is in Fig. 9.7.8.

The inverse secant and the inverse cosecant functions are defined in terms of $\cos^{-1}$ and $\sin^{-1}$, respectively.

9.7.5 Definition   The *inverse secant function*, denoted by $\sec^{-1}$, is defined by

$$\sec^{-1} x = \cos^{-1} \left(\frac{1}{x} \right) \qquad \text{for } |x| \geq 1$$

9.7.6 Definition   The *inverse cosecant function*, denoted by csc^{-1}, is defined by

$$\csc^{-1} x = \sin^{-1}\left(\frac{1}{x}\right) \qquad \text{for } |x| \geq 1$$

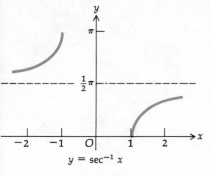

Figure 9.7.9

From Definition 9.7.5 it follows that the domain of sec^{-1} consists of the two intervals $(-\infty, -1]$ and $[1, +\infty)$, and the range consists of the two intervals $[0, \frac{1}{2}\pi)$ and $(\frac{1}{2}\pi, \pi]$. Note that the number $\frac{1}{2}\pi$ is not in the range because sec $\frac{1}{2}\pi$ is not defined. A sketch of the graph of sec^{-1} is shown in Fig. 9.7.9.

It follows from Definition 9.7.6 that the domain of csc^{-1} consists of the two intervals $(-\infty, -1]$ and $[1, +\infty)$, and the range consists of the two intervals $[-\frac{1}{2}\pi, 0)$ and $(0, \frac{1}{2}\pi]$. The number 0 is not in the range because csc 0 is not defined. A sketch of the graph of csc^{-1} is shown in Fig. 9.7.10.

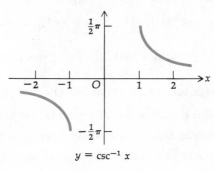

$y = \csc^{-1} x$

Figure 9.7.10

EXAMPLE 2:   Find the exact value of sec$[\sin^{-1}(-\frac{3}{4})]$.

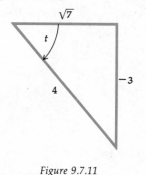

Figure 9.7.11

SOLUTION: Let $t = \sin^{-1}(-\frac{3}{4})$. Then $\sin t = -\frac{3}{4}$. Because the range of sin^{-1} is $[-\frac{1}{2}\pi, \frac{1}{2}\pi]$, and because sin t is negative, it follows that $-\frac{1}{2}\pi < t < 0$. Figure 9.7.11 shows an angle having radian measure t that satisfies these requirements. From the figure we see that sec $t = \frac{4}{7}\sqrt{7}$, and so we conclude that sec$[\sin^{-1}(-\frac{3}{4})] = \frac{4}{7}\sqrt{7}$.

EXAMPLE 3:   Find the exact value of sin$[2 \cos^{-1}(-\frac{3}{5})]$.

SOLUTION: Let $t = \cos^{-1}(-\frac{3}{5})$. So we wish to find the exact value of sin $2t$. From formula (14) of Sec. 9.1, we have

$$\sin 2t = 2 \sin t \cos t \tag{13}$$

Because $t = \cos^{-1}(-\frac{3}{5})$, it follows that $\cos t = -\frac{3}{5}$ and $\frac{1}{2}\pi < t < \pi$. From the identity, $\sin^2 t + \cos^2 t = 1$, and because $\sin t > 0$, since t is in $(\frac{1}{2}\pi, \pi)$, we obtain

$$\sin t = \sqrt{1 - \cos^2 t} = \sqrt{1 - (-\tfrac{3}{5})^2} = \tfrac{4}{5}$$

Therefore, from formula (13) we get

$$\sin 2t = 2(\tfrac{4}{5})(-\tfrac{3}{5}) = -\tfrac{24}{25}$$

from which we conclude that

$$\sin[2 \cos^{-1}(-\tfrac{3}{5})] = -\tfrac{24}{25}$$

Exercises 9.7

1. Find the value of each of the following: (a) $\sin^{-1}(-1)$; (b) $\cos^{-1}(-1)$; (c) $\tan^{-1}(-1)$; (d) $\cot^{-1}(-1)$; (e) $\sec^{-1}(-1)$; (f) $\csc^{-1}(-1)$.

2. Find the value of each of the following: (a) $\sin^{-1}(\frac{1}{2})$; (b) $\sin^{-1}(-\frac{1}{2})$; (c) $\cos^{-1}(\frac{1}{2})$; (d) $\cos^{-1}(-\frac{1}{2})$; (e) $\sec^{-1}(2)$; (f) $\csc^{-1}(-2)$.

3. Given: $y = \sin^{-1} \frac{1}{3}$. Find the exact value of each of the following: (a) $\cos y$; (b) $\tan y$; (c) $\cot y$; (d) $\sec y$; (e) $\csc y$.

4. Given: $y = \cos^{-1}(-\frac{2}{3})$. Find the exact value of each of the following: (a) $\sin y$; (b) $\tan y$; (c) $\cot y$; (d) $\sec y$; (e) $\csc y$.

5. Given: $y = \tan^{-1}(-2)$. Find the exact value of each of the following: (a) $\sin y$; (b) $\cos y$; (c) $\cot y$; (d) $\sec y$; (e) $\csc y$.

6. Given: $y = \cot^{-1}(-\frac{1}{2})$. Find the exact value of each of the following: (a) $\sin y$; (b) $\cos y$; (c) $\tan y$; (d) $\sec y$; (e) $\csc y$.

7. Find the exact value of each of the following: (a) $\tan[\sin^{-1}(\frac{1}{2}\sqrt{3})]$; (b) $\sin[\tan^{-1}(\frac{1}{2}\sqrt{3})]$.

8. Find the exact value of each of the following: (a) $\cos[\tan^{-1}(-3)]$; (b) $\tan[\sec^{-1}(-3)]$.

9. Find the exact value of each of the following: (a) $\sin^{-1}[\tan \frac{1}{4}\pi]$; (b) $\tan^{-1}[\sin(-\frac{1}{2}\pi)]$; (c) $\sec^{-1}[\tan(-\frac{1}{4}\pi)]$; (d) $\cot^{-1}[\csc(-\frac{1}{2}\pi)]$.

10. Find the exact value of each of the following: (a) $\cos^{-1}[\sin(-\frac{1}{6}\pi)]$; (b) $\sin^{-1}[\cos(-\frac{1}{6}\pi)]$; (c) $\cos^{-1}[\sin \frac{2}{3}\pi]$; (d) $\sin^{-1}[\cos \frac{2}{3}\pi]$.

In Exercises 11 through 18, find the exact value of the given quantity.

11. $\cos[2 \sin^{-1}(-\frac{5}{13})]$

12. $\tan[2 \sec^{-1}(-\frac{5}{4})]$

13. $\sin[\sin^{-1} \frac{2}{3} + \cos^{-1} \frac{1}{3}]$

14. $\cos[\sin^{-1}(-\frac{1}{2}) + \sin^{-1} \frac{1}{4}]$

15. $\tan(\tan^{-1} \frac{3}{4} - \sin^{-1} \frac{1}{2})$

16. $\tan[\sec^{-1} \frac{5}{3} + \csc^{-1}(-\frac{13}{12})]$

17. $\cos(\sin^{-1} \frac{1}{3} - \tan^{-1} \frac{1}{2})$

18. $\sin[\cos^{-1}(-\frac{2}{3}) + 2 \sin^{-1}(-\frac{1}{3})]$

19. Prove: $\cos^{-1}(3/\sqrt{10}) + \cos^{-1}(2/\sqrt{5}) = \frac{1}{4}\pi$.

20. Prove: $2 \tan^{-1} \frac{1}{3} - \tan^{-1}(-\frac{1}{7}) = \frac{1}{4}\pi$.

In Exercises 21 through 28, draw a sketch of the graph of the given equation.

21. $y = \frac{1}{2} \sin^{-1} x$

22. $y = \sin^{-1} \frac{1}{2}x$

23. $y = \tan^{-1} 2x$

24. $y = 2 \tan^{-1} x$

25. $y = \cos^{-1} 3x$

26. $y = \frac{1}{2} \sec^{-1} 2x$

27. $y = 2 \cot^{-1} \frac{1}{2}x$

28. $y = \frac{1}{2} \csc^{-1} \frac{1}{2}x$

9.8 DERIVATIVES OF THE INVERSE TRIGONOMETRIC FUNCTIONS

Because the inverse trigonometric functions are continuous and monotonic on their domains, it follows from Theorem 8.3.4 that they have derivatives. To derive the formula for the derivative of the inverse sine function, let

$$y = \sin^{-1} x$$

which is equivalent to

$$x = \sin y \quad \text{and} \quad y \text{ in } [-\tfrac{1}{2}\pi, \tfrac{1}{2}\pi] \tag{1}$$

Differentiating on both sides of (1) with respect to y, we obtain

$$D_y x = \cos y \quad \text{and} \quad y \text{ in } [-\tfrac{1}{2}\pi, \tfrac{1}{2}\pi] \tag{2}$$

From the identity $\sin^2 y + \cos^2 y = 1$, and replacing $\sin y$ by x, we obtain

$$\cos^2 y = 1 - x^2 \tag{3}$$

If y is in $[-\tfrac{1}{2}\pi, \tfrac{1}{2}\pi]$, $\cos y$ is nonnegative, and so from (3) it follows that

$$\cos y = \sqrt{1 - x^2} \quad \text{if } y \text{ is in } [-\tfrac{1}{2}\pi, \tfrac{1}{2}\pi] \tag{4}$$

Substituting from (4) into (2), we get

$$D_y x = \sqrt{1 - x^2}$$

From Theorem 8.3.4, $D_x y = 1/D_y x$; hence,

$$D_x(\sin^{-1} x) = \frac{1}{\sqrt{1 - x^2}} \tag{5}$$

The domain of the derivative of the inverse sine function is the open interval $(-1, 1)$.

If u is a differentiable function of x, we obtain from (5) and the chain rule

$$D_x(\sin^{-1} u) = \frac{1}{\sqrt{1 - u^2}} D_x u \tag{6}$$

To derive the formula for the derivative of the inverse cosine function, we use Eq. (9) of Sec. 9.7, which is

$$\cos^{-1} x = \tfrac{1}{2}\pi - \sin^{-1} x$$

Differentiating with respect to x, we have

$$D_x(\cos^{-1} x) = D_x(\tfrac{1}{2}\pi - \sin^{-1} x)$$

and so

$$D_x(\cos^{-1} x) = -\frac{1}{\sqrt{1 - x^2}} \tag{7}$$

where x is in $(-1, 1)$.

If u is a differentiable function of x, we obtain from (7) and the chain rule

$$D_x(\cos^{-1} u) = -\frac{1}{\sqrt{1 - u^2}} D_x u \tag{8}$$

We now derive the formula for the derivative of the inverse tangent function. If

$$y = \tan^{-1} x$$

then

$$x = \tan y \quad \text{and} \quad y \text{ is in } (-\tfrac{1}{2}\pi, \tfrac{1}{2}\pi)$$

Differentiating on both sides of the above equation with respect to y, we obtain

$$D_y x = \sec^2 y \quad \text{and} \quad y \text{ is in } (-\tfrac{1}{2}\pi, \tfrac{1}{2}\pi) \tag{9}$$

From the identity $\sec^2 y = 1 + \tan^2 y$, and replacing $\tan y$ by x, we have

$$\sec^2 y = 1 + x^2 \tag{10}$$

Substituting from (10) into (9), we get

$$D_y x = 1 + x^2$$

So from Theorem 8.3.4 we obtain

$$\maltese \ D_x(\tan^{-1} x) = \frac{1}{1 + x^2} \tag{11}$$

The domain of the derivative of the inverse tangent function is the set of all real numbers.

If u is a differentiable function of x, we obtain from (11) and the chain rule

$$D_x(\tan^{-1} u) = \frac{1}{1 + u^2} D_x u \tag{12}$$

From Definition 9.7.4 we have

$$\cot^{-1} x = \tfrac{1}{2}\pi - \tan^{-1} x$$

Differentiating with respect to x, we obtain the formula

$$D_x(\cot^{-1} x) = -\frac{1}{1 + x^2}$$

From this formula and the chain rule, it follows that if u is a differentiable function of x, then

$$D_x(\cot^{-1} u) = -\frac{1}{1 + u^2} D_x u \tag{13}$$

Definition 9.7.5 and formula (8) of this section are used to derive the formula for the derivative of the inverse secant function. From Definition 9.7.5 we have

$$\sec^{-1} x = \cos^{-1}\left(\frac{1}{x}\right) \qquad \text{for } |x| \geq 1$$

So

$$D_x(\sec^{-1} x) = -\frac{1}{\sqrt{1 - \left(\frac{1}{x}\right)^2}}\left(-\frac{1}{x^2}\right)$$

$$= \frac{1}{\dfrac{x^2 \sqrt{x^2 - 1}}{\sqrt{x^2}}}$$

$$= \frac{|x|}{x^2 \sqrt{x^2 - 1}}$$

Therefore, we have

$$\text{✗} \quad D_x(\sec^{-1} x) = \frac{1}{|x| \sqrt{x^2 - 1}} \tag{14}$$

where $|x| > 1$.

If u is a differentiable function of x, it follows from (14) and the chain rule that

$$D_x(\sec^{-1} u) = \frac{1}{|u| \sqrt{u^2 - 1}} D_x u \tag{15}$$

From (9) of Sec. 9.7 we have

$$\sin^{-1} x = \tfrac{1}{2}\pi - \cos^{-1} x \qquad \text{for } |x| \leq 1$$

Replacing x by $1/x$ in the above equation, we obtain

$$\sin^{-1}\left(\frac{1}{x}\right) = \frac{1}{2}\pi - \cos^{-1}\left(\frac{1}{x}\right) \qquad \text{for } |x| \geq 1$$

From the above equation and Definitions 9.7.5 and 9.7.6 it follows that

$$\csc^{-1} x = \tfrac{1}{2}\pi - \sec^{-1} x \qquad \text{for } |x| \geq 1 \tag{16}$$

Equations (16) and (14) are used to find the derivative of the inverse cosecant function. Differentiating on both sides of (16) with respect to x, we get

$$\text{✗} \quad D_x(\csc^{-1} x) = -\frac{1}{|x| \sqrt{x^2 - 1}} \tag{17}$$

where $|x| > 1$.

From (17) and the chain rule, if u is a differentiable function of x, we have

$$D_x(\csc^{-1} u) = -\frac{1}{|u|\sqrt{u^2-1}} D_x u \tag{18}$$

EXAMPLE 1: Given

$$y = \sin^{-1} x^2$$

find $D_x y$.

SOLUTION: Applying formula (6), we get

$$D_x y = \frac{1}{\sqrt{1-(x^2)^2}}(2x) = \frac{2x}{\sqrt{1-x^4}}$$

EXAMPLE 2: Given

$$y = x^3 \cot^{-1} \tfrac{1}{3}x$$

find $D_x y$.

SOLUTION:

$$D_x y = 3x^2 \cot^{-1} \frac{1}{3}x + x^3 \cdot \frac{-1}{1+\frac{1}{9}x^2} \cdot \frac{1}{3}$$

$$= 3x^2 \cot^{-1} \frac{1}{3}x - \frac{3x^3}{9+x^2}$$

EXAMPLE 3: Given

$$\ln(x+y) = \tan^{-1}\left(\frac{x}{y}\right)$$

find $D_x y$.

SOLUTION: Differentiating implicitly on both sides of the given equation with respect to x, we get

$$\frac{1}{x+y}(1+D_x y) = \frac{1}{1+\dfrac{x^2}{y^2}} \cdot \frac{y-x D_x y}{y^2}$$

or

$$\frac{1+D_x y}{x+y} = \frac{y-x D_x y}{y^2+x^2}$$

or

$$y^2+x^2+(y^2+x^2)D_x y = xy+y^2-(x^2+xy)D_x y$$

or

$$D_x y = \frac{xy-x^2}{2x^2+xy+y^2}$$

EXAMPLE 4: A picture 7 ft high is placed on a wall with its base 9 ft above the level of the eye of an observer. How far from the wall should the observer stand in order for the angle subtended at his eye by the picture to be the greatest?

SOLUTION: Let x ft be the distance of the observer from the wall, θ be the radian measure of the angle subtended at the observer's eye by the picture, α be the radian measure of the angle subtended at the observer's eye by the portion of the wall above his eye level and below the picture, and $\beta = \alpha + \theta$. Refer to Fig. 9.8.1.

We wish to find the value of x that will make θ an absolute maximum. Because x is in the interval $(0, +\infty)$, the absolute maximum value of θ will

Figure 9.8.1

be a relative maximum value. We see from the figure that

$$\cot \beta = \frac{x}{16} \qquad \text{and} \qquad \cot \alpha = \frac{x}{9}$$

Because $0 < \beta < \frac{1}{2}\pi$ and $0 < \alpha < \frac{1}{2}\pi$, we have

$$\beta = \cot^{-1} \frac{x}{16} \qquad \text{and} \qquad \alpha = \cot^{-1} \frac{x}{9}$$

Substituting these values of β and α in the equation $\theta = \beta - \alpha$, we get

$$\theta = \cot^{-1} \frac{x}{16} - \cot^{-1} \frac{x}{9}$$

Differentiating with respect to x gives

$$D_x \theta = -\frac{\frac{1}{16}}{1 + \left(\frac{x}{16}\right)^2} + \frac{\frac{1}{9}}{1 + \left(\frac{x}{9}\right)^2}$$

$$= -\frac{16}{16^2 + x^2} + \frac{9}{9^2 + x^2}$$

Setting $D_x \theta = 0$, we obtain

$$9(16^2 + x^2) - 16(9^2 + x^2) = 0$$

$$-7x^2 + 9 \cdot 16(16 - 9) = 0$$

$$x^2 = 9 \cdot 16$$

$$x = 12$$

The -12 is rejected because it is not in the interval $(0, +\infty)$. The results of the first-derivative test are shown in Table 9.8.1. Because the relative maximum value of θ is an absolute maximum value, we conclude that the observer should stand 12 ft from the wall.

Table 9.8.1

	$D_x \theta$	conclusion
$0 < x < 12$	$+$	
$x = 12$	0	θ has a relative maximum value
$12 < x < +\infty$	$-$	

Exercises 9.8

1. Derive the formula $D_x(\cot^{-1} x) = \dfrac{-1}{(1 + x^2)}$.

2. Derive the formula $D_x(\csc^{-1} x) = \dfrac{-1}{|x|\sqrt{x^2 - 1}}$.

In Exercises 3 through 22, find the derivative of the given function.

3. $f(x) = \sin^{-1} \frac{1}{2}x$

4. $g(x) = \tan^{-1} 2x$

5. $g(t) = \sec^{-1} 5t$

6. $F(x) = \cos^{-1}\sqrt{x}$

7. $F(x) = \cot^{-1}\dfrac{2}{x} + \tan^{-1}\dfrac{x}{2}$

8. $f(x) = \csc^{-1} 2x$

9. $h(y) = y \sin^{-1} 2y$

10. $f(t) = t^2 \cos^{-1} t$

11. $g(x) = x \csc^{-1}\dfrac{1}{x}$

12. $h(x) = \tan^{-1}\dfrac{2x}{1 - x^2}$

13. $f(x) = 4 \sin^{-1}\frac{1}{2}x + x\sqrt{4 - x^2}$

14. $g(s) = \cos^{-1} s + \dfrac{s}{1 - s^2}$

15. $f(t) = a \sin^{-1}\dfrac{t}{a} + \sqrt{a^2 - t^2}$

16. $F(x) = \ln(\tan^{-1} 3x)$

17. $g(x) = \cos^{-1}(\sin x)$

18. $f(x) = \sin^{-1} x + \cos^{-1} x$

19. $h(x) = \sec^{-1} x + \csc^{-1} x$

20. $F(x) = \sec^{-1}\sqrt{x^2 + 4}$

21. $G(x) = x \cot^{-1} x + \ln\sqrt{1 + x^2}$

22. $f(t) = \sin^{-1}\dfrac{t - 1}{t + 1}$

In Exercises 23 through 26, find $D_x y$ by implicit differentiation.

23. $e^x + y = \cos^{-1} x$

24. $\ln(\sin^2 3x) = e^x + \cot^{-1} y$

25. $x \sin y + x^3 = \tan^{-1} y$

26. $\sin^{-1}(xy) = \cos^{-1}(x + y)$

27. A light is 3 mi from a straight beach. If the light revolves and makes 2 rpm, find the speed of the spot of light along the beach when the spot is 2 mi from the point on the beach nearest the light.

28. A ladder 25 ft long is leaning against a vertical wall. If the bottom of the ladder is pulled horizontally away from the wall so that the top is sliding down at 3 ft/sec, how fast is the measure of the angle between the ladder and the ground changing when the bottom of the ladder is 15 ft from the wall?

29. A picture 4 ft high is placed on a wall with its base 3 ft above the level of the eye of an observer. If the observer is approaching the wall at the rate of 4 ft/sec, how fast is the measure of the angle subtended at his eye by the picture changing when the observer is 10 ft from the wall?

30. A man on a dock is pulling in at the rate of 2 ft/sec a rowboat by means of a rope. The man's hands are 20 ft above the level of the point where the rope is attached to the boat. How fast is the measure of the angle of depression of the rope changing when there are 52 ft of rope out?

31. A man is walking at the rate of 5 ft/sec along the diameter of a circular courtyard. A light at one end of a diameter perpendicular to his path casts a shadow on the circular wall. How fast is the shadow moving along the wall when the distance from the man to the center of the courtyard is $\frac{1}{2}r$, where r ft is the radius of the courtyard?

32. In Exercise 31, how far is the man from the center of the courtyard when the speed of his shadow along the wall is 9 ft/sec?

33. A rope is attached to a weight and it passes over a hook that is 8 ft above the ground. The rope is pulled over the hook at the rate of $\frac{3}{4}$ ft/sec and drags the weight along level ground. If the length of the rope between the weight and the hook is x ft when the radian measure of the angle between the rope and the floor is θ, find the time rate of change of θ in terms of x.

34. Given: $f(x) = \tan^{-1}(1/x) - \cot^{-1} x$. (a) Show that $f'(x) = 0$ for all x in the domain of f. (b) Prove that there is no constant C for which $f(x) = C$ for all x in its domain. (c) Why doesn't the statement in part (b) contradict Theorem 5.3.2?

9.9 INTEGRALS YIELDING INVERSE TRIGONOMETRIC FUNCTIONS

From the formulas for the derivatives of the inverse trigonometric functions, we obtain the following indefinite integral formulas:

$$\int \frac{du}{\sqrt{1 - u^2}} = \sin^{-1} u + C \tag{1}$$

$$\int \frac{du}{1+u^2} = \tan^{-1} u + C \tag{2}$$

$$\int \frac{du}{u\sqrt{u^2-1}} = \sec^{-1} |u| + C \tag{3}$$

Formulas (1) and (2) follow directly from the formulas for the derivatives of $\sin^{-1} u$ and $\tan^{-1} u$. Formula (3) needs an explanation.

If $u > 0$, then $u = |u|$, and we have

$$\int \frac{du}{u\sqrt{u^2-1}} = \int \frac{du}{|u|\sqrt{u^2-1}} = \sec^{-1} u + C = \sec^{-1} |u| + C$$

If $u < 0$, then $u = -|u|$, and we have

$$\int \frac{du}{u\sqrt{u^2-1}} = \int \frac{du}{-|u|\sqrt{u^2-1}}$$

$$= \int \frac{-du}{|u|\sqrt{u^2-1}}$$

$$= \int \frac{d(-u)}{|-u|\sqrt{(-u)^2-1}}$$

$$= \sec^{-1}(-u) + C$$

$$= \sec^{-1} |u| + C$$

Therefore, if $u > 0$ or $u < 0$, we obtain (3). We also have the following formulas.

$$\int \frac{du}{\sqrt{a^2-u^2}} = \sin^{-1} \frac{u}{a} + C \qquad \text{where } a > 0 \tag{4}$$

$$\int \frac{du}{a^2+u^2} = \frac{1}{a} \tan^{-1} \frac{u}{a} + C \tag{5}$$

$$\int \frac{du}{u\sqrt{u^2-a^2}} = \frac{1}{a} \sec^{-1} \left|\frac{u}{a}\right| + C \qquad \text{where } a > 0 \tag{6}$$

These formulas can be proved by finding the derivative of the right side and obtaining the integrand. This is illustrated by proving (4).

$$D_u\left(\sin^{-1} \frac{u}{a}\right) = \frac{1}{\sqrt{1-\left(\frac{u}{a}\right)^2}} D_u\left(\frac{u}{a}\right)$$

$$= \frac{\sqrt{a^2}}{\sqrt{a^2-u^2}} \cdot \frac{1}{a}$$

$$= \frac{a}{\sqrt{a^2-u^2}} \cdot \frac{1}{a} \qquad \text{if } a > 0$$

$$= \frac{1}{\sqrt{a^2 - u^2}} \qquad \text{if } a > 0$$

The proofs of (5) and (6) are left for the reader (see Exercises 1 and 2).

EXAMPLE 1: Evaluate

$$\int \frac{dx}{\sqrt{4 - 9x^2}}$$

$$\int \frac{du}{\sqrt{a^2 - u^2}} \quad \begin{aligned} a^2 &= 4 \\ u^2 &= 9x^2 \end{aligned}$$

SOLUTION:

$$\int \frac{dx}{\sqrt{4 - 9x^2}} = \frac{1}{3} \int \frac{d(3x)}{\sqrt{4 - (3x)^2}}$$

$$= \frac{1}{3} \sin^{-1} \frac{3x}{2} + C$$

EXAMPLE 2: Evaluate

$$\int \frac{dx}{3x^2 - 2x + 5}$$

SOLUTION:

$$\int \frac{dx}{3x^2 - 2x + 5} = \int \frac{dx}{3(x^2 - \frac{2}{3}x) + 5}$$

To complete the square of $x^2 - \frac{2}{3}x$ we add $\frac{1}{9}$, and because $\frac{1}{9}$ is multiplied by 3, we actually add $\frac{1}{3}$ to the denominator, and so we also subtract $\frac{1}{3}$ from the denominator. Therefore, we have

$$\int \frac{dx}{3x^2 - 2x + 5} = \int \frac{dx}{3(x^2 - \frac{2}{3}x + \frac{1}{9}) + 5 - \frac{1}{3}}$$

$$= \int \frac{dx}{3(x - \frac{1}{3})^2 + \frac{14}{3}} = \frac{1}{3} \int \frac{dx}{(x - \frac{1}{3})^2 + \frac{14}{9}}$$

$$= \frac{1}{3} \cdot \frac{3}{\sqrt{14}} \tan^{-1} \left(\frac{x - \frac{1}{3}}{\frac{1}{3}\sqrt{14}} \right) + C$$

$$= \frac{1}{\sqrt{14}} \tan^{-1} \left(\frac{3x - 1}{\sqrt{14}} \right) + C$$

EXAMPLE 3: Evaluate

$$\int \frac{(2x + 7)\, dx}{x^2 + 2x + 5}$$

SOLUTION: Because $d(x^2 + 2x + 5) = (2x + 2)\, dx$, we write the numerator as $(2x + 2)\, dx + 5\, dx$, and express the original integral as the sum of two integrals.

$$\int \frac{(2x + 7)\, dx}{x^2 + 2x + 5} = \int \frac{(2x + 2)\, dx}{x^2 + 2x + 5} + 5 \int \frac{dx}{x^2 + 2x + 5}$$

$$= \ln |x^2 + 2x + 5| + 5 \int \frac{dx}{(x + 1)^2 + 4}$$

$$= \ln(x^2 + 2x + 5) + \frac{5}{2} \tan^{-1} \frac{x + 1}{2} + C$$

NOTE: Because $x^2 + 2x + 5 > 0$, for all x, $|x^2 + 2x + 5| = x^2 + 2x + 5$.

EXAMPLE 4:   Evaluate

$$\int \frac{3\ dx}{(x+2)\ \sqrt{x^2+4x+3}}$$

SOLUTION:

$$\int \frac{3\ dx}{(x+2)\ \sqrt{x^2+4x+3}} = \int \frac{3\ dx}{(x+2)\ \sqrt{(x^2+4x+4)-1}}$$

$$= 3 \int \frac{d(x+2)}{(x+2)\ \sqrt{(x+2)^2-1}}$$

$$= 3 \sec^{-1} |x+2| + C$$

EXAMPLE 5:   Find the area of the region in the first quadrant bounded by the curve

$$y = \frac{1}{1+x^2}$$

the x axis, the y axis, and the line $x=1$.

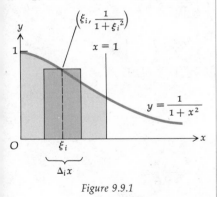

Figure 9.9.1

SOLUTION: Figure 9.9.1 shows the region and a rectangular element of area. If A square units is the area of the region, we have

$$A = \lim_{||\Delta|| \to 0} \sum_{i=1}^{n} \frac{1}{1+\xi_i^2}\ \Delta_i x$$

$$= \int_0^1 \frac{dx}{1+x^2}$$

$$= \tan^{-1} x\ \Big]_0^1$$

$$= \tan^{-1} 1 - \tan^{-1} 0$$

$$= \tfrac{1}{4}\pi - 0$$

$$= \tfrac{1}{4}\pi$$

The result of Example 5 states that the number π is four times the number of square units in the area of the region shown in Fig. 9.9.1.

Exercises 9.9

In Exercises 1 through 5, prove the given formula by showing that the derivative of the right side is equal to the integrand.

1. $\displaystyle\int \frac{du}{a^2+u^2} = \frac{1}{a}\ \tan^{-1}\frac{u}{a} + C$

2. $\displaystyle\int \frac{du}{u\ \sqrt{u^2-a^2}} = \frac{1}{a}\ \sec^{-1}\left|\frac{u}{a}\right| + C$ if $a > 0$

   Take two cases: $u > 0$ and $u < 0$.

3. $\displaystyle\int \frac{du}{\sqrt{1-u^2}} = -\cos^{-1} u + C$

   Is this formula equivalent to formula (1)? Why?

4. $\int \dfrac{du}{1 + u^2} = -\cot^{-1} u + C$

Is this formula equivalent to formula (2)? Why?

5. $\int \dfrac{du}{u \sqrt{u^2 - 1}} = -\csc^{-1} |u| + C$

Take two cases: $u > 0$ and $u < 0$. Is this formula equivalent to formula (3)? Why?

In Exercises 6 through 25, evaluate the indefinite integral.

6. $\int \dfrac{dx}{\sqrt{1 - 4x^2}}$

7. $\int \dfrac{dx}{x^2 + 25}$

8. $\int \dfrac{x \, dx}{x^4 + 16}$

9. $\int \dfrac{dx}{\sqrt{2 - 5x^2}}$

10. $\int \dfrac{3 \, dx}{x \sqrt{x^2 - 9}}$

11. $\int \dfrac{r \, dr}{\sqrt{16 - 9r^4}}$

12. $\int \dfrac{du}{u \sqrt{16u^2 - 9}}$

13. $\int \dfrac{e^x \, dx}{7 + e^{2x}}$

14. $\int \dfrac{\sin x \, dx}{\sqrt{2 - \cos^2 x}}$

15. $\int \dfrac{dx}{(1 + x) \sqrt{x}}$

16. $\int \dfrac{ds}{\sqrt{2s - s^2}}$

17. $\int \dfrac{dx}{x^2 - x + 2}$

18. $\int \dfrac{dx}{\sqrt{3x - x^2 - 2}}$

19. $\int \dfrac{dx}{\sqrt{15 + 2x - x^2}}$

20. $\int \dfrac{dx}{2x^2 + 2x + 3}$

21. $\int \dfrac{x \, dx}{\sqrt{3 - 2x - x^2}}$

22. $\int \dfrac{x \, dx}{x^2 + x + 1}$

23. $\int \dfrac{(2 + x) \, dx}{\sqrt{4 - 2x - x^2}}$

24. $\int \dfrac{3 \, dx}{(x + 2) \sqrt{x^2 + 4x + 3}}$

25. $\int \dfrac{2x^3 \, dx}{2x^2 - 4x + 3}$

In Exercises 26 through 33, evaluate the definite integral.

26. $\int_0^{1/2} \dfrac{dx}{\sqrt{1 - x^2}}$

27. $\int_0^1 \dfrac{1 + x}{1 + x^2} \, dx$

28. $\int_0^{\sqrt{3}} \dfrac{x \, dx}{\sqrt{1 + x^2}}$

29. $\int_{-4}^{-2} \dfrac{dt}{\sqrt{-t^2 - 6t - 5}}$

30. $\int_2^5 \dfrac{dx}{x^2 - 4x + 13}$

31. $\int_0^1 \dfrac{dx}{e^x + e^{-x}}$

32. $\int_{1/\sqrt{2}}^1 \dfrac{dx}{x \sqrt{4x^2 - 1}}$

33. $\int_1^e \dfrac{dx}{x[1 + (\ln x)^2]}$

34. Find the area of the region bounded by the curve $y = 8/(x^2 + 4)$, the x axis, the y axis, and the line $x = 2$.

35. Find the abscissa of the centroid of the region of Exercise 34.

36. Find the area of the region bounded by the curves $x^2 = 4ay$ and $y = 8a^3/(x^2 + 4a^2)$.

37. Find the circumference of the circle $x^2 + y^2 = r^2$ by integration.

38. A particle moving in a straight line is said to have *simple harmonic motion* if the measure of its acceleration is always proportional to the measure of its displacement from a fixed point on the line and its acceleration and displacement are oppositely directed. So if at t sec, s ft is the directed distance of the particle from the origin and v ft/sec is the velocity of the particle, then a differential equation for simple harmonic motion is

$$\dfrac{dv}{dt} = -k^2 s \qquad (7)$$

where k^2 is the constant of proportionality and the minus sign indicates that the acceleration is opposite in direction from the displacement. Because $dv/dt = (dv/ds)(ds/dt) = v(dv/ds)$, Eq. (7) may be written as

$$v\frac{dv}{ds} = -k^2 s \tag{8}$$

(a) Solve Eq. (8) for v to get $v = \pm k\sqrt{a^2 - s^2}$. Note: Take a^2k^2 as the arbitrary constant of integration and justify this choice. (b) Letting $v = ds/dt$ in the solution of part (a), we obtain the differential equation

$$\frac{ds}{dt} = \pm k\sqrt{a^2 - s^2} \tag{9}$$

Taking $t = 0$ at the instant when $v = 0$ (and hence $s = a$), solve Eq. (9) to obtain

$$s = a\cos kt \tag{10}$$

(c) Show that the largest value for $|s|$ is a. The number a is called the *amplitude* of the motion. (d) The particle will oscillate between the points where $s = a$ and $s = -a$. If T sec is the time for the particle to go from a to $-a$ and return, show that $T = 2\pi/k$. The number T is called the *period* of the motion.

39. A particle is moving in a straight line according to the equation of motion $s = 5 - 10\sin^2 2t$, where s ft is the directed distance of the particle from the origin at t sec. Use the result of part (b) of Exercise 38 to show that the motion is simple harmonic. Find the amplitude and period of this motion.

40. Show that the motion of Exercise 39 is simple harmonic by showing that differential equation (7) is satisfied.

9.10 THE HYPERBOLIC FUNCTIONS

Certain combinations of e^x and e^{-x} appear so frequently in applications of mathematics that they are given special names. Two of these functions are the *hyperbolic sine function* and the *hyperbolic cosine function*. The function values are related to the coordinates of the points of an equilateral hyperbola in a manner similar to that in which the values of the corresponding trigonometric functions are related to the coordinates of points of a circle (see Sec. 15.4) Following are the definitions of the hyperbolic sine function and the hyperbolic cosine function.

9.10.1 Definition   The *hyperbolic sine function* is defined by

$$\text{(1)}\qquad \sinh x = \frac{e^x - e^{-x}}{2}$$

The domain and range are the set of all real numbers.

9.10.2 Definition   The *hyperbolic cosine function* is defined by

$$\text{(2)}\qquad \cosh x = \frac{e^x + e^{-x}}{2}$$

The domain is the set of all real numbers and the range is the set of all numbers in the interval $[1, +\infty)$.

Sketches of the graphs of the hyperbolic sine function and the hyperbolic cosine function are shown in Figs. 9.10.1 and 9.10.2, respectively. The graphs are easily sketched by using values in the table of

$y = \sinh x$

Figure 9.10.1

$y = \cosh x$ Figure 9.10.2

hyperbolic functions in the Appendix. Note that these functions are not periodic.

The remaining four hyperbolic functions may be defined in terms of the hyperbolic sine and hyperbolic cosine functions. You should note that each satisfies a relation analogous to one satisfied by corresponding trigonometric functions.

9.10.3 Definition   The *hyperbolic tangent function, hyperbolic cotangent function, hyperbolic secant function,* and *hyperbolic cosecant function* are defined, respectively, as follows:

$$\tanh x = \frac{\sinh x}{\cosh x} = \frac{e^x - e^{-x}}{e^x + e^{-x}} \tag{1}$$

$$\coth x = \frac{\cosh x}{\sinh x} = \frac{e^x + e^{-x}}{e^x - e^{-x}} \tag{2}$$

$$\operatorname{sech} x = \frac{1}{\cosh x} = \frac{2}{e^x + e^{-x}} \tag{3}$$

$$\operatorname{csch} x = \frac{1}{\sinh x} = \frac{2}{e^x - e^{-x}} \tag{4}$$

A sketch of the graph of the hyperbolic tangent function is shown in Fig. 9.10.3.

There are identities that are satisfied by the hyperbolic functions which are similar to those satisfied by the trigonometric functions. Four of the fundamental identities are given in Definition 9.10.3. The other four fundamental identities are as follows:

$y = \tanh x$

Figure 9.10.3

$$\begin{cases} \tanh x = \dfrac{1}{\coth x} & (5) \\[2mm] \cosh^2 x - \sinh^2 x = 1 & (6) \\[2mm] 1 - \tanh^2 x = \operatorname{sech}^2 x & (7) \\[2mm] 1 - \coth^2 x = -\operatorname{csch}^2 x & (8) \end{cases}$$

Equation (5) follows immediately from (1) and (2). Following is the proof of (6).

$$\cosh^2 x - \sinh^2 x = \left(\frac{e^x + e^{-x}}{2}\right)^2 - \left(\frac{e^x - e^{-x}}{2}\right)^2$$

$$= \tfrac{1}{4}\left(e^{2x} + 2e^0 + e^{-2x} - e^{2x} + 2e^0 - e^{-2x}\right)$$

$$= 1$$

Equation (7) can be proved by using the definitions of tanh x and sech x in terms of e^x and e^{-x} as in the proof above, or an alternate proof is obtained by using other identities as follows:

$$1 - \tanh^2 x = 1 - \frac{\sinh^2 x}{\cosh^2 x} = \frac{\cosh^2 x - \sinh^2 x}{\cosh^2 x} = \frac{1}{\cosh^2 x} = \operatorname{sech}^2 x$$

The proof of (8) is left for the reader (see Exercise 1). From the eight fundamental identities, it is possible to prove others. Some of these are given in the exercises that follow. Other identities, such as the hyperbolic functions of the sum or difference of two numbers and the hyperbolic functions of twice a number or one-half a number, are similar to the corresponding trigonometric identities. Sometimes it is helpful to make use of the following two relations, which follow from Definitions 9.10.1 and 9.10.2.

$$\cosh x + \sinh x = e^x \tag{9}$$

$$\cosh x - \sinh x = e^{-x} \tag{10}$$

We use them in proving the following identity:

$$\sinh(x + y) = \sinh x \cosh y + \cosh x \sinh y \tag{11}$$

From Definition 9.10.1 we have

$$\sinh(x + y) = \frac{e^{x+y} - e^{-(x+y)}}{2} = \frac{e^x e^y - e^{-x} e^{-y}}{2}$$

Applying (9) and (10) to the right side of the above equation, we obtain

$$\sinh(x + y) = \tfrac{1}{2}[(\cosh x + \sinh x)(\cosh y + \sinh y)$$
$$- (\cosh x - \sinh x)(\cosh y - \sinh y)]$$

Expanding the right side of the above equation and combining terms, formula (11) is obtained.

In a similar manner we can prove

$$\cosh(x + y) = \cosh x \cosh y + \sinh x \sinh y \tag{12}$$

If in (11) and (12) y is replaced by x, the following two formulas are obtained:

$$\sinh 2x = 2 \sinh x \cosh x \tag{13}$$

and

$$\cosh 2x = \cosh^2 x + \sinh^2 x \tag{14}$$

Formula (14) combined with the identity (6) gives us two alternate formulas for $\cosh 2x$, which are

$$\boxed{\cosh 2x = 2 \sinh^2 x + 1} \tag{15}$$

and

$$\boxed{\cosh 2x = 2 \cosh^2 x - 1} \tag{16}$$

Solving (15) and (16) for $\sinh x$ and $\cosh x$, respectively, and replacing x by $\frac{1}{2}x$, we get

$$\sinh \frac{x}{2} = \pm \sqrt{\frac{\cosh x - 1}{2}} \tag{17}$$

and

$$\cosh \frac{x}{2} = \sqrt{\frac{\cosh x + 1}{2}} \tag{18}$$

We do not have a $\pm$ sign on the right side of (18) since the range of the hyperbolic cosine function is $[1, +\infty)$. The details of the proofs of Eqs. (12) through (18) are left for the reader (see Exercises 2, 4, and 5).

The formulas for the derivatives of the hyperbolic sine and hyperbolic cosine functions may be obtained by applying Definitions 9.10.1 and 9.10.2 and differentiating the resulting expressions involving exponential functions. For example,

$$D_x(\cosh x) = D_x \left(\frac{e^x + e^{-x}}{2} \right) = \frac{e^x - e^{-x}}{2} = \sinh x$$

In a similar manner, we find $D_x(\sinh x) = \cosh x$ (see Exercise 15). To find the derivative of the hyperbolic tangent function, we use some of the identities we have previously proved.

$$D_x(\tanh x) = D_x \left(\frac{\sinh x}{\cosh x} \right) = \frac{\cosh^2 x - \sinh^2 x}{\cosh^2 x} = \frac{1}{\cosh^2 x} = \operatorname{sech}^2 x$$

The formulas for the derivatives of the remaining hyperbolic functions are as follows: $D_x(\coth x) = -\operatorname{csch}^2 x$; $D_x(\operatorname{sech} x) = -\operatorname{sech} x \tanh x$; $D_x(\operatorname{csch} x) = -\operatorname{csch} x \coth x$. The proofs of these formulas are left for the reader (see Exercises 15 and 16).

From the above formulas and the chain rule, if u is a differentiable function of x, we have the following more general formulas:

$$D_x(\sinh u) = \cosh u \, D_x u \tag{19}$$

$$D_x(\cosh u) = \sinh u \, D_x u \tag{20}$$

$$D_x(\tanh u) = \operatorname{sech}^2 u \, D_x u \tag{21}$$

$$D_x(\coth u) = -\text{csch}^2\, u\, D_x u \tag{22}$$

$$D_x(\text{sech}\, u) = -\text{sech}\, u \tanh u\, D_x u \tag{23}$$

$$D_x(\text{csch}\, u) = -\text{csch}\, u \coth u\, D_x u \tag{24}$$

You should notice that the formulas for the derivatives of the hyperbolic sine, cosine, and tangent all have a plus sign, whereas the formulas for the derivatives of the hyperbolic cotangent, secant, and cosecant all have a minus sign. Otherwise, the formulas are similar to the corresponding formulas for the derivatives of the trigonometric functions.

EXAMPLE 1:   Given

$$y = \tanh(1 - x^2)$$

find $D_x y$.

SOLUTION: $D_x y = -2x\, \text{sech}^2(1 - x^2)$.

EXAMPLE 2:   Given

$$y = \ln \sinh x$$

find $D_x y$.

SOLUTION: $D_x y = \dfrac{1}{\sinh x} \cdot \cosh x = \dfrac{\cosh x}{\sinh x} = \coth x$.

Formulas (19) through (24) give rise to the following indefinite integration formulas:

$$\int \sinh u\, du = \cosh u + C \tag{25}$$

$$\int \cosh u\, du = \sinh u + C \tag{26}$$

$$\int \text{sech}^2\, u\, du = \tanh u + C \tag{27}$$

$$\int \text{csch}^2\, u\, du = -\coth u + C \tag{28}$$

$$\int \text{sech}\, u \tanh u\, du = -\text{sech}\, u + C \tag{29}$$

$$\int \text{csch}\, u \coth u\, du = -\text{csch}\, u + C \tag{30}$$

The methods used to integrate powers of the hyperbolic functions are similar to those used for powers of the trigonometric functions. The following two examples illustrate the method.

EXAMPLE 3:   Evaluate

$$\int \sinh^3 x \cosh^2 x \, dx$$

SOLUTION:

$$\int \sinh^3 x \cosh^2 x \, dx = \int \sinh^2 x \cosh^2 x \, (\sinh x \, dx)$$

$$= \int (\cosh^2 x - 1) \cosh^2 x \, (\sinh x \, dx)$$

$$= \int \cosh^4 x \, (\sinh x \, dx) - \int \cosh^2 x \, (\sinh x \, dx)$$

$$= \tfrac{1}{5} \cosh^5 x - \tfrac{1}{3} \cosh^3 x + C$$

EXAMPLE 4:   Evaluate

$$\int \text{sech}^4 x \, dx$$

SOLUTION:

$$\int \text{sech}^4 x \, dx = \int \text{sech}^2 x \, (\text{sech}^2 x \, dx)$$

$$= \int (1 - \tanh^2 x)(\text{sech}^2 x \, dx)$$

$$= \int \text{sech}^2 x \, dx - \int \tanh^2 x \, (\text{sech}^2 x \, dx)$$

$$= \tanh x - \tfrac{1}{3} \tanh^3 x + C$$

Figure 9.10.4

A *catenary* is the curve formed by a homogeneous flexible cable hanging from two points under its own weight. If the lowest point of the catenary is the point $(0, a)$, it can be shown that an equation of it is

$$y = a \cosh \left(\frac{x}{a}\right) \qquad a > 0 \tag{31}$$

A sketch of the graph of Eq. (31) is shown in Fig. 9.10.4.

EXAMPLE 5:   Find the length of arc of the catenary having equation (31) from the point $(0, a)$ to the point (x_1, y_1) where $x_1 > 0$.

SOLUTION: If

$$f(x) = a \cosh \left(\frac{x}{a}\right)$$

then

$$f'(x) = a \sinh \left(\frac{x}{a}\right) \cdot \left(\frac{1}{a}\right) = \sinh \left(\frac{x}{a}\right)$$

and using Theorem 7.10.2, if L units is the length of the given arc, we have

$$L = \int_0^{x_1} \sqrt{1 + [f'(x)]^2} \, dx$$

$$= \int_0^{x_1} \sqrt{1 + \sinh^2 \left(\frac{x}{a}\right)} \, dx \tag{32}$$

From formula (6), $1 + \sinh^2 x = \cosh^2 x$, and because $\cosh(x/a) \geq 1$, it follows that

$$\sqrt{1 + \sinh^2 \left(\frac{x}{a}\right)} = \sqrt{\cosh^2 \left(\frac{x}{a}\right)} = \cosh \left(\frac{x}{a}\right)$$

and substituting from the above into (32) we get

$$L = \int_0^{x_1} \cosh\left(\frac{x}{a}\right) dx$$

$$= a \sinh\left(\frac{x}{a}\right) \Big]_0^{x_1}$$

$$= a \sinh\left(\frac{x_1}{a}\right) - a \sinh 0$$

$$= a \sinh\left(\frac{x_1}{a}\right)$$

Exercises 9.10

In Exercises 1 through 10, prove the identities.

1. $1 - \coth^2 x = -\operatorname{csch}^2 x$

2. $\cosh(x + y) = \cosh x \cosh y + \sinh x \sinh y$

3. $\tanh(x + y) = \dfrac{\tanh x + \tanh y}{1 + \tanh x \tanh y}$

4. (a) $\sinh 2x = 2 \sinh x \cosh x$; (b) $\cosh 2x = \cosh^2 x + \sinh^2 x = 2 \sinh^2 x + 1 = 2 \cosh^2 x - 1$

5. (a) $\cosh \frac{1}{2}x = \sqrt{\dfrac{\cosh x + 1}{2}}$; (b) $\sinh \frac{1}{2}x = \pm \sqrt{\dfrac{\cosh x - 1}{2}}$

6. $\operatorname{csch} 2x = \frac{1}{2} \operatorname{sech} x \operatorname{csch} x$

7. (a) $\tanh(-x) = -\tanh x$; (b) $\operatorname{sech}(-x) = \operatorname{sech} x$

8. $\sinh 3x = 3 \sinh x + 4 \sinh^3 x$

9. $\cosh 3x = 4 \cosh^3 x - 3 \cosh x$

10. $\sinh^2 x - \sinh^2 y = \sinh(x + y) \sinh(x - y)$

11. Prove: $(\sinh x + \cosh x)^n = \cosh nx + \sinh nx$. (HINT: Use formula (9).)

12. Prove that the hyperbolic sine function is an odd function and the hyperbolic cosine function is an even function.

13. Prove: $\tanh(\ln x) = \dfrac{x^2 - 1}{x^2 + 1}$

14. Prove: $\dfrac{1 + \tanh x}{1 - \tanh x} = e^{2x}$

15. Prove: (a) $D_x(\sinh x) = \cosh x$; (b) $D_x(\coth x) = -\operatorname{csch}^2 x$.

16. Prove: (a) $D_x(\operatorname{sech} x) = -\operatorname{sech} x \tanh x$; (b) $D_x(\operatorname{csch} x) = -\operatorname{csch} x \coth x$.

In Exercises 17 through 26, find the derivative of the given function.

17. $f(x) = \tanh \dfrac{4x + 1}{5}$

18. $g(x) = \ln(\sinh x^3)$

19. $f(x) = e^x \cosh x$

20. $h(x) = \coth \dfrac{1}{x}$

21. $h(t) = \ln(\tanh t)$

22. $F(x) = \tan^{-1}(\sinh x^2)$

23. $G(x) = \sin^{-1}(\tanh x^2)$

24. $f(x) = \ln(\coth 3x - \operatorname{csch} 3x)$

25. $f(x) = x^{\sinh x}$

26. $g(x) = (\cosh x)^x$

27. Prove: (a) $\int \tanh u \, du = \ln |\cosh u| + C$; (b) $\int \coth u \, du = \ln |\sinh u| + C$.

28. Prove: $\int \operatorname{sech} u \, du = 2 \tan^{-1} e^u + C$.

29. Prove: $\int \operatorname{csch} u \, du = \ln |\tanh \tfrac{1}{2}u| + C$.

In Exercises 30 through 37, evaluate the indefinite integral.

30. $\displaystyle\int \sinh^4 x \cosh^3 x \, dx$

31. $\displaystyle\int \tanh x \ln(\cosh x) \, dx$

32. $\displaystyle\int \tanh^2 3x \, dx$

33. $\displaystyle\int \cosh^4 7x \, dx$

34. $\displaystyle\int x \sinh^2 x^2 \, dx$

35. $\displaystyle\int \operatorname{sech}^4 3x \, dx$

36. $\displaystyle\int \operatorname{sech} x \tanh^3 x \, dx$

37. $\displaystyle\int \frac{\sinh \sqrt{x}}{\sqrt{x}} \, dx$

In Exercises 38 and 39, evaluate the definite integral.

38. $\displaystyle\int_{-1}^{1} \cosh^2 x \, dx$

39. $\displaystyle\int_{0}^{2} \sinh^3 x \, dx$

40. Draw a sketch of the graph of the hyperbolic cotangent function. Find equations of the asymptotes.

41. Draw a sketch of the graph of the hyperbolic secant function. Find the relative extrema of the function, the points of inflection of the graph, the intervals on which the graph is concave upward, and the intervals on which the graph is concave downward.

42. Prove that a catenary is concave upward at each point.

43. Find the area of the region bounded by the catenary of Example 5, the y axis, the x axis, and the line $x = x_1$, where $x_1 > 0$.

44. Find the volume of the solid of revolution if the region of Exercise 43 is revolved about the x axis.

45. A particle is moving along a straight line according to the equation of motion

$$s = e^{-ct/2}(A \sinh t + B \cosh t)$$

where s ft is the directed distance of the particle from the origin at t sec. If v ft/sec and a ft/sec^2 are the velocity and acceleration, respectively, of the particle at t sec find v and a. Also show that a is the sum of two numbers, one of which is proportional to s and the other is proportional to v.

46. Prove that the hyperbolic sine function is continuous and increasing on its entire domain.

47. Prove that the hyperbolic tangent function is continuous and increasing on its entire domain.

48. Prove that the hyperbolic cosine function is continuous on its entire domain but is not monotonic on its entire domain. Find the intervals on which the function is increasing and the intervals on which the function is decreasing.

9.11 THE INVERSE HYPERBOLIC FUNCTIONS

From the graph of the hyperbolic sine function (Fig. 9.10.1), we see that a horizontal line intersects the graph in one and only one point; therefore, to each number in the range of the function there corresponds one and only one number in the domain. The hyperbolic sine function is continuous and increasing on its domain (see Exercise 46 in Exercises 9.10), and so by Theorem 8.3.2 the function has an inverse function.

9.11.1 Definition

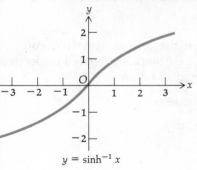

$y = \sinh^{-1} x$

Figure 9.11.1

The *inverse hyperbolic sine function*, denoted by $\sinh^{-1}$, is defined as follows:

$$y = \sinh^{-1} x \quad \text{if and only if} \quad x = \sinh y$$

A sketch of the graph of the inverse hyperbolic sine function is shown in Fig. 9.11.1. Its domain is the set of all real numbers, and its range is the set of all real numbers.

It follows from Definition 9.11.1 that

$$\sinh(\sinh^{-1} x) = x \tag{1}$$

and

$$\sinh^{-1}(\sinh y) = y \tag{2}$$

From Fig. 9.10.2, we notice that a horizontal line $y = k$, where $k > 1$, intersects the graph of the hyperbolic cosine function in two points. Therefore, for each number greater than 1 in the range of this function, there correspond two numbers in the domain. So the hyperbolic cosine function does not have an inverse function. However, we define a function F as follows:

$$F(x) = \cosh x \quad \text{for } x \geq 0 \tag{3}$$

$y = \cosh x, x \geq 0$

Figure 9.11.2

The domain of F is the interval $[0, +\infty)$, and the range is the interval $[1, +\infty)$. A sketch of the graph of F is shown in Fig. 9.11.2. The function F is continuous and increasing on its entire domain (see Exercise 1), and so by Theorem 8.3.2, F has an inverse function, which we call the *inverse hyperbolic cosine function*.

9.11.2 Definition

$y = \cosh^{-1} x$

Figure 9.11.3

The *inverse hyperbolic cosine function*, denoted by $\cosh^{-1}$, is defined as follows:

$$y = \cosh^{-1} x \quad \text{if and only if} \quad x = \cosh y \quad \text{and} \quad y \geq 0$$

A sketch of the graph of the inverse hyperbolic cosine function is shown in Fig. 9.11.3. The domain of this function is the interval $[1, +\infty)$, and the range is the interval $[0, +\infty)$. From Definition 9.11.2 we conclude that

$$\cosh(\cosh^{-1} x) = x \quad \text{if } x \geq 1 \tag{4}$$

and

$$\cosh^{-1}(\cosh y) = y \quad \text{if } y \geq 0 \tag{5}$$

As with the hyperbolic sine function, a horizontal line intersects each of the graphs of the hyperbolic tangent function, the hyperbolic cotangent function, and the hyperbolic cosecant function at one and only one point. For the hyperbolic tangent function, this may be seen in Fig. 9.10.3. Each of the above three functions is continuous and monotonic on its domain; hence, each has an inverse function.

9.11.3 Definition

The *inverse hyperbolic tangent function*, the *inverse hyperbolic cotangent function*, and the *inverse hyperbolic cosecant function*, denoted respectively by $\tanh^{-1}$, $\coth^{-1}$, and csch^{-1}, are defined as follows:

$$y = \tanh^{-1} x \quad \text{if and only if} \quad x = \tanh y$$

$$y = \coth^{-1} x \quad \text{if and only if} \quad x = \coth y$$

$$y = \operatorname{csch}^{-1} x \quad \text{if and only if} \quad x = \operatorname{csch} y$$

A sketch of the graph of the inverse hyperbolic tangent function is in Fig. 9.11.4.

The hyperbolic secant function does not have an inverse function. However, we proceed as we did with the hyperbolic cosine function and define a new function which has an inverse function. Let the function G be defined by

$$G(x) = \operatorname{sech} x \quad \text{for } x \geq 0 \tag{6}$$

It can be shown that G is continuous and monotonic on its entire domain (see Exercise 2); therefore, G has an inverse function, which we call the *inverse hyperbolic secant function*.

$y = \tanh^{-1} x$

Figure 9.11.4

9.11.4 Definition

The *inverse hyperbolic secant function*, denoted by sech^{-1}, is defined as follows:

$$y = \operatorname{sech}^{-1} x \quad \text{if and only if} \quad x = \operatorname{sech} y \quad \text{and} \quad y \geq 0 \tag{7}$$

The inverse hyperbolic functions can be expressed in terms of natural logarithms. This should not be surprising because the hyperbolic functions were defined in terms of the exponential function, and the natural logarithmic function is the inverse of the exponential function. Following are these expressions for $\sinh^{-1}$, $\cosh^{-1}$, $\tanh^{-1}$, and $\coth^{-1}$.

$$\sinh^{-1} x = \ln(x + \sqrt{x^2 + 1}) \quad x \text{ any real number} \tag{8}$$

$$\cosh^{-1} x = \ln(x + \sqrt{x^2 - 1}) \quad x \geq 1 \tag{9}$$

$$\tanh^{-1} x = \frac{1}{2} \ln \frac{1 + x}{1 - x} \quad |x| < 1 \tag{10}$$

$$\coth^{-1} x = \frac{1}{2} \ln \frac{x + 1}{x - 1} \quad |x| > 1 \tag{11}$$

We prove (9) and leave the proofs of the other three formulas for the reader (see Exercises 3 through 5).

To prove (9), let $y = \cosh^{-1} x$, $x \geq 1$. Then, by Definition 9.11.2, $x = \cosh y$, $y \geq 0$. Applying Definition 9.10.2 to $\cosh y$, we get

$$x = \frac{e^y + e^{-y}}{2} \qquad y \geq 0$$

from which we obtain

$$e^{2y} - 2xe^y + 1 = 0 \qquad y \geq 0$$

Solving this equation for e^y by the quadratic formula, we obtain

$$e^y = \frac{2x \pm \sqrt{4x^2 - 4}}{2} = x \pm \sqrt{x^2 - 1} \qquad y \geq 0 \qquad (12)$$

We know that $y \geq 0$ and $x \geq 1$. Therefore, $e^y \geq 1$. When $x = 1$, $x + \sqrt{x^2 - 1} = x - \sqrt{x^2 - 1} = 1$. Furthermore, when $x > 1$, $0 < x - 1 < x + 1$, and so $\sqrt{x - 1} < \sqrt{x + 1}$. Therefore,

$$\sqrt{x - 1}\,\sqrt{x - 1} < \sqrt{x - 1}\,\sqrt{x + 1}$$

giving us $x - 1 < \sqrt{x^2 - 1}$. Hence, when $x > 1$, $x - \sqrt{x^2 - 1} < 1$. Consequently, we can safely reject the minus sign in (12). And since $y = \cosh^{-1} x$, we have

$$\cosh^{-1} x = \ln(x + \sqrt{x^2 - 1}) \qquad x \geq 1$$

which is (9).

EXAMPLE 1: Express each of the following in terms of a natural logarithm: (a) $\tanh^{-1}(-\frac{4}{5})$; (b) $\sinh^{-1} 2$.

SOLUTION: (a) From (10), we obtain

$$\tanh^{-1}\left(-\frac{4}{5}\right) = \frac{1}{2}\ln\frac{\frac{1}{5}}{\frac{9}{5}} = \frac{1}{2}\ln\frac{1}{9} = \ln\frac{1}{3} = -\ln 3$$

(b) From (8), we get

$$\sinh^{-1} 2 = \ln(2 + \sqrt{5})$$

To obtain a formula for the derivative of the inverse hyperbolic sine function, let $y = \sinh^{-1} x$, and then $x = \sinh y$. Thus, because $D_y x = \cosh y$ and $D_x y = 1/D_y x$, we have

$$D_x y = \frac{1}{\cosh y} \qquad (13)$$

From the identity $\cosh^2 y - \sinh^2 y = 1$, it follows that $\cosh y = \sqrt{\sinh^2 y + 1}$. (NOTE: When taking the square root, the minus sign is rejected because $\cosh y \geq 1$.)

Hence, because $x = \sinh y$, $\cosh y = \sqrt{x^2 + 1}$. Substituting this in (13), we obtain

$$D_x(\sinh^{-1} x) = \frac{1}{\sqrt{x^2 + 1}} \qquad (14)$$

If u is a differentiable function of x, from (14) and the chain rule it follows that

$$D_x(\sinh^{-1} u) = \frac{1}{\sqrt{u^2 + 1}} D_x u \qquad (15)$$

Formula (14) can also be derived by using (8), as follows:

$$D_x(\sinh^{-1} x) = D_x \ln(x + \sqrt{x^2 + 1})$$

$$= \frac{1 + \dfrac{x}{\sqrt{x^2 + 1}}}{x + \sqrt{x^2 + 1}}$$

$$= \frac{\sqrt{x^2 + 1} + x}{\sqrt{x^2 + 1}\,(x + \sqrt{x^2 + 1})}$$

$$= \frac{1}{\sqrt{x^2 + 1}}$$

The following differentiation formulas can be obtained in analogous ways. Their proofs are left for the reader (see Exercises 6 through 10). In each formula u is a differentiable function of x.

$$D_x(\cosh^{-1} u) = \frac{1}{\sqrt{u^2 - 1}} D_x u \qquad u > 1 \qquad (16)$$

$$D_x(\tanh^{-1} u) = \frac{1}{1 - u^2} D_x u \qquad |u| < 1 \qquad (17)$$

$$D_x(\coth^{-1} u) = \frac{1}{1 - u^2} D_x u \qquad |u| > 1 \qquad (18)$$

$$D_x(\operatorname{sech}^{-1} u) = -\frac{1}{u\sqrt{1 - u^2}} D_x u \qquad 0 < u < 1 \qquad (19)$$

$$D_x(\operatorname{csch}^{-1} u) = -\frac{1}{|u|\sqrt{1 + u^2}} D_x u \qquad u \neq 0 \qquad (20)$$

EXAMPLE 2: Find $f'(x)$ if

$$f(x) = \tanh^{-1}(\cos 2x)$$

SOLUTION: Applying formula (17), we get

$$f'(x) = \frac{-2 \sin 2x}{1 - \cos^2 2x} = \frac{-2 \sin 2x}{\sin^2 2x} = -2 \csc 2x$$

EXAMPLE 3: Verify that

$$D_x(x \cosh^{-1} x - \sqrt{x^2 - 1})$$
$$= \cosh^{-1} x$$

SOLUTION:

$$D_x(x \cosh^{-1} x - \sqrt{x^2 - 1}) = \cosh^{-1} x + x \cdot \frac{1}{\sqrt{x^2 - 1}} - \frac{x}{\sqrt{x^2 - 1}}$$

$$= \cosh^{-1} x$$

The main use of the inverse hyperbolic functions is in connection with integration. The discussion of this topic is postponed until Sec. 10.6.

Exercises 9.11

1. If $F(x) = \cosh x$ and $x \geq 0$, prove that F is continuous and increasing on its entire domain.

2. If $G(x) = \operatorname{sech} x$ and $x \geq 0$, prove that G is continuous and monotonic on its entire domain.

In Exercises 3 through 10, prove the indicated formula of this section.

3. Formula (8)   4. Formula (10)   5. Formula (11)

6. Formula (16)   7. Formula (17)   8. Formula (18)

9. Formula (19)   10. Formula (20)

In Exercises 11 through 14, express the given quantity in terms of a natural logarithm.

11. $\sinh^{-1} \frac{1}{4}$ 12. $\cosh^{-1} 3$

13. $\tanh^{-1} \frac{1}{2}$ 14. $\coth^{-1}(-2)$

In Exercises 15 through 28, find the derivative of the given function.

15. $f(x) = \sinh^{-1} x^2$ 16. $G(x) = \cosh^{-1} \frac{1}{3}x$ 17. $F(x) = \tanh^{-1} 4x$

18. $h(w) = \tanh^{-1} w^3$ 19. $g(x) = \coth^{-1}(3x + 1)$ 20. $f(r) = \operatorname{csch}^{-1} \frac{1}{2}r^2$

21. $f(x) = x^2 \cosh^{-1} x^2$ 22. $h(x) = (\operatorname{sech}^{-1} x)^2$ 23. $f(x) = \sinh^{-1}(\tan x)$

24. $g(x) = \tanh^{-1}(\sin 3x)$ 25. $h(x) = \cosh^{-1}(\csc x)$ 26. $F(x) = \coth^{-1}(\cosh x)$

27. $G(x) = x \sinh^{-1} x - \sqrt{1 + x^2}$ 28. $H(x) = \ln \sqrt{x^2 - 1} - x \tanh^{-1} x$

In Exercises 29 through 32, draw a sketch of the graph of the indicated function.

29. The inverse hyperbolic tangent function.   30. The inverse hyperbolic cotangent function.

31. The inverse hyperbolic secant function.   32. The inverse hyperbolic cosecant function.

Review Exercises (*Chapter 9*)

In Exercises 1 through 4, evaluate the given limit, if it exists.

1. $\lim\limits_{x \to 0} \dfrac{\sin^2 x}{3x^2}$ 2. $\lim\limits_{x \to 0} \dfrac{\tan x}{2x}$

3. $\lim\limits_{x \to 0} \dfrac{\tan^4 2x}{4x^4}$ 4. $\lim\limits_{x \to \pi/2} \dfrac{\cos 5x}{\cos 7x}$

5. Show that $\dfrac{d(\ln \sin x)}{d(\ln x)} = x \cot x$ 6. Prove that $\lim\limits_{x \to 0} \dfrac{\sin x^2}{x} = 0$.

In Exercises 7 through 16, find the derivative of the function defined by the given equation.

7. $f(x) = \sqrt[4]{\sin 4x}$ 8. $f(x) = \sqrt{\csc 3x}$

9. $g(x) = x \cos \dfrac{1}{x}$ 10. $f(t) = \dfrac{\ln t}{\sec t}$

11. $F(x) = \tan^{-1} 2^x$ 12. $g(x) = \cot 3x \sqrt{\sin 2x}$

13. $f(w) = w^2 \sinh^{-1} 2w$

14. $f(x) = \tan^{-1}(\sinh x) - \sec^{-1}(\cosh x)$

15. $f(x) = (\tan x)^{1/x^2}$

16. $h(x) = (\cos x)^{e^x}$

In Exercises 17 and 18, find $D_x y$ by implicit differentiation.

17. $\cot^{-1} \dfrac{x^2}{3y} + xy^2 = 0$

18. $\sin(x + y) + \sin(x - y) = 1$

In Exercises 19 through 26, find the indefinite integral.

19. $\displaystyle\int \sin^4 \tfrac{1}{2}x \cos^2 \tfrac{1}{2}x \, dx$

20. $\displaystyle\int \sqrt{1 - \cos x} \, dx$

21. $\displaystyle\int \frac{dx}{2x^2 + 3x + 5}$

22. $\displaystyle\int (\csc 2x - \cot 2x) \, dx$

23. $\displaystyle\int \frac{dt}{1 + \sec 3t}$

24. $\displaystyle\int \frac{dx}{\sqrt{7 + 5x - 2x^2}}$

25. $\displaystyle\int \sin 3x \cos 5x \, dx$

26. $\displaystyle\int \sin^3 2x \cos^5 2x \, dx$

In Exercises 27 through 30, evaluate the definite integral.

27. $\displaystyle\int_0^{\pi/3} \sec^3 x \tan^5 x \, dx$

28. $\displaystyle\int_0^{\pi/6} \tan^4 2x \, dx$

29. $\displaystyle\int_1^2 \frac{(x + 2) \, dx}{\sqrt{4x - x^2}}$

30. $\displaystyle\int_{\pi/4}^{\pi/2} (\sin^4 2x - 2 \sin 4x) \, dx$

31. Find the length of the arc of the curve $y = \ln \cos x$ from the origin to the point $(\tfrac{1}{3}\pi, -\ln 2)$.

32. Find the average value of the cosine function on the closed interval $[a, a + 2\pi]$.

33. Find to the nearest degree the measurements of the four interior angles of the quadrilateral having vertices at $(5, 6)$, $(-2, 4)$, $(-2, 1)$ and $(3, 1)$ and verify that the sum is $360°$.

34. Find the volume of the solid generated if the region bounded by the curve $y = \sin^2 x$ and the x axis from $x = 0$ to $x = \pi$ is revolved about the x axis.

35. Two points A and B are diametrically opposite each other on the shores of a circular lake 1 mi in diameter. A man desires to go from point A to point B. He can row at the rate of $1\tfrac{1}{2}$ mi/hr and walk at the rate of 5 mi/hr. Find the least amount of time it can take for him to get from point A to point B.

36. Solve Exercise 35 if the rates of rowing and walking are, respectively, 2 mi/hr and 4 mi/hr.

37. A particle is moving along a straight line and

$$s = \sin(4t + \tfrac{1}{3}\pi) + \sin(4t + \tfrac{1}{6}\pi)$$

where s ft is the directed distance of the particle from the origin at t sec. Show that the motion is simple harmonic and find the amplitude of the motion. (See Exercise 38 in Exercises 9.9.)

38. If an equation of motion is $s = \cos 2t + \cos t$, prove that the motion is not simple harmonic.

39. Evaluate: $\displaystyle\int_0^{\pi} |\cos x + \tfrac{1}{2}| \, dx$.

40. Evaluate: $\displaystyle\int_0^{\pi/2} |\cos x - \sin x| \, dx$.

41. Find the area of the region in the first quadrant bounded by the y axis and the curves $y = \sec^2 x$ and $y = 2 \tan^2 x$.

42. Find an equation of the normal line to the curve $y = \cos x$ at the point $(\tfrac{2}{3}\pi, -\tfrac{1}{2})$.

43. A particle is moving along a straight line according to the equation of motion $s = 5 - 2\cos^2 t$ where s ft is the directed distance of the particle from the origin at t sec. If v ft/sec and a ft/sec² are, respectively, the velocity and acceleration of the particle at t sec, find v and a in terms of s.

44. If y ft is the range of a projectile then

$$y = \frac{v_0^2 \sin 2\theta}{g}$$

where v_0 ft/sec is the initial velocity, g ft/sec² is the acceleration due to gravity, and θ is the radian measure of the angle that the gun makes with the horizontal. Find the value of θ that makes the range a maximum.

45. A searchlight is $\frac{1}{2}$ mi from a straight road and it keeps a light trained on an automobile that is traveling at the constant speed of 60 mi/hr. Find the rate at which the light beam is changing direction (a) when the car is at the point on the road nearest the searchlight and (b) when the car is $\frac{1}{2}$ mi down the road from this point.

46. A helicopter leaves the ground at a point 800 ft from an observer and rises vertically at 25 ft/sec. Find the time rate of change of the measure of the observer's angle of elevation of the helicopter when the helicopter is 600 ft above the ground.

47. Find the length of the catenary $y = \cosh x$ from $(\ln 2, \frac{5}{4})$ to $(\ln 3, \frac{5}{3})$.

48. Find the area of the region bounded by the curve $y = 9/\sqrt{9 - x^2}$, the two coordinate axes, and the line $x = 2\sqrt{2}$.

49. In an electric circuit let $E = f(t)$ and $i = g(t)$ where E volts and i amperes are, respectively, the electromotive force and current at t sec. If P watts is the average power in the interval $[0, T]$, where T sec is the common period of f and g, then

$$P = \frac{1}{T} \int_0^T f(t)g(t)\, dt$$

If $E = 100 \sin t$ and $i = 4(\sin t - \frac{1}{3}\pi)$, first determine T and then find P.

50. The graph of the equation

$$x = a \sinh^{-1} \sqrt{\frac{a^2}{y^2} - 1} - \sqrt{a^2 - y^2}$$

is called a tractrix. Prove that the slope of the curve at any point (x, y) is $-y/\sqrt{a^2 - y^2}$.

51. Find the absolute maximum value attained by the function f if $f(x) = A \sin kx + B \cos kx$, where A, B, and k are positive constants.

52. Suppose the function f is defined on the open interval $(0, 1)$ and

$$f(x) = \frac{\sin \pi x}{x(x - 1)}$$

Define f at 0 and 1 so that f is continuous on the closed interval $[0, 1]$.

53. Prove: $D_x^n \sin x = \sin(x + \frac{1}{2}n\pi)$. (HINT: Use mathematical induction and the formulas $\sin(x + \frac{1}{2}\pi) = \cos x$ or $\cos(x + \frac{1}{2}\pi) = -\sin x$ after each differentiation.)

10
Techniques of Integration

10.1 INTRODUCTION

In Chapter 6 the definite integral of a function f from a to b was defined as the limit of a Riemann sum as follows:

$$\int_a^b f(x)\ dx = \lim_{||\Delta|| \to 0} \sum_{i=1}^n f(\xi_i)\ \Delta_i x \tag{1}$$

if the limit exists. We stated a theorem, proved in advanced calculus, that the limit on the right side of (1) exists if f is continuous on the closed interval $[a, b]$.

The exact value of a definite integral may be calculated by the fundamental theorem of the calculus, provided that we can find an antiderivative of the integrand. The process of finding the most general antiderivative of a given integrand is called *indefinite integration*. We use the term *indefinite integral* to mean the most general antiderivative of a given integrand. In practice, it is not always possible to find the indefinite integral. That is, we may have a definite integral that exists, but the integrand has no antiderivative that can be expressed in terms of elementary functions. An example of this is $\int_0^{1/2} e^{-t^2}\ dt$ (a method for computing the value of this definite integral to any required degree of accuracy by using infinite series is given in Sec. 14.9). However, many of the definite integrals that occur in practice can be evaluated by finding an antiderivative of the integrand. Some methods for doing this were given previously, and additional ones are presented in this chapter. Often you may find it desirable to resort to a *table of integrals* instead of performing a complicated integration. However, it may be necessary to employ some of the techniques of integration in order to express the integrand in a form that is found in a table. Therefore, you should acquire proficiency in recognizing which technique to apply to a given integral. Furthermore, development of computational skills is important in all branches of mathematics, and the exercises in this chapter provide a good training ground. For these reasons you are advised to use a table of integrals only after you have mastered integration.

The standard indefinite integration formulas, which we learned in previous chapters and which are used frequently, are listed below.

$$\int du = u + C$$

$$\int a\, du = au + C \quad \text{where } a \text{ is any constant}$$

$$\int [f(u) + g(u)]\, du = \int f(u)\, du + \int g(u)\, du$$

$$\int u^n\, du = \frac{u^{n+1}}{n+1} + C \quad n \neq -1$$

$$\int \frac{du}{u} = \ln |u| + C$$

$$\int a^u\, du = \frac{a^u}{\ln a} + C$$

$$\int e^u\, du = e^u + C$$

$$\int \sin u\, du = -\cos u + C$$

$$\int \cos u\, du = \sin u + C$$

$$\int \sec^2 u\, du = \tan u + C$$

$$\int \csc^2 u\, du = -\cot u + C$$

$$\int \sec u \tan u\, du = \sec u + C$$

$$\int \csc u \cot u\, du = -\csc u + C$$

$$\int \tan u\, du = \ln |\sec u| + C$$

$$\int \cot u\, du = \ln |\sin u| + C$$

$$\int \sec u\, du = \ln |\sec u + \tan u| + C$$

$$\int \csc u\, du = \ln |\csc u - \cot u| + C$$

$$\int \frac{du}{\sqrt{a^2 - u^2}} = \sin^{-1} \frac{u}{a} + C \quad \text{where } a > 0$$

$$\int \frac{du}{a^2 + u^2} = \frac{1}{a} \tan^{-1} \frac{u}{a} + C$$

$$\int \frac{du}{u\sqrt{u^2 - a^2}} = \frac{1}{a} \sec^{-1} \left| \frac{u}{a} \right| + C \quad \text{where } a > 0$$

$$\int \sinh u\, du = \cosh u + C$$

$$\int \cosh u\, du = \sinh u + C$$

$$\int \operatorname{sech}^2 u\, du = \tanh u + C$$

$$\int \operatorname{csch}^2 u\, du = -\coth u + C$$

$$\int \operatorname{sech} u \tanh u\, du = -\operatorname{sech} u + C$$

$$\int \operatorname{csch} u \coth u\, du = -\operatorname{csch} u + C$$

10.2 INTEGRATION BY PARTS   A method of integration that is quite useful is *integration by parts*. It depends on the formula for the differential of a product:

$$d(uv) = u\, dv + v\, du$$

or

$$u \, dv = d(uv) - v \, du \tag{1}$$

Integrating on both sides of (1), we have

$$\int u \, dv = uv - \int v \, du \tag{2}$$

THIS is THE GENERAL FORMULA

Formula (2) is called the *formula for integration by parts*. This formula expresses the integral $\int u \, dv$ in terms of another integral, $\int v \, du$. By a suitable choice of u and dv, it may be easier to integrate the second integral than the first. This method is shown by the following examples.

EXAMPLE 1: Find

$$\int \tan^{-1} x \, dx$$

SOLUTION: Let $u = \tan^{-1} x$ and $dv = dx$. Then

$$du = \frac{dx}{1 + x^2}$$

and

$$v = x + C_1$$

So from (2) we have

$$\int \tan^{-1} x \, dx = (\tan^{-1} x)(x + C_1) - \int (x + C_1) \frac{dx}{1 + x^2}$$

$$= x \tan^{-1} x + C_1 \tan^{-1} x - \int \frac{x \, dx}{1 + x^2} - C_1 \int \frac{dx}{1 + x^2}$$

$$= x \tan^{-1} x + C_1 \tan^{-1} x - \tfrac{1}{2} \ln |1 + x^2| - C_1 \tan^{-1} x + C_2$$

$$= x \tan^{-1} x - \tfrac{1}{2} \ln (1 + x^2) + C_2$$

Note that the first constant of integration C_1 does not appear in the final result. This is true in general, and we prove it as follows: By writing $v + C_1$ in place of v, we have

$$\int u \, dv = u(v + C_1) - \int (v + C_1) \, du$$

$$= uv + C_1 u - \int v \, du - C_1 \int du$$

$$= uv + C_1 u - \int v \, du - C_1 u$$

$$= uv - \int v \, du$$

Therefore, it is not necessary to write C_1 when finding v from dv.

EXAMPLE 2:   Find

$$\int x \ln x \, dx$$

SOLUTION: Let $u = \ln x$ and $dv = x \, dx$. Then

$$du = \frac{dx}{x} \qquad v = \frac{x^2}{2}$$

So

$$\int x \ln x \, dx = \frac{x^2}{2} \ln x - \int \frac{x^2}{2} \cdot \frac{dx}{x}$$

$$= \frac{x^2}{2} \ln x - \frac{1}{2} \int x \, dx$$

$$= \tfrac{1}{2} x^2 \ln x - \tfrac{1}{4} x^2 + C$$

EXAMPLE 3:   Find

$$\int x \sin x \, dx$$

SOLUTION: Let $u = x$ and $dv = \sin x \, dx$. Then

$$du = dx \quad \text{and} \quad v = -\cos x$$

Therefore, we have

$$\int x \sin x \, dx = -x \cos x + \int \cos x \, dx$$

$$= -x \cos x + \sin x + C$$

NOTE: In Example 3, if instead of our choices of u and dv as above, we let

$$u = \sin x \quad \text{and} \quad dv = x \, dx$$

we get

$$du = \cos x \, dx \quad \text{and} \quad v = \tfrac{1}{2} x^2$$

So we have

$$\int x \sin x \, dx = \frac{x^2}{2} \sin x - \frac{1}{2} \int x^2 \cos x \, dx$$

The integral on the right is more complicated than the integral with which we started, thereby indicating that these are not desirable choices for u and dv.

It may happen that a particular integral may require repeated applications of integration by parts. This is illustrated in the following example.

EXAMPLE 4:   Find

$$\int x^2 e^x \, dx$$

SOLUTION: Let $u = x^2$ and $dv = e^x \, dx$. Then

$$du = 2x \, dx \quad \text{and} \quad v = e^x$$

We have, then,

$$\int x^2 e^x \, dx = x^2 e^x - 2 \int x e^x \, dx$$

We now apply integration by parts to the integral on the right. Let

$$\bar{u} = x \quad \text{and} \quad d\bar{v} = e^x \, dx$$

Then

$$d\bar{u} = dx \quad \text{and} \quad \bar{v} = e^x$$

So we obtain

$$\int xe^x \, dx = xe^x - \int e^x \, dx$$

$$= xe^x - e^x + \overline{C}$$

Therefore,

$$\int x^2 e^x \, dx = x^2 e^x - 2[xe^x - e^x + \overline{C}]$$

$$= x^2 e^x - 2xe^x + 2e^x + C$$

Another situation that sometimes occurs when using integration by parts is shown in Example 5.

EXAMPLE 5: Find

$$\int e^x \sin x \, dx$$

SOLUTION: Let $u = e^x$ and $dv = \sin x \, dx$. Then

$$du = e^x \, dx \quad \text{and} \quad v = -\cos x$$

Therefore,

$$\int e^x \sin x \, dx = -e^x \cos x + \int e^x \cos x \, dx$$

The integral on the right is similar to the first integral, except it has $\cos x$ in place of $\sin x$. We apply integration by parts again by letting

$$\bar{u} = e^x \quad \text{and} \quad d\bar{v} = \cos x \, dx$$

So

$$d\bar{u} = e^x \, dx \quad \text{and} \quad \bar{v} = \sin x$$

Thus, we have

$$\int e^x \sin x \, dx = -e^x \cos x + [e^x \sin x - \int e^x \sin x \, dx]$$

Now we have on the right the same integral that we have on the left. So we add $\int e^x \sin x \, dx$ to both sides of the equation, thus giving us

$$2 \int e^x \sin x \, dx = -e^x \cos x + e^x \sin x + \overline{C}$$

Dividing on both sides by 2, we obtain

$$\int e^x \sin x \, dx = \tfrac{1}{2} e^x (\sin x - \cos x) + C$$

In Sec. 9.8 we noted that in order to integrate odd powers of the secant and cosecant we use integration by parts. This process is illustrated in Example 6.

EXAMPLE 6:   Find

$$\int \sec^3 x \, dx$$

SOLUTION: Let $u = \sec x$ and $dv = \sec^2 x \, dx$. Then

$$du = \sec x \tan x \, dx \quad \text{and} \quad v = \tan x$$

Therefore,

$$\int \sec^3 x \, dx = \sec x \tan x - \int \sec x \tan^2 x \, dx$$

or

$$\int \sec^3 x \, dx = \sec x \tan x - \int \sec x (\sec^2 x - 1) \, dx$$

or

$$\int \sec^3 x \, dx = \sec x \tan x - \int \sec^3 x \, dx + \int \sec x \, dx$$

Adding $\int \sec^3 x \, dx$ to both sides, we get

$$2 \int \sec^3 x \, dx = \sec x \tan x + \ln |\sec x + \tan x| + 2C$$

So

$$\int \sec^3 x \, dx = \tfrac{1}{2} \sec x \tan x + \tfrac{1}{2} \ln |\sec x + \tan x| + C$$

In applying integration by parts to a specific integral, one pair of choices for u and dv may work while another pair may not. We saw this in the note after Example 3.

Furthermore, in Example 5, in the step where we have

$$\int e^x \sin x \, dx = -e^x \cos x + \int e^x \cos x \, dx$$

if we evaluate the integral on the right by letting

$$\bar{u} = \cos x \quad \text{and} \quad d\bar{v} = e^x \, dx$$

$$d\bar{u} = -\sin x \, dx \quad \text{and} \quad \bar{v} = e^x$$

we get

$$\int e^x \sin x \, dx = -e^x \cos x + \left(e^x \cos x + \int e^x \sin x \, dx \right)$$

or

$$\int e^x \sin x \, dx = \int e^x \sin x \, dx$$

Integration by parts often is used when the integrand involves logarithms, inverse trigonometric functions, and products.

Exercises 10.2

In Exercises 1 through 16, evaluate the indefinite integral.

1. $\int \ln x \, dx$

2. $\int x \cos 2x \, dx$

3. $\int x \sec^2 x \, dx$

4. $\int x \, 3^x \, dx$

5. $\int \sin^{-1} x \, dx$

6. $\int x^2 \ln x \, dx$

7. $\int x \tan^{-1} x \, dx$

8. $\int x^2 \sin 3x \, dx$

9. $\int e^x \cos x \, dx$

10. $\int \sin(\ln x) \, dx$

11. $\int \dfrac{x^3 \, dx}{\sqrt{1 - x^2}}$

12. $\int x^3 e^{x^2} \, dx$

13. $\int x^2 \sinh x \, dx$

14. $\int \csc^3 x \, dx$

15. $\int \sec^5 x \, dx$

16. $\int \dfrac{\cot^{-1} \sqrt{x}}{\sqrt{x}} \, dx$

In Exercises 17 through 24, evaluate the definite integral.

17. $\displaystyle\int_0^{\pi/3} \sin 3x \cos x \, dx$

18. $\displaystyle\int_{-\pi}^{\pi} x^2 \cos 2x \, dx$

19. $\displaystyle\int_0^2 x e^{2x} \, dx$

20. $\displaystyle\int_0^{\pi^2/2} \cos \sqrt{2x} \, dx$

21. $\displaystyle\int_0^{\pi/4} e^{3x} \sin 4x \, dx$

22. $\displaystyle\int_{\pi/4}^{3\pi/4} x \cot x \csc x \, dx$

23. $\displaystyle\int_1^4 \sec^{-1} \sqrt{x} \, dx$

24. $\displaystyle\int_0^1 x \sin^{-1} x \, dx$

25. Find the area of the region bounded by the curve $y = \ln x$, the x axis, and the line $x = e^2$.

26. Find the volume of the solid generated by revolving the region in Exercise 25 about the x axis.

27. Find the volume of the solid generated by revolving the region in Exercise 25 about the y axis.

28. Find the centroid of the region bounded by the curve $y = e^x$, the coordinate axes, and the line $x = 3$.

29. The linear density of a rod at a point x ft from one end is $2e^{-x}$ slugs/ft. If the rod is 6 ft long find the mass and center of mass of the rod.

30. Find the centroid of the solid of revolution obtained by revolving about the x axis the region bounded by the curve $y = \sin x$, the x axis, and the line $x = \frac{1}{2}\pi$.

31. A board is in the shape of a region bounded by a straight line and one arch of the sine curve. If the board is submerged vertically in water so that the straight line is the lower boundary 2 ft below the surface of the water, find the force on the board due to liquid pressure.

32. A particle is moving along a straight line and s ft is the directed distance of the particle from the origin at t sec. If v ft/sec is the velocity at t sec, $s = 0$ when $t = 0$, and $v \cdot s = t \sin t$, find s in terms of t and also s when $t = \frac{1}{2}\pi$.

33. A water tank full of water is in the shape of the solid of revolution formed by rotating about the x axis the region bounded by the curve $y = e^{-x}$, the coordinate axes, and the line $x = 4$. Find the work done in pumping all the water to the top of the tank. Distance is measured in feet. Take the positive x axis vertically downward.

34. The face of a dam is in the shape of one arch of the curve $y = 100 \cos \frac{1}{200}\pi x$ and the surface of the water is at the top of the dam. Find the force due to liquid pressure on the face of the dam. Distance is measured in feet.

35. A manufacturer has discovered that if x hundreds of units of a particular commodity are produced per week, the marginal cost is determined by $x 2^{x/2}$ and the marginal revenue is determined by $8 \cdot 2^{-x/2}$, where both the production cost and the revenue are in thousands of dollars. If the weekly fixed costs amount to $2000, find the maximum weekly profit that can be obtained.

10.3 INTEGRATION BY TRIGONOMETRIC SUBSTITUTION

If the integrand contains an expression of the form $\sqrt{a^2 - u^2}$, $\sqrt{a^2 + u^2}$, or $\sqrt{u^2 - a^2}$, where $a > 0$, it is often possible to perform the integration by making a trigonometric substitution which results in an integral involving trigonometric functions. We consider each form as a separate case.

Case 1: The integrand contains an expression of the form $\sqrt{a^2 - u^2}$, $a > 0$. We introduce a new variable θ by letting $u = a \sin \theta$, where $0 \le \theta \le \frac{1}{2}\pi$ if $u \ge 0$ and $-\frac{1}{2}\pi \le \theta < 0$ if $u < 0$. Then $du = a \cos \theta \, d\theta$, and

$$\sqrt{a^2 - u^2} = \sqrt{a^2 - a^2 \sin^2 \theta} = \sqrt{a^2(1 - \sin^2 \theta)} = a\sqrt{\cos^2 \theta}$$

Because $-\frac{1}{2}\pi \le \theta \le \frac{1}{2}\pi$, $\cos \theta \ge 0$; hence, $\sqrt{\cos^2 \theta} = \cos \theta$, and we have $\sqrt{a^2 - u^2} = a \cos \theta$. Because $\sin \theta = u/a$ and $-\frac{1}{2}\pi \le \theta \le \frac{1}{2}\pi$, it follows that $\theta = \sin^{-1}(u/a)$.

EXAMPLE 1: Evaluate

$$\int \frac{\sqrt{9 - x^2}}{x^2} \, dx$$

$x \ge 0$

Figure 10.3.1

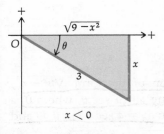

$x < 0$

Figure 10.3.2

SOLUTION: Let $x = 3 \sin \theta$, where $0 \le \theta \le \frac{1}{2}\pi$ if $x \ge 0$ and $-\frac{1}{2}\pi \le \theta < 0$ if $x < 0$. Then $dx = 3 \cos \theta \, d\theta$ and

$$\sqrt{9 - x^2} = \sqrt{9 - 9 \sin^2 \theta} = 3\sqrt{\cos^2 \theta} = 3 \cos \theta$$

Therefore,

$$\int \frac{\sqrt{9 - x^2}}{x^2} \, dx = \int \frac{3 \cos \theta}{9 \sin^2 \theta} (3 \cos \theta \, d\theta)$$

$$= \int \cot^2 \theta \, d\theta$$

$$= \int (\csc^2 \theta - 1) \, d\theta$$

$$= -\cot \theta - \theta + C$$

Because $\sin \theta = \frac{1}{3}x$ and $-\frac{1}{2}\pi \le \theta \le \frac{1}{2}\pi$, $\theta = \sin^{-1}(\frac{1}{3}x)$. To find $\cot \theta$ refer to Figs. 10.3.1 (for $x \ge 0$) and 10.3.2 (for $x < 0$). We see that $\cot \theta = \sqrt{9 - x^2}/x$. Therefore,

$$\int \frac{\sqrt{9 - x^2}}{x^2} \, dx = -\frac{\sqrt{9 - x^2}}{x} - \sin^{-1}\frac{x}{3} + C$$

Case 2: The integrand contains an expression of the form $\sqrt{a^2 + u^2}$, $a > 0$. We introduce a new variable θ by letting $u = a \tan \theta$, where $0 \le \theta < \frac{1}{2}\pi$ if $u \ge 0$ and $-\frac{1}{2}\pi < \theta < 0$ if $u < 0$. Then $du = a \sec^2 \theta \, d\theta$, and

$$\sqrt{a^2 + u^2} = \sqrt{a^2 + a^2 \tan^2 \theta} = a\sqrt{1 + \tan^2 \theta} = a\sqrt{\sec^2 \theta}$$

Because $-\frac{1}{2}\pi < \theta < \frac{1}{2}\pi$, sec $\theta \geq 1$; thus $\sqrt{\sec^2 \theta} = $ sec θ, and we have $\sqrt{a^2 + u^2} = $ sec θ. Because tan $\theta = u/a$ and $-\frac{1}{2}\pi < \theta < \frac{1}{2}\pi$, it follows that $\theta = \tan^{-1}(u/a)$.

EXAMPLE 2: Evaluate

$$\int \sqrt{x^2 + 5} \, dx$$

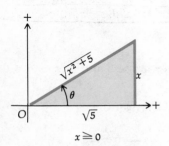

$x \geq 0$

Figure 10.3.3

$x < 0$

Figure 10.3.4

SOLUTION: Let $x = \sqrt{5} \tan \theta$, where $0 \leq \theta < \frac{1}{2}\pi$ if $x \geq 0$ and $-\frac{1}{2}\pi < \theta < 0$ if $x < 0$. Then $dx = \sqrt{5} \sec^2 \theta \, d\theta$ and

$$\sqrt{x^2 + 5} = \sqrt{5 \tan^2 \theta + 5} = \sqrt{5} \sqrt{\sec^2 \theta} = \sqrt{5} \sec \theta$$

Therefore,

$$\int \sqrt{x^2 + 5} \, dx = \int \sqrt{5} \sec \theta (\sqrt{5} \sec^2 \theta \, d\theta) = 5 \int \sec^3 \theta \, d\theta$$

Using the result of Example 6 of Sec. 10.2, we have

$$\int \sqrt{x^2 + 5} \, dx = \frac{5}{2} \sec \theta \tan \theta + \frac{5}{2} \ln |\sec \theta + \tan \theta| + C$$

We find sec θ from Figs. 10.3.3 (for $x \geq 0$) and 10.3.4 (for $x < 0$), where tan $\theta = x/\sqrt{5}$. We see that sec $\theta = \sqrt{x^2 + 5}/\sqrt{5}$. Hence,

$$\int \sqrt{x^2 + 5} \, dx = \frac{5}{2} \cdot \frac{\sqrt{x^2 + 5}}{\sqrt{5}} \cdot \frac{x}{\sqrt{5}} + \frac{5}{2} \ln \left| \frac{\sqrt{x^2 + 5}}{\sqrt{5}} + \frac{x}{\sqrt{5}} \right| + C$$

$$= \tfrac{1}{2} x \sqrt{x^2 + 5} + \tfrac{5}{2} \ln |\sqrt{x^2 + 5} + x| - \tfrac{5}{2} \ln \sqrt{5} + C$$

$$= \tfrac{1}{2} x \sqrt{x^2 + 5} + \tfrac{5}{2} \ln (\sqrt{x^2 + 5} + x) + C_1$$

NOTE: Because $\sqrt{x^2 + 5} + x > 0$, we drop the absolute-value bars.

Case 3: The integrand contains an expression of the form $\sqrt{u^2 - a^2}$, $a > 0$. We introduce a new variable θ by letting $u = a$ sec θ, where $0 \leq \theta < \frac{1}{2}\pi$ if $u \geq a$ and $\pi \leq \theta < \frac{3}{2}\pi$ if $u \leq -a$. Then $du = a$ sec θ tan $\theta \, d\theta$ and

$$\sqrt{u^2 - a^2} = \sqrt{a^2 \sec^2 \theta - a^2} = \sqrt{a^2 (\sec^2 \theta - 1)} = a \sqrt{\tan^2 \theta}$$

Because either $0 \leq \theta < \frac{1}{2}\pi$ or $\pi \leq \theta < \frac{3}{2}\pi$, tan $\theta \geq 0$; thus, $\sqrt{\tan^2 \theta} = $ tan θ, and we have $\sqrt{u^2 - a^2} = a \tan \theta$. Note in Fig. 10.3.5 that $u \geq a$, sec $\theta = u/a \geq 1$, and $0 \leq \theta < \frac{1}{2}\pi$. Hence, $\theta = \sec^{-1}(u/a)$ if $u \geq a$. In Fig. 10.3.6, $u \leq -a$, sec $\theta = u/a \leq -1$, and $\pi \leq \theta < \frac{3}{2}\pi$. Because when $u \leq -a, \frac{1}{2}\pi < \sec^{-1}(u/a) \leq \pi$, it follows that $\theta = 2\pi - \sec^{-1}(u/a)$.

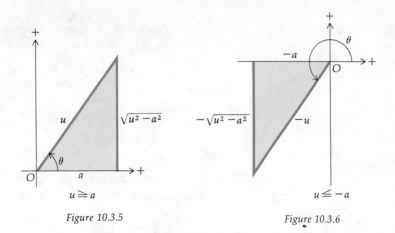

Figure 10.3.5

Figure 10.3.6

EXAMPLE 3:   **Evaluate**

$$\int \frac{dx}{x^3\sqrt{x^2-9}}$$

SOLUTION: Let $x = 3 \sec \theta$, where $0 < \theta < \frac{1}{2}\pi$ if $x > 3$ and $\pi < \theta < \frac{3}{2}\pi$ if $x < -3$. Then $dx = 3 \sec \theta \tan \theta \, d\theta$ and

$$\sqrt{x^2-9} = \sqrt{9 \sec^2 \theta - 9} = 3\sqrt{\tan^2 \theta} = 3 \tan \theta$$

Hence,

$$\int \frac{dx}{x^3\sqrt{x^2-9}} = \int \frac{3 \sec \theta \tan \theta \, d\theta}{27 \sec^3 \theta \cdot 3 \tan \theta} = \frac{1}{27} \int \cos^2 \theta \, d\theta$$

$$= \frac{1}{54} \int (1 + \cos 2\theta) \, d\theta = \tfrac{1}{54}(\theta + \tfrac{1}{2} \sin 2\theta) + C$$

$$= \tfrac{1}{54}(\theta + \sin \theta \cos \theta) + C$$

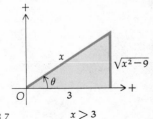

Figure 10.3.7 $x > 3$

When $x > 3$, $0 < \theta < \frac{1}{2}\pi$, and we obtain $\sin \theta$ and $\cos \theta$ from Fig. 10.3.7. When $x < -3$, $\pi < \theta < \frac{3}{2}\pi$, and we obtain $\sin \theta$ and $\cos \theta$ from Fig. 10.3.8. In either case, $\sin \theta = \sqrt{x^2-9}/x$ and $\cos \theta = 3/x$. To express θ in terms of x we must distinguish between the two cases: $x > 3$ and $x < -3$. When $x > 3$, $\theta = \sec^{-1} \frac{1}{3}x$. However, when $x < -3$, $\theta = 2\pi - \sec^{-1} \frac{1}{3}x$ (refer to Fig. 10.3.8). We have, then,

$$\int \frac{dx}{x^3\sqrt{x^2-9}} = \begin{cases} \frac{1}{54}\left(\sec^{-1}\frac{x}{3} + \frac{\sqrt{x^2-9}}{x} \cdot \frac{3}{x}\right) + C & \text{if } x > 3 \\[2mm] \frac{1}{54}\left(2\pi - \sec^{-1}\frac{x}{3} + \frac{\sqrt{x^2-9}}{x} \cdot \frac{3}{x}\right) + C_1 & \text{if } x < -3 \end{cases}$$

and letting $C = C_1 + \frac{1}{27}\pi$, we get

$$\int \frac{dx}{x^3\sqrt{x^2-9}} = \begin{cases} \dfrac{1}{54} \sec^{-1}\dfrac{x}{3} + \dfrac{\sqrt{x^2-9}}{18x^2} + C & \text{if } x > 3 \\[3mm] -\dfrac{1}{54} \sec^{-1}\dfrac{x}{3} + \dfrac{\sqrt{x^2-9}}{18x^2} + C & \text{if } x < -3 \end{cases}$$

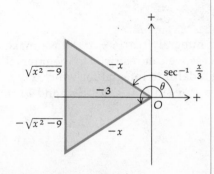

Figure 10.3.8 $x < -3$

EXAMPLE 4:   Evaluate

$$\int \frac{dx}{\sqrt{x^2 - 25}}$$

SOLUTION: Let $x = 5 \sec \theta$, where $0 < \theta < \frac{1}{2}\pi$ if $x > 5$ and $\pi < \theta < \frac{3}{2}\pi$ if $x < -5$. Then $dx = 5 \sec \theta \tan \theta \, d\theta$ and

$$\sqrt{x^2 - 25} = \sqrt{25 \sec^2 \theta - 25} = 5\sqrt{\tan^2 \theta} = 5 \tan \theta$$

Therefore,

$$\int \frac{dx}{\sqrt{x^2 - 25}} = \int \frac{5 \sec \theta \tan \theta \, d\theta}{5 \tan \theta} = \int \sec \theta \, d\theta$$

$$= \ln |\sec \theta + \tan \theta| + C$$

To find $\sec \theta$ and $\tan \theta$ refer to Fig. 10.3.9 (for $x > 5$) and Fig. 10.3.10 (for $x < -5$). In either case, $\sec \theta = \frac{1}{5}x$ and $\tan \theta = \frac{1}{5}\sqrt{x^2 - 25}$. We have, then,

$$\int \frac{dx}{\sqrt{x^2 - 25}} = \ln \left| \frac{x}{5} + \frac{\sqrt{x^2 - 25}}{5} \right| + C$$

$$= \ln |x + \sqrt{x^2 - 25}| - \ln 5 + C$$

$$= \ln |x + \sqrt{x^2 - 25}| + C_1$$

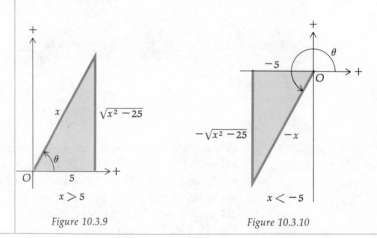

Figure 10.3.9   *Figure 10.3.10*

EXAMPLE 5:   Evaluate

$$\int_1^2 \frac{dx}{(6 - x^2)^{3/2}}$$

SOLUTION: To evaluate the indefinite integral $\int dx/(6 - x^2)^{3/2}$, we make the substitution $x = \sqrt{6} \sin \theta$. In this case we can restrict θ to the interval $0 < \theta < \frac{1}{2}\pi$ because we are evaluating a definite integral for which $x > 0$ because x is in $[1, 2]$. So we have $x = \sqrt{6} \sin \theta$, $0 < \theta < \frac{1}{2}\pi$, and $dx = \sqrt{6} \cos \theta \, d\theta$. Furthermore,

$$(6 - x^2)^{3/2} = (6 - 6 \sin^2 \theta)^{3/2}$$

$$= 6\sqrt{6} (1 - \sin^2 \theta)^{3/2}$$

$$= 6\sqrt{6} (\cos^2 \theta)^{3/2}$$

$$= 6\sqrt{6} \cos^3 \theta$$

Hence,

$$\int \frac{dx}{(6-x^2)^{3/2}} = \int \frac{\sqrt{6}\, \cos\theta\, d\theta}{6\sqrt{6}\, \cos^3\theta}$$

$$= \frac{1}{6}\int \frac{d\theta}{\cos^2\theta}$$

$$= \frac{1}{6}\int \sec^2\theta\, d\theta$$

$$= \tfrac{1}{6}\tan\theta + C$$

We find $\tan\theta$ from Fig. 10.3.11, in which $\sin\theta = x/\sqrt{6}$ and $0 < \theta < \tfrac{1}{2}\pi$. We see that $\tan\theta = x/\sqrt{6-x^2}$, and so we have

$$\int \frac{dx}{(6-x^2)^{3/2}} = \frac{x}{6\sqrt{6-x^2}} + C$$

Therefore,

$$\int_1^2 \frac{dx}{(6-x^2)^{3/2}} = \frac{x}{6\sqrt{6-x^2}}\,\bigg]_1^2$$

$$= \frac{1}{3\sqrt{2}} - \frac{1}{6\sqrt{5}}$$

$$= \frac{2\sqrt{5} - \sqrt{2}}{6\sqrt{10}}$$

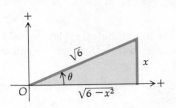

Figure 10.3.11

Exercises 10.3

In Exercises 1 through 18, evaluate the indefinite integral.

1. $\displaystyle\int \frac{dx}{x^2\sqrt{4-x^2}}$

2. $\displaystyle\int \frac{dx}{x\sqrt{x^2+4}}$

3. $\displaystyle\int \frac{\sqrt{9-x^2}}{x^2}\, dx$

4. $\displaystyle\int \frac{x^2\, dx}{\sqrt{x^2+6}}$

5. $\displaystyle\int \frac{dx}{x\sqrt{25-x^2}}$

6. $\displaystyle\int \frac{dx}{\sqrt{x^2-a^2}}$

7. $\displaystyle\int \sqrt{1-u^2}\, du$

8. $\displaystyle\int \frac{dw}{w^2\sqrt{w^2-7}}$

9. $\displaystyle\int x^2\sqrt{16-x^2}\, dx$

10. $\displaystyle\int \frac{dx}{(4+x^2)^{3/2}}$

11. $\displaystyle\int \frac{dx}{(4x^2-9)^{3/2}}$

12. $\displaystyle\int \frac{dx}{x^4\sqrt{16+x^2}}$

13. $\displaystyle\int \frac{dx}{\sqrt{4x+x^2}}$

14. $\displaystyle\int \frac{dx}{\sqrt{4x-x^2}}$

15. $\displaystyle\int \frac{dx}{(5-4x-x^2)^{3/2}}$

16. $\displaystyle\int \frac{dx}{x\sqrt{x^4-4}}$

17. $\displaystyle\int \frac{\sec^2 x\, dx}{(4-\tan^2 x)^{3/2}}$

18. $\displaystyle\int \frac{e^{-x}\, dx}{(9e^{-2x}+1)^{3/2}}$

In Exercises 19 through 26, evaluate the definite integral.

19. $\displaystyle\int_0^2 \frac{x^3\, dx}{\sqrt{16-x^2}}$

20. $\displaystyle\int_0^4 \frac{dx}{(16+x^2)^{3/2}}$

21. $\displaystyle\int_{\sqrt{3}}^{3\sqrt{3}} \frac{dx}{x^2\sqrt{x^2+9}}$

22. $\displaystyle\int_0^1 \frac{x^2\, dx}{\sqrt{4-x^2}}$

23. $\displaystyle\int_4^6 \frac{dx}{x\sqrt{x^2-4}}$

24. $\displaystyle\int_4^8 \frac{dw}{(w^2-4)^{3/2}}$

25. $\displaystyle\int_0^5 x^2\sqrt{25-x^2}\, dx$

26. $\displaystyle\int_1^3 \frac{dx}{x^4\sqrt{x^2+3}}$

27. Find the area of the region bounded by the curve $y = \sqrt{x^2-9}/x^2$, the x axis, and the line $x = 5$.

28. Find the centroid of the region of Exercise 27.

29. Find the length of the arc of the curve $y = \ln x$ from $x = 1$ to $x = 3$.

30. Find the volume of the solid generated by revolving the region of Exercise 27 about the y axis.

31. Find the centroid of the solid of revolution of Exercise 30.

32. The linear density of a rod at a point x ft from one end is $\sqrt{9 + x^2}$ slugs/ft. If the rod is 3 ft long find the mass and center of mass of the rod.

33. If an object is moving vertically due to the forces produced by a spring and gravity, then under certain conditions $v^2 = c^2 - k^2 s^2$, where at t sec, s ft is the directed distance of the object from the starting point and v ft/sec is the velocity of the object. Find s in terms of t where v is positive.

34. A gate in an irrigation ditch is in the shape of a segment of a circle of radius 4 ft. The top of the gate is horizontal and 3 ft above the lowest point on the gate. If the water level is 2 ft above the top of the gate, find the force on the gate due to the water pressure.

35. A cylindrical pipe is 4 ft in diameter and is closed at one end by a circular gate which just fits over the pipe. If the pipe contains water to a depth of 3 ft, find the force on the gate due to the water pressure.

36. An automobile's gasoline tank is in the shape of a right-circular cylinder of radius 8 in. with a horizontal axis. Find the total force on one end when the gasoline is 12 in. deep and w oz. is the weight of 1 in.^{3} of gasoline.

10.4 INTEGRATION OF RATIONAL FUNCTIONS BY PARTIAL FRACTIONS. CASES 1 AND 2: THE DENOMINATOR HAS ONLY LINEAR FACTORS

In Sec. 2.3 a rational function was defined as one which can be expressed as the quotient of two polynomial functions. That is, the function H is a rational function if $H(x) = P(x)/Q(x)$, where $P(x)$ and $Q(x)$ are polynomials. We saw previously that if the degree of the numerator is not less than the degree of the denominator we have an improper fraction, and in that case we divide the numerator by the denominator until we obtain a proper fraction, one in which the degree of the numerator is less than the degree of the denominator. For example,

$$\frac{x^4 - 10x^2 + 3x + 1}{x^2 - 4} = x^2 - 6 + \frac{3x - 23}{x^2 - 4}$$

So if we wish to integrate

$$\int \frac{x^4 - 10x^2 + 3x + 1}{x^2 - 4}\, dx$$

the problem is reduced to integrating

$$\int \frac{3x - 23}{x^2 - 4}\, dx$$

In general, then, we are concerned with the integration of expressions of the form

$$\int \frac{P(x)}{Q(x)}\, dx$$

where the degree of $P(x)$ is less than the degree of $Q(x)$.

To do this it is often necessary to write $P(x)/Q(x)$ as the sum of *partial fractions*. The denominators of the partial fractions are obtained by factoring $Q(x)$ into a product of linear and quadratic factors. Sometimes it may be difficult to find these factors of $Q(x)$; however, a theorem from advanced algebra states that theoretically this can always be done. We state this theorem without proof.

10.4.1 Theorem   Any polynomial with real coefficients can be expressed as a product of linear and quadratic factors in such a way that each of the factors has real coefficients.

After $Q(x)$ has been factored into products of linear and quadratic factors, the method of determining the partial fractions depends on the nature of these factors. We consider various cases separately. The results of advanced algebra, which we do not prove here, provide us with the form of the partial fractions in each case.

We may assume, without loss of generality, that if $Q(x)$ is a polynomial of the nth degree, then the coefficient of x^n is 1 because if

$$Q(x) = C_0 x^n + C_1 x^{n-1} + \cdots + C_{n-1} x + C_n$$

then if $C_0 \neq 1$ we divide the numerator and the denominator of the fraction $P(x)/Q(x)$ by C_0.

Case 1:   The factors of $Q(x)$ are all linear and none is repeated. That is,

$$Q(x) = (x - a_1)(x - a_2) \cdots (x - a_n)$$

where no two of the a_i are identical.

In this case we write

$$\frac{P(x)}{Q(x)} \equiv \frac{A_1}{x - a_1} + \frac{A_2}{x - a_2} + \cdots + \frac{A_n}{x - a_n} \tag{1}$$

where $A_1, A_2, \ldots, A_n$ are constants to be determined.

Note that we used "$\equiv$" (read as "identically equal") instead of "$=$" in (1). This is because (1) is an identity for the value of each A_i.

The following example illustrates how the values of A_i are found.

EXAMPLE 1:   Find

$$\int \frac{(x - 1)\, dx}{x^3 - x^2 - 2x}$$

SOLUTION: We factor the denominator, and we have

$$\frac{x - 1}{x^3 - x^2 - 2x} \equiv \frac{x - 1}{x(x - 2)(x + 1)}$$

So we write

$$\frac{x - 1}{x(x - 2)(x + 1)} \equiv \frac{A}{x} + \frac{B}{x - 2} + \frac{C}{x + 1} \tag{2}$$

Equation (2) is an identity for all x (except $x = 0, 2, -1$). From (2) we get

$$x - 1 \equiv A(x - 2)(x + 1) + Bx(x + 1) + Cx(x - 2) \tag{3}$$

Equation (3) is an identity which is true for all values of x including $0, 2,$ and -1. We wish to find the constants A, B, and C. Substituting 0 for x in (3), we obtain

$$-1 = -2A \quad \text{or} \quad A = \tfrac{1}{2}$$

Substituting 2 for x in (3), we get

$$1 = 6B \quad \text{or} \quad B = \tfrac{1}{6}$$

Substituting -1 for x in (3), we obtain

$$-2 = 3C \quad \text{or} \quad C = -\tfrac{2}{3}$$

There is another method for finding the values of A, B, and C. If on the right side of (3) we combine terms, we have

$$x - 1 \equiv (A + B + C)x^2 + (-A + B - 2C)x - 2A \tag{4}$$

For (4) to be an identity, the coefficients on the left must equal the corresponding coefficients on the right. Hence,

$$A + B + \ C = 0$$

$$-A + B - 2C = 1$$

$$- 2A = -1$$

Solving these equations simultaneously, we get $A = \tfrac{1}{2}$, $B = \tfrac{1}{6}$, and $C = -\tfrac{2}{3}$. Substituting these values in (2), we get

$$\frac{x-1}{x(x-2)(x+1)} = \frac{\tfrac{1}{2}}{x} + \frac{\tfrac{1}{6}}{x-2} + \frac{-\tfrac{2}{3}}{x+1}$$

So our given integral can be expressed as follows:

$$\int \frac{x-1}{x^3 - x^2 - 2x}\, dx = \frac{1}{2} \int \frac{dx}{x} + \frac{1}{6} \int \frac{dx}{x-2} - \frac{2}{3} \int \frac{dx}{x+1}$$

$$= \tfrac{1}{2} \ln |x| + \tfrac{1}{6} \ln |x-2| - \tfrac{2}{3} \ln |x+1| + \tfrac{1}{6} \ln C$$

$$= \tfrac{1}{6}(3 \ln |x| + \ln |x-2| - 4 \ln |x+1| + \ln C)$$

$$= \frac{1}{6} \ln \left| \frac{Cx^3(x-2)}{(x+1)^4} \right|$$

__Case 2:__　The factors of $Q(x)$ are all linear, and some are repeated.

Suppose that $(x - a_i)$ is a p-fold factor. Then, corresponding to this factor, there will be the sum of p partial fractions

$$\frac{A_1}{(x-a_i)^p} + \frac{A_2}{(x-a_i)^{p-1}} + \cdots + \frac{A_{p-1}}{(x-a_i)^2} + \frac{A_p}{x-a_i}$$

where $A_1, A_2, \ldots, A_p$ are constants to be determined.

Example 2 illustrates this case and the method of determining each A_i.

EXAMPLE 2:   Find

$$\int \frac{(x^3 - 1)\, dx}{x^2(x-2)^3}$$

SOLUTION: The fraction in the integrand is written as a sum of partial fractions as follows:

$$\frac{x^3 - 1}{x^2(x-2)^3} \equiv \frac{A}{x^2} + \frac{B}{x} + \frac{C}{(x-2)^3} + \frac{D}{(x-2)^2} + \frac{E}{x-2} \qquad (5)$$

The above is an identity for all x (except $x = 0, 2$). Multiplying on both sides of (5) by the lowest common denominator, we get

$$x^3 - 1 \equiv A(x-2)^3 + Bx(x-2)^3 + Cx^2 + Dx^2(x-2) + Ex^2(x-2)^2$$

or

$$x^3 - 1 \equiv A(x^3 - 6x^2 + 12x - 8) + Bx(x^3 - 6x^2 + 12x - 8)$$
$$+ Cx^2 + Dx^3 - 2Dx^2 + Ex^2(x^2 - 4x + 4)$$

or

$$x^3 - 1 \equiv (B + E)x^4 + (A - 6B + D - 4E)x^3$$
$$+ (-6A + 12B + C - 2D + 4E)x^2 + (12A - 8B)x - 8A$$

Equating the coefficients of like powers of x, we obtain

$$B + E = 0$$
$$A - 6B + D - 4E = 1$$
$$-6A + 12B + C - 2D + 4E = 0$$
$$12A - 8B = 0$$
$$-8A = -1$$

Solving, we get

$$A = \tfrac{1}{8} \qquad B = \tfrac{3}{16} \qquad C = \tfrac{7}{4} \qquad D = \tfrac{5}{4} \qquad E = -\tfrac{3}{16}$$

Therefore, from (5) we have

$$\frac{x^3 - 1}{x^2(x-2)^3} \equiv \frac{\tfrac{1}{8}}{x^2} + \frac{\tfrac{3}{16}}{x} + \frac{\tfrac{7}{4}}{(x-2)^3} + \frac{\tfrac{5}{4}}{(x-2)^2} + \frac{-\tfrac{3}{16}}{x-2}$$

Thus,

$$\int \frac{x^3 - 1}{x^2(x-2)^2}\, dx$$

$$= \frac{1}{8}\int \frac{dx}{x^2} + \frac{3}{16}\int \frac{dx}{x} + \frac{7}{4}\int \frac{dx}{(x-2)^3} + \frac{5}{4}\int \frac{dx}{(x-2)^2} - \frac{3}{16}\int \frac{dx}{x-2}$$

$$= -\frac{1}{8x} + \frac{3}{16}\ln|x| - \frac{7}{8(x-2)^2} - \frac{5}{4(x-2)} - \frac{3}{16}\ln|x-2| + C$$

$$= \frac{-11x^2 + 17x - 4}{8x(x-2)^2} + \frac{3}{16}\ln\left|\frac{x}{x-2}\right| + C$$

EXAMPLE 3: Find

$$\int \frac{du}{u^2 - a^2}$$

SOLUTION:

$$\frac{1}{u^2 - a^2} \equiv \frac{A}{u - a} + \frac{B}{u + a}$$

Multiplying by $(u - a)(u + a)$, we get

$$1 \equiv A(u + a) + B(u - a)$$

or

$$1 \equiv (A + B)u + Aa - Ba$$

Equating coefficients, we have

$$A + B = 0$$

$$Aa - Ba = 1$$

Solving simultaneously, we get

$$A = \frac{1}{2a} \quad \text{and} \quad B = -\frac{1}{2a}$$

Therefore,

$$\int \frac{du}{u^2 - a^2} = \frac{1}{2a} \int \frac{du}{u - a} - \frac{1}{2a} \int \frac{du}{u + a}$$

$$= \frac{1}{2a} \ln |u - a| - \frac{1}{2a} \ln |u + a| + C$$

or

$$\int \frac{du}{u^2 - a^2} = \frac{1}{2a} \ln \left| \frac{u - a}{u + a} \right| + C$$

The type of integral of the above example occurs frequently enough for it to be listed as a formula. It is not necessary to memorize it because an integration by partial fractions is fairly simple.

$$\int \frac{du}{u^2 - a^2} = \frac{1}{2a} \ln \left| \frac{u - a}{u + a} \right| + C \tag{6}$$

If we have $\int du/(a^2 - u^2)$, we write

$$\int \frac{du}{a^2 - u^2} = -\int \frac{du}{u^2 - a^2}$$

$$= -\frac{1}{2a} \ln \left| \frac{u - a}{u + a} \right| + C$$

$$= \frac{1}{2a} \ln \left| \frac{u + a}{u - a} \right| + C$$

This is also listed as a formula.

$$\int \frac{du}{a^2 - u^2} = \frac{1}{2a} \ln \left| \frac{u+a}{u-a} \right| + C \tag{7}$$

In chemistry, the *law of mass action* affords us an application of integration that leads to the use of partial fractions. Under certain conditions it is found that a substance A reacts with a substance B to form a third substance C in such a way that the rate of change of the amount of C is proportional to the product of the amounts of A and B remaining at any given time.

Suppose that initially there are α grams of A and β grams of B and that r grams of A combine with s grams of B to form $(r + s)$ grams of C. If we let x be the number of grams of substance C present at t units of time, then C contains $rx/(r + s)$ grams of A and $sx/(r + s)$ grams of B. The number of grams of substance A remaining is then $\alpha - rx/(r + s)$, and the number of grams of substance B remaining is $\beta - sx/(r + s)$. Therefore, the law of mass action gives us

$$\frac{dx}{dt} = K \left(\alpha - \frac{rx}{r+s} \right) \left(\beta - \frac{sx}{r+s} \right)$$

where K is the constant of proportionality. This equation can be written as

$$\frac{dx}{dt} = \frac{Krs}{(r+s)^2} \left(\frac{r+s}{r} \alpha - x \right) \left(\frac{r+s}{s} \beta - x \right) \tag{8}$$

Letting

$$k = \frac{Krs}{(r+s)^2} \qquad a = \frac{r+s}{r} \alpha \qquad b = \frac{r+s}{s} \beta$$

Eq. (8) becomes

$$\frac{dx}{dt} = k(a - x)(b - x) \tag{9}$$

We can separate the variables in Eq. (9) and get

$$\frac{dx}{(a-x)(b-x)} = k \, dt$$

If $a = b$, then the left side of the above equation can be integrated by the power formula. If $a \neq b$, partial fractions can be used for the integration.

EXAMPLE 4:   A chemical reaction causes a substance A to combine with a substance B to form a substance C so that the law of mass action is obeyed. If in Eq. (9) $a = 8$ and $b = 6$, and 2 g of substance C are formed in 10 min,

SOLUTION: Letting x grams be the amount of substance C present at t minutes, we have the initial conditions shown in Table 10.4.1. Equation (9) becomes

$$\frac{dx}{dt} = k(8 - x)(6 - x)$$

Separating the variables we have

how many grams of C are formed in 15 min?

Table 10.4.1

t	0	10	15
x	0	2	x_{15}

$$\int \frac{dx}{(8-x)(6-x)} = k \int dt \tag{10}$$

Writing the integrand as the sum of partial fractions gives

$$\frac{1}{(8-x)(6-x)} \equiv \frac{A}{8-x} + \frac{B}{6-x}$$

from which we obtain

$$1 \equiv A(6-x) + B(8-x)$$

Substituting 6 for x gives $B = \frac{1}{2}$, and substituting 8 for x gives $A = -\frac{1}{2}$. Hence, Eq. (10) is written as

$$-\frac{1}{2} \int \frac{dx}{8-x} + \frac{1}{2} \int \frac{dx}{6-x} = k \int dt$$

Integrating, we have

$$\frac{1}{2} \ln |8-x| - \frac{1}{2} \ln |6-x| - \frac{1}{2} \ln |C| = kt$$

$$\ln \left| \frac{6-x}{C(8-x)} \right| = -2kt$$

$$\frac{6-x}{8-x} = Ce^{-2kt} \tag{11}$$

Substituting $x=0$, $t=0$ in Eq. (11) we get $C = \frac{3}{4}$. Hence,

$$\frac{6-x}{8-x} = \frac{3}{4} e^{-2kt} \tag{12}$$

Substituting $x=2$, $t=10$ in Eq. (12), we have

$$\tfrac{4}{6} = \tfrac{3}{4} e^{-20k}$$

$$e^{-20k} = \tfrac{8}{9}$$

Substituting $x = x_{15}$, $t = 15$ into Eq. (12), we get

$$\frac{6-x_{15}}{8-x_{15}} = \frac{3}{4} e^{-30k}$$

$$4(6 - x_{15}) = 3(e^{-20k})^{3/2}(8 - x_{15})$$

$$24 - 4x_{15} = 3(\tfrac{8}{9})^{3/2}(8 - x_{15})$$

$$24 - 4x_{15} = \frac{16\sqrt{2}}{9}(8 - x_{15})$$

$$x_{15} = \frac{54 - 32\sqrt{2}}{9 - 4\sqrt{2}}$$

$$\approx 2.6$$

Therefore, there will be 2.6 g of substance C formed in 15 min.

Exercises 10.4

In Exercises 1 through 16, evaluate the indefinite integral.

1. $\displaystyle\int \frac{dx}{x^2 - 4}$

2. $\displaystyle\int \frac{x^2 \, dx}{x^2 + x - 6}$

3. $\displaystyle\int \frac{5x - 2}{x^2 - 4} \, dx$

4. $\displaystyle\int \frac{(4x - 2) \, dx}{x^3 - x^2 - 2x}$

5. $\displaystyle\int \frac{6x^2 - 2x - 1}{4x^3 - x} \, dx$

6. $\displaystyle\int \frac{x^2 + x + 2}{x^2 - 1} \, dx$

7. $\displaystyle\int \frac{dx}{x^3 + 3x^2}$

8. $\displaystyle\int \frac{3x^2 - x + 1}{x^3 - x^2} \, dx$

9. $\displaystyle\int \frac{dx}{(x + 2)^3}$

10. $\displaystyle\int \frac{dt}{(t + 2)^2 (t + 1)}$

11. $\displaystyle\int \frac{x^2 - 3x - 7}{(2x + 3)(x + 1)^2} \, dx$

12. $\displaystyle\int \frac{(5x^2 - 11x + 5) \, dx}{x^3 - 4x^2 + 5x - 2}$

13. $\displaystyle\int \frac{x^4 + 3x^3 - 5x^2 - 4x + 17}{x^3 + x^2 - 5x + 3} \, dx$

14. $\displaystyle\int \frac{2x^4 - 2x + 1}{2x^5 - x^4} \, dx$

15. $\displaystyle\int \frac{-24x^3 + 30x^2 + 52x + 17}{9x^4 - 6x^3 - 11x^2 + 4x + 4} \, dx$

16. $\displaystyle\int \frac{dx}{16x^4 - 8x^2 + 1}$

In Exercises 17 through 24, evaluate the definite integral.

17. $\displaystyle\int_1^2 \frac{x - 3}{x^3 + x^2} \, dx$

18. $\displaystyle\int_0^4 \frac{(x - 2) \, dx}{2x^2 + 7x + 3}$

19. $\displaystyle\int_1^3 \frac{x^2 - 4x + 3}{x(x + 1)^2} \, dx$

20. $\displaystyle\int_1^4 \frac{(2x^2 + 13x + 18) \, dx}{x^3 + 6x^2 + 9x}$

21. $\displaystyle\int_1^2 \frac{5x^2 - 3x + 18}{9x - x^3} \, dx$

22. $\displaystyle\int_0^1 \frac{(3x^2 + 7x) \, dx}{x^3 + 6x^2 + 11x + 6}$

23. $\displaystyle\int_0^5 \frac{(x^2 - 3) \, dx}{x^3 + 4x^2 + 5x + 2}$

24. $\displaystyle\int_0^4 \frac{x^2 \, dx}{2x^3 + 9x^2 + 12x + 4}$

25. Find the area of the region bounded by the curve $y = (x - 1)/(x^2 - 5x + 6)$, the x axis, and the lines $x = 4$ and $x = 6$.

26. Find the centroid of the region in Exercise 25.

27. Find the volume of the solid of revolution generated by revolving the region in Exercise 25 about the y axis.

28. Find the area of the region in the first quadrant bounded by the curve $(x + 2)^2 y = 4 - x$.

29. Find the centroid of the region of Exercise 28.

30. Find the volume of the solid of revolution generated if the region in Exercise 28 is revolved about the x axis.

31. Suppose in Example 4 that $a = 5$ and $b = 4$ and 1 g of substance C is formed in 5 min. How many grams of C are formed in 10 min?

32. Suppose in Example 4 that $a = 6$ and $b = 3$ and 1 g of substance C is formed in 4 min. How long will it take 2 g of substance C to be formed?

33. At any instant the rate at which a substance dissolves is proportional to the product of the amount of the substance present at that instant and the difference between the concentration of the substance in solution at that instant and the concentration of the substance in a saturated solution. A quantity of insoluble material is mixed with 10 lb of salt initially, and the salt is dissolving in a tank containing 20 gal of water. If 5 lb of salt dissolves in 10 min and the concentration of salt in a saturated solution is 3 lb/gal, how much salt will dissolve in 20 min?

34. A particle is moving along a straight line so that if v ft/sec is the velocity of the particle at t sec then

$$v = \frac{t + 3}{t^2 + 3t + 2}$$

Find the distance traveled by the particle from the time when $t = 0$ to the time when $t = 2$.

10.5 INTEGRATION OF RATIONAL FUNCTIONS BY PARTIAL FRACTIONS. CASES 3 AND 4: THE DENOMINATOR CONTAINS QUADRATIC FACTORS

Case 3: The factors of $Q(x)$ are linear and quadratic, and none of the quadratic factors is repeated.

Corresponding to the quadratic factor $x^2 + px + q$ in the denominator is the partial fraction of the form

$$\frac{Ax + B}{x^2 + px + q}$$

EXAMPLE 1: Find

$$\int \frac{(x^2 - 2x - 3)\,dx}{(x-1)(x^2+2x+2)}$$

SOLUTION: The fraction in the integrand is written as a sum of partial fractions as follows:

$$\frac{x^2 - 2x - 3}{(x-1)(x^2+2x+2)} \equiv \frac{Ax + B}{x^2 + 2x + 2} + \frac{C}{x - 1} \tag{1}$$

Multiplying on both sides of (1) by the lowest common denominator, we have

$$x^2 - 2x - 3 \equiv (Ax + B)(x - 1) + C(x^2 + 2x + 2)$$

or

$$x^2 - 2x - 3 \equiv (A + C)x^2 + (B - A + 2C)x + (2C - B)$$

Equating coefficients of like powers of x gives

$$A + C = 1$$
$$B - A + 2C = -2$$
$$2C - B = -3$$

Solving for A, B, and C, we obtain

$$A = \tfrac{9}{5} \qquad B = \tfrac{7}{5} \qquad C = -\tfrac{4}{5}$$

Substituting these values into (1), we get

$$\frac{x^2 - 2x - 3}{(x-1)(x^2+2x+2)} \equiv \frac{\tfrac{9}{5}x + \tfrac{7}{5}}{x^2 + 2x + 2} + \frac{-\tfrac{4}{5}}{x - 1}$$

So

$$\int \frac{x^2 - 2x - 3}{(x-1)(x^2+2x+2)}\,dx$$

$$= \frac{9}{5} \int \frac{x\,dx}{x^2 + 2x + 2} + \frac{7}{5} \int \frac{dx}{x^2 + 2x + 2} - \frac{4}{5} \int \frac{dx}{x - 1} \tag{2}$$

To integrate $\int (x\,dx)/(x^2 + 2x + 2)$, we see that the differential of the denominator is $2(x + 1)\,dx$; so we add and subtract 1 in the numerator, thereby giving us

$$\frac{9}{5} \int \frac{x\,dx}{x^2 + 2x + 2} = \frac{9}{5} \int \frac{(x+1)\,dx}{x^2 + 2x + 2} - \frac{9}{5} \int \frac{dx}{x^2 + 2x + 2} \tag{3}$$

Substituting from (3) into (2) and combining terms, we get

$$\int \frac{x^2 - 2x - 3}{(x-1)(x^2 + 2x + 2)}\, dx$$

$$= \frac{9}{5}\cdot\frac{1}{2}\int\frac{2(x+1)\,dx}{x^2+2x+2} - \frac{2}{5}\int\frac{dx}{x^2+2x+2} - \frac{4}{5}\int\frac{dx}{x-1} \tag{4}$$

$$= \frac{9}{10}\ln|x^2+2x+2| - \frac{2}{5}\int\frac{dx}{(x+1)^2+1} - \frac{4}{5}\ln|x-1|$$

$$= \tfrac{9}{10}\ln|x^2+2x+2| - \tfrac{2}{5}\tan^{-1}(x+1) - \tfrac{8}{10}\ln|x-1| + \tfrac{1}{10}\ln C$$

$$= \frac{1}{10}\ln\left|\frac{C(x^2+2x+2)^9}{(x-1)^8}\right| - \frac{2}{5}\tan^{-1}(x+1)$$

In the above example we would have saved some steps if instead of (1) we had expressed the original fraction as

$$\frac{x^2-2x-3}{(x-1)(x^2+2x+2)} \equiv \frac{D(2x+2)+E}{x^2+2x+2} + \frac{F}{x-1}$$

NOTE: We write $D(2x+2)+E$ instead of $Ax+B$ because

$$2x+2 = D_x(x^2+2x+2)$$

Then, solving for D, E, and F, we obtain

$$D = \tfrac{9}{10} \qquad E = -\tfrac{2}{5} \qquad F = -\tfrac{4}{5}$$

giving us (4) directly.

Case 4: The factors of $Q(x)$ are linear and quadratic, and some of the quadratic factors are repeated.

If $x^2 + px + q$ is an n-fold quadratic factor of $Q(x)$, then, corresponding to this factor $(x^2 + px + q)^n$, we have the sum of the following n partial fractions:

$$\frac{A_1 x + B_1}{(x^2+px+q)^n} + \frac{A_2 x + B_2}{(x^2+px+q)^{n-1}} + \cdots + \frac{A_n x + B_n}{x^2+px+q}$$

For example, if the denominator contains the factor $(x^2 - 5x + 2)^3$, we have, corresponding to this factor,

$$\frac{Ax+B}{(x^2-5x+2)^3} + \frac{Cx+D}{(x^2-5x+2)^2} + \frac{Ex+F}{x^2-5x+2}$$

or, more conveniently,

$$\frac{A(2x-5)+B}{(x^2-5x+2)^3} + \frac{C(2x-5)+D}{(x^2-5x+2)^2} + \frac{E(2x-5)+F}{x^2-5x+2}$$

EXAMPLE 2: Find

$$\int \frac{(x-2)\,dx}{x(x^2-4x+5)^2}$$

SOLUTION:

$$\frac{x-2}{x(x^2-4x+5)^2} \equiv \frac{A}{x} + \frac{B(2x-4)+C}{(x^2-4x+5)^2} + \frac{D(2x-4)+E}{x^2-4x+5} \tag{5}$$

Multiplying on both sides of (5) by the lowest common denominator, we have

$$x - 2 \equiv A(x^2 - 4x + 5)^2 + x(2Bx - 4B + C)$$
$$+ x(x^2 - 4x + 5)(2Dx - 4D + E)$$

or

$$x - 2 \equiv Ax^4 + 16Ax^2 + 25A - 8Ax^3 + 10Ax^2 - 40Ax + 2Bx^2 - 4Bx + Cx$$
$$+ 2Dx^4 - 12Dx^3 + Ex^3 + 26Dx^2 - 4Ex^2 - 20Dx + 5Ex$$

or

$$x - 2 \equiv (A + 2D)x^4 + (-8A - 12D + E)x^3 + (26A + 2B + 26D - 4E)x^2$$
$$+ (-40A - 4B + C - 20D + 5E)x + 25A$$

Equating coefficients and solving simultaneously, we obtain

$$A = -\tfrac{2}{25} \quad B = \tfrac{1}{5} \quad C = \tfrac{1}{5} \quad D = \tfrac{1}{25} \quad E = -\tfrac{4}{25}$$

Therefore,

$$\int \frac{(x - 2)\, dx}{x(x^2 - 4x + 5)^2}$$

$$= -\frac{2}{25} \int \frac{dx}{x} + \frac{1}{5} \int \frac{(2x - 4)\, dx}{(x^2 - 4x + 5)^2} + \frac{1}{5} \int \frac{dx}{(x^2 - 4x + 5)^2} + \frac{1}{25} \int \frac{(2x - 4)\, dx}{(x^2 - 4x + 5)}$$

$$- \frac{4}{25} \int \frac{dx}{x^2 - 4x + 5}$$

$$= -\frac{2}{25} \ln|x| - \frac{1}{5(x^2 - 4x + 5)} + \frac{1}{5} \int \frac{dx}{[(x^2 - 4x + 4) + 1]^2} + \frac{1}{25} \ln|x^2 - 4x + 5|$$

(6)

$$- \frac{4}{25} \int \frac{dx}{(x^2 - 4x + 4) + 1}$$

We evaluate separately the integrals in the third and fifth terms on the right side of (6).

$$\int \frac{dx}{[(x^2 - 4x + 4) + 1]^2} = \int \frac{dx}{[(x - 2)^2 + 1]^2}$$

Let $x - 2 = \tan\theta$, where $0 \le \theta < \tfrac{1}{2}\pi$, if $x \ge 2$ and $-\tfrac{1}{2}\pi < \theta < 0$ if $x < 2$. Then $dx = \sec^2\theta\, d\theta$ and $(x - 2)^2 + 1 = \tan^2\theta + 1 = \sec^2\theta$. Hence,

$$\int \frac{dx}{[(x - 2)^2 + 1]^2} = \int \frac{\sec^2\theta\, d\theta}{(\tan^2\theta + 1)^2}$$

$$= \int \frac{\sec^2\theta\, d\theta}{\sec^4\theta}$$

$$= \int \frac{d\theta}{\sec^2\theta}$$

$x \geq 2$

Figure 10.5.1

$x < 2$

Figure 10.5.2

$$= \int \cos^2 \theta \, d\theta$$

$$= \int \frac{1 + \cos 2\theta}{2} \, d\theta$$

$$= \frac{\theta}{2} + \frac{1}{4} \sin 2\theta + C_1$$

$$= \frac{\theta}{2} + \frac{1}{2} \sin \theta \cos \theta + C_1$$

Because $\tan \theta = x - 2$ and $-\frac{1}{2}\pi < \theta < \frac{1}{2}\pi$, $\theta = \tan^{-1}(x-2)$. We find $\sin \theta$ and $\cos \theta$ from Figs. 10.5.1 (if $x \geq 2$) and 10.5.2 (if $x < 2$). In either case

$$\sin \theta = \frac{x-2}{\sqrt{x^2 - 4x + 5}} \quad \text{and} \quad \cos \theta = \frac{1}{\sqrt{x^2 - 4x + 5}}$$

So we have

$$\int \frac{dx}{[(x-2)^2 + 1]^2} = \frac{1}{2} \tan^{-1}(x-2) + \frac{1}{2} \frac{x-2}{\sqrt{x^2 - 4x + 5}} \cdot \frac{1}{\sqrt{x^2 - 4x + 5}} + C_1$$

or

$$\int \frac{dx}{[(x-2)^2 + 1]^2} = \frac{1}{2} \tan^{-1}(x-2) + \frac{x-2}{2(x^2 - 4x + 5)} + C_1 \qquad (7)$$

Now considering the other integral on the right side of (6), we have

$$\int \frac{dx}{(x^2 - 4x + 4) + 1} = \int \frac{dx}{(x-2)^2 + 1} = \tan^{-1}(x-2) + C_2 \qquad (8)$$

Substituting from (7) and (8) into (6), we get

$$\int \frac{(x-2) \, dx}{x(x^2 - 4x + 5)^2}$$

$$= -\frac{2}{25} \ln |x| - \frac{1}{5(x^2 - 4x + 5)} + \frac{1}{10} \tan^{-1}(x-2) + \frac{x-2}{10(x^2 - 4x + 5)}$$

$$\qquad + \frac{1}{25} \ln |x^2 - 4x + 5| - \frac{4}{25} \tan^{-1}(x-2) + C$$

$$= \frac{1}{25} \ln \left| \frac{x^2 - 4x + 5}{x^2} \right| - \frac{3}{50} \tan^{-1}(x-2) + \frac{x-4}{10(x^2 - 4x + 5)} + C$$

Exercises 10.5

In Exercises 1 through 16, evaluate the indefinite integral.

1. $\displaystyle\int \frac{dx}{2x^3 + x}$

2. $\displaystyle\int \frac{(x+4) \, dx}{x(x^2 + 4)}$

3. $\displaystyle\int \frac{dx}{16x^4 - 1}$

4. $\int \dfrac{(x^2 - 4x - 4)\, dx}{x^3 - 2x^2 + 4x - 8}$

5. $\int \dfrac{(x^2 + x)\, dx}{x^3 - x^2 + x - 1}$

6. $\int \dfrac{dx}{9x^4 + x^2}$

7. $\int \dfrac{dx}{x^3 + x^2 + x}$

8. $\int \dfrac{(x + 3)\, dx}{4x^4 + 4x^3 + x^2}$

9. $\int \dfrac{(2x^2 - x + 2)\, dx}{x^5 + 2x^3 + x}$

10. $\int \dfrac{(2x^3 + 9x)\, dx}{(x^2 + 3)(x^2 - 2x + 3)}$

11. $\int \dfrac{(x^2 + 2x - 1)\, dx}{27x^3 - 1}$

12. $\int \dfrac{dx}{(x^2 + 1)^3}$

13. $\int \dfrac{18\, dx}{(4x^2 + 9)^2}$

14. $\int \dfrac{(2x^2 + 3x + 2)\, dx}{x^3 + 4x^2 + 6x + 4}$

15. $\int \dfrac{(\sec^2 x + 1)\sec^2 x\, dx}{1 + \tan^3 x}$

16. $\int \dfrac{e^{5x}\, dx}{(e^{2x} + 1)^2}$

In Exercises 17 through 24, evaluate the definite integral.

17. $\displaystyle\int_1^4 \dfrac{(4 + 5x^2)\, dx}{x^3 + 4x}$

18. $\displaystyle\int_0^1 \dfrac{x\, dx}{x^3 + 2x^2 + x + 2}$

19. $\displaystyle\int_3^4 \dfrac{(5x^3 - 4x)\, dx}{x^4 - 16}$

20. $\displaystyle\int_0^1 \dfrac{9\, dx}{8x^3 + 1}$

21. $\displaystyle\int_{-1}^0 \dfrac{x^2\, dx}{(2x^2 + 2x + 1)^2}$

22. $\displaystyle\int_0^{1/2} \dfrac{(x + 1)\, dx}{x^3 - 1}$

23. $\displaystyle\int_0^1 \dfrac{(x^2 + 3x + 3)\, dx}{x^3 + x^2 + x + 1}$

24. $\displaystyle\int_{\pi/6}^{\pi/2} \dfrac{\cos x\, dx}{\sin x + \sin^3 x}$

25. Find the area of the region bounded by the curve $y = 4/(x^3 + 8)$, the x axis, the y axis, and the line $x = 2$.

26. Find the abscissa of the centroid of the region in Exercise 25.

27. Find the mass of a lamina in the shape of the region of Exercise 25 if the area density at any point (x, y) is kx^2 slugs/ft².

28. Find the volume of the solid of revolution generated by revolving the region of Exercise 25 about the y axis.

29. A particle is moving along a straight line so that if v ft/sec is the velocity of the particle at t sec, then

$$v = \dfrac{t^2 - t + 1}{(t + 2)^2(t^2 + 1)}$$

Find a formula for the distance traveled by the particle from the time when $t = 0$ to the time when $t = t_1$.

10.6 INTEGRALS YIELDING INVERSE HYPERBOLIC FUNCTIONS

As mentioned in Sec. 9.11, the inverse hyperbolic functions can be applied in integration, and sometimes their use shortens the computation considerably. It should be noted, however, that no new types of integrals are evaluated by their use. Only new forms of the results are obtained. From formula (15) in Sec. 9.11 we have

$$D_x(\sinh^{-1} u) = \dfrac{1}{\sqrt{u^2 + 1}}\, D_x u$$

from which we obtain the integration formula

$$\int \dfrac{du}{\sqrt{u^2 + 1}} = \sinh^{-1} u + C$$

Expressing $\sinh^{-1} u$ as a natural logarithm by using formula (8) of Sec. 9.11, we get

$$\text{(1)} \quad \int \frac{du}{\sqrt{u^2 + 1}} = \sinh^{-1} u + C = \ln(u + \sqrt{u^2 + 1}) + C \tag{1}$$

Formula (16) in Sec. 9.11 is

$$D_x(\cosh^{-1} u) = \frac{1}{\sqrt{u^2 - 1}} D_x u \qquad \text{where } u > 1$$

from which it follows that

$$\int \frac{du}{\sqrt{u^2 - 1}} = \cosh^{-1} u + C \qquad u > 1$$

and combining this with formula (9) in Sec. 9.11, we obtain

$$\text{(2)} \quad \int \frac{du}{\sqrt{u^2 - 1}} = \cosh^{-1} u + C = \ln(u + \sqrt{u^2 - 1}) + C \qquad \text{if } u > 1 \tag{2}$$

Formulas (17) and (18) of Sec. 9.11 are, respectively,

$$D_x(\tanh^{-1} u) = \frac{1}{1 - u^2} D_x u \quad \text{where } |u| < 1$$

and

$$D_x(\coth^{-1} u) = \frac{1}{1 - u^2} D_x u \quad \text{where } |u| > 1$$

From the above two formulas we get

$$\int \frac{du}{1 - u^2} = \begin{cases} \tanh^{-1} u + C & \text{if } |u| < 1 \\ \coth^{-1} u + C & \text{if } |u| > 1 \end{cases}$$

and combining this with formulas (10) and (11) of Sec. 9.11 we have

$$\text{(3)} \quad \int \frac{du}{1 - u^2} = \begin{cases} \tanh^{-1} u + C & \text{if } |u| < 1 \\ \coth^{-1} u + C & \text{if } |u| > 1 \end{cases} = \frac{1}{2} \ln \left| \frac{1 + u}{1 - u} \right| + C \text{ if } u \neq 1 \tag{3}$$

We also have the following three formulas.

$$\text{(1)} \quad \int \frac{du}{\sqrt{u^2 + a^2}} = \sinh^{-1} \frac{u}{a} + C = \ln(u + \sqrt{u^2 + a^2}) + C \quad \text{if } a > 0 \tag{4}$$

$$\text{(2)} \quad \int \frac{du}{\sqrt{u^2 - a^2}} = \cosh^{-1} \frac{u}{a} + C = \ln(u + \sqrt{u^2 - a^2}) + C \quad \text{if } u > a > 0 \tag{5}$$

$$\text{(3)} \quad \int \frac{du}{a^2 - u^2} = \begin{cases} \dfrac{1}{a} \tanh^{-1} \dfrac{u}{a} + C & \text{if } |u| < a \\ \dfrac{1}{a} \coth^{-1} \dfrac{u}{a} + C & \text{if } |u| > a \end{cases} = \frac{1}{2a} \ln \left| \frac{a + u}{a - u} \right| + C \tag{6}$$

$$\text{if } u \neq a \text{ and } a \neq 0$$

These formulas can be proved by finding the derivative of the right side and obtaining the integrand, or else more directly by using a hyperbolic function substitution.

For example, the proof of (4) by differentiating the right side is as follows:

$$D_u\left(\sinh^{-1}\frac{u}{a}\right) = \frac{1}{\sqrt{\left(\dfrac{u}{a}\right)^2 + 1}} \cdot \frac{1}{a} = \frac{\sqrt{a^2}}{\sqrt{u^2 + a^2}} \cdot \frac{1}{a}$$

and because $a > 0$, $\sqrt{a^2} = a$, and we get

$$D_u\left(\sinh^{-1}\frac{u}{a}\right) = \frac{1}{\sqrt{u^2 + a^2}}$$

To obtain the natural logarithm representation we use formula (8) in Sec. 9.11 and we have

$$\sinh^{-1}\frac{u}{a} = \ln\left(\frac{u}{a} + \sqrt{\left(\frac{u}{a}\right)^2 + 1}\right)$$

$$= \ln\left(\frac{u}{a} + \frac{\sqrt{u^2 + a^2}}{a}\right)$$

$$= \ln(u + \sqrt{u^2 + a^2}) - \ln a$$

Therefore,

$$\sinh^{-1}\frac{u}{a} + C = \ln(u + \sqrt{u^2 + a^2}) - \ln a + C$$

$$= \ln(u + \sqrt{u^2 + a^2}) + C_1$$

where $C_1 = C - \ln a$.

The proof of (5) by a hyperbolic function substitution makes use of the identity $\cosh^2 x - \sinh^2 x = 1$. Letting $u = a \cosh x$, where $x > 0$, then $du = a \sinh x \, dx$, and $x = \cosh^{-1}(u/a)$. Substituting in the integrand, we get

$$\int \frac{du}{\sqrt{u^2 - a^2}} = \int \frac{a \sinh x \, dx}{\sqrt{a^2 \cosh^2 x - a^2}}$$

$$= \int \frac{a \sinh x \, dx}{\sqrt{a^2} \sqrt{\cosh^2 x - 1}}$$

$$= \int \frac{a \sinh x \, dx}{\sqrt{a^2} \sqrt{\sinh^2 x}}$$

Because $a > 0$, $\sqrt{a^2} = a$. Furthermore, because $x > 0$, $\sinh x > 0$, and so $\sqrt{\sinh^2 x} = \sinh x$. We have, then,

$$\int \frac{du}{\sqrt{u^2 - a^2}} = \int \frac{a \sinh x \, dx}{a \sinh x}$$

$$= \int dx$$

$$= x + C$$

$$= \cosh^{-1} \frac{u}{a} + C$$

The natural logarithm representation may be obtained in a way similar to the way we obtained the one for formula (4). The proof of formula (6) is left for the reader (see Exercise 17).

Note that formulas (1) through (6) give alternate representations of the integral in question. In evaluating a definite integral in which one of these forms occurs and a table of hyperbolic functions is available, the inverse hyperbolic function representation may be easier to use. Also the inverse hyperbolic function representation is a less cumbersome one to write for the indefinite integral. Also note that the natural logarithm form of formula (6) was obtained in Sec. 10.4 by using partial fractions.

EXAMPLE 1:   Evaluate

$$\int \frac{dx}{\sqrt{x^2 - 6x + 13}}$$

SOLUTION: We apply formula (4) after rewriting the denominator.

$$\int \frac{dx}{\sqrt{x^2 - 6x + 13}} = \int \frac{dx}{\sqrt{(x^2 - 6x + 9) + 4}}$$

$$= \int \frac{dx}{\sqrt{(x - 3)^2 + 4}}$$

$$= \sinh^{-1} \left(\frac{x - 3}{2} \right) + C$$

$$= \ln(x - 3 + \sqrt{x^2 - 6x + 13}) + C$$

EXAMPLE 2:   Evaluate

$$\int_6^{10} \frac{dx}{\sqrt{x^2 - 25}}$$

SOLUTION: Using formula (5), we get

$$\int_6^{10} \frac{dx}{\sqrt{x^2 - 25}} = \cosh^{-1} \frac{x}{5} \Big]_6^{10} = \cosh^{-1} 2 - \cosh^{-1} 1.2$$

Using Table 4 in the Appendix, we find

$$\cosh^{-1} 2 - \cosh^{-1}(1.2) = 1.32 - 0.62 = 0.70$$

Instead of applying the formulas, integrals of the forms of those in formulas (1) through (6) can be obtained by using a hyperbolic function substitution and proceeding in a manner similar to that using a trigonometric substitution.

EXAMPLE 3:   Evaluate the integral of Example 1 without using a formula but by using a hyperbolic function substitution.

SOLUTION: In the solution of Example 1, the given integral was rewritten as

$$\int \frac{dx}{\sqrt{(x - 3)^2 + 4}}$$

If we let $x - 3 = 2 \sinh u$, then $dx = 2 \cosh u \, du$ and $u = \sinh^{-1} \frac{1}{2}(x - 3)$. We have, therefore,

$$\int \frac{dx}{\sqrt{(x-3)^2 + 4}} = \int \frac{2 \cosh u \, du}{\sqrt{4 \sinh^2 u + 4}}$$

$$= \int \frac{2 \cosh u \, du}{2\sqrt{\sinh^2 u + 1}}$$

$$= \int \frac{\cosh u \, du}{\sqrt{\cosh^2 u}}$$

$$= \int \frac{\cosh u \, du}{\cosh u}$$

$$= \int du$$

$$= u + C$$

$$= \sinh^{-1}\left(\frac{x-3}{2}\right) + C$$

which agrees with the result of Example 1.

Exercises 10.6

In Exercises 1 through 10, express the indefinite integral in terms of an inverse hyperbolic function and as a natural logarithm.

1. $\displaystyle\int \frac{dx}{\sqrt{4 + x^2}}$

2. $\displaystyle\int \frac{dx}{\sqrt{4x^2 - 9}}$

3. $\displaystyle\int \frac{x \, dx}{\sqrt{x^4 - 1}}$

4. $\displaystyle\int \frac{dx}{25 - x^2}$

5. $\displaystyle\int \frac{dx}{9x^2 - 16}$

6. $\displaystyle\int \frac{dx}{4e^x - e^{-x}}$

7. $\displaystyle\int \frac{\cos x \, dx}{\sqrt{4 - \cos^2 x}}$

8. $\displaystyle\int \frac{dx}{\sqrt{x^2 - 4x + 1}}$

9. $\displaystyle\int \frac{dx}{2 - 4x - x^2}$

10. $\displaystyle\int \frac{3x \, dx}{\sqrt{x^4 + 6x^2 + 5}}$

In Exercises 11 through 16, evaluate the definite integral and express the answer in terms of a natural logarithm.

11. $\displaystyle\int_3^5 \frac{dx}{\sqrt{x^2 - 4}}$

12. $\displaystyle\int_1^2 \frac{dx}{\sqrt{x^2 + 2x}}$

13. $\displaystyle\int_{-1/2}^{1/2} \frac{dx}{1 - x^2}$

14. $\displaystyle\int_{-4}^{-3} \frac{dx}{1 - x^2}$

15. $\displaystyle\int_2^3 \frac{dx}{\sqrt{9x^2 - 12x - 5}}$

16. $\displaystyle\int_{-2}^2 \frac{dx}{\sqrt{16 + x^2}}$

17. Prove formula (6) by using a hyperbolic function substitution.

18. A curve goes through the point $(0, a)$, $a > 0$, and the slope at any point is $\sqrt{y^2/a^2 - 1}$. Prove that the curve is a catenary.

19. A man wearing a parachute falls out of an airplane and when the parachute opens his velocity is 200 ft/sec. If v ft/sec is his velocity t sec after the parachute opens

$$\frac{324}{g} \frac{dv}{dt} = 324 - v^2$$

Solve this differential equation to obtain

$$t = \frac{18}{g} \left(\coth^{-1} \frac{v}{18} - \coth^{-1} \frac{100}{9} \right)$$

10.7 INTEGRATION OF RATIONAL FUNCTIONS OF SINE AND COSINE

If an integrand is a rational function of $\sin x$ and $\cos x$, it can be reduced to a rational function of z by the substitution

$$z = \tan \tfrac{1}{2}x \tag{1}$$

Using the identity $\cos 2y \equiv 2 \cos^2 y - 1$ and letting $y = \tfrac{1}{2}x$, we have

$$\cos x = 2 \cos^2 \tfrac{1}{2}x - 1 = \frac{2}{\sec^2 \tfrac{1}{2}x} - 1 = \frac{2}{1 + \tan^2 \tfrac{1}{2}x} - 1 = \frac{2}{1 + z^2} - 1$$

So

$$\cos x = \frac{1 - z^2}{1 + z^2} \tag{2}$$

In a similar manner, from the identity $\sin 2y = 2 \sin y \cos y$ we have

$$\sin x = 2 \sin \tfrac{1}{2}x \cos \tfrac{1}{2}x = 2 \frac{\sin \tfrac{1}{2}x \cos^2 \tfrac{1}{2}x}{\cos \tfrac{1}{2}x}$$

$$= 2 \tan \tfrac{1}{2}x \cdot \frac{1}{\sec^2 \tfrac{1}{2}x} = \frac{2 \tan \tfrac{1}{2}x}{1 + \tan^2 \tfrac{1}{2}x}$$

Thus,

$$\sin x = \frac{2z}{1 + z^2} \tag{3}$$

Because $z = \tan \tfrac{1}{2}x$,

$$dz = \tfrac{1}{2} \sec^2 \tfrac{1}{2}x \, dx = \tfrac{1}{2}(1 + \tan^2 \tfrac{1}{2}x) \, dx$$

Hence,

$$dx = \frac{2 \, dz}{1 + z^2} \tag{4}$$

EXAMPLE 1: Find

$$\int \frac{dx}{1 - \sin x + \cos x}$$

SOLUTION: Letting $z = \tan \tfrac{1}{2}x$ and using (2), (3), and (4), we obtain

$$\int \frac{dx}{1 - \sin x + \cos x} = \int \frac{\dfrac{2 \, dz}{1 + z^2}}{1 - \dfrac{2z}{1 + z^2} + \dfrac{1 - z^2}{1 + z^2}}$$

$$= 2 \int \frac{dz}{(1 + z^2) - 2z + (1 - z^2)}$$

$$= 2 \int \frac{dz}{2 - 2z}$$

$$= \int \frac{dz}{1 - z}$$

$$= -\ln |1 - z| + C$$

$$= -\ln |1 - \tan \tfrac{1}{2}x| + C$$

EXAMPLE 2:   Find

$$\int \sec x \, dx$$

by using the substitution of this section.

SOLUTION: $\displaystyle \int \sec x \, dx = \int \frac{dx}{\cos x}$

Letting $z = \tan \tfrac{1}{2}x$ and using (2) and (4), we get

$$\int \frac{dx}{\cos x} = \int \frac{2 \, dz}{1 + z^2} \cdot \frac{1 + z^2}{1 - z^2} = 2 \int \frac{dz}{1 - z^2}$$

Using formula (7) from Sec. 10.4, we have

$$2 \int \frac{dz}{1 - z^2} = \ln \left| \frac{1 + z}{1 - z} \right| + C$$

Therefore,

$$\int \sec x \, dx = \ln \left| \frac{1 + \tan \tfrac{1}{2}x}{1 - \tan \tfrac{1}{2}x} \right| + C \qquad (5)$$

Equation (5) can be written in another form by noting that $1 = \tan \tfrac{1}{4}\pi$ and using the identity $\tan(\alpha + \beta) = (\tan \alpha + \tan \beta)/(1 - \tan \alpha \tan \beta)$. So we have

$$\int \sec x \, dx = \ln \left| \frac{\tan \tfrac{1}{4}\pi + \tan \tfrac{1}{2}x}{1 - \tan \tfrac{1}{4}\pi \cdot \tan \tfrac{1}{2}x} \right| + C$$

or

$$\int \sec x \, dx = \ln |\tan(\tfrac{1}{4}\pi + \tfrac{1}{2}x)| + C \qquad (6)$$

Formula (6) is an alternative form of the formula

$$\int \sec x \, dx = \ln |\sec x + \tan x| + C$$

which is obtained by the trick of multiplying the numerator and denominator of the integrand by $\sec x + \tan x$.

It is worth noting that still another form for $\int \sec x \, dx$ can be obtained as follows:

$$\int \sec x \, dx = \int \frac{dx}{\cos x} = \int \frac{\cos x \, dx}{\cos^2 x} = \int \frac{\cos x \, dx}{1 - \sin^2 x}$$

Substituting $u = \sin x$, $du = \cos x \, dx$, we have

$$\int \sec x \, dx = \int \frac{du}{1 - u^2} = \frac{1}{2} \ln \left| \frac{1 + u}{1 - u} \right| + C = \ln \left| \frac{1 + \sin x}{1 - \sin x} \right|^{1/2} + C$$

Because $-1 \le \sin x \le 1$ for all x, $1 + \sin x$ and $1 - \sin x$ are nonnegative; hence, the absolute-value bars can be removed and we have

$$\int \sec x \, dx = \ln \left(\frac{1 + \sin x}{1 - \sin x} \right)^{1/2} + C = \ln \sqrt{\frac{1 + \sin x}{1 - \sin x}} + C \qquad (7)$$

Exercises 10.7

In Exercises 1 through 12, evaluate the indefinite integral.

1. $\displaystyle\int \frac{dx}{5 + 4 \cos x}$

2. $\displaystyle\int \frac{dx}{3 - 5 \sin x}$

3. $\displaystyle\int \frac{dx}{\cos x - \sin x + 1}$

4. $\displaystyle\int \frac{dx}{\sin x - \cos x + 2}$

5. $\displaystyle\int \frac{dx}{\sin x + \tan x}$

6. $\displaystyle\int \frac{dx}{\tan x - 1}$

7. $\displaystyle\int \frac{8 \, dx}{3 \cos 2x + 1}$

8. $\displaystyle\int \frac{\cos x \, dx}{3 \cos x - 5}$

9. $\displaystyle\int \frac{5 \, dx}{6 + 4 \sec x}$

10. $\displaystyle\int \frac{dx}{\sin x - \tan x}$

11. $\displaystyle\int \frac{dx}{2 \sin x + 2 \cos x + 3}$

12. $\displaystyle\int \frac{dx}{\cot 2x(1 - \cos 2x)}$

In Exercises 13 through 18, evaluate the definite integral.

13. $\displaystyle\int_0^{\pi/2} \frac{dx}{5 \sin x + 3}$

14. $\displaystyle\int_0^{\pi/4} \frac{8 \, dx}{\tan x + 1}$

15. $\displaystyle\int_{-\pi/3}^{\pi/2} \frac{3 \, dx}{2 \cos x + 1}$

16. $\displaystyle\int_0^{\pi/2} \frac{dx}{3 + \cos 2x}$

17. $\displaystyle\int_{\pi/6}^{\pi/3} \frac{3 \, dx}{2 \sin 2x + 1}$

18. $\displaystyle\int_0^{\pi/2} \frac{\sin 2x \, dx}{2 + \cos x}$

19. Show that formula (7) of this section is equivalent to the formula: $\int \sec x \, dx = \ln|\sec x + \tan x| + C$. (HINT: Multiply the numerator and denominator under the radical sign by $(1 + \sin x)$.)

20. By using the substitution $z = \tan \frac{1}{2}x$, prove that

$$\int \csc x \, dx = \tfrac{1}{2} \ln \left| \frac{1 - \cos x}{1 + \cos x} \right| + C$$

21. Show that the result in Exercise 20 is equivalent to the formula $\int \csc x \, dx = \ln|\csc x - \cot x| + C$. (HINT: Use a method similar to that suggested in the hint for Exercise 19.)

10.8 MISCELLANEOUS SUBSTITUTIONS

If an integrand involves fractional powers of a variable x, the integrand can be simplified by the substitution

$$x = z^n$$

where n is the lowest common denominator of the denominators of the exponents. This is illustrated by the following example.

EXAMPLE 1:   Find

$$\int \frac{\sqrt{x} \, dx}{1 + \sqrt[3]{x}}$$

SOLUTION: We let $x = z^6$; then $dx = 6z^5 \, dz$. So

$$\int \frac{x^{1/2} \, dx}{1 + x^{1/3}} = \int \frac{z^3(6z^5 \, dz)}{1 + z^2} = 6 \int \frac{z^8}{z^2 + 1} \, dz$$

Dividing the numerator by the denominator, we have

$$\int \frac{x^{1/2}\,dx}{1 + x^{1/3}} = 6 \int \left(z^6 - z^4 + z^2 - 1 + \frac{1}{z^2 + 1} \right) dz$$

$$= 6 \left(\tfrac{1}{7}z^7 - \tfrac{1}{5}z^5 + \tfrac{1}{3}z^3 - z + \tan^{-1} z \right) + C$$

$$= \tfrac{6}{7}x^{7/6} - \tfrac{6}{5}x^{5/6} + 2x^{1/2} - 6x^{1/6} + 6 \tan^{-1} x^{1/6} + C$$

No general rule can be given to determine a substitution that will result in a simpler integrand. Sometimes a substitution which does not rationalize the given integrand may still result in a simpler integrand.

EXAMPLE 2:   Evaluate

$$\int x^5 \sqrt{x^2 + 4}\ dx$$

SOLUTION: Let $z = \sqrt{x^2 + 4}$. Then $z^2 = x^2 + 4$, and $2z\,dz = 2x\,dx$. So we have

$$\int x^5 \sqrt{x^2 + 4}\ dx = \int (x^2)^2 \sqrt{x^2 + 4}\ x\,dx = \int (z^2 - 4)^2 z (z\,dz)$$

$$= \int (z^6 - 8z^4 + 16z^2)\ dz = \tfrac{1}{7}z^7 - \tfrac{8}{5}z^5 + \tfrac{16}{3}z^3 + C$$

$$= \tfrac{1}{105}z^3 [15z^4 - 168z^2 + 560] + C$$

$$= \tfrac{1}{105}(x^2 + 4)^{3/2}[15(x^2 + 4)^2 - 168(x^2 + 4) + 560] + C$$

$$= \tfrac{1}{105}(x^2 + 4)^{3/2}[15x^4 - 48x^2 + 128] + C$$

EXAMPLE 3:   Evaluate

$$\int \frac{dx}{x^2 \sqrt{27x^2 + 6x - 1}}$$

by using the reciprocal substitution $x = 1/z$.

SOLUTION: If $x = 1/z$, then $dx = -dz/z^2$. We have, then,

$$\int \frac{dx}{x^2 \sqrt{27x^2 + 6x - 1}} = \int \frac{\dfrac{-dz}{z^2}}{\left(\dfrac{1}{z^2}\right) \sqrt{\dfrac{27}{z^2} + \dfrac{6}{z} - 1}}$$

$$= -\int \frac{\sqrt{z^2}\ dz}{\sqrt{27 + 6z - z^2}}$$

$$= -\int \frac{|z|\ dz}{\sqrt{27 + 6z - z^2}}$$

$$= \begin{cases} -\displaystyle\int \frac{z\,dz}{\sqrt{27 + 6z - z^2}} & \text{if } z > 0 \\[4mm] \displaystyle\int \frac{z\,dz}{\sqrt{27 + 6z - z^2}} & \text{if } z < 0 \end{cases} \tag{1}$$

We evaluate $\int z\,dz/\sqrt{27 + 6z - z^2}$.

$$\int \frac{z\,dz}{\sqrt{27 + 6z - z^2}} = -\frac{1}{2} \int \frac{(-2z + 6)\,dz}{\sqrt{27 + 6z - z^2}} + 3 \int \frac{dz}{\sqrt{27 + 6z - z^2}}$$

$$= -\frac{1}{2} \cdot 2\sqrt{27 + 6z - z^2} + 3\int \frac{dz}{\sqrt{27 + 9 - (z^2 - 6z + 9)}}$$

$$= -\sqrt{27 + 6z - z^2} + 3\int \frac{dz}{\sqrt{36 - (z - 3)^2}}$$

$$= -\sqrt{27 + 6z - z^2} + 3 \sin^{-1}\frac{z - 3}{6} + C$$

$$= -\sqrt{27 + \frac{6}{x} - \frac{1}{x^2}} + 3 \sin^{-1}\frac{\frac{1}{x} - 3}{6} + C$$

$$= -\frac{\sqrt{27x^2 + 6x - 1}}{\sqrt{x^2}} + 3 \sin^{-1}\frac{1 - 3x}{6x} + C$$

$$= -\frac{\sqrt{27x^2 + 6x - 1}}{|x|} + 3 \sin^{-1}\frac{1 - 3x}{6x} + C \qquad (2)$$

Substituting from (2) into (1) we get

$$\int \frac{dx}{x^2\sqrt{27x^2 + 6x - 1}}$$

$$= \begin{cases} \dfrac{\sqrt{27x^2 + 6x - 1}}{|x|} - 3 \sin^{-1}\dfrac{1 - 3x}{6x} + C & \text{if } x > 0 \\[3ex] \dfrac{-\sqrt{27x^2 + 6x - 1}}{|x|} + 3 \sin^{-1}\dfrac{1 - 3x}{6x} + C & \text{if } x < 0 \end{cases}$$

$$= \begin{cases} \dfrac{\sqrt{27x^2 + 6x - 1}}{x} - 3 \sin^{-1}\dfrac{1 - 3x}{6x} + C & \text{if } x > 0 \\[3ex] \dfrac{\sqrt{27x^2 + 6x - 1}}{x} + 3 \sin^{-1}\dfrac{1 - 3x}{6x} + C & \text{if } x < 0 \end{cases}$$

Exercises 10.8

In Exercises 1 through 16, evaluate the indefinite integral.

1. $\displaystyle\int \frac{x\,dx}{3 + \sqrt{x}}$

2. $\displaystyle\int \frac{dx}{\sqrt[3]{x} - x}$

3. $\displaystyle\int \frac{dx}{x\sqrt{1 + 4x}}$

4. $\displaystyle\int x(1 + x)^{2/3}\,dx$

5. $\displaystyle\int \frac{\sqrt{1 + x}}{1 - x}\,dx$

6. $\displaystyle\int \frac{dx}{3 + \sqrt{x + 2}}$

7. $\displaystyle\int \frac{dx}{1 + \sqrt[3]{x - 2}}$

8. $\displaystyle\int \frac{dx}{2\sqrt[3]{x} + \sqrt{x}}$

9. $\displaystyle\int \frac{dx}{\sqrt{2x} - \sqrt{x + 4}}$

THIS DOESN'T WORK BY PARTIAL SUBSTITUTIONS

10. $\displaystyle\int \frac{dx}{\sqrt{\sqrt{x}+1}}$

11. $\displaystyle\int \frac{dx}{\sqrt{x}\sqrt[3]{x}(1+\sqrt[3]{x})^2}$

12. $\displaystyle\int \frac{dx}{x\sqrt{x^2+2x-1}}$

Use the reciprocal substitution $x = 1/z$.

13. Do Exercise 12 by using the substitution: $\sqrt{x^2+2x-1} = z - x$.

14. $\displaystyle\int \frac{dx}{x\sqrt{x^2+4x-4}}$

15. $\displaystyle\int \frac{dx}{x\sqrt{1+x+x^2}}$

16. $\displaystyle\int \frac{dx}{x^2\sqrt{1+2x+3x^2}}$

In Exercises 17 through 22, evaluate the definite integral.

17. $\displaystyle\int_0^4 \frac{dx}{1+\sqrt{x}}$

18. $\displaystyle\int_0^1 \frac{x^{3/2}}{x+1}\,dx$

19. $\displaystyle\int_{1/2}^2 \frac{dx}{\sqrt{2x}(\sqrt{2x}+9)}$

20. $\displaystyle\int_{16}^{18} \frac{dx}{\sqrt{x}-\sqrt[4]{x^3}}$

21. $\displaystyle\int_{1/3}^3 \frac{\sqrt[3]{x-x^3}}{x^4}\,dx$

22. $\displaystyle\int_1^2 \frac{dx}{x\sqrt{x^2+4x-4}}$

10.9 THE TRAPEZOIDAL RULE

We have seen previously how many problems can be solved by evaluating definite integrals. In evaluating a definite integral by the fundamental theorem of the calculus, it is necessary to find an indefinite integral (or antiderivative). There are many functions for which there is no known method for finding an indefinite integral. However, if a function f is continuous on a closed interval $[a, b]$, the definite integral $\int_a^b f(x)\,dx$ exists and is a unique number. In this section and the next we learn two methods for computing an approximate value of a definite integral. These methods can often give us fairly good accuracy and can be used for evaluating a definite integral by electronic computers. The first method is known as the *trapezoidal rule*.

We know that if f is continuous on the closed interval $[a, b]$, the definite integral $\int_a^b f(x)\,dx$ is the limit of a Riemann sum

$$\int_a^b f(x)\,dx = \lim_{\|\Delta\|\to 0} \sum_{i=1}^n f(\xi_i)\,\Delta_i x$$

The geometric interpretation of the Riemann sum

$$\sum_{i=1}^n f(\xi_i)\,\Delta_i x$$

is that it is equal to the sum of the measures of the areas of the rectangles lying above the x axis plus the negative of the measures of the areas of the rectangles lying below the x axis (see Fig. 6.3.3).

To approximate the measure of the area of a region let us use trapezoids instead of rectangles. Let us also use regular partitions and function values at equally spaced points.

Thus, if we are considering the definite integral $\int_a^b f(x)\ dx$, we divide the interval $[a, b]$ into n subintervals, each of length $\Delta x = (b - a)/n$. This gives the following $(n + 1)$ points: $x_0 = a$, $x_1 = a + \Delta x$, $x_2 = a + 2\ \Delta x$, $\ldots$, $x_i = a + i\ \Delta x$, $\ldots$, $x_{n-1} = a + (n - 1)\ \Delta x$, $x_n = b$. Then the definite integral $\int_a^b f(x)\ dx$ may be expressed as the sum of n definite integrals as follows:

$$\int_a^b f(x)\ dx = \int_a^{x_1} f(x)\ dx + \int_{x_1}^{x_2} f(x)\ dx$$
$$+ \cdots + \int_{x_{i-1}}^{x_i} f(x)\ dx + \cdots + \int_{x_{n-1}}^b f(x)\ dx \quad (1)$$

To interpret (1) geometrically, refer to Fig. 10.9.1 in which we have taken $f(x) \geq 0$ for all x in $[a, b]$; however, (1) holds for any function which is continuous on $[a, b]$.

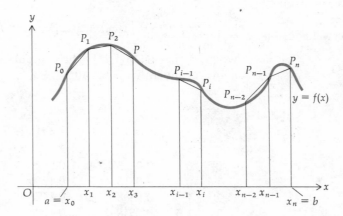

Figure 10.9.1

Then the integral $\int_a^{x_1} f(x)\ dx$ is the measure of the area of the region bounded by the x axis, the lines $x = a$ and $x = x_1$, and the portion of the curve from P_0 to P_1. This integral may be approximated by the measure of the area of the trapezoid formed by the lines $x = a$, $x = x_1$, P_0P_1, and the x axis. The measure of the area of this trapezoid is

$$\tfrac{1}{2}[f(x_0) + f(x_1)]\ \Delta x$$

Similarly, the other integrals on the right side of (1) may be approximated by the measure of the area of a trapezoid. Using the symbol "$\approx$" for "is approximately equal to," we have then for the ith integral

$$\int_{x_{i-1}}^{x_i} f(x)\ dx \approx \tfrac{1}{2}[f(x_{i-1}) + f(x_i)]\ \Delta x \quad (2)$$

So, using (2) for each of the integrals on the right side of (1), we have

$$\int_a^b f(x)\ dx \approx \tfrac{1}{2}[f(x_0) + f(x_1)]\ \Delta x + \tfrac{1}{2}[f(x_1) + f(x_2)]\ \Delta x + \cdots$$

$$+ \tfrac{1}{2}[f(x_{n-2}) + f(x_{n-1})]\ \Delta x + \tfrac{1}{2}[f(x_{n-1}) + f(x_n)]\ \Delta x$$

or

$$\int_a^b f(x)\ dx \approx \tfrac{1}{2}\Delta x[f(x_0) + 2f(x_1) + 2f(x_2) + \cdots + 2f(x_{n-1}) + f(x_n)] \quad (3)$$

Formula (3) is known as the *trapezoidal rule*.

EXAMPLE 1:   Compute

$$\int_0^3 \frac{dx}{16 + x^2}$$

by using the trapezoidal rule with $n = 6$. Express the result to three decimal places. Check by finding the exact value of the definite integral.

SOLUTION: Because $[a, b] = [0, 3]$ and $n = 6$, we have

$$\Delta x = \frac{b-a}{n} = \frac{3}{6} = 0.5$$

Therefore,

$$\int_0^3 \frac{dx}{16 + x^2} \approx \frac{0.5}{2}\ [f(x_0) + 2f(x_1) + 2f(x_2) + 2f(x_3) + 2f(x_4) + 2f(x_5) + f(x_6)]$$

where $f(x) = 1/(16 + x^2)$. The computation of the sum in brackets in the above is shown in Table 10.9.1. So,

Table 10.9.1

i	x_i	$f(x_i)$	k	$k \cdot f(x_i)$
0	0	0.0625	1	0.0625
1	0.5	0.0615	2	0.1230
2	1	0.0588	2	0.1176
3	1.5	0.0548	2	0.1096
4	2	0.0500	2	0.1000
5	2.5	0.0450	2	0.0900
6	3	0.0400	1	0.0400
sum:				0.6427

$$\int_0^3 \frac{dx}{16 + x^2} \approx 0.25(0.6427)$$

or

$$\int_0^3 \frac{dx}{16 + x^2} \approx 0.1607$$

Rounding the result off to three decimal places, we get

$$\int_0^3 \frac{dx}{16 + x^2} \approx 0.161$$

We check by finding the exact value. We have

$$\int_0^3 \frac{dx}{16 + x^2} = \frac{1}{4} \tan^{-1} \frac{x}{4} \Big]_0^3$$

$$= \tfrac{1}{4} \tan^{-1} \tfrac{3}{4} - \tfrac{1}{4} \tan^{-1} 0$$

$$= \tfrac{1}{4}(0.6435) - \tfrac{1}{4}(0)$$

$$= 0.1609 \quad \text{to four decimal places}$$

To consider the accuracy of the approximation of a definite integral by the trapezoidal rule, we prove first that as Δx approaches zero and n increases without bound, the limit of the approximation by the trapezoidal rule is the exact value of the definite integral. Let

$$T = \tfrac{1}{2} \Delta x [f(x_0) + 2f(x_1) + \cdots + 2f(x_{n-1}) + f(x_n)]$$

Then

$$T = [f(x_1) + f(x_2) + \cdots + f(x_n)] \Delta x + \tfrac{1}{2}[f(x_0) - f(x_n)] \Delta x$$

or

$$T = \sum_{i=1}^n f(x_i) \Delta x + \tfrac{1}{2}[f(a) - f(b)] \Delta x$$

Therefore, if $n \to +\infty$ and $\Delta x \to 0$, we have

$$\lim_{\Delta x \to 0} T = \lim_{\Delta x \to 0} \sum_{i=1}^n f(x_i) \Delta x + \lim_{\Delta x \to 0} \tfrac{1}{2}[f(a) - f(b)] \Delta x$$

$$= \int_a^b f(x) \, dx + 0$$

Thus, we can make the difference between T and the value of the definite integral as small as we please by taking n sufficiently large (and consequently Δx sufficiently small).

The following theorem, which is proved in advanced calculus, gives us a method for estimating the error obtained when using the trapezoidal rule. The error is denoted by ϵ_T.

10.9.1 Theorem   Let the function f be continuous on the closed interval $[a, b]$, and f' and f'' both exist on $[a, b]$. If

$$\epsilon_T = \int_a^b f(x) \, dx - T$$

where T is the approximate value of $\int_a^b f(x) \, dx$ found by the trapezoidal rule, then there is some number η in $[a, b]$ such that

$$\epsilon_T = -\tfrac{1}{12}(b - a)f''(\eta)(\Delta x)^2 \qquad (4)$$

EXAMPLE 2:   Find the bounds for the error in the result of Example 1.

SOLUTION: We first find the absolute minimum and absolute maximum values of $f''(x)$ on $[0, 3]$.

$$f(x) = (16 + x^2)^{-1}$$
$$f'(x) = -2x(16 + x^2)^{-2}$$
$$f''(x) = 8x^2(16 + x^2)^{-3} - 2(16 + x^2)^{-2} = (6x^2 - 32)(16 + x^2)^{-3}$$
$$f'''(x) = -6x(6x^2 - 32)(16 + x^2)^{-4} + 12x(16 + x^2)^{-3}$$
$$= 24x(16 - x^2)(16 + x^2)^{-4}$$

Because $f'''(x) > 0$ for all x in the open interval $(0, 3)$, then f'' is increasing on the open interval $(0, 3)$. Therefore, the absolute minimum value of f'' on $[0, 3]$ is $f''(0)$, and the absolute maximum value of f'' on $[0, 3]$ is $f''(3)$.

$$f''(0) = -\frac{1}{128} \quad \text{and} \quad f''(3) = \frac{22}{15{,}625}$$

Taking $\eta = 0$ on the right side of (4), we get

$$-\frac{3}{12}\left(-\frac{1}{128}\right)\frac{1}{4} \quad \text{or} \quad \frac{1}{2048}$$

Taking $\eta = 3$ on the right side of (4), we have

$$-\frac{3}{12}\left(\frac{22}{15{,}625}\right)\frac{1}{4} \quad \text{or} \quad -\frac{11}{45{,}000}$$

Therefore, if ϵ_T is the error in the result of Example 1, we conclude

$$-\frac{11}{45{,}000} \le \epsilon_T \le \frac{1}{2048}$$

or

$$-0.0002 \le \epsilon_T \le 0.0005$$

Exercises 10.9

In Exercises 1 through 14, compute the approximate value of the given definite integral by the trapezoidal rule for the indicated value of n. Express the result to three decimal places. In Exercises 1 through 8, find the exact value of the definite integral and compare the result with the approximation.

1. $\int_1^2 \frac{dx}{x}$; $n = 5$

2. $\int_2^{10} \frac{dx}{1 + x}$; $n = 8$

3. $\int_0^2 x^3 \, dx$; $n = 4$

4. $\int_0^2 x\sqrt{4 - x^2} \, dx$; $n = 8$

5. $\int_0^1 \frac{dx}{\sqrt{1 + x^2}}$; $n = 5$

6. $\int_2^3 \sqrt{1 + x^2} \, dx$; $n = 6$

7. $\int_0^\pi \sin x \, dx$; $n = 6$

8. $\int_0^\pi x \cos x^2 \, dx$; $n = 4$

9. $\int_{\pi/2}^{3\pi/2} \frac{\sin x}{x} \, dx$; $n = 6$

10. $\int_2^3 \ln(1 + x^2) \, dx$; $n = 4$

11. $\int_0^1 e^{x^2} \, dx$; $n = 5$

12. $\int_1^2 \frac{\sinh x}{x} \, dx$; $n = 4$

13. $\int_0^2 \sqrt{1+x^4}\, dx;\ n=6$
14. $\int_0^1 \sqrt{1+x^3}\, dx;\ n=4$

In Exercises 15 through 20, find the bounds for the error in the approximation of the indicated exercises.

15. Exercise 1
16. Exercise 2
17. Exercise 3

18. Exercise 6
19. Exercise 11
20. Exercise 12

21. The integral $\int_0^2 e^{-x^2}\, dx$ is very important in mathematical statistics. It is called a "probability integral" and it cannot be evaluated exactly in terms of elementary functions. Use the trapezoidal rule with $n=6$ to find an approximate value and express the result to three decimal places.

22. The region bounded by the curve whose equation is $y=e^{-x/2}$, the x axis, the y axis, and the line $x=2$ is revolved about the x axis. Find the volume of the solid of revolution generated. Approximate the definite integral by the trapezoidal rule to three decimal places, with $n=5$.

23. Show that the exact value of $\int_0^2 \sqrt{4-x^2}\, dx$ is π. Approximate the definite integral by the trapezoidal rule to three decimal places, with $n=8$, and compare the value so obtained with the exact value.

24. Show that the exact value of $\frac{1}{2}\int_0^3 dx/(x+1)$ is $\ln 2$. Approximate the definite integral by the trapezoidal rule with $n=6$ to three decimal places, and compare the value so obtained with the exact value of $\ln 2$ as given in a table.

10.10 SIMPSON'S RULE

Another method for approximating the value of a definite integral is provided by *Simpson's rule* (sometimes referred to as the *parabolic rule*). For a given partition of the closed interval $[a, b]$, Simpson's rule usually gives a better approximation than the trapezoidal rule. However, Simpson's rule requires more effort to apply. In the trapezoidal rule successive points on the graph of $y=f(x)$ are connected by segments of straight lines, whereas in Simpson's rule the points are connected by segments of parabolas. Before Simpson's rule is developed, we state and prove a theorem which will be needed.

10.10.1 Theorem

If $P_0(x_0, y_0)$, $P_1(x_1, y_1)$, and $P_2(x_2, y_2)$ are three noncollinear points on the parabola having the equation $y=Ax^2+Bx+C$, where $y_0 \geq 0$, $y_1 \geq 0$, $y_2 \geq 0$, $x_1=x_0+h$, and $x_2=x_0+2h$, then the measure of the area of the region bounded by the parabola, the x axis, and the lines $x=x_0$ and $x=x_2$ is given by

$$\tfrac{1}{3}h(y_0 + 4y_1 + y_2) \tag{1}$$

Figure 10.10.1

PROOF: The parabola whose equation is $y=Ax^2+Bx+C$ has a vertical axis. Refer to Fig. 10.10.1 which shows the region bounded by the parabola, the x axis, and the lines $x=x_0$ and $x=x_2$.

Because P_0, P_1, and P_2 are points on the parabola, their coordinates satisfy the equation of the parabola. So when we replace x_1 by x_0+h, and x_2 by x_0+2h, we have

$$y_0 = Ax_0^2 + Bx_0 + C$$

$$y_1 = A(x_0 + h)^2 + B(x_0 + h) + C = A(x_0^2 + 2hx_0 + h^2) + B(x_0 + h) + C$$
$$y_2 = A(x_0 + 2h)^2 + B(x_0 + 2h) + C = A(x_0^2 + 4hx_0 + 4h^2) + B(x_0 + 2h) + C$$

Therefore,

$$y_0 + 4y_1 + y_2 = A(6x_0^2 + 12hx_0 + 8h^2) + B(6x_0 + 6h) + 6C \qquad (2)$$

Now if K square units is the area of the region, then K can be computed by the limit of a Riemann sum, and we have

$$K = \lim_{\Delta x \to 0} \sum_{i=1}^{n} (A\xi_i^2 + B\xi_i + C)\, \Delta x$$

$$= \int_{x_0}^{x_0+2h} (Ax^2 + Bx + C)\, dx$$

or

$$K = \tfrac{1}{3}Ax^3 + \tfrac{1}{2}Bx^2 + Cx \Big]_{x_0}^{x_0+2h}$$

$$= \tfrac{1}{3}A(x_0 + 2h)^3 + \tfrac{1}{2}B(x_0 + 2h)^2 + C(x_0 + 2h) - (\tfrac{1}{3}Ax_0^3 + \tfrac{1}{2}Bx_0^2 + Cx_0)$$

$$= \tfrac{1}{3}h[A(6x_0^2 + 12hx_0 + 8h^2) + B(6x_0 + 6h) + 6C] \qquad (3)$$

Substituting from (2) in (3), we get

$$K = \tfrac{1}{3}h[y_0 + 4y_1 + y_2] \qquad \blacksquare$$

Let the function f be continuous on the closed interval $[a, b]$. Consider a regular partition of the interval $[a, b]$ of $2n$ subintervals ($2n$ is used instead of n because we want an even number of subintervals). The length of each subinterval is given by $\Delta x = (b - a)/2n$. Let the points on the curve $y = f(x)$ having these partitioning points as abscissas be denoted by $P_0(x_0, y_0), P_1(x_1, y_1), \dots, P_{2n}(x_{2n}, y_{2n})$; see Fig. 10.10.2 where $f(x) \geq 0$ for all x in $[a, b]$.

Figure 10.10.2

We approximate the segment of the curve $y = f(x)$ from P_0 to P_2 by the segment of the parabola with its vertical axis through P_0, P_1, and P_2. Then by Theorem 10.10.1 the measure of the area of the region bounded by this parabola, the x axis, and the lines $x = x_0$ and $x = x_2$, with $h = \Delta x$, is given by

$$\tfrac{1}{3} \Delta x (y_0 + 4y_1 + y_2) \quad \text{or} \quad \tfrac{1}{3} \Delta x [f(x_0) + 4f(x_1) + f(x_2)]$$

In a similar manner, we approximate the segment of the curve $y = f(x)$ from P_2 to P_4 by the segment of the parabola with its vertical axis through P_2, P_3, and P_4. The measure of the area of the region bounded by this parabola, the x axis, and the lines $x = x_2$ and $x = x_4$ is given by

$$\tfrac{1}{3} \Delta x (y_2 + 4y_3 + y_4) \quad \text{or} \quad \tfrac{1}{3} \Delta x [f(x_2) + 4f(x_3) + f(x_4)]$$

This process is continued until we have n such regions, and the measure of the area of the last region is given by

$$\tfrac{1}{3} \Delta x (y_{2n-2} + 4y_{2n-1} + y_{2n}) \quad \text{or} \quad \tfrac{1}{3} \Delta x [f(x_{2n-2}) + 4f(x_{2n-1}) + f(x_{2n})]$$

The sum of the measures of the areas of these regions approximates the measure of the area of the region bounded by the curve whose equation is $y = f(x)$, the x axis, and the lines $x = a$ and $x = b$. The measure of the area of this region is given by the definite integral $\int_a^b f(x)\, dx$. So we have as an approximation to the definite integral

$$\tfrac{1}{3} \Delta x [f(x_0) + 4f(x_1) + f(x_2)] + \tfrac{1}{3} \Delta x [f(x_2) + 4f(x_3) + f(x_4)] + \cdots$$
$$+ \tfrac{1}{3} \Delta x [f(x_{2n-4}) + 4f(x_{2n-3}) + f(x_{2n-2})] + \tfrac{1}{3} \Delta x [f(x_{2n-2}) + 4f(x_{2n-1}) + f(x_{2n})]$$

or

$$\int_a^b f(x)\, dx \approx \tfrac{1}{3} \Delta x [f(x_0) + 4f(x_1) + 2f(x_2) + 4f(x_3) + 2f(x_4) + \cdots$$
$$+ 2f(x_{2n-2}) + 4f(x_{2n-1}) + f(x_{2n})] \quad (4)$$

where $\Delta x = (b - a)/2n$.

Formula (4) is known as *Simpson's rule*.

EXAMPLE 1: Use Simpson's rule to approximate the value of

$$\int_0^1 \frac{dx}{x + 1}$$

with $2n = 4$. Give the result to four decimal places.

SOLUTION: Applying Simpson's rule with $2n = 4$, we have $\Delta x = \tfrac{1}{4}(1 - 0) = \tfrac{1}{4}$, and

$$\int_0^1 \frac{dx}{x + 1} \approx \frac{1}{12} [f(x_0) + 4f(x_1) + 2f(x_2) + 4f(x_3) + f(x_4)] \quad (5)$$

The computation of the expression in brackets on the right side of (5) is shown in Table 10.10.1, where $f(x) = 1/(x + 1)$.

Substituting the sum from Table 10.10.1 in (5), we get

$$\int_0^1 \frac{dx}{x + 1} \approx \frac{1}{12} (8.31906) \approx 0.69325^+$$

Table 10.10.1

i	x_i	$f(x_i)$	k	$k \cdot f(x_i)$
0	0	1.00000	1	1.00000
1	0.25	0.80000	4	3.20000
2	0.5	0.66667	2	1.33334
3	0.75	0.57143	4	2.28572
4	1	0.50000	1	0.50000
sum:				8.31906

Rounding off the result to four decimal places gives us

$$\int_0^1 \frac{dx}{x+1} \approx 0.6933$$

The exact value of $\int_0^1 dx/(x+1)$ is found as follows:

$$\int_0^1 \frac{dx}{x+1} = \ln |x+1| \Big]_0^1 = \ln 2 - \ln 1 = \ln 2$$

From a table of natural logarithms, the value of $\ln 2$ to four decimal places is 0.6931, which agrees with our approximation in the first three places. And the error in our approximation is -0.0002.

In applying Simpson's rule, the larger we take the value of $2n$, the smaller will be the value of Δx, and so geometrically it seems evident that the greater will be the accuracy of the approximation, because a parabola passing through three points of a curve that are close to each other will be close to the curve throughout the subinterval of width $2\,\Delta x$.

The following theorem, which is proved in advanced calculus, gives a method for determining the error in applying Simpson's rule. The error is denoted by ϵ_S.

10.10.2 Theorem   Let the function f be continuous on the closed interval $[a, b]$, and f', f'', f''', and $f^{(iv)}$ all exist on $[a, b]$. If

$$\epsilon_S = \int_a^b f(x)\ dx - S$$

where S is the approximate value of $\int_a^b f(x)\ dx$ found by Simpson's rule then there is some number η in $[a, b]$ such that

$$\epsilon_S = -\tfrac{1}{180}\,(b-a)f^{(iv)}(\eta)\,(\Delta x)^4 \tag{6}$$

EXAMPLE 2:   Find the bounds for the error in Example 1.

SOLUTION:

$$f(x) = (x+1)^{-1}$$

$$f'(x) = -1(x+1)^{-2}$$

$$f''(x) = 2(x+1)^{-3}$$

$$f'''(x) = -6(x+1)^{-4}$$

$$f^{(iv)}(x) = 24(x+1)^{-5}$$

$$f^{(v)}(x) = -120(x+1)^{-6}$$

Because $f^{(v)}(x) < 0$ for all x in $[0, 1]$, $f^{(iv)}$ is decreasing on $[0, 1]$. Thus, the absolute minimum value of $f^{(iv)}$ is at the right endpoint 1, and the absolute maximum value of $f^{(iv)}$ on $[0, 1]$ is at the left endpoint 0.

$$f^{(iv)}(0) = 24 \quad \text{and} \quad f^{(iv)}(1) = \tfrac{3}{4}$$

Substituting 0 for η in the right side of (6), we get

$$-\tfrac{1}{180}(b-a)f^{(iv)}(0)(\Delta x)^4 = -\tfrac{1}{180}(24)(\tfrac{1}{4})^4 = -\tfrac{1}{1920} = -0.00052$$

Substituting 1 for η in the right side of (6), we have

$$-\frac{1}{180}(b-a)f^{(iv)}(1)(\Delta x)^4 = -\frac{1}{180} \cdot \frac{3}{4}\left(\frac{1}{4}\right)^4 = -\frac{1}{61{,}440} = -0.00002$$

So we conclude that

$$-0.00052 \le \epsilon_S \le -0.00002 \tag{7}$$

The inequality (7) agrees with our previous discussion regarding the error in the approximation of $\int_0^1 dx/(x+1)$ by Simpson's rule because $-0.00052 < -0.0002 < -0.00002$.

If $f(x)$ is polynomial of degree three or less, then $f^{(iv)}(x) \equiv 0$ and therefore $\epsilon_S = 0$. In other words, Simpson's rule gives an exact result for a polynomial of the third degree or lower. This statement is geometrically obvious if $f(x)$ is of the second or first degree because in the first case the graph of $y = f(x)$ is a parabola, and in the second case the graph is a straight line (a degenerate parabola).

We apply Simpson's rule to the definite integral $\int_a^b f(x)\,dx$, where $f(x)$ is a third-degree polynomial, and take $2n = 2$. Here Simpson's rule gives an exact value for the definite integral. Because $2n = 2$, $x_0 = a$, $x_1 = \tfrac{1}{2}(a+b)$, and $x_2 = b$; and $\Delta x = \tfrac{1}{2}(b-a)$. So we have

$$\int_a^b f(x)\,dx = \frac{b-a}{6}\left[f(a) + 4f\left(\frac{a+b}{2}\right) + f(b)\right] \tag{8}$$

Formula (8) is known as the *prismoidal formula*.

In Sec. 7.4, we learned that $\int_a^b f(x)\, dx$ yields the measure of the volume of a solid for which $f(x)$ represents the measure of the area of a plane section formed by a plane perpendicular to the x axis at a distance x units from the origin. Therefore, if $f(x)$ is a polynomial of the third degree or less, the prismoidal formula gives the exact measure of the volume of such a solid.

EXAMPLE 3:   Find the volume of a right-circular cone of height h and base radius r by the prismoidal formula.

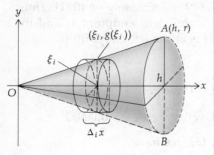

Figure 10.10.3

SOLUTION: Figure 10.10.3 illustrates a right-circular cone having its vertex at the origin and its axis along the positive side of the x axis. The area of the plane section ξ_i units from the origin is $\pi[g(\xi_i)]^2$ square units, where $g(x) = (r/h)x$, which is obtained from an equation of line OA in the xy plane. So if V cubic units is the volume of the right-circular cone, then

$$V = \lim_{||\Delta|| \to 0} \sum_{i=1}^n \pi[g(\xi_i)]^2\, \Delta_i x$$

$$= \int_0^h \pi[g(x)]^2\, dx$$

$$= \int_0^h \pi \frac{r^2}{h^2} x^2\, dx$$

$$= \frac{\pi r^2}{h^2} \int_0^h x^2\, dx$$

Evaluating $\int_0^h x^2\, dx$ by the prismoidal formula (8) with $f(x) = x^2$, $b = h$, $a = 0$, and $\frac{1}{2}(a+b) = \frac{1}{2}h$, we have

$$V = \frac{\pi r^2}{h^2} \cdot \frac{h}{6}\left(0 + 4 \cdot \frac{h^2}{4} + h^2\right) = \frac{\pi r^2}{6h}(2h^2) = \frac{1}{3}\pi r^2 h$$

Exercises 10.10

In Exercises 1 through 6, approximate the definite integral by Simpson's rule, using the indicated value of $2n$. Express the answers to three decimal places. Also, find the exact value of the definite integral and compare the results.

1. $\int_0^2 x^2\, dx;\ 2n = 4$

2. $\int_1^2 \frac{dx}{x+1};\ 2n = 8$

3. $\int_0^1 \frac{dx}{\sqrt{1+x^2}};\ 2n = 4$

4. $\int_{-1/2}^0 \frac{dx}{\sqrt{1-x^2}};\ 2n = 4$

5. $\int_0^1 \frac{dx}{x^2+x+1};\ 2n = 4$

6. $\int_0^\pi \sin x\, dx;\ 2n = 6$

In Exercises 7 through 9, find bounds for the error in the indicated exercise.

7. Exercise 1

8. Exercise 2

9. Exercise 6

Each of the definite integrals in Exercises 10 through 15 cannot be evaluated exactly in terms of elementary functions. Use Simpson's rule, with the indicated value of $2n$, to find an approximate value of the given definite integral. Express results to three decimal places.

10. $\displaystyle\int_0^{\pi/2} \sqrt{\sin x}\ dx;\ 2n = 6$

11. $\displaystyle\int_1^2 \frac{\sinh x}{x}\ dx;\ 2n = 4$

12. $\displaystyle\int_0^1 \sqrt[3]{1 - x^2}\ dx;\ 2n = 4$

13. $\displaystyle\int_0^2 e^{-x^2}\ dx;\ 2n = 4$

14. $\displaystyle\int_0^2 \sqrt{1 + x^4}\ dx;\ 2n = 6$

15. $\displaystyle\int_0^2 \frac{dx}{\sqrt{1 + x^3}};\ 2n = 8$

In Exercises 16 through 19, use the prismoidal formula to find the exact volume of the given solid.

16. A sphere of radius r.

17. A right-circular cylinder of height h and base radius r.

18. A right pyramid of height h and base a square having a side of length s.

19. A frustrum of a right-circular cone of height h_1 and base radii r_1 and r_2.

20. Show that the exact value of $4 \int_0^1 \sqrt{1 - x^2}\ dx$ is π. Then use Simpson's rule with $2n = 6$ to get an approximate value of $4 \int_0^1 \sqrt{1 - x^2}\ dx$ to three decimal places. Compare the results.

21. Find an approximate value to four decimal places of the definite integral $\int_0^{\pi/3} \log_{10} \cos x\ dx$, (a) by the prismoidal formula; (b) by Simpson's rule, taking $\Delta x = \frac{1}{12}\pi$; (c) by the trapezoidal rule, taking $\Delta x = \frac{1}{12}\pi$.

22. Find the area of the region enclosed by the loop of the curve whose equation is $y^2 = 8x^2 - x^5$. Evaluate the definite integral by Simpson's rule, with $2n = 8$. Express the result to three decimal places.

Review Exercises (Chapter 10)

In Exercises 1 through 62, evaluate the indefinite integral.

1. $\displaystyle\int \tan^2 4x \cos^4 4x\ dx$

2. $\displaystyle\int \frac{5x^2 - 3}{x^3 - x}\ dx$

3. $\displaystyle\int \frac{e^x\ dx}{\sqrt{4 - e^x}}$

4. $\displaystyle\int \frac{dx}{x^2 \sqrt{a^2 + x^2}}$

5. $\displaystyle\int \tan^{-1} \sqrt{x}\ dx$

6. $\displaystyle\int \frac{dt}{t^4 + 1}$

7. $\displaystyle\int \cos^2 \tfrac{1}{3}x\ dx$

8. $\displaystyle\int \frac{\sqrt{x + 1} + 1}{\sqrt{x + 1} - 1}\ dx$

9. $\displaystyle\int \frac{x^2 + 1}{(x - 1)^3}\ dx$

10. $\displaystyle\int \frac{dy}{\sqrt{y} + 1}$

11. $\displaystyle\int \sin x \sin 3x\ dx$

12. $\displaystyle\int \cos \theta \cos 2\theta\ d\theta$

13. $\displaystyle\int \frac{dx}{x + x^{4/3}}$

14. $\displaystyle\int t\sqrt{2t - t^2}\ dt$

15. $\displaystyle\int (\sec 3x + \csc 3x)^2\ dx$

16. $\displaystyle\int \frac{dx}{\sqrt{e^x - 1}}$

17. $\displaystyle\int \frac{2t^3 + 11t + 8}{t^3 + 4t^2 + 4t}\ dt$

18. $\displaystyle\int x^3 e^{3x}\ dx$

19. $\displaystyle\int \frac{x^4 + 1}{x^4 - 1}\ dx$

20. $\displaystyle\int \frac{\sqrt{x^2 - 4}}{x^2}\ dx$

21. $\displaystyle\int \sin^4 3x \cos^2 3x\ dx$

22. $\displaystyle\int t \sin^2 2t\ dt$

23. $\displaystyle\int \frac{dr}{\sqrt{3 - 4r - r^2}}$

24. $\displaystyle\int \frac{4x^2 + x - 2}{x^3 - 5x^2 + 8x - 4}\ dx$

25. $\displaystyle\int x \cosh x\ dx$

26. $\displaystyle\int \frac{y\ dy}{9 + 16y^4}$

27. $\displaystyle\int e^{t/2} \cos 2t\ dt$

28. $\displaystyle\int \frac{du}{u^{5/8} - u^{1/8}}$

29. $\displaystyle\int \frac{\sin x \cos x}{4 + \sin^4 x}\, dx$

30. $\displaystyle\int \frac{\sqrt{w - a}}{w}\, dw,\ a > 0$

31. $\displaystyle\int \sin^5 nx\, dx$

32. $\displaystyle\int \frac{dx}{x \ln x(\ln x - 1)}$

33. $\displaystyle\int \csc^5 x\, dx$

34. $\displaystyle\int \frac{dx}{5 + 4 \sec x}$

35. $\displaystyle\int \frac{2y^2 + 1}{y^3 - 6y^2 + 12y - 8}\, dy$

36. $\displaystyle\int \frac{x^5\, dx}{(x^2 - a^2)^3}$

37. $\displaystyle\int \frac{\sin x\, dx}{1 + \cos^2 x}$

38. $\displaystyle\int \frac{dx}{x\sqrt{x^2 + x + 1}}$

39. $\displaystyle\int \sqrt{4t - t^2}\, dt$

40. $\displaystyle\int \frac{dx}{\sqrt{1 - x + 3x^2}}$

41. $\displaystyle\int \frac{dx}{x^4 - x}$

42. $\displaystyle\int \frac{\sqrt{t} - 1}{\sqrt{t} + 1}\, dt$

43. $\displaystyle\int \frac{e^x\, dx}{\sqrt{4 - 9e^{2x}}}$

44. $\displaystyle\int \frac{dx}{5 + 4 \cos 2x}$

45. $\displaystyle\int \cot^2 3x \csc^4 3x\, dx$

46. $\displaystyle\int \frac{\cot x\, dx}{3 + 2 \sin x}$

47. $\displaystyle\int x^2 \sin^{-1} x\, dx$

48. $\displaystyle\int \frac{dx}{x\sqrt{5x - 6 - x^2}}$

49. $\displaystyle\int \frac{dx}{\sin x - 2 \csc x}$

50. $\displaystyle\int \cos x \ln(\sin x)\, dx$

51. $\displaystyle\int \frac{\cos 3t\, dt}{\sin 3t \sqrt{\sin^2 3t - \frac{1}{4}}}$

52. $\displaystyle\int \frac{dx}{(x^2 + 6x + 34)^2}$

53. $\displaystyle\int \frac{\sqrt{x^2 + a^2}}{x^4}\, dx$

54. $\displaystyle\int \sinh x \sin x\, dx$

55. $\displaystyle\int \frac{\sin^{-1} \sqrt{2t}}{\sqrt{1 - 2t}}\, dt$

56. $\displaystyle\int \ln(x^2 + 1)\, dx$

57. $\displaystyle\int \frac{dx}{\sqrt{2 + \sqrt{x - 1}}}$

58. $\displaystyle\int \frac{dx}{2 + 2 \sin x + \cos x}$

59. $\displaystyle\int \sqrt{\tan x}\, dx$

60. $\displaystyle\int \frac{dx}{\sqrt{1 + \sqrt[3]{x}}}$

61. $\displaystyle\int x^n \ln x\, dx$

62. $\displaystyle\int \tan^n x \sec^4 x\, dx,\ n > 0$

In Exercises 63 through 94, evaluate the definite integral.

63. $\displaystyle\int_0^\pi \sqrt{2 + 2 \cos x}\, dx$

64. $\displaystyle\int_{1/2}^1 \sqrt{\frac{1 - x}{x}}\, dx$

65. $\displaystyle\int_1^2 \frac{2x^2 + x + 4}{x^3 + 4x^2}\, dx$

66. $\displaystyle\int_0^1 \frac{dx}{e^x + e^{-x}}$

67. $\displaystyle\int_0^2 \frac{t^3\, dt}{\sqrt{4 + t^2}}$

68. $\displaystyle\int_0^{\pi/2} \sin^3 t \cos^3 t\, dt$

69. $\displaystyle\int_{-2}^{2\sqrt{3}} \frac{x^2\, dx}{(16 - x^2)^{3/2}}$

70. $\displaystyle\int_0^1 \frac{xe^x\, dx}{(1 + x)^2}$

71. $\displaystyle\int_0^1 \operatorname{sech}^2 x\, dx$

72. $\displaystyle\int_0^2 \frac{(1 - x)\, dx}{x^2 + 3x + 2}$

73. $\displaystyle\int_{\pi/12}^{\pi/8} \cot^3 2y\, dy$

74. $\displaystyle\int_0^2 (2^x + x^2)\, dx$

75. $\displaystyle\int_a^{a/2} \frac{\sqrt{(a^2 - x^2)^3}}{x^2}\, dx$

76. $\displaystyle\int_1^2 (\ln x)^2\, dx$

77. $\displaystyle\int_{\sqrt{3}/3}^1 \frac{(2x^2 - 2x + 1)\, dx}{x^3 + x}$

78. $\displaystyle\int_{\sqrt{2}/2}^1 \frac{x^3\, dx}{\sqrt{2 - x^2}}$

79. $\displaystyle\int_1^{10} \log_{10} \sqrt{ex}\, dx$

80. $\displaystyle\int_0^{2\pi} |\sin x - \cos x|\, dx$

81. $\int_1^2 \dfrac{x+2}{(x+1)^2}\,dx$

82. $\int_0^1 e^x \cosh x\,dx$

83. $\int_0^\pi |\cos^3 x|\,dx$

84. $\int_{-\pi/4}^{\pi/4} |\tan^5 x|\,dx$

85. $\int_0^{1/2} \dfrac{2x\,dx}{x^3 - x^2 - x + 1}$

86. $\int_0^1 x^3 \sqrt{1+x^2}\,dx$

87. $\int_0^{1/2} \dfrac{x\,dx}{\sqrt{1-4x^4}}$

88. $\int_0^{\pi/12} \dfrac{dx}{\cos^4 3x}$

89. $\int_0^1 \sqrt{2y + y^2}\,dy$

90. $\int_0^4 \dfrac{x^2\,dx}{x^3 + 4x^2 + 5x + 2}$

91. $\int_0^{\pi/2} \dfrac{dt}{12 + 13 \cos t}$

92. $\int_0^3 \dfrac{dr}{(r+2)\sqrt{r+1}}$

93. $\int_0^{16} \sqrt{4 - \sqrt{x}}\,dx$

94. $\int_{2\pi/3}^{\pi} \dfrac{\sin \frac{1}{2}t}{1 + \cos \frac{1}{2}t}\,dt$

In Exercises 95 and 96 find an approximate value for the given integral by using (a) the trapezoidal rule, and (b) Simpson's rule. Take four subintervals and express the results to three decimal places.

95. $\int_{1/10}^{1/2} \dfrac{\cos x}{x}\,dx$

96. $\int_1^{9/5} \sqrt{1 + x^3}\,dx$

In Exercises 97 and 98, obtain the given result by a hyperbolic function substitution.

97. $\int \dfrac{dx}{x^2 \sqrt{a^2 + x^2}} = -\dfrac{1}{a^2} \coth\left(\sinh^{-1}\dfrac{x}{a}\right) + C$

98. $\int \dfrac{dx}{(a^2 - x^2)^{3/2}} = \dfrac{1}{a^2} \sinh\left(\tanh^{-1}\dfrac{x}{a}\right) + C$

99. Find the length of the arc of the parabola $y^2 = 6x$ from $x = 6$ to $x = 12$.

100. Find the area of the region bounded by the curve $y = \sin^{-1} 2x$ and the line $x = \frac{1}{4}\sqrt{3}$.

101. Find the centroid of the solid of revolution obtained by revolving about the x axis the region bounded by the curve $y = e^{-x}$, the coordinate axes, and the line $x = 1$.

102. Find the centroid of the solid obtained by revolving the region of Exercise 101 about the y axis.

103. The vertical end of a water trough is 3 ft wide at the top, 2 ft deep, and has the form of the region bounded by the x axis and one arch of the curve $y = 2 \sin \frac{1}{3}\pi x$. If the trough is full of water, find the force due to liquid pressure on the end.

104. The linear density of a rod 3 ft long at a point x ft from one end is ke^{-3x} slugs/ft. Find the mass and center of mass of the rod.

105. Find the centroid of the region bounded by the curve $y = x \ln x$, the x axis, and the line $x = e$.

106. Find the area of the region enclosed by one loop of the curve $x^2 = y^4(1 - y^2)$.

107. Two chemicals A and B react to form a chemical C and the rate of change of the amount of C is proportional to the product of the amounts of A and B remaining at any given time. Initially there are 60 lb of chemical A and 60 lb of chemical B, and to form 5 lb of C, 3 lb of A and 2 lb of B are required. After 1 hr, 15 lb of C are formed. (a) If x lb of C are formed at t hr, find an expression for x in terms of t. (b) Find the amount of C after 3 hr.

108. A tank is in the shape of the solid of revolution formed by rotating about the x axis the region bounded by the curve $y = \ln x$, the x axis, and the lines $x = e$ and $x = e^2$. If the tank is full of water find the work done in pumping all the water to the top of the tank. Distance is measured in feet. Take the positive x axis vertically downward.

11

Polar Coordinates

11.1 THE POLAR COORDINATE SYSTEM

Figure 11.1.1

Figure 11.1.2

Figure 11.1.3

Until now we have located a point in a plane by its rectangular cartesian coordinates. There are other coordinate systems that can be used. Probably the next in importance to the cartesian coordinate system is the *polar coordinate system*. In the cartesian coordinate system, the coordinates are numbers called the abscissa and the ordinate, and these numbers are directed distances from two fixed lines. In the polar coordinate system, the coordinates consist of a distance and the measure of an angle relative to a fixed point and a fixed ray (or half line).

The fixed point is called the *pole* (or origin), and it is designated by the letter "O." The fixed ray is called the *polar axis* (or polar line), which we label *OA*. The ray *OA* is usually drawn horizontally and to the right, and it extends indefinitely (see Fig. 11.1.1).

Let *P* be any point in the plane distinct from *O*. Let θ be the radian measure of the directed angle *AOP*, positive when measured counterclockwise and negative when measured clockwise, having as its initial side the ray *OA* and, as its terminal side, the ray *OP*. Then if *r* is the undirected distance from *O* to *P* (i.e., $r = |\overline{OP}|$), one set of polar coordinates of *P* is given by *r* and θ, and we write these coordinates as (r, θ).

For example, the point $P(4, \tfrac{5}{6}\pi)$ is determined by first drawing the angle having radian measure $\tfrac{5}{6}\pi$, having its vertex at the pole and its initial side along the polar axis. Then the point on the terminal side, which is four units from the pole, is the point *P* (see Fig. 11.1.2). Another set of polar coordinates for this same point is $(4, -\tfrac{7}{6}\pi)$; see Fig. 11.1.3. Furthermore, the polar coordinates $(4, \tfrac{17}{6}\pi)$ would also yield the same point, as shown in Fig. 11.1.4.

$P\left(4, \frac{17}{6}\pi\right)$

$\frac{17}{6}\pi$

O A

Figure 11.1.4

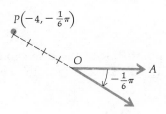

$P\left(-4, -\frac{1}{6}\pi\right)$

O A

$-\frac{1}{6}\pi$

Figure 11.1.5

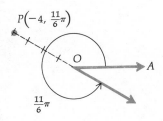

$P\left(-4, \frac{11}{6}\pi\right)$

O A

$\frac{11}{6}\pi$

Figure 11.1.6

Actually the coordinates $(4, \frac{5}{6}\pi + 2n\pi)$, where n is any integer, give the same point as $(4, \frac{5}{6}\pi)$. So a given point has an unlimited number of sets of polar coordinates. This is unlike the rectangular cartesian coordinate system because there is a one-to-one correspondence between the rectangular cartesian coordinates and the position of points in the plane, whereas there is no such one-to-one correspondence between the polar coordinates and the position of points in the plane. A further example is obtained by considering sets of polar coordinates for the pole. If $r = 0$ and θ is any real number, we have the pole, which is designated by $(0, \theta)$.

We consider polar coordinates for which r is negative. In this case, instead of the point being on the terminal side of the angle, it is on the extension of the terminal side, which is the ray from the pole extending in the direction opposite to the terminal side. So if P is on the extension of the terminal side of the angle of radian measure θ, a set of polar coordinates of P is (r, θ), where $r = -|\overline{OP}|$. For example, the point $(-4, -\frac{1}{6}\pi)$ shown in Fig. 11.1.5 is the same point as $(4, \frac{5}{6}\pi)$, $(4, -\frac{7}{6}\pi)$, and $(4, \frac{17}{6}\pi)$, as shown above. Still another set of polar coordinates for this same point is $(-4, \frac{11}{6}\pi)$; see Fig. 11.1.6.

The angle is usually measured in radians; thus, a set of polar coordinates of a point is an ordered pair of real numbers. To each ordered pair of real numbers there is a unique point having this set of polar coordinates. However, we have seen that a particular point can be given by an unlimited number of ordered pairs of real numbers. If the point P is not the pole, and r and θ are restricted so that $r > 0$ and $0 \le \theta < 2\pi$, then there is a unique set of polar coordinates for P.

EXAMPLE 1:   (a) Plot the point having polar coordinates $(3, -\frac{2}{3}\pi)$. Find another set of polar coordinates of this point for which (b) r is negative and $0 < \theta < 2\pi$; (c) r is positive and $0 < \theta < 2\pi$; (d) r is negative and $-2\pi < \theta < 0$.

SOLUTION: (a) The point is plotted by drawing the angle of radian measure $-\frac{2}{3}\pi$ in a clockwise direction from the polar axis. Because $r > 0$, P is on the terminal side of the angle, three units from the pole; see Fig. 11.1.7a. The answers to (b), (c), and (d) are, respectively, $(-3, \frac{1}{3}\pi)$, $(3, \frac{4}{3}\pi)$, and $(-3, -\frac{5}{3}\pi)$. They are illustrated in Fig. 11.1.7b, c, and d.

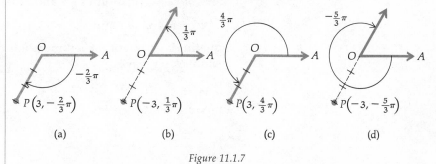

(a)   (b)   (c)   (d)

Figure 11.1.7

Often we wish to refer to both the rectangular cartesian coordinates and the polar coordinates of a point. To do this, we take the origin of the first system and the pole of the second system coincident, the polar

Figure 11.1.8

Figure 11.1.9

axis as the positive side of the x axis, and the ray for which $\theta = \frac{1}{2}\pi$ as the positive side of the y axis.

Suppose that P is a point whose representation in the rectangular cartesian coordinate system is (x, y) and (r, θ) is a polar-coordinate representation of P. We distinguish two cases: $r > 0$ and $r < 0$. In the first case, if $r > 0$, then the point P is on the terminal side of the angle of θ radians, and $r = |\overline{OP}|$. Such a case is shown in Fig. 11.1.8. Then $\cos \theta = x/|\overline{OP}| = x/r$ and $\sin \theta = y/|\overline{OP}| = y/r$; and so

$$x = r \cos \theta \quad \text{and} \quad y = r \sin \theta \tag{1}$$

In the second case, if $r < 0$, then the point P is on the extension of the terminal side and $r = -|\overline{OP}|$ (see Fig. 11.1.9). Then if Q is the point $(-x, -y)$, we have

$$\cos \theta = \frac{-x}{|\overline{OQ}|} = \frac{-x}{|\overline{OP}|} = \frac{-x}{-r} = \frac{x}{r}$$

So

$$x = r \cos \theta \tag{2}$$

Also,

$$\sin \theta = \frac{-y}{|\overline{OQ}|} = \frac{-y}{|\overline{OP}|} = \frac{-y}{-r} = \frac{y}{r}$$

Hence,

$$y = r \sin \theta \tag{3}$$

Formulas (2) and (3) are the same as the formulas in (1); thus, the formulas (1) hold in all cases.

From formulas (1) we can obtain the rectangular cartesian coordinates of a point when its polar coordinates are known. Also, from the formulas we can obtain a polar equation of a curve if a rectangular cartesian equation is known.

To obtain formulas which give a set of polar coordinates of a point when its rectangular cartesian coordinates are known, we square on both sides of each equation in (1) and obtain

$$x^2 = r^2 \cos^2 \theta \quad \text{and} \quad y^2 = r^2 \sin^2 \theta$$

Equating the sum of the left members of the above to the sum of the right members, we have

$$x^2 + y^2 = r^2 \cos^2 \theta + r^2 \sin^2 \theta$$

or, equivalently,

$$x^2 + y^2 = r^2 (\sin^2 \theta + \cos^2 \theta)$$

which gives us

$$x^2 + y^2 = r^2$$

and so

$$r = \pm \sqrt{x^2 + y^2} \tag{4}$$

From the equations in (1) and dividing, we have

$$\frac{r \sin \theta}{r \cos \theta} = \frac{y}{x}$$

or, equivalently,

$$\tan \theta = \frac{y}{x} \tag{5}$$

EXAMPLE 2: Plot the point whose polar coordinates are $(-6, \frac{7}{4}\pi)$ and find its rectangular cartesian coordinates.

Figure 11.1.10

SOLUTION: The point is plotted in Fig. 11.1.10. From (1) we have

$$x = r \cos \theta \qquad\qquad y = r \sin \theta$$

$$= -6 \cos \tfrac{7}{4}\pi \qquad = -6 \sin \tfrac{7}{4}\pi$$

$$= -6 \cdot \frac{\sqrt{2}}{2} \qquad\quad = -6 \left(-\frac{\sqrt{2}}{2}\right)$$

$$= -3\sqrt{2} \qquad\qquad = 3\sqrt{2}$$

So the point is $(-3\sqrt{2}, 3\sqrt{2})$.

The graph of an equation in polar coordinates r and θ consists of all those points and only those points P having at least one pair of coordinates which satisfy the equation. If an equation of a graph is given in polar coordinates, it is called a *polar equation* to distinguish it from a *cartesian equation*, which is the term used when an equation is given in rectangular cartesian coordinates.

EXAMPLE 3: Given a polar equation of a graph is

$$r^2 = 4 \sin 2\theta$$

find a cartesian equation.

SOLUTION: Because $r^2 = x^2 + y^2$ and $\sin 2\theta = 2 \sin \theta \cos \theta = 2(y/r)(x/r)$, from (1) we have, upon substituting in the given polar equation,

$$x^2 + y^2 = 4(2) \frac{y}{r} \cdot \frac{x}{r}$$

or

$$x^2 + y^2 = \frac{8xy}{r^2}$$

or, equivalently,

$$x^2 + y^2 = \frac{8xy}{x^2 + y^2}$$

or
$$(x^2 + y^2)^2 = 8xy$$

EXAMPLE 4:   Find (r, θ), if $r > 0$ and $0 \le \theta < 2\pi$ for the point whose rectangular cartesian coordinate representation is $(-\sqrt{3}, -1)$.

Figure 11.1.11

SOLUTION: The point $(-\sqrt{3}, -1)$ is plotted in Fig. 11.1.11. From (4), because $r > 0$, we have

$$r = \sqrt{1 + 3} = 2$$

From (5), $\tan \theta = -1/(-\sqrt{3})$, and since $\pi < \theta < \tfrac{3}{2}\pi$, we have

$$\theta = \tfrac{7}{6}\pi$$

So the point is $(2, \tfrac{7}{6}\pi)$.

EXAMPLE 5:   Given a cartesian equation of a graph is

$$x^2 + y^2 - 4x = 0$$

find a polar equation.

SOLUTION: Substituting $x = r \cos \theta$ and $y = r \sin \theta$ in

$$x^2 + y^2 - 4x = 0$$

we have

$$r^2 \cos^2 \theta + r^2 \sin^2 \theta - 4r \cos \theta = 0$$

or

$$r^2 - 4r \cos \theta = 0$$

or

$$r(r - 4 \cos \theta) = 0$$

Therefore,

$$r = 0 \quad \text{or} \quad r - 4 \cos \theta = 0$$

The graph of $r = 0$ is the pole. However, the pole is a point on the graph of $r - 4 \cos \theta = 0$ because $r = 0$ when $\theta = \tfrac{1}{2}\pi$. Therefore, a polar equation of the graph is

$$r = 4 \cos \theta$$

The graph of $x^2 + y^2 - 4x = 0$ is a circle. The equation may be written in the form

$$(x - 2)^2 + y^2 = 4$$

which is an equation of the circle with center at $(2, 0)$ and radius 2.

Exercises 11.1

In Exercises 1 through 6, plot the point having the given set of polar coordinates; then find another set of polar coordinates for the same point for which (a) $r < 0$ and $0 \leq \theta < 2\pi$; (b) $r > 0$ and $-2\pi < \theta \leq 0$; (c) $r < 0$ and $-2\pi < \theta \leq 0$.

1. $(4, \frac{1}{4}\pi)$

2. $(3, \frac{5}{6}\pi)$

3. $(2, \frac{1}{2}\pi)$

4. $(3, \frac{3}{2}\pi)$

5. $(\sqrt{2}, \frac{7}{4}\pi)$

6. $(2, \frac{4}{3}\pi)$

In Exercises 7 through 12, plot the point having the given set of polar coordinates; then give two other sets of polar coordinates of the same point, one with the same value of r and one with an r having opposite sign.

7. $(3, -\frac{2}{3}\pi)$

8. $(\sqrt{2}, -\frac{1}{4}\pi)$

9. $(-4, \frac{5}{6}\pi)$

10. $(-2, \frac{4}{3}\pi)$

11. $(-2, -\frac{5}{4}\pi)$

12. $(-3, -\pi)$

13. Find the rectangular cartesian coordinates of each of the following points whose polar coordinates are given: (a) $(3, \pi)$; (b) $(\sqrt{2}, -\frac{3}{4}\pi)$; (c) $(-4, \frac{2}{3}\pi)$; (d) $(-2, -\frac{1}{2}\pi)$; (e) $(-2, \frac{1}{4}\pi)$; (f) $(-1, -\frac{7}{6}\pi)$.

14. Find a set of polar coordinates for each of the following points whose rectangular cartesian coordinates are given. Take $r > 0$ and $0 \leq \theta < 2\pi$. (a) $(1, -1)$; (b) $(-\sqrt{3}, 1)$; (c) $(2, 2)$; (d) $(-5, 0)$; (e) $(0, -2)$; (f) $(-2, -2\sqrt{3})$.

In Exercises 15 through 22, find a polar equation of the graph having the given cartesian equation.

15. $x^2 + y^2 = a^2$

16. $x^3 = 4y^2$

17. $y^2 = 4(x + 1)$

18. $x^2 - y^2 = 16$

19. $(x^2 + y^2)^2 = 4(x^2 - y^2)$

20. $2xy = a^2$

21. $x^3 + y^3 - 3axy = 0$

22. $y = \dfrac{2x}{x^2 + 1}$

In Exercises 23 through 30, find a cartesian equation of the graph having the given polar equation.

23. $r^2 = 2 \sin 2\theta$

24. $r^2 \cos 2\theta = 10$

25. $r^2 = \cos \theta$

26. $r^2 = \theta$

27. $r^2 = 4 \cos 2\theta$

28. $r = 2 \sin 3\theta$

29. $r = \dfrac{6}{2 - 3 \sin \theta}$

30. $r = \dfrac{4}{3 - 2 \cos \theta}$

11.2 GRAPHS OF EQUATIONS IN POLAR COORDINATES

Let $r = f(\theta)$ be a polar equation of a curve. We first derive a formula for finding the slope of a tangent line to a polar curve at a point (r, θ) on the curve. Consider a rectangular cartesian coordinate system and a polar coordinate system in the same plane and having the positive side of the x axis coincident with the polar axis. In Sec. 11.1 we saw that the two sets of coordinates are related by the equations

$$x = r \cos \theta \quad \text{and} \quad y = r \sin \theta$$

x and y can be considered as functions of θ because $r = f(\theta)$. If we differentiate with respect to θ on both sides of these equations we get, by applying the chain rule,

$$\frac{dx}{d\theta} = \cos \theta \frac{dr}{d\theta} - r \sin \theta \tag{1}$$

and

$$\frac{dy}{d\theta} = \sin \theta \, \frac{dr}{d\theta} + r \cos \theta \tag{2}$$

If α is the radian measure of the inclination of the tangent line, then

$$\tan \alpha = \frac{dy}{dx}$$

and if $dx/d\theta \neq 0$, we have

$$\frac{dy}{dx} = \frac{\dfrac{dy}{d\theta}}{\dfrac{dx}{d\theta}} \tag{3}$$

Substituting from (1) and (2) into (3), we obtain

$$\frac{dy}{dx} = \frac{\sin \theta \, \dfrac{dr}{d\theta} + r \cos \theta}{\cos \theta \, \dfrac{dr}{d\theta} - r \sin \theta} \tag{4}$$

If $\cos \theta \neq 0$, we divide the numerator and the denominator of the right side of (4) by $\cos \theta$ and replace dy/dx by $\tan \alpha$, thereby giving us

$$\tan \alpha = \frac{\tan \theta \, \dfrac{dr}{d\theta} + r}{\dfrac{dr}{d\theta} - r \tan \theta} \tag{5}$$

EXAMPLE 1: Find the slope of the tangent line to the curve whose equation is $r = 1 - \cos \theta$ at the point $(1 - \frac{1}{2}\sqrt{2}, \frac{1}{4}\pi)$.

SOLUTION: Since $r = 1 - \cos \theta$, $dr/d\theta = \sin \theta$. So at the point $(1 - \frac{1}{2}\sqrt{2}, \frac{1}{4}\pi)$, $dr/d\theta = \frac{1}{2}\sqrt{2}$ and $\tan \theta = 1$; so from (5) we obtain

$$\tan \alpha = \frac{(1)\frac{1}{2}\sqrt{2} + (1 - \frac{1}{2}\sqrt{2})}{\frac{1}{2}\sqrt{2} - (1 - \frac{1}{2}\sqrt{2})(1)} = \frac{1}{\sqrt{2} - 1} = \sqrt{2} + 1$$

If we are to draw a sketch of the graph of a polar equation, it will be helpful to consider properties of symmetry of the graph. In Sec. 1.3 (Definition 1.3.4) we learned that two points P and Q are said to be symmetric with respect to a line if and only if the line is the perpendicular bisector of the line segment PQ, and that two points P and Q are said to be symmetric with respect to a third point if and only if the third point is the midpoint of the line segment PQ. Therefore, the points $(2, \frac{1}{3}\pi)$ and $(2, \frac{2}{3}\pi)$ are symmetric with respect to the $\frac{1}{2}\pi$ axis and the point $(2, \frac{1}{3}\pi)$ and $(2, -\frac{2}{3}\pi)$ are symmetric with respect to the pole. We also learned (Definition 1.3.5) that the graph of an equation is symmetric with respect to a line l if and only if for every point P on the graph there is a point Q, also on the graph, such that P and Q are symmetric with respect to l. Similarly, the graph of an equation is symmetric with respect to a point R if and only if for every point P on the graph there is a point S, also on the graph, such that P and S are symmetric with respect to R. We have the following rules of symmetry for graphs of polar equations.

Rule 1. If for an equation in polar coordinates an equivalent equation is obtained when (r, θ) is replaced by either $(r, -\theta + 2n\pi)$ or $(-r, \pi - \theta + 2n)$, where n is any integer, the graph of the equation is symmetric with respect to the polar axis.

Rule 2. If for an equation in polar coordinates an equivalent equation is obtained when (r, θ) is replaced by either $(r, \pi - \theta + 2n\pi)$ or $(-r, -\theta + 2n\pi)$, where n is any integer, the graph of the equation is symmetric with respect to the $\frac{1}{2}\pi$ axis.

Rule 3. If for an equation in polar coordinates an equivalent equation is obtained when (r, θ) is replaced by either $(-r, \theta + 2n\pi)$ or $(r, \pi + \theta + 2n\pi)$, where n is any integer, the graph of the equation is symmetric with respect to the pole.

The proof of Rule 1 is as follows: If the point $P(r, \theta)$ is a point on the graph of an equation, then the graph is symmetric with respect to the polar axis if there is a point $P_1(r_1, \theta_1)$ on the graph so that the polar axis is the perpendicular bisector of the line segment P_1P (see Fig. 11.2.1). So if $r_1 = r$, then θ_1 must equal $-\theta + 2n\pi$, where n is an integer. And if $r_1 = -r$, then θ_1 must be $\pi - \theta + 2n\pi$. The proofs of Rules 2 and 3 are similar and are omitted.

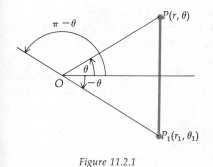

Figure 11.2.1

EXAMPLE 2: Test for symmetry with respect to the polar axis, the $\frac{1}{2}\pi$ axis, and the pole, the graph of the equation $r = 4 \cos 2\theta$.

SOLUTION: Using Rule 1 to test for symmetry with respect to the polar axis, we replace (r, θ) by $(r, -\theta)$ and obtain $r = 4 \cos(-2\theta)$, which is equivalent to $r = 4 \cos 2\theta$. So the graph is symmetric with respect to the polar axis.

Using Rule 2 to test for symmetry with respect to the $\frac{1}{2}\pi$ axis, we replace (r, θ) by $(r, \pi - \theta)$ and get $r = 4 \cos(2(\pi - \theta))$ or, equivalently, $r = 4 \cos(2\pi - 2\theta)$, which is equivalent to the equation $r = 4 \cos 2\theta$. Therefore, the graph is symmetric with respect to the $\frac{1}{2}\pi$ axis.

To test for symmetry with respect to the pole, we replace (r, θ) by $(-r, \theta)$ and obtain the equation $-r = 4 \cos 2\theta$, which is not equivalent to the equation. However, we must also determine if the other set of coordinates works. We replace (r, θ) by $(r, \pi + \theta)$ and obtain $r = 4 \cos 2(\pi + \theta)$ or, equivalently, $r = 4 \cos(2\pi + 2\theta)$, which is equivalent to the equation $r = 4 \cos 2\theta$. Therefore, the graph is symmetric with respect to the pole.

When drawing a sketch of a graph, it is desirable to determine if the pole is on the graph. This is done by substituting 0 for r and solving for θ. Also, it is advantageous to plot the points for which r has a relative maximum or relative minimum value. As a further aid in plotting, if a curve contains the pole it is sometimes helpful to find equations of the tangent lines to the graph at the pole.

To find the slope of the tangent line at the pole we use formula (5) with $r = 0$. If $dr/d\theta \neq 0$, we have

$$\tan \alpha = \tan \theta \qquad (6)$$

From (6) we conclude that the values of θ, where $0 \leq \theta < \pi$, which satisfy a polar equation of the curve when $r = 0$, are the inclinations of the tangent lines to the curve at the pole. So if $\theta_1, \theta_2, \ldots, \theta_k$ are these values of θ, then equations of the tangent lines to the curve at the pole are

$$\theta = \theta_1, \theta = \theta_2, \ldots, \theta = \theta_k$$

EXAMPLE 3:   Draw a sketch of the graph of

$$r = 1 - 2 \cos \theta$$

SOLUTION: Replacing (r, θ) by $(r, -\theta)$, we obtain an equivalent equation. Thus, the graph is symmetric with respect to the polar axis.

Table 11.2.1 gives the coordinates of some points on the graph. From these points we draw half of the graph and the remainder is drawn from its symmetry with respect to the polar axis.

If $r = 0$, we obtain $\cos \theta = \frac{1}{2}$, and if $0 \leq \theta < \pi$, $\theta = \frac{1}{3}\pi$. Therefore, the point $(0, \frac{1}{3}\pi)$ is on the graph, and an equation of the tangent line there

Table 11.2.1

θ	0	$\frac{1}{6}\pi$	$\frac{1}{3}\pi$	$\frac{1}{2}\pi$	$\frac{2}{3}\pi$	$\frac{5}{6}\pi$	π
r	-1	$1 - \sqrt{3}$	0	1	2	$1 + \sqrt{3}$	3

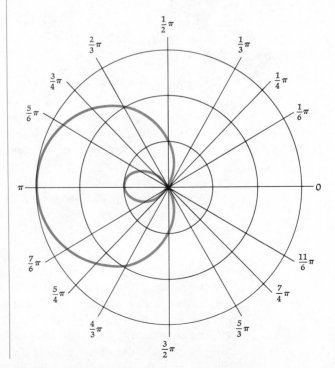

Figure 11.2.2

is $\theta = \frac{1}{3}\pi$. A sketch of the graph is shown in Fig. 11.2.2. It is called a *limaçon*.

The graph of an equation of the form

$$r = a \pm b \cos \theta$$

or

$$r = a \pm b \sin \theta$$

is a limaçon. If $b > a$, as is the case in Example 3, the limaçon has a loop. If $a = b$, the limaçon is a *cardioid*, which is heartshaped. If $a > b$, the limaçon has a shape similar to the one in Example 4.

EXAMPLE 4:   Draw a sketch of the graph of

$$r = 3 + 2 \sin \theta$$

SOLUTION: The graph is symmetric with respect to the $\frac{1}{2}\pi$ axis because if (r, θ) is replaced by $(r, \pi - \theta)$, an equivalent equation is obtained.

Table 11.2.2 gives the coordinates of some of the points on the graph.

Table 11.2.2

θ	0	$\frac{1}{6}\pi$	$\frac{1}{3}\pi$	$\frac{1}{2}\pi$	π	$\frac{7}{6}\pi$	$\frac{4}{3}\pi$	$\frac{3}{2}\pi$
r	3	4	$3 + \sqrt{3}$	5	3	2	$3 - \sqrt{3}$	1

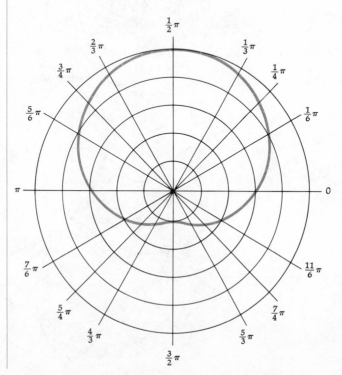

Figure 11.2.3

A sketch of the graph is shown in Fig. 11.2.3. It is drawn by plotting the points whose coordinates are given in Table 11.2.2 and using the symmetry property.

The graph of an equation of the form

$$r = a \cos n\theta \quad \text{or} \quad r = a \sin n\theta$$

is a *rose*, having n leaves if n is odd and $2n$ leaves if n is even.

EXAMPLE 5: Draw a sketch of the four-leafed rose

$$r = 4 \cos 2\theta$$

SOLUTION: In Example 2 we proved that the graph is symmetric with respect to the polar axis, the $\frac{1}{2}\pi$ axis, and the pole. Substituting 0 for r in the given equation, we get

$$\cos 2\theta = 0$$

from which we obtain, for $0 \leq \theta < 2\pi$, $\theta = \frac{1}{4}\pi, \frac{3}{4}\pi, \frac{7}{4}\pi$, and $\frac{11}{4}\pi$.

Table 11.2.3 gives values of r for some values of θ from 0 to $\frac{1}{2}\pi$. From these values and the symmetry properties, we draw a sketch of the graph as shown in Fig. 11.2.4.

Table 11.2.3

θ	0	$\frac{1}{12}\pi$	$\frac{1}{6}\pi$	$\frac{1}{4}\pi$	$\frac{1}{3}\pi$	$\frac{5}{12}\pi$	$\frac{1}{2}\pi$
r	4	$2\sqrt{3}$	2	0	-2	$-2\sqrt{3}$	-4

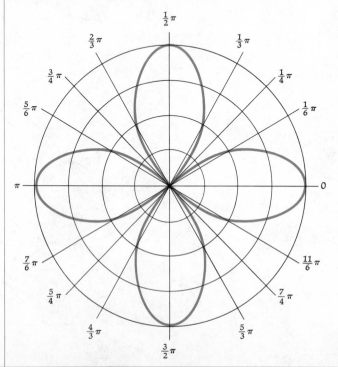

Figure 11.2.4

The graph of the equation

$$\theta = C$$

where C is any constant, is a straight line through the pole and makes an angle of C radians with the polar axis. The same line is given by the equation

$$\theta = C \pm n\pi$$

where n is any integer.

In general, the polar form of an equation of a line is not so simple as the cartesian form. However, if the line is parallel to either the polar axis or the $\frac{1}{2}\pi$ axis, the equation is fairly simple.

If a line is parallel to the polar axis and contains the point B whose cartesian coordinates are $(0, b)$ and polar coordinates are $(b, \frac{1}{2}\pi)$, then a cartesian equation is $y = b$. If we replace y by $r \sin \theta$, we have

$$r \sin \theta = b$$

which is a polar equation of any line parallel to the polar axis. If b is positive, the line is above the polar axis. If b is negative, it is below the polar axis.

If a line is parallel to the $\frac{1}{2}\pi$ axis or, equivalently, perpendicular to the polar axis, and goes through the point A whose cartesian coordinates are $(a, 0)$ and polar coordinates are $(a, 0)$, a cartesian equation is $x = a$. Replacing x by $r \cos \theta$, we obtain

$$r \cos \theta = a$$

which is an equation of any line perpendicular to the polar axis. If a is positive, the line is to the right of the $\frac{1}{2}\pi$ axis. If a is negative, the line is to the left of the $\frac{1}{2}\pi$ axis.

EXAMPLE 6:   Draw a sketch of the graph of each of the following equations: (a) $r \sin \theta = 3$; (b) $r \cos \theta = 3$; (c) $r \sin \theta = -3$; (d) $r \cos \theta = -3$.

SOLUTION: Each graph is a line, and they are shown in Fig. 11.2.5a,b, c, and d.

Figure 11.2.5

The graph of the equation

$$r = C$$

where C is any constant, is a circle whose center is at the pole and radius is $|C|$. The same circle is given by the equation

$$r = -C$$

As was the case with the straight line, the general polar equation of a circle is not so simple as the cartesian form. However, there are special cases of an equation of a circle which are worth considering in polar form.

If a circle has its center on the polar axis at the point having polar coordinates $(a, 0)$ and is tangent to the $\frac{1}{2}\pi$ axis, then its radius is $|a|$. The points of intersection of such a circle with the polar axis are the pole $(0, 0)$ and the point $(2a, 0)$ (see Fig. 11.2.6). Then if $P(r, \theta)$ is any point on the circle, the angle at P inscribed in the circle is a right angle. Therefore, $\cos \theta = r/2a$ or, equivalently,

$$r = 2a \cos \theta$$

which is a polar equation of the circle having its center on the polar axis or its extension, and tangent to the $\frac{1}{2}\pi$ axis. If a is a positive number, the circle is to the right of the pole. If a is a negative number, the circle is to the left of the pole.

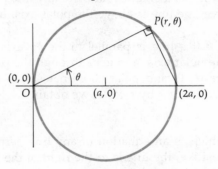

Figure 11.2.6

In a similar manner, it may be shown that

$$r = 2b \sin \theta$$

is a polar equation of the circle having its center on the $\frac{1}{2}\pi$ axis or its extension, and tangent to the polar axis. If b is positive, the circle is above the pole. If b is negative, the circle is below the pole.

EXAMPLE 7: Draw a sketch of the graph of

$$r = \theta \qquad \theta \geq 0$$

SOLUTION: When $\theta = n\pi$, where n is any integer, the graph intersects the polar axis or its extension, and when $\theta = \frac{1}{2}n\pi$, where n is any odd integer, the graph intersects the $\frac{1}{2}\pi$ axis or its extension. When $r = 0$, $\theta = 0$; thus, the tangent line to the curve at the pole is the polar axis. A sketch of the graph is shown in Fig. 11.2.7. The curve is called a *spiral of Archimedes*.

Figure 11.2.7

Exercises 11.2

In Exercises 1 through 40, draw a sketch of the graph of the given equation.

1. $r \cos \theta = 4$

2. $r \sin \theta = 2$

3. $r = 4 \cos \theta$

4. $r = 2 \sin \theta$

5. $\theta = 5$

6. $\theta = -4$

7. $r = 5$

8. $r = -4$

9. $r \sin \theta = -4$

10. $r \cos \theta = -5$

11. $r = -4 \sin \theta$

12. $r = -5 \cos \theta$

13. $r = e^{\theta}$ (logarithmic spiral)

14. $r = e^{\theta/3}$ (logarithmic spiral)

15. $r = 1/\theta$ (reciprocal spiral)

16. $r = 2\theta$ (spiral of Archimedes)

17. $r = 2 \sin 3\theta$ (three-leafed rose)

18. $r = 3 \cos 2\theta$ (four-leafed rose)

19. $r = 2 \cos 4\theta$ (eight-leafed rose)

20. $r = 4 \sin 5\theta$ (five-leafed rose)

21. $r = 4 \sin 2\theta$ (four-leafed rose)

22. $r = 3 \cos 3\theta$ (three-leafed rose)

23. $r = 2 + 2 \sin \theta$ (cardioid)

24. $r = 3 + 3 \cos \theta$ (cardioid)

25. $r = 4 - 4 \cos \theta$ (cardioid)

26. $r = 3 - 3 \sin \theta$ (cardioid)

27. $r = 4 - 3 \cos \theta$ (limaçon)

28. $r = 3 - 4 \cos \theta$ (limaçon)

29. $r = 4 + 2 \sin \theta$ (limaçon)

30. $r = 2 - 3 \sin \theta$ (limaçon)

31. $r^2 = 9 \sin 2\theta$ (lemniscate)

32. $r^2 = -4 \sin 2\theta$ (lemniscate)

33. $r^2 = -25 \cos 2\theta$ (lemniscate)

34. $r^2 = 16 \cos 2\theta$ (lemniscate)

35. $r = 2 \sin \theta \tan \theta$ (cissoid)

36. $(r - 2)^2 = 8\theta$ (parabolic spiral)

37. $r = 2 \sec \theta - 1$ (conchoid of Nicomedes)

38. $r = 2 \csc \theta + 3$ (conchoid of Nicomedes)

39. $r = |\sin 2\theta|$

40. $r = 2|\cos \theta|$

In Exercises 41 through 44, find an equation of each of the tangent lines to the given curve at the pole.

41. $r = 4 \cos \theta + 2$

42. $r = 2 \sin 3\theta$

43. $r^2 = 4 \cos 2\theta$

44. $r^2 = 9 \sin 2\theta$

45. Find the slope of the tangent line to the curve $r = 4$ at $(4, \frac{1}{4}\pi)$.

46. Find a polar equation of the tangent line to the curve $r = -6 \sin \theta$ at the point $(6, \frac{3}{2}\pi)$.

11.3 INTERSECTION OF GRAPHS IN POLAR COORDINATES

To find the points of intersection of two curves whose equations are in cartesian coordinates, we solve the two equations simultaneously. The common solutions give all the points of intersection. However, because a point has an unlimited number of sets of polar coordinates, it is possible to have as the intersection of two curves a point for which no single pair of polar coordinates satisfies both equations. This is illustrated in the following example.

EXAMPLE 1:   Draw sketches of the graphs of $r = 2 \sin 2\theta$ and $r = 1$, and find the points of intersection.

SOLUTION: The graph of $r = 2 \sin 2\theta$ is a four-leafed rose. The graph of $r = 1$ is the circle with its center at the pole and radius 1. Sketches of the graphs are shown in Fig. 11.3.1. Solving the two equations simultaneously, we have $1 = 2 \sin 2\theta$ or $\sin 2\theta = \frac{1}{2}$. Therefore, we get

$$2\theta = \tfrac{1}{6}\pi, \tfrac{5}{6}\pi, \tfrac{13}{6}\pi, \text{ and } \tfrac{17}{6}\pi$$

or

$$\theta = \tfrac{1}{12}\pi, \tfrac{5}{12}\pi, \tfrac{13}{12}\pi, \text{ and } \tfrac{17}{12}\pi$$

Hence, we obtain the points of intersection $(1, \frac{1}{12}\pi)$, $(1, \frac{5}{12}\pi)$, $(1, \frac{13}{12}\pi)$, and $(1, \frac{17}{12}\pi)$. We notice in Fig. 11.3.1 that eight points of intersection are shown. The other four points are obtained if we take another form of the equation of the circle $r = 1$; that is, consider the equation $r = -1$, which is the same circle. Solving this equation simultaneously with the equation of the four-leafed rose, we have $\sin 2\theta = -\frac{1}{2}$. Then we get

$$2\theta = \tfrac{7}{6}\pi, \tfrac{11}{6}\pi, \tfrac{19}{16}\pi, \text{ and } \tfrac{23}{6}\pi$$

or

$$\theta = \tfrac{7}{12}\pi, \tfrac{11}{12}\pi, \tfrac{19}{12}\pi, \text{ and } \tfrac{23}{12}\pi$$

Thus, we have the four points $(-1, \frac{7}{12}\pi)$, $(-1, \frac{11}{12}\pi)$, $(-1, \frac{19}{12}\pi)$, and $(-1, \frac{23}{12}\pi)$.

Incidentally, $(-1, \frac{7}{12}\pi)$ also can be written as $(1, \frac{19}{12}\pi)$, $(-1, \frac{11}{12}\pi)$ can be written as $(1, \frac{23}{12}\pi)$, $(-1, \frac{19}{12}\pi)$ can be written as $(1, \frac{7}{12}\pi)$, and $(-1, \frac{23}{12}\pi)$ can be written as $(1, \frac{11}{12}\pi)$.

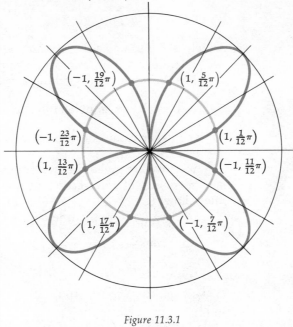

Figure 11.3.1

Because $(0, \theta)$ represents the pole for any θ, we determine if the pole is a point of intersection by setting $r = 0$ in each equation and solving for θ.

Often the coordinates of the points of intersection of two curves can be found directly from their graphs. However, the following is a general method.

If an equation of a curve in polar coordinates is given by

$$r = f(\theta) \tag{1}$$

then the same curve is given by

$$(-1)^n r = f(\theta + n\pi) \tag{2}$$

where n is any integer. In particular, consider the curves of Example 1. The graph of $r = 2 \sin 2\theta$ also has the equation (by taking $n = 1$ in Eq. (2))

$$(-1)r = 2 \sin 2(\theta + \pi)$$

or, equivalently,

$$-r = 2 \sin 2\theta$$

If we take $n = 2$ in Eq. (2), the graph of $r = 2 \sin 2\theta$ also has the equation

$$(-1)^2 r = 2 \sin 2(\theta + 2\pi)$$

or, equivalently,

$$r = 2 \sin 2\theta$$

which is the same as the original equation. Taking n any other integer, we get either $r = 2 \sin 2\theta$ or $r = -2 \sin 2\theta$. The graph of the equation $r = 1$ also has the equation (by taking $n = 1$ in Eq. (2))

$$(-1)r = 1 \quad \text{or, equivalently,} \quad r = -1$$

Other integer values of n in (2) applied to the equation $r = 1$ give either $r = 1$ or $r = -1$.

So if we are given the two equations $r = f(\theta)$ and $r = g(\theta)$, we obtain all the points of intersection of the graphs of the equations by doing the following.

(a) Use (2) to determine all the distinct equations of the two curves:

$$r = f_1(\theta), \ r = f_2(\theta), \ r = f_3(\theta), \ \ldots \tag{3}$$

$$r = g_1(\theta), r = g_2(\theta), r = g_3(\theta), \ \ldots \tag{4}$$

(b) Solve each equation in (3) simultaneously with each equation in (4).

(c) Check to see if the pole is a point of intersection by setting $r = 0$ in each equation, thereby giving

$$f(\theta) = 0 \quad \text{and} \quad g(\theta) = 0 \tag{5}$$

If Eqs. (5) each have a solution for θ, not necessarily the same, then the pole lies on both curves.

EXAMPLE 2: Find the points of intersection of the two curves $r = 2 - 2 \cos \theta$ and $r = 2 \cos \theta$. Draw sketches of their graphs.

SOLUTION: To find other equations of the curve represented by $r = 2 - 2 \cos \theta$, we have

$$(-1)r = 2 - 2 \cos(\theta + \pi)$$

or

$$-r = 2 + 2 \cos \theta$$

$$(-1)^2 r = 2 - 2 \cos(\theta + 2\pi)$$

or

$$r = 2 - 2 \cos \theta$$

which is the same as the original equation.

In a similar manner, we find other equations of the curve given by $r = 2 \cos \theta$:

$$(-1)r = 2 \cos(\theta + \pi)$$

or

$$-r = -2 \cos \theta$$

$$r = 2 \cos \theta$$

which is the same as the original equation.

So there are two possible equations for the first curve, $r = 2 - 2 \cos \theta$ and $-r = 2 + 2 \cos \theta$, and one equation for the second curve, $r = 2 \cos \theta$. Solving simultaneously $r = 2 - 2 \cos \theta$ and $r = 2 \cos \theta$ gives

$$2 \cos \theta = 2 - 2 \cos \theta$$

$$4 \cos \theta = 2$$

$$\cos \theta = \tfrac{1}{2}$$

Thus, $\theta = \tfrac{1}{3}\pi$ and $\tfrac{5}{3}\pi$, giving the points $(1, \tfrac{1}{3}\pi)$ and $(1, \tfrac{5}{3}\pi)$. Solving simultaneously $-r = 2 + 2 \cos \theta$ and $r = 2 \cos \theta$ yields

$$2 + 2 \cos \theta = -2 \cos \theta$$

$$4 \cos \theta = -2$$

$$\cos \theta = -\tfrac{1}{2}$$

Hence, $\theta = \tfrac{2}{3}\pi$ and $\theta = \tfrac{4}{3}\pi$, giving the points $(-1, \tfrac{2}{3}\pi)$ and $(-1, \tfrac{4}{3}\pi)$. However, $(-1, \tfrac{2}{3}\pi)$ is the same point as $(1, \tfrac{5}{3}\pi)$, and $(-1, \tfrac{4}{3}\pi)$ is the same point as $(1, \tfrac{1}{3}\pi)$.

Checking to see if the pole is on the first curve by substituting $r = 0$ in the equation $r = 2 - 2 \cos \theta$, we have

$$0 = 2 - 2 \cos \theta$$

$$\cos \theta = 1$$

$$\theta = 0$$

Therefore, the pole lies on the first curve. In a similar fashion, by substituting $r = 0$ in $r = 2 \cos \theta$, we get

$$0 = 2 \cos \theta$$

$$\cos \theta = 0$$

$$\theta = \tfrac{1}{2}\pi \quad \text{or} \quad \tfrac{3}{2}\pi$$

So the pole lies on the second curve.

Therefore, the points of intersection of the two curves are $(1, \frac{1}{3}\pi)$, $(1, \frac{5}{3}\pi)$, and the pole. Sketches of the two curves are shown in Fig. 11.3.2.

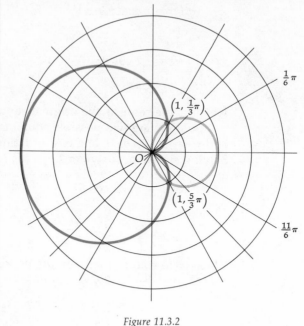

Figure 11.3.2

Exercises 11.3

In Exercises 1 through 14, find the points of intersection of the graphs of the given pair of equations. Draw a sketch of each pair of graphs with the same pole and polar axis.

1. $\begin{cases} 2r = 3 \\ r = 3 \sin \theta \end{cases}$

2. $\begin{cases} 2r = 3 \\ r = 1 + \cos \theta \end{cases}$

3. $\begin{cases} r = 2 \cos \theta \\ r = 2 \sin \theta \end{cases}$

4. $\begin{cases} r = 2 \cos 2\theta \\ r = 2 \sin \theta \end{cases}$

5. $\begin{cases} r = 4\theta \\ r = \frac{1}{2}\pi \end{cases}$

6. $\begin{cases} \theta = \frac{1}{6}\pi \\ r = 2 \end{cases}$

7. $\begin{cases} r = \cos \theta - 1 \\ r = \cos 2\theta \end{cases}$

8. $\begin{cases} r = 1 - \sin \theta \\ r = \cos 2\theta \end{cases}$

9. $\begin{cases} r = \sin 2\theta \\ r = \cos 2\theta \end{cases}$

10. $\begin{cases} r^2 = 2 \cos \theta \\ r = 1 \end{cases}$

11. $\begin{cases} r = \tan \theta \\ r = 4 \sin \theta \end{cases}$

12. $\begin{cases} r = 4 \tan \theta \sin \theta \\ r = 4 \cos \theta \end{cases}$

13. $\begin{cases} r = 4(1 + \sin \theta) \\ r(1 - \sin \theta) = 3 \end{cases}$

14. $\begin{cases} r^2 \sin 2\theta = 8 \\ r \cos \theta = 2 \end{cases}$

In Exercises 15 and 16, the graph of the given equation intersects itself. Find the points at which this occurs.

15. $r = \sin \frac{3}{2}\theta$

16. $r = 1 + 2 \cos 2\theta$

11.4 TANGENT LINES OF POLAR CURVES　In Sec. 11.2, we derived a formula for finding the slope of a tangent line to a polar curve whose equation is $r = f(\theta)$. If α radians is the measure of the inclination of the tangent line to the curve at (r, θ), we have

$$\tan \alpha = \frac{\tan \theta \dfrac{dr}{d\theta} + r}{\dfrac{dr}{d\theta} - r \tan \theta} \tag{1}$$

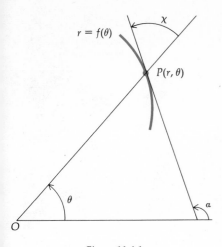

$r = f(\theta)$

χ

$P(r, \theta)$

θ

α

O

Figure 11.4.1

Formula (1) is generally complicated to apply. A simpler formula is obtained by considering the angle between the line OP and the tangent line. This angle will have radian measure χ and is measured from the line OP counterclockwise to the tangent line, $0 \leq \chi < \pi$.

There are two possible cases: $\alpha \geq \theta$ and $\alpha < \theta$. These two cases are illustrated in Figs. 11.4.1 and 11.4.2. In Fig. 11.4.1, $\alpha > \theta$ and $\chi = \alpha - \theta$. In Fig. 11.4.2, $\alpha < \theta$ and $\chi = \pi - (\theta - \alpha)$. In each case,

$$\tan \chi = \tan(\alpha - \theta)$$

or, equivalently,

$$\tan \chi = \frac{\tan \alpha - \tan \theta}{1 + \tan \alpha \tan \theta} \tag{2}$$

Substituting the value of $\tan \alpha$ from (1) in (2), we get

$$\tan \chi = \frac{\left(\tan \theta \dfrac{dr}{d\theta} + r\right) \Big/ \left(\dfrac{dr}{d\theta} - r \tan \theta\right) - \tan \theta}{1 + \left[\left(\tan \theta \dfrac{dr}{d\theta} + r\right) \Big/ \left(\dfrac{dr}{d\theta} - r \tan \theta\right)\right] (\tan \theta)}$$

$$= \frac{\tan \theta \dfrac{dr}{d\theta} + r - \tan \theta \dfrac{dr}{d\theta} + r \tan^2 \theta}{\dfrac{dr}{d\theta} - r \tan \theta + \tan^2 \theta \dfrac{dr}{d\theta} + r \tan \theta}$$

$$= \frac{r(1 + \tan^2 \theta)}{(1 + \tan^2 \theta) \dfrac{dr}{d\theta}}$$

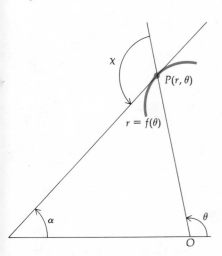

χ

$P(r, \theta)$

$r = f(\theta)$

α

θ

O

Figure 11.4.2

or

$$\tan \chi = \frac{r}{\dfrac{dr}{d\theta}} \tag{3}$$

Comparing formula (3) with formula (1), you can see why it is more desirable to consider χ instead of α when working with polar coordinates.

EXAMPLE 1: Find χ for the cardioid $r = a + a \sin \theta$ at the point $(\frac{3}{2}a, \frac{1}{6}\pi)$.

SOLUTION: See Fig. 11.4.3. Because $r = a + a \sin \theta$, we have

$$\frac{dr}{d\theta} = a \cos \theta$$

Applying formula (3), we get

$$\tan \chi = \frac{a + a \sin \theta}{a \cos \theta} = \frac{1 + \sin \theta}{\cos \theta}$$

Therefore, at the point $(\frac{3}{2}a, \frac{1}{6}\pi)$,

$$\tan \chi = \frac{1 + \frac{1}{2}}{\frac{1}{2}\sqrt{3}} = \frac{3}{\sqrt{3}} = \sqrt{3}$$

So

$$\chi = \frac{1}{3}\pi$$

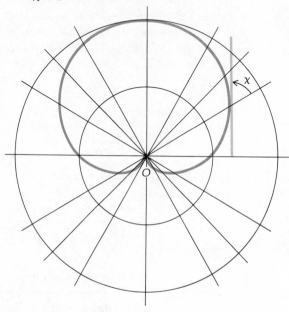

Figure 11.4.3

EXAMPLE 2: Find to the nearest 10 min the measurement of the smaller angle between the tangent lines to the curves $r = 3 \cos 2\theta$ and $r = 3 \sin 2\theta$ at the point $P(\frac{3}{2}\sqrt{2}, \frac{1}{8}\pi)$.

SOLUTION: Let χ_1 be the radian measure of the angle between the line OP and the tangent line to the curve $r = 3 \cos 2\theta$, and let χ_2 be the radian measure of the angle between the line OP and the tangent line to the curve $r = 3 \sin 2\theta$. The graph of each equation is a four-leafed rose (see Fig. 11.4.4).

If β is the radian measure of the angle between the tangent lines at $P(\frac{3}{2}\sqrt{2}, \frac{1}{8}\pi)$, then

$$\beta = \chi_1 - \chi_2$$

So

$$\tan \beta = \tan(\chi_1 - \chi_2)$$

or, equivalently,

$$\tan \beta = \frac{\tan \chi_1 - \tan \chi_2}{1 + \tan \chi_1 \tan \chi_2} \tag{4}$$

Tan χ_1 and tan χ_2 are found from formula (3). For tan χ_1, $r = 3 \cos 2\theta$ and $dr/d\theta = -6 \sin 2\theta$. So

$$\tan \chi_1 = \frac{3 \cos 2\theta}{-6 \sin 2\theta} = -\frac{1}{2} \cot 2\theta$$

When $\theta = \frac{1}{8}\pi$, $\tan \chi_1 = -\frac{1}{2} \cot \frac{1}{4}\pi = -\frac{1}{2}$.
For tan χ_2, $r = 3 \sin 2\theta$ and $dr/d\theta = 6\cos 2\theta$. So

$$\tan \chi_2 = \frac{3 \sin 2\theta}{6 \cos 2\theta} = \frac{1}{2} \tan 2\theta$$

When $\theta = \frac{1}{8}\pi$, $\tan \chi_2 = \frac{1}{2} \tan \frac{1}{4}\pi = \frac{1}{2}$.
Substituting $\tan \chi_1 = -\frac{1}{2}$ and $\tan \chi_2 = \frac{1}{2}$ in (4), we obtain

$$\tan \beta = \frac{-\frac{1}{2} - \frac{1}{2}}{1 + (-\frac{1}{2})(\frac{1}{2})} = \frac{-1}{1 - \frac{1}{4}} = -\frac{4}{3}$$

The angle of radian measure β has a measurement of 126°50′ to the nearest 10 min. So the measurement of the smaller angle between the two tangent lines is $180° - 126°50' = 53°10'$.

Figure 11.4.4

Exercises 11.4

In Exercises 1 through 8, find χ at the point indicated.

1. $r\theta = a$; $(a, 1)$

2. $r = a\theta$; $(\frac{5}{2}\pi a, \frac{5}{2}\pi)$

3. $r = a \sec 2\theta$; $(\sqrt{2}a, -\frac{1}{8}\pi)$

4. $r = a \sin \frac{1}{2}\theta$; $(\frac{1}{2}a, \frac{1}{3}\pi)$

5. $r = \theta^2$; $(\frac{1}{4}\pi^2, \frac{1}{2}\pi)$

6. $r = a \cos 2\theta$; $(\frac{1}{2}\sqrt{3}a, \frac{1}{12}\pi)$

7. $r^2 = a^2 \cos 2\theta$; $\left(\frac{a}{\sqrt{2}}, \frac{1}{6}\pi\right)$

8. $r = a(1 - \sin \theta)$; (a, π)

In Exercises 9 through 12, find a measurement of the angle between the tangent lines of the given pair of curves at the indicated point of intersection.

9. $\begin{cases} r = a \cos \theta \\ r = a \sin \theta \end{cases}$; $(\frac{1}{2}\sqrt{2}a, \frac{1}{4}\pi)$

10. $\begin{cases} r = a \\ r = 2a \sin \theta \end{cases}$; $(a, \frac{1}{6}\pi)$

11. $\begin{cases} r = 4 \cos \theta \\ r = 4 \cos^2 \theta - 3 \end{cases}$; $(-2, \frac{2}{3}\pi)$

12. $\begin{cases} r = -a \sin \theta \\ r = a \cos 2\theta \end{cases}$; the pole

In Exercises 13 through 16, find a measurement of the angle between the tangent lines of the given pair of curves at all points of intersection.

13. $\begin{cases} r = 1 - \sin \theta \\ r = 1 + \sin \theta \end{cases}$

14. $\begin{cases} r = 3 \cos \theta \\ r = 1 + \cos \theta \end{cases}$

15. $\begin{cases} r = \cos \theta \\ r = \sin 2\theta \end{cases}$

16. $\begin{cases} r = 2 \sec \theta \\ r = \csc^2 \frac{1}{2}\theta \end{cases}$

17. Prove that $\tan \chi = \tan \frac{1}{2}\theta$ at all points of the cardioid $r = 2(1 - \cos \theta)$.

18. Prove that at each point of the logarithmic spiral $r = be^{a\theta}$, χ is the same.

19. Prove that at the points of intersection of the cardioids $r = a(1 + \sin \theta)$ and $r = b(1 - \sin \theta)$ their tangent lines are perpendicular for all values of a and b.

20. Prove that at the points of intersection of the two curves $r = a \sec^2 \frac{1}{2}\theta$ and $r = b \csc^2 \frac{1}{2}\theta$ their tangent lines are perpendicular.

11.5 AREA OF A REGION IN POLAR COORDINATES

In this section a method is developed for finding the area of a region bounded by a curve whose equation is given in polar coordinates and by two lines through the pole.

Let the function f be continuous and nonnegative on the closed interval $[\alpha, \beta]$. Let R be the region bounded by the curve whose equation is $r = f(\theta)$ and by the lines $\theta = \alpha$ and $\theta = \beta$. Then the region R is the region AOB shown in Fig. 11.5.1.

Figure 11.5.1

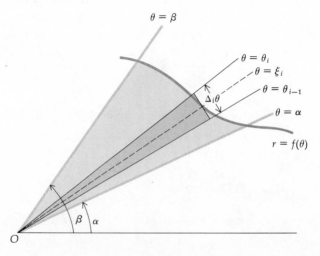

Figure 11.5.2

Consider a partition Δ of $[\alpha, \beta]$ defined by $\alpha = \theta_0 < \theta_1 < \theta_2 < \cdots < \theta_{i-1} < \theta_i < \cdots < \theta_{n-1} < \theta_n = \beta$. Therefore, we have n subintervals of the form $[\theta_{i-1}, \theta_i]$, where $i = 1, 2, \ldots, n$. Let ξ_i be a value of θ in the ith subinterval $[\theta_{i-1}, \theta_i]$. See Fig. 11.5.2 where the ith subinterval is shown together with $\theta = \xi_i$. The radian measure of the angle between the lines $\theta = \theta_{i-1}$ and $\theta = \theta_i$ is denoted by $\Delta_i\theta$. The number of square units in the area of the circular sector of radius $f(\xi_i)$ units and central angle of radian measure $\Delta_i\theta$ is given by

$$\tfrac{1}{2}[f(\xi_i)]^2\,\Delta_i\theta$$

There is such a circular sector for each of the n subintervals. The sum of the measures of the areas of these n circular sectors is

$$\tfrac{1}{2}[f(\xi_1)]^2\,\Delta_1\theta + \tfrac{1}{2}[f(\xi_2)]^2\,\Delta_2\theta + \cdots + \tfrac{1}{2}[f(\xi_i)]^2\,\Delta_i\theta + \cdots + \tfrac{1}{2}[f(\xi_n)]^2\,\Delta_n\theta$$

which can be written, using sigma notation, as

$$\sum_{i=1}^{n} \tfrac{1}{2}[f(\xi_i)]^2\,\Delta_i\theta$$

Let $\|\Delta\|$ be the norm of the partition Δ; that is, $\|\Delta\|$ is the measure of the largest $\Delta_i\theta$. Then if we let A square units be the area of the region R, we define

$$A = \lim_{\|\Delta\| \to 0} \sum_{i=1}^{n} \tfrac{1}{2}[f(\xi_i)]^2\,\Delta_i\theta \tag{1}$$

The limit in (1) is a definite integral, and we have

$$A = \tfrac{1}{2}\int_{\alpha}^{\beta} [f(\theta)]^2\,d\theta \tag{2}$$

EXAMPLE 1:   Find the area of the region bounded by the graph of $r = 2 + 2\cos\theta$.

SOLUTION: The region together with an element of area is shown in Fig. 11.5.3. Because the curve is symmetric with respect to the polar axis, we take the θ limits from 0 to π which determine the area of the region bounded by the curve above the polar axis. Then the area of the entire region is determined by multiplying that area by 2. Thus, if A square units is the measure of the required area,

$$A = 2 \lim_{\|\Delta\| \to 0} \sum_{i=1}^{n} \tfrac{1}{2}(2 + 2\cos\xi_i)^2\,\Delta_i\theta$$

$$= 2 \int_0^{\pi} \tfrac{1}{2}(2 + 2\cos\theta)^2\,d\theta$$

$$= 4 \int_0^{\pi} (1 + 2\cos\theta + \cos^2\theta)\,d\theta$$

$$= 4 \left[\theta + 2\sin\theta + \tfrac{1}{2}\theta + \tfrac{1}{4}\sin 2\theta \right]_0^{\pi}$$

$$= 4(\pi + 0 + \tfrac{1}{2}\pi + 0 - 0)$$

$$= 6\pi$$

Therefore, the area is 6π square units.

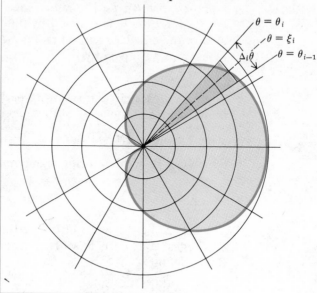

Figure 11.5.3

EXAMPLE 2:   Find the area of the region inside the circle $r = 3 \sin \theta$ and outside the limaçon $r = 2 - \sin \theta$.

SOLUTION: To find the points of intersection, we set

$$3 \sin \theta = 2 - \sin \theta$$

$$\sin \theta = \tfrac{1}{2}$$

So

$$\theta = \tfrac{1}{6}\pi \quad \text{and} \quad \tfrac{5}{6}\pi$$

The curves are sketched and the region is shown together with an element of area in Fig. 11.5.4.

If we let $f(\theta) = 3 \sin \theta$ and $g(\theta) = 2 - \sin \theta$, then the equation of the circle is $r = f(\theta)$, and the equation of the limaçon is $r = g(\theta)$.

The measure of the area of the element of area is the difference of the measures of the areas of two circular sectors.

$$\tfrac{1}{2}[f(\xi_i)]^2 \, \Delta_i\theta - \tfrac{1}{2}[g(\xi_i)]^2 \, \Delta_i\theta = \tfrac{1}{2}([f(\xi_i)]^2 - [g(\xi_i)]^2) \, \Delta_i\theta$$

The sum of the measures of the areas of n such elements is given by

$$\sum_{i=1}^{n} \tfrac{1}{2}([f(\xi_i)]^2 - [g(\xi_i)]^2) \, \Delta_i\theta$$

Hence, if A square units is the area of the region desired, we have

$$A = \lim_{\|\Delta\| \to 0} \sum_{i=1}^{n} \tfrac{1}{2}([f(\xi_i)]^2 - [g(\xi_i)]^2) \, \Delta_i\theta$$

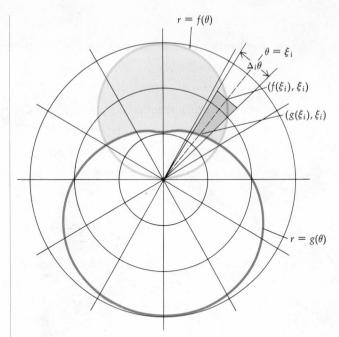

Figure 11.5.4

This limit is a definite integral. Instead of taking the limits $\frac{1}{6}\pi$ to $\frac{5}{6}\pi$, we use the property of symmetry with respect to the $\frac{1}{2}\pi$ axis and take the limits from $\frac{1}{6}\pi$ to $\frac{1}{2}\pi$ and multiply by 2. We have, then,

$$A = 2 \cdot \frac{1}{2} \int_{\pi/6}^{\pi/2} ([f(\theta)]^2 - [g(\theta)]^2)\ d\theta$$

$$= \int_{\pi/6}^{\pi/2} [9\ \sin^2\theta - (2 - \sin\theta)^2]\ d\theta$$

$$= 8 \int_{\pi/6}^{\pi/2} \sin^2\theta\ d\theta + 4 \int_{\pi/6}^{\pi/2} \sin\theta\ d\theta - 4 \int_{\pi/6}^{\pi/2} d\theta$$

$$= 8 \int_{\pi/6}^{\pi/2} (1 - \cos 2\theta)\ d\theta + \left[-4\ \cos\theta - 4\theta \right]_{\pi/6}^{\pi/2}$$

$$= 4\theta - 2\ \sin 2\theta - 4\ \cos\theta - 4\theta \Big]_{\pi/6}^{\pi/2}$$

$$= -2\ \sin 2\theta - 4\ \cos\theta \Big]_{\pi/6}^{\pi/2}$$

$$= (-2\ \sin\pi - 4\ \cos\tfrac{1}{2}\pi) - (-2\ \sin\tfrac{1}{3}\pi - 4\ \cos\tfrac{1}{6}\pi)$$

$$= 2 \cdot \tfrac{1}{2}\sqrt{3} + 4 \cdot \tfrac{1}{2}\sqrt{3}$$

$$= 3\sqrt{3}$$

Therefore, the area is $3\sqrt{3}$ square units.

Exercises 11.5

In Exercises 1 through 6, find the area of the region enclosed by the graph of the given equation.

1. $r = 3 \cos \theta$

2. $r = 2 - \sin \theta$

3. $r = 4 \cos 3\theta$

4. $r = 4 \sin^2 \frac{1}{2}\theta$

5. $r^2 = 4 \sin 2\theta$

6. $r = 4 \sin^2 \theta \cos \theta$

In Exercises 7 through 10, find the area of the region enclosed by one loop of the graph of the given equation.

7. $r = 3 \cos 2\theta$

8. $r = a \sin 3\theta$

9. $r = 1 + 3 \sin \theta$

10. $r = a(1 - 2 \cos \theta)$

In Exercises 11 through 14, find the area of the region which is enclosed by both of the graphs of the two given equations.

11. $\begin{cases} r = 2 \\ r = 3 - 2 \cos \theta \end{cases}$

12. $\begin{cases} r = 4 \sin \theta \\ r = 4 \cos \theta \end{cases}$

13. $\begin{cases} r = 3 \sin 2\theta \\ r = 3 \cos 2\theta \end{cases}$

14. $\begin{cases} r^2 = 2 \cos 2\theta \\ r = 1 \end{cases}$

In Exercises 15 through 18, find the area of the region which is inside the graph of the first equation and outside the graph of the second equation.

15. $\begin{cases} r = a \\ r = a(1 - \cos \theta) \end{cases}$

16. $\begin{cases} r = 2a \sin \theta \\ r = a \end{cases}$

17. $\begin{cases} r = 2 \sin \theta \\ r = \sin \theta + \cos \theta \end{cases}$

18. $\begin{cases} r^2 = 4 \sin 2\theta \\ r = \sqrt{2} \end{cases}$

19. The face of a bow tie is the region enclosed by the graph of the equation $r^2 = 4 \cos 2\theta$. How much material is necessary to cover the face of the tie?

20. Find the area of the region swept out by the radius vector of the spiral $r = a\theta$ during its second revolution which was not swept out during its first revolution.

21. Find the area of the region swept out by the radius vector of the curve of Exercise 20 during its third revolution which was not swept out during its second revolution.

Review Exercises (Chapter 11)

In Exercises 1 and 2, find a polar equation of the graph having the given cartesian equation.

1. $x^2 + y^2 - 9x + 8y = 0$

2. $y^4 = x^2(a^2 - y^2)$

In Exercises 3 and 4, find a cartesian equation of the graph having the given polar equation.

3. $r = 9 \sin^2 \frac{1}{2}\theta$

4. $r = a \tan^2 \theta$

5. Draw a sketch of the graph of (a) $r = 3/\theta$ (reciprocal spiral) and (b) $r = \theta/3$ (spiral of Archimedes).

6. Show that the equations $r = 1 + \sin \theta$ and $r = \sin \theta - 1$ have the same graph.

7. Draw a sketch of the graph of $r = \sqrt{|\cos \theta|}$.

8. Draw a sketch of the graph of $r = \sqrt{|\cos 2\theta|}$.

9. Find an equation of each of the tangent lines at the pole to the cardioid $r = 3 - 3 \sin \theta$.

10. Find an equation of each of the tangent lines at the pole to the four-leafed rose $r = 4 \cos 2\theta$.

11. Find the area of the region inside the graph of $r = 2a \sin \theta$ and outside the graph of $r = a$.

12. Find the area of the region enclosed by both of the graphs of the two equations $r = a \cos \theta$ and $r = 1 - \cos \theta$, $a > 0$.

13. Find the area of the region swept out by the radius vector of the logarithmic spiral $r = e^{k\theta}$ ($k > 0$) as θ varies from 0 to 2π.

14. Find the area of the region inside the graph of the lemniscate $r^2 = 2 \sin 2\theta$ and outside the graph of the circle $r = 1$.

15. Find a polar equation of the tangent line to the curve $r = \theta$ at the point (π, π).

In Exercises 16 and 17, find all the points of intersection of the graphs of the two given equations.

16. $\begin{cases} r \cos \theta = 1 \\ r = 1 + 2 \cos \theta \end{cases}$
17. $\begin{cases} r = 2(1 + \cos \theta) \\ r^2 = 2 \cos \theta \end{cases}$

18. Prove that the graphs of $r = a\theta$ and $r\theta = a$ have an unlimited number of points of intersection. Also prove that the tangent lines are perpendicular at only two of these points of intersection, and find these points.

19. Find the radian measure of the angle between the tangent lines at each point of intersection of the graphs of the equations $r = -6 \cos \theta$ and $r = 2(1 - \cos \theta)$.

20. Find the slope of the tangent line to the curve $r = 6 \cos \theta - 2$ at the point $(1, \tfrac{5}{3}\pi)$.

21. Find the area of the region enclosed by the loop of the limaçon $r = 4(1 + 2 \cos \theta)$ and also the area of the region enclosed by the outer part of the limaçon.

22. Find the area enclosed by one loop of the curve $r = a \sin n\theta$, where n is a positive integer.

23. Prove that the distance between the two points $P_1(r_1, \theta_1)$ and $P_2(r_2, \theta_2)$ is

$$\sqrt{r_1^2 + r_2^2 - 2r_1r_2 \cos(\theta_2 - \theta_1)}$$

24. Find the points of intersection of the graphs of the equations $r = \tan \theta$ and $r = \cot \theta$.

25. (a) Use the formula of Exercise 23 to find a polar equation of the parabola having its focus at $(2, \tfrac{1}{2}\pi)$ and the line $\theta = 0$ as its directrix. (b) Write a cartesian equation of the parabola having its focus at $(0, 2)$ and the x axis as its directrix. Compare the results of parts (a) and (b).

26. Find a polar equation of the circle having its center at (r_0, θ_0) and a radius of a units. (HINT: Apply the law of cosines to the triangle having vertices at the pole, (r_0, θ_0), and (r, θ).)

12 The Conic Sections

12.1 SOME PROPERTIES OF CONICS

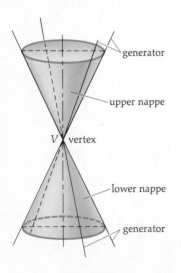

Figure 12.1.1

In Sec. 1.7 we stated that a *conic section* (or *conic*) is a curve of intersection of a plane with a right-circular cone of two nappes, and three types of curves of intersection that occur are the *parabola*, the *ellipse*, and the *hyperbola*. The Greek mathematician Apollonius studied conic sections, in terms of geometry, by using this concept. We studied the parabola in Sec. 1.7, where an analytic definition (1.7.1) of a parabola was given. In this chapter, an analytic definition of a conic section is given and the three types of curves are obtained as special cases of this definition.

In a consideration of the geometry of conic sections, a cone is regarded as having two nappes, extending indefinitely far in both directions. A portion of a right-circular cone of two nappes is shown in Fig. 12.1.1. A *generator* (or element) of the cone is a line lying in the cone, and all the generators of a cone contain the point V, called the *vertex* of the cone.

In Fig. 12.1.2 we have a cone and a cutting plane which is parallel to one and only one generator of the cone. This conic is a *parabola*. If the cutting plane is parallel to two generators, it intersects both nappes of the cone and we have a *hyperbola* (Fig. 12.1.3). An *ellipse* is obtained if the cutting plane is parallel to no generator, in which case the cutting plane intersects each generator, as in Fig. 12.1.4.

A special case of the ellipse is a *circle*, which is formed if the cutting plane, which intersects each generator, is also perpendicular to the axis of the cone. Degenerate cases of the conic sections include a point, a straight line, and two intersecting straight lines. A point is obtained if the cutting plane contains the vertex of the cone but does not contain a

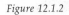

Figure 12.1.2   *Figure 12.1.3*   *Figure 12.1.4*

generator. This is a degenerate ellipse. If the cutting plane contains the vertex of the cone and only one generator, then a straight line is obtained, and this is a degenerate parabola. A degenerate hyperbola is formed when the cutting plane contains the vertex of the cone and two generators, thereby giving two intersecting straight lines.

There are many applications of conic sections to both pure and applied mathematics. We shall mention a few of them. The orbits of planets and satellites are ellipses. Ellipses are used in making machine gears. Arches of bridges are sometimes elliptical or parabolic in shape. The path of a projectile is a parabola if motion is considered to be in a plane and air resistance is neglected. Parabolas are used in the design of parabolic mirrors, searchlights, and automobile headlights. Hyperbolas are used in combat in "sound ranging" to locate the position of enemy guns by the sound of the firing of those guns. If a quantity varies inversely as another quantity, such as pressure and volume in Boyle's law for a perfect gas at a constant temperature, the graph is a hyperbola.

To discuss conics analytically as plane curves, we first state a definition which gives a property common to all conics.

12.1.1 Definition   A *conic* is the set of all points P in a plane such that the undirected distance of P from a fixed point is in a constant ratio to the undirected distance of P from a fixed line which does not contain the fixed point.

The constant ratio in the above definition is called the *eccentricity* of the conic and is denoted by e. The eccentricity e is a nonnegative number because it is the ratio of two undirected distances. Actually for nondegenerate conics, $e > 0$. (Later we see that when $e = 0$, we have a point.) If $e = 1$, we see by comparing Definitions 12.1.1 and 1.7.1 that the conic is a parabola. If $e < 1$, the conic is an ellipse, and if $e > 1$, the conic is a hyperbola.

The fixed point, referred to in Definition 12.1.1, is called a *focus* of the conic, and the fixed line is called the corresponding *directrix*. We learned in Sec. 1.7 that a parabola has one focus and one directrix. Later we see that an ellipse and a hyperbola each have two foci and two directrices, with each focus corresponding to a particular directrix.

The line through a focus of a conic perpendicular to its directrix is called the *principal axis* of the conic. The points of intersection of the conic and its principal axis are called the *vertices* of the conic. From our study of the parabola, we know that a parabola has one vertex. However, both the ellipse and the hyperbola have two vertices. This is proved in the following theorem.

12.1.2 Theorem   If e is the eccentricity of a nondegenerate conic, then if $e \neq 1$, the conic has two vertices; if $e = 1$, the conic has only one vertex.

Figure 12.1.5

PROOF: Let F denote the focus of the conic and D denote the point of intersection of the directrix and the principal axis. Let d denote the undirected distance between the focus and its directrix. In Fig. 12.1.5, F is to the right of the directrix, and in Fig. 12.1.6, F is to the left of the directrix. Let V denote a vertex of the conic. We wish to show that if $e \neq 1$, there are two possible vertices V, and if $e = 1$, there is only one vertex V.

From Definition 12.1.1, we have

$$|\overline{FV}| = e|\overline{DV}|$$

Removing the absolute-value bars, we obtain

$$\overline{FV} = \pm e(\overline{DV}) \tag{1}$$

Because D, F, and V are all on the principal axis,

$$\overline{DV} = \overline{DF} + \overline{FV}$$

If F is to the right of D, $\overline{DF} = d$. Thus, we have from the above

$$\overline{DV} = d + \overline{FV} \tag{2}$$

Substituting from (1) into (2) gives

$$\overline{DV} = d \pm e(\overline{DV})$$

from which we get

$$\overline{DV} = \frac{d}{1 \pm e} \tag{3}$$

Figure 12.1.6

If $e = 1$, the minus sign in the above equations must be rejected because we would be dividing by zero. So if $e \neq 1$, two points V are obtained; if $e = 1$, we obtain only one point V.

If F is to the left of D, $\overline{DF} = -d$. Instead of (3), we get

$$\overline{DV} = \frac{-d}{1 \mp e}$$

from which the same conclusion follows. So the theorem is proved.   ■

The point on the principal axis of an ellipse or a hyperbola that lies halfway between the two vertices is called the *center* of the conic. Hence, the ellipse and the hyperbola are called *central conics* in contrast to the parabola that has no center because it has only one vertex.

12.1.3 Theorem   A conic is symmetric with respect to its principal axis.

The proof of this theorem is left for the reader (see Exercise 7).

EXAMPLE 1: Use Definition 12.1.1 to find an equation of the conic whose eccentricity is $\frac{4}{5}$ and having a focus at the point $F(1, -2)$ with the line $4y + 17 = 0$ as the corresponding directrix.

SOLUTION: Figure 12.1.7 shows the focus, the directrix, and the point $P(x, y)$ representing any point on the conic. Letting the point D be the foot of the perpendicular from P to the directrix, we have from Definition 12.1.1

$$\frac{|\overline{PF}|}{|\overline{PD}|} = \frac{4}{5}$$

and so

$$|\overline{PF}| = \tfrac{4}{5}|\overline{PD}|$$

Using the distance formula to find $|\overline{PF}|$ and $|\overline{PD}|$ and substituting into the above equation, we get

$$\sqrt{(x - 1)^2 + (y + 2)^2} = \tfrac{4}{5}|y + \tfrac{17}{4}|$$

Squaring on both sides of this equation and simplifying, we get

$$x^2 - 2x + 1 + y^2 + 4y + 4 = \tfrac{16}{25}(y^2 + \tfrac{17}{2}y + \tfrac{289}{16})$$

$$25x^2 - 50x + 25y^2 + 100y + 125 = 16y^2 + 136y + 289$$

$$25x^2 + 9y^2 - 50x - 36y = 164$$

Because $e = \frac{4}{5} < 1$, the equation is that of an ellipse.

Figure 12.1.7

Exercises 12.1

In Exercises 1 through 6, use Definition 12.1.1 and the formula of Exercise 24 of Exercises 4.9 to find an equation of the conic having the given properties.

1. Focus at $(2, 0)$; directrix: $x = -4$; $e = \frac{1}{2}$.

2. Focus at $(0, -4)$; directrix: $y = -2$; $e = \frac{3}{4}$.

3. Focus at $(-3, 2)$; directrix: $x = 1$; $e = 3$.

4. Focus at $(1, 3)$; directrix: $y = 8$; $e = \frac{3}{2}$.

5. Focus at $(4, -3)$; directrix: $2x - y - 2 = 0$; $e = \frac{1}{2}$.

6. Focus at $(-1, 4)$; directrix: $2x - y + 3 = 0$; $e = 2$.

7. Prove Theorem 12.1.3.

8. Find an equation whose graph consists of all points P in a plane such that the undirected distance of P from the point $(ae, 0)$ is in a constant ratio e to the undirected distance of P from the line $x = a/e$. Let $a^2(1 - e^2) = \pm b^2$ and consider the three cases: $e = 1$, $e < 1$, and $e > 1$.

9. Solve Exercise 8 if the point is $(-ae, 0)$ and the line is $x = -a/e$.

12.2 POLAR EQUATIONS OF THE CONICS

Figure 12.2.1

Fairly simple polar equations of conics are obtained by taking the pole at a focus and the polar axis and its extension along the principal axis. We first consider this situation when the directrix corresponding to the focus at the pole is to the left of the focus. Let D be the point of intersection of this directrix with the principal axis, and let d denote the undirected distance between a focus and its directrix (refer to Fig. 12.2.1). Let $P(r, \theta)$ be any point on the conic to the right of the directrix and on the terminal side of the angle of measure θ. Draw perpendiculars PQ and PR to the principal axis and the directrix, respectively. By Definition 12.1.1, the point P is on the conic if and only if

$$|\overline{OP}| = e|\overline{RP}| \tag{1}$$

Because P is to the right of the directrix, $\overline{RP} > 0$; thus, $|\overline{RP}| = \overline{RP}$. $|\overline{OP}| = r$ because $r > 0$. So from (1) we have

$$r = e(\overline{RP}) \tag{2}$$

However, $\overline{RP} = \overline{DQ} = \overline{DO} + \overline{OQ} = d + r \cos \theta$. Substituting this expression for $\overline{RP}$ in (2), we get

$$r = e(d + r \cos \theta)$$

from which we obtain

$$r = \frac{ed}{1 - e \cos \theta} \tag{3}$$

In a similar manner, we can derive an equation of a conic if the directrix corresponding to the focus at the pole is to the right of the focus, and we obtain

$$r = \frac{ed}{1 + e \cos \theta} \tag{4}$$

The derivation of (4) is left for the reader (see Exercise 1).

If a focus of a conic is at the pole and the polar axis is parallel to the corresponding directrix, then the $\frac{1}{2}\pi$ axis and its extension are along the principal axis. We obtain the following equation:

$$r = \frac{ed}{1 \pm e \sin \theta} \tag{5}$$

where e and d are, respectively, the eccentricity and the undirected distance between the focus and the corresponding directrix. The plus sign is taken when the directrix corresponding to the focus at the pole is above the focus, and the minus sign is taken when it is below the focus. The derivation of Eqs. (5) is left for the reader (see Exercises 2 and 3).

We now discuss the graph of Eq. (3) for each of the three cases: $e = 1$, $e < 1$, and $e > 1$. Similar discussions apply to the graphs of Eqs. (4) and (5).

Case 1: $e = 1$. The conic is a parabola.

Equation (3) becomes

$$r = \frac{d}{1 - \cos \theta} \tag{6}$$

r is not defined when $\theta = 0$; however, r is defined for all other values of θ for which $0 < \theta < 2\pi$. Differentiating in (6), we obtain

$$D_\theta r = \frac{-d \sin \theta}{(1 - \cos \theta)^2}$$

Setting $D_\theta r = 0$, for values of θ in the interval $(0, 2\pi)$ we obtain $\theta = \pi$. Because when $0 < \theta < \pi$, $D_\theta r < 0$, and when $\pi < \theta < 2\pi$, $D_\theta r > 0$, r has an absolute minimum value at $\theta = \pi$. When $\theta = \pi$, $r = \frac{1}{2}d$, and the point $(\frac{1}{2}d, \pi)$ is the vertex. Therefore, the undirected distance from the focus to a point on the parabola is shortest when the point on the parabola is the vertex.

By Theorem 12.1.3, the parabola is symmetric with respect to its principal axis; by Theorem 12.1.2 there is one vertex. Note that the curve does not contain the pole because there is no value of θ which will give a value of 0 for r. A sketch of the parabola is shown in Fig. 12.2.2.

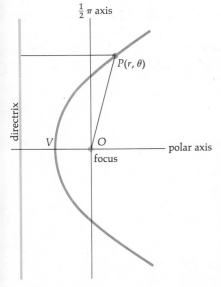

Figure 12.2.2

EXAMPLE 1:   A parabola has its focus at the pole and its vertex at $(4, \pi)$. Find an equation of the

SOLUTION: Because the focus is at the pole and the vertex is at $(4, \pi)$, the polar axis and its extension are along the principal axis of the parabola. Furthermore, the vertex is to the left of the focus, and so the directrix is parabola and an equation of the directrix. Draw a sketch of the parabola and the directrix.

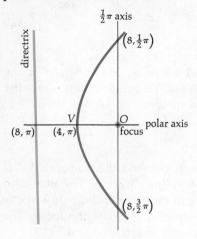

Figure 12.2.3

also to the left of the focus. Hence, an equation of the parabola is of the form of Eq. (3). Because the vertex is at $(4, \pi)$, $\frac{1}{2}d = 4$; thus, $d = 8$. The eccentricity $e = 1$, and therefore we obtain the equation

$$r = \frac{8}{1 - \cos \theta}$$

An equation of the directrix is given by $r \cos \theta = -d$, and because $d = 8$, we have $r \cos \theta = -8$. Figure 12.2.3 shows a sketch of the parabola and the directrix.

EXAMPLE 2:   Follow the instructions of Example 1 if the parabola has its focus at the pole and its vertex at $(3, \frac{3}{2}\pi)$.

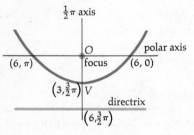

Figure 12.2.4

SOLUTION: The vertex of the parabola is below the focus, and the $\frac{1}{2}\pi$ axis and its extension are along the principal axis. Therefore, the directrix is also below the focus, and an equation of the parabola is of the form of Eq. (5) with the minus sign. The undirected distance from the focus to the vertex is $\frac{1}{2}d = 3$; thus $d = 6$. Therefore, from Eqs. (5) an equation of the parabola is

$$r = \frac{6}{1 - \sin \theta}$$

An equation of the directrix is given by $r \sin \theta = -d$. Because $d = 6$, we have $r \sin \theta = -6$. Sketches of the parabola and the directrix are shown in Fig. 12.2.4.

Case 2: $e < 1$. The conic is an ellipse.

When $e < 1$, the denominator of the fraction in Eq. (3) is never zero, and so r exists for all values of θ. To find the absolute extrema of r on the interval $[0, 2\pi)$, we find $D_\theta r$ and obtain

$$D_\theta r = \frac{-e^2 d \sin \theta}{(1 - e \cos \theta)^2} \qquad (7)$$

For θ in the interval $[0, 2\pi)$, $D_\theta r = 0$ when $\theta = 0$ and π. When $-\frac{1}{2}\pi < \theta < 0$, $D_\theta r > 0$; and when $0 < \theta < \frac{1}{2}\pi$, $D_\theta r < 0$. Hence, when $\theta = 0$, r has

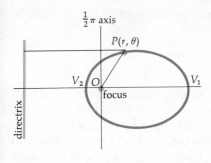

Figure 12.2.5

an absolute maximum value of $ed/(1 - e)$. When $\frac{1}{2}\pi < \theta < \pi$, $D_\theta r < 0$; and when $\pi < \theta < \frac{3}{2}\pi$, $D_\theta r > 0$. Thus, r has an absolute minimum value of $ed/(1 + e)$ when $\theta = \pi$. The points $(ed/(1 - e), 0)$ and $(ed/(1 + e), \pi)$ are the vertices of the ellipse. We denote them by V_1 and V_2, respectively. It follows, then, that the undirected distance from the focus $(0, 0)$ to a point on the ellipse is greatest when the point on the ellipse is V_1 and smallest when it is V_2.

By Theorem 12.1.3, the ellipse is symmetric with respect to its principal axis. There is no value of θ that will give a value of 0 for r, and so the curve does not contain the pole. A sketch of the ellipse is shown in Fig. 12.2.5.

EXAMPLE 3: Find an equation of the ellipse having a focus at the pole and vertices at $(5, 0)$ and $(2, \pi)$. Write an equation of the directrix corresponding to the focus at the pole. Draw a sketch of the ellipse.

SOLUTION: Because the vertices are at $(5, 0)$ and $(2, \pi)$, the polar axis and its extension are along the principal axis of the ellipse. The directrix corresponding to the focus at the pole is to the left of the focus because the vertex closest to this focus is at $(2, \pi)$. The required equation is therefore of the form of Eq. (3). The vertex V_1 is at $(5, 0)$ and V_2 is at $(2, \pi)$. It follows from the discussion of Case 2 that

$$\frac{ed}{1 - e} = 5 \quad \text{and} \quad \frac{ed}{1 + e} = 2$$

Solving these two equations simultaneously, we obtain $e = \frac{3}{7}$ and $d = \frac{20}{3}$. Hence, from Eq. (3) an equation of the ellipse is

$$r = \frac{\frac{3}{7} \cdot \frac{20}{3}}{1 - \frac{3}{7} \cos \theta}$$

or, equivalently,

$$r = \frac{20}{7 - 3 \cos \theta}$$

Because $d = \frac{20}{3}$, an equation of the directrix corresponding to the focus at the pole is $r \cos \theta = -\frac{20}{3}$ or, equivalently, $3r \cos \theta = -20$. A sketch of of the ellipse is shown in Fig. 12.2.6.

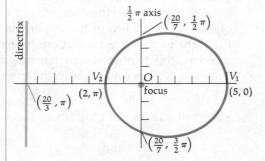

Figure 12.2.6

EXAMPLE 4: An equation of a conic is

$$r = \frac{5}{3 + 2 \sin \theta}$$

Find the eccentricity, identify the conic, write an equation of the directrix corresponding to the focus at the pole, find the vertices, and draw a sketch of the curve.

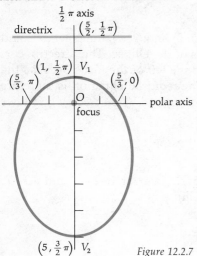

Figure 12.2.7

SOLUTION: Dividing the numerator and denominator of the fraction in the given equation by 3, we obtain

$$r = \frac{\frac{5}{3}}{1 + \frac{2}{3} \sin \theta}$$

which is of the form of Eqs. (5) with the plus sign. The eccentricity $e = \frac{2}{3} < 1$, and so the conic is an ellipse. Because $ed = \frac{5}{3}$, $d = \frac{5}{3} \div \frac{2}{3} = \frac{5}{2}$. The $\frac{1}{2}\pi$ axis and its extension are along the principal axis. The directrix corresponding to the focus at the pole is above the focus, and an equation of it is $r \sin \theta = \frac{5}{2}$. When $\theta = \frac{1}{2}\pi$, $r = 1$. And when $\theta = \frac{3}{2}\pi$, $r = 5$. The vertices are therefore at $(1, \frac{1}{2}\pi)$ and $(5, \frac{3}{2}\pi)$. A sketch of the ellipse is shown in Fig. 12.2.7.

Case 3: $e > 1$. The conic is a hyperbola.

In the derivation of Eq. (3) we assumed that the point P on the conic is to the right of the given directrix and that P is on the terminal side of the angle of θ radians, thus making r positive. In the previous two cases, when the conic is an ellipse or a parabola, we obtain the entire curve with these assumptions. However, when $e > 1$, we shall see that we obtain only one of two branches of the hyperbola when $r > 0$, and this branch is to the right of the directrix. There is also a branch to the left of the given directrix; this is obtained by letting r assume negative as well as positive values as θ takes on values in the interval $[0, 2\pi)$.

If $e > 1$ in Eq. (3), r is undefined when $\cos \theta = 1/e$. There are two values of θ in $[0, 2\pi)$ that satisfy this equation. These values are

$$\theta_1 = \cos^{-1} \frac{1}{e} \quad \text{and} \quad \theta_2 = 2\pi - \cos^{-1} \frac{1}{e}$$

We investigate the values of r as θ increases from 0 to θ_1. When $\theta = 0$, $r = ed/(1 - e)$, and because $e > 1$, $r < 0$. So the point $(ed/(1 - e), 0)$ is the left vertex of the hyperbola. The cosine function is decreasing in the interval $(0, \theta_1)$; therefore, when $0 < \theta < \theta_1$, $\cos \theta > \cos \theta_1 = 1/e$ or, equivalently, $1 - e \cos \theta < 0$. Hence, for values of θ in the interval $(0, \theta_1)$, $r = ed/(1 - e \cos \theta) < 0$. When $\theta = \theta_1$, r is undefined; however,

$$\lim_{\theta \to \theta_1^-} r = \lim_{\theta \to \theta_1^-} \frac{ed}{1 - e \cos \theta} = -\infty$$

We conclude, then, that as θ increases from 0 to θ_1, $r < 0$ and $|r|$ increases without bound. From these values of θ we obtain the lower half of the left branch of the curve. See Fig. 12.2.8. We show later that a hyperbola has two asymptotes. For this hyperbola one of the asymptotes is parallel to the line $\theta = \theta_1$.

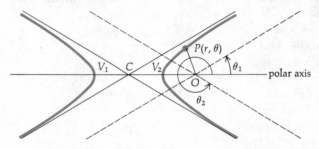

Figure 12.2.8

Now we consider the points on the hyperbola as θ increases through values between θ_1 and θ_2. When $\theta_1 < \theta < \theta_2$, $\cos \theta < \cos \theta_1 = 1/e$ or, equivalently, $1 - e \cos \theta > 0$. Therefore, for values of θ in the interval (θ_1, θ_2), $r > 0$.

$$\lim_{\theta \to \theta_1^+} r = \lim_{\theta \to \theta_1^+} \frac{ed}{1 - e \cos \theta} = +\infty$$

When $\theta = \pi$, $r = ed/(1 + e)$; so the point $(ed/(1 + e), \pi)$ is the right vertex of the hyperbola. Finding $D_\theta r$ from Eq. (3), we get

$$D_\theta r = -\frac{e^2 d \sin \theta}{(1 - e \cos \theta)^2} \tag{8}$$

When $\theta_1 < \theta < \pi$, $\sin \theta > 0$; hence, $D_\theta r < 0$, from which we conclude that r is decreasing when θ is in the interval (θ_1, π). Therefore, for values of θ in the interval (θ_1, π) we obtain the top half of the right branch of the hyperbola shown in Fig. 12.2.8.

When $\pi < \theta < \theta_2$, $\sin \theta < 0$; so from Eq. (8), $D_\theta r > 0$. Hence, r is increasing when θ is in the interval (π, θ_2). Furthermore,

$$\lim_{\theta \to \theta_2^-} r = \lim_{\theta \to \theta_2^-} \frac{ed}{1 - e \cos \theta} = +\infty$$

Consequently, for values of θ in the interval (π, θ_2) we have the lower half of the right branch of the hyperbola. The other asymptote of the hyperbola is parallel to the line $\theta = \theta_2$.

The cosine function is increasing in the interval $(\theta_2, 2\pi)$. So when $\theta_2 < \theta < 2\pi$, $\cos \theta > \cos \theta_2 = 1/e$ or, equivalently, $1 - e \cos \theta < 0$. Thus, we see from Eq. (3) that for values of θ in the interval $(\theta_2, 2\pi)$, $r < 0$. Also,

$$\lim_{\theta \to \theta_2^+} r = \lim_{\theta \to \theta_2^+} \frac{ed}{1 - e \cos \theta} = -\infty$$

It follows from Eq. (8) that $D_\theta r > 0$; hence, r is increasing when $\theta_2 < \theta < 2\pi$. When $r < 0$ and r is increasing, $|r|$ is decreasing. Thus, for values of θ in the interval $(\theta_2, 2\pi)$ we obtain the upper half of the left branch of the hyperbola, and so the curve of Fig. 12.2.8 is complete.

EXAMPLE 5: The polar axis and its extension are along the principal axis of a hyperbola having a focus at the pole. The corresponding directrix is to the left of the focus. If the hyperbola contains the point $(1, \frac{2}{3}\pi)$ and $e = 2$, find (a) an equation of the hyperbola; (b) the vertices; (c) the center; and (d) an equation of the directrix corresponding to the focus at the pole. Draw a sketch of the hyperbola.

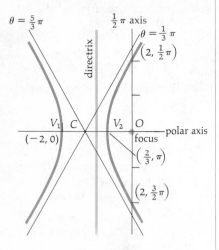

Figure 12.2.9

SOLUTION: An equation of the hyperbola is of the form of Eq. (3) with $e = 2$. We have, then,

$$r = \frac{2d}{1 - 2 \cos \theta}$$

Because the point $(1, \frac{2}{3}\pi)$ lies on the hyperbola, its coordinates satisfy the equation. Therefore,

$$1 = \frac{2d}{1 - 2(-\frac{1}{2})}$$

from which we obtain $d = 1$. Hence, an equation of the hyperbola is

$$r = \frac{2}{1 - 2 \cos \theta} \qquad (9)$$

The vertices are the points on the hyperbola for which $\theta = 0$ and $\theta = \pi$. From Eq. (9) we see that when $\theta = 0$, $r = -2$; and when $\theta = \pi$, $r = \frac{2}{3}$. Consequently, the left vertex V_1 is at the point $(-2, 0)$, and the right vertex V_2 is at the point $(\frac{2}{3}, \pi)$.

The center of the hyperbola is the point on the principal axis halfway between the two vertices. This is the point $(\frac{4}{3}, \pi)$.

An equation of the directrix corresponding to the focus at the pole is given by $r \cos \theta = -d$. Because $d = 1$, this equation is $r \cos \theta = -1$.

As an aid in drawing a sketch of the hyperbola, we first draw the two asymptotes. In our discussion of Case 3 we stated that these are lines through the center of the hyperbola that are parallel to the lines $\theta = \theta_1$ and $\theta = \theta_2$, where θ_1 and θ_2 are the values of θ in the interval $[0, 2\pi)$ for which r is not defined. From Eq. (9), r is not defined when $1 - 2 \cos \theta = 0$. Therefore, $\theta_1 = \frac{1}{3}\pi$ and $\theta_2 = \frac{5}{3}\pi$. Figure 12.2.9 shows a sketch of the hyperbola as well as the two asymptotes, and the directrix corresponding to the focus at the pole.

EXAMPLE 6: Find a polar equation of the hyperbola having the line $r \cos \theta = 4$ as the directrix

SOLUTION: The given directrix is perpendicular to the polar axis and is four units to the right of the focus at the pole. Therefore, an equation of the hyperbola is of the form of Eq. (4), which is corresponding to a focus at the pole, and $e = \frac{3}{2}$.

$$r = \frac{ed}{1 + e \cos \theta}$$

Because $d = 4$ and $e = \frac{3}{2}$, the equation becomes

$$r = \frac{\frac{3}{2} \cdot 4}{1 + \frac{3}{2} \cos \theta}$$

or, equivalently,

$$r = \frac{12}{2 + 3 \cos \theta}$$

Exercises 12.2

1. Show that an equation of a conic having its principal axis along the polar axis and its extension, a focus at the pole, and the corresponding directrix to the right of the focus is $r = ed/(1 + e \cos \theta)$.

2. Show that an equation of a conic having its principal axis along the $\frac{1}{2}\pi$ axis and its extension, a focus at the pole, and the corresponding directrix above the focus is $r = ed/(1 + e \sin \theta)$.

3. Show that an equation of a conic having its principal axis along the $\frac{1}{2}\pi$ axis and its extension, a focus at the pole, and the corresponding directrix below the focus is $r = ed/(1 - e \sin \theta)$.

4. Show that the equation $r = k \csc^2 \frac{1}{2}\theta$, where k is a constant, is a polar equation of a parabola.

In Exercises 5 through 14, the equation is that of a conic having a focus at the pole. In each Exercise, (a) find the eccentricity; (b) identify the conic; (c) write an equation of the directrix which corresponds to the focus at the pole; (d) draw a sketch of the curve.

5. $r = \dfrac{2}{1 - \cos \theta}$
6. $r = \dfrac{4}{1 + \cos \theta}$
7. $r = \dfrac{5}{2 + \sin \theta}$

8. $r = \dfrac{4}{1 - 3 \cos \theta}$
9. $r = \dfrac{6}{3 - 2 \cos \theta}$
10. $r = \dfrac{1}{2 + \sin \theta}$

11. $r = \dfrac{9}{5 - 6 \sin \theta}$
12. $r = \dfrac{1}{1 - 2 \sin \theta}$
13. $r = \dfrac{10}{7 - 2 \sin \theta}$

14. $r = \dfrac{7}{3 + 4 \cos \theta}$

In Exercises 15 through 18, find an equation of the conic having a focus at the pole and satisfying the given conditions.

15. Parabola; vertex at $(4, \frac{3}{2}\pi)$.

16. Ellipse; $e = \frac{1}{2}$; a vertex at $(4, \pi)$.

17. Hyperbola; vertices at $(1, \frac{1}{2}\pi)$ and $(3, \frac{1}{2}\pi)$.

18. Hyperbola; $e = \frac{4}{3}$; $r \cos \theta = 9$ is the directrix corresponding to the focus at the pole.

19. Find the area of the region inside the ellipse $r = 6/(2 - \sin \theta)$ and above the parabola $r = 3/(1 + \sin \theta)$.

20. For the ellipse and parabola of Exercise 19, find the area of the region inside the ellipse and below the parabola.

21. A comet is moving in a parabolic orbit around the sun at the focus of the parabola. When the comet is 80,000,000 miles from the sun the line segment from the sun to the comet makes an angle of $\frac{1}{3}\pi$ radians with the axis of the orbit. (a) Find an equation of the comet's orbit. (b) How close does the comet come to the sun?

22. The orbit of a planet is in the form of an ellipse having the equation $r = p/(1 + e \cos \theta)$ where the pole is at the sun. Find the average measure of the distance of the planet from the sun with respect to θ.

23. Using Definition 12.1.1, find a polar equation of a central conic for which the center is at the pole, the principal axis is along the polar axis and its extension, and the distance from the pole to a directrix is a/e.

24. Show that the tangent lines at the points of intersection of the parabolas $r = a/(1 + \cos \theta)$ and $r = b/(1 - \cos \theta)$ are perpendicular.

12.3 CARTESIAN EQUATIONS OF THE CONICS

In Sec. 12.2 we learned that a polar equation of a conic is

$$r = \frac{ed}{1 - e \cos \theta}$$

or, equivalently,

$$r = e(r \cos \theta + d) \tag{1}$$

A cartesian representation of Eq. (1) can be obtained by replacing r by $\pm\sqrt{x^2 + y^2}$ and $r \cos \theta$ by x. Making these substitutions, we get

$$\pm\sqrt{x^2 + y^2} = e(x + d)$$

Squaring on both sides of the above equation gives

$$x^2 + y^2 = e^2 x^2 + 2e^2 dx + e^2 d^2$$

or, equivalently,

$$y^2 + x^2(1 - e^2) = 2e^2 dx + e^2 d^2 \tag{2}$$

If $e = 1$, Eq. (2) becomes

$$y^2 = 2d(x + \tfrac{1}{2}d) \tag{3}$$

If we translate the origin to the point $(-\tfrac{1}{2}d, 0)$ by replacing x by $\bar{x} - \tfrac{1}{2}d$ and y by $\bar{y}$, Eq. (3) becomes

$$\bar{y}^2 = 2d\bar{x} \tag{4}$$

Equation (4) resembles Eq. (1) of Sec. 1.7

$$y^2 = 4px$$

which is an equation of the parabola having its focus at $(p, 0)$ and its directrix the line $x = -p$. Therefore, relative to the $\bar{x}$ and $\bar{y}$ axes, (4) is an equation of a parabola having its focus at $(\tfrac{1}{2}d, 0)$, which is the origin relative to the x and y axes. The parabola having its axis parallel to one of the coordinate axes was discussed in detail in Secs. 1.7 and 1.8.

If $e \neq 1$, we divide on both sides of Eq. (2) by $1 - e^2$ and obtain

$$x^2 - \frac{2e^2 d}{1 - e^2} x + \frac{1}{1 - e^2} y^2 = \frac{e^2 d^2}{1 - e^2}$$

Completing the square for the terms involving x by adding $e^4 d^2/(1 - e^2)^2$

on both sides of the above equation, we get

$$\left(x - \frac{e^2 d}{1 - e^2}\right)^2 + \frac{1}{1 - e^2} y^2 = \frac{e^2 d^2}{(1 - e^2)^2} \tag{5}$$

If the origin is translated to the point $(e^2 d/(1 - e^2), 0)$, Eq. (5) becomes

$$\bar{x}^2 + \frac{1}{1 - e^2} \bar{y}^2 = \frac{e^2 d^2}{(1 - e^2)^2}$$

or, equivalently,

$$\frac{\bar{x}^2}{\dfrac{e^2 d^2}{(1 - e^2)^2}} + \frac{\bar{y}^2}{\dfrac{e^2 d^2}{1 - e^2}} = 1 \tag{6}$$

Now let $e^2 d^2/(1 - e^2)^2 = a^2$, where $a > 0$. Then

$$a = \begin{cases} \dfrac{ed}{1 - e^2} & \text{if } 0 < e < 1 \\[2ex] \dfrac{ed}{e^2 - 1} & \text{if } e > 1 \end{cases} \tag{7}$$

Then Eq. (6) can be written as

$$\frac{\bar{x}^2}{a^2} + \frac{\bar{y}^2}{a^2(1 - e^2)} = 1$$

Replacing $\bar{x}$ and $\bar{y}$ by x and y, we get

$$\frac{x^2}{a^2} + \frac{y^2}{a^2(1 - e^2)} = 1 \tag{8}$$

Equation (8) is a standard form of a cartesian equation of a central conic having its principal axis on the x axis. Because (5) is an equation of a conic having a focus at the origin (pole), and (8) is obtained from (5) by translating the origin to the point $(e^2 d/(1 - e^2), 0)$, it follows that the central conic having Eq. (8) has a focus at the point $(-e^2 d/(1 - e^2), 0)$. However, from (7) it follows that

$$\frac{-e^2 d}{1 - e^2} = \begin{cases} -ae & \text{if } 0 < e < 1 \\ ae & \text{if } e > 1 \end{cases}$$

Therefore, we conclude that if (8) is an equation of an ellipse $(0 < e < 1)$, there is a focus at the point $(-ae, 0)$. If (8) is an equation of a hyperbola $(e > 1)$, there is a focus at $(ae, 0)$. In each case the corresponding directrix is d units to the left of the focus. So if the graph of (8) is an ellipse, the directrix corresponding to the focus at $(-ae, 0)$ has as an equation

$$x = -ae - d$$

Because when $0 < e < 1$, $d = a(1 - e^2)/e$, this equation becomes

$$x = -ae - \frac{a(1 - e^2)}{e}$$

or

$$x = -\frac{a}{e}$$

Similarly, if the graph of (8) is a hyperbola, the directrix corresponding to the focus at $(ae, 0)$ has as an equation

$$x = ae - d$$

When $e > 1$, $d = a(e^2 - 1)/e$; thus, the above equation of the directrix can be written as

$$x = \frac{a}{e}$$

Hence, we have shown that if (8) is an equation of an ellipse, a focus and its corresponding directrix are $(-ae, 0)$ and $x = -a/e$; and if (8) is an equation of a hyperbola, a focus and its corresponding directrix are $(ae, 0)$ and $x = a/e$.

Because Eq. (8) contains only even powers of x and y, its graph is symmetric with respect to both the x and y axes. Therefore, if there is a focus at $(-ae, 0)$ having a corresponding directrix of $x = -a/e$, by symmetry there is also a focus at $(ae, 0)$ having a corresponding directrix of $x = a/e$. Similarly, for a focus at $(ae, 0)$ and a corresponding directrix of $x = a/e$, there is also a focus at $(-ae, 0)$ and a corresponding directrix of $x = -a/e$. These results are summarized in the following theorem.

12.3.1 Theorem   The central conic having as an equation

$$\frac{x^2}{a^2} + \frac{y^2}{a^2(1 - e^2)} = 1 \tag{9}$$

where $a > 0$, has a focus at $(-ae, 0)$, whose corresponding directrix is $x = -a/e$, and a focus at $(ae, 0)$, whose corresponding directrix is $x = a/e$.

Figures 12.3.1 and 12.3.2 show sketches of the graph of Eq. (9) together with the foci and directrices in the respective cases of an ellipse and a hyperbola.

Suppose that in Eq. (9) $0 < e < 1$. Then the conic is an ellipse. Because in this case $1 - e^2 > 0$, we conclude that $\sqrt{1 - e^2}$ is a real number. Therefore, we let

$$b = a\sqrt{1 - e^2} \tag{10}$$

Because $a > 0$, it follows that $b > 0$. Substituting from (10) into (9), we obtain

$$\frac{x^2}{a^2} + \frac{y^2}{b^2} = 1 \tag{11}$$

Equation (11) is an equation of an ellipse having its principal axis

Figure 12.3.1

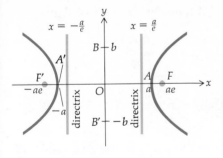

Figure 12.3.2

on the x axis. Because the vertices are the points of intersection of the ellipse with its principal axis, they are at $(-a, 0)$ and $(a, 0)$. The center of the ellipse is at the origin because it is the point midway between the vertices. Figure 12.3.1 shows a sketch of this ellipse. Refer to this figure as you read the next two paragraphs.

If we denote the vertices $(-a, 0)$ and $(a, 0)$ by A' and A, respectively, the segment $A'A$ of the principal axis is called the *major axis* of the ellipse, and its length is $2a$ units. Then we state that a is the number of units in the length of the semimajor axis of the ellipse.

The ellipse having Eq. (11) intersects the y axis at the points $(-b, 0)$ and $(b, 0)$, which we denote by B' and B, respectively. The segment $B'B$ is called the *minor axis* of the ellipse. Its length is $2b$ units. Hence, b is the number of units in the length of the semiminor axis of the ellipse. Because a and b are positive numbers and $0 < e < 1$, it follows from Eq. (10) that $b < a$.

EXAMPLE 1: Given the ellipse having the equation

$$\frac{x^2}{25} + \frac{y^2}{16} = 1$$

find the vertices, foci, directrices, eccentricity, and extremities of the minor axis. Draw a sketch of the ellipse and show the foci and directrices.

Figure 12.3.3

SOLUTION: From the equation of the ellipse, we have $a^2 = 25$ and $b^2 = 16$; thus, $a = 5$ and $b = 4$. Therefore, the vertices are at the points $A'(-5, 0)$ and $A(5, 0)$, and the extremities of the minor axis are at the points $B'(0, -4)$ and $B(0, 4)$. From (10) we have $4 = 5\sqrt{1 - e^2}$, from which it follows that $e = \frac{3}{5}$. The foci and the directrices are obtained by applying Theorem 12.3.1. Because $ae = 3$ and $a/e = \frac{25}{3}$, we conclude that one focus F is at $(3, 0)$ and its corresponding directrix has the equation $x = \frac{25}{3}$; the other focus F' is at $(-3, 0)$ and its corresponding directrix has the equation $x = -\frac{25}{3}$. A sketch of the ellipse, the foci F and F', and the directrices are in Fig. 12.3.3. From the definition of a conic (12.1.1) it follows that if P is any point on this ellipse, the ratio of the undirected distance of P from a focus to the undirected distance of P from the corresponding directrix is equal to the eccentricity $\frac{3}{5}$.

EXAMPLE 2: An arch is in the form of a semiellipse. It is 48 ft wide at the base and has a height of 20 ft. How wide is the arch at a height of 10 ft above the base?

SOLUTION: Figure 12.3.4 shows a sketch of the arch and the coordinate axes which are chosen so that the x axis is along the base and the origin is at the midpoint of the base. Then the ellipse has its principal axis on the x axis, its center at the origin, $a = 24$, and $b = 20$. An equation of the ellipse is of the form of Eq. (11):

$$\frac{x^2}{576} + \frac{y^2}{400} = 1$$

Let $2\bar{x}$ be the number of feet in the width of the arch at a height of 10 ft

Figure 12.3.4

above the base. Therefore, the point $(\bar{x}, 10)$ lies on the ellipse. Thus,

$$\frac{\bar{x}^2}{576} + \frac{100}{400} = 1$$

and so

$$\bar{x}^2 = 432$$

$$\bar{x} = 12\sqrt{3}$$

Hence, at a height of 10 ft above the base the width of the arch is $24\sqrt{3}$ ft.

Consider now the central conic of Theorem 12.3.1 when $e > 1$, that is, when the conic is a hyperbola. Because $e > 1$, $1 - e^2 < 0$; hence, $e^2 - 1 > 0$. Therefore, for a hyperbola we let

$$b = a\sqrt{e^2 - 1} \tag{12}$$

It follows from Eq. (12) that b is a positive number. Also, from (12), if $1 < e < \sqrt{2}$, $b < a$; if $e = \sqrt{2}$, $b = a$; and if $e > \sqrt{2}$, $b > a$. Substituting from (12) into (9), we get

$$\frac{x^2}{a^2} - \frac{y^2}{b^2} = 1 \tag{13}$$

Equation (13) is an equation of a hyperbola having its principal axis on the x axis, its vertices at the points $(-a, 0)$ and $(a, 0)$, and its center at the origin. A sketch of this hyperbola is in Fig. 12.3.2. If we denote the vertices $(-a, 0)$ and $(a, 0)$ by A' and A, the segment $A'A$ is called the *transverse axis* of the hyperbola. The length of the transverse axis is $2a$ units, and so a is the number of units in the length of the semitransverse axis.

Substituting 0 for x in Eq. (13), we obtain $y^2 = -b^2$, which has no real roots. Consequently, the hyperbola does not intersect the y axis. However, the line segment having extremities at the points $(0, -b)$ and $(0, b)$ is called the *conjugate axis* of the hyperbola, and its length is $2b$ units. Hence, b is the number of units in the length of the semiconjugate axis.

Solving Eq. (13) for y in terms of x, we obtain

$$y = \pm \frac{b}{a} \sqrt{x^2 - a^2} \tag{14}$$

We conclude from (14) that if $|x| < a$, there is no real value of y. Therefore, there are no points (x, y) on the hyperbola for which $-a < x < a$. We also see from (14) that if $|x| \geq a$, then y has two real values. As previously learned, the hyperbola has two branches. One branch contains the vertex $A(a, 0)$ and extends indefinitely far to the right of A. The other branch contains the vertex $A'(-a, 0)$ and extends indefinitely far to the left of A'.

EXAMPLE 3: Given the hyperbola

$$\frac{x^2}{9} - \frac{y^2}{16} = 1$$

find the vertices, foci, directrices, eccentricity, and lengths of the transverse and conjugate axes. Draw a sketch of the hyperbola and show the foci and the directrices.

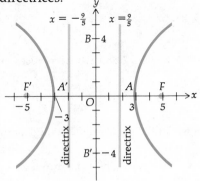

Figure 12.3.5

SOLUTION: The given equation is of the form of Eq. (13); thus, $a = 3$ and $b = 4$. The vertices are therefore at the points $A'(-3, 0)$ and $A(3, 0)$. The number of units in the length of the transverse axis is $2a = 6$, and the number of units in the length of the conjugate axis is $2b = 8$. Because from (12), $b = a\sqrt{e^2 - 1}$, we have $4 = 3\sqrt{e^2 - 1}$, and so $e = \frac{5}{3}$. Therefore, $ae = 5$ and $a/e = \frac{9}{5}$. Hence, the foci are at $F'(-5, 0)$ and $F(5, 0)$. The corresponding directrices have, respectively, the equations $x = -\frac{9}{5}$ and $x = \frac{9}{5}$. A sketch of the hyperbola and the foci and directrices are in Fig. 12.3.5. From Definition 12.1.1 it follows that if P is any point on this hyperbola the ratio of the undirected distance of P from a focus to the undirected distance of P from the corresponding directrix is equal to the eccentricity $\frac{5}{3}$.

EXAMPLE 4: Find an equation of the hyperbola having the ends of its conjugate axis at $(0,-2)$ and $(0, 2)$ and an eccentricity equal to $\frac{3}{5}\sqrt{5}$.

SOLUTION: Because the ends of the conjugate axis are at $(0, -2)$ and $(0, 2)$, it follows that $b = 2$, the transverse axis is along the x axis, and the center is at the origin. Hence, an equation is of the form

$$\frac{x^2}{a^2} - \frac{y^2}{b^2} = 1$$

To find a we use the equation $b = a\sqrt{e^2 - 1}$ and let $b = 2$ and $e = \frac{3}{5}\sqrt{5}$, thereby yielding $2 = a\sqrt{\frac{9}{5} - 1}$. Therefore, $a = \sqrt{5}$, and an equation of the hyperbola is

$$\frac{x^2}{5} - \frac{y^2}{4} = 1$$

Exercises 12.3

In Exercises 1 through 4, find the vertices, foci, directrices, eccentricity, and ends of the minor axis of the given ellipse. Draw a sketch of the curve and show the foci and the directrices.

1. $4x^2 + 9y^2 = 36$ 2. $4x^2 + 9y^2 = 4$ 3. $2x^2 + 3y^2 = 18$ 4. $3x^2 + 4y^2 = 9$

In Exercises 5 through 9, find the vertices, foci, directrices, eccentricity, and lengths of the transverse and conjugate axes of the given hyperbola. Draw a sketch of the curve and show the foci and the directrices.

5. $9x^2 - 4y^2 = 36$ 6. $x^2 - 9y^2 = 9$ 7. $9x^2 - 16y^2 = 1$ 8. $25x^2 - 25y^2 = 1$

In Exercises 9 through 14, find an equation of the given conic satisfying the given conditions and draw a sketch of the graph.

9. Hyperbola having vertices at $(-2, 0)$ and $(2, 0)$ and a conjugate axis of length 6.

10. Ellipse having foci at $(-5, 0)$ and $(5, 0)$ and one directrix the line $x = -20$.

11. Ellipse having vertices at $(-\frac{5}{2}, 0)$ and $(\frac{5}{2}, 0)$ and one focus $(\frac{3}{2}, 0)$.

12. Hyperbola having the ends of its conjugate axis at $(0, -3)$ and $(0, 3)$ and $e = 2$.

13. Hyperbola having its center at the origin, its foci on the x axis, and passing through the points $(4, -2)$ and $(7, -6)$.

14. Ellipse having its center at the origin, its foci on the x axis, the length of the major axis equal to three times the length of the minor axis, and passing through the point $(3, 3)$.

15. Find an equation of the tangent line to the ellipse $4x^2 + 9y^2 = 72$ at the point $(3, 2)$.

16. Find an equation of the normal line to the hyperbola $4x^2 - 3y^2 = 24$ at the point $(3, 2)$.

17. Find an equation of the hyperbola whose foci are the vertices of the ellipse $7x^2 + 11y^2 = 77$ and whose vertices are the foci of this ellipse.

18. Find an equation of the ellipse whose foci are the vertices of the hyperbola $11x^2 - 7y^2 = 77$ and whose vertices are the foci of this hyperbola.

19. The ceiling in a hallway 20 ft wide is in the shape of a semiellipse and is 18 ft high in the center and 12 ft high at the side walls. Find the height of the ceiling 4 ft from either wall.

20. A football is 12 in. long, and a plane section containing a seam is an ellipse, of which the length of the minor axis is 7 in. Find the volume of the football if the leather is so stiff that every cross section is a square.

21. Solve Exercise 20 if every cross section is a circle.

22. The orbit of the earth around the sun is elliptical in shape with the sun at one focus, a semimajor axis of length 92.9 million miles, and an eccentricity of 0.017. Find (a) how close the earth gets to the sun and (b) the greatest possible distance between the earth and the sun.

23. The cost of production of a commodity is $12 less per unit at a point A than it is at a point B and the distance between A and B is 100 miles. Assuming that the route of delivery of the commodity is along a straight line, and that the delivery cost is 20 cents per unit per mile, find the curve at any point of which the commodity can be supplied from either A or B at the same total cost. (HINT: Take points A and B at $(-50, 0)$ and $(50, 0)$, respectively.)

24. Prove that there is no tangent line to the hyperbola $x^2 - y^2 = 1$ that passes through the origin.

25. Find the volume of the solid of revolution generated by revolving the region bounded by the hyperbola $x^2/a^2 - y^2/b^2 = 1$ and the line $x = 2a$ about the x axis.

26. Find the centroid of the solid of revolution of Exercise 25.

27. A tank has a horizontal axis of length 20 ft and its ends are semiellipses. The width across the top of the tank is 10 ft and the depth is 6 ft. If the tank is full of water, how much work is necessary to pump all the water to the top of the tank?

12.4 THE ELLIPSE   In Sec. 12.3 we considered ellipses for which the center is at the origin and the principal axis is on the x axis. Now more general equations of ellipses will be discussed.

   If an ellipse has its center at the origin and its principal axis on the y axis, then an equation of the ellipse is of the form

$$\frac{y^2}{a^2} + \frac{x^2}{b^2} = 1 \tag{1}$$

which is obtained from Eq. (11) of Sec. 12.3 by interchanging x and y. Because for an ellipse $a > b$, it follows that the ellipse having the equation $x^2/16 + y^2/25 = 1$ has its foci on the y axis. This ellipse has the same shape as the ellipse of Example 1 in Sec. 12.3. The vertices are at $(0, -5)$ and $(0, 5)$, and the foci are at $(0, -3)$ and $(0, 3)$, and their corresponding directrices have the equations $y = -\frac{25}{3}$ and $y = \frac{25}{3}$, respectively.

If the center of an ellipse is at the point (h, k) rather than at the origin, and if the principal axis is parallel to one of the coordinate axes, then by a translation of axes so that the point (h, k) is the new origin, an equation of the ellipse is $\bar{x}^2/a^2 + \bar{y}^2/b^2 = 1$ if the principal axis is horizontal, and $\bar{y}^2/a^2 + \bar{x}^2/b^2 = 1$ if the principal axis is vertical. Because $\bar{x} = x - h$ and $\bar{y} = y - k$, these equations become the following in x and y:

$$\frac{(x-h)^2}{a^2} + \frac{(y-k)^2}{b^2} = 1 \tag{2}$$

if the principal axis is horizontal, and

$$\frac{(y-k)^2}{a^2} + \frac{(x-h)^2}{b^2} = 1 \tag{3}$$

if the principal axis is vertical.

In Sec. 1.6 we discussed the general equation of the second degree in two variables:

$$Ax^2 + Bxy + Cy^2 + Dx + Ey + F = 0 \tag{4}$$

where $B = 0$ and $A = C$. In such a case, the graph of (4) is either a circle or a degenerate case of a circle, which is either a point-circle or no real locus. If we eliminate the fractions and combine terms in Eqs. (2) and (3), we obtain an equation of the form

$$Ax^2 + Cy^2 + Dx + Ey + F = 0 \tag{5}$$

where $A \neq C$ if $a \neq b$ and $AC > 0$. It can be shown by completing the squares in x and y that an equation of the form (5) can be put in the form

$$\frac{(x-h)^2}{\dfrac{1}{A}} + \frac{(y-k)^2}{\dfrac{1}{C}} = G \tag{6}$$

If $AC > 0$, then A and C have the same sign. If G has the same sign as A and C, then Eq. (6) can be written in the form of (2) or (3). Thus, the graph of (5) is an ellipse. Suppose, for example, that we have the equation

$$6x^2 + 9y^2 - 24x - 54y + 51 = 0$$

which can be written as

$$6(x^2 - 4x) + 9(y^2 - 6y) = -51$$

Completing the squares in x and y, we get

$$6(x^2 - 4x + 4) + 9(y^2 - 6y + 9) = -51 + 24 + 81$$

or, equivalently,

$$6(x - 2)^2 + 9(y - 3)^2 = 54$$

which can be put in the form

$$\frac{(x - 2)^2}{\frac{1}{6}} + \frac{(y - 3)^2}{\frac{1}{9}} = 54$$

This is an equation of the form of Eq. (6). By dividing on both sides by 54 we have

$$\frac{(x - 2)^2}{9} + \frac{(y - 3)^2}{6} = 1$$

which has the form of Eq. (2).

If in Eq. (6) G has a sign opposite to that of A and C, then (6) is not satisfied by any real values of x and y. Hence, the graph of (5) is no real locus. For example, suppose that Eq. (5) is

$$6x^2 + 9y^2 - 24x - 54y + 115 = 0$$

Then, upon completing the squares in x and y, we get

$$6(x - 2)^2 + 9(y - 3)^2 = -115 + 24 + 81$$

which can be written as

$$\frac{(x - 2)^2}{\frac{1}{6}} + \frac{(y - 3)^2}{\frac{1}{9}} = -10 \tag{7}$$

This is of the form of Eq. (6), where $G = -10$, $A = 6$, and $C = 9$. For all values of x and y the left side of Eq. (7) is nonnegative; hence, the graph of (7) is no real locus.

If $G = 0$ in (6), then the equation is satisfied by only the point (h, k). Therefore, the graph of (5) is a single point, which we call a *point-ellipse*. In particular, because

$$6x^2 + 9y^2 - 24x - 54y + 105 = 0$$

can be written as

$$\frac{(x - 2)^2}{\frac{1}{6}} + \frac{(y - 3)^2}{\frac{1}{9}} = 0$$

its graph is the point $(2, 3)$. For a point-ellipse or no real locus the graph is said to be degenerate.

If $A = C$ in (5), we have either a circle or a degenerate circle, as mentioned above. A circle is a limiting form of an ellipse. This can be shown by considering the formula relating a, b, and e for an ellipse:

$$b^2 = a^2(1 - e^2)$$

From this formula, it is seen that as e approaches zero, b^2 approaches a^2. If $b^2 = a^2$, Eqs. (2) and (3) become

$$(x - h)^2 + (y - k)^2 = a^2$$

which is an equation of a circle having its center at (h, k) and radius a. We see that the results of Sec. 1.6 for a circle are the same as those obtained for Eq. (5) applied to an ellipse.

The results of the above discussion are summarized in the following theorem.

12.4.1 Theorem   If in the general second-degree Eq. (4) $B = 0$ and $AC > 0$, then the graph is either an ellipse, a point-ellipse, or no real locus. In addition, if $A = C$, then the graph is either a circle, a point-circle, or no real locus.

EXAMPLE 1:   Determine the graph of the equation $25x^2 + 16y^2 + 150x - 128y - 1119 = 0$.

SOLUTION: From Theorem 12.4.1, because $B = 0$ and $AC = (25)(16) = 400 > 0$, the graph is either an ellipse or is degenerate. Completing the squares in x and y, we have

$$25(x^2 + 6x + 9) + 16(y^2 - 8y + 16) = 1119 + 225 + 256$$

or

$$25(x + 3)^2 + 16(y - 4)^2 = 1600$$

or

$$\frac{(x + 3)^2}{64} + \frac{(y - 4)^2}{100} = 1 \tag{8}$$

Equation (8) is of the form of Eq. (3), and so the graph is an ellipse having its principal axis parallel to the y axis and its center at $(-3, 4)$.

EXAMPLE 2:   For the ellipse of Example 1, find the vertices, foci, directrices, eccentricity, and extremities of the minor axis. Draw a sketch of the ellipse and show the foci and the directrices.

SOLUTION: From Eq. (8) it follows that $a = 10$ and $b = 8$. Because the center of the ellipse is at $(-3, 4)$ and the principal axis is vertical, the vertices are at the points $V'(-3, -6)$ and $V(-3, 14)$. The extremities of the minor axis are at the points $B'(-11, 4)$ and $B(5, 4)$. Because $b = a\sqrt{1 - e^2}$, we have

$$8 = 10\sqrt{1 - e^2}$$

and, solving for e, we get $e = \frac{3}{5}$. Consequently, $ae = 6$ and $a/e = \frac{50}{3}$. Therefore, the foci are at the points $F'(-3, -2)$ and $F(-3, 10)$. The corresponding directrices have, respectively, the equations $y = -\frac{38}{3}$ and $y = \frac{62}{3}$. A sketch of the ellipse, the foci, and the directrices are in Fig. 12.4.1.

$y = \frac{62}{3}$ directrix

$(-3, 14)$ V

$(-3, 10)$ F

$(-11, 4)$ B' $(-3, 4)$ B $(5, 4)$

$(-3, -2)$ F'

$(-3, -6)$ V'

$y = -\frac{38}{3}$ directrix

Figure 12.4.1

EXAMPLE 3: Find an equation of the ellipse for which the foci are at $(-8, 2)$ and $(4, 2)$ and the eccentricity is $\frac{2}{3}$. Draw a sketch of the ellipse.

SOLUTION: The center of the ellipse which is halfway between the foci is the point $(-2, 2)$. The distance between the foci of any ellipse is $2ae$, and the distance between $(-8, 2)$ and $(4, 2)$ is 12. Therefore, we have the equation $2ae = 12$. Replacing e by $\frac{2}{3}$, we get $2a(\frac{2}{3}) = 12$, and so $a = 9$. Because $b = a\sqrt{1 - e^2}$, we have

$$b = 9\sqrt{1 - (\tfrac{2}{3})^2} = 9\sqrt{1 - \tfrac{4}{9}} = 3\sqrt{5}$$

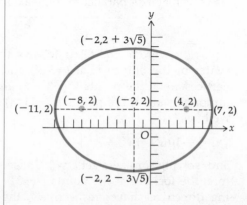

$(-2, 2 + 3\sqrt{5})$

$(-11, 2)$ $(-8, 2)$ $(-2, 2)$ $(4, 2)$ $(7, 2)$

O

$(-2, 2 - 3\sqrt{5})$

Figure 12.4.2

The principal axis is parallel to the x axis; hence, an equation of the ellipse is of the form of Eq. (2). Because $(h, k) = (-2, 2)$, $a = 9$, and $b = 3\sqrt{5}$, the required equation is

$$\frac{(x + 2)^2}{81} + \frac{(y - 2)^2}{45} = 1$$

A sketch of this ellipse is shown in Fig. 12.4.2.

We conclude this section with a theorem that gives an alternative definition of an ellipse. The theorem is based on a characteristic property of the ellipse.

12.4.2 Theorem   An ellipse can be defined as the set of points such that the sum of the distances from any point of the set to two given points (the foci) is a constant.

PROOF: The proof consists of two parts. In the first part we show that the set of points defined in the theorem is an ellipse. In the second part we prove that any ellipse is such a set of points. Refer to Fig. 12.4.3 in both parts of the proof.

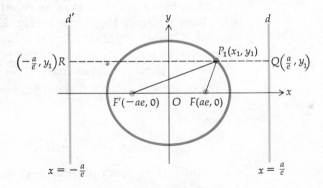

Figure 12.4.3

Let the point $P_1(x_1, y_1)$ be any point in the given set. Let the foci be the points $F'(-ae, 0)$ and $F(ae, 0)$, and let the constant sum of the distances be $2a$. Then

$$|\overline{FP_1}| + |\overline{F'P_1}| = 2a$$

Using the distance formula, we get

$$\sqrt{(x_1 - ae)^2 + y_1{}^2} + \sqrt{(x_1 + ae)^2 + y_1{}^2} = 2a$$

or

$$\sqrt{(x_1 - ae)^2 + y_1{}^2} = 2a - \sqrt{(x_1 + ae)^2 + y_1{}^2}$$

Squaring on both sides of the above equation, we obtain

$$x_1{}^2 - 2aex_1 + a^2e^2 + y_1{}^2 = 4a^2 - 4a\sqrt{(x_1 + ae)^2 + y_1{}^2}$$
$$+ x_1{}^2 + 2aex_1 + a^2e^2 + y_1{}^2$$

or

$$\sqrt{(x_1 + ae)^2 + y_1{}^2} = a + ex_1$$

Squaring on both sides again, we get

$$x_1{}^2 + 2aex_1 + a^2e^2 + y_1{}^2 = a^2 + 2aex_1 + e^2x_1{}^2$$

or

$$(1 - e^2)x_1{}^2 + y_1{}^2 = a^2(1 - e^2)$$

or

$$\frac{x_1{}^2}{a^2} + \frac{y_1{}^2}{a^2(1 - e^2)} = 1$$

Because $b^2 = a^2(1 - e^2)$, and replacing x_1 and y_1 by x and y, respectively, we obtain

$$\frac{x^2}{a^2} + \frac{y^2}{b^2} = 1$$

which is the required form of an equation of an ellipse.

Now consider the ellipse in Fig. 12.4.3; $P_1(x_1, y_1)$ is any point on the ellipse. Through P_1 draw a line that is parallel to the x axis and that intersects the directrices d and d' at the points Q and R, respectively. From Definition 12.1.1 it follows that

$$|\overline{F'P_1}| = e|\overline{RP_1}| \quad \text{and} \quad |\overline{FP_1}| = e|\overline{P_1Q}|$$

Therefore,

$$|\overline{F'P_1}| + |\overline{FP_1}| = e(|\overline{RP_1}| + |\overline{P_1Q}|) \tag{9}$$

$\overline{RP_1}$ and $\overline{P_1Q}$ are both positive because an ellipse lies between its directrices. Hence,

$$|\overline{RP_1}| + |\overline{P_1Q}| = \overline{RP_1} + \overline{P_1Q} = \overline{RQ} = \frac{a}{e} - \left(-\frac{a}{e}\right) = \frac{2a}{e} \tag{10}$$

Substituting from (10) into (9), we get

$$|\overline{F'P_1}| + |\overline{FP_1}| = 2a$$

which proves that an ellipse is a set of points as described in the theorem. ∎

The ellipse of Example 1 has foci at $(-3, -2)$ and $(-3, 10)$, and $2a = 20$. Therefore, by Theorem 12.4.2 this ellipse can be defined as the set of points such that the sum of the distances from any point of the set to the points $(-3, -2)$ and $(-3, 10)$ is equal to 20. Similarly, the ellipse of

Example 3 can be defined as the set of points such that the sum of the distances from any point of the set to the points $(-8, 2)$ and $(4, 2)$ is equal to 18.

Exercises 12.4

In Exercises 1 through 6, find the eccentricity, center, foci, and directrices of each of the given ellipses and draw a sketch of the graph.

1. $6x^2 + 9y^2 - 24x - 54y + 51 = 0$
2. $9x^2 + 4y^2 - 18x + 16y - 11 = 0$
3. $5x^2 + 3y^2 - 3y - 12 = 0$
4. $2x^2 + 2y^2 - 2x + 18y + 33 = 0$
5. $4x^2 + 4y^2 + 20x - 32y + 89 = 0$
6. $3x^2 + 4y^2 - 30x + 16y + 100 = 0$

In Exercises 7 through 12, find an equation of the ellipse satisfying the given conditions and draw a sketch of the graph.

7. Foci at $(5, 0)$ and $(-5, 0)$; one directrix is the line $x = -20$.

8. Vertices at $(0, 5)$ and $(0, -5)$ and passing through the point $(2, -\frac{5}{3}\sqrt{5})$.

9. Center at $(4, -2)$, a vertex at $(9, -2)$, and one focus at $(0, -2)$.

10. Foci at $(2, 3)$ and $(2, -7)$ and eccentricity of $\frac{2}{3}$.

11. Foci at $(-1, -1)$ and $(-1, 7)$ and the semimajor axis of length 8 units.

12. Directrices the lines $y = 3 \pm \frac{16.9}{12}$ and a focus at $(0, -2)$.

13. The following graphical method for sketching the graph of an ellipse is based on Theorem 12.4.2. To draw a sketch of the graph of the ellipse $4x^2 + y^2 = 16$, first locate the points of intersection with the axes and then locate the foci on the y axis by use of compasses set with center at one point of intersection with the x axis and with radius of 4. Then fasten thumbtacks at each focus and tie one end of a string at one thumbtack and the other end of the string at the second thumbtack in such a way that the length of the string between the tacks is $2a = 8$. Place a pencil against the string, drawing it taut, and describe a curve with the point of the pencil by moving it against the taut string. When the curve is completed, it will necessarily be an ellipse, because the pencil point describes a locus of points whose sum of distances from the two tacks is a constant.

14. Use Theorem 12.4.2 to find an equation of the ellipse for which the sum of the distances from any point on the ellipse to $(4, -1)$ and $(4, 7)$ is equal to 12.

15. Solve Exercise 14 if the sum of the distances from $(-4, -5)$ and $(6, -5)$ is equal to 16.

16. A plate is in the shape of the region bounded by the ellipse having a semimajor axis of length 3 ft and a semiminor axis of length 2 ft. If the plate is lowered vertically in a tank of water until the minor axis lies in the surface of the water, find the force due to liquid pressure on one side of the submerged portion of the plate.

17. If the plate of Exercise 16 is lowered until the center is 3 ft below the surface of the water, find the force due to liquid pressure on one side of the plate. The minor axis is still horizontal.

12.5 THE HYPERBOLA   In Sec. 12.3 we learned that an equation of a hyperbola having its center at the origin and its principal axis on the x axis is of the form $x^2/a^2 - y^2/b^2 = 1$. Interchanging x and y in this equation, we obtain

$$\frac{y^2}{a^2} - \frac{x^2}{b^2} = 1 \tag{1}$$

which is an equation of a hyperbola having its center at the origin and its principal axis on the y axis. For example, the hyperbola with an equation $y^2/9 - x^2/16 = 1$ has its foci on the y axis because the equation is of the form (1). Note that there is no general inequality involving a and b corresponding to the inequality $a > b$ for an ellipse. That is, for a hyperbola, it is possible to have $a < b$, as in the example just mentioned, where $a = 3$ and $b = 4$; or it is possible to have $a > b$, as for the hyperbola having the equation $y^2/25 - x^2/16 = 1$, where $a = 5$ and $b = 4$. If, for a hyperbola, $a = b$, then the hyperbola is said to be *equilateral*.

We stated in Sec. 12.2 that a hyperbola has asymptotes, and we now show how to obtain equations of these asymptotes. In Sec. 2.9 horizontal and vertical asymptotes of the graph of a function were defined. What follows is a more general definition, of which the definitions in Sec. 2.9 are special cases.

12.5.1 Definition The graph of the equation $y = f(x)$ has the line $y = mx + b$ as an *asymptote* if either of the following statements is true:

(i) $\lim\limits_{x \to +\infty} [f(x) - (mx + b)] = 0$

(ii) $\lim\limits_{x \to -\infty} [f(x) - (mx + b)] = 0$

Statement (i) indicates that for any $\epsilon > 0$ there exists a number $N > 0$ such that

$$|f(x) - (mx + b)| < \epsilon \qquad \text{whenever } x > N$$

that is, we can make the function value $f(x)$ as close to the value of $mx + b$ as we please by taking x large enough. This is consistent with our intuitive notion of an asymptote of a graph. A similar statement may be made for part (ii) of Definition 12.5.1.

For the hyperbola $x^2/a^2 - y^2/b^2 = 1$, upon solving for y, we get

$$y = \pm \frac{b}{a} \sqrt{x^2 - a^2}$$

So if

$$f(x) = \frac{b}{a} \sqrt{x^2 - a^2}$$

we have

$$\lim_{x \to +\infty} \left[f(x) - \frac{b}{a} x \right] = \lim_{x \to +\infty} \left[\frac{b}{a} \sqrt{x^2 - a^2} - \frac{b}{a} x \right]$$

$$= \frac{b}{a} \lim_{x \to +\infty} \frac{(\sqrt{x^2 - a^2} - x)(\sqrt{x^2 - a^2} + x)}{\sqrt{x^2 + a^2} + x}$$

$$= \frac{b}{a} \lim_{x \to +\infty} \frac{-a^2}{\sqrt{x^2 - a^2} + x}$$

$$= 0$$

Therefore, by Definition 12.5.1, we conclude that the line $y = bx/a$ is an asymptote of the graph of $y = b\sqrt{x^2 - a^2}/a$. Similarly, it can be shown that the line $y = bx/a$ is an asymptote of the graph of $y = -b\sqrt{x^2 - a^2}/a$. Consequently, the line $y = bx/a$ is an asymptote of the hyperbola $x^2/a^2 - y^2/b^2 = 1$. In an analogous manner, we can demonstrate that the line $y = -bx/a$ is an asymptote of this same hyperbola. We have, then, the following theorem.

12.5.2 Theorem The lines

$$y = \frac{b}{a}x \quad \text{and} \quad y = -\frac{b}{a}x$$

are asymptotes of the hyperbola

$$\frac{x^2}{a^2} - \frac{y^2}{b^2} = 1$$

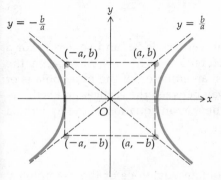

Figure 12.5.1

Figure 12.5.1 shows a sketch of the hyperbola of Theorem 12.5.2 together with its asymptotes. In the figure note that the diagonals of the rectangle having vertices at (a, b), $(a, -b)$, $(-a, b)$, and $(-a, -b)$ are on the asymptotes of the hyperbola. This rectangle is called the *auxiliary rectangle* of the hyperbola. The vertices of the hyperbola are the points of intersection of the principal axis and the auxiliary rectangle. A fairly good sketch of a hyperbola can be made by first drawing the auxiliary rectangle and then drawing the branch of the hyperbola through each vertex tangent to the side of the auxiliary rectangle there and approaching asymptotically the lines on which the diagonals of the rectangle lie.

There is a mnemonic device for obtaining equations of the asymptotes of a hyperbola. For example, for the hyperbola having the equation $x^2/a^2 - y^2/b^2 = 1$, if the right side is replaced by zero, we obtain $x^2/a^2 - y^2/b^2 = 0$. Upon factoring, this equation becomes $(x/a - y/b)(x/a + y/b) = 0$, which is equivalent to the two equations $x/a - y/b = 0$ and $x/a + y/b = 0$, which, by Theorem 12.5.2, are equations of the asymptotes of the given hyperbola. Using this device for the hyperbola having Eq. (1), we see that the asymptotes are the lines having equations $y/a - x/b = 0$ and $y/a + x/b = 0$, which are the same lines as the asymptotes of the hyperbola with the equation $x^2/b^2 - y^2/a^2 = 1$. These two hyperbolas are called *conjugate hyperbolas*.

The asymptotes of an equilateral hyperbola ($a = b$) are perpendicular to each other. The auxiliary rectangle for such a hyperbola is a square, and the transverse and conjugate axes have equal lengths.

If the center of a hyperbola is at (h, k) and its principal axis is parallel to the x axis, then if the axes are translated so that the point (h, k) is the new origin, an equation of the hyperbola relative to this new coordinate system is

$$\frac{\bar{x}^2}{a^2} - \frac{\bar{y}^2}{b^2} = 1$$

If we replace $\bar{x}$ by $x - h$ and $\bar{y}$ by $y - k$, this equation becomes

$$\frac{(x - h)^2}{a^2} - \frac{(y - k)^2}{b^2} = 1 \tag{2}$$

Similarly, an equation of a hyperbola having its center at (h, k) and its principal axis parallel to the y axis is

$$\frac{(y - k)^2}{a^2} - \frac{(x - h)^2}{b^2} = 1 \tag{3}$$

EXAMPLE 1: The vertices of a hyperbola are at $(-5, -3)$ and $(-5, -1)$, and the eccentricity is $\sqrt{5}$. Find an equation of the hyperbola and equations of the asymptotes. Draw a sketch of the hyperbola and the asymptotes.

SOLUTION: The distance between the vertices is $2a$, and so $a = 1$. For a hyperbola, $b = a\sqrt{e^2 - 1}$, and therefore $b = 1\sqrt{5 - 1} = 2$. Because the principal axis is parallel to the y axis, an equation of the hyperbola is of the form (3). The center (h, k) is halfway between the vertices and is therefore at the point $(-5, -2)$. We have, then, as an equation of the hyperbola

$$\frac{(y + 2)^2}{1} - \frac{(x + 5)^2}{4} = 1$$

Using the mnemonic device to obtain equations of the asymptotes, we have

$$\left(\frac{y + 2}{1} - \frac{x + 5}{2}\right)\left(\frac{y + 2}{1} + \frac{x + 5}{2}\right) = 0$$

which gives

$$y + 2 = \tfrac{1}{2}(x + 5) \quad \text{and} \quad y + 2 = -\tfrac{1}{2}(x + 5)$$

A sketch of the hyperbola and the asymptotes are in Fig. 12.5.2.

Figure 12.5.2

If in Eqs. (2) and (3) we eliminate fractions and combine terms, the resulting equations are of the form

$$Ax^2 + Cy^2 + Dx + Ey + F = 0 \tag{4}$$

where A and C have different signs; that is, $AC < 0$. We now wish to show that the graph of an equation of the form (4), where $AC < 0$, is either a hyperbola or it degenerates. Completing the squares in x and y in Eq. (4), where $AC < 0$, the resulting equation has the form

$$\alpha^2(x - h)^2 - \beta^2(y - k)^2 = H \tag{5}$$

If $H > 0$, Eq. (5) can be written as

$$\frac{(x - h)^2}{\dfrac{H}{\alpha^2}} - \frac{(y - k)^2}{\dfrac{H}{\beta^2}} = 1$$

which has the form of Eq. (2). For example, the equation

$$4x^2 - 12y^2 + 24x + 96y - 181 = 0$$

can be written as

$$4(x^2 + 6x) - 12(y^2 - 8y) = 181$$

and upon completing the squares in x and y, we have

$$4(x^2 + 6x + 9) - 12(y^2 - 8y + 16) = 181 + 36 - 192$$

which is equivalent to

$$4(x + 3)^2 - 12(y - 4)^2 = 25$$

This has the form of Eq. (5), where $H = 25 > 0$. It may be written as

$$\frac{(x + 3)^2}{\frac{25}{4}} - \frac{(y - 4)^2}{\frac{25}{12}} = 1$$

which has the form of Eq. (2).

If in Eq. (5), $H < 0$, then (5) may be written as

$$\frac{(y - k)^2}{\dfrac{|H|}{\alpha^2}} - \frac{(x - h)^2}{\dfrac{|H|}{\beta^2}} = 1$$

which has the form of Eq. (3). For instance, suppose that Eq. (4) is

$$4x^2 - 12y^2 + 24x + 96y - 131 = 0$$

Upon completing the squares in x and y, we get

$$4(x + 3)^2 - 12(y - 4)^2 = -25$$

This has the form of Eq. (5), where $H = -25 < 0$, and it may be written as

$$\frac{(y-4)^2}{\frac{25}{12}} - \frac{(x+3)^2}{\frac{25}{4}} = 1$$

which has the form of Eq. (3).

If $H = 0$ in Eq. (5), then (5) is equivalent to the two equations

$$\alpha(x-h) - \beta(y-k) = 0 \quad \text{and} \quad \alpha(x-h) + \beta(y-k) = 0$$

which are equations of two straight lines through the point (h, k). This is the degenerate case of the hyperbola.

The following theorem summarizes the results of the above discussion.

12.5.3 Theorem   If in the general second-degree equation

$$Ax^2 + Bxy + Cy^2 + Dx + Ey + F = 0$$

$B = 0$ and $AC < 0$, then the graph is either a hyperbola or two intersecting straight lines.

EXAMPLE 2:   Determine the graph of the equation

$$9x^2 - 4y^2 - 18x - 16y + 29 = 0$$

SOLUTION: From Theorem 12.5.3, because $B = 0$ and $AC = (9)(-4) = -36 < 0$, the graph is either a hyperbola or two intersecting straight lines. Completing the squares in x and y, we get

$$9(x^2 - 2x + 1) - 4(y^2 + 4y + 4) = -29 + 9 - 16$$

or

$$9(x-1)^2 - 4(y+2)^2 = -36$$

or

$$\frac{(y+2)^2}{9} - \frac{(x-1)^2}{4} = 1 \tag{6}$$

Equation (6) has the form of Eq. (3), and so the graph is a hyperbola whose principal axis is parallel to the y axis and whose center is at $(1, -2)$.

EXAMPLE 3:   For the hyperbola of Example 2, find the eccentricity, the vertices, the foci, and the directrices. Draw a sketch of the hyperbola and show the foci and the directrices.

SOLUTION: From Eq. (6) we see that $a = 3$ and $b = 2$. For a hyperbola, $b = a\sqrt{e^2 - 1}$; thus,

$$2 = 3\sqrt{e^2 - 1}$$

and solving for e, we obtain $e = \frac{1}{3}\sqrt{13}$. Because the center is at $(1, -2)$, the principal axis is vertical, and $a = 3$, it follows that the vertices are at the points $V'(1, -5)$ and $V(1, 1)$. Because $ae = \sqrt{13}$, the foci are at the points $F'(1, -2 - \sqrt{13})$ and $F(1, -2 + \sqrt{13})$. Furthermore, $a/e = \frac{9}{13}\sqrt{13}$; hence, the directrix corresponding to the focus at F' has as an equation $y = -2 - \frac{9}{13}\sqrt{13}$, and the directrix corresponding to the focus at F has as an equation $y = -2 + \frac{9}{13}\sqrt{13}$. Figure 12.5.3 shows a sketch of the hyperbola and the foci and directrices.

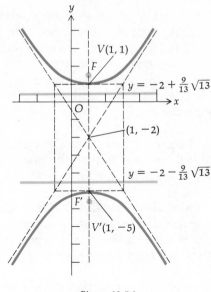

$$y = -2 + \tfrac{9}{13}\sqrt{13}$$

$$y = -2 - \tfrac{9}{13}\sqrt{13}$$

Figure 12.5.3

Just as Theorem 12.4.2 gives an alternate definition of an ellipse, the following theorem gives an alternate definition of a hyperbola.

12.5.4 Theorem   A hyperbola can be defined as the set of points such that the absolute value of the difference of the distances from any point of the set to two given points (the foci) is a constant.

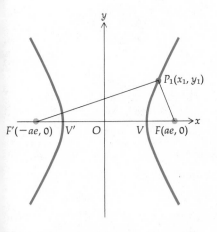

Figure 12.5.4

The proof of this theorem is similar to the proof of Theorem 12.4.2 and is left for the reader (see Exercises 13 and 14). In the proof, take the foci at the points $F'(-ae, 0)$ and $F(ae, 0)$, and let the constant absolute value of the difference of the distances be $2a$. See Fig. 12.5.4.

Because the hyperbola of Example 2 has foci at $(1, -2 - \sqrt{13})$ and $(1, -2 + \sqrt{13})$ and $2a = 6$, it follows from Theorem 12.5.4 that this hyperbola can be defined as the set of points such that the absolute value of the difference of the distances from any point of the set to the points $(1, -2 - \sqrt{13})$ and $(1, -2 + \sqrt{13})$ is 6.

The graph of the general second-degree equation

$$Ax^2 + Bxy + Cy^2 + Dx + Ey + F = 0 \tag{7}$$

where $B = 0$ and $AC > 0$, was discussed in Sec. 12.4. In this section we have so far considered the equation when $B = 0$ and $AC < 0$. Now if for Eq. (7), $B = 0$ and $AC = 0$, then either $A = 0$ or $C = 0$ (we do not consider $A = B = C = 0$ because then Eq. (7) would not be a quadratic equation). Suppose that in Eq. (7), $B = 0$, $A = 0$, and $C \neq 0$. The equation becomes

$$Cy^2 + Dx + Ey + F = 0 \tag{8}$$

If $D \neq 0$, (8) is an equation of a parabola. If $D = 0$, then the graph of (8) may be two parallel lines, one line, or no real locus. For example, $4y^2 - 9 = 0$ is an equation of two parallel lines; $9y^2 + 6y + 1 = 0$ is an equation of one line; and $2y^2 + y + 1 = 0$ is satisfied by no real values of y. These are the degenerate cases of the parabola. A similar discussion holds if $B = 0$, $C = 0$, and $A \neq 0$. The results are summarized in the following theorem.

12.5.5 Theorem   If in the general second-degree Eq. (7), $B = 0$ and either $A = 0$ and $C \neq 0$ or $C = 0$ and $A \neq 0$, then the graph is one of the following: a parabola, two parallel lines, one line, or no real locus.

From Theorems 12.4.1, 12.5.3, and 12.5.5, it may be concluded that the graph of the general quadratic equation in two unknowns when $B = 0$ is either a conic or a degenerate conic. The type of conic can be determined from the product of A and C. We have the following theorem.

12.5.6 Theorem   The graph of the equation $Ax^2 + Cy^2 + Dx + Ey + F = 0$, where A and C are not both zero, is either a conic or a degenerate conic; if it is a conic, then the graph is

(i) a *parabola* if either $A = 0$ or $C = 0$, that is, if $AC = 0$;
(ii) an *ellipse* if A and C have the same sign, that is, if $AC > 0$;
(iii) a *hyperbola* if A and C have opposite signs, that is, if $AC < 0$.

A discussion of the graph of the general quadratic equation, where $B \neq 0$, is given in Sec. 12.6.

Exercises 12.5

In Exercises 1 through 6, find the eccentricity, center, foci, directrices, and equations of the asymptotes of the given hyperbolas and draw a sketch of the graph.

1. $9x^2 - 18y^2 + 54x - 36y + 79 = 0$
2. $x^2 - y^2 + 6x + 10y - 4 = 0$
3. $3y^2 - 4x^2 - 8x - 24y - 40 = 0$
4. $4x^2 - y^2 + 56x + 2y + 195 = 0$
5. $4y^2 - 9x^2 + 16y + 18x = 29$
6. $y^2 - x^2 + 2y - 2x - 1 = 0$

In Exercises 7 through 12, find an equation of the hyperbola satisfying the given conditions and draw a sketch of the graph.

7. One focus at $(26, 0)$ and asymptotes the lines $12y = \pm 5x$.
8. Center at $(3, -5)$, a vertex at $(7, -5)$, and a focus at $(8, -5)$.
9. Center at $(-2, -1)$, a focus at $(-2, 14)$, and a directrix the line $5y = -53$.
10. Foci at $(3, 6)$ and $(3, 0)$ and passing through the point $(5, 3 + 6/\sqrt{5})$.
11. One focus at $(-3 - 3\sqrt{13}, 1)$, asymptotes intersecting at $(-3, 1)$, and one asymptote passing through the point $(1, 7)$.
12. Foci at $(-1, 4)$ and $(7, 4)$ and eccentricity of 3.

13. Prove that the set of points, such that the absolute value of the difference of the distances from any point of the set to two given points (the foci) is a constant, is a hyperbola.

14. Prove that any hyperbola is a set of points such that the absolute value of the difference of the distances from any point of the set to two given points (the foci) is a constant.

15. Use Theorem 12.5.4 to find an equation of the hyperbola for which the difference of the distances from any point on the hyperbola to $(2, 1)$ and $(2, 9)$ is equal to 4.

16. Solve Exercise 15 if the difference of the distances from $(-8, -4)$ and $(2, -4)$ is equal to 6.

17. Three listening posts are located at the points $A(0, 0)$, $B(0, \frac{21}{4})$, and $C(\frac{25}{3}, 0)$, the unit being 1 mile. Microphones located at these points show that a gun is $\frac{5}{3}$ mi closer to A than to C, and $\frac{7}{4}$ mi closer to B than to A. Locate the position of the gun by use of Theorem 12.5.4.

18. Prove that the eccentricity of an equilateral hyperbola is equal to $\sqrt{2}$.

12.6 ROTATION OF AXES   We have previously shown how a translation of coordinate axes can simplify the form of certain equations. A translation of axes gives a new coordinate system whose axes are parallel to the original axes. We now consider a rotation of coordinate axes.

Suppose that we have two rectangular cartesian coordinate systems with the same origin. Let one system be the xy system and the other the $\bar{x}\bar{y}$ system. Suppose further that the $\bar{x}$ axis makes an angle of radian measure α with the x axis. Then of course the $\bar{y}$ axis makes an angle of radian measure α with the y axis. In such a case, we state that the xy system of coordinates is *rotated* through an angle of radian measure α to form the $\bar{x}\bar{y}$ system of coordinates. A point P having coordinates (x, y) with respect to the original coordinate system will have coordinates $(\bar{x}, \bar{y})$ with respect to the new one. We now obtain relationships between these two sets of coordinates. To do this, we introduce two polar coordinate systems, each system having the pole at the origin. In the first polar coordinate system the positive side of the x axis is taken as the polar axis; in the second polar coordinate system the positive side of the $\bar{x}$ axis is taken as the polar axis (see Fig. 12.6.1). Point P has two sets of polar coordinates, (r, θ) and $(\bar{r}, \bar{\theta})$, where

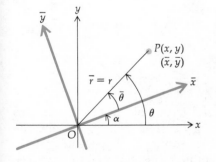

Figure 12.6.1

$$\bar{r} = r \quad \text{and} \quad \bar{\theta} = \theta - \alpha \tag{1}$$

The following equations hold:

$$\bar{x} = \bar{r} \cos \bar{\theta} \quad \text{and} \quad \bar{y} = \bar{r} \sin \bar{\theta} \tag{2}$$

Substituting from (1) into (2), we get

$$\bar{x} = r \cos(\theta - \alpha) \quad \text{and} \quad \bar{y} = r \sin(\theta - \alpha) \tag{3}$$

Using the trigonometric identities for the sine and cosine of the difference of two numbers, Eqs. (3) become

$$\bar{x} = r \cos \theta \cos \alpha + r \sin \theta \sin \alpha$$

and

$$\bar{y} = r \sin \theta \cos \alpha - r \cos \theta \sin \alpha$$

Because $r \cos \theta = x$ and $r \sin \theta = y$, we obtain from the above two equations

$$\bar{x} = x \cos \alpha + y \sin \alpha \tag{4}$$

and

$$\bar{y} = -x \sin \alpha + y \cos \alpha \tag{5}$$

Solving Eqs. (4) and (5) simultaneously for x and y in terms of $\bar{x}$ and $\bar{y}$, we obtain

$$x = \bar{x} \cos \alpha - \bar{y} \sin \alpha \tag{6}$$

and

$$y = \bar{x} \sin \alpha + \bar{y} \cos \alpha \tag{7}$$

It is left for the reader to fill in the steps in going from (4) and (5) to (6) and (7) (see Exercise 1).

EXAMPLE 1:   Given the equation $xy = 1$, find an equation of the graph with respect to the $\bar{x}$ and $\bar{y}$ axes after a rotation of axes through an angle of radian measure $\frac{1}{4}\pi$.

Figure 12.6.2

SOLUTION: Taking $\alpha = \frac{1}{4}\pi$ in Eqs. (6) and (7), we obtain

$$x = \frac{1}{\sqrt{2}} \bar{x} - \frac{1}{\sqrt{2}} \bar{y} \quad \text{and} \quad y = \frac{1}{\sqrt{2}} \bar{x} + \frac{1}{\sqrt{2}} \bar{y}$$

Substituting these expressions for x and y in the equation $xy = 1$, we get

$$\left(\frac{1}{\sqrt{2}} \bar{x} - \frac{1}{\sqrt{2}} \bar{y} \right)\left(\frac{1}{\sqrt{2}} \bar{x} + \frac{1}{\sqrt{2}} \bar{y} \right) = 1$$

or, equivalently,

$$\frac{\bar{x}^2}{2} - \frac{\bar{y}^2}{2} = 1$$

This is an equation of an equilateral hyperbola whose asymptotes are the bisectors of the quadrants in the $\bar{x}\bar{y}$ system. Hence, we conclude that the graph of the equation $xy = 1$ is an equilateral hyperbola lying in the first and third quadrants whose asymptotes are the x and y axes (see Fig. 12.6.2).

In Sec. 12.5 we showed that when $B = 0$ and A and C are not both zero, the graph of the general second-degree equation in two unknowns,

$$Ax^2 + Bxy + Cy^2 + Dx + Ey + F = 0 \tag{8}$$

is either a conic or a degenerate conic. We now show that if $B \neq 0$, then any equation of the form (8) can be transformed by a suitable rotation of axes into an equation of the form

$$\bar{A}\bar{x}^2 + \bar{C}\bar{y}^2 + \bar{D}\bar{x} + \bar{E}\bar{y} + \bar{F} = 0 \tag{9}$$

where $\bar{A}$ and $\bar{C}$ are not both zero.

If the xy system is rotated through an angle of radian measure α, then to obtain an equation of the graph of (8) with respect to the $\bar{x}\bar{y}$ system, we replace x by $\bar{x} \cos \alpha - \bar{y} \sin \alpha$ and y by $\bar{x} \sin \alpha + \bar{y} \cos \alpha$. We get

$$\bar{A}\bar{x}^2 + \bar{B}\bar{x}\bar{y} + \bar{C}\bar{y}^2 + \bar{D}\bar{x} + \bar{E}\bar{y} + \bar{F} = 0 \tag{10}$$

where

$$\bar{A} = A \cos^2 \alpha + B \sin \alpha \cos \alpha + C \sin^2 \alpha$$

$$\bar{B} = -2A \sin \alpha \cos \alpha + B(\cos^2 \alpha - \sin^2 \alpha) + 2C \sin \alpha \cos \alpha \tag{11}$$

$$\bar{C} = A \sin^2 \alpha - B \sin \alpha \cos \alpha + C \cos^2 \alpha$$

We wish to find an α so that the rotation transforms Eq. (8) into an equation of the form (9). Setting $\bar{B}$ from (11) equal to zero, we have

$$B(\cos^2 \alpha - \sin^2 \alpha) + (C - A)(2 \sin \alpha \cos \alpha) = 0$$

or, equivalently, with trigonometric identities,

$$B \cos 2\alpha + (C - A) \sin 2\alpha = 0$$

Because $B \neq 0$, this gives

$$\cot 2\alpha = \frac{A - C}{B} \tag{12}$$

We have shown, then, that an equation of the form (8), where $B \neq 0$, can be transformed to an equation of the form (9) by a rotation of axes through an angle of radian measure α satisfying (12). We wish to show that $\bar{A}$ and $\bar{C}$ in (9) are not both zero. To prove this, notice that Eq. (10) is obtained from (8) by rotating the axes through the angle of radian measure α. Also, Eq. (8) can be obtained from (10) by rotating the axes back through the angle of radian measure $(-\alpha)$. If $\bar{A}$ and $\bar{C}$ in (10) are both zero, then the substitutions

$$\bar{x} = x \cos \alpha + y \sin \alpha \quad \text{and} \quad \bar{y} = -x \sin \alpha + y \cos \alpha$$

in (10) would result in the equation

$$\bar{D}(x \cos \alpha + y \sin \alpha) + \bar{E}(-x \sin \alpha + y \cos \alpha) + \bar{F} = 0$$

which is an equation of the first degree and hence different from (8) because we have assumed that at least $B \neq 0$. The following theorem has, therefore, been proved.

12.6.1 Theorem   If $B \neq 0$, the equation $Ax^2 + Bxy + Cy^2 + Dx + Ey + F = 0$ can be transformed into the equation $\bar{A}\bar{x}^2 + \bar{C}\bar{y}^2 + \bar{D}\bar{x} + \bar{E}\bar{y} + \bar{F} = 0$, where $\bar{A}$ and $\bar{C}$ are not both zero, by a rotation of axes through an angle of radian measure α for which $\cot 2\alpha = (A - C)/B$.

By Theorems 12.6.1 and 12.5.6, it follows that the graph of an equation of the form (8) is either a conic or a degenerate conic. To determine which type of conic is the graph of a particular equation, we use the fact that A, B, and C of Eq. (8) and $\bar{A}$, $\bar{B}$, and $\bar{C}$ of Eq. (10) satisfy the relation

$$B^2 - 4AC = \bar{B}^2 - 4\bar{A}\bar{C} \tag{13}$$

which can be proved by substituting the expressions for $\bar{A}$, $\bar{B}$, and $\bar{C}$ given in Eqs. (11) in the right side of (13). This is left for the reader (see Exercise 15).

The expression $B^2 - 4AC$ is called the *discriminant* of Eq. (8). Equation (13) states that the discriminant of the general quadratic equation in two variables is *invariant* under a rotation of axes. If the angle of rotation is chosen so that $\bar{B} = 0$, then (13) becomes

$$B^2 - 4AC = -4\bar{A}\bar{C} \tag{14}$$

From Theorem 12.5.6 it follows that if the graph of (9) is not degenerate, then it is a parabola if $\bar{A}\bar{C} = 0$, an ellipse if $\bar{A}\bar{C} > 0$, and a hyperbola if $\bar{A}\bar{C} < 0$. So we conclude that the graph of (9) is a parabola, an ellipse, or a hyperbola depending on whether $-4\bar{A}\bar{C}$ is zero, negative, or positive. Because the graph of (8) is the same as the graph of (9), it follows from (14) that if the graph of (8) is not degenerate, then it is a parabola, an ellipse, or a hyperbola depending on whether the discriminant $B^2 - 4AC$ is zero, negative, or positive. We have proved the following theorem.

12.6.2 Theorem   The graph of the equation

$$Ax^2 + Bxy + Cy^2 + Dx + Ey + F = 0$$

is either a conic or a degenerate conic. If it is a conic, then it is

  (i) a *parabola* if $B^2 - 4AC = 0$;
  (ii) an *ellipse* if $B^2 - 4AC < 0$;
  (iii) a *hyperbola* if $B^2 - 4AC > 0$.

EXAMPLE 2:   Given the equation $17x^2 - 12xy + 8y^2 - 80 = 0$, simplify the equation by a rotation of axes. Draw a sketch of the graph of the equation showing both sets of axes.

SOLUTION: $B^2 - 4AC = (-12)^2 - 4(17)(8) = -400 < 0$. Therefore, by Theorem 12.6.2, the graph is an ellipse or else it is degenerate. To eliminate the xy term by a rotation of axes, we must choose an α such that

$$\cot 2\alpha = \frac{A - C}{B} = \frac{17 - 8}{-12} = -\frac{3}{4}$$

There is a 2α in the interval $(0, \pi)$ for which $\cot 2\alpha = -\frac{3}{4}$. Therefore, α is in the interval $(0, \frac{1}{2}\pi)$. To apply (6) and (7) it is not necessary to find α so long as we find $\cos \alpha$ and $\sin \alpha$. These functions can be found from the value of $\cot 2\alpha$ by the trigonometric identities

$$\cos \alpha = \sqrt{\frac{1 + \cos 2\alpha}{2}} \quad \text{and} \quad \sin \alpha = \sqrt{\frac{1 - \cos 2\alpha}{2}}$$

Because $\cot 2\alpha = -\frac{3}{4}$ and $0 < \alpha < \frac{1}{2}\pi$, it follows that $\cos 2\alpha = -\frac{3}{5}$. So

$$\cos \alpha = \sqrt{\frac{1 - \frac{3}{5}}{2}} = \frac{1}{\sqrt{5}}$$

and

$$\sin \alpha = \sqrt{\frac{1 + \frac{3}{5}}{2}} = \frac{2}{\sqrt{5}}$$

Substituting $x = \bar{x}/\sqrt{5} - 2\bar{y}/\sqrt{5}$ and $y = 2\bar{x}/\sqrt{5} + \bar{y}/\sqrt{5}$ in the given equation, we obtain

$$17\left(\frac{\bar{x}^2 - 4\bar{x}\bar{y} + 4\bar{y}^2}{5}\right) - 12\left(\frac{2\bar{x}^2 - 3\bar{x}\bar{y} - 2\bar{y}^2}{5}\right) + 8\left(\frac{4\bar{x}^2 + 4\bar{x}\bar{y} + \bar{y}^2}{5}\right) - 80 = 0$$

Upon simplification, this equation becomes

$$\bar{x}^2 + 4\bar{y}^2 = 16$$

or, equivalently,

$$\frac{\bar{x}^2}{16} + \frac{\bar{y}^2}{4} = 1$$

So the graph is an ellipse whose major axis is 8 units long and whose minor axis is 4 units long. A sketch of the ellipse with both sets of axes is shown in Fig. 12.6.3.

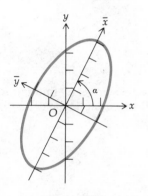

Figure 12.6.3

Exercises 12.6

1. Derive Eqs. (6) and (7) of this section by solving Eqs. (4) and (5) for x and y in terms of $\bar{x}$ and $\bar{y}$.

In Exercises 2 through 8, remove the xy term from the given equation by a rotation of axes. Draw a sketch of the graph and show both sets of axes.

2. $x^2 + xy + y^2 = 3$

3. $24xy - 7y^2 + 36 = 0$

4. $4xy + 3x^2 = 4$

5. $xy = 8$

6. $5x^2 + 6xy + 5y^2 = 9$

7. $31x^2 + 10\sqrt{3}xy + 21y^2 = 144$

8. $6x^2 + 20\sqrt{3}xy + 26y^2 = 324$

In Exercises 9 through 14, simplify the given equation by a rotation and translation of axes. Draw a sketch of the graph and show the three sets of axes.

9. $x^2 + xy + y^2 - 3y - 6 = 0$

10. $x^2 - 10xy + y^2 + x + y + 1 = 0$

11. $17x^2 - 12xy + 8y^2 - 68x + 24y - 12 = 0$

12. $3x^2 - 4xy + 8x - 1 = 0$

13. $11x^2 - 24xy + 4y^2 + 30x + 40y - 45 = 0$

14. $19x^2 + 6xy + 11y^2 - 26x + 38y + 31 = 0$

15. Show that for the general second-degree equation in two variables, the discriminant $B^2 - 4AC$ is invariant under a rotation of axes.

Review Exercises (Chapter 12)

In Exercises 1 through 6, find a cartesian equation of the conic satisfying the given conditions and draw a sketch of the graph.

1. Vertices at $(1, 8)$ and $(1, -4)$; $e = \frac{2}{3}$.

2. Foci at $(-5, 1)$ and $(1, 1)$; one vertex at $(-4, 1)$.

3. Center at the origin; foci on the x axis; $e = 2$; containing the point $(2, 3)$.

4. Vertex at $(4, 2)$; focus at $(4, -3)$; $e = 1$.

5. A focus at $(-5, 3)$; directrix: $x = -3$; $e = \frac{3}{4}$.

6. A focus at $(4, -2)$; directrix: $y = 2$; $e = \frac{3}{2}$.

In Exercises 7 through 10, find a polar equation of the conic satisfying the given conditions and draw a sketch of the graph.

7. A focus at the pole; vertices at $(2, \pi)$ and $(4, \pi)$.

8. A focus at the pole; a vertex at $(6, \frac{1}{2}\pi)$; $e = \frac{3}{4}$.

9. A focus at the pole; a vertex at $(3, \frac{3}{2}\pi)$; $e = 1$.

10. The line $r \sin \theta = 6$ is the directrix corresponding to the focus at the pole and $e = \frac{5}{3}$.

In Exercises 11 through 14, the equation is that of a conic having a focus at the pole. In each Exercise, (a) find the eccentricity; (b) identify the conic; (c) write an equation of the directrix which corresponds to the focus at the pole; (d) draw a sketch of the curve.

11. $r = \dfrac{2}{2 - \sin \theta}$

12. $r = \dfrac{5}{3 + 3 \sin \theta}$

13. $r = \dfrac{4}{2 + 3 \cos \theta}$

14. $r = \dfrac{4}{3 - 2 \cos \theta}$

In Exercises 15 through 18, the equation is that of either an ellipse or a hyperbola. Find the eccentricity, center, foci, and directrices, and draw a sketch of the graph. If it is a hyperbola, also find equations of the asymptotes.

15. $4x^2 + y^2 + 24x - 16y + 84 = 0$

16. $3x^2 - 2y^2 + 6x - 8y + 11 = 0$

17. $25x^2 - y^2 + 50x + 6y - 9 = 0$

18. $4x^2 + 9y^2 + 32x - 18y + 37 = 0$

In Exercises 19 and 20, simplify the given equation by a rotation and translation of axes. Draw a sketch of the graph and show the three sets of axes.

19. $3x^2 - 3xy - y^2 - 6y = 0$

20. $4x^2 + 3xy + y^2 - 6x + 12y = 0$

21. Find a polar equation of the parabola containing the point $(2, \frac{1}{3}\pi)$, whose focus is at the pole and whose vertex is on the extension of the polar axis.

22. If the distance between the two directrices of an ellipse is three times the distance between the foci, find the eccentricity.

23. Find the volume of the solid of revolution generated if the region bounded by the hyperbola $x^2/a^2 - y^2/b^2 = 1$ and the line $x = 2a$ is revolved about the y axis.

24. Show that the hyperbola $x^2 - y^2 = 4$ has the same foci as the ellipse $x^2 + 9y^2 = 9$.

25. A satellite is traveling around the earth in an elliptical orbit having the earth at one focus and an eccentricity of $\frac{1}{3}$. The closest distance that the satellite gets to the earth is 300 mi. Find the farthest distance that the satellite gets from the earth.

26. The orbit of the planet Mercury around the sun is elliptical in shape with the sun at one focus, a semimajor axis of length 36 million miles and an eccentricity of 0.206. Find (a) how close Mercury gets to the sun and (b) the greatest possible distance between Mercury and the sun.

27. A comet is moving in a parabolic orbit around the sun at the focus F of the parabola. An observation of the comet is made when it is at point P_1, 15 million miles from the sun, and a second observation is made when it is at point P_2, 5 million miles from the sun. The line segments FP_1 and FP_2 are perpendicular. With this information there are two possible orbits for the comet. Find how close the comet comes to the sun for each orbit.

28. The arch of a bridge is in the shape of a semiellipse having a horizontal span of 40 ft and a height of 16 ft at its center. How high is the arch 9 ft to the right or left of the center?

29. Points A and B are 1000 ft apart and it is determined from the sound of an explosion heard at these points at different times that the location of the explosion is 600 ft closer to A than to B. Show that the location of the explosion is restricted to a particular curve and find an equation of it.

30. Find the area of the region bounded by the two parabolas: $r = 2/(1 - \cos \theta)$ and $r = 2/(1 + \cos \theta)$.

31. A focal chord of a conic is a line segment passing through a focus and having its endpoints on the conic. Prove that if two focal chords of a parabola are perpendicular, the sum of the reciprocals of the measures of their lengths is a constant. (HINT: Use polar coordinates.)

32. A focal chord of a conic is divided into two segments by the focus. Prove that the sum of the reciprocals of the measures of the lengths of the two segments is the same, regardless of what chord is taken. (HINT: Use polar coordinates.)

13

Indeterminate Forms, Improper Integrals, and Taylor's Formula

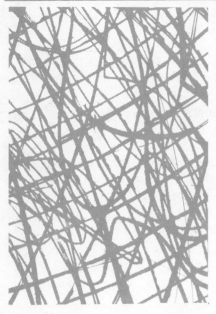

13.1 THE INDETERMINATE FORM 0/0

Limit theorem 9 (2.5.9) states that if $\lim\limits_{x \to a} f(x)$ and $\lim\limits_{x \to a} g(x)$ both exist, then

$$\lim_{x \to a} \frac{f(x)}{g(x)} = \frac{\lim\limits_{x \to a} f(x)}{\lim\limits_{x \to a} g(x)}$$

provided that $\lim\limits_{x \to a} g(x) \neq 0$.

There are various situations for which this theorem cannot be used. In particular, if $\lim\limits_{x \to a} g(x) = 0$ and $\lim\limits_{x \to a} f(x) = k$, where k is a constant not equal to 0, then Limit theorem 13 (2.8.5) can be applied. Consider the case when both $\lim\limits_{x \to a} f(x) = 0$ and $\lim\limits_{x \to a} g(x) = 0$. Some limits of this type have previously been considered. For example,

$$\lim_{x \to 4} \frac{x^2 - x - 12}{x^2 - 3x - 4}$$

Here, $\lim\limits_{x \to 4} (x^2 - x - 12) = 0$ and $\lim\limits_{x \to 4} (x^2 - 3x - 4) = 0$. However, the numerator and denominator can be factored which gives

$$\lim_{x \to 4} \frac{x^2 - x - 12}{x^2 - 3x - 4} = \lim_{x \to 4} \frac{(x - 4)(x + 3)}{(x - 4)(x + 1)}$$

Because $x \neq 4$, the numerator and denominator can be divided by $(x - 4)$, and we obtain

$$\lim_{x \to 4} \frac{x^2 - x - 12}{x^2 - 3x - 4} = \lim_{x \to 4} \frac{x + 3}{x + 1} = \frac{7}{5}$$

Another example of this case is $\lim_{x \to 0} (\sin x/x)$, which equals 1 by Theorem 9.2.1.

13.1.1 Definition   If f and g are two functions such that $\lim_{x \to a} f(x) = 0$ and $\lim_{x \to a} g(x) = 0$, then the function f/g has the *indeterminate form* 0/0 *at* a.

From Definition 13.1.1 it follows that $(x^2 - x - 12)/(x^2 - 3x - 4)$ has the indeterminate form 0/0 at 4; however, we saw above that

$$\lim_{x \to 4} \frac{x^2 - x - 12}{x^2 - 3x - 4} = \frac{7}{5}$$

Also, $(\sin x/x)$ has the indeterminate form 0/0 at 0, while $\lim_{x \to 0} (\sin x/x) = 1$.

We now consider a general method for finding the limit, if it exists, of a function at a number where it has the indeterminate form 0/0. This method is attributed to the French mathematician Guillaume François de L'Hôpital (1661–1707), who wrote the first calculus textbook, published in 1696. It is known as *L'Hôpital's rule.*

13.1.2 Theorem
L'Hôpital's Rule

Let f and g be functions which are differentiable on an open interval I, except possibly at the number a in I. Suppose that for all $x \neq a$ in I, $g'(x) \neq 0$. Then if $\lim_{x \to a} f(x) = 0$ and $\lim_{x \to a} g(x) = 0$, and if

$$\lim_{x \to a} \frac{f'(x)}{g'(x)} = L$$

it follows that

$$\lim_{x \to a} \frac{f(x)}{g(x)} = L$$

The theorem is valid if all the limits are right-hand limits or all the limits are left-hand limits.

Before we prove Theorem 13.1.2, we illustrate the use of the theorem by some examples.

EXAMPLE 1:   Use L'Hôpital's rule to show that

(a) $\lim_{x \to 4} \dfrac{x^2 - x - 12}{x^2 - 3x - 4} = \dfrac{7}{5}$

and

(b) $\lim_{x \to 0} \dfrac{\sin x}{x} = 1$

SOLUTION: (a) Because $\lim_{x \to 4} (x^2 - x - 12) = 0$ and $\lim_{x \to 4} (x^2 - 3x - 4) = 0$, we can apply L'Hôpital's rule and obtain

$$\lim_{x \to 4} \frac{x^2 - x - 12}{x^2 - 3x - 4} = \lim_{x \to 4} \frac{2x - 1}{2x - 3} = \frac{7}{5}$$

(b) We can apply L'Hôpital's rule because $\lim_{x \to 0} \sin x = 0$ and $\lim_{x \to 0} x = 0$. We have, then,

$$\lim_{x \to 0} \frac{\sin x}{x} = \lim_{x \to 0} \frac{\cos x}{1} = 1$$

EXAMPLE 2: Find

$$\lim_{x \to 0} \frac{x}{1 - e^x}$$

if it exists.

SOLUTION: Because $\lim\limits_{x \to 0} x = 0$ and $\lim\limits_{x \to 0} (1 - e^x) = 0$, L'Hôpital's rule can be applied, and we have

$$\lim_{x \to 0} \frac{x}{1 - e^x} = \lim_{x \to 0} \frac{1}{-e^x} = \frac{1}{-1} = -1$$

EXAMPLE 3: Find

$$\lim_{x \to 1} \frac{1 - x + \ln x}{x^3 - 3x + 2}$$

if it exists.

SOLUTION:

$$\lim_{x \to 1} (1 - x + \ln x) = 1 - 1 + 0 = 0$$

and

$$\lim_{x \to 1} (x^3 - 3x + 2) = 1 - 3 + 2 = 0$$

Therefore, applying L'Hôpital's rule, we have

$$\lim_{x \to 1} \frac{1 - x + \ln x}{x^3 - 3x + 2} = \lim_{x \to 1} \frac{-1 + \dfrac{1}{x}}{3x^2 - 3}$$

Now, because $\lim\limits_{x \to 1} (-1 + 1/x) = 0$ and $\lim\limits_{x \to 1} (3x^2 - 3) = 0$, we apply L'Hôpital's rule again giving

$$\lim_{x \to 1} \frac{-1 + \dfrac{1}{x}}{3x^2 - 3} = \lim_{x \to 1} \frac{-\dfrac{1}{x^2}}{6x} = -\frac{1}{6}$$

Therefore, we conclude

$$\lim_{x \to 1} \frac{1 - x + \ln x}{x^3 - 3x + 2} = -\frac{1}{6}$$

To prove Theorem 13.1.2 we need to use the theorem known as *Cauchy's mean-value theorem,* which extends to two functions the mean-value theorem (4.5.2) for a single function. This theorem is attributed to the French mathematician Augustin L. Cauchy (1789–1857).

13.1.3 Theorem
Cauchy's Mean-Value Theorem

If f and g are two functions such that

(i) f and g are continuous on the closed interval $[a, b]$;
(ii) f and g are differentiable on the open interval (a, b);
(iii) for all x in the open interval (a, b), $g'(x) \neq 0$

then there exists a number z in the open interval (a, b) such that

$$\frac{f(b) - f(a)}{g(b) - g(a)} = \frac{f'(z)}{g'(z)}$$

PROOF: We first show that $g(b) \neq g(a)$. Assume $g(b) = g(a)$. Because g satisfies the two conditions in the hypothesis of the mean-value theorem (4.5.2), there is some number c in (a, b) such that $g'(c) = [g(b) - g(a)]/(b - a)$. But if $g(b) = g(a)$, then there is some number c in (a, b) such that $g'(c) = 0$. But condition (iii) of the hypothesis of this theorem states that for all x in (a, b), $g'(x) \neq 0$. Therefore, we have a contradiction. Hence, our assumption that $g(b) = g(a)$ is false. So, $g(b) \neq g(a)$, and consequently $g(b) - g(a) \neq 0$.

Now let us consider the function h defined by

$$h(x) = f(x) - f(a) - \left[\frac{f(b) - f(a)}{g(b) - g(a)}\right] [g(x) - g(a)]$$

Then,

$$h'(x) = f'(x) - \left[\frac{f(b) - f(a)}{g(b) - g(a)}\right] g'(x) \tag{1}$$

Therefore, h is differentiable on (a, b) because f and g are differentiable there, and h is continuous on $[a, b]$ because f and g are continuous there.

$$h(a) = f(a) - f(a) - \left[\frac{f(b) - f(a)}{g(b) - g(a)}\right] [g(a) - g(a)] = 0$$

$$h(b) = f(b) - f(a) - \left[\frac{f(b) - f(a)}{g(b) - g(a)}\right] [g(b) - g(a)] = 0$$

Hence, the three conditions of the hypothesis of Rolle's theorem are satisfied by the function h. So there exists a number z in the open interval (a, b) such that $h'(z) = 0$. Thus, from (1) we have

$$f'(z) - \frac{f(b) - f(a)}{g(b) - g(a)} g'(z) = 0 \tag{2}$$

Because $g'(z) \neq 0$ on (a, b), we have from (2)

$$\frac{f(b) - f(a)}{g(b) - g(a)} = \frac{f'(z)}{g'(z)}$$

where z is some number in (a, b). This proves the theorem. ∎

We should note that if g is the function such that $g(x) = x$, then the conclusion of Cauchy's mean-value theorem becomes the conclusion of the former mean-value theorem because then $g'(z) = 1$. So the former mean-value theorem is a special case of Cauchy's mean-value theorem.

A geometric interpretation of Cauchy's mean-value theorem is given in Sec. 15.4. It is postponed until then because parametric equations are needed.

EXAMPLE 4: Given

$$f(x) = 3x^2 + 3x - 1$$

and $g(x) = x^3 - 4x + 2$, find a number z in $(0, 1)$ predicted by Theorem 13.1.3.

SOLUTION: $f'(x) = 6x + 3$ and $g'(x) = 3x^2 - 4$. Hence, f and g are differentiable and continuous everywhere, and for all x in $(0, 1)$, $g'(x) \neq 0$. Hence, by Theorem 13.1.3, there exists a z in $(0, 1)$ such that

$$\frac{f(1) - f(0)}{g(1) - g(0)} = \frac{6z + 3}{3z^2 - 4}$$

$$\frac{f(b) - f(a)}{f(b) - f(a)} = \frac{f'(x)}{f'(x)}.$$

Substituting $f(1) = 5$, $g(1) = -1$, $f(0) = -1$, and $g(0) = 2$, and solving for z, we have

$$\frac{5 - (-1)}{-1 - 2} = \frac{6z + 3}{3z^2 - 4}$$

$$6z^2 + 6z - 5 = 0$$

$$z = \frac{-6 \pm \sqrt{36 + 120}}{12}$$

$$= \frac{-6 \pm 2\sqrt{39}}{12}$$

$$= \frac{-3 \pm \sqrt{39}}{6}$$

Only one of these numbers is in $(0, 1)$, namely, $z = \frac{1}{6}(-3 + \sqrt{39})$.

We are now in a position to prove Theorem 13.1.2. We distinguish three cases: (i) $x \to a^+$; (ii) $x \to a^-$; (iii) $x \to a$.

PROOF OF (i):   Because in the hypothesis it is not assumed that f and g are defined at a, we consider two new functions F and G for which

$$F(x) = f(x) \quad \text{if } x \neq a \quad \text{and} \quad F(a) = 0$$
$$G(x) = g(x) \quad \text{if } x \neq a \quad \text{and} \quad G(a) = 0 \tag{3}$$

Let b be the right endpoint of the open interval I given in the hypothesis. Because f and g are both differentiable on I, except possibly at a, we conclude that F and G are both differentiable on the interval $(a, x]$, where $a < x < b$. Therefore, F and G are both continuous on $(a, x]$. The functions F and G are also both continuous from the right at a because $\lim_{x \to a^+} F(x) = \lim_{x \to a^+} f(x) = 0 = F(a)$, and $\lim_{x \to a^+} G(x) = \lim_{x \to a^+} g(x) = 0 = G(a)$. Therefore, F and G are continuous on the closed interval $[a, x]$. So F and G satisfy the three conditions of the hypothesis of Cauchy's mean-value theorem (Theorem 13.1.3) on the interval $[a, x]$. Hence,

$$\frac{F(x) - F(a)}{G(x) - G(a)} = \frac{F'(z)}{G'(z)} \tag{4}$$

where z is some number such that $a < z < x$. From (3) and (4) we have

$$\frac{f(x)}{g(x)} = \frac{f'(z)}{g'(z)} \tag{5}$$

Because $a < z < x$, it follows that as $x \to a^+$, $z \to a^+$; therefore,

$$\lim_{x \to a^+} \frac{f(x)}{g(x)} = \lim_{x \to a^+} \frac{f'(z)}{g'(z)} = \lim_{z \to a^+} \frac{f'(z)}{g'(z)} \tag{6}$$

But by hypothesis, the limit on the right side of (6) is L. Therefore,

$$\lim_{x \to a^+} \frac{f(x)}{g(x)} = L$$

which proves case (i).

The proof of case (ii) is similar to the proof of case (i) and is left for the reader (see Exercise 28). The proof of case (iii) is based on the results of cases (i) and (ii) and is also left for the reader (see Exercise 29).

L'Hôpital's rule also holds if either x increases without bound or x decreases without bound, as given in the next theorem.

13.1.4 Theorem
L'Hôpital's Rule

Let f and g be functions which are differentiable for all $x > N$, where N is a positive constant, and suppose that for all $x > N$, $g'(x) \neq 0$. Then if $\lim_{x \to +\infty} f(x) = 0$ and $\lim_{x \to +\infty} g(x) = 0$ and if

$$\left(\lim_{x \to +\infty} \frac{f'(x)}{g'(x)} = L \right.$$

it follows that

$$\left(\lim_{x \to +\infty} \frac{f(x)}{g(x)} = L \right.$$

The theorem is also valid if "$x \to +\infty$" is replaced by "$x \to -\infty$."

PROOF: We prove the theorem for $x \to +\infty$. The proof for $x \to -\infty$ is left for the reader (see Exercise 30).

For all $x > N$, let $x = 1/t$; then $t = 1/x$. Let F and G be the functions defined by $F(t) = f(1/t)$ and $G(t) = g(1/t)$, if $t \neq 0$. Then $f(x) = F(t)$ and $g(x) = G(t)$, where $x > N$ and $0 < t < 1/N$. From Definitions 2.7.1 and 2.6.1, it may be shown that the statements

$$\lim_{x \to +\infty} f(x) = M \quad \text{and} \quad \lim_{t \to 0^+} F(t) = M$$

have the same meaning. It is left for the reader to prove this (see Exercise 31). Because by hypothesis, $\lim_{x \to +\infty} f(x) = 0$ and $\lim_{x \to +\infty} g(x) = 0$, we can conclude that

$$\lim_{t \to 0^+} F(t) = 0 \quad \text{and} \quad \lim_{t \to 0^+} G(t) = 0 \tag{7}$$

Considering the quotient $F'(t)/G'(t)$, we have, using the chain rule,

$$\frac{F'(t)}{G'(t)} = \frac{-\frac{1}{t^2} f'\left(\frac{1}{t}\right)}{-\frac{1}{t^2} g'\left(\frac{1}{t}\right)} = \frac{f'\left(\frac{1}{t}\right)}{g'\left(\frac{1}{t}\right)} = \frac{f'(x)}{g'(x)}$$

Because by hypothesis $\lim_{x \to +\infty} f'(x)/g'(x) = L$, it follows from the above that

$$\lim_{t \to 0^+} \frac{F'(t)}{G'(t)} = L \qquad (8)$$

Because for all $x > N$, $g'(x) \neq 0$

$$G'(t) \neq 0 \qquad \text{for all } 0 < t < \frac{1}{N} \qquad (9)$$

From (7), (8), and (9), it follows from Theorem 13.1.2 that

$$\lim_{t \to 0^+} \frac{F(t)}{G(t)} = L$$

But because $F(t)/G(t) = f(x)/g(x)$ for all $x > N$ and $t \neq 0$, we have

$$\lim_{x \to +\infty} \frac{f(x)}{g(x)} = L$$

and so the theorem is proved. ∎

Theorems 13.1.2 and 13.1.4 also hold if L is replaced by $+\infty, -\infty,$ or ∞. The proofs for these cases are omitted.

EXAMPLE 5: Find

$$\lim_{x \to +\infty} \frac{\sin \frac{1}{x}}{\tan^{-1}\left(\frac{1}{x}\right)}$$

if it exists.

SOLUTION: $\lim_{x \to +\infty} \sin(1/x) = 0$ and $\lim_{x \to +\infty} \tan^{-1}(1/x) = 0$. So applying L'Hô-pital's rule we get

$$\lim_{x \to +\infty} \frac{\sin \frac{1}{x}}{\tan^{-1}\left(\frac{1}{x}\right)} = \lim_{x \to +\infty} \frac{\cos \frac{1}{x} \cdot \left(-\frac{1}{x^2}\right)}{\frac{1}{1+\frac{1}{x^2}} \cdot \left(-\frac{1}{x^2}\right)} = \lim_{x \to +\infty} \frac{\cos \frac{1}{x}}{\frac{x^2}{x^2+1}}$$

Because

$$\lim_{x \to +\infty} \cos \frac{1}{x} = 1 \quad \text{and} \quad \lim_{x \to +\infty} \frac{x^2}{x^2+1} = \lim_{x \to +\infty} \frac{1}{1+\frac{1}{x^2}} = 1$$

it follows that

$$\lim_{x \to +\infty} \frac{\cos \frac{1}{x}}{\frac{x^2}{x^2+1}} = 1$$

Therefore, the given limit is 1.

Exercises 13.1

In Exercises 1 through 4, find all values of z in the given interval (a, b) satisfying the conclusion of Theorem 13.1.3 for the given pair of functions.

1. $f(x) = x^3$, $g(x) = x^2$; $(a, b) = (0, 2)$

2. $f(x) = \dfrac{2x}{1 + x^2}$, $g(x) = \dfrac{1 - x^2}{1 + x^2}$; $(a, b) = (0, 2)$

3. $f(x) = \sin x$, $g(x) = \cos x$; $(a, b) = (0, \pi)$

4. $f(x) = \cos 2x$, $g(x) = \sin x$; $(a, b) = (0, \tfrac{1}{2}\pi)$

In Exercises 5 through 24, evaluate the limit, if it exists.

5. $\displaystyle\lim_{x \to 0} \frac{x}{\tan x}$

6. $\displaystyle\lim_{x \to 0} \frac{\tan x - x}{x - \sin x}$

7. $\displaystyle\lim_{x \to +\infty} \frac{\sin \dfrac{2}{x}}{\dfrac{1}{x}}$

8. $\displaystyle\lim_{x \to 2} \frac{\sin \pi x}{2 - x}$

9. $\displaystyle\lim_{x \to 0^+} \frac{e^{-1/x}}{x}$

10. $\displaystyle\lim_{x \to 0} \frac{\sin^{-1} x}{x}$

11. $\displaystyle\lim_{x \to \pi/2} \frac{\ln(\sin x)}{(\pi - 2x)^2}$

12. $\displaystyle\lim_{x \to 0} \frac{e^x - \cos x}{x \sin x}$

13. $\displaystyle\lim_{x \to 0} \frac{2^x - 3^x}{x}$

14. $\displaystyle\lim_{x \to 0} \frac{e^{2x^2} - 1}{\sin^2 x}$

15. $\displaystyle\lim_{\theta \to 0} \frac{\theta - \sin \theta}{\tan^3 \theta}$

16. $\displaystyle\lim_{t \to 2} \frac{t^n - 2^n}{t - 2}$

17. $\displaystyle\lim_{t \to 0} \frac{\sin^2 t}{\sin t^2}$

18. $\displaystyle\lim_{x \to 0} \frac{\tanh 2x}{\tanh x}$

19. $\displaystyle\lim_{x \to 0} \frac{(1 + x)^{1/5} - (1 - x)^{1/5}}{(1 + x)^{1/3} - (1 - x)^{1/3}}$

20. $\displaystyle\lim_{x \to 0} \frac{e^x - 10^x}{x}$

21. $\displaystyle\lim_{x \to \pi} \frac{1 + \cos 2x}{1 - \sin x}$

22. $\displaystyle\lim_{x \to +\infty} \frac{\dfrac{1}{x^2} - 2 \tan^{-1} \dfrac{1}{x}}{\dfrac{1}{x}}$

23. $\displaystyle\lim_{x \to 0} \frac{\cos x - \cosh x}{x^2}$

24. $\displaystyle\lim_{x \to 0} \frac{\sinh x - \sin x}{\sin^3 x}$

25. An electrical circuit has a resistance of R ohms, an inductance of L henries, and an electromotive force of E volts, where R, L, and E are positive. If I amperes is the current flowing in the circuit t sec after a switch is turned on, then

$$I = \frac{E}{R}\left(1 - e^{-Rt/L}\right)$$

For specific values of t, E, and L, find $\displaystyle\lim_{R \to 0^+} I$.

26. In a geometric progression, if a is the first term, r is the common ratio of two successive terms, and S is the sum of the first n terms, then if $r \neq 1$

$$S = \frac{a(r^n - 1)}{r - 1}$$

Find $\displaystyle\lim_{r \to 1} S$. Is the result consistent with the sum of the first n terms if $r = 1$?

27. (a) Prove that $\displaystyle\lim_{x \to 0} \left(e^{-1/x^2}/x^n\right) = 0$ for any positive integer n. (b) If $f(x) = e^{-1/x^2}$, use the result of (a) to prove that the limit of f and all of its derivatives, as x approaches 0, is 0.

28. Prove Theorem 13.1.2(ii).

29. Prove Theorem 13.1.2(iii).

30. Prove Theorem 13.1.4 for $x \to -\infty$.

31. Suppose that f is a function defined for all $x > N$, where N is a positive constant. If $t = 1/x$ and $F(t) = f(1/t)$, where $t \neq 0$, prove that the statements $\lim\limits_{x \to +\infty} f(x) = M$ and $\lim\limits_{t \to 0^+} F(t) = M$ have the same meaning.

13.2 OTHER INDETERMINATE FORMS

Suppose that we wish to determine if $\lim\limits_{x \to \pi/2} (\sec^2 x / \sec^2 3x)$ exists. We cannot apply the theorem involving the limit of a quotient because $\lim\limits_{x \to \pi/2} \sec^2 x = +\infty$ and $\lim\limits_{x \to \pi/2} \sec^2 3x = +\infty$. In this case we say that the function defined by $\sec^2 x / \sec^2 3x$ has the indeterminate form $(+\infty/+\infty)$ at $x = \frac{1}{2}\pi$. L'Hôpital's rule also applies to an indeterminate form of this type as well as to $(-\infty/-\infty)$, $(-\infty/+\infty)$, $(+\infty/-\infty)$, and (∞/∞). This is given by the following theorems, for which the proofs are omitted because they are beyond the scope of this book.

13.2.1 Theorem
L'Hôpital's Rule

Let f and g be functions which are differentiable on an open interval I, except possibly at the number a in I, and suppose that for all $x \neq a$ in I, $g'(x) \neq 0$. Then if $\lim\limits_{x \to a} f(x) = +\infty, -\infty$, or ∞, and $\lim\limits_{x \to a} g(x) = +\infty, -\infty$, or ∞, and if

$$\lim_{x \to a} \frac{f'(x)}{g'(x)} = L$$

it follows that

$$\lim_{x \to a} \frac{f(x)}{g(x)} = L$$

The theorem is valid if all the limits are right-hand limits or if all the limits are left-hand limits.

13.2.2 Theorem
L'Hôpital's Rule

Let f and g be functions which are differentiable for all $x > N$, where N is a positive constant, and suppose that for all $x > N$, $g'(x) \neq 0$. Then if $\lim\limits_{x \to +\infty} f(x) = +\infty, -\infty$, or ∞, and $\lim\limits_{x \to +\infty} g(x) = +\infty, -\infty$, or ∞, and if

$$\lim_{x \to +\infty} \frac{f'(x)}{g'(x)} = L$$

it follows that

$$\lim_{x \to +\infty} \frac{f(x)}{g(x)} = L$$

The theorem is also valid if "$x \to +\infty$" is replaced by "$x \to -\infty$."

Theorems 13.2.1 and 13.2.2 also hold if L is replaced by $+\infty, -\infty$, or ∞, and the proofs for these cases are also omitted.

EXAMPLE 1:   Find

$$\lim_{x\to 0^+} \frac{\ln x}{\frac{1}{x}}$$

if it exists.

SOLUTION: Because $\lim_{x\to 0^+} \ln x = -\infty$ and $\lim_{x\to 0^+} (1/x) = +\infty$, we apply L'Hôpital's rule and get

$$\lim_{x\to 0^+} \frac{\ln x}{\frac{1}{x}} = \lim_{x\to 0^+} \frac{\frac{1}{x}}{-\frac{1}{x^2}} = \lim_{x\to 0^+} (-x) = 0$$

EXAMPLE 2:   Find

$$\lim_{x\to +\infty} \frac{x^2}{e^x}$$

if it exists.

SOLUTION: Because $\lim_{x\to +\infty} x^2 = +\infty$ and $\lim_{x\to +\infty} e^x = +\infty$, by applying L'Hôpital's rule we obtain

$$\lim_{x\to +\infty} \frac{x^2}{e^x} = \lim_{x\to +\infty} \frac{2x}{e^x}$$

Now because $\lim_{x\to +\infty} 2x = +\infty$ and $\lim_{x\to +\infty} e^x = +\infty$, we apply L'Hôpital's rule again and get

$$\lim_{x\to +\infty} \frac{2x}{e^x} = \lim_{x\to +\infty} \frac{2}{e^x} = 0$$

Therefore,

$$\lim_{x\to +\infty} \frac{x^2}{e^x} = 0$$

EXAMPLE 3:   Find

$$\lim_{x\to \pi/2} \frac{\sec^2 x}{\sec^2 3x}$$

if it exists.

SOLUTION: $\lim_{x\to \pi/2} \sec^2 x = +\infty$ and $\lim_{x\to \pi/2} \sec^2 3x = +\infty$. So by applying L'Hôpital's rule we get $\sec^2 x = 2\sec^2 x \tan x.$

$$\lim_{x\to \pi/2} \frac{\sec^2 x}{\sec^2 3x} = \lim_{x\to \pi/2} \frac{2 \sec^2 x \tan x}{6 \sec^2 3x \tan 3x}$$

$$\lim_{x\to \pi/2} 2 \sec^2 x \tan x = \infty \quad \text{and} \quad \lim_{x\to \pi/2} 6 \sec^2 3x \tan 3x = \infty$$

It may be seen that further applications of L'Hôpital's rule will not help us. However, the original quotient may be rewritten and we have

$$\lim_{x\to \pi/2} \frac{\sec^2 x}{\sec^2 3x} = \lim_{x\to \pi/2} \frac{\cos^2 3x}{\cos^2 x}$$

Now, because $\lim_{x\to \pi/2} \cos^2 3x = 0$ and $\lim_{x\to \pi/2} \cos^2 x = 0$, we may apply L'Hôpital's rule giving

$$\lim_{x\to \pi/2} \frac{\cos^2 3x}{\cos^2 x} = \lim_{x\to \pi/2} \frac{-6 \cos 3x \sin 3x}{-2 \cos x \sin x}$$

$$= \lim_{x\to \pi/2} \frac{3(2 \cos 3x \sin 3x)}{(2 \cos x \sin x)}$$

$$= \lim_{x\to \pi/2} \frac{3 \sin 6x}{\sin 2x}$$

Because $\lim\limits_{x \to \pi/2} 3 \sin 6x = 0$ and $\lim\limits_{x \to \pi/2} \sin 2x = 0$, we apply L'Hôpital's rule again and we have

$$\lim_{x \to \pi/2} \frac{3 \sin 6x}{\sin 2x} = \lim_{x \to \pi/2} \frac{18 \cos 6x}{2 \cos 2x} = \frac{18(-1)}{2(-1)} = 9$$

Therefore,

$$\lim_{x \to \pi/2} \frac{\sec^2 x}{\sec^2 3x} = 9$$

The limit in Example 3 can be evaluated without L'Hôpital's rule by using Eqs. (11) in Sec. 9.1 and Theorem 9.2.1. This is left for the reader (see Exercise 25).

In addition to $0/0$ and $\pm(\infty/\infty)$, other indeterminate forms are $0 \cdot \infty$, $\infty - \infty$, 0^0, ∞^0, 1^∞, and corresponding forms where ∞ is replaced by either $+\infty$ or $-\infty$. These indeterminate forms are defined analogously to the other two. For example, if $\lim\limits_{x \to a} f(x) = \infty$ and $\lim\limits_{x \to a} g(x) = 0$, then the function defined by $f(x)^{g(x)}$ has the indeterminate form ∞^0 at a. To find the limit of a function having one of these indeterminate forms, it must be changed to either the form $0/0$ or $\pm(\infty/\infty)$ before L'Hôpital's rule can be applied. The following examples illustrate the method.

EXAMPLE 4: Find

$$\lim_{x \to 0} \sin^{-1} x \csc x$$

if it exists.

SOLUTION: Because $\lim\limits_{x \to 0} \sin^{-1} x = 0$ and $\lim\limits_{x \to 0} \csc x = \infty$, the function defined by $\sin^{-1} x \csc x$ has the indeterminate form $0 \cdot \infty$ at 0. Before we can apply L'Hôpital's rule we rewrite $\sin^{-1} x \csc x$ as $\sin^{-1} x/\sin x$, and consider $\lim\limits_{x \to 0} (\sin^{-1} x/\sin x)$. Now $\lim\limits_{x \to 0} \sin^{-1} x = 0$ and $\lim\limits_{x \to 0} \sin x = 0$, and so we have the indeterminate form $0/0$. Therefore, we apply L'Hôpital's rule and obtain

$$\lim_{x \to 0} \frac{\sin^{-1} x}{\sin x} = \lim_{x \to 0} \frac{\dfrac{1}{\sqrt{1 - x^2}}}{\cos x} = \frac{1}{1} = 1$$

EXAMPLE 5: Find

$$\lim_{x \to 0} \left(\frac{1}{x^2} - \frac{1}{x^2 \sec x} \right)$$

if it exists.

SOLUTION: Because

$$\lim_{x \to 0} \frac{1}{x^2} = +\infty \quad \text{and} \quad \lim_{x \to 0} \frac{1}{x^2 \sec x} = +\infty$$

we have the indeterminate form $+\infty - (+\infty)$. Rewriting the expression, we have

$$\lim_{x \to 0} \left(\frac{1}{x^2} - \frac{1}{x^2 \sec x} \right) = \lim_{x \to 0} \frac{\sec x - 1}{x^2 \sec x}$$

$\lim\limits_{x \to 0} (\sec x - 1) = 0$ and $\lim\limits_{x \to 0} (x^2 \sec x) = 0$; so we apply L'Hôpital's rule and obtain

$$\lim_{x \to 0} \frac{\sec x - 1}{x^2 \sec x} = \lim_{x \to 0} \frac{\sec x \tan x}{2x \sec x + x^2 \sec x \tan x}$$

$$= \lim_{x \to 0} \frac{\tan x}{2x + x^2 \tan x}$$

$$\lim_{x \to 0} \tan x = 0 \quad \text{and} \quad \lim_{x \to 0} (2x + x^2 \tan x) = 0$$

and so we apply the rule again and obtain

$$\lim_{x \to 0} \frac{\tan x}{2x + x^2 \tan x} = \lim_{x \to 0} \frac{\sec^2 x}{2 + 2x \tan x + x^2 \sec^2 x} = \frac{1}{2}$$

Therefore,

$$\lim_{x \to 0} \left(\frac{1}{x^2} - \frac{1}{x^2 \sec x} \right) = \frac{1}{2}$$

If we have one of the indeterminate forms, 0^0, ∞^0, or 1^∞, the procedure for evaluating the limit is illustrated in Example 6.

EXAMPLE 6:   Find

$$\lim_{x \to 0} (x + 1)^{\cot x}$$

if it exists.

SOLUTION: Because $\lim_{x \to 0} (x + 1) = 1$ and $\lim_{x \to 0} \cot x = \infty$, we have the indeterminate form 1^∞. Let

$$y = (x + 1)^{\cot x} \tag{1}$$

Then

$$\ln y = \cot x \ln(x + 1)$$

or

$$\ln y = \frac{\ln(x + 1)}{\tan x}$$

So

$$\lim_{x \to 0} \ln y = \lim_{x \to 0} \frac{\ln(x + 1)}{\tan x} \tag{2}$$

Because $\lim_{x \to 0} \ln(x + 1) = 0$ and $\lim_{x \to 0} \tan x = 0$, we may apply L'Hôpital's rule to the right side of (2) and obtain

$$\lim_{x \to 0} \frac{\ln(x + 1)}{\tan x} = \lim_{x \to 0} \frac{\dfrac{1}{x + 1}}{\sec^2 x} = 1$$

Therefore, substituting 1 on the right side of (2), we have

$$\lim_{x \to 0} \ln y = 1 \tag{3}$$

Because the natural logarithmic function is continuous on its entire domain, which is the set of all positive numbers, we may apply Theorem 2.12.5 and we have from (3)

$$\ln \lim_{x \to 0} y = 1$$

Therefore,

$$\lim_{x \to 0} y = e^1$$

But from (1), $y = (x + 1)^{\cot x}$, and so we have

$$\lim_{x \to 0} (x + 1)^{\cot x} = e$$

Exercises 13.2

In Exercises 1 through 24, evaluate the limit, if it exists.

1. $\lim\limits_{x \to +\infty} \dfrac{x^2}{e^x}$

2. $\lim\limits_{x \to \pi/2^-} \dfrac{\ln(\cos x)}{\ln(\tan x)}$

3. $\lim\limits_{x \to 1/2^-} \dfrac{\ln(1 - 2x)}{\tan \pi x}$

4. $\lim\limits_{x \to +\infty} \dfrac{(\ln x)^3}{x}$

5. $\lim\limits_{x \to 0} x \csc x$

6. $\lim\limits_{x \to 0} \sin^{-1} x \csc x$

7. $\lim\limits_{x \to 1} \left(\dfrac{1}{\ln x} - \dfrac{1}{x - 1} \right)$

8. $\lim\limits_{x \to 0^+} (\sinh x)^{\tan x}$

9. $\lim\limits_{x \to 0^+} x^{\sin x}$

10. $\lim\limits_{x \to 0} (x + e^{2x})^{1/x}$

11. $\lim\limits_{x \to +\infty} (x^2 - \sqrt{x^4 - x^2 + 2})$

12. $\lim\limits_{x \to 2} \left(\dfrac{5}{x^2 + x - 6} - \dfrac{1}{x - 2} \right)$

13. $\lim\limits_{x \to +\infty} x^{1/x}$

14. $\lim\limits_{x \to 0^+} (1 + x)^{\ln x}$

15. $\lim\limits_{x \to +\infty} (e^x + x)^{2/x}$

16. $\lim\limits_{x \to 0^+} x^{1/\ln x}$

17. $\lim\limits_{x \to 0} (1 + ax)^{1/x}; a \neq 0$

18. $\lim\limits_{x \to +\infty} \left(1 + \dfrac{1}{2x} \right)^{x^2}$

19. $\lim\limits_{x \to 0} (1 + \sinh x)^{2/x}$

20. $\lim\limits_{x \to 2} (x - 2) \tan \frac{1}{4} \pi x$

21. $\lim\limits_{x \to 0} [(\cos x)e^{x^2/2}]^{4/x^4}$

22. $\lim\limits_{x \to 0} (\cos x)^{1/x^2}$

23. $\lim\limits_{x \to +\infty} [(x^6 + 3x^5 + 4)^{1/6} - x]$

24. $\lim\limits_{x \to 0^+} x^{x^x}$

25. Evaluate the limit in Example 3 without using L'Hôpital's rule, but by using Eqs. (11) in Sec. 9.1 and Theorem 9.2.1.

26. If $\lim\limits_{x \to +\infty} \left(\dfrac{nx + 1}{nx - 1} \right)^x = 9$, find n.

27. Suppose $f(x) = \displaystyle\int_1^x e^{3t} \sqrt{9t^4 + 1} \, dt$ and $g(x) = x^n e^{3x}$. If $\lim\limits_{x \to +\infty} \left[\dfrac{f'(x)}{g'(x)} \right] = 1$, find n.

13.3 IMPROPER INTEGRALS WITH INFINITE LIMITS OF INTEGRATION In defining the definite integral $\int_a^b f(x) \, dx$, the function f was assumed to be defined on the closed interval $[a, b]$. We now extend the definition of the definite integral to consider an infinite interval of integration and call such an integral an *improper integral.* In Sec. 13.4 we discuss another kind of improper integral.

Consider the problem of finding the area of the region bounded by the curve $y = e^{-x}$, the x axis, the y axis, and the line $x = b$, where $b > 0$.

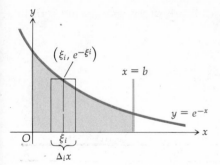

Figure 13.3.1

This region is shown in Fig. 13.3.1. Letting A square units be the area of this region, we have

$$A = \lim_{\|\Delta\| \to 0} \sum_{i=1}^{n} e^{-\xi_i} \Delta_i x$$

$$= \int_0^b e^{-x} \, dx$$

$$= -e^{-x} \bigg]_0^b$$

$$= 1 - e^{-b}$$

If we let b increase without bound, then

$$\lim_{b \to +\infty} \int_0^b e^{-x} \, dx = \lim_{b \to +\infty} (1 - e^{-b})$$

or

$$\lim_{b \to +\infty} \int_0^b e^{-x} \, dx = 1 \tag{1}$$

Equation (1) states that if $b > 0$, for any $\epsilon > 0$ there exists an $N > 0$ such that

$$\left| \int_0^b e^{-x} \, dx - 1 \right| < \epsilon \qquad \text{whenever } b > N$$

In place of (1) we write

$$\int_0^{+\infty} e^{-x} \, dx = 1$$

We conclude from Eq. (1) that no matter how large a value we take for b, the area of the region shown in Fig. 13.3.1 will always be less than 1 square unit.

In general, we have the following definition.

13.3.1 Definition If f is continuous for all $x \geq a$, then

$$\int_a^{+\infty} f(x) \, dx = \lim_{b \to +\infty} \int_a^b f(x) \, dx$$

if this limit exists.

If the lower limit of integration is infinite, we have the following definition.

13.3.2 Definition If f is continuous for all $x \leq b$, then

$$\int_{-\infty}^b f(x) \, dx = \lim_{a \to -\infty} \int_a^b f(x) \, dx$$

if this limit exists.

Finally, we have the case when both limits of integration are infinite.

13.3.3 Definition   If f is continuous for all values of x, then

$$\int_{-\infty}^{+\infty} f(x)\ dx = \lim_{a \to -\infty} \int_a^0 f(x)\ dx + \lim_{b \to +\infty} \int_0^b f(x)\ dx$$

if these limits exist.

In Definitions 13.3.1, 13.3.2, and 13.3.3, if the limits exist, we say that the improper integral is *convergent*. If the limits do not exist, we say that the improper integral is *divergent*.

[handwritten in margin: HOW DOES IT AFFECT THE RESULT IF WE CHANGE THE FORMULA]

EXAMPLE 1:   Evaluate

$$\int_{-\infty}^2 \frac{dx}{(4-x)^2}$$

if it converges.

SOLUTION:

$$\int_{-\infty}^2 \frac{dx}{(4-x)^2} = \lim_{a \to -\infty} \int_a^2 \frac{dx}{(4-x)^2}$$

$$= \lim_{a \to -\infty} \left[\frac{1}{4-x} \right]_a^2$$

$$= \lim_{a \to -\infty} \left(\frac{1}{2} - \frac{1}{4-a} \right)$$

$$= \tfrac{1}{2} - 0$$

$$= \tfrac{1}{2} \quad \text{[handwritten: IT CONVERGES]}$$

EXAMPLE 2:   Evaluate if they exist:

(a) $\displaystyle\int_{-\infty}^{+\infty} x\ dx$

and

(b) $\displaystyle\lim_{r \to +\infty} \int_{-r}^r x\ dx$

SOLUTION: (a) Using Definition 13.3.3, we have

$$\int_{-\infty}^{+\infty} x\ dx = \lim_{a \to -\infty} \int_a^0 x\ dx + \lim_{b \to +\infty} \int_0^b x\ dx$$

$$= \lim_{a \to -\infty} \left[\tfrac{1}{2}x^2 \right]_a^0 + \lim_{b \to +\infty} \left[\tfrac{1}{2}x^2 \right]_0^b$$

$$= \lim_{a \to -\infty} \left(-\tfrac{1}{2}a^2 \right) + \lim_{b \to +\infty} \tfrac{1}{2}b^2$$

Because neither of these two limits exists, the improper integral diverges.

(b) $\displaystyle\lim_{r \to +\infty} \int_{-r}^r x\ dx = \lim_{r \to +\infty} \left[\tfrac{1}{2}x^2 \right]_{-r}^r$

$$= \lim_{r \to +\infty} \left(\tfrac{1}{2}r^2 - \tfrac{1}{2}r^2 \right)$$

$$= \lim_{r \to +\infty} 0$$

$$= 0$$

Example 2 illustrates why we cannot use the limit in (b) as the definition of an improper integral where both limits of integration are infinite. That is, the improper integral in (a) is divergent, but the limit in (b) exists and is zero.

EXAMPLE 3: Evaluate

$$\int_{-\infty}^{+\infty} \frac{dx}{x^2 + 6x + 12}$$

if it converges.

SOLUTION:

$$\int_{-\infty}^{+\infty} \frac{dx}{x^2 + 6x + 12} = \lim_{a \to -\infty} \int_a^0 \frac{dx}{(x + 3)^2 + 3} + \lim_{b \to +\infty} \int_0^b \frac{dx}{(x + 3)^2 + 3}$$

$$= \lim_{a \to -\infty} \left[\frac{1}{\sqrt{3}} \tan^{-1} \frac{x + 3}{\sqrt{3}} \right]_a^0 + \lim_{b \to +\infty} \left[\frac{1}{\sqrt{3}} \tan^{-1} \frac{x + 3}{\sqrt{3}} \right]_0^b$$

$$= \lim_{a \to -\infty} \left(\frac{1}{\sqrt{3}} \tan^{-1} \sqrt{3} - \frac{1}{\sqrt{3}} \tan^{-1} \frac{a + 3}{\sqrt{3}} \right)$$

$$+ \lim_{b \to +\infty} \left(\frac{1}{\sqrt{3}} \tan^{-1} \frac{b + 3}{\sqrt{3}} - \frac{1}{\sqrt{3}} \tan^{-1} \sqrt{3} \right)$$

$$= \frac{1}{\sqrt{3}} \left[\lim_{a \to -\infty} \left(-\tan^{-1} \frac{a + 3}{\sqrt{3}} \right) + \lim_{b \to +\infty} \tan^{-1} \frac{b + 3}{\sqrt{3}} \right]$$

$$= \frac{1}{\sqrt{3}} \left[-\left(-\frac{\pi}{2} \right) + \frac{\pi}{2} \right]$$

$$= \frac{\pi}{\sqrt{3}}$$

EXAMPLE 4: Is it possible to assign a finite number to represent the measure of the area of the region bounded by the graphs of the equations $y = 1/x$, $y = 0$, and $x = 1$?

Figure 13.3.2

SOLUTION: The region is shown in Fig. 13.3.2. Let L be the number we wish to assign to the measure of the area, if possible. Let A be the measure of the area of the region bounded by the graphs of the equations $y = 1/x$, $y = 0$, $x = 1$, and $x = b$ where $b > 1$. Then

$$A = \lim_{\|\Delta\| \to 0} \sum_{i=1}^n \frac{1}{\xi_i} \Delta_i x = \int_1^b \frac{1}{x} dx$$

So we shall let $L = \lim_{b \to +\infty} A$ if this limit exists. But

$$\lim_{b \to +\infty} A = \lim_{b \to +\infty} \int_1^b \frac{1}{x} dx$$

$$= \lim_{b \to +\infty} [\ln b - \ln 1]$$

$$= +\infty$$

Therefore, it is not possible to assign a finite number to represent the measure of the area of the region.

EXAMPLE 5: Is it possible to assign a finite number to represent the measure of the volume of the solid formed by revolving the region in Example 4 about the x axis?

SOLUTION: The element of volume is a circular disk having a thickness of $\Delta_i x$ and a base radius of $1/\xi_i$. Let L be the number we wish to assign to the measure of the volume, and let V be the measure of the volume of the solid formed by revolving about the x axis the region bounded by the graphs of the equations $y = 1/x$, $y = 0$, $x = 1$, and $x = b$ where $b > 1$. Then

$$V = \lim_{||\Delta|| \to 0} \sum_{i=1}^{n} \pi \left(\frac{1}{\xi_i}\right)^2 \Delta_i x = \pi \int_{1}^{b} \frac{1}{x^2}\, dx$$

We shall let $L = \lim_{b \to +\infty} V$, if the limit exists.

$$\lim_{b \to +\infty} V = \lim_{b \to +\infty} \pi \int_{1}^{b} \frac{dx}{x^2}$$

$$= \pi \lim_{b \to +\infty} \left[-\frac{1}{x}\right]_{1}^{b}$$

$$= \pi \lim_{b \to +\infty} \left(-\frac{1}{b} + 1\right)$$

$$= \pi$$

Therefore, we assign π to represent the measure of the volume of the solid.

EXAMPLE 6: Determine if

$$\int_{0}^{+\infty} \sin x\, dx$$

is convergent or divergent.

SOLUTION:

$$\int_{0}^{+\infty} \sin x\, dx = \lim_{b \to +\infty} \int_{0}^{b} \sin x\, dx$$

$$= \lim_{b \to +\infty} \left[-\cos x\right]_{0}^{b}$$

$$= \lim_{b \to +\infty} (-\cos b + 1)$$

For any integer n, as b takes on all values from $n\pi$ to $2n\pi$, $\cos b$ takes on all values from -1 to 1. Hence, $\lim_{b \to +\infty} \cos b$ does not exist. Therefore, the improper integral is divergent.

Example 6 illustrates the case for which an improper integral is divergent where the limit is not infinite.

Exercises 13.3

In Exercises 1 through 14, determine whether the improper integral is convergent or divergent. If it is convergent, evaluate it.

1. $\displaystyle\int_{0}^{+\infty} e^{-x}\, dx$

2. $\displaystyle\int_{-\infty}^{1} e^{x}\, dx$

3. $\displaystyle\int_{-\infty}^{0} x\, 5^{-x^2}\, dx$

4. $\displaystyle\int_{1}^{+\infty} 2^{-x}\, dx$

5. $\displaystyle\int_{0}^{+\infty} x e^{-x}\, dx$

6. $\int_{5}^{+\infty} \dfrac{dx}{\sqrt{x-1}}$ 7. $\int_{-\infty}^{+\infty} x \cosh x \, dx$ 8. $\int_{-\infty}^{0} x^2 e^x \, dx$ 9. $\int_{-\infty}^{+\infty} e^{-|x|} \, dx$ 10. $\int_{-\infty}^{+\infty} x e^{-x^2} \, dx$

11. $\int_{e}^{+\infty} \dfrac{dx}{x(\ln x)^2}$ 12. $\int_{-\infty}^{+\infty} \dfrac{dx}{16 + x^2}$ 13. $\int_{1}^{+\infty} \ln x \, dx$ 14. $\int_{0}^{+\infty} e^{-x} \cos x \, dx$

15. Evaluate if they exist: (a) $\int_{-\infty}^{+\infty} \sin x \, dx$; (b) $\lim\limits_{r \to +\infty} \int_{-r}^{r} \sin x \, dx$.

16. Prove that if $\int_{-\infty}^{b} f(x) \, dx$ is convergent, then $\int_{-b}^{+\infty} f(-x) \, dx$ is also convergent and has the same value.

17. Show that the improper integral $\int_{-\infty}^{+\infty} x(1 + x^2)^{-2} \, dx$ is convergent and the improper integral $\int_{-\infty}^{+\infty} x(1 + x^2)^{-1} \, dx$ is divergent.

18. Prove that the improper integral $\int_{1}^{+\infty} dx/x^n$ is convergent if and only if $n > 1$.

19. Determine if it is possible to assign a finite number to represent the measure of the area of the region bounded by the curve whose equation is $y = 1/(e^x + e^{-x})$ and the x axis. If a finite number can be assigned, find it.

20. Determine if it is possible to assign a finite number to represent the measure of the area of the region bounded by the x axis, the line $x = 2$, and the curve whose equation is $y = 1/(x^2 - 1)$. If a finite number can be assigned, find it.

21. Determine if it is possible to assign a finite number to represent the measure of the volume of the solid formed by revolving about the x axis the region to the right of the line $x = 1$ and bounded by the curve whose equation is $y = 1/x\sqrt{x}$ and the x axis. If a finite number can be assigned, find it.

22. Determine a value of n for which the improper integral
$$\int_{1}^{+\infty} \left(\frac{nx^2}{x^3 + 1} - \frac{1}{3x + 1} \right) dx$$
is convergent and evaluate the integral for this value of n.

23. Determine a value of n for which the improper integral
$$\int_{1}^{+\infty} \left(\frac{n}{x + 1} - \frac{3x}{2x^2 + n} \right) dx$$
is convergent and evaluate the integral for this value of n.

Exercises 24, 25, and 26 show an interesting application of improper integrals in the field of economics. Suppose there is a continuous flow of income for which interest is compounded continuously at the annual rate of $100i$ percent and $f(t)$ dollars is the income per year at any time t years. If the income continues indefinitely, the present value, V dollars, of all future income is defined by
$$V = \int_{0}^{+\infty} f(t) e^{-it} \, dt$$

24. A continuous flow of income is decreasing with time and at t years the number of dollars in the annual income is $1000 \cdot 2^{-t}$. Find the present value of this income if it continues indefinitely using an interest rate of 8 percent compounded continuously.

25. The continuous flow of profit for a company is increasing with time, and at t years the number of dollars in the profit per year is proportional to t. Show that the present value of the company is inversely proportional to i^2, where $100i$ percent is the interest rate compounded continuously.

26. The British Consol is a bond with no maturity (i.e., it never comes due), and it affords the holder an annual lump-sum payment. By finding the present value of a flow of payments of R dollars annually and using the current interest rate of $100i$ percent, compounded continuously, show that the fair selling price of a British Consol is R/i dollars.

13.4 OTHER IMPROPER INTEGRALS

Figure 13.4.1

Figure 13.4.1 shows the region bounded by the curve whose equation is $y = 1/\sqrt{x}$, the x axis, the y axis, and the line $x = 4$. If it is possible to assign a finite number to represent the measure of the area of this region, it would be given by

$$\lim_{\|\Delta\|\to 0} \sum_{i=1}^{n} \frac{1}{\sqrt{\xi_i}} \Delta_i x$$

If this limit exists it is the definite integral denoted by

$$\int_0^4 \frac{dx}{\sqrt{x}} \tag{1}$$

However, the integrand is discontinuous at the lower limit zero. Furthermore, $\lim_{x\to 0^+} 1/\sqrt{x} = +\infty$, and so we state that the integrand has an infinite discontinuity at the lower limit. Such an integral is improper, and its existence can be determined from the following definition.

13.4.1 Definition   If f is continuous at all x in the interval half open on the left $(a, b]$, then

$$\int_a^b f(x)\ dx = \lim_{\epsilon\to 0^+} \int_{a+\epsilon}^b f(x)\ dx$$

if this limit exists.

EXAMPLE 1:   Determine if it is possible to assign a finite number to represent the measure of the area of the region shown in Fig. 13.4.1.

SOLUTION: From the discussion preceding Definition 13.4.1 the measure of the area of the given region will be the improper integral (1) if it exists. By Definition 13.4.1, we have

$$\int_0^4 \frac{dx}{\sqrt{x}} = \lim_{\epsilon\to 0^+} \int_\epsilon^4 \frac{dx}{\sqrt{x}}$$

$$= \lim_{\epsilon\to 0^+} 2x^{1/2} \Big]_\epsilon^4$$

$$= \lim_{\epsilon\to 0^+} [4 - 2\sqrt{\epsilon}]$$

$$= 4 - 0$$

$$= 4$$

Therefore, we assign 4 to the measure of the area of the given region.

If the integrand has an infinite discontinuity at the upper limit of integration, we use the following definition to determine the existence of the improper integral.

13.4.2 Definition   If f is continuous at all x in the interval half open on the right $[a, b)$, then

$$\int_a^b f(x)\ dx = \lim_{\epsilon\to 0^+} \int_a^{b-\epsilon} f(x)\ dx$$

if this limit exists.

If there is an infinite discontinuity at an interior point of the interval of integration, the existence of the improper integral is determined from the following definition.

13.4.3 Definition   If f is continuous at all x in the interval $[a, b]$ except c when $a < c < b$, then

$$\left(\int_a^b f(x)\ dx = \lim_{\epsilon \to 0^+} \int_a^{c-\epsilon} f(x)\ dx + \lim_{\delta \to 0^+} \int_{c+\delta}^b f(x)\ dx \right.$$

if these limits exist.

If $\int_a^b f(x)\ dx$ is an improper integral, it is convergent if the corresponding limit exists; otherwise, it is divergent.

EXAMPLE 2:   Evaluate

$$\int_0^2 \frac{dx}{(x-1)^2}$$

if it is convergent.

SOLUTION: The integrand has an infinite discontinuity at 1. Applying Definition 13.4.3, we have

$$\int_0^2 \frac{dx}{(x-1)^2} = \lim_{\epsilon \to 0^+} \int_0^{1-\epsilon} \frac{dx}{(x-1)^2} + \lim_{\delta \to 0^+} \int_{1+\delta}^2 \frac{dx}{(x-1)^2}$$

$$= \lim_{\epsilon \to 0^+} \left[-\frac{1}{x-1} \right]_0^{1-\epsilon} + \lim_{\delta \to 0^+} \left[-\frac{1}{x-1} \right]_{1+\delta}^2$$

$$= \lim_{\epsilon \to 0^+} \left[\frac{1}{\epsilon} - 1 \right] + \lim_{\delta \to 0^+} \left[-1 + \frac{1}{\delta} \right]$$

Because neither of these limits exist, the improper integral is divergent.

Suppose that in evaluating the integral in Example 2 we had failed to note the infinite discontinuity of the integrand at 1. We would have obtained

$$-\frac{1}{x-1} \Big]_0^2 = -\frac{1}{1} + \frac{1}{-1} = -2$$

This is obviously an incorrect result because the integrand $1/(x-1)^2$ is never negative; hence, the integral from 0 to 2 could not possibly be a negative number.

EXAMPLE 3:   Evaluate

$$\int_0^1 x \ln x\ dx$$

if it is convergent.

SOLUTION: The integrand has a discontinuity at the lower limit. Applying Definition 13.4.1, we have

$$\int_0^1 x \ln x\ dx = \lim_{\epsilon \to 0^+} \int_\epsilon^1 x \ln x\ dx$$

$$= \lim_{\epsilon \to 0^+} \left[\tfrac{1}{2} x^2 \ln x - \tfrac{1}{4} x^2 \right]_\epsilon^1$$

$$= \lim_{\epsilon \to 0^+} \left[\tfrac{1}{2} \ln 1 - \tfrac{1}{4} - \tfrac{1}{2} \epsilon^2 \ln \epsilon - \tfrac{1}{4} \epsilon^2 \right]$$

Hence,

$$\int_0^1 x \ln x \, dx = 0 - \tfrac{1}{4} - \tfrac{1}{2} \lim_{\epsilon \to 0^+} \epsilon^2 \ln \epsilon - 0 \tag{2}$$

To evaluate

$$\lim_{\epsilon \to 0^+} \epsilon^2 \ln \epsilon = \lim_{\epsilon \to 0^+} \frac{\ln \epsilon}{\dfrac{1}{\epsilon^2}}$$

we apply L'Hôpital's rule because $\lim\limits_{\epsilon \to 0^+} \ln \epsilon = -\infty$ and $\lim\limits_{\epsilon \to 0^+} 1/\epsilon^2 = +\infty$. We have

$$\lim_{\epsilon \to 0^+} \frac{\ln \epsilon}{\dfrac{1}{\epsilon^2}} = \lim_{\epsilon \to 0^+} \frac{\dfrac{1}{\epsilon}}{-\dfrac{2}{\epsilon^3}} = \lim_{\epsilon \to 0^+} \left[-\frac{\epsilon^2}{2} \right] = 0$$

Therefore, from (2) we have

$$\int_0^1 x \ln x \, dx = -\tfrac{1}{4}$$

EXAMPLE 4: Evaluate

$$\int_1^{+\infty} \frac{dx}{x\sqrt{x^2 - 1}}$$

if it is convergent.

SOLUTION: For this integral, there is both an infinite upper limit and an infinite discontinuity of the integrand at the lower limit. We proceed as follows.

$$\int_1^{+\infty} \frac{dx}{x\sqrt{x^2 - 1}} = \lim_{a \to 1^+} \int_a^2 \frac{dx}{x\sqrt{x^2 - 1}} + \lim_{b \to +\infty} \int_2^b \frac{dx}{x\sqrt{x^2 - 1}}$$

$$= \lim_{a \to 1^+} \left[\sec^{-1} x \right]_a^2 + \lim_{b \to +\infty} \left[\sec^{-1} x \right]_2^b$$

$$= \lim_{a \to 1^+} (\sec^{-1} 2 - \sec^{-1} a) + \lim_{b \to +\infty} (\sec^{-1} b - \sec^{-1} 2)$$

$$= -\lim_{a \to 1^+} \sec^{-1} a + \lim_{b \to +\infty} \sec^{-1} b$$

$$= 0 + \tfrac{1}{2}\pi$$

$$= \tfrac{1}{2}\pi$$

Exercises 13.4

In Exercises 1 through 20, determine whether the improper integral is convergent or divergent. If it is convergent, evaluate it.

1. $\displaystyle \int_0^1 \frac{dx}{\sqrt{1 - x}}$

2. $\displaystyle \int_0^2 \frac{dx}{\sqrt{4 - x^2}}$

3. $\displaystyle \int_{\pi/4}^{\pi/2} \sec x \, dx$

4. $\displaystyle \int_0^4 \frac{x \, dx}{\sqrt{16 - x^2}}$

5. $\displaystyle \int_0^{+\infty} \frac{dx}{x^3}$

6. $\displaystyle \int_0^{\pi/2} \tan \theta \, d\theta$

7. $\displaystyle \int_0^{\pi/2} \frac{dt}{1 - \sin t}$

8. $\displaystyle \int_0^2 \frac{dx}{(x - 1)^{2/3}}$

9. $\displaystyle \int_0^4 \frac{dx}{x^2 - 2x - 3}$

10. $\displaystyle\int_{2}^{+\infty} \frac{dx}{x\sqrt{x^2 - 4}}$

11. $\displaystyle\int_{0}^{+\infty} \ln x \, dx$

12. $\displaystyle\int_{-1}^{1} \frac{dx}{x^2}$

13. $\displaystyle\int_{-2}^{0} \frac{dt}{(t+1)^{1/3}}$

14. $\displaystyle\int_{0}^{2} \frac{dx}{\sqrt{2x - x^2}}$

15. $\displaystyle\int_{-2}^{2} \frac{dx}{x^3}$

16. $\displaystyle\int_{0}^{+\infty} \frac{e^{-\sqrt{x}}}{\sqrt{x}} \, dx$

17. $\displaystyle\int_{1/2}^{2} \frac{dt}{t(\ln t)^{1/5}}$

18. $\displaystyle\int_{0}^{2} \frac{x \, dx}{1 - x}$

19. $\displaystyle\int_{1}^{2} \frac{dx}{x\sqrt{x^2 - 1}}$

20. $\displaystyle\int_{0}^{1} \frac{dx}{x\sqrt{4 - x^2}}$

21. Evaluate, if they exist:

(a) $\displaystyle\int_{-1}^{1} \frac{dx}{x}$; (b) $\displaystyle\lim_{r \to 0^+} \left[\int_{-1}^{-r} \frac{dx}{x} + \int_{r}^{1} \frac{dx}{x} \right]$

22. Show that it is possible to assign a finite number to represent the measure of the area of the region bounded by the curve whose equation is $y = 1/\sqrt{x}$, the line $x = 1$, and the x and y axes, but that it is not possible to assign a finite number to represent the measure of the volume of the solid of revolution generated if this region is revolved about the x axis.

In Exercises 23 through 25, find the values of n for which the improper integral converges and evaluate the integral for these values of n.

23. $\displaystyle\int_{0}^{1} x^n \, dx$

24. $\displaystyle\int_{0}^{1} x^n \ln x \, dx$

25. $\displaystyle\int_{0}^{1} x^n \ln^2 x \, dx$

13.5 TAYLOR'S FORMULA

Values of polynomial functions can be found by performing a finite number of additions and multiplications. However, there are other functions, such as the logarithmic, exponential, and trigonometric functions, that cannot be evaluated as easily. We show in this section that many functions can be approximated by polynomials and that the polynomial, instead of the original function, can be used for computations when the difference between the actual function value and the polynomial approximation is sufficiently small.

There are various methods of approximating a given function by polynomials. One of the most widely used is that involving *Taylor's formula* named in honor of the English mathematician Brook Taylor (1685–1731). The following theorem, which can be considered as a generalization of the mean-value theorem (4.5.2), gives us Taylor's formula.

13.5.1 Theorem   Let f be a function such that f and its first n derivatives are continuous on the closed interval $[a, b]$. Furthermore, let $f^{(n+1)}(x)$ exist for all x in the open interval (a, b). Then there is a number ξ in the open interval (a, b) such that

$$f(b) = f(a) + \frac{f'(a)}{1!} (b - a) + \frac{f''(a)}{2!} (b - a)^2 + \cdots$$

$$+ \frac{f^{(n)}(a)}{n!} (b - a)^n + \frac{f^{(n+1)}(\xi)}{(n + 1)!} (b - a)^{n+1} \qquad (1)$$

Equation (1) also holds if $b < a$; in such a case, $[a, b]$ is replaced by $[b, a]$, and (a, b) is replaced by (b, a).

Before proving this theorem, note that when $n = 0$, (1) becomes

$$f(b) = f(a) + f'(\xi)(b - a)$$

where ξ is between a and b. This is the mean-value theorem (4.5.2).

There are several known proofs of Theorem 13.5.1, although none is very well motivated. The one following makes use of Cauchy's mean-value theorem (13.1.3).

PROOF OF THEOREM 13.5.1:   Let F and G be two functions defined by

$$F(x) = f(b) - f(x) - f'(x)(b - x) - \frac{f''(x)}{2!}(b - x)^2 - \cdots$$
$$- \frac{f^{(n-1)}(x)}{(n-1)!}(b - x)^{n-1} - \frac{f^{(n)}(x)}{n!}(b - x)^n \quad (2)$$

and

$$G(x) = \frac{(b - x)^{n+1}}{(n + 1)!} \tag{3}$$

It follows that $F(b) = 0$ and $G(b) = 0$. Differentiating in (2), we get

$$F'(x) = -f'(x) + f'(x) - f''(x)(b - x) + \frac{2f''(x)(b - x)}{2!}$$

$$- \frac{f'''(x)(b - x)^2}{2!} + \frac{3f'''(x)(b - x)^2}{3!} - \frac{f^{(iv)}(x)(b - x)^3}{3!} + \cdots$$

$$+ \frac{(n-1)f^{(n-1)}(x)(b - x)^{n-2}}{(n-1)!} - \frac{f^{(n)}(x)(b - x)^{n-1}}{(n-1)!}$$

$$+ \frac{nf^{(n)}(x)(b - x)^{n-1}}{n!} - \frac{f^{(n+1)}(x)(b - x)^n}{n!}$$

Combining terms, we see that the sum of every odd-numbered term with the following even-numbered term is zero, and so only the last term remains. Therefore,

$$F'(x) = -\frac{f^{(n+1)}(x)}{n!}(b - x)^n \tag{4}$$

Differentiating in (3), we obtain

$$G'(x) = -\frac{1}{n!}(b - x)^n \tag{5}$$

Checking the hypothesis of Theorem 13.1.3, we see that

  (i) F and G are continuous on $[a, b]$;
  (ii) F and G are differentiable on (a, b);
  (iii) for all x in (a, b), $G'(x) \neq 0$.

So by the conclusion of Theorem 13.1.3 it follows that

$$\frac{F(b) - F(a)}{G(b) - G(a)} = \frac{F'(\xi)}{G'(\xi)}$$

where ξ is in (a, b). But $F(b) = 0$ and $G(b) = 0$. So $\rightarrow \dfrac{F'(\xi)}{G'(\xi)} = \dfrac{F(a)}{G(a)}$

$$F(a) = \frac{F'(\xi)}{G'(\xi)} G(a) \tag{6}$$

for some ξ in (a, b).

Letting $x = a$ in (3), $x = \xi$ in (4), and $x = \xi$ in (5) and substituting into (6), we obtain

$$F(a) = -\frac{f^{(n+1)}(\xi)}{n!} (b - \xi)^n \left[-\frac{n!}{(b - \xi)^n} \right] \frac{(b - a)^{n+1}}{(n + 1)!}$$

or, equivalently,

$$F(a) = \frac{f^{(n+1)}(\xi)}{(n + 1)!} (b - a)^{n+1} \tag{7}$$

Letting $x = a$ in (2), we obtain

$$F(a) = f(b) - f(a) - f'(a)(b - a) - \frac{f''(a)}{2!} (b - a)^2 - \cdots$$

$$- \frac{f^{(n-1)}(a)}{(n - 1)!} (b - a)^{n-1} - \frac{f^{(n)}(a)}{n!} (b - a)^n \tag{8}$$

Substituting from (7) into (8), we get

$$f(b) = f(a) + f'(a)(b - a) + \frac{f''(a)}{2!} (b - a)^2 + \cdots$$

$$+ \frac{f^{(n)}(a)}{n!} (b - a)^n + \frac{f^{(n+1)}(\xi)}{(n + 1)!} (b - a)^{n+1}$$

which is the desired result. The theorem holds if $b < a$ because the conclusion of Theorem 13.1.3 is unaffected if a and b are interchanged. ∎

If in (1) b is replaced by x, Taylor's formula is obtained. It is

$$f(x) = f(a) + \frac{f'(a)}{1!} (x - a) + \frac{f''(a)}{2!} (x - a)^2 + \cdots$$

$$+ \frac{f^{(n)}(a)}{n!} (x - a)^n + \frac{f^{(n+1)}(\xi)}{(n + 1)!} (x - a)^{n+1} \tag{9}$$

where ξ is between a and x.

The condition under which (9) holds is that f and its first n derivatives must be continuous on a closed interval containing a and x, and the $(n + 1)$st derivative of f must exist at all points of the corresponding open interval. Formula (9) may be written as

$$f(x) = P_n(x) + R_n(x) \tag{10}$$

where

$$P_n(x) = f(a) + \frac{f'(a)}{1!}(x-a) + \frac{f''(a)}{2!}(x-a)^2 + \cdots$$

$$+ \frac{f^{(n)}(a)}{n!}(x-a)^n \qquad (11)$$

and

$$R_n(x) = \frac{f^{(n+1)}(\xi)}{(n+1)!}(x-a)^{n+1} \qquad \text{where } \xi \text{ is between } a \text{ and } x \qquad (12)$$

$P_n(x)$ is called the *n*th-degree *Taylor polynomial* of the function f at the number a, and $R_n(x)$ is called the *remainder*. The term $R_n(x)$ as given in (12) is called the *Lagrange form* of the remainder, named in honor of the French mathematician Joseph L. Lagrange (1736–1813).

EXAMPLE 1: Find the third-degree Taylor polynomial of the cosine function at $\frac{1}{4}\pi$ and the Lagrange form of the remainder.

SOLUTION: Letting $f(x) = \cos x$, we have from (11)

$$P_3(x) = f\left(\frac{\pi}{4}\right) + f'\left(\frac{\pi}{4}\right)\left(x - \frac{\pi}{4}\right) + \frac{f''(\frac{1}{4}\pi)}{2!}\left(x - \frac{\pi}{4}\right)^2 + \frac{f'''(\frac{1}{4}\pi)}{3!}\left(x - \frac{\pi}{4}\right)^3$$

Because $f(x) = \cos x$, $f(\frac{1}{4}\pi) = \frac{1}{2}\sqrt{2}$; $f'(x) = -\sin x$, $f'(\frac{1}{4}\pi) = -\frac{1}{2}\sqrt{2}$; $f''(x) = -\cos x$, $f''(\frac{1}{4}\pi) = -\frac{1}{2}\sqrt{2}$; $f'''(x) = \sin x$, $f'''(\frac{1}{4}\pi) = \frac{1}{2}\sqrt{2}$. Therefore,

$$P_3(x) = \frac{1}{2}\sqrt{2} - \frac{1}{2}\sqrt{2}(x - \frac{1}{4}\pi) - \frac{1}{4}\sqrt{2}(x - \frac{1}{4}\pi)^2 + \frac{1}{12}\sqrt{2}(x - \frac{1}{4}\pi)^3$$

Because $f^{(iv)}(x) = \cos x$, we obtain from (12)

$$R_3(x) = \frac{1}{24}(\cos \xi)(x - \frac{1}{4}\pi)^4 \qquad \text{where } \xi \text{ is between } \frac{1}{4}\pi \text{ and } x$$

Because $|\cos \xi| \le 1$, we may conclude that for all x, $|R_3(x)| \le \frac{1}{24}(x - \frac{1}{4}\pi)^4$.

Taylor's formula may be used to approximate a function by means of a Taylor polynomial. From (10) we obtain

$$|R_n(x)| = |f(x) - P_n(x)| \qquad (13)$$

If $P_n(x)$ is used to approximate $f(x)$, we can obtain an upper bound for the error of this approximation if we can find a number $E > 0$ such that $|R_n(x)| \le E$ or, because of (13), such that $|f(x) - P_n(x)| \le E$ or, equivalently,

$$P_n(x) - E \le f(x) \le P_n(x) + E$$

EXAMPLE 2: Use the result of Example 1 to compute an approximate value of cos 47° and determine the accuracy of the result.

SOLUTION: $47° \sim \frac{47}{180}\pi$ radians. Thus, in the solution of Example 1, we take $x = \frac{47}{180}\pi$ and $x - \frac{1}{4}\pi = \frac{1}{90}\pi$, and we have

$$\cos 47° = \frac{1}{2}\sqrt{2}[1 - \frac{1}{90}\pi - \frac{1}{2}(\frac{1}{90}\pi)^2 + \frac{1}{6}(\frac{1}{90}\pi)^3] + R_3(\frac{47}{180}\pi)$$

where

$$R_3(\tfrac{47}{180}\pi) = \frac{1}{24}\cos \xi \, (\tfrac{1}{90}\pi)^4 \qquad \text{with } \tfrac{1}{4}\pi < \xi < \tfrac{47}{180}\pi$$

Because $0 < \cos \xi < 1$,

$$0 < R_3(\tfrac{47}{180}\pi) < \frac{1}{24}(\tfrac{1}{90}\pi)^4 < 0.00000004$$

Taking $\frac{1}{90}\pi \approx 0.034907$, we obtain

$$\cos 47° \approx 0.68200$$

which is accurate to five decimal places.

EXAMPLE 3: Use a Taylor polynomial at zero to find the value of $\sqrt{e}$, accurate to four decimal places.

SOLUTION: If we let $f(x) = e^x$, all the derivatives of f at x are e^x and all the derivatives evaluated at zero are 1. Therefore, from (11) we have

$$P_n(x) = 1 + x + \frac{x^2}{2!} + \frac{x^3}{3!} + \cdots + \frac{x^n}{n!}$$

and from (12) we get

$$R_n(x) = \frac{e^\xi}{(n+1)!} x^{n+1} \qquad \text{where } \xi \text{ is between } 0 \text{ and } x$$

We want $|R_n(\tfrac{1}{2})|$ to be less than 0.00005. If we take $x = \tfrac{1}{2}$ in the above and because $e^{1/2} < 2$, we get

$$|R_n(\tfrac{1}{2})| < \frac{e^{1/2}}{2^{n+1}(n+1)!} < \frac{2}{2^{n+1}(n+1)!} = \frac{1}{2^n(n+1)!}$$

$|R_n(\tfrac{1}{2})|$ will be less than 0.00005 if $1/2^n(n+1)! < 0.00005$. When $n = 5$,

$$\frac{1}{2^n(n+1)!} = \frac{1}{(32)(720)} = 0.00004 < 0.00005$$

So

$$\sqrt{e} \approx P_5(\tfrac{1}{2}) = 1 + \tfrac{1}{2} + \tfrac{1}{8} + \tfrac{1}{48} + \tfrac{1}{384} + \tfrac{1}{3840}$$

from which we obtain $\sqrt{e} \approx 1.64870$.

A special case of Taylor's formula is obtained by taking $a = 0$ in (9) and we get

$$f(x) = f(0) + \frac{f'(0)}{1!} x + \frac{f''(0)}{2!} x^2 + \cdots + \frac{f^{(n)}(0)}{n!} x^n + \frac{f^{(n+1)}(\xi)}{(n+1)!} x^{n+1} \quad (14)$$

where ξ is between 0 and x. Formula (14) is called Maclaurin's formula, named in honor of the Scotch mathematician Colin Maclaurin (1698–1746). However, the formula was obtained earlier by Taylor and by another English mathematician, James Stirling (1692–1770).

There are other forms of the remainder in Taylor's formula. Depending on the function, one form of the remainder may be more desirable to use than another. The following theorem expresses the remainder as an integral, and it is known as *Taylor's formula with integral form of the remainder*.

13.5.2 Theorem   If f is a function whose first $n + 1$ derivatives are continuous on a closed interval containing a and x, then $f(x) = P_n(x) + R_n(x)$, where $P_n(x)$ is the nth-degree Taylor polynomial of f at a and $R_n(x)$ is the remainder given by

$$R_n(x) = \frac{1}{n!} \int_a^x (x-t)^n f^{(n+1)}(t) \, dt \tag{15}$$

The proof of this theorem is left for the reader (see Exercise 22).

Exercises 13.5

In Exercises 1 through 10, find the Taylor polynomial of degree n with the Lagrange form of the remainder at the number a for the function defined by the given equation.

1. $f(x) = \sin x$; $a = \frac{1}{6}\pi$; $n = 3$
2. $f(x) = \tan x$; $a = 0$; $n = 3$
3. $f(x) = \sinh x$; $a = 0$; $n = 4$
4. $f(x) = \cosh x$; $a = 0$; $n = 4$
5. $f(x) = \ln x$; $a = 1$; $n = 3$
6. $f(x) = \sqrt{x}$; $a = 4$; $n = 4$
7. $f(x) = \ln \cos x$; $a = \frac{1}{3}\pi$; $n = 3$
8. $f(x) = e^{-x^2}$; $a = 0$; $n = 3$
9. $f(x) = (1+x)^{3/2}$; $a = 0$; $n = 3$
10. $f(x) = (1-x)^{-1/2}$; $a = 0$; $n = 3$

11. Compute the value of e correct to five decimal places, and prove that your answer has the required accuracy.

12. Use the Taylor polynomial in Exercise 6 to compute $\sqrt{5}$ accurate to as many places as is justified when R_4 is neglected.

13. Compute $\sin 31°$ accurate to three decimal places by using the Taylor polynomial in Exercise 1 at $\frac{1}{6}\pi$. (Use the approximation $\frac{1}{180}\pi \approx 0.0175$.)

14. Use a Taylor polynomial at 0 for the function defined by $f(x) = \ln(1+x)$ to compute the value of $\ln 1.2$, accurate to four decimal places.

15. Use a Taylor polynomial at 0 for the function defined by

$$f(x) = \ln \frac{1+x}{1-x}$$

to compute the value of $\ln 1.2$ accurate to four decimal places. Compare the computation with that of Exercise 14.

16. Show that the formula

$$(1+x)^{3/2} \approx 1 + \tfrac{3}{2}x$$

is accurate to three decimal places if $-0.03 \le x \le 0$.

17. Show that the formula

$$(1+x)^{-1/2} \approx 1 - \tfrac{1}{2}x$$

is accurate to two decimal places if $-0.1 \le x \le 0$.

18. Show that if $0 \le x \le \frac{1}{2}$,

$$\sin x = x - \frac{x^3}{3!} + R(x)$$

where $|R(x)| < \frac{1}{3840}$.

19. Use the result of Exercise 18 to find an approximate value of $\int_0^{1/\sqrt{2}} \sin x^2 \, dx$ and estimate the error.

20. Draw sketches of the graphs of $y = \sin x$ and $y = mx$ on the same set of axes. Note that if m is positive and close to

zero, then the graphs intersect at a point whose abscissa is close to π. By finding the second-degree Taylor polynomial at π for the function f defined by $f(x) = \sin x - mx$, show that an approximate solution of the equation $\sin x = mx$, when m is positive and close to zero, is given by $x \approx \pi/(1 + m)$.

21. Use the method described in Exercise 20 to find an approximate solution of the equation $\cot x = mx$ when m is positive and close to zero.

22. Prove Theorem 13.5.2. (HINT: Let

$$\int_a^x f'(t)\, dt = f(x) - f(a)$$

Solve for $f(x)$ and integrate

$$\int_a^x f'(t)\, dt$$

by parts by letting $u = f'(t)$ and $dv = dt$. Repeat this process, and the desired result follows by mathematical induction.)

Review Exercises (Chapter 13)

In Exercises 1 through 14, evaluate the limit, if it exists.

1. $\displaystyle \lim_{x \to 0} \frac{\tanh 2x}{\sinh^2 x}$

2. $\displaystyle \lim_{x \to \pi/2} \left(\frac{1}{1 - \sin x} - \frac{2}{\cos^2 x} \right)$

3. $\displaystyle \lim_{x \to 0} (\csc^2 x - x^{-2})$

4. $\displaystyle \lim_{x \to 0} \frac{e - (1 + x)^{1/x}}{x}$

5. $\displaystyle \lim_{t \to +\infty} \frac{\ln(1 + e^{2t}/t)}{t^{1/2}}$

6. $\displaystyle \lim_{x \to +\infty} x \ln \frac{x + 1}{x - 1}$

7. $\displaystyle \lim_{x \to \pi/2} (\sin^2 x)^{\tan x}$

8. $\displaystyle \lim_{t \to +\infty} \frac{t^{100}}{e^t}$

9. $\displaystyle \lim_{x \to +\infty} \frac{\ln(\ln x)}{\ln(x - \ln x)}$

10. $\displaystyle \lim_{x \to 0} \frac{x - \tan^{-1} x}{4x^3}$

11. $\displaystyle \lim_{\theta \to \pi/2} \frac{\tan \theta + 3}{\sec \theta - 1}$

12. $\displaystyle \lim_{x \to 0} \left(\frac{\sin x}{x} \right)^{1/x}$

13. $\displaystyle \lim_{x \to +\infty} (e^x - x)^{1/x}$

14. $\displaystyle \lim_{x \to 0^+} \left(\frac{1}{x} \right)^{\tan x}$

In Exercises 15 through 24, determine whether the improper integral is convergent or divergent. If it is convergent, evaluate it.

15. $\displaystyle \int_{-2}^0 \frac{dx}{2x + 3}$

16. $\displaystyle \int_0^{+\infty} \frac{dx}{\sqrt{e^x}}$

17. $\displaystyle \int_{-\infty}^0 \frac{dx}{(x - 2)^2}$

18. $\displaystyle \int_2^4 \frac{x\, dx}{\sqrt{x - 2}}$

19. $\displaystyle \int_0^{\pi/4} \cot^2 \theta\, d\theta$

20. $\displaystyle \int_1^{+\infty} \frac{dt}{t^4 + t^2}$

21. $\displaystyle \int_{-\infty}^{+\infty} \frac{dx}{4x^2 + 4x + 5}$

22. $\displaystyle \int_0^1 \frac{\ln x}{x}\, dx$

23. $\displaystyle \int_0^1 \frac{dx}{x + x^3}$

24. $\displaystyle \int_{-3}^0 \frac{dx}{\sqrt{3 - 2x - x^2}}$

In Exercises 25 and 26, find the Taylor polynomial of degree n with the Lagrange form of the remainder at the number a for the function defined by the given equation.

25. $f(x) = \cos x;\ a = 0;\ n = 6$

26. $f(x) = (1 + x^2)^{-1};\ a = 1;\ n = 3$

27. Given:

$$f(x) = \begin{cases} \dfrac{e^x - 1}{x} & \text{if } x \neq 0 \\ 1 & \text{if } x = 0 \end{cases}$$

(a) Prove that f is continuous at 0. (b) Prove that f is differentiable at 0 and find $f'(0)$.

28. For the function of Exercise 27, find, if they exist: (a) $\lim\limits_{x \to +\infty} f(x)$; (b) $\lim\limits_{x \to -\infty} f(x)$.

29. Given:

$$f(x) = \begin{cases} \dfrac{e^x - e^{-x}}{e^{2x} - e^{-2x}} & \text{if } x \neq 0 \\ 1 & \text{if } x = 0 \end{cases}$$

(a) Is f continuous at 0? (b) Find $\lim\limits_{x \to +\infty} f(x)$, if it exists.

30. If the normal line to the curve $y = \ln x$ at the point $(x_1, \ln x_1)$ intersects the x axis at the point having an abscissa of a, prove that $\lim\limits_{x_1 \to +\infty} (a - x_1) = 0$.

31. If the first four terms of the Taylor polynomial at 0 are used to approximate the value of $\sqrt{e}$, how accurate is the result?

32. Express both e^{x^2} and $\cos x$ as a Taylor polynomial of degree 4 at 0 and use them to evaluate

$$\lim_{x \to 0} \frac{e^{x^2} - \cos x}{x^4}$$

33. Evaluate the limit in Exercise 32 by L'Hôpital's rule.

34. Apply Taylor's formula to express the polynomial

$$P(x) = 4x^3 + 5x^2 - 2x + 1$$

as a polynomial in powers of $(x + 2)$.

35. Determine if it is possible to assign a finite number to represent the measure of the area of the region to the right of the y axis bounded by the curve $4y^2 - xy^2 - x^2 = 0$ and its asymptote. If a finite number can be assigned, find it.

36. Determine if it is possible to assign a finite number to represent the measure of the area of the region in the first quadrant and below the curve having the equation $y = e^{-x}$. If a finite number can be assigned, find it.

37. Assuming a continuous flow of income for a particular business and that at t years from now the number of dollars in the income per year is given by $1000t - 300$, what is the present value of all future income if 8% is the interest rate compounded continuously? (HINT: See the paragraph preceding Exercise 24 in Sec. 13.3.)

38. Find the values of n for which the improper integral $\displaystyle\int_1^{+\infty} \frac{\ln x}{x^n}\, dx$ converges and evaluate the integral for those values of n.

39. (a) Prove that $\lim\limits_{x \to +\infty} (x^n/e^x) = 0$, for n any positive integer. (b) Find $\lim\limits_{x \to 0} (e^{-1/x}/x^n)$, where $x > 0$ and n is any positive integer, by letting $x = 1/t$ and using the result of part (a).

14

Infinite Series

14.1 SEQUENCES

You have undoubtedly encountered sequences of numbers in your previous study of mathematics. For example, the numbers 5, 7, 9, 11, 13, 15 define a sequence. This sequence is said to be *finite* because there is a first and last number. If the set of numbers which defines a sequence does not have both a first and last number, the sequence is said to be *infinite*. For example, the sequence defined by

$$\tfrac{1}{3}, \tfrac{2}{5}, \tfrac{3}{7}, \tfrac{4}{9}, \ldots \tag{1}$$

is infinite because the three dots with no number following indicate that there is no last number. We are concerned here with infinite sequences, and when we use the word "sequence" it is understood that we are referring to an infinite sequence. We define a sequence as a particular kind of function.

14.1.1 Definition (A *sequence* is a function whose domain is the set of positive integers.)

The numbers in the range of the sequence, which are called the *elements* of the sequence, are restricted to real numbers in this book.

If the nth element is given by $f(n)$, then the sequence is the set of ordered pairs of the form $(n, f(n))$, where n is a positive integer. In particular, if $f(n) = n/(2n + 1)$, then

$$f(1) = \tfrac{1}{3} \qquad f(2) = \tfrac{2}{5} \qquad f(3) = \tfrac{3}{7} \qquad f(4) = \tfrac{4}{9}$$

and so on. We see that the range of f consists of the elements of sequence

(1). Some of the ordered pairs in the sequence f are $(1, \frac{1}{3})$, $(2, \frac{2}{5})$, $(3, \frac{3}{7})$, $(4, \frac{4}{9})$, and $(5, \frac{5}{11})$. A sketch of the graph of this sequence is shown in Fig. 14.1.1.

Figure 14.1.1

Usually the nth element $f(n)$ of the sequence is stated when the elements are listed in order. Thus, for the elements of sequence (1) we would write

$$\frac{1}{3}, \frac{2}{5}, \frac{3}{7}, \frac{4}{9}, \ldots, \frac{n}{2n+1}, \ldots$$

Because the domain of every sequence is the same, we can use the notation $\{f(n)\}$ to denote a sequence. So the sequence (1) can be denoted by $\{n/(2n+1)\}$. We also use the subscript notation $\{a_n\}$ to denote the sequence for which $f(n) = a_n$.

You should distinguish between the elements of a sequence and the sequence itself. For example, the sequence $\{1/n\}$ has as its elements the reciprocals of the positive integers

$$1, \frac{1}{2}, \frac{1}{3}, \frac{1}{4}, \ldots, \frac{1}{n}, \ldots \tag{2}$$

The sequence for which

$$f(n) = \begin{cases} 1 & \text{if } n \text{ is odd} \\ \dfrac{2}{n+2} & \text{if } n \text{ is even} \end{cases}$$

has as its elements

$$1, \tfrac{1}{2}, 1, \tfrac{1}{3}, 1, \tfrac{1}{4}, \ldots \tag{3}$$

The elements of sequences (2) and (3) are the same; however, the sequences are different. Sketches of the graphs of sequences (2) and (3) are shown in Figs. 14.1.2 and 14.1.3, respectively.

We now plot on a horizontal axis the points corresponding to successive elements of a sequence. This is done in Fig. 14.1.4 for sequence (1) which is $\{n/(2n+1)\}$. We see that the successive elements of the sequence get closer and closer to $\frac{1}{2}$, even though no element in the sequence has the value $\frac{1}{2}$. Intuitively we see that the element will be as close to $\frac{1}{2}$ as we please by taking the number of the element sufficiently large. Or stating this another way, we can make $|n/(2n+1) - \frac{1}{2}|$ less than any

Figure 14.1.2

Figure 14.1.3

Figure 14.1.4

given ϵ by taking n large enough. Because of this we state that the limit of the sequence $\{n/(2n + 1)\}$ is $\frac{1}{2}$.

In general, if there is a number L such that $|a_n - L|$ is arbitrarily small for n sufficiently large, we say the sequence $\{a_n\}$ has the limit L. Following is the precise definition of the limit of a sequence.

14.1.2 Definition   A sequence $\{a_n\}$ is said to have the limit L if for every $\epsilon > 0$ there exists a number $N > 0$ such that $|a_n - L| < \epsilon$ for every integer $n > N$; and we write

$$\lim_{n \to +\infty} a_n = L$$

EXAMPLE 1: Use Definition 14.1.2 to prove that the sequence
$$\left\{ \frac{n}{2n + 1} \right\}$$
has the limit $\frac{1}{2}$.

SOLUTION: We must show that for any $\epsilon > 0$ there exists a number $N > 0$ such that

$$\left| \frac{n}{2n + 1} - \frac{1}{2} \right| < \epsilon \qquad \text{for every integer } n > N$$

$$\left| \frac{n}{2n + 1} - \frac{1}{2} \right| = \left| \frac{2n - 2n - 1}{2(2n + 1)} \right| = \left| \frac{-1}{4n + 2} \right| = \frac{1}{4n + 2}$$

Hence, we must find a number $N > 0$ such that

$$\frac{1}{4n + 2} < \epsilon \qquad \text{for every integer } n > N$$

But

$$\frac{1}{4n+2} < \epsilon \quad \text{is equivalent to} \quad 2n+1 > \frac{1}{2\epsilon}$$

which is equivalent to

$$n > \frac{1-2\epsilon}{4\epsilon}$$

So it follows that

$$\left|\frac{n}{2n+1} - \frac{1}{2}\right| < \epsilon \qquad \text{for every integer } n > \frac{1-2\epsilon}{4\epsilon}$$

Therefore, if $N = (1-2\epsilon)/4\epsilon$, Definition 14.1.2 holds.
In particular, if $\epsilon = \frac{1}{8}$, $N = (1-\frac{1}{4})/\frac{1}{2} = \frac{3}{2}$. So

$$\left|\frac{n}{2n+1} - \frac{1}{2}\right| < \frac{1}{8} \qquad \text{for every integer } n > \frac{3}{2}$$

In particular, if $n = 4$,

$$\left|\frac{n}{2n+1} - \frac{1}{2}\right| = \left|\frac{4}{9} - \frac{1}{2}\right| = \left|\frac{-1}{18}\right| = \frac{1}{18} < \frac{1}{8}$$

Consider now the sequence $\{(-1)^{n+1}/n\}$. Note that the nth element of this sequence is $(-1)^{n+1}/n$ and $(-1)^{n+1}$ is equal to $+1$ when n is odd and to -1 when n is even. Hence, the elements of the sequence can be written

$$1, -\frac{1}{2}, \frac{1}{3}, -\frac{1}{4}, \frac{1}{5}, \cdots, \frac{(-1)^{n+1}}{n}, \cdots$$

In Fig. 14.1.5 are plotted points corresponding to successive elements of this sequence. In the figure, $a_1 = 1$, $a_2 = -\frac{1}{2}$, $a_3 = \frac{1}{3}$, $a_4 = -\frac{1}{4}$, $a_5 = \frac{1}{5}$, $a_6 = -\frac{1}{6}$, $a_7 = \frac{1}{7}$, $a_8 = -\frac{1}{8}$, $a_9 = \frac{1}{9}$, $a_{10} = -\frac{1}{10}$. The limit of the sequence is 0 and the elements oscillate about 0.

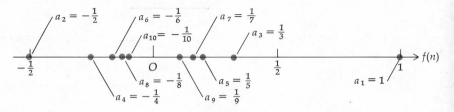

Figure 14.1.5

Compare Definition 14.1.2 with Definition 2.7.1 of the limit of $f(x)$ as x increases without bound. The two definitions are almost identical; however, when we state that $\lim\limits_{x \to +\infty} f(x) = L$, the function f is defined for all real numbers greater than some real number R, while when we consider $\lim\limits_{n\to+\infty} a_n$, n is restricted to positive integers. We have, however, the following theorem which follows immediately from Definition 2.7.1.

14.1.3 Theorem If $\lim\limits_{x\to+\infty} f(x) = L$, and f is defined for every positive integer, then also $\lim\limits_{n\to+\infty} f(n) = L$ when n is any positive integer.

The proof is left for the reader (see Exercise 20).

EXAMPLE 2: Verify Theorem 14.1.3 for the sequence of Example 1.

SOLUTION: For the sequence of Example 1, $f(n) = n/(2n+1)$. Hence, $f(x) = x/(2x+1)$ and

$$\lim_{x\to+\infty} \frac{x}{2x+1} = \lim_{x\to+\infty} \frac{1}{2+\dfrac{1}{x}} = \frac{1}{2}$$

It follows then from Theorem 14.1.3 that $\lim\limits_{n\to+\infty} f(n) = \tfrac{1}{2}$ when n is any positive integer. This agrees with the solution of Example 1.

14.1.4 Definition If a sequence $\{a_n\}$ has a limit, the sequence is said to be *convergent*, and we say that a_n *converges* to that limit. If the sequence is not convergent, it is said to be *divergent*.

EXAMPLE 3: Determine if the sequence

$$\left\{\frac{4n^2}{2n^2+1}\right\}$$

is convergent or divergent.

SOLUTION: We wish to determine if $\lim\limits_{n\to+\infty} 4n^2/(2n^2+1)$ exists. Let $f(x) = 4x^2/(2x^2+1)$ and investigate $\lim\limits_{x\to+\infty} f(x)$.

$$\lim_{x\to+\infty} \frac{4x^2}{2x^2+1} = \lim_{x\to+\infty} \frac{4}{2+\dfrac{1}{x^2}} = 2$$

Therefore, by Theorem 14.1.3, $\lim\limits_{n\to+\infty} f(n) = 2$. We conclude that the given sequence is convergent and that $4n^2/(2n^2+1)$ converges to 2.

EXAMPLE 4: Prove that if $|r| < 1$, the sequence $\{r^n\}$ is convergent and that r^n converges to zero.

SOLUTION: First of all, if $r = 0$, the sequence is $\{0\}$ and $\lim\limits_{x\to+\infty} 0 = 0$. Hence, the sequence is convergent and the nth element converges to zero.

If $0 < |r| < 1$, we consider the function f defined by $f(x) = r^x$, where x is any positive number, and show that $\lim\limits_{x\to+\infty} r^x = 0$. Then from Theorem 14.1.3 it will follow that $\lim\limits_{n\to+\infty} r^n = 0$ when n is any positive integer.

To prove that $\lim\limits_{x\to+\infty} r^x = 0$ $(0 < |r| < 1)$, we shall show that for any $\epsilon > 0$ there exists a number $N > 0$ such that

$$|r^x - 0| < \epsilon \qquad \text{whenever } x > N \tag{4}$$

Statement (4) is equivalent to

$$|r|^x < \epsilon \qquad \text{whenever } x > N$$

which is true if and only if

$$\ln |r|^x < \ln \epsilon \qquad \text{whenever } x > N$$

or, equivalently,

$$x \ln |r| < \ln \epsilon \qquad \text{whenever } x > N \tag{5}$$

Because $0 < |r| < 1$, $\ln |r| < 0$. Thus, (5) is equivalent to

$$x > \frac{\ln \epsilon}{\ln |r|} \qquad \text{whenever } x > N$$

Therefore, if we take $N = \ln \epsilon / \ln |r|$, we may conclude (4). Consequently, $\lim_{x \to +\infty} r^x = 0$, and so $\lim_{n \to +\infty} r^n = 0$ if n is any positive integer. Hence, by Definitions 14.1.2 and 14.1.4, $\{r^n\}$ is convergent and r^n converges to zero.

EXAMPLE 5: Determine if the sequence $\{(-1)^n + 1\}$ is convergent or divergent.

SOLUTION: The elements of this sequence are 0, 2, 0, 2, 0, 2, . . . , $(-1)^n + 1$, ... Because $a_n = 0$ if n is odd, and $a_n = 2$ if n is even, it appears that the sequence is divergent. To prove this, let us assume that the sequence is convergent and show that this assumption leads to a contradiction. If the sequence has the limit L, then by Definition 14.1.2, for every $\epsilon > 0$ there exists a number $N > 0$ such that $|a_n - L| < \epsilon$ for every integer $n > N$. In particular, when $\epsilon = \frac{1}{2}$, there exists a number $N > 0$ such that

$$|a_n - L| < \tfrac{1}{2} \qquad \text{for every integer } n > N$$

or, equivalently,

$$-\tfrac{1}{2} < a_n - L < \tfrac{1}{2} \qquad \text{for every integer } n > N \tag{6}$$

Because $a_n = 0$ if n is odd and $a_n = 2$ if n is even, it follows from (6) that

$$-\tfrac{1}{2} < -L < \tfrac{1}{2} \quad \text{and} \quad -\tfrac{1}{2} < 2 - L < \tfrac{1}{2}$$

But if $-L > -\frac{1}{2}$, then $2 - L > \frac{3}{2}$; hence, $2 - L$ cannot be less than $\frac{1}{2}$. So we have a contradiction, and therefore the given sequence is divergent.

EXAMPLE 6: Determine if the sequence

$$\left\{ n \sin \frac{\pi}{n} \right\}$$

is convergent or divergent.

SOLUTION: We wish to determine if $\lim_{n \to +\infty} n \sin(\pi/n)$ exists. Let $f(x) = x \sin(\pi/x)$ and investigate $\lim_{x \to +\infty} f(x)$. Because $f(x)$ can be written as $[\sin(\pi/x)]/(1/x)$ and $\lim_{x \to +\infty} \sin(\pi/x) = 0$ and $\lim_{x \to +\infty} (1/x) = 0$, we can apply L'Hôpital's rule and obtain

$$\lim_{x \to +\infty} f(x) = \lim_{x \to +\infty} \frac{-\dfrac{\pi}{x^2} \cos \dfrac{\pi}{x}}{-\dfrac{1}{x^2}} = \lim_{x \to +\infty} \pi \cos \frac{\pi}{x} = \pi$$

Therefore, $\lim\limits_{n \to +\infty} f(n) = \pi$ when n is a positive integer. So the given sequence is convergent and $n \sin(\pi/n)$ converges to π.

We have limit theorems for sequences, which are analogous to limit theorems for functions given in Chapter 2. We state these theorems by using the terminology of sequences. The proofs are omitted because they are almost identical to the proofs of the corresponding theorems given in Chapter 2.

14.1.5 Theorem If $\{a_n\}$ and $\{b_n\}$ are convergent sequences and c is a constant, then

  (i) the constant sequence $\{c\}$ has c as its limit;

  (ii) $\lim\limits_{n \to +\infty} c a_n = c \lim\limits_{n \to +\infty} a_n$;

  (iii) $\lim\limits_{n \to +\infty} (a_n \pm b_n) = \lim\limits_{n \to +\infty} a_n \pm \lim\limits_{n \to +\infty} b_n$;

  (iv) $\lim\limits_{n \to +\infty} a_n b_n = (\lim\limits_{n \to +\infty} a_n)(\lim\limits_{n \to +\infty} b_n)$;

  (v) $\lim\limits_{n \to +\infty} \dfrac{a_n}{b_n} = \dfrac{\lim\limits_{n \to +\infty} a_n}{\lim\limits_{n \to +\infty} b_n}$ if $\lim\limits_{n \to +\infty} b_n \neq 0$.

EXAMPLE 7: Use Theorem 14.1.5 to prove that the sequence

$$\left\{ \frac{n^2}{2n + 1} \sin \frac{\pi}{n} \right\}$$

is convergent and find the limit of the sequence.

SOLUTION:

$$\frac{n^2}{2n + 1} \sin \frac{\pi}{n} = \frac{n}{2n + 1} \cdot n \sin \frac{\pi}{n}$$

In Example 1 we showed that the sequence $\{n/(2n + 1)\}$ is convergent and $\lim\limits_{n \to +\infty} [n/(2n + 1)] = \frac{1}{2}$. In Example 6 we showed that the sequence $\{n \sin(\pi/n)\}$ is convergent and $\lim\limits_{n \to +\infty} [n \sin (\pi/n)] = \pi$. Hence, by Theorem 14.1.5(iv)

$$\lim_{n \to +\infty} \left[\frac{n}{2n + 1} \cdot n \sin \frac{\pi}{n} \right] = \lim_{n \to +\infty} \frac{n}{2n + 1} \cdot \lim_{n \to +\infty} n \sin \frac{\pi}{n} = \frac{1}{2} \cdot \pi$$

Thus, the given sequence is convergent, and its limit is $\frac{1}{2}\pi$.

Exercises 14.1

In Exercises 1 through 4, use Definition 14.1.2 to prove that the given sequence has the limit L.

1. $\left\{ \dfrac{3}{n - 1} \right\}$; $L = 0$

2. $\left\{ \dfrac{1}{\sqrt{n}} \right\}$; $L = 0$

3. $\left\{ \dfrac{8n}{2n + 3} \right\}$; $L = 4$

4. $\left\{ \dfrac{5 - n}{2 + 3n} \right\}$; $L = -\frac{1}{3}$

In Exercises 5 through 19, determine if the sequence is convergent or divergent. If the sequence converges, find its limit.

5. $\left\{ \dfrac{n + 1}{2n - 1} \right\}$

6. $\left\{ \dfrac{2n^2 + 1}{3n^2 - n} \right\}$

7. $\left\{ \dfrac{n^2 + 1}{n} \right\}$

8. $\left\{\dfrac{3n^3 + 1}{2n^2 + n}\right\}$ 9. $\left\{\dfrac{\ln n}{n^2}\right\}$ 10. $\left\{\dfrac{e^n}{n}\right\}$

11. $\{\tanh n\}$ 12. $\left\{\dfrac{\log_b n}{n}\right\}, b > 1$ 13. $\left\{\dfrac{n}{n+1}\sin\dfrac{n\pi}{2}\right\}$

14. $\left\{\dfrac{\sinh n}{\sin n}\right\}$ 15. $\left\{\dfrac{1}{\sqrt{n^2+1}-n}\right\}$ 16. $\{\sqrt{n+1}-\sqrt{n}\}$

17. $\left\{\left(1+\dfrac{1}{3n}\right)^n\right\}$ 18. $\left\{\left(1+\dfrac{2}{n}\right)^n\right\}$

    (HINT: Use $\lim\limits_{x\to 0}(1+x)^{1/x} = e$.)   See Hint for Exercise 17.

19. $\{r^{1/n}\}$ and $r > 0$. (HINT: Consider two cases: $r \le 1$ and $r > 1$.)

20. Prove Theorem 14.1.3.

21. Prove that if $|r| < 1$, the sequence $\{nr^n\}$ is convergent and nr^n converges to zero.

22. Prove that if the sequence $\{a_n\}$ is convergent and $\lim\limits_{n\to+\infty} a_n = L$, then the sequence $\{|a_n|\}$ is also convergent and $\lim\limits_{n\to+\infty} |a_n| = |L|$.

23. Prove that if the sequence $\{a_n\}$ is convergent and $\lim\limits_{n\to+\infty} a_n = L$, then the sequence $\{a_n^2\}$ is also convergent and $\lim\limits_{n\to+\infty} a_n^2 = L^2$.

24. Prove that if the sequence $\{a_n\}$ converges, then $\lim\limits_{n\to+\infty} a_n$ is unique. (HINT: Assume that $\lim\limits_{n\to+\infty} a_n$ has two different values, L and M, and show that this is impossible by taking $\epsilon = \frac{1}{2}|L - M|$ in Definition 14.1.2.)

14.2 MONOTONIC AND BOUNDED SEQUENCES

We shall be concerned with certain kinds of sequences which are given special names.

14.2.1 Definition   A sequence $\{a_n\}$ is said to be

    (i) *increasing* if $a_n \le a_{n+1}$ for all n;
    (ii) *decreasing* if $a_n \ge a_{n+1}$ for all n.

If a sequence is increasing or if it is decreasing, it is called *monotonic*.

    Note that if $a_n < a_{n+1}$ (a special case of $a_n \le a_{n+1}$) we have a *strictly increasing* sequence; if $a_n > a_{n+1}$ we have a *strictly decreasing* sequence.

EXAMPLE 1: For each of the following sequences determine if it is increasing, decreasing, or not monotonic:

    (a) $\{n/(2n+1)\}$
    (b) $\{1/n\}$
    (c) $\{(-1)^{n+1}/n\}$

SOLUTION: (a) The elements of the sequence can be written

$$\frac{1}{3}, \frac{2}{5}, \frac{3}{7}, \frac{4}{9}, \cdots , \frac{n}{2n+1}, \frac{n+1}{2n+3}, \cdots$$

Note that a_{n+1} is obtained from a_n by replacing n by $n + 1$. Therefore, because $a_n = n/(2n+1)$,

$$a_{n+1} = \frac{n+1}{2(n+1)+1} = \frac{n+1}{2n+3}$$

Looking at the first four elements of the sequence, we see that the elements increase as n increases. Thus, we suspect in general that

$$\frac{n}{2n+1} \le \frac{n+1}{2n+3} \tag{1}$$

Inequality (1) can be verified if we find an equivalent inequality which we know is valid. Multiplying each member of inequality (1) by $(2n+1)(2n+3)$, we obtain

$$n(2n+3) \le (n+1)(2n+1) \tag{2}$$

Inequality (2) is equivalent to inequality (1) because (1) may be obtained from (2) by dividing each member by $(2n+1)(2n+3)$. Inequality (2) is equivalent to

$$2n^2 + 3n \le 2n^2 + 3n + 1 \tag{3}$$

Inequality (3) obviously holds because the right member is 1 greater than the left member. Therefore, inequality (1) holds and so the given sequence is increasing.

(b) The elements of the sequence can be written

$$1, \frac{1}{2}, \frac{1}{3}, \frac{1}{4}, \ldots, \frac{1}{n}, \frac{1}{n+1}, \ldots$$

Because

$$\frac{1}{n} > \frac{1}{n+1}$$

for all n, the sequence is decreasing.

(c) The elements of the sequence can be written

$$1, -\frac{1}{2}, \frac{1}{3}, -\frac{1}{4}, \ldots, \frac{(-1)^{n+1}}{n}, \frac{(-1)^{n+2}}{n+1}, \ldots$$

$a_1 = 1$ and $a_2 = -\frac{1}{2}$, and so $a_1 > a_2$. But $a_3 = \frac{1}{3}$, and so $a_2 < a_3$. In a more general sense, consider three consecutive elements $a_n = (-1)^{n+1}/n$, $a_{n+1} = (-1)^{n+2}/(n+1)$, and $a_{n+2} = (-1)^{n+3}/(n+2)$. If n is odd, $a_n > a_{n+1}$ and $a_{n+1} < a_{n+2}$, and if n is even, $a_n < a_{n+1}$ and $a_{n+1} > a_{n+2}$. Hence, the sequence is neither increasing nor decreasing and so is not monotonic.

14.2.2 Definition The number C is called a *lower bound* of the sequence $\{a_n\}$ if $C \le a_n$ for all positive integers n, and the number D is called an *upper bound* of the sequence $\{a_n\}$ if $a_n \le D$ for all positive integers n.

The number zero is a lower bound of the sequence $\{n/(2n+1)\}$ whose elements are

$$\frac{1}{3}, \frac{2}{5}, \frac{3}{7}, \frac{4}{9}, \ldots, \frac{n}{2n+1}, \ldots$$

Another lower bound of this sequence is $\frac{1}{3}$. Actually any number which is less than or equal to $\frac{1}{3}$ is a lower bound of this sequence.

For the sequence $\{1/n\}$ whose elements are

$$1, \frac{1}{2}, \frac{1}{3}, \frac{1}{4}, \; \cdots \; , \frac{1}{n}, \; \cdots$$

1 is an upper bound; 26 is also an upper bound. Any number which is greater than or equal to 1 is an upper bound of this sequence, and any nonpositive number will serve as a lower bound. We see, then, that a sequence may have many upper or lower bounds.

14.2.3 Definition If A is a lower bound of a sequence $\{a_n\}$ and if A has the property that for every lower bound C of $\{a_n\}$, $C \leq A$, then A is called the *greatest lower bound* of the sequence. Similarly, if B is an upper bound of a sequence $\{a_n\}$ and if B has the property that for every upper bound D of $\{a_n\}$, $B \leq D$, then B is called the *least upper bound* of the sequence.

The greatest lower bound of the sequence $\{n/(2n+1)\}$ is $\frac{1}{3}$ because every lower bound of the sequence is less than or equal to $\frac{1}{3}$. The least upper bound of the sequence $\{1/n\}$ is 1 because every upper bound of the sequence is greater than or equal to 1.

14.2.4 Definition A sequence $\{a_n\}$ is said to be *bounded* if and only if it has an upper bound and a lower bound.

Because the sequence $\{1/n\}$ has an upper bound and a lower bound, it is bounded. This sequence is also a decreasing sequence and hence is a bounded monotonic sequence. There is a theorem (14.2.6) that guarantees that a bounded monotonic sequence is convergent. In particular, the sequence $\{1/n\}$ is convergent because $\lim\limits_{n \to +\infty} (1/n) = 0$. The sequence $\{n\}$ whose elements are

$$1, 2, 3, \; \ldots \; , n, \; \ldots$$

is monotonic (because it is increasing) but is not bounded (because there is no upper bound). It is not convergent because $\lim\limits_{n \to +\infty} n = +\infty$.

For the proof of Theorem 14.2.6 we need a very important property of the real-number system which we now state.

14.2.5 The Axiom of Completeness Every set of real numbers which has a lower bound has a greatest lower bound. Also, every set of real numbers which has an upper bound has a least upper bound.

The axiom of completeness, together with the fundamental algebraic properties of the real numbers (1.1.1 through 1.1.7) and the axiom of order

(1.1.10), completely describes the real-number system. Actually, the second sentence in our statement of the axiom of completeness is unnecessary because it can be proved from the first sentence. It is included in the axiom here to expedite the discussion.

Suppose that $\{a_n\}$ is an increasing sequence that is bounded. Let D be an upper bound of the sequence. Then if the points corresponding to successive elements of the sequence are plotted on a horizontal axis, these points will all lie to the left of the point corresponding to the number D. Furthermore, because the sequence is increasing, each point will be either to the right of or coincide with the preceding point. See Fig. 14.2.1. Hence, as n increases, the elements increase toward D. Intuitively it appears that the sequence $\{a_n\}$ has a limit which is either D or some number less than D. This is indeed the case and is proved in the following theorem.

Figure 14.2.1

14.2.6 Theorem   A bounded monotonic sequence is convergent.

PROOF: We prove the theorem for the case when the monotonic sequence is increasing. Let the sequence be $\{a_n\}$.

Because $\{a_n\}$ is bounded, there is an upper bound for the sequence. By the axiom of completeness (14.2.5), $\{a_n\}$ has a least upper bound, which we call B. Then if ϵ is a positive number, $B - \epsilon$ cannot be an upper bound of the sequence because $B - \epsilon < B$ and B is the least upper bound of the sequence. So for some positive integer N

$$B - \epsilon < a_N \tag{4}$$

Because B is the least upper bound of $\{a_n\}$, by Definition 14.2.2 it follows that

$$a_n \leq B \quad \text{for every positive integer } n \tag{5}$$

Because $\{a_n\}$ is an increasing sequence, we have from Definition 14.2.1(i)

$$a_n \leq a_{n+1} \quad \text{for every positive integer } n$$

and so

$$a_N \leq a_n \quad \text{whenever } n \geq N \tag{6}$$

From (4), (5), and (6), it follows that

$$B - \epsilon < a_N \leq a_n \leq B < B + \epsilon \quad \text{whenever } n \geq N$$

from which we get

$$B - \epsilon < a_n < B + \epsilon \quad \text{whenever } n \geq N$$

or, equivalently,

$$-\epsilon < a_n - B < \epsilon \quad \text{whenever } n \geq N$$

which can be written as

$$|a_n - B| < \epsilon \qquad \text{whenever } n \geq N \tag{7}$$

But by Definition 14.1.2, (7) is the condition that $\lim\limits_{n \to +\infty} a_n = B$. Therefore, the sequence $\{a_n\}$ is convergent.

To prove the theorem when $\{a_n\}$ is a decreasing sequence, we consider the sequence $\{-a_n\}$, which will be increasing, and apply the above results. We leave it to the reader to fill in the steps (see Exercise 13). ■

Theorem 14.2.6 states that if $\{a_n\}$ is a bounded monotonic sequence, there exists a number L such that $\lim\limits_{n \to +\infty} a_n = L$, but it does not state how to find L. For this reason, Theorem 14.2.6 is called an *existence theorem*. Many important concepts in mathematics are based on existence theorems. In particular, there are many sequences for which we cannot find the limit by direct use of the definition or by using limit theorems, but the knowledge that such a limit exists can be of great value to a mathematician.

In the proof of Theorem 14.2.6 we saw that the limit of the bounded increasing sequence is the least upper bound B of the sequence. Hence, if D is an upper bound of the sequence, $\lim\limits_{n \to +\infty} a_n = B \leq D$. We have, then, the following theorem.

14.2.7 Theorem   Let $\{a_n\}$ be an increasing sequence, and suppose that D is an upper bound of this sequence. Then $\{a_n\}$ is convergent and

$$\lim_{n \to +\infty} a_n \leq D$$

In proving Theorem 14.2.6 for the case when the bounded monotonic sequence is decreasing, the limit of the sequence is the greatest lower bound. The following theorem follows in a way similar to that of Theorem 14.2.7.

14.2.8 Theorem   Let $\{a_n\}$ be a decreasing sequence, and suppose that C is a lower bound of this sequence. Then $\{a_n\}$ is convergent and

$$\lim_{n \to +\infty} a_n \geq C$$

EXAMPLE 2:   Use Theorem 14.2.6 to prove that the sequence

$$\left\{ \frac{2^n}{n!} \right\}$$

is convergent.

SOLUTION: The elements of the given sequence are

$$\frac{2^1}{1!}, \frac{2^2}{2!}, \frac{2^3}{3!}, \frac{2^4}{4!}, \ldots, \frac{2^n}{n!}, \frac{2^{n+1}}{(n+1)!}, \ldots$$

$1! = 1$, $2! = 1 \cdot 2 = 2$, $3! = 1 \cdot 2 \cdot 3 = 6$, $4! = 1 \cdot 2 \cdot 3 \cdot 4 = 24$. Hence, the elements of the sequence can be written as

$$2, 2, \frac{4}{3}, \frac{2}{3}, \ldots, \frac{2^n}{n!}, \frac{2^{n+1}}{(n+1)!}, \ldots$$

We see, then, that $a_1 = a_2 > a_3 > a_4$, and so the given sequence may be decreasing. We must check to see if $a_n \geq a_{n+1}$; that is, we must determine if

$$\frac{2^n}{n!} \geq \frac{2^{n+1}}{(n+1)!} \tag{8}$$

which is equivalent to

$$2^n(n+1)! \geq 2^{n+1}n!$$

which is equivalent to

$$2^n n!(n+1) \geq 2 \cdot 2^n n!$$

which is equivalent to

$$n+1 \geq 2 \tag{9}$$

When $n = 1$, inequality (9) becomes $2 = 2$, and (9) obviously holds when $n > 2$. Because inequality (8) is equivalent to (9), it follows that the given sequence is decreasing and hence monotonic. An upper bound for the given sequence is 2, and a lower bound is 0. Therefore, the sequence is bounded.

The sequence $\{2^n/n!\}$ is therefore a bounded monotonic sequence, and by Theorem 14.2.6 it is convergent.

Theorem 14.2.6 states that a sufficient condition for a monotonic sequence to be convergent is that it be bounded. This is also a necessary condition and is given in the following theorem.

14.2.9 Theorem   A convergent monotonic sequence is bounded.

PROOF: We prove the theorem for the case when the monotonic sequence is increasing. Let the sequence be $\{a_n\}$.

To prove that $\{a_n\}$ is bounded we must show that it has a lower bound and an upper bound. Because $\{a_n\}$ is an increasing sequence, its first element serves as a lower bound. We must now find an upper bound.

Because $\{a_n\}$ is convergent, the sequence has a limit; call this limit L. Therefore, $\lim\limits_{n \to +\infty} a_n = L$, and so by Definition 14.1.2, for any $\epsilon > 0$ there exists a number $N > 0$ such that

$$|a_n - L| < \epsilon \qquad \text{for every positive integer } n > N$$

or, equivalently,

$$-\epsilon < a_n - L < \epsilon \qquad \text{whenever } n > N$$

or, equivalently,

$$L - \epsilon < a_n < L + \epsilon \qquad \text{whenever } n > N$$

Because $\{a_n\}$ is increasing, we conclude that

$$a_n < L + \epsilon \qquad \text{for all positive integers } n$$

Therefore, $L + \epsilon$ will serve as an upper bound of the sequence $\{a_n\}$.

To prove the theorem when $\{a_n\}$ is a decreasing sequence we do as suggested in the proof of Theorem 14.2.6: Consider the sequence $\{-a_n\}$, which will be increasing, and apply the above results. You are asked to do this proof in Exercise 14. ∎

Exercises 14.2

In Exercises 1 through 12, determine if the given sequence is increasing, decreasing, or not monotonic.

1. $\left\{\dfrac{3n - 1}{4n + 5}\right\}$

2. $\{\sin n\pi\}$

3. $\left\{\dfrac{1}{n + \sin n^2}\right\}$

4. $\left\{\dfrac{2^n}{1 + 2^n}\right\}$

5. $\left\{\dfrac{5^n}{1 + 5^{2n}}\right\}$

6. $\left\{\dfrac{n^3 - 1}{n}\right\}$

7. $\left\{\dfrac{n!}{3^n}\right\}$

8. $\left\{\dfrac{n}{2^n}\right\}$

9. $\left\{\dfrac{n^n}{n!}\right\}$

10. $\{n^2 + (-1)^n n\}$

11. $\left\{\dfrac{n!}{1 \cdot 3 \cdot 5 \cdot \ldots \cdot (2n - 1)}\right\}$

12. $\left\{\dfrac{1 \cdot 3 \cdot 5 \cdot \ldots \cdot (2n - 1)}{2^n \cdot n!}\right\}$

13. Use the fact that Theorem 14.2.6 holds for an increasing sequence to prove that the theorem holds when $\{a_n\}$ is a decreasing sequence. (HINT: Consider the sequence $\{-a_n\}$.)

14. Prove Theorem 14.2.9 by a method similar to that used in Exercise 13.

In Exercises 15 through 21 prove that the given sequence is convergent by using Theorem 14.2.6.

15. The sequence of Exercise 1.

16. The sequence of Exercise 4.

17. The sequence of Exercise 5.

18. The sequence of Exercise 8.

19. The sequence of Exercise 11.

20. The sequence of Exercise 12.

21. $\left\{\dfrac{n^2}{2^n}\right\}$

14.3 INFINITE SERIES OF CONSTANT TERMS

The familiar operation of addition applies only to a finite set of numbers. We now wish to extend addition to infinitely many numbers and to define what we mean by such a sum. To carry this out we deal with a limiting process by considering sequences.

14.3.1 Definition

If $\{u_n\}$ is a sequence and

$$s_n = \sum_{i=1}^{n} u_i = u_1 + u_2 + u_3 + \cdots + u_n$$

then the sequence $\{s_n\}$ is called an *infinite series*.

The numbers $u_1, u_2, u_3, \ldots$ are called the *terms* of the infinite series. We use the following symbolism to denote an infinite series:

$$\sum_{n=1}^{+\infty} u_n = u_1 + u_2 + u_3 + \cdots + u_n + \cdots \tag{1}$$

Given the infinite series denoted by (1), $s_1 = u_1$, $s_2 = u_1 + u_2$, $s_3 = u_1 + u_2 + u_3$, and in general

$$s_k = \sum_{i=1}^{k} u_i = u_1 + u_2 + u_3 + \cdots + u_k \tag{2}$$

where s_k, defined by (2), is called the kth *partial sum* of the given series, and the sequence $\{s_n\}$ is a sequence of partial sums.

Because $s_{n-1} = u_1 + u_2 + \cdots + u_{n-1}$ and $s_n = u_1 + u_2 + \cdots + u_{n-1} + u_n$, we have the formula

$$s_n = s_{n-1} + u_n \tag{3}$$

EXAMPLE 1: Given the infinite series

$$\sum_{n=1}^{+\infty} u_n = \sum_{n=1}^{+\infty} \frac{1}{n(n+1)}$$

find the first four terms of the sequence of partial sums $\{s_n\}$, and find a formula for s_n in terms of n.

SOLUTION: Applying formula (3), we get

$$s_1 = u_1 = \frac{1}{1 \cdot 2} = \frac{1}{2}$$

$$s_2 = s_1 + u_2 = \frac{1}{2} + \frac{1}{2 \cdot 3} = \frac{2}{3}$$

$$s_3 = s_2 + u_3 = \frac{2}{3} + \frac{1}{3 \cdot 4} = \frac{3}{4}$$

$$s_4 = s_3 + u_4 = \frac{3}{4} + \frac{1}{4 \cdot 5} = \frac{4}{5}$$

$S_4 = S_1 + S_2 + S_3 + U_4$

By partial fractions, we see that

$$u_k = \frac{1}{k(k+1)} = \frac{1}{k} - \frac{1}{k+1}$$

WHERE IS THAT COMING FROM?

Therefore,

$$u_1 = 1 - \frac{1}{2}, \; u_2 = \frac{1}{2} - \frac{1}{3}, \; u_3 = \frac{1}{3} - \frac{1}{4}, \; \cdots, \; u_{n-1} = \frac{1}{n-1} - \frac{1}{n}, \; u_n = \frac{1}{n} - \frac{1}{n+1}$$

Thus, because $s_n = u_1 + u_2 + \cdots + u_{n-1} + u_n$, we have

$$s_n = \left(1 - \frac{1}{2}\right) + \left(\frac{1}{2} - \frac{1}{3}\right) + \left(\frac{1}{3} - \frac{1}{4}\right) + \cdots + \left(\frac{1}{n-1} - \frac{1}{n}\right) + \left(\frac{1}{n} - \frac{1}{n+1}\right)$$

Upon removing parentheses and combining terms, we obtain

$$s_n = 1 - \frac{1}{n+1} = \frac{n}{n+1}$$

Taking $n = 1, 2, 3$, and 4, we see that our previous results agree.

Note that the method of solution of the above example applies only to a special case. In general, it is not possible to obtain such an expression for s_n.

We now define what we mean by the "sum" of an infinite series.

14.3.2 Definition   Let $\sum\limits_{n=1}^{+\infty} u_n$ be a given infinite series, and let $\{s_n\}$ be the sequence of partial sums defining this infinite series. Then if $\lim\limits_{n\to+\infty} s_n$ exists and is equal to S, we say that the given series is *convergent* and that S is the *sum* of the given infinite series. If $\lim\limits_{n\to+\infty} s_n$ does not exist, the series is said to be *divergent* and the series does not have a sum.

If an infinite series has a sum S, we also say that the series converges to S.

Note that the sum of a convergent series is the limit of a sequence of partial sums and is not obtained by ordinary addition. For a convergent series we use the symbolism

$$\sum_{n=1}^{+\infty} a_n$$

to denote both the series and the sum of the series. The use of the same symbol should not be confusing because the correct interpretation is apparent from the context in which it is used.

EXAMPLE 2:   Determine if the infinite series of Example 1 has a sum.

SOLUTION: In the solution of Example 1, we showed that the sequence of partial sums for the given series is $\{s_n\} = \{n/(n+1)\}$. Therefore,

$$\lim_{n\to+\infty} s_n = \lim_{n\to+\infty} \frac{n}{n+1} = \lim_{n\to+\infty} \frac{1}{1+\dfrac{1}{n}} = 1$$

So we conclude that the infinite series has a sum equal to 1. We can write

$$\sum_{n=1}^{+\infty} \frac{1}{n(n+1)} = \frac{1}{2} + \frac{1}{6} + \frac{1}{12} + \frac{1}{20} + \cdots + \frac{1}{n(n+1)} + \cdots = 1$$

As we mentioned above, in most cases it is not possible to obtain an expression for s_n in terms of n, and so we must have other methods for determining whether or not a given infinite series has a sum or, equivalently, whether a given infinite series is convergent or divergent.

14.3.3 Theorem   If the infinite series $\sum\limits_{n=1}^{+\infty} u_n$ is convergent, then $\lim\limits_{n\to+\infty} u_n = 0$.

PROOF: Letting $\{s_n\}$ be the sequence of partial sums for the given series, and denoting the sum of the series by S, we have, from Definition 14.3.2, $\lim\limits_{n\to+\infty} s_n = S$. Therefore, for any $\epsilon > 0$ there exists a number $N > 0$ such that $|S - s_n| < \frac{1}{2}\epsilon$ for every integer $n > N$. Also, for these integers $n > N$

we know that $|S - s_{n+1}| < \frac{1}{2}\epsilon$. We have, then,

$$|u_{n+1}| = |s_{n+1} - s_n| = |S - s_n + s_{n+1} - S| \le |S - s_n| + |s_{n+1} - S|$$

So

$$|u_{n+1}| < \tfrac{1}{2}\epsilon + \tfrac{1}{2}\epsilon = \epsilon \qquad \text{for every integer } n > N$$

Therefore, $\lim_{n \to +\infty} u_n = 0$.

The following theorem is a corollary of the preceding one.

14.3.4 Theorem   If $\lim_{n \to +\infty} u_n \ne 0$, then the series $\sum_{n=1}^{+\infty} u_n$ is divergent.

PROOF: Assume that $\sum_{n=1}^{+\infty} u_n$ is convergent. Then by Theorem 14.3.3 $\lim_{n \to +\infty} u_n = 0$. But this contradicts the hypothesis. Therefore, the series is divergent.

EXAMPLE 3:   Prove that the following two series are divergent.

(a) $\displaystyle\sum_{n=1}^{+\infty} \frac{n^2 + 1}{n^2}$

$= 2 + \dfrac{5}{4} + \dfrac{10}{9} + \dfrac{17}{16} + \cdots$

(b) $\displaystyle\sum_{n=1}^{+\infty} (-1)^{n+1}3$

$= 3 - 3 + 3 - 3 + \cdots$

SOLUTION: (a) $\displaystyle\lim_{n \to +\infty} u_n = \lim_{n \to +\infty} \frac{n^2 + 1}{n^2}$

$$= \lim_{n \to +\infty} \frac{1 + \dfrac{1}{n^2}}{1}$$

$$= 1$$

$$\ne 0$$

Therefore, by Theorem 14.3.4 the series is divergent.

(b) $\displaystyle\lim_{n \to +\infty} u_n = \lim_{n \to +\infty} (-1)^{n+1}3$, which does not exist. Therefore, by Theorem 14.3.4 the series is divergent.

Note that the converse of Theorem 14.3.3 is false. That is, if $\lim_{n \to +\infty} u_n = 0$, it does not follow that the series is necessarily convergent. In other words, it is possible to have a divergent series for which $\lim_{n \to +\infty} u_n = 0$. An example of such a series is the one known as the *harmonic series*, which is

$$\sum_{n=1}^{+\infty} \frac{1}{n} = 1 + \frac{1}{2} + \frac{1}{3} + \frac{1}{4} + \cdots + \frac{1}{n} + \cdots \tag{4}$$

Clearly, $\lim_{n \to +\infty} 1/n = 0$. To prove that the harmonic series diverges we use the following theorem, which states that the difference between two partial sums s_R and s_T of a convergent series can be made as small as we please by taking R and T sufficiently large.

14.3.5 Theorem   Let $\{s_n\}$ be the sequence of partial sums for a given convergent series $\sum\limits_{n=1}^{+\infty} u_n$. Then for any $\epsilon > 0$ there exists a number N such that

$$|s_R - s_T| < \epsilon \qquad \text{whenever } R > N \text{ and } T > N$$

PROOF: Because the series $\sum\limits_{n=1}^{+\infty} u_n$ is convergent, call its sum S. Then for any $\epsilon > 0$ there exists an $N > 0$ such that $|S - s_n| < \frac{1}{2}\epsilon$ whenever $n > N$. Therefore, if $R > N$ and $T > N$,

$$|s_R - s_T| = |s_R - S + S - s_T| \leq |s_R - S| + |S - s_T| < \tfrac{1}{2}\epsilon + \tfrac{1}{2}\epsilon$$

So

$$|s_R - s_T| < \epsilon \qquad \text{whenever } R > N \text{ and } T > N \qquad \blacksquare$$

We now prove that the harmonic series (4) is divergent. For this series,

$$s_n = 1 + \frac{1}{2} + \cdots + \frac{1}{n}$$

and

$$s_{2n} = 1 + \frac{1}{2} + \cdots + \frac{1}{n} + \frac{1}{n+1} + \cdots + \frac{1}{2n}$$

So

$$s_{2n} - s_n = \frac{1}{n+1} + \frac{1}{n+2} + \frac{1}{n+3} + \cdots + \frac{1}{2n} \qquad (5)$$

If $n > 1$,

$$\frac{1}{n+1} + \frac{1}{n+2} + \frac{1}{n+3} + \cdots + \frac{1}{2n} > \frac{1}{2n} + \frac{1}{2n} + \frac{1}{2n} + \cdots + \frac{1}{2n} \qquad (6)$$

There are n terms on each side of the inequality sign in (6); so the right side is $n(1/2n) = \frac{1}{2}$. Therefore, from (5) and (6) we have

$$s_{2n} - s_n > \tfrac{1}{2} \qquad \text{whenever } n > 1 \qquad (7)$$

But Theorem 14.3.5 states that if the given series is convergent, then $s_{2n} - s_n$ may be made as small as we please by taking n large enough; that is, if we take $\epsilon = \frac{1}{2}$, there exists an N such that $s_{2n} - s_n < \frac{1}{2}$ whenever $2n > N$ and $n > N$. But this would contradict (7). Therefore, we conclude that the harmonic series is divergent even though $\lim\limits_{n \to +\infty} 1/n = 0$.

A *geometric series* is a series of the form

$$\sum_{n=1}^{+\infty} ar^{n-1} = a + ar + ar^2 + \cdots + ar^{n-1} + \cdots \qquad (8)$$

The nth partial sum of this series is given by

$$s_n = a(1 + r + r^2 + \cdots + r^{n-1}) \qquad (9)$$

From the identity

$$1 - r^n = (1 - r)(1 + r + r^2 + \cdots + r^{n-1})$$

we can write (9) as

$$s_n = \frac{a(1 - r^n)}{1 - r} \qquad \text{if } r \neq 1 \tag{10}$$

14.3.6 Theorem   The geometric series converges to the sum $a/(1 - r)$ if $|r| < 1$, and the geometric series diverges if $|r| \geq 1$.

PROOF: In Example 4, Sec. 14.1, we showed that $\lim\limits_{n \to +\infty} r^n = 0$ if $|r| < 1$. Therefore, from (10) we can conclude that if $|r| < 1$,

$$\lim_{n \to +\infty} s_n = \frac{a}{1 - r}$$

So if $|r| < 1$, the geometric series converges, and its sum is $a/(1 - r)$.

If $r = 1$, $s_n = na$. Then $\lim\limits_{n \to +\infty} s_n = +\infty$ if $a > 0$, and $\lim\limits_{n \to +\infty} s_n = -\infty$ if $a < 0$.

If $r = -1$, the geometric series becomes $a - a + a - \cdots + (-1)^{n-1}a + \cdots$; so $s_n = 0$ if n is even, and $s_n = a$ if n is odd. Therefore, $\lim\limits_{n \to +\infty} s_n$ does not exist. Hence, the geometric series diverges when $|r| = 1$.

If $|r| > 1$, $\lim\limits_{n \to +\infty} ar^{n-1} = a \lim\limits_{n \to +\infty} r^{n-1}$. Clearly, $\lim\limits_{n \to +\infty} r^{n-1} \neq 0$ because we can make $|r^{n-1}|$ as large as we please by taking n large enough. Therefore, by Theorem 14.3.4 the series is divergent. This completes the proof.   ∎

EXAMPLE 4:   Determine whether the infinite series

$$\sum_{n=1}^{+\infty} \frac{1}{2^{n-1}}$$

is convergent or divergent.

SOLUTION:

$$\sum_{n=1}^{+\infty} \frac{1}{2^{n-1}} = 1 + \frac{1}{2} + \frac{1}{4} + \frac{1}{8} + \cdots + \frac{1}{2^{n-1}} + \cdots$$

THE SERIES IS CONVERGENT BECAUSE

which is the geometric series, with $a = 1$ and $r = \frac{1}{2}$. Therefore, by Theorem 14.3.6 the series is convergent. Because $a/(1 - r) = 1/(1 - \frac{1}{2}) = 2$, the sum of the series is 2.

The following example illustrates how Theorem 14.3.6 can be used to express a nonterminating repeating decimal as a rational number.

EXAMPLE 5:   Express the decimal 0.3333 . . . as a rational number.

SOLUTION:

$$0.3333\ldots = \frac{3}{10} + \frac{3}{100} + \frac{3}{1,000} + \frac{3}{10,000} + \cdots + \frac{3}{10^n} + \cdots$$

We have a geometric series in which $a = \frac{3}{10}$ and $r = \frac{1}{10}$. Because $r < 1$, it follows from Theorem 14.3.6 that the series converges and its sum is $a/(1 - r)$. Therefore,

$$0.3333\ldots = \frac{\frac{3}{10}}{1 - \frac{1}{10}} = \frac{1}{3}$$

The next theorem states that the convergence or divergence of an infinite series is not affected by changing a finite number of terms.

14.3.7 Theorem If $\sum\limits_{n=1}^{+\infty} a_n$ and $\sum\limits_{n=1}^{+\infty} b_n$ are two infinite series, differing only in their first m terms (i.e., $a_k = b_k$ if $k > m$), then either both series converge or both series diverge.

PROOF: Let $\{s_n\}$ and $\{t_n\}$ be the sequences of partial sums of the series $\sum\limits_{n=1}^{+\infty} a_n$ and $\sum\limits_{n=1}^{+\infty} b_n$, respectively. Then

$$s_n = a_1 + a_2 + \cdots + a_m + a_{m+1} + a_{m+2} + \cdots + a_n$$

and

$$t_n = b_1 + b_2 + \cdots + b_m + b_{m+1} + b_{m+2} + \cdots + b_n$$

Because $a_k = b_k$ if $k > m$, then if $n \geq m$, we have

$$s_n - t_n = (a_1 + a_2 + \cdots + a_m) - (b_1 + b_2 + \cdots + b_m)$$

So

$$s_n - t_n = s_m - t_m \qquad \text{whenever } n \geq m \tag{11}$$

We wish to show that either both $\lim\limits_{n \to +\infty} s_n$ and $\lim\limits_{n \to +\infty} t_n$ exist or do not exist.

Suppose that $\lim\limits_{n \to +\infty} t_n$ exists. Then from Eq. (11) we have

$$s_n = t_n + (s_m - t_m) \qquad \text{whenever } n \geq m$$

and so

$$\lim_{n \to +\infty} s_n = \lim_{n \to +\infty} t_n + (s_m - t_m)$$

Hence, when $\lim\limits_{n \to +\infty} t_n$ exists, $\lim\limits_{n \to +\infty} s_n$ also exists and both series converge.

Now suppose that $\lim\limits_{n \to +\infty} t_n$ does not exist and $\lim\limits_{n \to +\infty} s_n$ exists. From Eq. (11) we have

$$t_n = s_n + (t_m - s_m) \qquad \text{whenever } n \geq m$$

Because $\lim\limits_{n \to +\infty} s_n$ exists, it follows that

$$\lim_{n \to +\infty} t_n = \lim_{n \to +\infty} s_n + (t_m - s_m)$$

and so $\lim\limits_{n \to +\infty} t_n$ has to exist, which is a contradiction. Hence, if $\lim\limits_{n \to +\infty} t_n$ does not exist, then $\lim\limits_{n \to +\infty} s_n$ does not exist, and both series diverge. ∎

EXAMPLE 6:   Determine whether the infinite series

$$\sum_{n=1}^{+\infty} \frac{1}{n+4}$$

is convergent or divergent.

SOLUTION: The given series is

$$\frac{1}{5} + \frac{1}{6} + \frac{1}{7} + \cdots + \frac{1}{n+4} + \cdots$$

which can be written as

$$0 + 0 + 0 + 0 + \frac{1}{5} + \frac{1}{6} + \frac{1}{7} + \cdots + \frac{1}{n} + \cdots \qquad (12)$$

Now the harmonic series which is known to be divergent is

$$1 + \frac{1}{2} + \frac{1}{3} + \frac{1}{4} + \frac{1}{5} + \frac{1}{6} + \frac{1}{7} + \cdots + \frac{1}{n} + \cdots \qquad (13)$$

Series (12) differs from series (13) only in the first four terms. Hence, by Theorem 14.3.7 series (12) is also divergent.

EXAMPLE 7:   Determine whether the following infinite series is convergent or divergent:

$$\sum_{n=1}^{+\infty} \frac{\left[\!\left[\cos \frac{3}{n} \pi + 2\right]\!\right]}{3^n}$$

SOLUTION: The given series can be written as

$$\frac{[\![\cos 3\pi + 2]\!]}{3} + \frac{[\![\cos \frac{3}{2}\pi + 2]\!]}{3^2} + \frac{[\![\cos \pi + 2]\!]}{3^3} + \frac{[\![\cos \frac{3}{4}\pi + 2]\!]}{3^4}$$

$$+ \frac{[\![\cos \frac{3}{5}\pi + 2]\!]}{3^5} + \frac{[\![\cos \frac{1}{2}\pi + 2]\!]}{3^6} + \frac{[\![\cos \frac{3}{7}\pi + 2]\!]}{3^7} + \cdots$$

$$= \frac{1}{3} + \frac{2}{3^2} + \frac{1}{3^3} + \frac{1}{3^4} + \frac{1}{3^5} + \frac{2}{3^6} + \frac{2}{3^7} + \frac{2}{3^8} + \cdots \qquad (14)$$

Consider the geometric series with $a = \frac{2}{3}$ and $r = \frac{1}{3}$:

$$\frac{2}{3} + \frac{2}{3^2} + \frac{2}{3^3} + \frac{2}{3^4} + \frac{2}{3^5} + \frac{2}{3^6} + \frac{2}{3^7} + \frac{2}{3^8} + \cdots \qquad (15)$$

This series is convergent by Theorem 14.3.6. Because series (14) differs from series (15) only in the first five terms, it follows from Theorem 14.3.7 that series (14) is also convergent.

As a consequence of Theorem 14.3.7, for a given infinite series, we can add or subtract a finite number of terms without affecting its convergence or divergence. For instance, in Example 6 the given series may be thought of as being obtained from the harmonic series by subtracting the first four terms. And because the harmonic series is divergent, the given series is divergent. In Example 7, we could consider the convergent geometric series

$$\frac{2}{3^6} + \frac{2}{3^7} + \frac{2}{3^8} + \cdots \qquad (16)$$

and obtain the given series (14) by adding five terms. Because series (16) is convergent, it follows that series (14) is convergent.

The following theorem states that if an infinite series is multiplied term by term by a nonzero constant, its convergence or divergence is not affected.

14.3.8 Theorem Let c be any nonzero constant.

(i) If the series $\sum\limits_{n=1}^{+\infty} u_n$ is convergent and its sum is S, then the series $\sum\limits_{n=1}^{+\infty} cu_n$ is also convergent and its sum is $c \cdot S$.

(ii) If the series $\sum\limits_{n=1}^{+\infty} u_n$ is divergent, then the series $\sum\limits_{n=1}^{+\infty} cu_n$ is also divergent.

PROOF: Let the nth partial sum of the series $\sum\limits_{n=1}^{+\infty} u_n$ be s_n. Therefore, $s_n = u_1 + u_2 + \cdots + u_n$. The nth partial sum of the series $\sum\limits_{n=1}^{+\infty} cu_n$ is $c(u_1 + u_2 + \cdots + u_n) = cs_n$.

Part (i): If the series $\sum\limits_{n=1}^{+\infty} u_n$ is convergent, then $\lim\limits_{n \to +\infty} s_n$ exists and is S. Therefore,

$$\lim_{n \to +\infty} cs_n = c \lim_{n \to +\infty} s_n = c \cdot S$$

Hence, the series $\sum\limits_{n=1}^{+\infty} cu_n$ is convergent and its sum is $c \cdot S$.

Part (ii): If the series $\sum\limits_{n=1}^{+\infty} u_n$ is divergent, then $\lim\limits_{n \to +\infty} s_n$ does not exist. Now suppose that the series $\sum\limits_{n=1}^{+\infty} cu_n$ is convergent. Then $\lim\limits_{n \to +\infty} cs_n$ exists. But $s_n = cs_n/c$, and so

$$\lim_{n \to +\infty} s_n = \lim_{n \to +\infty} \frac{1}{c}(cs_n) = \frac{1}{c} \lim_{n \to +\infty} cs_n$$

Thus, $\lim\limits_{n \to +\infty} s_n$ must exist, which is a contradiction. Therefore, the series $\sum\limits_{n=1}^{+\infty} cu_n$ is divergent. ∎

EXAMPLE 8: Determine whether the infinite series

$$\sum_{n=1}^{+\infty} \frac{1}{4n}$$

is convergent or divergent.

SOLUTION:
$$\sum_{n=1}^{+\infty} \frac{1}{4n} = \frac{1}{4} + \frac{1}{8} + \frac{1}{12} + \frac{1}{16} + \cdots + \frac{1}{4n} + \cdots$$

Because $\sum\limits_{n=1}^{+\infty} 1/n$ is the harmonic series which is divergent, then by Theorem 14.3.8(ii) with $c = \frac{1}{4}$, the given series is divergent.

Note that Theorem 14.3.8(i) is an extension to convergent infinite series of the following property of finite sums:

$$\sum_{k=1}^{n} ca_k = c \sum_{k=1}^{n} a_k$$

Another property of finite sums is

$$\sum_{k=1}^{n} (a_k \pm b_k) = \sum_{k=1}^{n} a_k \pm \sum_{k=1}^{n} b_k$$

and its extension to convergent infinite series is given by the following theorem.

14.3.9 Theorem   If $\sum_{n=1}^{+\infty} a_n$ and $\sum_{n=1}^{+\infty} b_n$ are convergent infinite series whose sums are S and R, respectively, then

(i) $\sum_{n=1}^{+\infty} (a_n + b_n)$ is a convergent series and its sum is $S + R$;

(ii) $\sum_{n=1}^{+\infty} (a_n - b_n)$ is a convergent series and its sum is $S - R$.

The proof of this theorem is left for the reader (see Exercise 11).

The next theorem is a corollary of the above theorem and is sometimes used to prove that a series is divergent.

14.3.10 Theorem   If the series $\sum_{n=1}^{+\infty} a_n$ is convergent and the series $\sum_{n=1}^{+\infty} b_n$ is divergent, then the series $\sum_{n=1}^{+\infty} (a_n + b_n)$ is divergent.

PROOF: Assume that $\sum_{n=1}^{+\infty} (a_n + b_n)$ is convergent and its sum is S. Let the sum of the series $\sum_{n=1}^{+\infty} a_n$ be R. Then because

$$\sum_{n=1}^{+\infty} b_n = \sum_{n=1}^{+\infty} [(a_n + b_n) - a_n]$$

it follows from Theorem 14.3.9(ii) that $\sum_{n=1}^{+\infty} b_n$ is convergent and its sum is $S - R$. But this is a contradiction to the hypothesis that $\sum_{n=1}^{+\infty} b_n$ is divergent.

Hence, $\sum_{n=1}^{+\infty} (a_n + b_n)$ is divergent.   ■

EXAMPLE 9:   Determine whether the infinite series

$$\sum_{n=1}^{+\infty} \left(\frac{1}{4n} + \frac{1}{4^n} \right)$$

is convergent or divergent.

SOLUTION: In Example 8 we proved that the series $\sum_{n=1}^{+\infty} 1/4n$ is divergent. Because the series $\sum_{n=1}^{+\infty} 1/4^n$ is a geometric series with $|r| = \frac{1}{4} < 1$, it is convergent. Hence, by Theorem 14.3.10 the given series is divergent.

Note that if both series $\sum_{n=1}^{+\infty} a_n$ and $\sum_{n=1}^{+\infty} b_n$ are divergent, the series $\sum_{n=1}^{+\infty} (a_n + b_n)$ may or may not be convergent. For example, if $a_n = 1/n$ and $b_n = 1/n$, then $a_n + b_n = 2/n$ and $\sum_{n=1}^{+\infty} 2/n$ is divergent. But if $a_n = 1/n$ and $b_n = -1/n$, then $a_n + b_n = 0$ and $\sum_{n=1}^{+\infty} 0$ is convergent.

Exercises 14.3

In Exercises 1 through 6, find the first four terms of the sequence of partial sums $\{s_n\}$ and find a formula for s_n in terms of n; also, determine if the infinite series is convergent or divergent, and if it is convergent, find its sum.

1. $\sum_{n=1}^{+\infty} \dfrac{1}{(2n-1)(2n+1)}$

2. $\sum_{n=1}^{+\infty} \dfrac{2}{(4n-3)(4n+1)}$

3. $\sum_{n=1}^{+\infty} \ln \dfrac{n}{n+1}$

4. $\sum_{n=1}^{+\infty} n$

5. $\sum_{n=1}^{+\infty} \dfrac{2n+1}{n^2(n+1)^2}$

6. $\sum_{n=1}^{+\infty} \dfrac{2^{n-1}}{3^n}$

In Exercises 7 through 10, find the infinite series which is the given sequence of partial sums; also determine if the infinite series is convergent or divergent, and if it is convergent, find its sum.

7. $\{s_n\} = \left\{ \dfrac{2n}{3n+1} \right\}$

8. $\{s_n\} = \left\{ \dfrac{n^2}{n+1} \right\}$

9. $\{s_n\} = \left\{ \dfrac{1}{2^n} \right\}$

10. $\{s_n\} = \{3^n\}$

11. Prove Theorem 14.3.9.

In Exercises 12 through 25, write the first four terms of the given infinite series and determine if the series is convergent or divergent. If the series is convergent, find its sum.

12. $\sum_{n=1}^{+\infty} \dfrac{n}{n+1}$

13. $\sum_{n=1}^{+\infty} \dfrac{2n+1}{3n+2}$

14. $\sum_{n=1}^{+\infty} \dfrac{2}{3n}$

15. $\sum_{n=1}^{+\infty} \left(\dfrac{2}{3} \right)^n$

16. $\sum_{n=1}^{+\infty} \dfrac{2}{3^{n-1}}$

17. $\sum_{n=1}^{+\infty} (-1)^{n+1} \dfrac{3}{2^n}$

18. $\sum_{n=1}^{+\infty} \ln \dfrac{1}{n}$

19. $\sum_{n=1}^{+\infty} e^{-n}$

20. $\sum_{n=1}^{+\infty} \sin \pi n$

21. $\sum_{n=1}^{+\infty} \cos \pi n$

22. $\sum_{n=1}^{+\infty} \dfrac{\sinh n}{n}$

23. $\sum_{n=1}^{+\infty} (2^{-n} + 3^{-n})$

24. $\sum_{n=1}^{+\infty} [1 + (-1)^n]$

25. $\sum_{n=1}^{+\infty} \left(\dfrac{1}{2n} - \dfrac{1}{3n} \right)$

In Exercises 26 through 29, express the given nonterminating repeating decimal as a rational number.

26. 0.27 27 27 . . .

27. 1.234 234 234 . . .

28. 2.045 45 45 . . .

29. 0.4653 4653 4653 . . .

30. A ball is dropped from a height of 12 ft. Each time it strikes the ground, it bounces back to a height of three-fourths the distance from which it fell. Find the total distance traveled by the ball before it comes to rest.

14.4 INFINITE SERIES OF POSITIVE TERMS

If all the terms of an infinite series are positive, the sequence of partial sums is increasing. Thus, the following theorem follows immediately from Theorems 14.2.6 and 14.2.9.

14.4.1 Theorem

An infinite series of positive terms is convergent if and only if its sequence of partial sums has an upper bound.

EXAMPLE 1: Prove that the series

$$\sum_{n=1}^{+\infty} \frac{1}{n!}$$

is convergent by using Theorem 14.4.1.

SOLUTION: We must find an upper bound for the sequence of partial sums of the series $\sum_{n=1}^{+\infty} 1/n!$.

$$s_1 = 1, \quad s_2 = 1 + \frac{1}{1 \cdot 2}, \quad s_3 = 1 + \frac{1}{1 \cdot 2} + \frac{1}{1 \cdot 2 \cdot 3}$$

$$s_4 = 1 + \frac{1}{1 \cdot 2} + \frac{1}{1 \cdot 2 \cdot 3} + \frac{1}{1 \cdot 2 \cdot 3 \cdot 4}, \cdots,$$

$$s_n = 1 + \frac{1}{1 \cdot 2} + \frac{1}{1 \cdot 2 \cdot 3} + \frac{1}{1 \cdot 2 \cdot 3 \cdot 4} + \cdots + \frac{1}{1 \cdot 2 \cdot 3 \cdot \ldots \cdot n} \quad (1)$$

Now consider the first n terms of the geometric series with $a = 1$ and $r = \frac{1}{2}$:

$$\sum_{k=1}^{n} \frac{1}{2^{k-1}} = 1 + \frac{1}{2} + \frac{1}{2^2} + \frac{1}{2^3} + \cdots + \frac{1}{2^{n-1}} \quad (2)$$

By Theorem 14.3.6 the geometric series with $a = 1$ and $r = \frac{1}{2}$ has the sum $a/(1 - r) = 1/(1 - \frac{1}{2}) = 2$. Hence, summation (2) is less than 2. Observe that each term of summation (1) is less than or equal to the corresponding term of summation (2); that is,

$$\frac{1}{k!} \leq \frac{1}{2^{k-1}}$$

This is true because $k! = 1 \cdot 2 \cdot 3 \cdot \ldots \cdot k$, which in addition to the factor 1 contains $k - 1$ factors each greater than or equal to 2. Hence,

$$s_n = \sum_{k=1}^{n} \frac{1}{k!} \leq \sum_{k=1}^{n} \frac{1}{2^{k-1}} < 2$$

From the above we see that s_n has an upper bound of 2. Therefore, by Theorem 14.4.1 the given series is convergent.

In the above example the terms of the given series were compared with those of a known convergent series. This is a particular case of the following theorem known as the *comparison test*.

14.4.2 Theorem
Comparison Test

Let the series $\sum\limits_{n=1}^{+\infty} u_n$ be a series of positive terms.

(i) If $\sum\limits_{n=1}^{+\infty} v_n$ is a series of positive terms which is known to be convergent, and $u_n \leq v_n$ for all positive integers n, then $\sum\limits_{n=1}^{+\infty} u_n$ is convergent.

(ii) If $\sum\limits_{n=1}^{+\infty} w_n$ is a series of positive terms which is known to be divergent, and $u_n \geq w_n$ for all positive integers n, then $\sum\limits_{n=1}^{+\infty} u_n$ is divergent.

PROOF OF (i):   Let $\{s_n\}$ be the sequence of partial sums for the series $\sum\limits_{n=1}^{+\infty} u_n$ and $\{t_n\}$ be the sequence of partial sums for the series $\sum\limits_{n=1}^{+\infty} v_n$. Because $\sum\limits_{n=1}^{+\infty} v_n$ is a series of positive terms which is convergent, it follows from Theorem 14.4.1 that the sequence $\{t_n\}$ has an upper bound; call it B. Because $u_n \leq v_n$ for all positive integers n, we can conclude that $s_n \leq t_n \leq B$ for all positive integers n. Therefore, B is an upper bound of the sequence $\{s_n\}$. And because the terms of the series $\sum\limits_{n=1}^{+\infty} u_n$ are all positive, it follows from Theorem 14.4.1 that $\sum\limits_{n=1}^{+\infty} u_n$ is convergent.

PROOF OF (ii):   Assume that $\sum\limits_{n=1}^{+\infty} u_n$ is convergent. Then because both $\sum\limits_{n=1}^{+\infty} u_n$ and $\sum\limits_{n=1}^{+\infty} w_n$ are infinite series of positive terms and $w_n \leq u_n$ for all positive integers n, it follows from part (i) that $\sum\limits_{n=1}^{+\infty} w_n$ is convergent. However, this contradicts the hypothesis, and so our assumption is false. Therefore, $\sum\limits_{n=1}^{+\infty} u_n$ is divergent.   ∎

As we stated in Sec. 14.3, as a result of Theorem 14.3.7, the convergence or divergence of an infinite series is not affected by discarding a finite number of terms. Therefore, when applying the comparison test, if $u_i \leq v_i$ or $u_i \geq w_i$ when $i > m$, the test is valid regardless of how the first m terms of the two series compare.

EXAMPLE 2:   Determine whether the infinite series

$$\sum_{n=1}^{+\infty} \frac{4}{3^n + 1}$$

is convergent or divergent.

SOLUTION: The given series is

$$\frac{4}{4} + \frac{4}{10} + \frac{4}{28} + \frac{4}{82} + \cdots + \frac{4}{3^n + 1} + \cdots$$

Comparing the nth term of this series with the nth term of the convergent geometric series

$$\frac{4}{3} + \frac{4}{9} + \frac{4}{27} + \frac{4}{81} + \cdots + \frac{4}{3^n} + \cdots \qquad r = \frac{1}{3} < 1$$

we . ve

$$\frac{4}{3^n + 1} < \frac{4}{3^n}$$

for every positive integer n. Therefore, by the comparison test, Theorem 14.4.2(i), the given series is convergent.

EXAMPLE 3:   Determine whether the infinite series

$$\sum_{n=1}^{+\infty} \frac{1}{\sqrt{n}}$$

is convergent or divergent.

SOLUTION: The given series is

$$\sum_{n=1}^{+\infty} \frac{1}{\sqrt{n}} = \frac{1}{\sqrt{1}} + \frac{1}{\sqrt{2}} + \frac{1}{\sqrt{3}} + \cdots + \frac{1}{\sqrt{n}} + \cdots$$

Comparing the nth term of this series with the nth term of the divergent harmonic series, we have

$$\frac{1}{\sqrt{n}} \geq \frac{1}{n} \qquad \text{for every positive integer } n$$

So by Theorem 14.4.2(ii) the given series $\sum_{n=1}^{+\infty} 1/\sqrt{n}$ is divergent.

The following theorem, known as the *limit comparison test*, is a consequence of Theorem 14.4.2 and is often easier to apply.

14.4.3 Theorem
Limit Comparison Test

Let $\sum_{n=1}^{+\infty} u_n$ and $\sum_{n=1}^{+\infty} v_n$ be two series of positive terms.

(i) If $\lim_{n \to +\infty} (u_n/v_n) = c > 0$, then the two series either both converge or both diverge.

(ii) If $\lim_{n \to +\infty} (u_n/v_n) = 0$, and if $\sum_{n=1}^{+\infty} v_n$ converges, then $\sum_{n=1}^{+\infty} u_n$ converges.

(iii) If $\lim_{n \to +\infty} (u_n/v_n) = +\infty$, and if $\sum_{n=1}^{+\infty} v_n$ diverges, then $\sum_{n=1}^{+\infty} u_n$ diverges.

PROOF OF (i):   Because $\lim\limits_{n \to +\infty} (u_n/v_n) = c$, it follows that there exists an $N > 0$ such that

$$\left| \frac{u_n}{v_n} - c \right| < \frac{c}{2} \qquad \text{for all } n > N$$

or, equivalently,

$$-\frac{c}{2} < \frac{u_n}{v_n} - c < \frac{c}{2} \qquad \text{for all } n > N$$

or, equivalently,

$$\frac{c}{2} < \frac{u_n}{v_n} < \frac{3c}{2} \qquad \text{for all } n > N \tag{3}$$

From the right-hand inequality (3) we get

$$u_n < \tfrac{3}{2} c v_n \tag{4}$$

If $\sum\limits_{n=1}^{+\infty} v_n$ is convergent, so is $\sum\limits_{n=1}^{+\infty} \tfrac{3}{2} c v_n$. It follows from inequality (4) and the comparison test that $\sum\limits_{n=1}^{+\infty} u_n$ is convergent.

From the left-hand inequality (3) we get

$$v_n < \frac{2}{c} u_n \tag{5}$$

If $\sum\limits_{n=1}^{+\infty} u_n$ is convergent, so is $\sum\limits_{n=1}^{+\infty} \frac{2}{c} u_n$. From inequality (5) and the comparison test it follows that $\sum\limits_{n=1}^{+\infty} v_n$ is convergent.

If $\sum\limits_{n=1}^{+\infty} v_n$ is divergent, we can show that $\sum\limits_{n=1}^{+\infty} u_n$ is divergent by assuming that $\sum\limits_{n=1}^{+\infty} u_n$ is convergent and getting a contradiction by applying inequality (5) and the comparison test.

In a similar manner, if $\sum\limits_{n=1}^{+\infty} u_n$ is divergent, it follows that $\sum\limits_{n=1}^{+\infty} v_n$ is divergent because a contradiction is obtained from inequality (4) and the comparison test if $\sum\limits_{n=1}^{+\infty} v_n$ is assumed to be convergent.

We have therefore proved part (i). The proofs of parts (ii) and (iii) are left for the reader (see Exercises 19 and 20).   ∎

A word of caution is in order regarding part (ii) of Theorem 14.4.3. Note that when $\lim\limits_{n \to +\infty} (u_n/v_n) = 0$, the divergence of the series $\sum\limits_{n=1}^{+\infty} v_n$ does not imply that the series $\sum\limits_{n=1}^{+\infty} u_n$ diverges.

EXAMPLE 4:   Solve Example 2 by using the limit comparison test.

SOLUTION: Let u_n be the nth term of the given series $\sum\limits_{n=1}^{+\infty} 4/(3^n + 1)$ and v_n be the nth term of the convergent geometric series $\sum\limits_{n=1}^{+\infty} 4/3^n$. Therefore,

$$\lim_{n \to +\infty} \frac{u_n}{v_n} = \lim_{n \to +\infty} \frac{\dfrac{4}{3^n + 1}}{\dfrac{4}{3^n}}$$

$$= \lim_{n \to +\infty} \frac{3^n}{3^n + 1}$$

$$= \lim_{n \to +\infty} \frac{1}{1 + 3^{-n}}$$

$$= 1$$

Hence, by part (i) of the limit comparison test, it follows that the given series is convergent.

EXAMPLE 5:   Solve Example 3 by using the limit comparison test.

SOLUTION: Let u_n be the nth term of the given series $\sum\limits_{n=1}^{+\infty} 1/\sqrt{n}$ and v_n be the nth term of the divergent harmonic series. Then

$$\lim_{n \to +\infty} \frac{u_n}{v_n} = \lim_{n \to +\infty} \frac{\dfrac{1}{\sqrt{n}}}{\dfrac{1}{n}} = \lim_{n \to +\infty} \sqrt{n} = +\infty$$

Therefore, by part (iii) of the limit comparison test, we conclude that the given series is divergent.

EXAMPLE 6:   Determine whether the series

$$\sum_{n=1}^{+\infty} \frac{n^3}{n!}$$

is convergent or divergent.

SOLUTION: In Example 1, we proved that the series $\sum\limits_{n=1}^{+\infty} 1/n!$ is convergent. Using the limit comparison test with $u_n = n^3/n!$ and $v_n = 1/n!$, we have

$$\lim_{n \to +\infty} \frac{u_n}{v_n} = \lim_{n \to +\infty} \frac{\dfrac{n^3}{n!}}{\dfrac{1}{n!}} = \lim_{n \to +\infty} n^3 = +\infty$$

Part (iii) of the limit comparison test is not applicable because $\sum\limits_{n=1}^{+\infty} v_n$ converges. However, there is a way that we can use the limit comparison test. The given series can be written as

$$\frac{1^3}{1!} + \frac{2^3}{2!} + \frac{3^3}{3!} + \frac{4^3}{4!} + \frac{5^3}{5!} + \cdots + \frac{n^3}{n!} + \cdots$$

Because Theorem 14.3.7 allows us to subtract a finite number of terms without affecting the behavior (convergence or divergence) of a series, we discard the first three terms and obtain

$$\frac{4^3}{4!} + \frac{5^3}{5!} + \frac{6^3}{6!} + \cdots + \frac{(n+3)^3}{(n+3)!} + \cdots$$

Now letting $u_n = (n+3)^3/(n+3)!$ and, as before, letting $v_n = 1/n!$, we have

$$\lim_{n \to +\infty} \frac{u_n}{v_n} = \lim_{n \to +\infty} \frac{\dfrac{(n+3)^3}{(n+3)!}}{\dfrac{1}{n!}}$$

$$= \lim_{n \to +\infty} \frac{(n+3)^3 n!}{(n+3)!}$$

$$= \lim_{n \to +\infty} \frac{(n+3)^3 n!}{n!(n+1)(n+2)(n+3)}$$

$$= \lim_{n \to +\infty} \frac{(n+3)^2}{(n+1)(n+2)}$$

$$= \lim_{n \to +\infty} \frac{n^2 + 6n + 9}{n^2 + 3n + 2}$$

$$= \lim_{n \to +\infty} \frac{1 + \dfrac{6}{n} + \dfrac{9}{n^2}}{1 + \dfrac{3}{n} + \dfrac{2}{n^2}}$$

$$= 1$$

It follows from part (i) of the limit comparison test that the given series is convergent.

Consider now the geometric series

$$1 + \frac{1}{2} + \frac{1}{4} + \frac{1}{8} + \frac{1}{16} + \frac{1}{32} + \cdots + \frac{1}{2^{n-1}} + \cdots \tag{6}$$

which converges to 2 as shown in Example 4 of Sec. 14.3. Regrouping the terms of this series, we have

$$\left(1 + \frac{1}{2}\right) + \left(\frac{1}{4} + \frac{1}{8}\right) + \left(\frac{1}{16} + \frac{1}{32}\right) + \cdots + \left(\frac{1}{4^{n-1}} + \frac{1}{2 \cdot 4^{n-1}}\right) + \cdots$$

which is the series

$$\frac{3}{2} + \frac{3}{8} + \frac{3}{32} + \cdots + \frac{3}{2 \cdot 4^{n-1}} + \cdots \tag{7}$$

Series (7) is the geometric series with $a = \frac{3}{2}$ and $r = \frac{1}{4}$. Thus, by Theorem 14.3.6 it is convergent, and its sum is

$$\frac{a}{1-r} = \frac{\frac{3}{2}}{1 - \frac{1}{4}} = 2$$

We see, then, that series (7), which is obtained from the convergent series (6) by regrouping the terms, is also convergent. Its sum is the same as that of series (6). This is a particular case of the following theorem.

14.4.4 Theorem   If $\sum\limits_{n=1}^{+\infty} u_n$ is a given convergent series of positive terms, its terms can be grouped in any manner, and the resulting series also will be convergent and will have the same sum as the given series.

PROOF: Let $\{s_n\}$ be the sequence of partial sums for the given convergent series of positive terms. Then $\lim\limits_{n \to +\infty} s_n$ exists; let this limit be S. Consider a series $\sum\limits_{n=1}^{+\infty} v_n$ whose terms are obtained by grouping the terms of $\sum\limits_{n=1}^{+\infty} u_n$ in some manner. For example, $\sum\limits_{n=1}^{+\infty} v_n$ may be the series

$$u_1 + (u_2 + u_3) + (u_4 + u_5 + u_6) + (u_7 + u_8 + u_9 + u_{10}) + \cdots$$

or it may be the series

$$(u_1 + u_2) + (u_3 + u_4) + (u_5 + u_6) + (u_7 + u_8) + \cdots$$

and so forth. Let $\{t_m\}$ be the sequence of partial sums for the series $\sum\limits_{n=1}^{+\infty} v_n$. Each partial sum of the sequence $\{t_m\}$ is also a partial sum of the sequence $\{s_n\}$. Therefore, as m increases without bound, so does n. Because $\lim\limits_{n \to +\infty} s_n = S$, we conclude that $\lim\limits_{m \to +\infty} t_m = S$. This proves the theorem.   ∎

Theorem 14.4.4 and the next theorem state properties of the sum of a convergent series of positive terms that are similar to properties that hold for the sum of a finite number of terms.

14.4.5 Theorem   If $\sum\limits_{n=1}^{+\infty} u_n$ is a given convergent series of positive terms, the order of the terms can be rearranged, and the resulting series also will be convergent and will have the same sum as the given series.

PROOF: Let $\{s_n\}$ be the sequence of partial sums for the given convergent series of positive terms, and let $\lim\limits_{n \to +\infty} s_n = S$. Let $\sum\limits_{n=1}^{+\infty} v_n$ be a series formed by rearranging the order of the terms of $\sum\limits_{n=1}^{+\infty} u_n$. For example, $\sum\limits_{n=1}^{+\infty} v_n$ may be the series

$$u_4 + u_3 + u_7 + u_1 + u_9 + u_5 + \cdots$$

Let $\{t_n\}$ be the sequence of partial sums for the series $\sum\limits_{n=1}^{+\infty} v_n$. Each partial sum of the sequence $\{t_n\}$ will be less than S because it is the sum of n terms of the infinite series $\sum\limits_{n=1}^{+\infty} u_n$. Therefore, S is an upper bound of the sequence $\{t_n\}$. Furthermore, because all the terms of the series $\sum\limits_{n=1}^{+\infty} v_n$ are positive, $\{t_n\}$ is a monotonic increasing sequence. Hence, by Theorem 14.2.7 the sequence $\{t_n\}$ is convergent, and $\lim\limits_{n \to +\infty} t_n = T \leq S$. Now because the given series $\sum\limits_{n=1}^{+\infty} u_n$ can be obtained from the series $\sum\limits_{n=1}^{+\infty} v_n$ by rearranging the order of the terms, we can use the same argument and conclude that $S \leq T$. If both inequalities, $T \leq S$ and $S \leq T$, must hold, it follows that $S = T$. This proves the theorem. ∎

A series which is often used in the comparison test is the one known as the *p series,* or the *hyperharmonic series.* It is

$$\frac{1}{1^p} + \frac{1}{2^p} + \frac{1}{3^p} + \cdots + \frac{1}{n^p} + \cdots \qquad \text{where } p \text{ is a constant} \qquad (8)$$

EXAMPLE 7: Prove that the p series diverges if $p \leq 1$ and converges if $p > 1$.

SOLUTION: If $p = 1$, the p series is the harmonic series, which diverges. If $p < 1$, then $n^p \leq n$, and so

$$\frac{1}{n^p} \geq \frac{1}{n} \qquad \text{for every positive integer } n$$

Hence, by Theorem 14.4.2(ii) the p series is divergent if $p < 1$.

If $p > 1$, we group the terms as follows:

$$\frac{1}{1^p} + \left(\frac{1}{2^p} + \frac{1}{3^p}\right) + \left(\frac{1}{4^p} + \frac{1}{5^p} + \frac{1}{6^p} + \frac{1}{7^p}\right) + \left(\frac{1}{8^p} + \frac{1}{9^p} + \cdots + \frac{1}{15^p}\right) + \cdots \qquad (9)$$

Consider the series

$$\frac{1}{1^p} + \frac{2}{2^p} + \frac{4}{4^p} + \frac{8}{8^p} + \cdots + \frac{2^{n-1}}{(2^{n-1})^p} + \cdots \qquad (10)$$

This is a geometric series whose ratio is $2/2^p = 1/2^{p-1}$, which is a positive number less than 1. Hence, series (10) is convergent. Rewriting the terms of series (10), we get

$$\frac{1}{1^p} + \left(\frac{1}{2^p} + \frac{1}{2^p}\right) + \left(\frac{1}{4^p} + \frac{1}{4^p} + \frac{1}{4^p} + \frac{1}{4^p}\right) + \left(\frac{1}{8^p} + \frac{1}{8^p} + \cdots + \frac{1}{8^p}\right) + \cdots \qquad (11)$$

Comparing series (9) and series (11), we see that the group of terms in each set of parentheses after the first group is less in sum for (9) than it is for (11). Therefore, by the comparison test, series (9) is convergent. Because (9) is merely a regrouping of the terms of the p series when $p > 1$, we conclude from Theorem 14.4.4 that the p series is convergent if $p > 1$.

Note that the series in Example 3 is the p series where $p = \frac{1}{2} < 1$; therefore, it is divergent.

EXAMPLE 8:   Determine whether the infinite series

$$\sum_{n=1}^{+\infty} \frac{1}{(n^2 + 2)^{1/3}}$$

is convergent or divergent.

SOLUTION: Because for large values of n the number $n^2 + 2$ is close to the number n^2, so is the number $1/(n^2 + 2)^{1/3}$ close to the number $1/n^{2/3}$. The series $\sum_{n=1}^{+\infty} 1/n^{2/3}$ is divergent because it is the p series with $p = \frac{2}{3} < 1$. Using the limit comparison test with $u_n = 1/(n^2 + 2)^{1/3}$ and $v_n = 1/n^{2/3}$, we have

$$\lim_{n \to +\infty} \frac{u_n}{v_n} = \lim_{n \to +\infty} \frac{\dfrac{1}{(n^2 + 2)^{1/3}}}{\dfrac{1}{n^{2/3}}}$$

$$= \lim_{n \to +\infty} \frac{n^{2/3}}{(n^2 + 2)^{1/3}}$$

$$= \lim_{n \to +\infty} \left(\frac{n^2}{n^2 + 2} \right)^{1/3}$$

$$= \lim_{n \to +\infty} \left(\frac{1}{1 + \dfrac{2}{n^2}} \right)^{1/3}$$

$$= 1$$

Therefore, the given series is divergent.

Exercises 14.4

In Exercises 1 through 18, determine if the given series is convergent or divergent.

1. $\displaystyle\sum_{n=1}^{+\infty} \frac{1}{n2^n}$

2. $\displaystyle\sum_{n=1}^{+\infty} \frac{1}{\sqrt{2n+1}}$

3. $\displaystyle\sum_{n=1}^{+\infty} \frac{1}{n^n}$

4. $\displaystyle\sum_{n=1}^{+\infty} \frac{n^2}{4n^3 + 1}$

5. $\displaystyle\sum_{n=1}^{+\infty} \frac{1}{\sqrt{n^2 + 4n}}$

6. $\displaystyle\sum_{n=1}^{+\infty} \frac{|\sin n|}{n^2}$

7. $\displaystyle\sum_{n=1}^{+\infty} \frac{n!}{(n+2)!}$

8. $\displaystyle\sum_{n=1}^{+\infty} \frac{1}{\sqrt{n^3 + 1}}$

9. $\displaystyle\sum_{n=1}^{+\infty} \frac{n}{5n^2 + 3}$

10. $\displaystyle\sum_{n=1}^{+\infty} \sin \frac{1}{n}$

11. $\displaystyle\sum_{n=1}^{+\infty} \frac{n!}{(2n)!}$

12. $\displaystyle\sum_{n=1}^{+\infty} \frac{2^n}{n!}$

13. $\displaystyle\sum_{n=1}^{+\infty} \frac{|\csc n|}{\sqrt{n}}$

14. $\displaystyle\sum_{n=1}^{+\infty} \frac{1}{n + \sqrt{n}}$

15. $\displaystyle\sum_{n=2}^{+\infty} \frac{1}{n\sqrt{n^2 - 1}}$

16. $\displaystyle\sum_{n=1}^{+\infty} \frac{1}{(n+2)(n+4)}$

17. $\displaystyle\sum_{n=1}^{+\infty} \frac{\ln n}{n^2 + 2}$

18. $\displaystyle\sum_{n=1}^{+\infty} \frac{1}{3^n - \cos n}$

19. Prove Theorem 14.4.3(ii).   20. Prove Theorem 14.4.3(iii).

21. If $\sum\limits_{n=1}^{+\infty} a_n$ and $\sum\limits_{n=1}^{+\infty} b_n$ are two convergent series of positive terms, use the Limit Comparison Test to prove that the series $\sum\limits_{n=1}^{+\infty} a_n b_n$ is also convergent.

22. Suppose f is a function such that $f(n) > 0$ for n any positive integer. Furthermore, suppose that if p is any positive number $\lim\limits_{n \to +\infty} n^p f(n)$ exists and is positive. Prove that the series $\sum\limits_{n=1}^{+\infty} f(n)$ is convergent if $p > 1$ and divergent if $0 < p \le 1$.

14.5 THE INTEGRAL TEST

The theorem known as the *integral test* makes use of the theory of improper integrals to test an infinite series of positive terms for convergence.

14.5.1 Theorem
Integral Test

Let f be a function which is continuous, decreasing, and positive-valued for all $x \ge 1$. Then the infinite series

$$\sum_{n=1}^{+\infty} f(n) = f(1) + f(2) + f(3) + \cdots + f(n) + \cdots$$

is convergent if the improper integral

$$\int_1^{+\infty} f(x)\ dx$$

exists, and it is divergent if the improper integral increases without bound.

PROOF: If i is a positive integer, by the mean-value theorem for integrals (6.5.2) there exists a number X such that $i - 1 \le X \le i$ and

$$\int_{i-1}^i f(x)\ dx = f(X) \cdot 1 \tag{1}$$

Because f is a decreasing function,

$$f(i - 1) \ge f(X) \ge f(i)$$

and so from (1) we have

$$f(i - 1) \ge \int_{i-1}^i f(x)\ dx \ge f(i)$$

Therefore, if n is any positive integer,

$$\sum_{i=2}^n f(i - 1) \ge \sum_{i=2}^n \int_{i-1}^i f(x)\ dx \ge \sum_{i=2}^n f(i)$$

or, equivalently,

$$\sum_{i=1}^{n-1} f(i) \ge \int_1^n f(x)\ dx \ge \sum_{i=1}^n f(i) - f(1) \tag{2}$$

Figures 14.5.1 and 14.5.2 show the geometric interpretation of the above discussion for $n = 6$. In Fig. 14.5.1, we have a sketch of the graph of a function f satisfying the hypothesis. The sum of the measures of the areas of the shaded rectangles is $f(1) + f(2) + f(3) + f(4) + f(5)$, which is the left member of inequality (2) when $n = 6$. Clearly, the sum of the measures of the areas of these rectangles is greater than the measure of the area given by the definite integral when $n = 6$. In Fig. 14.5.2 the sum of the measures of the areas of the shaded rectangles is $f(2) + f(3) + f(4) + f(5) + f(6)$, which is the right member of the inequality (2) when $n = 6$. This sum is less than the value of the definite integral when $n = 6$.

If the given improper integral exists, let L be its value. Then

$$\int_1^n f(x) \, dx \leq L \tag{3}$$

From the second and third members of the inequality (2) and from (3) we obtain

$$\sum_{i=1}^n f(i) \leq f(1) + \int_1^n f(x) \, dx \leq f(1) + L \tag{4}$$

Consider now the infinite series $\sum_{n=1}^{+\infty} f(n)$. Let the sequence of partial sums of this series be $\{s_n\}$, where $s_n = \sum_{i=1}^n f(i)$. From (4) we see that $\{s_n\}$ has an upper bound of $f(1) + L$. Hence, by Theorem 14.4.1 we conclude that $\sum_{n=1}^{+\infty} f(n)$ is convergent.

Suppose that the given improper integral increases without bound. From (2) we have

$$\sum_{i=1}^{n-1} f(i) \geq \int_1^n f(x) \, dx$$

for all positive integers n. Thus, $\sum_{i=1}^{n-1} f(i)$ must also increase without bound as $n \to +\infty$. Therefore, $\lim_{n \to +\infty} s_n = \lim_{n \to +\infty} \sum_{i=1}^n f(i) = +\infty$. Hence, $\sum_{n=1}^{+\infty} f(n)$ is divergent. ∎

Figure 14.5.1

Figure 14.5.2

EXAMPLE 1: Use the integral test to show that the p series diverges if $p \leq 1$ and converges if $p > 1$.

SOLUTION: The p series is $\sum_{n=1}^{+\infty} 1/n^p$. The function f, defined by $f(x) = 1/x^p$, satisfies the hypothesis of Theorem 14.5.1. Thus, considering the improper integral, we have

$$\int_1^{+\infty} \frac{dx}{x^p} = \lim_{b \to +\infty} \int_1^b \frac{dx}{x^p}$$

If $p = 1$, the above integral gives

$$\lim_{b \to +\infty} \ln x \Big]_1^b = \lim_{b \to +\infty} \ln b = +\infty$$

If $p \neq 1$, the integral gives

$$\lim_{b \to +\infty} \frac{x^{1-p}}{1-p} \Big]_1^b = \lim_{b \to +\infty} \frac{b^{1-p} - 1}{1-p}$$

This limit is $+\infty$ when $p < 1$; it is $-1/(1-p)$ if $p > 1$. Therefore, by the integral test, it follows that the p series converges for $p > 1$ and diverges for $p \le 1$.

EXAMPLE 2:   Determine if the infinite series

$$\sum_{n=1}^{+\infty} n e^{-n}$$

is convergent or divergent.

SOLUTION: Letting $f(x) = xe^{-x}$, we see that f is continuous, decreasing, and positive valued for $x \ge 1$; thus, the hypothesis of the integral test is satisfied. Using integration by parts, we have $\int xe^{-x} \, dx = -e^{-x}(x+1) + C$. Hence,

$$\int_1^{+\infty} xe^{-x} \, dx = \lim_{b \to +\infty} \left[-e^{-x}(x+1) \right]_1^b = \lim_{b \to +\infty} \left[-\frac{b+1}{e^b} + \frac{2}{e} \right]$$

Because $\lim_{b \to +\infty} (b+1) = +\infty$ and $\lim_{b \to +\infty} e^b = +\infty$, we can use L'Hôpital's rule and obtain

$$\lim_{b \to +\infty} \frac{b+1}{e^b} = \lim_{b \to +\infty} \frac{1}{e^b} = 0$$

Therefore,

$$\int_1^{+\infty} xe^{-x} \, dx = \frac{2}{e}$$

and so the given series is convergent.

EXAMPLE 3:   Determine if the series

$$\sum_{n=1}^{+\infty} \frac{1}{(n+1) \sqrt{\ln(n+1)}}$$

is convergent or divergent.

SOLUTION: The function f defined by $f(x) = 1/(x+1) \sqrt{\ln(x+1)}$ is continuous, decreasing, and positive valued for $x \ge 1$; hence, the integral test can be applied.

$$\int_1^{+\infty} \frac{dx}{(x+1) \sqrt{\ln(x+1)}} = \lim_{b \to +\infty} \int_1^b [\ln(x+1)]^{-1/2} \frac{dx}{x+1}$$

$$= \lim_{b \to +\infty} \left[2\sqrt{\ln(x+1)} \right]_1^b$$

$$= \lim_{b \to +\infty} [2\sqrt{\ln(b+1)} - 2\sqrt{\ln 2}]$$

$$= +\infty$$

We conclude that the given series is divergent.

Exercises 14.5

In Exercises 1 through 12, determine if the given series is convergent or divergent.

1. $\displaystyle\sum_{n=1}^{+\infty} \frac{\ln n}{n}$

2. $\displaystyle\sum_{n=2}^{+\infty} \frac{1}{n \ln n}$

3. $\displaystyle\sum_{n=1}^{+\infty} \frac{\tan^{-1} n}{n^2 + 1}$

4. $\displaystyle\sum_{n=1}^{+\infty} ne^{-n^2}$

5. $\displaystyle\sum_{n=1}^{+\infty} n^2 e^{-n}$

6. $\displaystyle\sum_{n=1}^{+\infty} \cot^{-1} n$

7. $\displaystyle\sum_{n=1}^{+\infty} \operatorname{csch} n$

8. $\displaystyle\sum_{n=1}^{+\infty} \frac{e^{\tan^{-1} n}}{n^2 + 1}$

9. $\displaystyle\sum_{n=1}^{+\infty} \frac{e^{1/n}}{n^2}$

10. $\displaystyle\sum_{n=1}^{+\infty} \operatorname{sech}^2 n$

11. $\displaystyle\sum_{n=1}^{+\infty} \ln\left(\frac{n + 3}{n}\right)$

12. $\displaystyle\sum_{n=2}^{+\infty} \frac{1}{n(\ln n)^3}$

13. Prove that the series $\displaystyle\sum_{n=2}^{+\infty} \frac{1}{n(\ln n)^p}$ is convergent if and only if $p > 1$.

14. Prove that the series $\displaystyle\sum_{n=3}^{+\infty} \frac{1}{n(\ln n)[\ln(\ln n)]^p}$ is convergent if and only if $p > 1$.

15. If s_k is the kth partial sum of the harmonic series, prove that

$$\ln(k + 1) < s_k < 1 + \ln k$$

(HINT: $\dfrac{1}{m + 1} \leq \dfrac{1}{x} \leq \dfrac{1}{m}$ if $0 < m \leq x \leq m + 1$

Integrate each member of the inequality from m to $m + 1$; let m take on successively the values $1, 2, \ldots, n - 1$, and add the results.)

16. Use the result of Exercise 15 to estimate the sum $\displaystyle\sum_{m=50}^{100} \frac{1}{m} = \frac{1}{50} + \frac{1}{51} + \cdots + \frac{1}{100}$.

14.6 INFINITE SERIES OF POSITIVE AND NEGATIVE TERMS

In this section we consider infinite series having both positive and negative terms. The first type of such a series which we discuss is one whose terms are alternately positive and negative—an *alternating series.*

14.6.1 Definition   If $a_n > 0$ for all positive integers n, then the series

$$\sum_{n=1}^{+\infty} (-1)^{n+1} a_n = a_1 - a_2 + a_3 - a_4 + \cdots + (-1)^{n+1} a_n + \cdots$$

and the series

$$\sum_{n=1}^{+\infty} (-1)^n a_n = -a_1 + a_2 - a_3 + a_4 - \cdots + (-1)^n a_n + \cdots$$

are called *alternating series.*

The following theorem gives a test for the convergence of an alternating series.

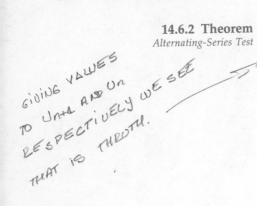

GIVING VALUES TO U_{n+1} AND U_n RESPECTIVELY WE SEE THAT IS THE 4TH.

14.6.2 Theorem
Alternating-Series Test

If the numbers $u_1, u_2, u_3, \ldots, u_n, \ldots$ are alternately positive and negative, $|u_{n+1}| < |u_n|$ for all positive integers n, and $\lim\limits_{n \to +\infty} u_n = 0$, then the alternating series $\sum\limits_{n=1}^{+\infty} u_n$ is convergent.

PROOF: We assume that the odd-numbered terms of the given series are positive and the even-numbered terms are negative. This assumption is not a loss of generality because if this is not the case, then we consider the series whose first term is u_2 because discarding a finite number of terms does not affect the convergence of the series. So $u_{2n-1} > 0$ and $u_{2n} < 0$ for every positive integer n. Consider the partial sum

$$s_{2n} = (u_1 + u_2) + (u_3 + u_4) + \cdots + (u_{2n-1} + u_{2n}) \tag{1}$$

The first term of each quantity in parentheses in (1) is positive and the second term is negative. Because by hypothesis $|u_{n+1}| < |u_n|$, we conclude that each quantity in parentheses is positive. Therefore,

$$0 < s_2 < s_4 < s_6 < \cdots < s_{2n} < \cdots \tag{2}$$

We also can write s_{2n} as

$$s_{2n} = u_1 + (u_2 + u_3) + (u_4 + u_5) + \cdots + (u_{2n-2} + u_{2n-1}) + u_{2n} \tag{3}$$

Because $|u_{n+1}| < |u_n|$, each quantity in parentheses in (3) is negative and so also is u_{2n}. Therefore,

$$s_{2n} < u_1 \qquad \text{for every positive integer } n \tag{4}$$

From (2) and (4) we have

$$0 < s_{2n} < u_1 \qquad \text{for every positive integer } n$$

So the sequence $\{s_{2n}\}$ is bounded. Furthermore, from (2) the sequence $\{s_{2n}\}$ is monotonic. Therefore, by Theorem 14.2.6 the sequence $\{s_{2n}\}$ is convergent. Let $\lim\limits_{n \to +\infty} s_{2n} = S$, and from Theorem 14.2.7 we know that $S \leq u_1$.

Because $s_{2n+1} = s_{2n} + u_{2n+1}$, we have

$$\lim_{n \to +\infty} s_{2n+1} = \lim_{n \to +\infty} s_{2n} + \lim_{n \to +\infty} u_{2n+1}$$

but, by hypothesis, $\lim\limits_{n \to +\infty} u_{2n+1} = 0$, and so $\lim\limits_{n \to +\infty} s_{2n+1} = \lim\limits_{n \to +\infty} s_{2n}$. Therefore, the sequence of partial sums of the even-numbered terms and the sequence of partial sums of the odd-numbered terms have the same limit S.

We now show that $\lim\limits_{n \to +\infty} s_n = S$. Because $\lim\limits_{n \to +\infty} s_{2n} = S$, then for any $\epsilon > 0$ there exists an integer $N_1 > 0$ such that

$$|s_{2n} - S| < \epsilon \qquad \text{whenever } 2n \geq N_1$$

And because $\lim\limits_{n \to +\infty} s_{2n+1} = S$, there exists an integer $N_2 > 0$ such that

$$|s_{2n+1} - S| < \epsilon \qquad \text{whenever } 2n + 1 \geq N_2$$

If N is the larger of the two integers N_1 and N_2, it follows that if n is any integer, either odd or even, then

$$|s_n - S| < \epsilon \qquad \text{whenever } n \geq N$$

Therefore, $\lim\limits_{n \to +\infty} s_n = S$, and so the series $\sum\limits_{n=1}^{+\infty} u_n$ is convergent.   ∎

EXAMPLE 1: Prove that the alternating series

$$\sum_{n=1}^{+\infty} \frac{(-1)^{n+1}}{n}$$

is convergent.

SOLUTION: The given series is

$$1 - \frac{1}{2} + \frac{1}{3} - \frac{1}{4} + \cdots + (-1)^{n+1}\frac{1}{n} + (-1)^{n+2}\frac{1}{n+1} + \cdots$$

Because $1/(n+1) < 1/n$ for all positive integers n, and $\lim\limits_{n \to +\infty} (1/n) = 0$, it follows from Theorem 14.6.2 that the given alternating series is convergent.

EXAMPLE 2: Determine if the series

$$\sum_{n=1}^{+\infty} (-1)^n \frac{n+2}{n(n+1)}$$

is convergent or divergent.

SOLUTION: The given series is an alternating series, with

$$u_n = (-1)^n \frac{n+2}{n(n+1)} \quad \text{and} \quad u_{n+1} = (-1)^{n+1}\frac{n+3}{(n+1)(n+2)}$$

$$\lim_{n \to +\infty} \frac{n+2}{n(n+1)} = \lim_{n \to +\infty} \frac{\frac{1}{n} + \frac{2}{n^2}}{1 + \frac{1}{n}} = 0$$

Before we can apply the alternating-series test we must also show that $|u_{n+1}| < |u_n|$ or, equivalently, $|u_{n+1}|/|u_n| < 1$.

$$\frac{|u_{n+1}|}{|u_n|} = \frac{n+3}{(n+1)(n+2)} \cdot \frac{n(n+1)}{n+2} = \frac{n(n+3)}{(n+2)^2} = \frac{n^2+3n}{n^2+4n+4} < 1$$

Then it follows from Theorem 14.6.2 that the given series is convergent.

14.6.3 Definition   If an infinite series $\sum\limits_{n=1}^{+\infty} u_n$ is convergent and its sum is S, then the remainder obtained by approximating the sum of the series by the kth partial sum s_k is denoted by R_k and

$$\left(R_k = S - s_k \right)$$

14.6.4 Theorem   Suppose $\sum\limits_{n=1}^{+\infty} u_n$ is an alternating series, $|u_{n+1}| < |u_n|$, and $\lim\limits_{n \to +\infty} u_n = 0$. Then, if R_k is the remainder obtained by approximating the sum of the series by the sum of the first k terms, $|R_k| < |u_{k+1}|$.

PROOF: Assume that the odd-numbered terms of the given series are positive and the even-numbered terms are negative. Then, from (2) in the proof of Theorem 14.6.2, we see that the sequence $\{s_{2n}\}$ is increasing. So if S is the sum of the given series, we have

$$s_{2k} < s_{2k+2} < S \qquad \text{for all } k \geq 1 \tag{5}$$

To show that the sequence $\{s_{2n-1}\}$ is decreasing, we write

$$s_{2n-1} = u_1 + (u_2 + u_3) + (u_4 + u_5) + \cdots + (u_{2n-2} + u_{2n-1}) \tag{6}$$

The first term of each quantity in parentheses in (6) is negative and the second term is positive, and because $|u_{n+1}| < |u_n|$, it follows that each quantity in parentheses is negative. Therefore, because $u_1 > 0$, we conclude that $s_1 > s_3 > s_5 > \cdots > s_{2n-1} > \cdots$; and so the sequence $\{s_{2n-1}\}$ is decreasing. Thus,

$$S < s_{2k+1} < s_{2k-1} \qquad \text{for all } k \geq 1 \tag{7}$$

From (7) we have $S - s_{2k} < s_{2k+1} - s_{2k} = u_{2k+1}$, and from (5) we have $0 < S - s_{2k}$. Therefore,

$$0 < S - s_{2k} < u_{2k+1} \qquad \text{for all } k \geq 1 \tag{8}$$

From (5) we have $-S < -s_{2k}$; hence, $s_{2k-1} - S < s_{2k-1} - s_{2k} = -u_{2k}$. Because from (7) it follows that $0 < s_{2k-1} - S$, we have

$$0 < s_{2k-1} - S < -u_{2k} \qquad \text{for all } k \geq 1 \tag{9}$$

Because from Definition 14.6.3, $R_k = S - s_k$, (8) can be written as $0 < |R_{2k}| < |u_{2k+1}|$ and (9) can be written as $0 < |R_{2k-1}| < |u_{2k}|$. Hence, we have $|R_k| < |u_{k+1}|$ for all $k \geq 1$, and the theorem is proved. ∎

EXAMPLE 3: A series for computing $\ln(1 - x)$ if x is in the open interval $(-1, 1)$ is

$$\ln(1 - x) = \sum_{n=1}^{+\infty} -\frac{x^n}{n}$$

Find an estimate of the error when the first three terms of this series are used to approximate the value of $\ln 1.1$.

SOLUTION: Using the given series with $x = -0.1$, we get

$$\ln 1.1 = 0.1 - \frac{(0.1)^2}{2} + \frac{(0.1)^3}{3} - \frac{(0.1)^4}{4} + \cdots$$

This series satisfies the conditions of Theorem 14.6.4; so if R_3 is the difference between the actual value of $\ln 1.1$ and the sum of the first three terms, then

$$|R_3| < |u_4| = 0.000025$$

Thus, we know that the sum of the first three terms will yield a value of $\ln 1.1$ accurate at least to four decimal places. Using the first three terms, we get

$$\ln 1.1 = 0.0953$$

Associated with each infinite series is the series whose terms are the absolute values of the terms of that series.

THEY TALK OF THIS SERIES BEING AN ALTERNATING SERIES AT THAT MOMENT.

14.6.5 Definition The infinite series $\sum\limits_{n=1}^{+\infty} u_n$ is said to be *absolutely convergent* if the series

$\sum\limits_{n=1}^{+\infty} |u_n|$ is convergent. *THE ABSOLUTE SIGN CHANGES ALL THE NEGATIVE VALUES TO POSITIVES*

EXAMPLE 4: Determine if the series

$$\sum_{n=1}^{+\infty} (-1)^{n+1} \frac{2}{3^n}$$

is absolutely convergent.

SOLUTION: The given series is

$$\sum_{n=1}^{+\infty} (-1)^{n+1} \frac{2}{3^n} = \frac{2}{3} - \frac{2}{3^2} + \frac{2}{3^3} - \frac{2}{3^4} + \cdots + (-1)^{n+1} \frac{2}{3^n} + \cdots$$

This series will be absolutely convergent if the series

$$\sum_{n=1}^{+\infty} \frac{2}{3^n} = \frac{2}{3} + \frac{2}{3^2} + \frac{2}{3^3} + \frac{2}{3^4} + \cdots + \frac{2}{3^n} + \cdots$$

is convergent. Because this is the geometric series with $r = \frac{1}{3} < 1$, it is convergent. Therefore, the given series is absolutely convergent.

An example of a convergent series which is not absolutely convergent is the series $\sum\limits_{n=1}^{+\infty} (-1)^{n+1}/n$. In Example 1 we proved that this series is convergent. The series is not absolutely convergent because the series of absolute values is the harmonic series which is divergent. The series $\sum\limits_{m=1}^{+\infty} (-1)^{n+1}/n$ is an example of a *conditionally convergent* series.

14.6.6 Definition A series which is convergent, but not absolutely convergent, is said to be *conditionally convergent.*

It is possible, then, for a series to be convergent but not absolutely convergent. If a series is absolutely convergent it must be convergent, however, and this is given by the next theorem.

14.6.7 Theorem If the infinite series $\sum\limits_{n=1}^{+\infty} u_n$ is absolutely convergent, it is convergent and

$$\left| \sum_{n=1}^{+\infty} u_n \right| \leq \sum_{n=1}^{+\infty} |u_n|$$

PROOF: Consider the three infinite series $\sum\limits_{n=1}^{+\infty} u_n$, $\sum\limits_{n=1}^{+\infty} |u_n|$, and $\sum\limits_{n=1}^{+\infty} (u_n + |u_n|)$, and let their sequences of partial sums be $\{s_n\}$, $\{t_n\}$, and $\{r_n\}$, respectively. For every positive integer n, $u_n + |u_n|$ is either 0 or $2|u_n|$; so we have the inequality

$$0 \leq u_n + |u_n| \leq 2|u_n| \tag{10}$$

Because $\sum\limits_{n=1}^{+\infty} |u_n|$ is convergent, it has a sum, which we denote by T.

$\{t_n\}$ is an increasing sequence of positive numbers, and so $t_n \leq T$ for all positive integers n. From (10), it follows that

$$0 \leq r_n \leq 2t_n \leq 2T$$

Therefore, the sequence $\{r_n\}$ has an upper bound of $2T$. Thus, by Theorem 14.4.1 the series $\sum\limits_{n=1}^{+\infty} (u_n + |u_n|)$ is convergent, and we call its sum R. Because from (10), $\{r_n\}$ is an increasing sequence, it may be concluded from Theorem 14.2.7 that $R \leq 2T$.

Each of the series $\sum\limits_{n=1}^{+\infty} (u_n + |u_n|)$ and $\sum\limits_{n=1}^{+\infty} |u_n|$ is convergent; hence, from Theorem 14.3.9 the series

$$\sum_{n=1}^{+\infty} [(u_n + |u_n|) - |u_n|] = \sum_{n=1}^{+\infty} u_n$$

is also convergent.

Let the sum of the series $\sum\limits_{n=1}^{+\infty} u_n$ be S. Then, also from Theorem 14.3.9, $S = R - T$. And because $R \leq 2T$, $S \leq 2T - T = T$.

Because $\sum\limits_{n=1}^{+\infty} u_n$ is convergent and has the sum S, it follows from Theorem 14.3.8 that $\sum\limits_{n=1}^{+\infty} (-u_n)$ is convergent and has the sum $-S$. Because $\sum\limits_{n=1}^{+\infty} |-u_n| = \sum\limits_{n=1}^{+\infty} |u_n| = T$, we can replace $\sum\limits_{n=1}^{+\infty} u_n$ by $\sum\limits_{n=1}^{+\infty} (-u_n)$ in the above discussion and show that $-S \leq T$. Because $S \leq T$ and $-S \leq T$, we have $|S| \leq T$; therefore, $\left| \sum\limits_{n=1}^{+\infty} u_n \right| \leq \sum\limits_{n=1}^{+\infty} |u_n|$, and the theorem is proved.   ∎

EXAMPLE 5:   **Determine if the series**

$$\sum_{n=1}^{+\infty} \frac{\cos \frac{1}{3}n\pi}{n^2}$$

is convergent or divergent.

SOLUTION: Denote the given series by $\sum\limits_{n=1}^{+\infty} u_n$. Therefore,

$$\sum_{n=1}^{+\infty} u_n = \frac{\frac{1}{2}}{1^2} - \frac{\frac{1}{2}}{2^2} - \frac{1}{3^2} - \frac{\frac{1}{2}}{4^2} + \frac{\frac{1}{2}}{5^2} + \frac{1}{6^2} + \frac{\frac{1}{2}}{7^2} - \cdots + \frac{\cos\frac{1}{3}n\pi}{n^2} + \cdots$$

$$= \tfrac{1}{2} - \tfrac{1}{8} - \tfrac{1}{9} - \tfrac{1}{32} + \tfrac{1}{50} + \tfrac{1}{36} + \tfrac{1}{98} - \cdots$$

We have a series of positive and negative terms. We can prove this series is convergent if we can show that it is absolutely convergent.

$$\sum_{n=1}^{+\infty} |u_n| = \sum_{n=1}^{+\infty} \frac{|\cos \frac{1}{3}n\pi|}{n^2}$$

Because

$$|\cos \tfrac{1}{3}n\pi| \leq 1 \qquad \text{for all } n$$

$$\frac{|\cos \tfrac{1}{3}n\pi|}{n^2} \leq \frac{1}{n^2} \qquad \text{for all positive integers } n$$

The series $\sum\limits_{n=1}^{+\infty} 1/n^2$ is the p series, with $p = 2$, and is therefore convergent.

So by the comparison test $\sum\limits_{n=1}^{+\infty} |u_n|$ is convergent. The given series is therefore absolutely convergent; hence, by Theorem 14.6.7 it is convergent.

You will note that the terms of the series $\sum\limits_{n=1}^{+\infty} |u_n|$ neither increase monotonically nor decrease monotonically. For example, $|u_4| = \frac{1}{32}$, $|u_5| = \frac{1}{50}$, $|u_6| = \frac{1}{36}$; and so $|u_5| < |u_4|$, but $|u_6| > |u_5|$.

The *ratio test*, given in the next theorem, is used frequently to determine whether a given series is absolutely convergent.

14.6.8 Theorem
The Ratio Test

Let $\sum\limits_{n=1}^{+\infty} u_n$ be a given infinite series for which every u_n is nonzero. Then

(i) if $\lim\limits_{n \to +\infty} |u_{n+1}/u_n| = L < 1$, the given series is absolutely convergent;

(ii) if $\lim\limits_{n \to +\infty} |u_{n+1}/u_n| = L > 1$ or if $\lim\limits_{n \to +\infty} |u_{n+1}/u_n| = +\infty$, the series is divergent;

(iii) if $\lim\limits_{n \to +\infty} |u_{n+1}/u_n| = 1$, no conclusion regarding convergence may be made.

PROOF OF (i): We are given that $L < 1$, and let R be a number such that $L < R < 1$. Let $R - L = \epsilon < 1$. Because $\lim\limits_{n \to +\infty} |u_{n+1}/u_n| = L$, there exists an integer $N > 0$ such that

$$\left| \left| \frac{u_{n+1}}{u_n} \right| - L \right| < \epsilon \qquad \text{whenever } n \geq N$$

or, equivalently,

$$0 < \left| \frac{u_{n+1}}{u_n} \right| < L + \epsilon = R \qquad \text{whenever } n \geq N \tag{11}$$

Letting n take on the successive values $N, N+1, N+2, \ldots$, and so forth, we obtain from (11)

$$|u_{N+1}| < R|u_N|$$

$$|u_{N+2}| < R|u_{N+1}| < R^2|u_N|$$

$$|u_{N+3}| < R|u_{N+2}| < R^3|u_N|$$

$$\cdots$$

In general, we have

$$|u_{N+k}| < R^k|u_N| \qquad \text{for every positive integer } k \tag{12}$$

The series

$$\sum_{k=1}^{+\infty} |u_N| R^k = |u_N| R + |u_N| R^2 + \cdots + |u_N| R^n + \cdots$$

is convergent because it is a geometric series whose ratio is less than 1. So from (12) and the comparison test, it follows that the series $\sum_{k=1}^{+\infty} |u_{N+k}|$ is convergent. The series $\sum_{k=1}^{+\infty} |u_{N+k}|$ differs from the series $\sum_{n=1}^{+\infty} |u_n|$ in only the first N terms. Therefore, $\sum_{n=1}^{+\infty} |u_n|$ is convergent, and so the given series is absolutely convergent.

PROOF OF (ii):   If $\lim_{n \to +\infty} |u_{n+1}/u_n| = L > 1$ or $\lim_{n \to +\infty} |u_{n+1}/u_n| = +\infty$, then in either case there is an integer $N > 0$ such that $|u_{n+1}/u_n| > 1$ for all $n \geq N$. Letting n take on the successive values $N, N+1, N+2, \ldots$, and so on, we obtain

$$|u_{N+1}| > |u_N|$$

$$|u_{N+2}| > |u_{N+1}| > |u_N|$$

$$|u_{N+3}| > |u_{N+2}| > |u_N|$$

$$\cdots$$

So we may conclude that $|u_n| > |u_N|$ for all $n > N$. Hence, $\lim_{n \to +\infty} u_n \neq 0$, and so the given series is divergent.

PROOF OF (iii):   If we apply the ratio test to the p series, we have

$$\lim_{n \to +\infty} \left| \frac{u_{n+1}}{u_n} \right| = \lim_{n \to +\infty} \left| \frac{\dfrac{1}{(n+1)^p}}{\dfrac{1}{n^p}} \right| = \lim_{n \to +\infty} \left| \left(\frac{n}{n+1} \right)^p \right| = 1$$

Because the p series diverges if $p \leq 1$ and converges if $p > 1$, we have shown that it is possible to have both convergent and divergent series for which we have $\lim_{n \to +\infty} |u_{n+1}/u_n| = 1$. This proves part (iii). ∎

EXAMPLE 6:   Determine if the series

$$\sum_{n=1}^{+\infty} \frac{(-1)^{n+1} n}{2^n}$$

is convergent or divergent.

SOLUTION: $u_n = (-1)^{n+1} n / 2^n$ and $u_{n+1} = (-1)^{n+2} (n+1) / 2^{n+1}$.

Therefore,

$$\left| \frac{u_{n+1}}{u_n} \right| = \frac{n+1}{2^{n+1}} \cdot \frac{2^n}{n} = \frac{n+1}{2n}$$

So

$$\lim_{n \to +\infty} \left| \frac{u_{n+1}}{u_n} \right| = \lim_{n \to +\infty} \frac{1 + \dfrac{1}{n}}{2} = \frac{1}{2} < 1$$

Therefore, by the ratio test, the given series is absolutely convergent and hence, by Theorem 14.6.7, it is convergent.

EXAMPLE 7: In Example 2, the series

$$\sum_{n=1}^{+\infty} (-1)^n \frac{n+2}{n(n+1)}$$

was shown to be convergent. Is this series absolutely convergent or conditionally convergent?

SOLUTION: To test for absolute convergence we apply the ratio test. In the solution of Example 2 we showed that $|u_{n+1}|/|u_n| = (n^2 + 3n)/(n^2 + 4n + 4)$. Hence,

$$\lim_{n \to +\infty} \left| \frac{u_{n+1}}{u_n} \right| = \lim_{n \to +\infty} \frac{1 + \dfrac{3}{n}}{1 + \dfrac{4}{n} + \dfrac{4}{n^2}} = 1$$

So the ratio test fails. Because

$$|u_n| = \frac{n+2}{n(n+1)} = \frac{n+2}{n+1} \cdot \frac{1}{n} > \frac{1}{n}$$

we can apply the comparison test. And because the series $\sum_{n=1}^{+\infty} 1/n$ is the harmonic series, which diverges, we conclude that the series $\sum_{n=1}^{+\infty} |u_n|$ is divergent and hence $\sum_{n=1}^{+\infty} u_n$ is not absolutely convergent. Therefore, the series is conditionally convergent.

It should be noted that the ratio test does not include all possibilities for $\lim_{n \to +\infty} |u_{n+1}/u_n|$ as it is possible that the limit does not exist and is not $+\infty$. The discussion of such cases is beyond the scope of this book.

To conclude the discussion of infinite series of constant terms, we suggest a possible procedure to follow for determining the convergence or divergence of a given series. First of all, if $\lim_{n \to +\infty} u_n \neq 0$, we may conclude that the series is divergent. If $\lim_{n \to +\infty} u_n = 0$ and the series is an alternating series, then try the alternating-series test. If this test is not applicable, try the ratio test. If in applying the ratio test, $L = 1$, then another test must be used. The integral test may work when the ratio test does not; this was shown for the p series. Also, the comparison test can be tried.

Exercises 14.6

In Exercises 1 through 8, determine if the given alternating series is convergent or divergent.

1. $\sum_{n=2}^{+\infty} (-1)^n \frac{1}{\ln n}$

2. $\sum_{n=1}^{+\infty} (-1)^{n+1} \sin \frac{\pi}{n}$

3. $\sum_{n=1}^{+\infty} (-1)^{n+1} \frac{n^2}{n^3 + 2}$

4. $\sum_{n=1}^{+\infty} (-1)^{n+1} \frac{\ln n}{n}$

5. $\sum_{n=1}^{+\infty} (-1)^{n+1} \frac{\ln n}{n^2}$

6. $\sum_{n=1}^{+\infty} (-1)^n \frac{e^n}{n}$

7. $\sum_{n=1}^{+\infty} (-1)^n \frac{n}{2^n}$

8. $\sum_{n=1}^{+\infty} (-1)^n \frac{\sqrt{n}}{3n - 1}$

In Exercises 9 through 12, find the error if the sum of the first four terms is used as an approximation to the sum of the given infinite series.

9. $\displaystyle\sum_{n=1}^{+\infty} (-1)^{n+1} \frac{1}{n}$

10. $\displaystyle\sum_{n=1}^{+\infty} (-1)^n \frac{1}{n!}$

11. $\displaystyle\sum_{n=1}^{+\infty} (-1)^{n+1} \frac{1}{(2n-1)^2}$

12. $\displaystyle\sum_{n=1}^{+\infty} (-1)^{n+1} \frac{1}{n^n}$

In Exercises 13 through 16, find the sum of the given infinite series, accurate to three decimal places.

13. $\displaystyle\sum_{n=1}^{+\infty} (-1)^{n+1} \frac{1}{(2n)^3}$

14. $\displaystyle\sum_{n=1}^{+\infty} (-1)^{n+1} \frac{1}{(2n)!}$

15. $\displaystyle\sum_{n=1}^{+\infty} (-1)^{n+1} \frac{1}{n2^n}$

16. $\displaystyle\sum_{n=1}^{+\infty} (-1)^n \frac{1}{(2n+1)^3}$

In Exercises 17 through 28, determine if the given series is absolutely convergent, conditionally convergent, or divergent. Prove your answer.

17. $\displaystyle\sum_{n=1}^{+\infty} (-1)^{n+1} \frac{2^n}{n!}$

18. $\displaystyle\sum_{n=1}^{+\infty} (-1)^{n+1} \frac{1}{(2n-1)!}$

19. $\displaystyle\sum_{n=1}^{+\infty} \frac{n^2}{n!}$

20. $\displaystyle\sum_{n=1}^{+\infty} n \left(\frac{2}{3}\right)^n$

21. $\displaystyle\sum_{n=1}^{+\infty} (-1)^n \frac{n!}{2^{n+1}}$

22. $\displaystyle\sum_{n=1}^{+\infty} (-1)^{n+1} \frac{1}{n(n+2)}$

23. $\displaystyle\sum_{n=1}^{+\infty} (-1)^{n+1} \frac{3^n}{n!}$

24. $\displaystyle\sum_{n=1}^{+\infty} (-1)^n \frac{n^2+1}{n^3}$

25. $\displaystyle\sum_{n=2}^{+\infty} (-1)^{n+1} \frac{1}{n(\ln n)^2}$

26. $\displaystyle\sum_{n=1}^{+\infty} (-1)^n \frac{\cos n}{n^2}$

27. $\displaystyle\sum_{n=1}^{+\infty} \frac{n^n}{n!}$

28. $\displaystyle\sum_{n=1}^{+\infty} \frac{1 \cdot 3 \cdot 5 \cdot \ldots \cdot (2n-1)}{1 \cdot 4 \cdot 7 \cdot \ldots \cdot (3n-2)}$

29. Prove by mathematical induction that $1/n! \le 1/2^{n-1}$.

30. Prove that if $\displaystyle\sum_{n=1}^{+\infty} u_n$ is absolutely convergent and $u_n \ne 0$ for all n, then $\displaystyle\sum_{n=1}^{+\infty} 1/|u_n|$ is divergent.

31. Prove that if $\displaystyle\sum_{n=1}^{+\infty} u_n$ is absolutely convergent, then $\displaystyle\sum_{n=1}^{+\infty} u_n{}^2$ is convergent.

32. Show by means of an example that the converse of Exercise 31 is not true.

14.7 POWER SERIES
14.7.1 Definition

A *power series* in $(x - a)$ is a series of the form

$$c_0 + c_1(x-a) + c_2(x-a)^2 + \cdots + c_n(x-a)^n + \cdots \qquad (1)$$

We use the notation $\displaystyle\sum_{n=0}^{+\infty} c_n(x-a)^n$ to represent series (1). (Note that we take $(x-a)^0 = 1$ even when $x = a$, for convenience in writing the general term.) If x is a particular number, the power series (1) becomes an infinite series of constant terms, as was discussed in previous sections. A special case of (1) is obtained when $a = 0$ and the series becomes a power series in x, which is

$$\sum_{n=0}^{+\infty} c_n x^n = c_0 + c_1 x + c_2 x^2 + \cdots + c_n x^n + \cdots \qquad (2)$$

In addition to power series in $(x - a)$ and x, there are power series of the form

$$\sum_{n=0}^{+\infty} c_n[\phi(x)]^n = c_0 + c_1\phi(x) + c_2[\phi(x)]^2 + \cdots + c_n[\phi(x)]^n + \cdots$$

where ϕ is a function of x. Such a series is called a power series in $\phi(x)$. In this book, we are concerned exclusively with power series of the forms (1) and (2), and when we use the term "power series," we mean either of these forms. In discussing the theory of power series, we confine ourselves to series (2). The more general power series (1) can be obtained from (2) by the translation $x = \bar{x} - a$; therefore, our results can be applied to series (1) as well.

In dealing with an infinite series of constant terms, we were concerned with the question of convergence or divergence of the series. In considering a power series, we ask, For what values of x, if any, does the power series converge? For each value of x for which the power series converges, the series represents the number which is the sum of the series. Therefore, we can think of a power series as defining a function. The function f, with function values

$$f(x) = \sum_{n=0}^{+\infty} c_n x^n \tag{3}$$

has as its domain all values of x for which the power series in (3) converges. It is apparent that every power series (2) is convergent for $x = 0$. There are some series (see Example 3) which are convergent for no other value of x, and there are also series which converge for every value of x (see Example 2).

The following three examples illustrate how the ratio test can be used to determine the values of x for which a power series is convergent. Note that when $n!$ is used in representing the nth term of a power series (as in Example 2), we take $0! = 1$ so that the expression for the nth term will hold when $n = 0$.

EXAMPLE 1: Find the values of x for which the power series

$$\sum_{n=1}^{+\infty} (-1)^{n+1} \frac{2^n x^n}{n3^n}$$

is convergent.

SOLUTION: For the given series,

$$u_n = (-1)^{n+1} \frac{2^n x^n}{n3^n} \quad \text{and} \quad u_{n+1} = (-1)^{n+2} \frac{2^{n+1} x^{n+1}}{(n+1)3^{n+1}}$$

So

$$\lim_{n \to +\infty} \left| \frac{u_{n+1}}{u_n} \right| = \lim_{n \to +\infty} \left| \frac{2^{n+1}x^{n+1}}{(n+1)3^{n+1}} \cdot \frac{n3^n}{2^n x^n} \right| = \lim_{n \to +\infty} \frac{2}{3}|x| \frac{n}{n+1} = \frac{2}{3}|x|$$

Therefore, the power series is absolutely convergent when $\frac{2}{3}|x| < 1$ or, equivalently, when $|x| < \frac{3}{2}$. The series is divergent when $\frac{2}{3}|x| > 1$ or, equivalently, when $|x| > \frac{3}{2}$. When $\frac{2}{3}|x| = 1$ (i.e., when $x = \pm\frac{3}{2}$), the ratio test fails. When $x = \frac{3}{2}$, the given power series becomes

$$\frac{1}{1} - \frac{1}{2} + \frac{1}{3} - \frac{1}{4} + \cdots + (-1)^{n+1} \frac{1}{n} + \cdots$$

which is convergent, as was shown in Example 1 of Sec. 14.6. When $x = -\frac{3}{2}$, we have

$$-\frac{1}{1} - \frac{1}{2} - \frac{1}{3} - \frac{1}{4} \cdots - \frac{1}{n} - \cdots$$

which by Theorem 14.3.8 is divergent. We conclude, then, that the given power series is convergent when $-\frac{3}{2} < x \leq \frac{3}{2}$. The series is absolutely convergent when $-\frac{3}{2} < x < \frac{3}{2}$ and is conditionally convergent when $x = \frac{3}{2}$. If $x \leq -\frac{3}{2}$ or $x > \frac{3}{2}$, the series is divergent.

EXAMPLE 2:   Find the values of x for which the power series

$$\sum_{n=0}^{+\infty} \frac{x^n}{n!}$$

is convergent.

SOLUTION: For the given series, $u_n = x^n/n!$ and $u_{n+1} = x^{n+1}/(n+1)!$. So by applying the ratio test, we have

$$\lim_{n \to +\infty} \left| \frac{u_{n+1}}{u_n} \right| = \lim_{n \to +\infty} \left| \frac{x^{n+1}}{(n+1)!} \cdot \frac{n!}{x^n} \right| = |x| \lim_{n \to +\infty} \frac{1}{n+1} = 0 < 1$$

We conclude that the given power series is absolutely convergent for all values of x.

EXAMPLE 3:   Find the values of x for which the power series

$$\sum_{n=0}^{+\infty} n! x^n$$

is convergent.

SOLUTION: For the given series $u_n = n!x^n$ and $u_{n+1} = (n+1)!x^{n+1}$. Applying the ratio test, we have

$$\lim_{n \to +\infty} \left| \frac{u_{n+1}}{u_n} \right| = \lim_{n \to +\infty} \left| \frac{(n+1)!x^{n+1}}{n!x^n} \right|$$

$$= \lim_{n \to +\infty} |(n+1)x|$$

$$= |x| \lim_{n \to +\infty} (n+1)$$

When $x = 0$, $|x| \lim_{n \to +\infty} (n+1) = 0$; when $x \neq 0$, $|x| \lim_{n \to +\infty} (n+1) = +\infty$. It follows that the series is divergent for all values of x except 0.

14.7.2 Theorem   If the power series $\sum_{n=0}^{+\infty} c_n x^n$ is convergent for $x = x_1$ ($x_1 \neq 0$), then it is absolutely convergent for all values of x for which $|x| < |x_1|$.

PROOF: If $\sum_{n=0}^{+\infty} c_n x_1{}^n$ is convergent, then $\lim_{n \to +\infty} c_n x_1{}^n = 0$. Therefore, if we take $\epsilon = 1$ in Definition 2.7.1, there exists an integer $N > 0$ such that

$$|c_n x_1{}^n| < 1 \qquad \text{whenever } n \geq N$$

Now if x is any number such that $|x| < |x_1|$, we have

$$|c_n x^n| = \left| c_n x_1{}^n \frac{x^n}{x_1{}^n} \right| = |c_n x_1{}^n| \left| \frac{x}{x_1} \right|^n < \left| \frac{x}{x_1} \right|^n \qquad \text{whenever } n > N \qquad (4)$$

The series

$$\sum_{n=N}^{+\infty} \left| \frac{x}{x_1} \right|^n \tag{5}$$

is convergent because it is a geometric series with $r = |x/x_1| < 1$ (because $|x| < |x_1|$). Comparing the series $\sum_{n=N}^{+\infty} |c_n x^n|$, where $|x| < |x_1|$, with series (5), we see from (4) and the comparison test that $\sum_{n=N}^{+\infty} |c_n x^n|$ is convergent for $|x| < |x_1|$. So the given power series is absolutely convergent for all values of x for which $|x| < |x_1|$. ■

An illustration of the above theorem is given in Example 1. The power series is convergent for $x = \frac{3}{2}$ and is absolutely convergent for all values of x for which $|x| < \frac{3}{2}$.

A corollary of Theorem 14.7.2 is the following one.

14.7.3 Theorem   If the power series $\sum_{n=0}^{+\infty} c_n x^n$ is divergent for $x = x_2$, it is divergent for all values of x for which $|x| > |x_2|$.

PROOF: Suppose that the given power series is convergent for some number x for which $|x| > |x_2|$. Then by Theorem 14.7.2 the series must converge when $x = x_2$. However, this contradicts the hypothesis. Therefore, the given power series is divergent for all values of x for which $|x| > |x_2|$. ■

To illustrate Theorem 14.7.3 consider again the power series of Example 1. It is divergent for $x = -\frac{3}{2}$ and is also divergent for all values of x for which $|x| > |-\frac{3}{2}|$.

From Theorems 14.7.2 and 14.7.3, we can prove the following important theorem.

14.7.4 Theorem   Let $\sum_{n=0}^{+\infty} c_n x^n$ be a given power series. Then exactly one of the following conditions holds:

(i) the series converges only when $x = 0$;
(ii) the series is absolutely convergent for all values of x;
(iii) there exists a number $R > 0$ such that the series is absolutely convergent for all values of x for which $|x| < R$ and is divergent for all values of x for which $|x| > R$.

PROOF: If we replace x by zero in the given power series, we have $c_0 + 0$

$+0+\cdots$, which is obviously convergent. Therefore, every power series of the form $\sum\limits_{n=0}^{+\infty} c_n x^n$ is convergent when $x=0$. If this is the only value of x for which the series converges, then condition (i) holds.

Suppose that the given series is convergent for $x = x_1$ where $x_1 \neq 0$. Then it follows from Theorem 14.7.2 that the series is absolutely convergent for all values of x for which $|x| < |x_1|$. Now if in addition there is no value of x for which the given series is divergent, we can conclude that the series is absolutely convergent for all values of x. This is condition (ii).

If the given series is convergent for $x = x_1$, where $x_1 \neq 0$, and is divergent for $x = x_2$, where $|x_2| > |x_1|$, it follows from Theorem 14.7.3 that the series is divergent for all values of x for which $|x| > |x_2|$. Hence, $|x_2|$ is an upper bound of the set of values of $|x|$ for which the series is absolutely convergent. Therefore, by the axiom of completeness (14.2.5), this set of numbers has a least upper bound, which is the number R of condition (iii). This proves that exactly one of the three conditions holds. ∎

Theorem 14.7.4(iii) can be illustrated on the number line. See Fig. 14.7.1.

If instead of the power series $\sum\limits_{n=0}^{+\infty} c_n x^n$ we have the series $\sum\limits_{n=0}^{+\infty} c_n (x-a)^n$, in conditions (i) and (iii) of Theorem 14.7.4, x is replaced by $x - a$. The conditions become

(i) the series converges only when $x = a$;
(iii) there exists a number $R > 0$ such that the series is absolutely convergent for all values of x for which $|x - a| < R$ and is divergent for all values of x for which $|x - a| > R$. (See Fig. 14.7.2 for an illustration of this on the number line.)

series convergent for $|x| < R$

series divergent for $|x| > R$

Figure 14.7.1

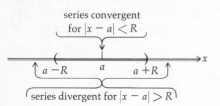

series convergent for $|x - a| < R$

series divergent for $|x - a| > R$

Figure 14.7.2

The set of all values of x for which a given power series is convergent is called the *interval of convergence* of the power series. The number R of condition (iii) of Theorem 14.7.4 is called the *radius of convergence* of the power series. If condition (i) holds, we take $R = 0$; if condition (ii) holds, we write $R = +\infty$.

For the power series of Example 1, $R = \frac{3}{2}$ and the interval of convergence is $(-\frac{3}{2}, \frac{3}{2}]$. In Example 2, $R = +\infty$, and we write the interval of convergence as $(-\infty, +\infty)$.

If R is the radius of convergence of the power series $\sum\limits_{n=0}^{+\infty} c_n x^n$, the interval of convergence is one of the following intervals: $(-R, R)$, $[-R, R]$, $(-R, R]$, or $[-R, R)$. For the more general power series $\sum\limits_{n=0}^{+\infty} c_n (x-a)^n$, the interval of convergence is one of the following: $(a - R, a + R)$, $[a - R, a + R]$, $(a - R, a + R]$, or $[a - R, a + R)$.

A given power series defines a function having the interval of convergence as its domain. The most useful method at our disposal for determining the interval of convergence of a power series is the ratio test. However, the ratio test will not reveal anything about the convergence or divergence of the power series at the endpoints of the interval of convergence. At an endpoint, a power series may be either absolutely convergent, conditionally convergent, or divergent. If a power series converges absolutely at one endpoint, it follows from the definition of absolute convergence that the series is absolutely convergent at each endpoint (see Exercise 21). If a power series converges at one endpoint and diverges at the other, the series is conditionally convergent at the endpoint at which it converges (see Exercise 22). There are cases for which the convergence or divergence of a power series at the endpoints cannot be determined by the methods of elementary calculus.

EXAMPLE 4: Determine the interval of convergence of the power series

$$\sum_{n=1}^{+\infty} n(x-2)^n$$

SOLUTION: The given series is

$$(x-2) + 2(x-2)^2 + \cdots + n(x-2)^n + (n+1)(x-2)^{n+1} + \cdots$$

Applying the ratio test, we have

$$\lim_{n \to +\infty} \left| \frac{u_{n+1}}{u_n} \right| = \lim_{n \to +\infty} \left| \frac{(n+1)(x-2)^{n+1}}{n(x-2)^n} \right| = |x-2| \lim_{n \to +\infty} \frac{n+1}{n} = |x-2|$$

The given series then will be absolutely convergent if $|x-2| < 1$ or, equivalently, $-1 < x-2 < 1$ or, equivalently, $1 < x < 3$.

When $x = 1$, the series is $\sum_{n=1}^{+\infty} (-1)^n n$, which is divergent because $\lim_{n \to +\infty} u_n \neq 0$. When $x = 3$, the series is $\sum_{n=1}^{+\infty} n$, which is also divergent because $\lim_{n \to +\infty} u_n \neq 0$. Therefore, the interval of convergence is $(1, 3)$. So the given power series defines a function having the interval $(1, 3)$ as its domain.

EXAMPLE 5: Determine the interval of convergence of the power series

$$\sum_{n=1}^{+\infty} \frac{x^n}{2+n^2}$$

SOLUTION: The given series is

$$\frac{x}{2+1^2} + \frac{x^2}{2+2^2} + \frac{x^3}{2+3^2} + \cdots + \frac{x^n}{2+n^2} + \frac{x^{n+1}}{2+(n+1)^2} + \cdots$$

Applying the ratio test, we have

$$\lim_{n \to +\infty} \left| \frac{u_{n+1}}{u_n} \right| = \lim_{n \to +\infty} \left| \frac{x^{n+1}}{2+(n+1)^2} \cdot \frac{2+n^2}{x^n} \right| = |x| \lim_{n \to +\infty} \frac{2+n^2}{2+n^2+2n+1} = |x|$$

So the given series will be absolutely convergent if $|x| < 1$ or, equivalently, $-1 < x < 1$. When $x = 1$, we have the series

$$\frac{1}{2+1^2} + \frac{1}{2+2^2} + \frac{1}{2+3^2} + \cdots + \frac{1}{2+n^2} + \cdots$$

Because $1/(2 + n^2) < 1/n^2$ for all positive integers n, and because $\sum\limits_{n=1}^{+\infty} 1/n^2$ is a convergent p series, it follows from the comparison test that the given power series is convergent when $x = 1$. When $x = -1$, we have the series $\sum\limits_{n=1}^{+\infty} (-1)^n/(2 + n^2)$, which is convergent because we have just seen that it is absolutely convergent. Hence, the interval of convergence of the given power series is $[-1, 1]$.

Exercises 14.7

In Exercises 1 through 20, find the interval of convergence of the given power series.

1. $\sum\limits_{n=1}^{+\infty} (-1)^{n+1} \dfrac{x^{2n-1}}{(2n-1)!}$

2. $\sum\limits_{n=0}^{+\infty} \dfrac{x^n}{n+1}$

3. $\sum\limits_{n=1}^{+\infty} \dfrac{2^n x^n}{n^2}$

4. $\sum\limits_{n=1}^{+\infty} (-1)^n \dfrac{x^{2n}}{(2n)!}$

5. $\sum\limits_{n=1}^{+\infty} n! x^n$

6. $\sum\limits_{n=0}^{+\infty} \dfrac{x^n}{(n+1)5^n}$

7. $\sum\limits_{n=1}^{+\infty} (-1)^n \dfrac{x^n}{(2n-1)3^{2n-1}}$

8. $\sum\limits_{n=1}^{+\infty} (-1)^{n+1} \dfrac{(n+1)x}{n!}$

9. $\sum\limits_{n=1}^{+\infty} (-1)^{n+1} \dfrac{(x-1)^n}{n}$

10. $\sum\limits_{n=1}^{+\infty} \dfrac{(x+2)^n}{(n+1)2^n}$

11. $\sum\limits_{n=0}^{+\infty} (\sinh 2n)x^n$

12. $\sum\limits_{n=1}^{+\infty} \dfrac{x^n}{\ln(n+1)}$

13. $\sum\limits_{n=2}^{+\infty} (-1)^{n+1} \dfrac{x^n}{n(\ln n)^2}$

14. $\sum\limits_{n=1}^{+\infty} \dfrac{(x+5)^{n-1}}{n^2}$

15. $\sum\limits_{n=1}^{+\infty} \dfrac{n! x^n}{n^n}$

16. $\sum\limits_{n=1}^{+\infty} \dfrac{n^n}{n!} x^n$

17. $\sum\limits_{n=1}^{+\infty} \dfrac{\ln n (x-5)^n}{n+1}$

18. $\sum\limits_{n=1}^{+\infty} n^n(x-3)^n$

19. $\sum\limits_{n=1}^{+\infty} (-1)^n \dfrac{1 \cdot 3 \cdot 5 \cdot \ldots \cdot (2n-1)}{2 \cdot 4 \cdot 6 \cdot \ldots \cdot 2n} x^{2n+1}$

20. $\sum\limits_{n=1}^{+\infty} \dfrac{(-1)^{n+1} 1 \cdot 3 \cdot 5 \cdot \ldots \cdot (2n-1)}{2 \cdot 4 \cdot 6 \cdot \ldots \cdot 2n} x^n$

21. Prove that if a power series converges absolutely at one endpoint of its interval of convergence, then the power series is absolutely convergent at each endpoint.

22. Prove that if a power series converges at one endpoint of its interval of convergence and diverges at the other endpoint, then the power series is conditionally convergent at the endpoint at which it converges.

23. Prove that if the radius of convergence of the power series $\sum\limits_{n=1}^{+\infty} u_n x^n$ is r, then the radius of convergence of the series $\sum\limits_{n=1}^{+\infty} u_n x^{2n}$ is $\sqrt{r}$.

24. Prove that if $\lim\limits_{n \to +\infty} \sqrt[n]{|u_n|} = L$ ($L \neq 0$), then the radius of convergence of the power series $\sum\limits_{n=1}^{+\infty} u_n x^n$ is $1/L$.

14.8 DIFFERENTIATION OF POWER SERIES

A power series $\sum_{n=0}^{+\infty} c_n x^n$ defines a function whose domain is the interval of convergence of the series. For example, consider the geometric series with $a = 1$ and $r = x$, which is $\sum_{n=0}^{+\infty} x^n$. By Theorem 14.3.6 this series converges to the sum $1/(1-x)$ if $|x| < 1$. Therefore, the power series $\sum_{n=0}^{+\infty} x^n$ defines the function f for which $f(x) = 1/(1-x)$ and $|x| < 1$. Hence, we can write

$$1 + x + x^2 + x^3 + \cdots + x^n + \cdots = \frac{1}{1-x} \qquad \text{if } |x| < 1 \qquad (1)$$

The series in (1) can be used to form other power series whose sums can be determined. For example, if in (1) we replace x by $-x$, we have

$$1 - x + x^2 - x^3 + \cdots + (-1)^n x^n + \cdots = \frac{1}{1+x} \qquad \text{if } |x| < 1 \qquad (2)$$

Letting $x = x^2$ in (1), we get

$$1 + x^2 + x^4 + x^6 + \cdots + x^{2n} + \cdots = \frac{1}{1-x^2} \qquad \text{if } |x| < 1 \qquad (3)$$

If x is replaced by $-x^2$ in (1) we obtain

$$1 - x^2 + x^4 - x^6 + \cdots + (-1)^n x^{2n} + \cdots = \frac{1}{1+x^2} \qquad \text{if } |x| < 1 \quad (4)$$

In this section and the next we learn that other interesting series can be obtained from those like the above by differentiation and integration. We prove that if $R \neq 0$ is the radius of convergence of a power series which defines a function f, then f is differentiable on the open interval $(-R, R)$ and the derivative of f can be obtained by differentiating the power series term by term. Furthermore, we show that f is integrable on every closed subinterval of $(-R, R)$, and the integral of f is evaluated by integrating the power series term by term. We first need some preliminary theorems.

14.8.1 Theorem   If $\sum_{n=0}^{+\infty} c_n x^n$ is a power series having a radius of convergence of $R > 0$, then the series $\sum_{n=1}^{+\infty} n c_n x^{n-1}$ also has R as its radius of convergence.

This theorem states that the series, obtained by differentiating term by term each term of a given power series, will have the same radius of convergence as the given series.

PROOF: Let x be any number in the open interval $(-R, R)$. Then $|x| < R$.

Choose a number x_1 so that $|x| < |x_1| < R$. Because $|x_1| < R$, $\sum\limits_{n=0}^{+\infty} c_n x_1{}^n$ is convergent. Hence, $\lim\limits_{n\to+\infty} c_n x_1{}^n = 0$. So if we take $\epsilon = 1$ in Definition 2.7.1, there exists a number $N > 0$ such that

$$|c_n x_1{}^n| < 1 \qquad \text{whenever } n > N$$

Let M be the largest of the numbers $|c_1 x_1|, |c_2 x_1{}^2|, |c_3 x_1{}^3|, \ldots , |c_N x_1{}^N|, 1$. Then

$$|c_n x_1{}^n| \le M \qquad \text{for all positive integers } n \tag{5}$$

Now

$$\left| n c_n x^{n-1} \right| = \left| n c_n \cdot \frac{x^{n-1}}{x_1{}^n} \cdot x_1{}^n \right| = n \frac{|c_n x_1{}^n|}{|x_1|} \left| \frac{x}{x_1} \right|^{n-1}$$

From (5) and the above equation, we get

$$\left| n c_n x^{n-1} \right| \le n \frac{M}{|x_1|} \left| \frac{x}{x_1} \right|^{n-1} \tag{6}$$

Applying the ratio test to the series

$$\frac{M}{|x_1|} \sum_{n=1}^{+\infty} n \left| \frac{x}{x_1} \right|^{n-1} \tag{7}$$

we have

$$\lim_{n\to+\infty} \left| \frac{u_{n+1}}{u_n} \right| = \lim_{n\to+\infty} \left| \frac{(n+1)|x|^n}{|x_1|^n} \cdot \frac{|x_1|^{n-1}}{n|x|^{n-1}} \right|$$

$$= \left| \frac{x}{x_1} \right| \lim_{n\to+\infty} \frac{n+1}{n}$$

$$= \left| \frac{x}{x_1} \right| < 1$$

Therefore, series (7) is absolutely convergent; so from (6) and the comparison test, the series $\sum\limits_{n=1}^{+\infty} n c_n x^{n-1}$ is also absolutely convergent. Because x is any number in $(-R, R)$, it follows that if the radius of convergence of $\sum\limits_{n=1}^{+\infty} n c_n x^{n-1}$ is R', then $R' \ge R$.

To complete the proof we must show that R' cannot be greater than R. Assume that $R' > R$ and let x_2 be a number such that $R < |x_2| < R'$. Because $|x_2| > R$, it follows that

$$\sum_{n=0}^{+\infty} c_n x_2{}^n \quad \text{is divergent} \tag{8}$$

Because $|x_2| < R'$, it follows that $\sum\limits_{n=1}^{+\infty} nc_n x_2^{n-1}$ is absolutely convergent. Furthermore,

$$|x_2| \sum_{n=1}^{+\infty} |nc_n x_2^{n-1}| = \sum_{n=1}^{+\infty} |nc_n x_2^n|$$

and so from Theorem 14.3.8 we may conclude that

$$\sum_{n=1}^{+\infty} |nc_n x_2^n| \quad \text{is convergent} \tag{9}$$

If n is any positive integer

$$|c_n x_2^n| \le n|c_n x_2^n| = |nc_n x_2^n| \tag{10}$$

From statement (9), inequality (10), and the comparison test it follows that $\sum\limits_{n=1}^{+\infty} |c_n x_2^n|$ is convergent. Therefore, the series $\sum\limits_{n=0}^{+\infty} c_n x_2^n$ is convergent, which contradicts statement (8). Hence, the assumption that $R' > R$ is false. Therefore, R' cannot be greater than R; and because we showed that $R' \ge R$, it follows that $R' = R$, which proves the theorem. ∎

EXAMPLE 1: Verify Theorem 14.8.1 for the power series

$$\sum_{n=0}^{+\infty} \frac{x^{n+1}}{(n+1)^2}$$

SOLUTION: The given power series is

$$\sum_{n=0}^{+\infty} \frac{x^{n+1}}{(n+1)^2} = x + \frac{x^2}{4} + \frac{x^3}{9} + \cdots + \frac{x^{n+1}}{(n+1)^2} + \frac{x^{n+2}}{(n+2)^2} + \cdots$$

To find the radius of convergence, we apply the ratio test.

$$\lim_{n \to +\infty} \left| \frac{u_{n+1}}{u_n} \right| = \lim_{n \to +\infty} \left| \frac{(n+1)^2 x^{n+2}}{(n+2)^2 x^{n+1}} \right| = |x| \lim_{n \to +\infty} \left| \frac{n^2 + 2n + 1}{n^2 + 4n + 4} \right| = |x|$$

Hence, the power series is convergent when $|x| < 1$, and so its radius of convergence $R = 1$.

The power series obtained from the given series by differentiating term by term is

$$\sum_{n=0}^{+\infty} \frac{(n+1)x^n}{(n+1)^2} = \sum_{n=0}^{+\infty} \frac{x^n}{n+1} = 1 + \frac{x}{2} + \frac{x^2}{3} + \frac{x^3}{4} + \cdots + \frac{x^n}{n+1} + \frac{x^{n+1}}{n+2} + \cdots$$

Applying the ratio test for this power series, we have

$$\lim_{n \to +\infty} \left| \frac{u_{n+1}}{u_n} \right| = \lim_{n \to +\infty} \left| \frac{(n+1)x^{n+1}}{(n+2)x^n} \right| = |x| \lim_{n \to +\infty} \left| \frac{n+1}{n+2} \right| = |x|$$

This power series is convergent when $|x| < 1$; thus, its radius of convergence $R' = 1$. Because $R = R'$, Theorem 14.8.1 is verified.

14.8.2 Theorem If the radius of convergence of the power series $\sum\limits_{n=0}^{+\infty} c_n x^n$ is $R > 0$, then R is also the radius of convergence of the series $\sum\limits_{n=2}^{+\infty} n(n-1)c_n x^{n-2}$.

PROOF: If we apply Theorem 14.8.1 to the series $\sum\limits_{n=1}^{+\infty} nc_n x^{n-1}$, we have the desired result. ∎

We are now in a position to prove the theorem regarding term-by-term differentiation of a power series.

14.8.3 Theorem Let $\sum\limits_{n=0}^{+\infty} c_n x^n$ be a power series whose radius of convergence is $R > 0$. Then if f is the function defined by

$$f(x) = \sum_{n=0}^{+\infty} c_n x^n \qquad (11)$$

$f'(x)$ exists for every x in the open interval $(-R, R)$, and it is given by

$$f'(x) = \sum_{n=1}^{+\infty} nc_n x^{n-1}$$

PROOF: Let x and a be two distinct numbers in the open interval $(-R, R)$. Taylor's formula (formula (9) in Sec. 13.5), with $n = 1$, is

$$f(x) = f(a) + \frac{f'(a)}{1!}(x-a) + \frac{f''(\xi)}{2!}(x-a)^2$$

Using this formula with $f(x) = x^n$, we have for every positive integer n

$$x^n = a^n + na^{n-1}(x-a) + \tfrac{1}{2}n(n-1)(\xi_n)^{n-2}(x-a)^2 \qquad (12)$$

where ξ_n is between a and x for every positive integer n. From (11) we have

$$f(x) - f(a) = \sum_{n=0}^{+\infty} c_n x^n - \sum_{n=0}^{+\infty} c_n a^n$$

$$= c_0 + \sum_{n=1}^{+\infty} c_n x^n - c_0 - \sum_{n=1}^{+\infty} c_n a^n$$

$$= \sum_{n=1}^{+\infty} c_n (x^n - a^n)$$

Dividing by $x - a$ (because $x \neq a$) and using (12), we have from the above equation

$$\frac{f(x) - f(a)}{x - a} = \frac{1}{x-a} \sum_{n=1}^{+\infty} c_n[na^{n-1}(x-a) + \tfrac{1}{2}n(n-1)(\xi_n)^{n-2}(x-a)^2]$$

So

$$\frac{f(x) - f(a)}{x - a} = \sum_{n=1}^{+\infty} n c_n a^{n-1} + \tfrac{1}{2}(x - a) \sum_{n=2}^{+\infty} n(n-1)c_n(\xi_n)^{n-2} \qquad (13)$$

Because a is in $(-R, R)$, it follows from Theorem 14.8.1 that $\sum_{n=1}^{+\infty} n c_n a^{n-1}$ is absolutely convergent.

Because both a and x are in $(-R, R)$, there is some number $K > 0$ such that $|a| < K < R$ and $|x| < K < R$. It follows from Theorem 14.8.2 that

$$\sum_{n=2}^{+\infty} n(n-1)c_n K^{n-2}$$

is absolutely convergent. Then because

$$|n(n-1)c_n(\xi_n)^{n-2}| < |n(n-1)c_n K^{n-2}| \qquad (14)$$

for each ξ_n, we can conclude from the comparison test that

$$\sum_{n=2}^{+\infty} n(n-1)c_n(\xi_n)^{n-2}$$

is absolutely convergent.

It follows from (13) that

$$\left| \frac{f(x) - f(a)}{x - a} - \sum_{n=1}^{+\infty} n c_n a^{n-1} \right| = \left| \tfrac{1}{2}(x - a) \sum_{n=2}^{+\infty} n(n-1)c_n(\xi_n)^{n-2} \right| \qquad (15)$$

However, from Theorem 14.6.7 we know that if $\sum_{n=1}^{+\infty} u_n$ is absolutely convergent, then

$$\left| \sum_{n=1}^{+\infty} u_n \right| \leq \sum_{n=1}^{+\infty} |u_n|$$

Applying this to the right side of (15), we obtain

$$\left| \frac{f(x) - f(a)}{x - a} - \sum_{n=1}^{+\infty} n c_n a^{n-1} \right| \leq \tfrac{1}{2}|x - a| \sum_{n=2}^{+\infty} n(n-1)|c_n||\xi_n|^{n-2} \qquad (16)$$

From (14) and (16) we get

$$\left| \frac{f(x) - f(a)}{x - a} - \sum_{n=1}^{+\infty} n c_n a^{n-1} \right| \leq \tfrac{1}{2}|x - a| \sum_{n=2}^{+\infty} n(n-1)|c_n|K^{n-2} \qquad (17)$$

where $0 < K < R$. Because the series on the right side of (17) is absolutely convergent, the limit of the right side, as x approaches a, is zero. Therefore, from (17) and Theorem 2.10.5 it follows that

$$\lim_{x \to a} \frac{f(x) - f(a)}{x - a} = \sum_{n=1}^{+\infty} n c_n a^{n-1}$$

or, equivalently,

$$f'(a) = \sum_{n=1}^{+\infty} n c_n a^{n-1}$$

and because a may be any number in the open interval $(-R, R)$, the theorem is proved. ∎

EXAMPLE 2: Let f be the function defined by the power series of Example 1. (a) Find the domain of f; (b) write the power series which defines the function f' and find the domain of f'.

SOLUTION:

(a) $f(x) = \sum_{n=0}^{+\infty} \frac{x^{n+1}}{(n + 1)^2}$

The domain of f is the interval of convergence of the power series. In Example 1 we showed that the radius of convergence of the power series is 1; that is, the series converges when $|x| < 1$. We now consider the power series when $|x| = 1$. When $x = 1$, the series is

$$1 + \frac{1}{4} + \frac{1}{9} + \cdots + \frac{1}{(n + 1)^2} + \cdots$$

which is convergent because it is the p series with $p = 2$. When $x = -1$, we have the series $\sum_{n=0}^{+\infty} (-1)^{n+1}/(n + 2)^2$, which is convergent because it is absolutely convergent. Hence, the domain of f is the interval $[-1, 1]$.

(b) From Theorem 14.8.3 it follows that f' is defined by

$$f'(x) = \sum_{n=0}^{+\infty} \frac{x^n}{n + 1} \tag{18}$$

and that $f'(x)$ exists for every x in the open interval $(-1, 1)$. In Example 1 we showed that the radius of convergence of the power series in (18) is 1. We now consider the power series in (18) when $x = \pm 1$. When $x = 1$, the series is

$$1 + \frac{1}{2} + \frac{1}{3} + \frac{1}{4} + \cdots + \frac{1}{n + 1} + \cdots$$

which is the harmonic series and hence is divergent. When $x = -1$, the series is

$$1 - \frac{1}{2} + \frac{1}{3} - \frac{1}{4} + \cdots + (-1)^n \frac{1}{n + 1} + \cdots$$

which is a convergent alternating series. Therefore, the domain of f' is the interval $[-1, 1)$.

Example 2 illustrates the fact that if a function f is defined by a power series and this power series is differentiated term by term, the resulting power series, which defines f', has the same radius of convergence but not necessarily the same interval of convergence.

EXAMPLE 3: Obtain a power-series representation of

$$\frac{1}{(1-x)^2}$$

SOLUTION: From (1) we have

$$\frac{1}{1-x} = 1 + x + x^2 + x^3 + \cdots + x^n + \cdots \qquad \text{if } |x| < 1$$

Using Theorem 14.8.3, differentiating on both sides of the above, we get

$$\frac{1}{(1-x)^2} = 1 + 2x + 3x^2 + \cdots + nx^{n-1} + \cdots \qquad \text{if } |x| < 1$$

EXAMPLE 4: Show that

$$e^x = \sum_{n=0}^{+\infty} \frac{x^n}{n!}$$

$$= 1 + x + \frac{x^2}{2!} + \frac{x^3}{3!} + \cdots$$

for all real values of x.

SOLUTION: In Example 2 of Sec. 14.7 we showed that the power series $\sum_{n=0}^{+\infty} x^n/n!$ is absolutely convergent for all real values of x. Therefore, if f is the function defined by

$$f(x) = \sum_{n=0}^{+\infty} \frac{x^n}{n!} \tag{19}$$

the domain of f is the set of all real numbers; that is, the interval of convergence is $(-\infty, +\infty)$. It follows from Theorem 14.8.3 that for all real values of x

$$f'(x) = \sum_{n=1}^{+\infty} \frac{nx^{n-1}}{n!} \tag{20}$$

Because $n/n! = 1/(n-1)!$, (20) can be written as

$$f'(x) = \sum_{n=1}^{+\infty} \frac{x^{n-1}}{(n-1)!}$$

or, equivalently,

$$f'(x) = \sum_{n=0}^{+\infty} \frac{x^n}{n!} \tag{21}$$

Comparing (19) and (21), we see that $f'(x) = f(x)$ for all real values of x. Therefore, the function f satisfies the differential equation

$$\frac{dy}{dx} = y$$

for which the general solution is $y = Ce^x$. Hence, for some constant C, $f(x) = Ce^x$. From (19) we see that $f(0) = 1$. (Remember that we take $x^0 = 1$ even when $x = 0$ for convenience in writing the general term.) Therefore, $C = 1$, and so $f(x) = e^x$, and we have the desired result.

EXAMPLE 5: Use the result of Example 4 to find a power-series representation of e^{-x}.

SOLUTION: If we replace x by $-x$ in the series for e^x, it follows that

$$e^{-x} = 1 - x + \frac{x^2}{2!} - \frac{x^3}{3!} + \cdots + (-1)^n \frac{x^n}{n!} + \cdots$$

for all real values of x.

EXAMPLE 6: Use the series of Example 5 to find the value of e^{-1} correct to five decimal places.

SOLUTION: Taking $x = 1$ in the series for e^{-x}, we have

$$e^{-1} = 1 - 1 + \frac{1}{2!} - \frac{1}{3!} + \frac{1}{4!} - \frac{1}{5!} + \frac{1}{6!} - \frac{1}{7!} + \frac{1}{8!} - \frac{1}{9!} + \frac{1}{10!} - \cdots$$

$$= 1 - 1 + \frac{1}{2} - \frac{1}{6} + \frac{1}{24} - \frac{1}{120} + \frac{1}{720} - \frac{1}{5,040} + \frac{1}{40,320} - \frac{1}{362,880}$$

$$+ \frac{1}{3,628,800} - \cdots$$

$$= 1 - 1 + 0.5 - 0.166667 + 0.041667 - 0.008333 + 0.001389$$

$$- 0.000198 + 0.000025 - 0.000003 + 0.0000003 - \cdots$$

We have a convergent alternating series for which $|u_{n+1}| < |u_n|$. So if we use the first ten terms to approximate the sum, by Theorem 14.6.4 the error is less than the absolute value of the eleventh term. Adding the first ten terms, we obtain 0.367880. Rounding off to five decimal places gives

$$e^{-1} \approx 0.36788$$

In computation with infinite series two kinds of errors occur. One is the error given by the remainder after the first n terms. The other is the round-off error which occurs when each term of the series is approximated by a decimal with a finite number of places. In particular, in Example 6 we wanted the result accurate to five decimal places so we rounded off each term to six decimal places. After computing the sum, we rounded off this result to five decimal places. Of course, the error given by the remainder can be reduced by considering additional terms of the series, whereas the round-off error can be reduced by using more decimal places.

Exercises 14.8

In Exercises 1 through 8 a function f is defined by a power series. In each exercise do the following: (a) Find the radius of convergence of the given power series and the domain of f; (b) write the power series which defines the function f' and find its radius of convergence by using methods of Sec. 14.7 (thus verifying Theorem 14.8.1); (c) find the domain of f'.

1. $f(x) = \sum\limits_{n=1}^{+\infty} \frac{x^n}{n^2}$

2. $f(x) = \sum\limits_{n=1}^{+\infty} (-1)^{n-1} \frac{x^n}{n}$

3. $f(x) = \sum\limits_{n=1}^{+\infty} \frac{x^n}{\sqrt{n}}$

4. $f(x) = \sum\limits_{n=2}^{+\infty} \frac{(x-2)^n}{\sqrt{n-1}}$

5. $f(x) = \sum\limits_{n=1}^{+\infty} (-1)^{n-1} \frac{x^{2n-1}}{(2n-1)!}$

6. $f(x) = \sum\limits_{n=1}^{+\infty} \frac{x^{2n-2}}{(2n-2)!}$

7. $f(x) = \displaystyle\sum_{n=1}^{+\infty} \frac{(x-1)^n}{n3^n}$

8. $f(x) = \displaystyle\sum_{n=2}^{+\infty} (-1)^n \frac{(x-3)^n}{n(n-1)}$

9. Use the result of Example 3 to find a power-series representation of $1/(1-x)^3$.

10. Use the result of Example 4 to find a power-series representation of $e^{\sqrt{x}}$.

11. Obtain a power-series representation of $1/(1+x)^2$ if $|x| < 1$ by differentiating series (2) term by term.

12. Obtain a power-series representation of $x/(1+x^2)^2$ if $|x| < 1$ by differentiating series (4) term by term.

13. Use the result of Example 5 to find the value of $1/\sqrt{e}$ correct to five decimal places.

14. If $f(x) = \displaystyle\sum_{n=0}^{+\infty} (-1)^n \frac{x^{2n}}{3^n}$, find $f'(\tfrac{1}{2})$ correct to four decimal places.

15. Use the results of Examples 4 and 5 to find a power-series representation of (a) $\sinh x$ and (b) $\cosh x$.

16. Show that each of the power series in parts (a) and (b) of Exercise 15 can be obtained from the other by term-by-term differentiation.

17. Use the result of Example 3 to find the sum of the series $\displaystyle\sum_{n=1}^{+\infty} \frac{n}{2^n}$.

18. (a) Find a power-series representation for $(e^x - 1)/x$.

    (b) By differentiating term by term the power series in part (a) show that $\displaystyle\sum_{n=1}^{+\infty} \frac{n}{(n+1)!} = 1$.

19. (a) Find a power-series representation for $x^2 e^{-x}$. (b) By differentiating term by term the power series in part (a) show

    that $\displaystyle\sum_{n=1}^{+\infty} (-2)^{n+1} \frac{n+2}{n!} = 4$.

20. Assume that the constant 0 has a power-series representation $\displaystyle\sum_{n=0}^{+\infty} c_n x^n$, where the radius of convergence $R > 0$. Prove

    that $c_n = 0$ for all n.

21. Suppose a function f has the power-series representation $\displaystyle\sum_{n=0}^{+\infty} c_n x^n$, where the radius of convergence $R > 0$. If $f'(x) = f(x)$

    and $f(0) = 1$, find the power series by using only properties of power series and nothing about the exponential function.

22. (a) Using only properties of power series find a power-series representation of the function f for which $f(x) > 0$ and $f'(x) = 2xf(x)$ for all x, and $f(0) = 1$. (b) Verify your result in part (a) by solving the differential equation $D_x y = 2xy$ having the boundary condition $y = 1$ when $x = 0$.

14.9 INTEGRATION OF POWER SERIES   The theorem regarding the term-by-term integration of a power series is a consequence of Theorem 14.8.3.

14.9.1 Theorem   Let $\displaystyle\sum_{n=0}^{+\infty} c_n x^n$ be a power series whose radius of convergence is $R > 0$. Then

if f is the function defined by

$$f(x) = \sum_{n=0}^{+\infty} c_n x^n$$

f is integrable on every closed subinterval of $(-R, R)$, and we evaluate the integral of f by integrating the given power series term by term; that is, if x is in $(-R, R)$, then

$$\int_0^x f(t) \, dt = \sum_{n=0}^{+\infty} \frac{c_n}{n+1} x^{n+1}$$

Furthermore, R is the radius of convergence of the resulting series.

PROOF: Let g be the function defined by

$$g(x) = \sum_{n=0}^{+\infty} \frac{c_n}{n+1} x^{n+1}$$

Because the terms of the power-series representation of $f(x)$ are the derivatives of the terms of the power-series representation of $g(x)$, the two series have, by Theorem 14.8.1, the same radius of convergence. By Theorem 14.8.3 it follows that

$$g'(x) = f(x) \qquad \text{for every } x \text{ in } (-R, R)$$

By Theorem 14.8.2, it follows that $f'(x) = g''(x)$ for every x in $(-R, R)$. Because f is differentiable on $(-R, R)$, f is continuous there; consequently, f is continuous on every closed subinterval of $(-R, R)$. From Theorem 6.6.2 it follows that if x is in $(-R, R)$, then

$$\int_0^x f(t) \, dt = g(x) - g(0) = g(x)$$

or, equivalently,

$$\int_0^x f(t) \, dt = \sum_{n=0}^{+\infty} \frac{c_n}{n+1} x^{n+1}$$

∎

Theorem 14.9.1 often is used to compute a definite integral which cannot be evaluated directly by finding an antiderivative of the integrand. Examples 1 and 2 illustrate the technique. The definite integral $\int_0^x e^{-t^2} \, dt$ appearing in these two examples represents the measure of the area of a region under the "normal probability curve."

EXAMPLE 1: Find a power-series representation of

$$\int_0^x e^{-t^2} \, dt$$

SOLUTION: In Example 5 of Sec. 14.8 we showed that

$$e^{-x} = \sum_{n=0}^{+\infty} \frac{(-1)^n x^n}{n!}$$

for all values of x. Replacing x by t^2, we get

$$e^{-t^2} = 1 - t^2 + \frac{t^4}{2!} - \frac{t^6}{3!} + \cdots + (-1)^n \frac{t^{2n}}{n!} + \cdots \qquad \text{for all values of } t$$

Applying Theorem 14.9.1, we integrate term by term and obtain

$$\int_0^x e^{-t^2}\, dt = \sum_{n=0}^{+\infty} \int_0^x (-1)^n \frac{t^{2n}}{n!}\, dt$$

$$= x - \frac{x^3}{3} + \frac{x^5}{2! \cdot 5} - \frac{x^7}{3! \cdot 7} + \cdots + (-1)^n \frac{x^{2n+1}}{n!(2n+1)} + \cdots$$

The power series represents the integral for all values of x.

EXAMPLE 2: Using the result of Example 1, compute accurate to three decimal places the value of

$$\int_0^{1/2} e^{-t^2}\, dt$$

SOLUTION: Replacing x by $\tfrac{1}{2}$ in the power series obtained in Example 1, we have

$$\int_0^{1/2} e^{-t^2}\, dt = \tfrac{1}{2} - \tfrac{1}{24} + \tfrac{1}{320} - \tfrac{1}{5376} + \cdots$$

$$= 0.5 - 0.0417 + 0.0031 - 0.0002 + \cdots$$

We have a convergent alternating series with $|u_{n+1}| < |u_n|$. Thus, if we use the first three terms to approximate the sum, by Theorem 14.6.4 the error is less than the absolute value of the fourth term. From the first three terms we get

$$\int_0^{1/2} e^{-t^2}\, dt \approx 0.461$$

EXAMPLE 3: Obtain a power-series representation of $\ln(1 + x)$.

SOLUTION: Consider the function f defined by $f(t) = 1/(1 + t)$. A power-series representation of this function is given by series (2) in Sec. 14.8, which is

$$\frac{1}{1+t} = 1 - t + t^2 - t^3 + \cdots + (-1)^n t^n + \cdots \qquad \text{if } |t| < 1$$

Applying Theorem 14.9.1, we integrate term by term and obtain

$$\int_0^x \frac{dt}{1+t} = \sum_{n=0}^{+\infty} \int_0^x (-1)^n t^n\, dt \qquad \text{if } |x| < 1$$

and so

$$\ln(1 + x) = x - \frac{x^2}{2} + \frac{x^3}{3} - \frac{x^4}{4} + \cdots + (-1)^n \frac{x^{n+1}}{n+1} + \cdots \qquad \text{if } |x| < 1$$

or, equivalently,

$$\ln(1 + x) = \sum_{n=1}^{+\infty} (-1)^{n-1} \frac{x^n}{n} \qquad \text{if } |x| < 1 \tag{1}$$

Note that because $|x| < 1$, $|1 + x| = (1 + x)$. Thus, the absolute-value bars are not needed when writing $\ln(1 + x)$.

In Example 3, Theorem 14.9.1 allows us to conclude that the power series in (1) represents the function only for values of x in the open interval $(-1, 1)$. However, the power series is convergent at the right endpoint 1, as was shown in Example 1 of Sec. 14.6. When $x = -1$, the power series becomes the harmonic series, which is divergent. Hence, the interval of convergence of the power series in (1) is $(-1, 1]$.

The following example shows that the power series represents $\ln(1 + x)$ at $x = 1$.

EXAMPLE 4:   Show that the power series in (1) represents $\ln(x + 1)$ at $x = 1$ by proving that the sum of the series

$$\sum_{n=1}^{+\infty} \frac{(-1)^{n-1}}{n}$$

is $\ln 2$.

SOLUTION: For the infinite series $\sum\limits_{n=1}^{+\infty} (-1)^{n-1}/n$, the nth partial sum is

$$s_n = 1 - \frac{1}{2} + \frac{1}{3} - \frac{1}{4} + \cdots + (-1)^{n-1} \frac{1}{n} \qquad (2)$$

It follows from Definition 14.3.2 that if we show $\lim\limits_{n \to +\infty} s_n = \ln 2$, we will have proved that the sum of the series is $\ln 2$.

From algebra we have the following formula for the sum of a geometric progression:

$$a + ar + ar^2 + ar^3 + \cdots + ar^{n-1} = \frac{a - ar^n}{1 - r}$$

Using this formula with $a = 1$ and $r = -t$, we have

$$1 - t + t^2 - t^3 + \cdots + (-t)^{n-1} = \frac{1 - (-t)^n}{1 + t}$$

which we can write as

$$1 - t + t^2 - t^3 + \cdots + (-1)^{n-1}t^{n-1} = \frac{1}{1 + t} + (-1)^{n+1} \frac{t^n}{1 + t}$$

Integrating from 0 to 1, we get

$$\int_0^1 [1 - t + t^2 - t^3 + \cdots + (-1)^{n-1}t^{n-1}]\, dt = \int_0^1 \frac{dt}{1 + t} + (-1)^{n+1} \int_0^1 \frac{t^n}{1 + t}\, dt$$

which gives

$$1 - \frac{1}{2} + \frac{1}{3} - \frac{1}{4} + \cdots + (-1)^{n-1} \frac{1}{n} = \ln 2 + (-1)^{n+1} \int_0^1 \frac{t^n}{1 + t}\, dt \qquad (3)$$

Referring to Eq. (2), we see that the left side of Eq. (3) is s_n. Letting

$$R_n = (-1)^{n+1} \int_0^1 \frac{t^n}{1 + t}\, dt$$

Eq. (3) may be written as

$$s_n = \ln 2 + R_n \qquad (4)$$

Because $t^n/(1 + t) \leq t^n$ for all t in $[0, 1]$ it follows from Theorem 6.4.8 that

$$\int_0^1 \frac{t^n}{1 + t}\, dt \leq \int_0^1 t^n\, dt$$

Hence,

$$0 \leq |R_n| = \int_0^1 \frac{t^n}{1 + t}\, dt \leq \int_0^1 t^n\, dt = \frac{1}{n + 1}$$

Because $\lim\limits_{n \to +\infty} 1/(n + 1) = 0$, it follows from the above inequality and the squeeze theorem (2.10.5) that $\lim\limits_{n \to +\infty} R_n = 0$. So from Eq. (4), we get

$$\lim_{n \to +\infty} s_n = \ln 2 + \lim_{n \to +\infty} R_n$$

$$= \ln 2$$

Therefore,

$$\sum_{n=1}^{+\infty} (-1)^{n-1} \frac{1}{n} = 1 - \frac{1}{2} + \frac{1}{3} - \frac{1}{4} + \cdots = \ln 2 \tag{5}$$

The solution of Example 3 showed that the power series in (1) represents $\ln(x + 1)$ if $|x| < 1$. Hence, with the result of Example 4 we can conclude that the power series in (1) represents $\ln(x + 1)$ for all x in its interval of convergence $(-1, 1]$.

Although it is interesting that the sum of the series in (5) is $\ln 2$, this series converges too slowly to use it to calculate $\ln 2$. We now proceed to obtain a power series for computation of natural logarithms.

From (1) we have

$$\left(\ln(1 + x) = x - \frac{x^2}{2} + \frac{x^3}{3} - \cdots + (-1)^{n-1} \frac{x^n}{n} + \cdots \quad \text{for } x \text{ in } (-1, 1] \quad (6) \right.$$

Replacing x by $-x$ in this series, we get

$$\left(\ln(1 - x) = -x - \frac{x^2}{2} - \frac{x^3}{3} - \frac{x^4}{4} - \cdots - \frac{x^n}{n} - \cdots \quad \text{for } x \text{ in } [-1, 1) \quad (7) \right)$$

Subtracting term by term (7) from (6), we obtain

$$\ln \frac{1 + x}{1 - x} = 2\left(x + \frac{x^3}{3} + \frac{x^5}{5} + \cdots + \frac{x^{2n-1}}{2n - 1} + \cdots \right) \quad \text{if } |x| < 1 \tag{8}$$

The series in (8) can be used to compute the value of the natural logarithm of any positive number. If y is any positive number, let

$$y = \frac{1 + x}{1 - x} \quad \text{and then} \quad x = \frac{y - 1}{y + 1} \quad \text{and } |x| < 1$$

For example, if $y = 2$, then $x = \frac{1}{3}$. We have from (8)

$$\ln 2 = 2\left(\frac{1}{3} + \frac{1}{3^4} + \frac{1}{5 \cdot 3^5} + \frac{1}{7 \cdot 3^7} + \frac{1}{9 \cdot 3^9} + \frac{1}{11 \cdot 3^{11}} + \cdots\right)$$

$$= 2\left(\frac{1}{3} + \frac{1}{81} + \frac{1}{1{,}215} + \frac{1}{15{,}309} + \frac{1}{177{,}147} + \frac{1}{1{,}948{,}617} + \cdots\right)$$

$$= 2(0.333333 + 0.012346 + 0.000823 + 0.000065 + 0.000006$$
$$+ 0.000001 + \cdots)$$

Using the first six terms in parentheses, multiplying by 2, and rounding off to five decimal places, we get

$$\ln 2 \approx 0.69315$$

EXAMPLE 5: Obtain a power-series representation of $\tan^{-1} x$.

SOLUTION: From series (4) in Sec. 14.8 we have

$$\frac{1}{1 + x^2} = 1 - x^2 + x^4 - x^6 + \cdots + (-1)^n x^{2n} + \cdots \qquad \text{if } |x| < 1$$

Applying Theorem 14.9.1 and integrating term by term, we get

$$\int_0^x \frac{1}{1 + t^2}\, dt = x - \frac{x^3}{3} + \frac{x^5}{5} - \cdots + (-1)^n \frac{x^{2n+1}}{2n + 1} + \cdots$$

Therefore,

$$\tan^{-1} x = \sum_{n=0}^{+\infty} (-1)^n \frac{x^{2n+1}}{2n + 1} \qquad \text{if } |x| < 1 \tag{9}$$

Although Theorem 14.9.1 allows us to conclude that the power series in (9) represents $\tan^{-1} x$ only for values of x such that $|x| < 1$, it can be shown that the interval of convergence of the power series is $[-1, 1]$ and that the power series is a representation of $\tan^{-1} x$ for all x in its interval of convergence. (You are asked to do this in Exercise 16.) We therefore have

$$\tan^{-1} x = \sum_{n=0}^{+\infty} (-1)^n \frac{x^{2n+1}}{2n + 1} = x - \frac{x^3}{3} + \frac{x^5}{5} \cdots \qquad \text{if } |x| \leq 1 \tag{10}$$

Taking $x = 1$ in (10), we get

$$\frac{\pi}{4} = 1 - \frac{1}{3} + \frac{1}{5} - \frac{1}{7} + \cdots + (-1)^n \frac{1}{2n + 1} + \cdots$$

This series is not suitable for computing π because it converges too slowly. The following example gives a better method.

EXAMPLE 6:   Prove that

$\frac{1}{4}\pi = \tan^{-1}\frac{1}{2} + \tan^{-1}\frac{1}{3}$

Use this formula and the power series for $\tan^{-1} x$ of Example 5 to compute the value of π accurate to four decimal places.

SOLUTION: Let $\alpha = \tan^{-1}\frac{1}{2}$ and $\beta = \tan^{-1}\frac{1}{3}$. Then

$$\tan(\alpha + \beta) = \frac{\tan \alpha + \tan \beta}{1 - \tan \alpha \tan \beta}$$

$$= \frac{\frac{1}{2} + \frac{1}{3}}{1 - \frac{1}{2} \cdot \frac{1}{3}}$$

$$= \frac{3 + 2}{6 - 1}$$

$$= 1$$

$$= \tan \tfrac{1}{4}\pi$$

Therefore,

$$\tfrac{1}{4}\pi = \alpha + \beta = \tan^{-1}\tfrac{1}{2} + \tan^{-1}\tfrac{1}{3} \qquad (11)$$

From formula (10) with $x = \frac{1}{2}$ we get

$$\tan^{-1}\frac{1}{2} = \frac{1}{2} - \frac{1}{3}\left(\frac{1}{2}\right)^3 + \frac{1}{5}\left(\frac{1}{2}\right)^5 - \frac{1}{7}\left(\frac{1}{2}\right)^7 + \frac{1}{9}\left(\frac{1}{2}\right)^9 - \frac{1}{11}\left(\frac{1}{2}\right)^{11} + \frac{1}{13}\left(\frac{1}{2}\right)^{13}$$

$$- \frac{1}{15}\left(\frac{1}{2}\right)^{15} + \cdots$$

$$= \frac{1}{2} - \frac{1}{24} + \frac{1}{160} - \frac{1}{896} + \frac{1}{4{,}608} - \frac{1}{22{,}528} + \frac{1}{106{,}492} - \frac{1}{491{,}520} + \cdots$$

$$= 0.5 - 0.04167 + 0.00625 - 0.00112 + 0.00022 - 0.00004$$

$$+ 0.00001 - 0.000002 + \cdots$$

Because the series is alternating and $|u_{n+1}| < |u_n|$, we know by Theorem 14.6.4 that if the first seven terms are used to approximate the sum of the series, the error is less than the absolute value of the eighth term. Therefore,

$$\tan^{-1}\tfrac{1}{2} \approx 0.46365 \qquad (12)$$

Using formula (10) with $x = \frac{1}{3}$, we have

$$\tan^{-1}\frac{1}{3} = \frac{1}{3} - \frac{1}{3}\left(\frac{1}{3}\right)^3 + \frac{1}{5}\left(\frac{1}{3}\right)^5 - \frac{1}{7}\left(\frac{1}{3}\right)^7 + \frac{1}{9}\left(\frac{1}{3}\right)^9 - \frac{1}{11}\left(\frac{1}{3}\right)^{11} + \cdots$$

$$= \frac{1}{3} - \frac{1}{81} + \frac{1}{1{,}215} - \frac{1}{15{,}309} + \frac{1}{177{,}147} - \frac{1}{1{,}948{,}617} + \cdots$$

$$= 0.33333 - 0.01235 + 0.00082 - 0.00007 + 0.00001$$

$$- 0.000001 + \cdots$$

Using the first five terms to approximate the sum, we get

$$\tan^{-1}\tfrac{1}{3} \approx 0.32174 \qquad (13)$$

Substituting from (12) and (13) into (11), we get

$\frac{1}{4}\pi \approx 0.46365 + 0.32174 = 0.78539$

Multiplying by 4 and rounding off to four decimal places gives $\pi \approx 3.1416$.

Exercises 14.9

In Exercises 1 through 7, compute the value of the given integral, accurate to four decimal places by using series.

1. $\displaystyle\int_0^{1/2} \frac{dx}{1+x^3}$

2. $\displaystyle\int_0^{1/3} \frac{dx}{1+x^4}$

3. $\displaystyle\int_0^1 e^{-x^2}\, dx$

4. $\displaystyle\int_0^{1/2} f(x)\, dx$, where $f(x) = \begin{cases} \dfrac{\ln(1+x)}{x} & \text{if } x \neq 0 \\ 1 & \text{if } x = 0 \end{cases}$

5. $\displaystyle\int_0^{1/4} g(x)\, dx$, where $g(x) = \begin{cases} \dfrac{\tan^{-1} x}{x} & \text{if } x \neq 0 \\ 1 & \text{if } x = 0 \end{cases}$

6. $\displaystyle\int_0^1 h(x)\, dx$, where $h(x) = \begin{cases} \dfrac{\sinh x}{x} & \text{if } x \neq 0 \\ 1 & \text{if } x = 0 \end{cases}$

7. $\displaystyle\int_0^1 f(x)\, dx$, where $f(x) = \begin{cases} \dfrac{e^x - 1}{x} & \text{if } x \neq 0 \\ 1 & \text{if } x = 0 \end{cases}$

8. Use the power series in Eq. (8) to compute ln 3 accurate to four decimal places.

9. Use the power series in Eq. (9) to compute $\tan^{-1} \frac{1}{4}$ accurate to four decimal places.

10. Integrate term by term from 0 to x a power-series representation for $(1 - t^2)^{-1}$ to obtain the power series in Eq. (8) for $\ln[(1+x)/(1-x)]$.

11. Find a power-series representation for $\tanh^{-1} x$ by integrating term by term from 0 to x a power-series representation for $(1 - t^2)^{-1}$.

12. Find a power series for xe^x by multiplying the series for e^x by x, and then integrate the resulting series term by term from 0 to 1 and show that $\displaystyle\sum_{n=1}^{+\infty} \frac{1}{n!(n+2)} = \frac{1}{2}$.

13. By integrating term by term from 0 to x a power-series representation for $\ln(1-t)$, show that

$$\sum_{n=2}^{+\infty} \frac{x^n}{(n-1)n} = x + (1-x)\ln(1-x)$$

14. By integrating term by term from 0 to x a power-series representation for $t \tan^{-1} t$, show that

$$\sum_{n=1}^{+\infty} (-1)^{n+1} \frac{x^{2n+1}}{(2n-1)(2n+1)} = \frac{1}{2}[(x^2 + 1)\tan^{-1} x - x]$$

15. Find the power series in x of $f(x)$ if $f''(x) = -f(x)$, $f(0) = 0$, and $f'(0) = 1$. Also, find the radius of convergence of the resulting series.

16. Show that the interval of convergence of the power series in Eq. (9) is $[-1, 1]$ and that the power series is a representation of $\tan^{-1} x$ for all x in its interval of convergence.

14.10 TAYLOR SERIES   If f is the function defined by

$$f(x) = \sum_{n=0}^{+\infty} c_n x^n = c_0 + c_1 x + c_2 x^2 + c_3 x^3 + \cdots + c_n x^n + \cdots \qquad (1)$$

whose radius of convergence is $R > 0$, it follows from successive applications of Theorem 14.8.3 that f has derivatives of all orders on $(-R, R)$. We say that such a function is *infinitely differentiable on* $(-R, R)$. Successive differentiations of the function in (1) give

$$f'(x) = c_1 + 2c_2x + 3c_3x^2 + 4c_4x^3 + \cdots + nc_nx^{n-1} + \cdots \tag{2}$$

$$f''(x) = 2c_2 + 2 \cdot 3c_3x + 3 \cdot 4c_4x^2 + \cdots + (n-1)nc_nx^{n-2} + \cdots \tag{3}$$

$$f'''(x) = 2 \cdot 3c_3 + 2 \cdot 3 \cdot 4c_4x + \cdots + (n-2)(n-1)nc_nx^{n-3} + \cdots \tag{4}$$

$$f^{(iv)}(x) = 2 \cdot 3 \cdot 4c_4 + \cdots + (n-3)(n-2)(n-1)nc_nx^{n-4} + \cdots \tag{5}$$

etc. Letting $x = 0$ in (1), we get

$$f(0) = c_0$$

For $x = 0$ in (2) we see that

$$f'(0) = c_1$$

If in (3) we take $x = 0$, we have

$$f''(0) = 2c_2 \quad \text{and so} \quad c_2 = \frac{f''(0)}{2!}$$

From (4), taking $x = 0$, we get

$$f'''(0) = 2 \cdot 3c_3 \quad \text{and so} \quad c_3 = \frac{f'''(0)}{3!}$$

In a similar manner from (5), if $x = 0$, we obtain

$$f^{(iv)}(0) = 2 \cdot 3 \cdot 4c_4 \quad \text{and so} \quad c_4 = \frac{f^{(iv)}(0)}{4!}$$

In general, we have

$$c_n = \frac{f^{(n)}(0)}{n!} \quad \text{for every positive integer } n \tag{6}$$

Formula (6) also holds when $n = 0$ if we take $f^{(0)}(0)$ to be $f(0)$ and $0! = 1$. So from (1) and (6) we can write the power series of f in x as

[handwritten note: MCLAURIN. SERIES. WHEN a=0]

$$\sum_{n=0}^{+\infty} \frac{f^{(n)}(0)}{n!} x^n = f(0) + f'(0)x + \frac{f''(0)}{2!} x^2 + \cdots + \frac{f^{(n)}(0)}{n!} x^n + \cdots \tag{7}$$

In a more general sense, consider the function f as a power series in $(x - a)$; that is,

$$f(x) = \sum_{n=0}^{+\infty} c_n(x - a)^n$$

$$= c_0 + c_1(x - a) + c_2(x - a)^2 + \cdots + c_n(x - a)^n + \cdots \tag{8}$$

If the radius of convergence of this series is R, then f is infinitely differentiable on $(a - R, a + R)$. Successive differentiations of the function in (8) give

$$f'(x) = c_1 + 2c_2(x - a) + 3c_3(x - a)^2 + 4c_4(x - a)^3 + \cdots$$
$$+ nc_n(x - a)^{n-1} + \cdots$$

$$f''(x) = 2c_2 + 2 \cdot 3c_3(x - a) + 3 \cdot 4c_4(x - a)^2 + \cdots$$
$$+ (n - 1)nc_n(x - a)^{n-2} + \cdots$$

$$f'''(x) = 2 \cdot 3c_3 + 2 \cdot 3 \cdot 4c_4(x - a) + \cdots$$
$$+ (n - 2)(n - 1)nc_n(x - a)^{n-3} + \cdots$$

etc. Letting $x = a$ in the power-series representations of f and its derivatives, we get

$$c_0 = f(a) \qquad c_1 = f'(a) \qquad c_2 = \frac{f''(a)}{2!} \qquad c_3 = \frac{f'''(a)}{3!}$$

and in general

$$c_n = \frac{f^{(n)}(a)}{n!} \tag{9}$$

TAYLOR'S SERIES

From (8) and (9) we can write the power series of f in $(x - a)$ as

$$\sum_{n=0}^{+\infty} \frac{f^{(n)}(a)}{n!}(x - a)^n = f(a) + f'(a)(x - a) + \frac{f''(a)}{2!}(x - a)^2$$
$$+ \cdots + \frac{f^{(n)}(a)}{n!}(x - a)^n + \cdots \tag{10}$$

The series in (10) is called the *Taylor series* of f at a. The special case of (10), when $a = 0$, is Eq. (7), which is called the *Maclaurin series*.

EXAMPLE 1: Find the Maclaurin series for e^x.

SOLUTION: If $f(x) = e^x$, $f^{(n)}(x) = e^x$ for all x; therefore, $f^{(n)}(0) = 1$ for all n. So from (7) we have the Maclaurin series for e^x:

$$1 + x + \frac{x^2}{2!} + \frac{x^3}{3!} + \cdots + \frac{x^n}{n!} + \cdots \tag{11}$$

Note that series (11) is the same as the series for e^x obtained in Example 4 of Sec. 14.8.

EXAMPLE 2: Find the Taylor series for $\sin x$ at a.

SOLUTION: If $f(x) = \sin x$, $f'(x) = \cos x$, $f''(x) = -\sin x$, $f'''(x) = -\cos x$, $f^{(\text{iv})}(x) = \sin x$, and so forth. Thus, from formula (9) we have $c_0 = \sin a$, $c_1 = \cos a$, $c_2 = (-\sin a)/2!$, $c_3 = (-\cos a)/3!$, $c_4 = (\sin a)/4!$, and so on. The required Taylor series is obtained from (10), and it is

$$\sin a + \cos a(x - a) - \sin a \frac{(x - a)^2}{2!} - \cos a \frac{(x - a)^3}{3!}$$
$$+ \sin a \frac{(x - a)^4}{4!} + \cdots \tag{12}$$

We can deduce that a power-series representation of a function is unique. That is, if two functions have the same function values in some interval containing the number a, and if both functions have a power-series representation in $(x - a)$, then these series must be the same because the coefficients in the series are obtained from the values of the functions and their derivatives at a. <u>Therefore, if a function has a power-series representation in $(x - a)$, this series must be its Taylor series at a.</u> Hence, the Taylor series for a given function does not have to be obtained by using formula (10). Any method that gives a power series in $(x - a)$ representing the function will be the Taylor series of the function at a. For example, to find the Taylor series for e^x at a, we can write $e^x = e^a e^{x-a}$ and then use series (11), where x is replaced by $(x - a)$. We then have

$$e^x = e^a \left[1 + (x - a) + \frac{(x-a)^2}{2!} + \frac{(x-a)^3}{3!} + \cdots + \frac{(x-a)^n}{n!} + \cdots \right]$$

We can use the series for $\ln(1 + x)$ found in Example 3 of Sec. 14.9 to find the Taylor series for $\ln x$ at a $(a > 0)$ by writing

$$\ln x = \ln[a + (x - a)] = \ln a + \ln\left(1 + \frac{x - a}{a}\right)$$

Then because

$$\ln(1 + x) = \sum_{n=1}^{+\infty} (-1)^{n-1} \frac{x^n}{n} \qquad \text{if} \ -1 < x \le 1$$

we have

$$\ln x = \ln a + \frac{x - a}{a} - \frac{(x - a)^2}{2a^2} + \frac{(x - a)^3}{3a^3} - \cdots$$

and the series represents $\ln x$ if $-1 < (x - a)/a \le 1$ or, equivalently, $0 < x \le 2a$.

A natural question that arises is: If a function has a Taylor series in $(x - a)$ having radius of convergence $R > 0$, does this series represent the function for all values of x in the interval $(a - R, a + R)$? For most elementary functions the answer is yes. However, in general the answer is no. The following example shows this.

EXAMPLE 3: Let f be the function defined by

$$f(x) = \begin{cases} e^{-1/x^2} & \text{if } x \ne 0 \\ 0 & \text{if } x = 0 \end{cases}$$

Find the Maclaurin series for f and show that it converges for all values of x but that it represents $f(x)$ only when $x = 0$.

SOLUTION: To find $f'(0)$ we use the definition of a derivative. We have

$$f'(0) = \lim_{x \to 0} \frac{e^{-1/x^2} - 0}{x - 0} = \lim_{x \to 0} \frac{\dfrac{1}{x}}{e^{1/x^2}}$$

Because $\lim_{x \to 0} (1/x) = +\infty$ and $\lim_{x \to 0} e^{1/x^2} = +\infty$, we use L'Hôpital's rule and get

$$f'(0) = \lim_{x \to 0} \frac{-\dfrac{1}{x^2}}{e^{1/x^2}\left(-\dfrac{2}{x^3}\right)} = \lim_{x \to 0} \frac{x}{2e^{1/x^2}} = 0$$

By a similar method, using the definition of a derivative and L'Hôpital's rule, we get 0 for every derivative. So $f^{(n)}(0) = 0$ for all n. Therefore, the Maclaurin series for the given function is $0 + 0 + 0 + \cdots + 0 + \cdots$. This series converges to 0 for all x; however, if $x \neq 0$, $f(x) = e^{-1/x^2} \neq 0$.

A theorem that gives a test for determining whether a function is represented by its Taylor series is the following.

14.10.1 Theorem   Let f be a function such that f and all of its derivatives exist in some interval $(a - r, a + r)$. Then the function is represented by its Taylor series

$$\left(\sum_{n=0}^{+\infty} \frac{f^{(n)}(a)}{n!} (x - a)^n \right.$$

for all x such that $|x - a| < r$ if and only if

$$\left(\lim_{n \to +\infty} R_n(x) = \lim_{n \to +\infty} \frac{f^{(n+1)}(\xi_n)}{(n + 1)!} (x - a)^{n+1} = 0 \right.$$

where each ξ_n is between x and a.

PROOF: In the interval $(a - r, a + r)$, the function f satisfies the hypothesis of Theorem 13.5.1 for which

$$f(x) = P_n(x) + R_n(x) \tag{13}$$

where $P_n(x)$ is the nth-degree Taylor polynomial of f at a and $R_n(x)$ is the remainder, given by

$$R_n(x) = \frac{f^{(n+1)}(\xi_n)}{(n + 1)!} (x - a)^{n+1} \tag{14}$$

where each ξ_n is between x and a.

Now $P_n(x)$ is the nth partial sum of the Taylor series of f at a. So if we show that $\lim_{n \to +\infty} P_n(x)$ exists and equals $f(x)$ if and only if $\lim_{n \to +\infty} R_n(x) = 0$, the theorem will be proved. From Eq. (13) we have

$$P_n(x) = f(x) - R_n(x) \tag{15}$$

If $\lim_{n \to +\infty} R_n(x) = 0$, it follows from Eq. (15) that

$$\lim_{n \to +\infty} P_n(x) = f(x) - \lim_{n \to +\infty} R_n(x)$$
$$= f(x) - 0$$
$$= f(x)$$

Now under the hypothesis that $\lim_{n \to +\infty} P_n(x) = f(x)$ we wish to show that $\lim_{n \to +\infty} R_n(x) = 0$. From Eq. (13) we have

$$R_n(x) = f(x) - P_n(x)$$

and so

$$\lim_{n \to +\infty} R_n(x) = f(x) - \lim_{n \to +\infty} P_n(x)$$

$$= f(x) - f(x)$$

$$= 0$$

This proves the theorem.   ∎

Theorem 14.10.1 also holds for other forms of the remainder $R_n(x)$ besides the Lagrange form.

It is often difficult to apply Theorem 14.10.1 in practice because the values of ξ_n are arbitrary. However, sometimes an upper bound for $R_n(x)$ can be found, and we may be able to prove that the limit of the upper bound is zero as $n \to +\infty$. The following limit is helpful in some cases:

$$\lim_{n \to +\infty} \frac{x^n}{n!} = 0 \qquad \text{for all } x \tag{16}$$

This follows from Example 2 of Sec. 14.7, where we showed that the power series $\sum_{n=0}^{+\infty} x^n/n!$ is convergent for all values of x and hence the limit of its nth term must be zero. In a similar manner, because $\sum_{n=0}^{+\infty} (x - a)^n/n!$ is convergent for all values of x, we have

$$\lim_{n \to +\infty} \frac{(x - a)^n}{n!} = 0 \qquad \text{for all } x \tag{17}$$

EXAMPLE 4: Use Theorem 14.10.1 to show that the Maclaurin series for e^x, found in Example 1, represents the function for all values of x.

SOLUTION: The Maclaurin series for e^x is series (11) and

$$R_n(x) = \frac{e^{\xi_n}}{(n + 1)!} x^{n+1}$$

where each ξ_n is between 0 and x.

We must show that $\lim_{n \to +\infty} R_n = 0$ for all x. We distinguish three cases: $x > 0$, $x < 0$, and $x = 0$.

If $x > 0$, then $0 < \xi_n < x$; hence, $e^\xi < e^x$. So

$$0 < \frac{e^{\xi_n}}{(n + 1)!} x^{n+1} < e^x \frac{x^{n+1}}{(n + 1)!} \tag{18}$$

From (16) it follows that $\lim_{n \to +\infty} x^{n+1}/(n + 1)! = 0$, and so

$$\lim_{n \to +\infty} e^x \frac{x^{n+1}}{(n + 1)!} = 0$$

Therefore, from (18) and the squeeze theorem (2.10.5) we can conclude that $\lim_{n \to +\infty} R_n(x) = 0$.

If $x < 0$, then $x < \xi_n < 0$ and $0 < e^{\xi_n} < 1$. Therefore, if $x^{n+1} > 0$,

$$0 < \frac{e^{\xi_n}}{(n+1)!} x^{n+1} < \frac{x^{n+1}}{(n+1)!}$$

and if $x^{n+1} < 0$,

$$\frac{x^{n+1}}{(n+1)!} < \frac{e^{\xi_n}}{(n+1)!} x^{n+1} < 0$$

In either case, because $\lim_{n \to +\infty} x^{n+1}/(n+1)! = 0$, it follows that $\lim_{n \to +\infty} R_n = 0$. Finally, if $x = 0$, the series has the sum of 1 which is e^0. Hence, we can conclude that the series (11) represents e^x for all values of x.

From the results of the above example we can write

$$e^x = \sum_{n=0}^{+\infty} \frac{x^n}{n!} = 1 + x + \frac{x^2}{2!} + \frac{x^3}{3!} + \cdots \qquad \text{for all } x \qquad (19)$$

and this agrees with Example 4 of Sec. 14.8.

EXAMPLE 5: Show that the Taylor series for $\sin x$ at a, found in Example 2, represents the function for all values of x.

SOLUTION: We use Theorem 14.10.1; so we must show that

$$\lim_{n \to +\infty} R_n(x) = \lim_{n \to +\infty} \frac{f^{(n+1)}(\xi_n)}{(n+1)!} (x-a)^{n+1} = 0$$

Because $f(x) = \sin x$, $f^{(n+1)}(\xi_n)$ will be one of the following numbers: $\cos \xi_n$, $\sin \xi_n$, $-\cos \xi_n$, or $-\sin \xi_n$. In any case, $|f^{(n+1)}(\xi_n)| \leq 1$. Hence,

$$0 < |R_n(x)| \leq \frac{|x-a|^{n+1}}{(n+1)!} \qquad (20)$$

From (17) we know that $\lim_{n \to +\infty} |x-a|^{n+1}/(n+1)! = 0$. Thus, by the squeeze theorem (2.10.5) and (20) it follows that $\lim_{n \to +\infty} R_n(x) = 0$.

EXAMPLE 6: Compute the value of $\sin 47°$ accurate to four decimal places.

SOLUTION: In Examples 2 and 5 we obtained the Taylor series for $\sin x$ at a which represents the function for all values of x. It is

$$\sin x = \sin a + \cos a (x-a) - \sin a \frac{(x-a)^2}{2!} - \cos a \frac{(x-a)^3}{3!} + \cdots$$

To make $(x-a)$ small we choose a value of a near the value of x for which we are computing the function value. We also need to know the sine and cosine of a. We therefore choose $a = \frac{1}{4}\pi$ and have

$$\sin x = \sin \tfrac{1}{4}\pi + \cos \tfrac{1}{4}\pi (x - \tfrac{1}{4}\pi) - \sin \tfrac{1}{4}\pi \frac{(x - \tfrac{1}{4}\pi)^2}{2!}$$

$$- \cos \tfrac{1}{4}\pi \frac{(x - \tfrac{1}{4}\pi)^3}{3!} + \cdots \qquad (21)$$

Because $47°$ is equivalent to $\frac{47}{180}\pi$ radians $= (\frac{1}{4}\pi + \frac{1}{90}\pi)$ radians, from Eq.

(21) we have

$$\sin \tfrac{47}{180}\pi = \tfrac{1}{2}\sqrt{2} + \tfrac{1}{2}\sqrt{2} \cdot \tfrac{1}{90}\pi - \tfrac{1}{2}\sqrt{2} \cdot \tfrac{1}{2}(\tfrac{1}{90}\pi)^2 - \tfrac{1}{2}\sqrt{2} \cdot \tfrac{1}{6}(\tfrac{1}{90}\pi)^3 + \cdots$$

$$= \tfrac{1}{2}\sqrt{2}(1 + 0.03490 - 0.00061 - 0.000002 + \cdots)$$

Taking $\sqrt{2} = 1.41421$ and using the first three terms of the series, we get

$$\sin \tfrac{47}{180}\pi \approx (0.70711)(1.03429) = 0.73136$$

Rounding off to four decimal places gives $\sin 47° \approx 0.7314$. The error introduced by using the first three terms is $R_2(\tfrac{47}{180}\pi)$, and from (20) we have

$$\left| R_2\left(\frac{47}{180}\pi\right) \right| \le \frac{(\tfrac{1}{90}\pi)^3}{3!} = 0.00001$$

Our result, then, is accurate to four decimal places.

The following Maclaurin series represent the function for all values of x:

$$\sin x = \sum_{n=0}^{+\infty} \frac{(-1)^n x^{2n+1}}{(2n+1)!} = x - \frac{x^3}{3!} + \frac{x^5}{5!} - \frac{x^7}{7!} + \cdots \tag{22}$$

$$\cos x = \sum_{n=0}^{+\infty} \frac{(-1)^n x^{2n}}{(2n)!} = 1 - \frac{x^2}{2!} + \frac{x^4}{4!} - \frac{x^6}{6!} + \cdots \tag{23}$$

$$\sinh x = \sum_{n=0}^{+\infty} \frac{x^{2n+1}}{(2n+1)!} = x + \frac{x^3}{3!} + \frac{x^5}{5!} + \frac{x^7}{7!} + \cdots \tag{24}$$

$$\cosh x = \sum_{n=0}^{+\infty} \frac{x^{2n}}{(2n)!} = 1 + \frac{x^2}{2!} + \frac{x^4}{4!} + \frac{x^6}{6!} + \cdots \tag{25}$$

Series (22) is a direct result of Examples 2 and 5 with $a = 0$. You are asked to verify series (23), (24), and (25) in Exercises 1, 2, and 3.

EXAMPLE 7:   Evaluate

$$\int_{1/2}^{1} \frac{\sin x}{x}\, dx$$

accurate to six decimal places.

SOLUTION: We cannot find an antiderivative of the integrand in terms of elementary functions. However, using series (22) we have

$$\frac{\sin x}{x} = \frac{1}{x} \cdot \sin x$$

$$= \frac{1}{x}\left(x - \frac{x^3}{3!} + \frac{x^5}{5!} - \frac{x^7}{7!} + \frac{x^9}{9!} - \cdots \right)$$

$$= 1 - \frac{x^2}{3!} + \frac{x^4}{5!} - \frac{x^6}{7!} + \frac{x^8}{9!} - \cdots$$

which is true for all $x \neq 0$. Using term-by-term integration we get

$$\int_{1/2}^{1} \frac{\sin x}{x}\, dx = x - \frac{x^3}{3 \cdot 3!} + \frac{x^5}{5 \cdot 5!} - \frac{x^7}{7 \cdot 7!} + \frac{x^9}{9 \cdot 9!} - \cdots \Big]_{1/2}^{1}$$

$$= (1 - 0.0555555 + 0.0016667 - 0.0000283 + 0.0000003 - \cdots)$$

$$- (0.5 - 0.0069444 + 0.0000521 - 0.0000002 + \cdots)$$

In each set of parentheses we have a convergent alternating series with $|u_{n+1}| < |u_n|$. In the first set of parentheses we use the first four terms because the error obtained is less than 0.0000003. In the second set of parentheses we use the first three terms where the error obtained is less than 0.0000002. Doing the arithmetic and rounding off to six decimal places, we get

$$\int_{1/2}^{1} \frac{\sin x}{x}\, dx \approx 0.452975$$

Exercises 14.10

1. Prove that the series

$$\sum_{n=0}^{+\infty} \frac{(-1)^n x^{2n}}{(2n)!}$$

represents cos x for all values of x.

2. Prove that the series

$$\sum_{n=0}^{+\infty} \frac{x^{2n+1}}{(2n+1)!}$$

represents sinh x for all values of x.

3. Prove that the series

$$\sum_{n=0}^{+\infty} \frac{x^{2n}}{(2n)!}$$

represents cosh x for all values of x.

4. Obtain the Maclaurin series for the cosine function by differentiating the Maclaurin series for the sine function. Also obtain the Maclaurin series for the sine function by differentiating the one for the cosine function.

5. Obtain the Maclaurin series for the hyperbolic sine function by differentiating the Maclaurin series for the hyperbolic cosine function. Also differentiate the Maclaurin series for the hyperbolic sine function to obtain the one for the hyperbolic cosine function.

6. Find the Taylor series for e^x at 3 by using the Maclaurin series for e^x.

7. Use the Maclaurin series for $\ln(1 + x)$ to find the Taylor series for $\ln x$ at 2.

8. Given $\ln 2 = 0.6931$, use the series obtained in Exercise 7 to find $\ln 3$ accurate to four decimal places.

In Exercises 9 through 14, find a power-series representation for the given function at the number a and determine its radius of convergence.

9. $f(x) = \ln(1 + x)$; $a = 1$

10. $f(x) = \dfrac{1}{x}$; $a = 1$

11. $f(x) = \sqrt{x}$; $a = 4$

12. $f(x) = 2^x$; $a = 0$

13. $f(x) = \cos x$; $a = \frac{1}{3}\pi$

14. $f(x) = \ln |x|$; $a = -1$

15. Find the Maclaurin series for $\sin^2 x$. (HINT: Use $\sin^2 x = \frac{1}{2}(1 - \cos 2x)$.)

16. Find the Maclaurin series for $\cos^2 x$. (HINT: Use $\cos^2 x = \frac{1}{2}(1 + \cos 2x)$.)

17. (a) Find the first three nonzero terms of the Maclaurin series for tan x. (b) Use the result of part (a) and term-by-term differentiation to find the first three nonzero terms of the Maclaurin series for sec^2 x. (c) Use the result of part (a) and term-by-term integration to find the first three nonzero terms of the Maclaurin series for ln cos x.

In Exercises 18 through 23, use a power series to compute the value of the given quantity to the indicated accuracy.

18. sinh $\frac{1}{2}$; five decimal places.

19. cos 58°; four decimal places.

20. $\sqrt[5]{e}$; four decimal places.

21. $\sqrt[5]{30}$; five decimal places.

22. $\sqrt[3]{29}$; three decimal places.

23. ln(0.8); four decimal places.

24. Compute the value of e correct to seven decimal places, and prove that your answer has the required accuracy.

In Exercises 25 through 29, compute the value of the definite integral accurate to four decimal places.

25. $\displaystyle\int_{0}^{1/2} \sin x^2 \, dx$

26. $\displaystyle\int_{0}^{1} \cos \sqrt{x} \, dx$

27. $\displaystyle\int_{0}^{0.1} \ln(1 + \sin x) \, dx$

28. $\displaystyle\int_0^{1/3} f(x)\,dx$, where $f(x) = \begin{cases} \dfrac{\sin x}{x} & \text{if } x \neq 0 \\ 1 & \text{if } x = 0 \end{cases}$

29. $\displaystyle\int_0^1 g(x)\,dx$, where $g(x) = \begin{cases} \dfrac{1-\cos x}{x} & \text{if } x \neq 0 \\ 0 & \text{if } x = 0 \end{cases}$

30. The function E defined by

$$E(x) = \frac{2}{\sqrt{\pi}} \int_0^x e^{-t^2}\,dt$$

is called the *error function,* and it is important in mathematical statistics. Find the Maclaurin series for the error function.

31. Determine a_n $(n = 0, 1, 2, 3, 4)$ so that the polynomial

$$f(x) = 3x^4 - 17x^3 + 35x^2 - 32x + 17$$

is written in the form

$$f(x) = a_4(x-1)^4 + a_3(x-1)^3 + a_2(x-1)^2 + a_1(x-1) + a_0$$

14.11 THE BINOMIAL SERIES

In elementary algebra you learned that the binomial theorem expresses $(a+b)^m$ as a sum of powers of a and b, where m is a positive integer, as follows:

$$\left(\begin{array}{l} (a+b)^m = a^m + ma^{m-1}b + \dfrac{m(m-1)}{2!}\,a^{m-2}b^2 + \cdots \\[2mm] \qquad + \dfrac{m(m-1)\,\cdot\,\ldots\,\cdot\,(m-k+1)}{k!}\,a^{m-k}b^k + \cdots + b^m \end{array}\right)$$

We now take $a = 1$ and $b = x$, and apply the binomial theorem to the expression $(1+x)^m$, where m is not a positive integer. We obtain the power series

$$1 + mx + \frac{m(m-1)}{2!}\,x^2 + \frac{m(m-1)(m-2)}{3!}\,x^3 + \cdots$$

$$\qquad + \frac{m(m-1)(m-2)\,\cdot\,\ldots\,\cdot\,(m-n+1)}{n!}\,x^n + \cdots \tag{1}$$

Series (1) is the Maclaurin series for $(1+x)^m$. It is called a *binomial series.* To find the radius of convergence of series (1), we apply the ratio test and get

$$\lim_{n \to +\infty} \left| \frac{u_{n+1}}{u_n} \right|$$

$$= \lim_{n \to +\infty} \left| \frac{\dfrac{m(m-1)\,\cdot\,\ldots\,\cdot\,(m-n+1)(m-n)}{(n+1)!}\,x^{n+1}}{\dfrac{m(m-1)\,\cdot\,\ldots\,\cdot\,(m-n+1)}{n!}\,x^n} \right|$$

$$= \lim_{n \to +\infty} \left| \frac{m-n}{n+1} \right| |x|$$

$$= \lim_{n \to +\infty} \left| \frac{\dfrac{m}{n} - 1}{1 + \dfrac{1}{n}} \right| |x|$$

$$= |x|$$

So the series is convergent if $|x| < 1$. We now prove that series (1) represents $(1 + x)^m$ for all real numbers m if x is in the open interval $(-1, 1)$. We do not do this by calculating $R_n(x)$ and showing that its limit is zero because this is quite difficult, as you will soon see if you attempt to do so. Instead, we use the following method. Let

$$f(x) = 1 + \sum_{n=1}^{+\infty} \frac{m(m-1) \cdot \ldots \cdot (m-n+1)}{n!} x^n \qquad |x| < 1 \qquad (2)$$

We wish to show that $f(x) = (1 + x)^m$, where $|x| < 1$. By Theorem 14.8.3 we have

$$f'(x) = \sum_{n=1}^{+\infty} \frac{m(m-1) \cdot \ldots \cdot (m-n+1)}{(n-1)!} x^{n-1} \qquad |x| < 1 \qquad (3)$$

Multiplying on both sides of Eq. (3) by x, we get from Theorem 14.3.8

$$xf'(x) = \sum_{n=1}^{+\infty} \frac{m(m-1) \cdot \ldots \cdot (m-n+1)}{(n-1)!} x^n \qquad (4)$$

Rewriting the right side of (3), we have

$$f'(x) = m + \sum_{n=2}^{+\infty} \frac{m(m-1) \cdot \ldots \cdot (m-n+1)}{(n-1)!} x^{n-1} \qquad (5)$$

Rewriting the summation in (5) by decreasing the lower limit by 1 and replacing n by $n + 1$, we get

$$f'(x) = m + \sum_{n=1}^{+\infty} (m-n) \frac{m(m-1) \cdot \ldots \cdot (m-n+1)}{n!} x^n \qquad (6)$$

If in (4) we multiply the numerator and the denominator by n, we get

$$xf'(x) = \sum_{n=1}^{+\infty} n \frac{m(m-1) \cdot \ldots \cdot (m-n+1)}{n!} x^n \qquad (7)$$

Because the series in (6) and (7) are absolutely convergent for $|x| < 1$, then by Theorem 14.3.9 we can add them term by term, and the resulting series will be absolutely convergent for $|x| < 1$. When we add we get

$$(1 + x)f'(x) = m \left[1 + \sum_{n=1}^{+\infty} \frac{m(m-1) \cdot \ldots \cdot (m-n+1)}{n!} x^n \right]$$

Because by (2) the expression in brackets is $f(x)$, we have

$$(1 + x)f'(x) = mf(x)$$

or, equivalently,

$$\frac{f'(x)}{f(x)} = \frac{m}{1+x}$$

The left side of the above equation is $D_x[\ln f(x)]$; so we can write

$$D_x[\ln f(x)] = \frac{m}{1+x}$$

However, we also know that

$$D_x[\ln(1+x)^m] = \frac{m}{1+x}$$

Because $\ln f(x)$ and $\ln(1+x)^m$ have the same derivative, they differ by a constant. Hence,

$$\ln f(x) = \ln(1+x)^m + C$$

We see from (2) that $f(0) = 1$. Therefore, $C = 0$ and we get

$$f(x) = (1+x)^m$$

We have proved the general binomial theorem, which we now state.

14.11.1 Theorem
Binomial Theorem

If m is any real number, then

$$(1+x)^m = 1 + \sum_{n=1}^{+\infty} \frac{m(m-1)(m-2)\cdot\,\ldots\,\cdot(m-n+1)}{n!}\,x^n \qquad (8)$$

for all values of x such that $|x| < 1$.

If m is a positive integer, the binomial series will terminate after a finite number of terms.

EXAMPLE 1: Express

$$\frac{1}{\sqrt{1+x}}$$

as a power series in x.

SOLUTION: From Theorem 14.11.1 we have, when $|x| < 1$,

$$(1+x)^{-1/2} = 1 - \frac{1}{2}x + \frac{(-\frac{1}{2})(-\frac{1}{2}-1)}{2!}x^2 + \frac{(-\frac{1}{2})(-\frac{1}{2}-1)(-\frac{1}{2}-2)}{3!}x^3$$

$$+\cdots+ \frac{(-\frac{1}{2})(-\frac{3}{2})(-\frac{5}{2})\cdot\,\ldots\,\cdot(-\frac{1}{2}-n+1)\,x^n}{n!} +\cdots$$

$$= 1 - \frac{1}{2}x + \frac{1\cdot3}{2^2\cdot2!}x^2 - \frac{1\cdot3\cdot5}{2^3\cdot3!}x^3 +\cdots$$

$$+ (-1)^n \frac{1\cdot3\cdot5\cdot\,\ldots\,\cdot(2n-1)}{2^n n!}x^n +\cdots$$

EXAMPLE 2: From the result of Example 1 obtain a binomial series for $(1-x^2)^{-1/2}$ and use it to find a power series for $\sin^{-1} x$.

SOLUTION: Replacing x by $-x^2$ in the series for $(1+x)^{-1/2}$, we get for $|x| < 1$

$$(1-x^2)^{-1/2} = 1 + \frac{1}{2}x^2 + \frac{1\cdot3}{2^2\cdot2!}x^4 + \frac{1\cdot3\cdot5}{2^3\cdot3!}x^6 +\cdots$$

$$+ \frac{1\cdot3\cdot5\cdot\,\ldots\,\cdot(2n-1)}{2^n n!}x^{2n} +\cdots$$

Applying Theorem 14.9.1, we integrate term by term and obtain

$$\int_0^x \frac{dt}{\sqrt{1-t^2}} = x + \frac{1}{2} \cdot \frac{x^3}{3} + \frac{1 \cdot 3}{2^2 \cdot 2!} \cdot \frac{x^5}{5} + \frac{1 \cdot 3 \cdot 5}{2^3 \cdot 3!} \cdot \frac{x^7}{7} + \cdots$$

$$+ \frac{1 \cdot 3 \cdot 5 \cdot \ldots \cdot (2n-1)}{2^n n!} \cdot \frac{x^{2n+1}}{2n+1} + \cdots$$

and so

$$\sin^{-1} x = x + \sum_{n=1}^{+\infty} \frac{1 \cdot 3 \cdot 5 \cdot \ldots \cdot (2n-1)}{2^n n!} \cdot \frac{x^{2n+1}}{2n+1} \qquad \text{for } |x| < 1$$

EXAMPLE 3:   Compute the value of $\sqrt[3]{25}$ accurate to three decimal places by using the binomial series for $(1+x)^{1/3}$.

SOLUTION: From Eq. (8) we have

$$(1+x)^{1/3} = 1 + \frac{1}{3}x + \left(\frac{1}{3}\right)\left(-\frac{2}{3}\right)\frac{x^2}{2!} + \left(\frac{1}{3}\right)\left(-\frac{2}{3}\right)\left(-\frac{5}{3}\right)\frac{x^3}{3!} + \cdots \qquad (9)$$

$$\text{if } |x| < 1$$

We can write

$$\sqrt[3]{25} = \sqrt[3]{27}\,\sqrt[3]{\tfrac{25}{27}} = 3\sqrt[3]{1 - \tfrac{2}{27}} = 3\left(1 - \tfrac{2}{27}\right)^{1/3} \qquad (10)$$

Using Eq. (9) with $x = -\frac{2}{27}$, we get

$$\left(1 - \frac{2}{27}\right)^{1/3} = 1 + \frac{1}{3}\left(-\frac{2}{27}\right) - \frac{2}{3^2 \cdot 2!}\left(-\frac{2}{27}\right)^2 + \frac{2 \cdot 5}{3^3 \cdot 3!}\left(-\frac{2}{27}\right)^3 + \cdots$$

$$= 1 - 0.0247 - 0.0006 - 0.00003 - \cdots \qquad (11)$$

If the first three terms of the above series are used, we see from Eq. (14) of Sec. 14.10 that the remainder is

$$R_2\left(-\frac{2}{27}\right) = \frac{f'''(\xi_2)}{3!}\left(-\frac{2}{27}\right)^3$$

$$= \left(\frac{1}{3}\right)\left(-\frac{2}{3}\right)\left(-\frac{5}{3}\right)\left(\frac{1}{3!}\right)(1+\xi_2)^{(1/3)-3}\left(-\frac{2}{27}\right)^3$$

where $-\frac{2}{27} < \xi_2 < 0$. Therefore,

$$\left|R_2\left(-\frac{2}{27}\right)\right| = \left(\frac{2 \cdot 5}{3^3 \cdot 3!}\right)\frac{(1+\xi_2)^{1/3}}{(1+\xi_2)^3}\left(\frac{2}{27}\right)^3 \qquad (12)$$

Because $-\frac{2}{27} < \xi_2 < 0$, it follows that

$$(1+\xi_2)^{1/3} < 1^{1/3} = 1 \quad \text{and} \quad \frac{1}{(1+\xi_2)^3} < \frac{1}{\left(\frac{25}{27}\right)^3} \qquad (13)$$

Furthermore,

$$\frac{2 \cdot 5}{3^3 \cdot 3!} = \frac{2 \cdot 5}{3 \cdot 3 \cdot 3 \cdot 1 \cdot 2 \cdot 3} = \frac{2}{3} \cdot \frac{5}{6} \cdot \frac{1}{9} < \frac{1}{9} \qquad (14)$$

and so using inequalities (13) and (14) in (12) we see that

$$\left| R\left(-\frac{2}{27}\right) \right| < \frac{1}{9} \cdot \frac{1}{(\frac{25}{27})^3} \cdot \left(\frac{2}{27}\right)^3 = \frac{8}{140,625} < 0.00006$$

Using, then, the first three terms of series (11) gives

$$\left(1 - \frac{2}{27}\right)^{1/3} \approx 0.9747$$

with an error less than 0.00006. From (10) we obtain

$$\sqrt[3]{25} \approx 3(0.9747) = 2.9241$$

with an error less than $3(0.00006) = 0.00018$. Rounding off to three decimal places gives $\sqrt[3]{25} \approx 2.924$.

Exercises 14.11

In Exercises 1 through 6, use a binomial series to find the Maclaurin series for the given function. Determine the radius of convergence of the resulting series.

1. $f(x) = \sqrt{1 + x}$
2. $f(x) = (9 + x^4)^{-1/2}$
3. $f(x) = (4 + x^2)^{-1}$

4. $f(x) = \sqrt[3]{8 + x}$
5. $f(x) = \dfrac{x^2}{\sqrt{1 + x}}$
6. $f(x) = \dfrac{x}{\sqrt[3]{1 + x^2}}$

7. Integrate term by term from 0 to x the binomial series for $(1 + t^2)^{-1/2}$ to obtain the Maclaurin series for $\sinh^{-1} x$. Determine the radius of convergence.

8. Use a method similar to that of Exercise 7 to find the Maclaurin series for $\tanh^{-1} x$. Determine the radius of convergence.

In Exercises 9 through 12 compute the value of the given quantity accurate to three decimal places by using a binomial series.

9. $\sqrt{24}$
10. $\sqrt[3]{66}$
11. $\sqrt[4]{630}$

12. $\dfrac{1}{\sqrt[5]{31}}$

In Exercises 13 through 16 compute the value of the definite integral accurate to four decimal places.

13. $\displaystyle\int_0^{1/3} \frac{dx}{\sqrt[3]{x^2 + 1}}$
14. $\displaystyle\int_0^1 \sqrt{1 - x^3}\, dx$
15. $\displaystyle\int_0^{1/2} \frac{dx}{\sqrt{1 - x^3}}$

16. $\displaystyle\int_0^{1/2} f(x)\, dx$, where $f(x) = \begin{cases} \dfrac{\sin^{-1} x}{x} & \text{if } x \neq 0 \\ 1 & \text{if } x = 0 \end{cases}$

Review Exercises (Chapter 14)

In Exercises 1 through 6, write the first four numbers of the sequence and find the limit of the sequence, if it exists.

1. $\left\{\dfrac{3n}{n + 2}\right\}$
2. $\left\{\dfrac{(-1)^{n-1}}{(n + 1)^2}\right\}$
3. $\left\{\dfrac{n^2 - 1}{n^2 + 1}\right\}$
4. $\left\{\dfrac{n + 3n^2}{4 + 2n^3}\right\}$
5. $\{2 + (-1)^n\}$
6. $\left\{\dfrac{n^2}{n + 2} - \dfrac{n^2}{n - 2}\right\}$

In Exercises 7 through 11, determine if the series is convergent or divergent. If the series is convergent, find its sum.

7. $\displaystyle\sum_{n=1}^{+\infty} \left(\frac{3}{4}\right)^n$

8. $\displaystyle\sum_{n=1}^{+\infty} e^{-2n}$

9. $\displaystyle\sum_{n=1}^{+\infty} \frac{n-1}{n+1}$

10. $\displaystyle\sum_{n=0}^{+\infty} [(-1)^n + (-1)^{n+1}]$

11. $\displaystyle\sum_{n=0}^{+\infty} \sin^n \tfrac{1}{3}\pi$

12. $\displaystyle\sum_{n=0}^{+\infty} \cos^n \tfrac{1}{3}\pi$

13. $\displaystyle\sum_{n=1}^{+\infty} \frac{1}{(3n-1)(3n+2)}$ (HINT: To find the sum, first find the sequence of partial sums.)

In Exercises 14 through 25, determine if the series is convergent or divergent.

14. $\displaystyle\sum_{n=1}^{+\infty} \frac{1}{(2n+1)^3}$

15. $\displaystyle\sum_{n=1}^{+\infty} \frac{2}{n^2+6n}$

16. $\displaystyle\sum_{n=1}^{+\infty} \frac{3+\sin n}{n^2}$

17. $\displaystyle\sum_{n=1}^{+\infty} \cos\left(\frac{\pi}{2n^2-1}\right)$

18. $\displaystyle\sum_{n=1}^{+\infty} \frac{n}{\sqrt{3n+2}}$

19. $\displaystyle\sum_{n=1}^{+\infty} \frac{(n!)^2}{(2n)!}$

20. $\displaystyle\sum_{n=1}^{+\infty} \frac{(-1)^{n+1}}{1+\sqrt{n}}$

21. $\displaystyle\sum_{n=1}^{+\infty} (-1)^n \ln \frac{1}{n}$

22. $\displaystyle\sum_{n=1}^{+\infty} \frac{\ln n}{n^2}$

23. $\displaystyle\sum_{n=2}^{+\infty} \frac{1}{n(\ln n)^2}$

24. $\displaystyle\sum_{n=0}^{+\infty} \frac{n!}{10^n}$

25. $\displaystyle\sum_{n=1}^{+\infty} \frac{1}{1+2\ln n}$

In Exercises 26 through 33, determine if the given series is absolutely convergent, conditionally convergent, or divergent. Prove your answer.

26. $\displaystyle\sum_{n=0}^{+\infty} (-1)^n \frac{5^{2n+1}}{(2n+1)!}$

27. $\displaystyle\sum_{n=0}^{+\infty} (-1)^n \frac{n^2}{3^n}$

28. $\displaystyle\sum_{n=1}^{+\infty} (-1)^{n-1} \frac{6^n}{5^{n+1}}$

29. $\displaystyle\sum_{n=1}^{+\infty} (-1)^{n-1} \frac{1}{(n+1)^{3/4}}$

30. $\displaystyle\sum_{n=1}^{+\infty} (-1)^n \frac{\sqrt{2n-1}}{n}$

31. $\displaystyle\sum_{n=1}^{+\infty} (-1)^n \frac{n!}{10n}$

32. $\displaystyle\sum_{n=1}^{+\infty} c_n$, where $c_n = \begin{cases} -\dfrac{1}{n} & \text{if } \tfrac{1}{4}n \text{ is an integer} \\ \dfrac{1}{n^2} & \text{if } \tfrac{1}{4}n \text{ is not an integer} \end{cases}$

33. $\displaystyle\sum_{n=1}^{+\infty} c_n$, where $c_n = \begin{cases} -\dfrac{1}{n} & \text{if } n \text{ is a perfect square} \\ \dfrac{1}{n^2} & \text{if } n \text{ is not a perfect square} \end{cases}$

In Exercises 34 through 42, find the interval of convergence of the given power series.

34. $\displaystyle\sum_{n=0}^{+\infty} \frac{x^n}{2^n}$

35. $\displaystyle\sum_{n=1}^{+\infty} \frac{x^n}{\sqrt{n}}$

36. $\displaystyle\sum_{n=1}^{+\infty} \frac{(x-2)^n}{n}$

37. $\displaystyle\sum_{n=1}^{+\infty} \frac{x^n}{3^n(n^2+n)}$

38. $\displaystyle\sum_{n=1}^{+\infty} n(2x-1)^n$

39. $\displaystyle\sum_{n=0}^{+\infty} \frac{n!}{2^n} (x-3)^n$

40. $\displaystyle\sum_{n=1}^{+\infty} \frac{(-1)^{n-1} x^{2n-1}}{(2n-1)!}$

41. $\displaystyle\sum_{n=1}^{+\infty} \frac{n^2}{6^n} (x+1)^n$

42. $\displaystyle\sum_{n=1}^{+\infty} n^n x^n$

In Exercises 43 through 50, use a power series to compute the value of the given quantity accurate to four decimal places.

43. $\tan^{-1} \frac{1}{5}$

44. $\sin 0.3$

45. $\sqrt[3]{130}$

46. $\sin^{-1} 1$

47. $\cos 3°$

48. $\sqrt[4]{e}$

49. $\displaystyle\int_0^{1/4} \sqrt{x} \sin x \, dx$

50. $\displaystyle\int_0^1 \cos x^3 \, dx$

In Exercises 51 through 53, find the Maclaurin series for the given function and find its interval of convergence.

51. $f(x) = a^x (a > 0)$

52. $f(x) = \dfrac{1}{2 - x}$

53. $f(x) = \sin^3 x$

In Exercises 54 through 56, find the Taylor series for the given function at the given number.

54. $f(x) = e^{x-2}$; at 2

55. $f(x) = \sin 3x$; at $-\frac{1}{3}\pi$

56. $f(x) = \dfrac{1}{x}$; at 2

Exercises 57 through 61 pertain to the functions J_0 and J_1 defined by power series as follows:

$$J_0(x) = \sum_{n=0}^{+\infty} (-1)^n \frac{x^{2n}}{n!n!2^{2n}} \qquad J_1(x) = \sum_{n=0}^{+\infty} (-1)^n \frac{x^{2n+1}}{n!(n+1)!2^{2n+1}}$$

The functions J_0 and J_1 are called *Bessel functions of the first kind* of orders zero and one, respectively.

57. Show that both J_0 and J_1 converge for all real values of x.

58. Show that $J_0'(x) = -J_1(x)$.

59. Show that $D_x(xJ_1(x)) = xJ_0(x)$.

60. Show that $y = J_0(x)$ is a solution of the differential equation

$$x \frac{d^2y}{dx^2} + \frac{dy}{dx} + xy = 0$$

61. Show that $y = J_1(x)$ is a solution of the differential equation

$$x^2 \frac{d^2y}{dx^2} + x \frac{dy}{dx} + (x^2 - 1)y = 0$$

15

Vectors in the Plane and Parametric Equations

15.1 VECTORS IN THE PLANE

In the application of mathematics to physics and engineering, we are often concerned with quantities that possess both *magnitude* and *direction;* examples of these are *force, velocity, acceleration,* and *displacement.* Such quantities may be represented geometrically by a *directed line segment.* Physicists and engineers refer to a directed line segment as a *vector,* and the quantities that have both magnitude and direction are called *vector quantities.* The study of vectors is called *vector analysis.*

The approach to vector analysis can be on either a geometric or an analytic basis. If the geometric approach is taken, we first define a directed line segment as a line segment from a point P to a point Q and denote this directed line segment by $\overrightarrow{PQ}$. The point P is called the *initial point,* and the point Q is called the *terminal point.* Then two directed line segments $\overrightarrow{PQ}$ and $\overrightarrow{RS}$ are said to be equal if they have the same *length* and *direction,* and we write $\overrightarrow{PQ} = \overrightarrow{RS}$ (see Fig. 15.1.1). The directed line segment $\overrightarrow{PQ}$ is called the *vector* from P to Q. A vector is denoted by a single letter, set in boldface type, such as **A**. In some books, a letter in lightface type, with an arrow above it, is used to indicate a vector, for example, $\overrightarrow{A}$.

Continuing with the geometric approach to vector analysis, we note that if the directed line segment $\overrightarrow{PQ}$ is the vector **A**, and $\overrightarrow{PQ} = \overrightarrow{RS}$, the directed line segment $\overrightarrow{RS}$ is also the vector **A**. Then a vector is considered to be remaining unchanged if it is moved parallel to itself. With this interpretation of a vector, we can assume for convenience that every vector has its initial point at some fixed reference point. By taking this point as

$$\overrightarrow{PQ} = \overrightarrow{RS}$$

Figure 15.1.1

the origin of a rectangular cartesian-coordinate system, a vector can be defined analytically in terms of real numbers. Such a definition enables us to study vector analysis from a purely mathematical viewpoint.

In this book, we use the analytic approach; however, the geometric interpretation is used for illustrative purposes. We denote a vector in the plane by an ordered pair of real numbers and use the notation $\langle x, y \rangle$ instead of (x, y) to avoid confusing the notation for a vector with the notation for a point. We let V_2 be the set of all such ordered pairs. Following is the formal definition.

15.1.1 Definition   A *vector in the plane* is an ordered pair of real numbers $\langle x, y \rangle$. The numbers x and y are called the *components* of the vector $\langle x, y \rangle$.

There is a one-to-one correspondence between the vectors $\langle x, y \rangle$ in the plane and the points (x, y) in the plane. Let the vector **A** be the ordered pair of real numbers $\langle a_1, a_2 \rangle$. If we let A denote the point (a_1, a_2), then the vector **A** may be represented geometrically by the directed line segment $\overrightarrow{OA}$. Such a directed line segment is called a *representation* of vector **A**. Any directed line segment which is equal to $\overrightarrow{OA}$ is also a representation of vector **A**. The particular representation of a vector which has its initial point at the origin is called the *position representation* of the vector. For example, the vector $\langle 2, 3 \rangle$ has as its position representation the directed line segment from the origin to the point $(2, 3)$. The representation of the vector $\langle 2, 3 \rangle$ whose initial point is (h, k) has as its terminal point $(h + 2, 3 + k)$; refer to Fig. 15.1.2.

The vector $\langle 0, 0 \rangle$ is called the *zero vector*, and we denote it by **0**; that is,

$$\mathbf{0} = \langle 0, 0 \rangle$$

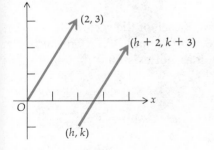

Figure 15.1.2

Any point is a representation of the zero vector. The zero vector has no direction.

15.1.2 Definition   The *magnitude* of a vector is the length of any of its representations, and the *direction* of a vector is the direction of any of its representations.

The magnitude of the vector **A** is denoted by $|\mathbf{A}|$.

15.1.3 Theorem   If **A** is the vector $\langle a_1, a_2 \rangle$, then $|\mathbf{A}| = \sqrt{a_1{}^2 + a_2{}^2}$

PROOF: Because by Definition 15.1.2, $|\mathbf{A}|$ is the length of any of the representations of **A**, then $|\mathbf{A}|$ will be the length of the position representation of **A**, which is the distance from the origin to the point (a_1, a_2). So from the formula for the distance between two points, we have

$$|\mathbf{A}| = \sqrt{(a_1 - 0)^2 + (a_2 - 0)^2} = \sqrt{a_1{}^2 + a_2{}^2} \qquad \blacksquare$$

It should be noted that $|\mathbf{A}|$ is a nonnegative number and not a vector. From Theorem 15.1.3 it follows that $|\mathbf{0}| = 0$.

EXAMPLE 1: Find the magnitude of the vector $\mathbf{A} = \langle -3, 5 \rangle$.

SOLUTION: $|\mathbf{A}| = \sqrt{(-3)^2 + 5^2} = \sqrt{34}$.

$$\tan \theta = \frac{a_2}{a_1}$$

The direction of any nonzero vector is given by the radian measure θ of the angle from the positive x axis counterclockwise to the position representation of the vector: $0 \le \theta < 2\pi$. So if $\mathbf{A} = \langle a_1, a_2 \rangle$, then $\tan \theta = a_2/a_1$ if $a_1 \ne 0$. If $a_1 = 0$, and $a_2 > 0$, then $\theta = \frac{1}{2}\pi$. If $a_1 = 0$ and $a_2 < 0$, then $\theta = \frac{3}{2}\pi$. Figures 15.1.3, 15.1.4, and 15.1.5 show the angle of radian measure θ for specific vectors $\langle a_1, a_2 \rangle$ whose position representations are drawn.

Figure 15.1.3

Figure 15.1.4

Figure 15.1.5

EXAMPLE 2: Find the radian measure of the angle giving the direction of each of the following vectors: (a) $\langle -1, 1 \rangle$; (b) $\langle 0, -5 \rangle$; (c) $\langle 1, -2 \rangle$.

SOLUTION: The position representation of each of the vectors in (a), (b), and (c) is shown in Figures 15.1.6, 15.1.7, and 15.1.8, respectively. (a) $\tan \theta = -1$; so $\theta = \frac{3}{4}\pi$; (b) $\tan \theta$ does not exist and $a_2 < 0$; $\theta = \frac{3}{2}\pi$; (c) $\tan \theta = -2$; $\theta = \tan^{-1}(-2) + 2\pi$.

Figure 15.1.6

Figure 15.1.7

Figure 15.1.8

If the vector $\mathbf{A} = \langle a_1, a_2 \rangle$, then the representation of $\mathbf{A}$ whose initial point is (x, y) has as its endpoint $(x + a_1, y + a_2)$. In this way a vector may be thought of as a translation of the plane into itself. Figure 15.1.9 illustrates five representations of the vector $\mathbf{A} = \langle a_1, a_2 \rangle$. In each case, $\mathbf{A}$ translates the point (x_i, y_i) into the point $(x_i + a_1, y_i + a_2)$. A two-dimensional vector, then, can be considered as a function whose domain and range are the set of points in the plane. If $\mathbf{A}$ is the vector which translates the point P into the point Q, we write $\mathbf{A}(P) = Q$. So if P is the point (x, y) and $\mathbf{A} = \langle a_1, a_2 \rangle$, then

$$\mathbf{A}(P) = (x + a_1, y + a_2) = Q$$

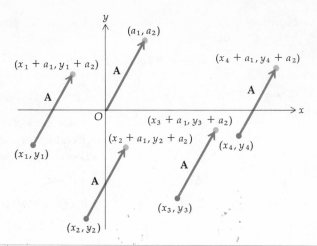

Figure 15.1.9

EXAMPLE 3: Given $\mathbf{A} = \langle 3, -4 \rangle$; $P_1 = (0, 0)$; $P_2 = (1, 4)$; $P_3 = (-6, 5)$, find $\mathbf{A}(P_1)$; $\mathbf{A}(P_2)$; $\mathbf{A}(P_3)$.	SOLUTION: $\mathbf{A}(P_1) = (3, -4)$; $\mathbf{A}(P_2) = (4, 0)$; $\mathbf{A}(P_3) = (-3, 1)$.

It should be noted that $\mathbf{A}(P) = P$ if and only if $\mathbf{A} = \langle 0, 0 \rangle$. Also, if $P = (x_1, y_1)$ and $Q = (x_2, y_2)$, there exists a unique vector $\mathbf{B}$ for which $\mathbf{B}(P) = Q$; and $\mathbf{B} = \langle x_2 - x_1, y_2 - y_1 \rangle$.

Exercises 15.1

In Exercises 1 through 6, draw the position representation of the given vector $\mathbf{A}$ and also the particular representation through the given point P; find the magnitude of $\mathbf{A}$.

1. $\mathbf{A} = \langle 3, 4 \rangle$; $P = (2, 1)$

2. $\mathbf{A} = \langle -2, 5 \rangle$; $P = (3, -4)$

3. $\mathbf{A} = \langle 0, -2 \rangle$; $P = (-3, 4)$

4. $\mathbf{A} = \langle 4, 0 \rangle$; $P = (2, 6)$

5. $\mathbf{A} = \langle 3, \sqrt{2} \rangle$; $P = (4, -\sqrt{2})$

6. $\mathbf{A} = \langle e, -\frac{1}{2} \rangle$; $P = (-2, -e)$

In Exercises 7 through 12, find $\mathbf{A}(P)$ for the given $\mathbf{A}$ and P. If $Q = \mathbf{A}(P)$, draw $\overrightarrow{PQ}$.

7. $\mathbf{A} = \langle 2, 6 \rangle$; $P = (1, 3)$

8. $\mathbf{A} = \langle -4, 1 \rangle$; $P = (-2, -3)$

9. $\mathbf{A} = \langle 0, 4 \rangle$; $P = (3, -4)$

10. $\mathbf{A} = \langle -3, 0 \rangle$; $P = (-1, -6)$

11. $\mathbf{A} = \langle \frac{1}{2}, \frac{1}{3} \rangle$; $P = (-\frac{1}{3}, -\frac{1}{2})$

12. $\mathbf{A} = \langle -3, -7 \rangle$; $P = (3, 7)$

In Exercises 13 through 18, find the vector $\mathbf{A}$ having $\overrightarrow{PQ}$ as a representation. Draw $\overrightarrow{PQ}$ and the position representation of $\mathbf{A}$.

13. $P = (3, 7)$; $Q = (5, 4)$

14. $P = (5, 4)$; $Q = (3, 7)$

15. $P = (-3, 5)$; $Q = (-5, -2)$

16. $P = (0, \sqrt{3})$; $Q = (2, 3\sqrt{3})$

17. $P = (-5, -3)$; $Q = (0, 3)$

18. $P = (-\sqrt{2}, 0)$; $Q = (0, 0)$

In Exercises 19 through 22, find the point S so that $\overrightarrow{PQ}$ and $\overrightarrow{RS}$ are each representations of the same vector.

19. $P = (2, 5)$; $Q = (1, 6)$; $R = (-3, 2)$

20. $P = (-1, 4)$; $Q = (2, -3)$; $R = (-5, -2)$

21. $P = (0, 3)$; $Q = (5, -2)$; $R = (7, 0)$

22. $P = (-2, 0)$; $Q = (-3, -4)$; $R = (4, 2)$

15.2 VECTOR ADDITION, SUBTRACTION, AND SCALAR MULTIPLICATION

The following definition gives the method for adding two vectors.

15.2.1 Definition

The *sum* of two vectors $\mathbf{A} = \langle a_1, a_2 \rangle$ and $\mathbf{B} = \langle b_1, b_2 \rangle$ is the vector $\mathbf{A} + \mathbf{B}$, defined by

$$\mathbf{A} + \mathbf{B} = \langle a_1 + b_1, a_2 + b_2 \rangle$$

EXAMPLE 1: Given $\mathbf{A} = \langle 3, -1 \rangle$, $\mathbf{B} = \langle -4, 5 \rangle$, find $\mathbf{A} + \mathbf{B}$.	SOLUTION: $\mathbf{A} + \mathbf{B} = \langle 3 + (-4), -1 + 5 \rangle = \langle -1, 4 \rangle$.

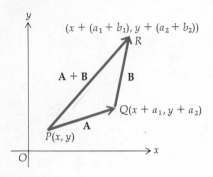

Figure 15.2.1

The geometric interpretation of the sum of two vectors is shown in Fig. 15.2.1. Let $\mathbf{A} = \langle a_1, a_2 \rangle$ and $\mathbf{B} = \langle b_1, b_2 \rangle$ and P be the point (x, y). Then

$$\mathbf{A}(P) = (x + a_1, y + a_2) = Q$$
$$\mathbf{B}(Q) = ((x + a_1) + b_1, (y + a_2) + b_2)$$
$$= (x + (a_1 + b_1), y + (a_2 + b_2))$$
$$= R$$

But

$$\mathbf{A} + \mathbf{B} = \langle a_1 + b_1, a_2 + b_2 \rangle$$

So

$$(\mathbf{A} + \mathbf{B})(P) = (x + (a_1 + b_1), y + (a_2 + b_2))$$
$$= R$$

Thus, in Fig. 15.2.1 $\overrightarrow{PQ}$ is a representation of the vector $\mathbf{A}$, $\overrightarrow{QR}$ is a representation of the vector $\mathbf{B}$, and $\overrightarrow{PR}$ is a representation of the vector $\mathbf{A} + \mathbf{B}$. The representations of the vectors $\mathbf{A}$ and $\mathbf{B}$ are adjacent sides of a parallelogram, and the representation of the vector $\mathbf{A} + \mathbf{B}$ is a diagonal of the parallelogram. Thus, the rule for the addition of vectors is sometimes referred to as the *parallelogram law*.

15.2.2 Definition

If $\mathbf{A} = \langle a_1, a_2 \rangle$, then the vector $\langle -a_1, -a_2 \rangle$ is defined to be the *negative* of $\mathbf{A}$, denoted by $-\mathbf{A}$.

Figure 15.2.2

If the directed line segment $\overrightarrow{PQ}$ is a representation of the vector $\mathbf{A}$, then the directed line segment $\overrightarrow{QP}$ is a representation of $-\mathbf{A}$. Any directed line segment which is parallel to $\overrightarrow{PQ}$, has the same length as $\overrightarrow{PQ}$, and has a direction opposite to that of $\overrightarrow{PQ}$ is also a representation of $-\mathbf{A}$ (see Fig. 15.2.2). We now define subtraction of two vectors.

15.2.3 Definition

The *difference* of the two vectors $\mathbf{A}$ and $\mathbf{B}$, denoted by $\mathbf{A} - \mathbf{B}$, is the vector obtained by adding $\mathbf{A}$ to the negative of $\mathbf{B}$; that is,

$$\mathbf{A} - \mathbf{B} = \mathbf{A} + (-\mathbf{B})$$

So if $\mathbf{A} = \langle a_1, a_2 \rangle$ and $\mathbf{B} = \langle b_1, b_2 \rangle$, then $-\mathbf{B} = \langle -b_1, -b_2 \rangle$, and so

$$\mathbf{A} - \mathbf{B} = \langle a_1 - b_1, a_2 - b_2 \rangle$$

EXAMPLE 2:   Given $\mathbf{A} = \langle 4, -2 \rangle$, $\mathbf{B} = \langle 6, -3 \rangle$, find $\mathbf{A} - \mathbf{B}$.

SOLUTION:

$$\mathbf{A} - \mathbf{B} = \langle 4, -2 \rangle - \langle 6, -3 \rangle$$
$$= \langle 4, -2 \rangle + \langle -6, 3 \rangle$$
$$= \langle -2, 1 \rangle$$

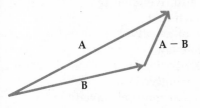

Figure 15.2.3

To interpret the difference of two vectors geometrically, let the representations of the vectors $\mathbf{A}$ and $\mathbf{B}$ have the same initial point. Then the directed line segment from the endpoint of the representation of $\mathbf{B}$ to the endpoint of the representation of $\mathbf{A}$ is a representation of the vector $\mathbf{A} - \mathbf{B}$. This obeys the parallelogram law $\mathbf{B} + (\mathbf{A} - \mathbf{B}) = \mathbf{A}$ (see Fig. 15.2.3).

Another operation with vectors is *scalar multiplication*. A *scalar* is a real number. Following is the definition of the multiplication of a vector by a scalar.

15.2.4 Definition If c is a scalar and $\mathbf{A}$ is the vector $\langle a_1, a_2 \rangle$, then the *product* of c and $\mathbf{A}$, denoted by $c\mathbf{A}$, is a vector and is given by

$$c\mathbf{A} = c\langle a_1, a_2 \rangle = \langle ca_1, ca_2 \rangle$$

EXAMPLE 3:   Given $\mathbf{A} = \langle 4, -5 \rangle$, find $3\mathbf{A}$.

SOLUTION: $3\mathbf{A} = 3\langle 4, -5 \rangle = \langle 12, -15 \rangle$.

EXAMPLE 4:   If $\mathbf{A}$ is any vector and c is any scalar, show that $0(\mathbf{A}) = \mathbf{0}$ and $c(\mathbf{0}) = \mathbf{0}$.

SOLUTION: From Definition 15.2.4 it follows that

$$0(\mathbf{A}) = 0\langle a_1, a_2 \rangle = \langle 0, 0 \rangle = \mathbf{0}$$

and

$$c(\mathbf{0}) = c\langle 0, 0 \rangle = \langle 0, 0 \rangle = \mathbf{0}$$

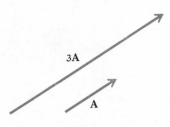

Figure 15.2.4

We compute the magnitude of the vector $c\mathbf{A}$ as follows.

$$c\mathbf{A} = \sqrt{(ca_1)^2 + (ca_2)^2}$$
$$= \sqrt{c^2(a_1{}^2 + a_2{}^2)}$$
$$= \sqrt{c^2}\ \sqrt{a_1{}^2 + a_2{}^2}$$
$$= |c||\mathbf{A}|$$

Therefore, the magnitude of $c\mathbf{A}$ is the absolute value of c times the magnitude of $\mathbf{A}$.

The geometric interpretation of the vector $c\mathbf{A}$ is given in Figs. 15.2.4 and 15.2.5. If $c > 0$, then $c\mathbf{A}$ is a vector whose representation has a length c times the magnitude of $\mathbf{A}$ and the same direction as $\mathbf{A}$; an example of this is shown in Fig. 15.2.4, where $c = 3$. If $c < 0$, then $c\mathbf{A}$ is a vector whose representation has a length which is $|c|$ times the magnitude of $\mathbf{A}$ and a direction opposite to that of $\mathbf{A}$. This is shown in Fig. 15.2.5, where $c = -\frac{1}{2}$.

The following theorem gives laws satisfied by the operations of vector addition and scalar multiplication of any vectors in V_2.

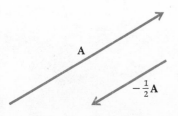

Figure 15.2.5

15.2.5 Theorem   If $\mathbf{A}$, $\mathbf{B}$, and $\mathbf{C}$ are any vectors in V_2, and c and d are any scalars, then vector addition and scalar multiplication satisfy the following properties:

$$
\begin{cases}
\text{(i)} & \mathbf{A} + \mathbf{B} = \mathbf{B} + \mathbf{A} \quad \text{(commutative law)} \\
\text{(ii)} & \mathbf{A} + (\mathbf{B} + \mathbf{C}) = (\mathbf{A} + \mathbf{B}) + \mathbf{C} \quad \text{(associative law)} \\
\text{(iii)} & \text{There is a vector } \mathbf{0} \text{ in } V_2 \text{ for which} \\
& \qquad \mathbf{A} + \mathbf{0} = \mathbf{A} \quad \text{(existence of additive identity)} \\
\text{(iv)} & \text{There is a vector } -\mathbf{A} \text{ in } V_2 \text{ such that} \\
& \qquad \mathbf{A} + (-\mathbf{A}) = \mathbf{0} \quad \text{(existence of negative)} \\
\text{(v)} & (cd)\mathbf{A} = c(d\mathbf{A}) \quad \text{(associative law)} \\
\text{(vi)} & c(\mathbf{A} + \mathbf{B}) = c\mathbf{A} + c\mathbf{B} \quad \text{(distributive law)} \\
\text{(vii)} & (c + d)\mathbf{A} = c\mathbf{A} + d\mathbf{A} \quad \text{(distributive law)} \\
\text{(viii)} & 1(\mathbf{A}) = \mathbf{A} \quad \text{(existence of scalar multiplicative identity)}
\end{cases}
$$

PROOF: We give the proofs of (i), (iv), and (vi) and leave the others for the reader (see Exercises 13 through 16). Let $\mathbf{A} = \langle a_1, a_2 \rangle$ and $\mathbf{B} = \langle b_1, b_2 \rangle$.

PROOF OF (i):   By the commutative law for real numbers, $a_1 + b_1 = b_1 + a_1$ and $a_2 + b_2 = b_2 + a_2$, and so we have

$$
\begin{aligned}
\mathbf{A} + \mathbf{B} &= \langle a_1, a_2 \rangle + \langle b_1, b_2 \rangle \\
&= \langle a_1 + b_1, a_2 + b_2 \rangle \\
&= \langle b_1 + a_1, b_2 + a_2 \rangle \\
&= \langle b_1, b_2 \rangle + \langle a_1, a_2 \rangle \\
&= \mathbf{B} + \mathbf{A}
\end{aligned}
$$

PROOF OF (iv):   The vector $-\mathbf{A}$ is given by Definition 15.2.2, and we have

$$
\begin{aligned}
\mathbf{A} + (-\mathbf{A}) &= \langle a_1, a_2 \rangle + \langle -a_1, -a_2 \rangle \\
&= \langle a_1 + (-a_1), a_2 + (-a_2) \rangle \\
&= \langle 0, 0 \rangle \\
&= \mathbf{0}
\end{aligned}
$$

PROOF OF (vi):

$$
\begin{aligned}
c(\mathbf{A} + \mathbf{B}) &= c(\langle a_1, a_2 \rangle + \langle b_1, b_2 \rangle) \\
&= c(\langle a_1 + b_1, a_2 + b_2 \rangle) \\
&= \langle c(a_1 + b_1), c(a_2 + b_2) \rangle \\
&= \langle ca_1 + cb_1, ca_2 + cb_2 \rangle \\
&= \langle ca_1, ca_2 \rangle + \langle cb_1, cb_2 \rangle \\
&= c\langle a_1, a_2 \rangle + c\langle b_1, b_2 \rangle \\
&= c\mathbf{A} + c\mathbf{B}
\end{aligned}
$$

EXAMPLE 5: Verify (ii), (iii), (v), (vii), and (viii) of Theorem 15.2.5 if $\mathbf{A} = \langle 3, 4 \rangle$, $\mathbf{B} = \langle -2, 1 \rangle$, $\mathbf{C} = \langle 5, -3 \rangle$, $c = 2$, and $d = -6$.

SOLUTION:

$$\mathbf{A} + (\mathbf{B} + \mathbf{C}) = \langle 3, 4 \rangle + (\langle -2, 1 \rangle + \langle 5, -3 \rangle)$$
$$= \langle 3, 4 \rangle + \langle 3, -2 \rangle$$
$$= \langle 6, 2 \rangle$$

$$(\mathbf{A} + \mathbf{B}) + \mathbf{C} = (\langle 3, 4 \rangle + \langle -2, 1 \rangle) + \langle 5, -3 \rangle$$
$$= \langle 1, 5 \rangle + \langle 5, -3 \rangle$$
$$= \langle 6, 2 \rangle$$

Therefore, $\mathbf{A} + (\mathbf{B} + \mathbf{C}) = (\mathbf{A} + \mathbf{B}) + \mathbf{C}$, and so (ii) holds.

$$\mathbf{A} + \mathbf{0} = \langle 3, 4 \rangle + \langle 0, 0 \rangle = \langle 3, 4 \rangle = \mathbf{A}$$

Hence, (iii) holds.

$$(cd)\mathbf{A} = [(2)(-6)]\langle 3, 4 \rangle$$
$$= (-12)\langle 3, 4 \rangle$$
$$= \langle -36, -48 \rangle$$

$$c(d\mathbf{A}) = 2(-6\langle 3, 4 \rangle)$$
$$= 2\langle -18, -24 \rangle$$
$$= \langle -36, -48 \rangle$$

Thus, $(cd)\mathbf{A} = c(d\mathbf{A})$, and so (v) holds.

$$(c + d)\mathbf{A} = [2 + (-6)]\langle 3, 4 \rangle = (-4)\langle 3, 4 \rangle = \langle -12, -16 \rangle$$
$$c\mathbf{A} + d\mathbf{A} = 2\langle 3, 4 \rangle + (-6)\langle 3, 4 \rangle = \langle 6, 8 \rangle + \langle -18, -24 \rangle = \langle -12, -16 \rangle$$

Therefore, $(c + d)\mathbf{A} = c\mathbf{A} + d\mathbf{A}$, and (vii) holds.

$$1\mathbf{A} = 1\langle 3, 4 \rangle = \langle (1)(3), (1)(4) \rangle = \langle 3, 4 \rangle = \mathbf{A}$$

and so (viii) holds.

Theorem 15.2.5 is very important because every algebraic law for the operations of vector addition and scalar multiplication of vectors in V_2 can be derived from the eight properties stated in the theorem. These laws are similar to the laws of arithmetic of real numbers. Furthermore, in linear algebra, a *vector space* is defined as a set of vectors together with a set of scalars and the two operations of vector addition and scalar multiplication which satisfy the eight properties given in Theorem 15.2.5. Following is the formal definition.

15.2.6 Definition A *vector space* V is a set of elements, called *vectors*, together with a set of elements, called *scalars*, with two operations called *vector addition* and *scalar multiplication* such that for every pair of vectors **A** and **B** in V and for every scalar c, a vector $\mathbf{A} + \mathbf{B}$ and a vector $c\mathbf{A}$ are defined so that properties (i)–(viii) of Theorem 15.2.5 are satisfied.

From Definition 15.2.6 and Theorem 15.2.5 it follows that V_2 is a set of vectors in a vector space. We denote this vector space by V_2. The use of the same symbol V_2 to name both the set of vectors and the vector space having these vectors as its vector elements should not cause confusion because the context makes the meaning clear.

We now take an arbitrary vector in V_2 and write it in a special form.

$$\mathbf{A} = \langle a_1, a_2 \rangle = \langle a_1, 0 \rangle + \langle 0, a_2 \rangle = a_1 \langle 1, 0 \rangle + a_2 \langle 0, 1 \rangle$$

Because the magnitude of each of the two vectors $\langle 1, 0 \rangle$ and $\langle 0, 1 \rangle$ is one unit, they are called *unit vectors*. We introduce the following notations for these two unit vectors:

$$\mathbf{i} = \langle 1, 0 \rangle \quad \text{and} \quad \mathbf{j} = \langle 0, 1 \rangle$$

The position representation of each of these unit vectors is shown in Fig. 15.2.6. Because

$$\langle a_1, a_2 \rangle = a_1 \langle 1, 0 \rangle + a_2 \langle 0, 1 \rangle = a_1 \mathbf{i} + a_2 \mathbf{j}$$

it follows that any vector in V_2 can be written as a linear combination of the two vectors **i** and **j**. Because of this the vectors **i** and **j** are said to form a *basis* for the vector space V_2. The number of elements in a basis of a vector space is called the *dimension* of the vector space. Hence, V_2 is a two-dimensional vector space.

Figure 15.2.6

EXAMPLE 6: Express the vector $\langle 3, -4 \rangle$ in terms of **i** and **j**.

SOLUTION: $\langle 3, -4 \rangle = 3\langle 1, 0 \rangle + (-4)\langle 0, 1 \rangle = 3\mathbf{i} - 4\mathbf{j}.$

Figure 15.2.7

Let **A** be the vector $\langle a_1, a_2 \rangle$ and θ be the radian measure of the angle giving the direction of **A** (see Fig. 15.2.7 where (a_1, a_2) is in the second quadrant). $a_1 = |\mathbf{A}| \cos \theta$ and $a_2 = |\mathbf{A}| \sin \theta$. Because $\mathbf{A} = a_1 \mathbf{i} + a_2 \mathbf{j}$, we can write

$$\mathbf{A} = |\mathbf{A}| \cos \theta \mathbf{i} + |\mathbf{A}| \sin \theta \mathbf{j}$$

or, equivalently,

$$\mathbf{A} = |\mathbf{A}|(\cos \theta \mathbf{i} + \sin \theta \mathbf{j}) \tag{1}$$

Equation (1) expresses the vector **A** in terms of its magnitude, the cosine and sine of the radian measure of the angle giving the direction of **A**, and the unit vectors **i** and **j**.

EXAMPLE 7: Express the vector $\langle -5, -2 \rangle$ in the form of Eq. (1).

SOLUTION: Refer to Fig. 15.2.8, which shows the position representation of the vector $\langle -5, -2 \rangle$.

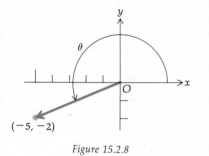

Figure 15.2.8

$$|\langle -5, -2 \rangle| = \sqrt{(-5)^2 + (-2)^2} = \sqrt{25 + 4} = \sqrt{29}$$

$$\sin \theta = -\frac{2}{\sqrt{29}} \quad \text{and} \quad \cos \theta = -\frac{5}{\sqrt{29}}$$

So from (1) we have

$$\langle -5, -2 \rangle = \sqrt{29} \left(-\frac{5}{\sqrt{29}} \, \mathbf{i} - \frac{2}{\sqrt{29}} \, \mathbf{j} \right)$$

15.2.7 Theorem   If the nonzero vector $\mathbf{A} = a_1\mathbf{i} + a_2\mathbf{j}$, then the unit vector $\mathbf{U}$ having the same direction as $\mathbf{A}$ is given by

$$\mathbf{U} = \frac{a_1}{|\mathbf{A}|} \, \mathbf{i} + \frac{a_2}{|\mathbf{A}|} \, \mathbf{j} \tag{2}$$

PROOF: From (2),

$$\mathbf{U} = \frac{1}{|\mathbf{A}|} (a_1\mathbf{i} + a_2\mathbf{j}) = \frac{1}{|\mathbf{A}|} (\mathbf{A})$$

Therefore, $\mathbf{U}$ is a positive scalar times the vector $\mathbf{A}$, and so the direction of $\mathbf{U}$ is the same as the direction of $\mathbf{A}$. Furthermore,

$$|\mathbf{U}| = \sqrt{\left(\frac{a_1}{|\mathbf{A}|} \right)^2 + \left(\frac{a_2}{|\mathbf{A}|} \right)^2}$$

$$= \frac{\sqrt{a_1^2 + a_2^2}}{|\mathbf{A}|}$$

$$= \frac{|\mathbf{A}|}{|\mathbf{A}|}$$

$$= 1$$

Therefore, $\mathbf{U}$ is the unit vector having the same direction as $\mathbf{A}$, and the theorem is proved.   ∎

EXAMPLE 8:   Given $\mathbf{A} = \langle 3, 1 \rangle$ and $\mathbf{B} = \langle -2, 4 \rangle$, find the unit vector having the same direction as $\mathbf{A} - \mathbf{B}$.

SOLUTION: $\mathbf{A} - \mathbf{B} = \langle 3, 1 \rangle - \langle -2, 4 \rangle = \langle 5, -3 \rangle$. So we may write

$$\mathbf{A} - \mathbf{B} = 5\mathbf{i} - 3\mathbf{j}$$

Then

$$|\mathbf{A} - \mathbf{B}| = \sqrt{5^2 + (-3)^2} = \sqrt{34}$$

By Theorem 15.2.7, the desired unit vector is given by

$$\mathbf{U} = \frac{5}{\sqrt{34}} \, \mathbf{i} - \frac{3}{\sqrt{34}} \, \mathbf{j}$$

Exercises 15.2

In Exercises 1 through 6, find the sum of the given pairs of vectors and illustrate geometrically.

1. $\langle 2, 4 \rangle$; $\langle -3, 5 \rangle$ 2. $\langle 0, 3 \rangle$; $\langle -2, 3 \rangle$ 3. $\langle -3, 0 \rangle$; $\langle 4, -5 \rangle$

4. $\langle 2, 3 \rangle$; $\langle -\sqrt{2}, -1 \rangle$ 5. $\langle 0, 0 \rangle$; $\langle -2, 2 \rangle$ 6. $\langle 2, 5 \rangle$; $\langle 2, 5 \rangle$

In Exercises 7 through 12, subtract the second vector from the first, and illustrate geometrically.

7. $\langle 4, 5 \rangle$; $\langle -3, 2 \rangle$ 8. $\langle 0, 5 \rangle$; $\langle 2, 8 \rangle$ 9. $\langle -3, -4 \rangle$; $\langle 6, 0 \rangle$

10. $\langle 1, e \rangle$; $\langle -3, 2e \rangle$ 11. $\langle 0, \sqrt{3} \rangle$; $\langle -\sqrt{2}, 0 \rangle$ 12. $\langle 3, 7 \rangle$; $\langle 3, 7 \rangle$

13. Prove Theorem 15.2.5(ii).   14. Prove Theorem 15.2.5(v).   15. Prove Theorem 15.2.5(vii).

16. Prove Theorem 15.2.5(iii) and (viii).

17. Given $\mathbf{A} = \langle 2, -5 \rangle$; $\mathbf{B} = \langle 3, 1 \rangle$; $\mathbf{C} = \langle -4, 2 \rangle$. (a) Find $\mathbf{A} + (\mathbf{B} + \mathbf{C})$ and illustrate geometrically. (b) Find $(\mathbf{A} + \mathbf{B}) + \mathbf{C}$ and illustrate geometrically.

In Exercises 18 through 23, let $\mathbf{A} = \langle 2, 4 \rangle$, $\mathbf{B} = \langle 4, -3 \rangle$, and $\mathbf{C} = \langle -3, 2 \rangle$.

18. Find $\mathbf{A} + \mathbf{B}$ 19. Find $\mathbf{A} - \mathbf{B}$ 20. Find $|\mathbf{C}|$

21. Find $|\mathbf{C} - \mathbf{B}|$ 22. Find $2\mathbf{A} + 3\mathbf{B}$ 23. Find $|7\mathbf{A} - \mathbf{B}|$

In Exercises 26 through 31, let $\mathbf{A} = 2\mathbf{i} + 3\mathbf{j}$ and $\mathbf{B} = 4\mathbf{i} - \mathbf{j}$.

24. Find $\mathbf{A} + \mathbf{B}$ 25. Find $\mathbf{A} - \mathbf{B}$ 26. Find $5\mathbf{A} - 6\mathbf{B}$

27. Find $|\mathbf{A}||\mathbf{B}|$ 28. Find $|\mathbf{A} + \mathbf{B}|$ 29. Find $|\mathbf{A}| + |\mathbf{B}|$

30. Find $|3\mathbf{A} - 2\mathbf{B}|$ 31. Find $|3\mathbf{A}| - |2\mathbf{B}|$

32. Given $\mathbf{A} = \langle 3, 2 \rangle$; $\mathbf{C} = \langle 8, 8 \rangle$; $\mathbf{A} + \mathbf{B} = \mathbf{C}$; find $|\mathbf{B}|$.

33. Given $\mathbf{A} = 8\mathbf{i} + 5\mathbf{j}$ and $\mathbf{B} = 3\mathbf{i} - \mathbf{j}$; find a unit vector having the same direction as $\mathbf{A} + \mathbf{B}$.

34. Given $\mathbf{A} = -8\mathbf{i} + 7\mathbf{j}$; $\mathbf{B} = 6\mathbf{i} - 9\mathbf{j}$; $\mathbf{C} = -\mathbf{i} - \mathbf{j}$; find $|2\mathbf{A} - 3\mathbf{B} - \mathbf{C}|$.

35. Given $\mathbf{A} = -2\mathbf{i} + \mathbf{j}$; $\mathbf{B} = 3\mathbf{i} - 2\mathbf{j}$; $\mathbf{C} = 5\mathbf{i} - 4\mathbf{j}$; find scalars h and k such that $\mathbf{C} = h\mathbf{A} + k\mathbf{B}$.

36. Write each of the following vectors in the form $r(\cos \theta \mathbf{i} + \sin \theta \mathbf{j})$, where r is the magnitude of the vector and θ is the radian measure of the angle giving the direction of the vector: (a) $\mathbf{A} = 3\mathbf{i} - 3\mathbf{j}$; (b) $\mathbf{B} = -4\mathbf{i} + 4\sqrt{3}\mathbf{j}$; (c) $\mathbf{C} = -16\mathbf{i}$; (d) $\mathbf{D} = 2\mathbf{j}$.

37. For each of the vectors in Exercise 36, find a unit vector having the same direction.

38. Let $\overrightarrow{PQ}$ be a representation of vector $\mathbf{A}$, $\overrightarrow{QR}$ be a representation of vector $\mathbf{B}$, and $\overrightarrow{RS}$ be a representation of vector $\mathbf{C}$. Prove that if $\overrightarrow{PQ}$, $\overrightarrow{QR}$, and $\overrightarrow{RS}$ are sides of a triangle, then $\mathbf{A} + \mathbf{B} + \mathbf{C} = \mathbf{0}$.

39. Prove analytically the triangle inequality for vectors $|\mathbf{A} + \mathbf{B}| \leq |\mathbf{A}| + |\mathbf{B}|$.

40. Two vectors are said to be *independent* if and only if their position representations are not collinear. Furthermore, two vectors $\mathbf{A}$ and $\mathbf{B}$ are said to form a *basis* for the vector space V_2 if and only if any vector in V_2 can be written as a linear combination of $\mathbf{A}$ and $\mathbf{B}$. A theorem can be proved which states that two vectors form a basis for the vector space V_2 if they are independent. Show that this theorem holds for the two vectors $\langle 2, 5 \rangle$ and $\langle 3, -1 \rangle$ by doing the following: (a) Verify that the vectors are independent by showing that their position representations are not collinear; (b) verify that the vectors form a basis by showing that any vector $a_1\mathbf{i} + a_2\mathbf{j}$ can be written as $c(2\mathbf{i} + 5\mathbf{j}) + d(3\mathbf{i} - \mathbf{j})$, where c and d are scalars. (HINT: Find c and d in terms of a_1 and a_2.)

41. Refer to the first two sentences of Exercise 40. A theorem can be proved which states that two vectors form a basis for the vector space V_2 only if they are independent. Show that this theorem holds for the two vectors $\langle 3, -2 \rangle$ and $\langle -6, 4 \rangle$ by doing the following: (a) Verify that the vectors are dependent (not independent) by showing that their position rep-

resentations are collinear; (b) verify that the vectors do not form a basis by taking a particular vector and showing that it cannot be written as $c(3\mathbf{i} + 2\mathbf{j}) + d(-6\mathbf{i} + 4\mathbf{j})$, where c and d are scalars.

15.3 DOT PRODUCT

In Sec. 15.2 we defined addition and subtraction of vectors and multiplication of a vector by a scalar. However, we did not consider the multiplication of two vectors. We now define a multiplication operation on two vectors which gives what is called the *dot product*.

15.3.1 Definition

If $\mathbf{A} = \langle a_1, a_2 \rangle$ and $\mathbf{B} = \langle b_1, b_2 \rangle$ are two vectors in V_2, then the *dot product* of $\mathbf{A}$ and $\mathbf{B}$, denoted by $\mathbf{A} \cdot \mathbf{B}$, is given by

$$\mathbf{A} \cdot \mathbf{B} = \langle a_1, a_2 \rangle \cdot \langle b_1, b_2 \rangle = a_1 b_1 + a_2 b_2$$

The dot product of two vectors is a real number (or scalar) and not a vector. It is sometimes called the *scalar product* or *inner product*.

EXAMPLE 1:   Given $\mathbf{A} = \langle 2, -3 \rangle$ and $\mathbf{B} = \langle -\frac{1}{2}, 4 \rangle$, find $\mathbf{A} \cdot \mathbf{B}$.

SOLUTION: $\mathbf{A} \cdot \mathbf{B} = \langle 2, -3 \rangle \cdot \langle -\frac{1}{2}, 4 \rangle = (2)(-\frac{1}{2}) + (-3)(4) = -13.$

The following dot products are useful and are easily verified (see Exercise 5).

$$\mathbf{i} \cdot \mathbf{i} = 1 \tag{1}$$
$$\mathbf{j} \cdot \mathbf{j} = 1 \tag{2}$$
$$\mathbf{i} \cdot \mathbf{j} = 0 \tag{3}$$

The following theorem states that dot multiplication is commutative and distributive with respect to vector addition.

15.3.2 Theorem

If $\mathbf{A}$, $\mathbf{B}$, and $\mathbf{C}$ are any vectors in V_2, then

(i) $\mathbf{A} \cdot \mathbf{B} = \mathbf{B} \cdot \mathbf{A}$ (commutative law)
(ii) $\mathbf{A} \cdot (\mathbf{B} + \mathbf{C}) = \mathbf{A} \cdot \mathbf{B} + \mathbf{A} \cdot \mathbf{C}$ (distributive law)

The proofs of (i) and (ii) are left for the reader (see Exercises 6 and 7).

Note that because $\mathbf{A} \cdot \mathbf{B}$ is a scalar, the expression $(\mathbf{A} \cdot \mathbf{B}) \cdot \mathbf{C}$ is meaningless. Hence, we do not consider associativity of dot multiplication.

Some other laws of dot multiplication are given in the following theorem.

15.3.3 Theorem

If $\mathbf{A}$ and $\mathbf{B}$ are any vectors in V_2 and c is any scalar, then

(i) $c(\mathbf{A} \cdot \mathbf{B}) = (c\mathbf{A}) \cdot \mathbf{B}$;
(ii) $\mathbf{0} \cdot \mathbf{A} = 0$;
(iii) $\mathbf{A} \cdot \mathbf{A} = |\mathbf{A}|^2$.

The proofs are left for the reader (see Exercises 8 through 10). We now consider what is meant by the angle between two vectors, and this leads to another expression for the dot product of two vectors.

15.3.4 Definition Let **A** and **B** be two nonzero vectors such that **A** is not a scalar multiple of **B**. If $\overrightarrow{OP}$ is the position representation of **A** and $\overrightarrow{OQ}$ is the position representation of **B**, then the *angle between the vectors* **A** and **B** is defined to be the angle of positive measure between $\overrightarrow{OP}$ and $\overrightarrow{OQ}$ interior to the triangle POQ. If $\mathbf{A} = c\mathbf{B}$, where c is a scalar, then if $c > 0$ the angle between the vectors has radian measure 0; if $c < 0$, the angle between the vectors has radian measure π.

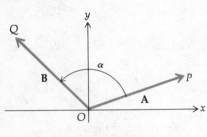

Figure 15.3.1

It follows from Definition 15.3.4 that if α is the radian measure of the angle between two vectors, then $0 \le \alpha \le \pi$. Figure 15.3.1 shows the angle between two vectors if **A** is not a scalar multiple of **B**.

The following theorem is perhaps the most important fact about the dot product of two vectors.

15.3.5 Theorem If α is the radian measure of the angle between the two nonzero vectors **A** and **B**, then

$$\mathbf{A} \cdot \mathbf{B} = |\mathbf{A}||\mathbf{B}| \cos \alpha \qquad (4)$$

PROOF: Let $\mathbf{A} = a_1\mathbf{i} + a_2\mathbf{j}$ and $\mathbf{B} = b_1\mathbf{i} + b_2\mathbf{j}$. Let $\overrightarrow{OP}$ be the position representation of **A** and $\overrightarrow{OQ}$ be the position representation of **B**. Then the angle between the vectors **A** and **B** is the angle at the origin in triangle POQ (see Fig. 15.3.2); P is the point (a_1, a_2) and Q is the point (b_1, b_2). In triangle OPQ, $|\mathbf{A}|$ is the length of the side OP and $|\mathbf{B}|$ is the length of the side OQ. So from the law of cosines we obtain

$$\cos \alpha = \frac{|\mathbf{A}|^2 + |\mathbf{B}|^2 - |\overline{PQ}|^2}{2|\mathbf{A}||\mathbf{B}|}$$

$$= \frac{(a_1^2 + a_2^2) + (b_1^2 + b_2^2) - [(a_1 - b_1)^2 + (a_2 - b_2)^2]}{2|\mathbf{A}||\mathbf{B}|}$$

$$= \frac{2a_1b_1 + 2a_2b_2}{2|\mathbf{A}||\mathbf{B}|}$$

$$= \frac{a_1b_1 + a_2b_2}{|\mathbf{A}||\mathbf{B}|}$$

Figure 15.3.2

Hence,

$$\cos \alpha = \frac{\mathbf{A} \cdot \mathbf{B}}{|\mathbf{A}||\mathbf{B}|}$$

from which we obtain

$$\mathbf{A} \cdot \mathbf{B} = |\mathbf{A}||\mathbf{B}| \cos \alpha$$

Theorem 15.3.5 states that the dot product of two vectors is the product of the magnitudes of the vectors and the cosine of the radian measure of the angle between them.

EXAMPLE 2:   Given $\mathbf{A} = 3\mathbf{i} - 2\mathbf{j}$ and $\mathbf{B} = 2\mathbf{i} + \mathbf{j}$, find $\cos \alpha$ if α is the radian measure of the angle between $\mathbf{A}$ and $\mathbf{B}$.

SOLUTION: From Theorem 15.3.5, we have

$$\cos \alpha = \frac{\mathbf{A} \cdot \mathbf{B}}{|\mathbf{A}||\mathbf{B}|}$$

$$= \frac{(3)(2) + (-2)(1)}{\sqrt{9+4} \ \sqrt{4+1}}$$

$$= \frac{6-2}{\sqrt{13} \ \sqrt{5}}$$

$$= \frac{4}{\sqrt{65}}$$

15.3.6 Definition   Two nonzero vectors are said to be *parallel* if and only if the radian measure of the angle between them is zero or π.

15.3.7 Definition   Two nonzero vectors are said to be *orthogonal* if and only if the radian measure of the angle between them is $\frac{1}{2}\pi$.

The following theorem gives a method for determining if two vectors are orthogonal.

15.3.8 Theorem   Two nonzero vectors $\mathbf{A}$ and $\mathbf{B}$ are orthogonal if and only if $\mathbf{A} \cdot \mathbf{B} = 0$.

PROOF: From Definition 15.3.7, if α is the radian measure of the angle between the two vectors $\mathbf{A}$ and $\mathbf{B}$, $\mathbf{A}$ and $\mathbf{B}$ are orthogonal if and only if $\alpha = \frac{1}{2}\pi$. Because $0 \le \alpha \le \pi$, it follows that

$$\mathbf{A} \text{ and } \mathbf{B} \text{ are orthogonal if and only if } \cos \alpha = 0 \tag{5}$$

But from Theorem 15.3.5, we have

$$\mathbf{A} \cdot \mathbf{B} = |\mathbf{A}||\mathbf{B}| \cos \alpha \tag{6}$$

Because neither $\mathbf{A}$ nor $\mathbf{B}$ is the zero vector, $|\mathbf{A}| \ne 0$ and $|\mathbf{B}| \ne 0$. Therefore, from (6) we conclude that

$$\mathbf{A} \cdot \mathbf{B} = 0 \quad \text{if and only if} \quad \cos \alpha = 0 \tag{7}$$

From (5) and (7) we have the desired result:

$$\mathbf{A} \text{ and } \mathbf{B} \text{ are orthogonal if and only if } \mathbf{A} \cdot \mathbf{B} = 0 \qquad \blacksquare$$

EXAMPLE 3:   Given $\mathbf{A} = 3\mathbf{i} + 2\mathbf{j}$ and $\mathbf{B} = 2\mathbf{i} + k\mathbf{j}$, where k is a

SOLUTION: (a) By Theorem 15.3.8, $\mathbf{A}$ and $\mathbf{B}$ are orthogonal if and only if

$$\mathbf{A} \cdot \mathbf{B} = 0$$

scalar, find (a) k so that **A** and **B** are orthogonal; (b) k so that **A** and **B** are parallel.

or

$$(3)(2) + 2(k) = 0$$

So

$$k = -3$$

(b) If α is the radian measure of the angle between **A** and **B**, **A** and **B** are parallel if and only if either $\alpha = 0$ or $\alpha = \pi$, that is, if and only if

$$\cos \alpha = \pm 1 \tag{8}$$

Substituting from (8) into (4), we obtain

$$\mathbf{A} \cdot \mathbf{B} = \pm |\mathbf{A}||\mathbf{B}|$$

or

$$6 + 2k = \pm \sqrt{13}\ \sqrt{4 + k^2}$$

Squaring on both sides of this equation gives

$$36 + 24k + 4k^2 = 52 + 13k^2$$

$$9k^2 - 24k + 16 = 0$$

$$(3k - 4)^2 = 0$$

$$k = \tfrac{4}{3}$$

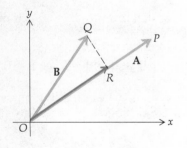

Figure 15.3.3

A geometric interpretation of the dot product is obtained by considering the *projection* of a vector onto another vector. Let $\overrightarrow{OP}$ and $\overrightarrow{OQ}$ be representations of the vectors **A** and **B**, respectively. See Fig. 15.3.3. The projection of $\overrightarrow{OQ}$ in the direction of $\overrightarrow{OP}$ is the directed line segment $\overrightarrow{OR}$, where R is the foot of the perpendicular from Q to the line containing $\overrightarrow{OP}$. Then the vector for which $\overrightarrow{OR}$ is a representation is called the *vector projection* of the vector **B** onto the vector **A**. The *scalar projection* of **B** onto **A** is defined to be $|\mathbf{B}| \cos \alpha$, where α is the radian measure of the angle between **A** and **B**. Note that $|\mathbf{B}| \cos \alpha$ may be either positive or negative depending on α. Because $\mathbf{A} \cdot \mathbf{B} = |\mathbf{A}||\mathbf{B}| \cos \alpha$, it follows that

$$\mathbf{A} \cdot \mathbf{B} = |\mathbf{A}|(|\mathbf{B}| \cos \alpha) \tag{9}$$

Hence, the dot product of **A** and **B** is the magnitude of **A** multiplied by the scalar projection of **B** onto **A**. See Fig. 15.3.4a and b. Because dot mul-

$|\mathbf{B}| \cos \alpha > 0$

(a)

$|\mathbf{B}| \cos \alpha < 0$

(b)

Figure 15.3.4

tiplication is commutative, $\mathbf{A} \cdot \mathbf{B}$ is also the magnitude of $\mathbf{B}$ multiplied by the scalar projection of $\mathbf{A}$ onto $\mathbf{B}$.

EXAMPLE 4:   Given $\mathbf{A} = -5\mathbf{i} + \mathbf{j}$ and $\mathbf{B} = 4\mathbf{i} + 2\mathbf{j}$, find the vector projection of $\mathbf{B}$ onto $\mathbf{A}$.

Figure 15.3.5

SOLUTION: Figure 15.3.5 shows the position representations of vectors $\mathbf{A}$ and $\mathbf{B}$ as well as that of $\mathbf{C}$, which is the vector projection of $\mathbf{B}$ onto $\mathbf{A}$. From (6) we get

$$|\mathbf{B}| \cos \alpha = \frac{\mathbf{A} \cdot \mathbf{B}}{|\mathbf{A}|} = \frac{(-5)(4) + (1)(2)}{\sqrt{26}} = \frac{-18}{\sqrt{26}}$$

Therefore, $|\mathbf{C}| = 18/\sqrt{26}$. Because $\cos \alpha < 0, \frac{1}{2}\pi < \alpha < \pi$, and so the direction of $\mathbf{C}$ is opposite that of $\mathbf{A}$. Hence, $\mathbf{C} = c\mathbf{A}$, and $c < 0$. Then we have

$$\mathbf{C} = -5c\mathbf{i} + c\mathbf{j}$$

Because $|\mathbf{C}| = 18/\sqrt{26}$, we get

$$\frac{18}{\sqrt{26}} = \sqrt{25c^2 + c^2} \quad \longrightarrow \quad \frac{18}{\sqrt{26}} = c \cdot \sqrt{26} = \frac{18}{26} \quad \boxed{c = -\frac{9}{13}}$$

and so $c = -\frac{9}{13}$, from which it follows that

$$\mathbf{C} = \frac{45}{13}\mathbf{i} - \frac{9}{13}\mathbf{j}$$

If $\mathbf{A} = a_1\mathbf{i} + a_2\mathbf{j}$, then

$$\mathbf{A} \cdot \mathbf{i} = a_1 \quad \text{and} \quad \mathbf{A} \cdot \mathbf{j} = a_2$$

Hence, the dot product of $\mathbf{A}$ and $\mathbf{i}$ gives the component of $\mathbf{A}$ in the direction of $\mathbf{i}$ and the dot product of $\mathbf{A}$ and $\mathbf{j}$ gives the component of $\mathbf{A}$ in the direction $\mathbf{j}$. To generalize this result, let $\mathbf{U}$ be any unit vector. Then from (9)

$$\mathbf{A} \cdot \mathbf{U} = |\mathbf{A}|(|\mathbf{U}| \cos \alpha) = |\mathbf{A}| \cos \alpha$$

and so $\mathbf{A} \cdot \mathbf{U}$ is the scalar projection of $\mathbf{A}$ onto $\mathbf{U}$, which is called the *component* of the vector $\mathbf{A}$ in the direction of $\mathbf{U}$. More generally, the *component* of a vector $\mathbf{A}$ in the direction of a vector $\mathbf{B}$ is the scalar projection of $\mathbf{A}$ onto a unit vector in the direction of $\mathbf{B}$.

In Sec. 7.5 we stated that if a constant force of F pounds moves an object a distance d feet along a straight line and the force is acting in the direction of motion, then if W is the number of foot-pounds in the work done by the force, $W = Fd$. Suppose, however, that the constant force is not directed along the line of motion. In this case the physicist defines the *work* done as the *product of the component of the force along the line of motion times the displacement.* If the object moves from the point A to the point B, we call the vector, having $\overrightarrow{AB}$ as a representation, the *displacement vector* and denote it by $\mathbf{V}(\overrightarrow{AB})$. So if the magnitude of a constant force vector $\mathbf{F}$ is expressed in pounds and the distance from A to B is expressed in feet, and

α is the radian measure of the angle between the vectors $\mathbf{F}$ and $\mathbf{V}(\overrightarrow{AB})$, then if W is the number of foot-pounds in the work done by the force $\mathbf{F}$ in moving an object from A to B,

$$W = (|\mathbf{F}| \cos \alpha)|\mathbf{V}(\overrightarrow{AB})|$$
$$= |\mathbf{F}||\mathbf{V}(\overrightarrow{AB})| \cos \alpha$$
$$= \mathbf{F} \cdot \mathbf{V}(\overrightarrow{AB})$$

EXAMPLE 5: Suppose that a force $\mathbf{F}$ has a magnitude of 6 lb and $\frac{1}{6}\pi$ is the radian measure of the angle giving its direction. Find the work done by $\mathbf{F}$ in moving an object along a straight line from the origin to the point $P(7, 1)$, where distance is measured in feet.

SOLUTION: Figure 15.3.6 shows the position representations of $\mathbf{F}$ and $\mathbf{V}(\overrightarrow{OP})$. If W ft-lb is the work done, then

$$W = \mathbf{F} \cdot \mathbf{V}(\overrightarrow{OP})$$

$\mathbf{F} = \langle 6 \cos \frac{1}{6}\pi, 6 \sin \frac{1}{6}\pi \rangle = \langle 3\sqrt{3}, 3 \rangle$, and $\mathbf{V}(\overrightarrow{OP}) = \langle 7, 1 \rangle$. So

$$W = \langle 3\sqrt{3}, 3 \rangle \cdot \langle 7, 1 \rangle = 21\sqrt{3} + 3 \approx 39.37$$

Therefore, the work done is 39.37 ft-lb.

Figure 15.3.6

Vectors have geometric representations which are independent of the coordinate system used. Because of this, vector analysis can be used to prove certain theorems of plane geometry. This is illustrated in the following example.

EXAMPLE 6: Prove by vector analysis that the altitudes of a triangle meet in a point.

Figure 15.3.7

SOLUTION: Let ABC be a triangle having altitudes AP and BQ intersecting at point S. Draw a line through C and S intersecting AB at point R. We wish to prove that RC is perpendicular to AB (see Fig. 15.3.7).

Let $\overrightarrow{AB}$, $\overrightarrow{BC}$, $\overrightarrow{AC}$, $\overrightarrow{AS}$, $\overrightarrow{BS}$, $\overrightarrow{CS}$ be representations of vectors. Let $\mathbf{V}(\overrightarrow{AB})$ be the vector having directed line segment $\overrightarrow{AB}$ as a representation. In a similar manner, let $\mathbf{V}(\overrightarrow{BC})$, $\mathbf{V}(\overrightarrow{AC})$, $\mathbf{V}(\overrightarrow{AS})$, $\mathbf{V}(\overrightarrow{BS})$, and $\mathbf{V}(\overrightarrow{CS})$ be the vectors having the directed line segment in parentheses as a representation.

Because AP is an altitude of the triangle,

$$\mathbf{V}(\overrightarrow{AS}) \cdot \mathbf{V}(\overrightarrow{BC}) = 0 \tag{10}$$

Also, because BQ is an altitude of the triangle,

$$\mathbf{V}(\overrightarrow{BS}) \cdot \mathbf{V}(\overrightarrow{AC}) = 0 \tag{11}$$

To prove that RC is perpendicular to AB, we shall show that

$$\mathbf{V}(\overrightarrow{CS}) \cdot \mathbf{V}(\overrightarrow{AB}) = 0$$

$$\mathbf{V}(\vec{CS}) \cdot \mathbf{V}(\vec{AB}) = \mathbf{V}(\vec{CS}) \cdot [\mathbf{V}(\vec{AC}) + \mathbf{V}(\vec{CB})]$$
$$= \mathbf{V}(\vec{CS}) \cdot \mathbf{V}(\vec{AC}) + \mathbf{V}(\vec{CS}) \cdot \mathbf{V}(\vec{CB})$$
$$= [\mathbf{V}(\vec{CB}) + \mathbf{V}(\vec{BS})] \cdot \mathbf{V}(\vec{AC})$$
$$\qquad + [\mathbf{V}(\vec{CA}) + \mathbf{V}(\vec{AS})] \cdot \mathbf{V}(\vec{CB})$$
$$= \mathbf{V}(\vec{CB}) \cdot \mathbf{V}(\vec{AC}) + \mathbf{V}(\vec{BS}) \cdot \mathbf{V}(\vec{AC})$$
$$\qquad + \mathbf{V}(\vec{CA}) \cdot \mathbf{V}(\vec{CB}) + \mathbf{V}(\vec{AS}) \cdot \mathbf{V}(\vec{CB})$$

Replacing $\mathbf{V}(\vec{CA})$ by $-\mathbf{V}(\vec{AC})$ and using (10) and (11), we obtain

$$\mathbf{V}(\vec{CS}) \cdot \mathbf{V}(\vec{AB}) = \mathbf{V}(\vec{CB}) \cdot \mathbf{V}(\vec{AC}) + 0 + [-\mathbf{V}(\vec{AC})] \cdot \mathbf{V}(\vec{CB}) + 0$$
$$= 0$$

Therefore, altitudes AP, BQ, and RC meet in a point.

Exercises 15.3

In Exercises 1 through 4, find $\mathbf{A} \cdot \mathbf{B}$.

1. $\mathbf{A} = \langle -1, 2 \rangle$; $\mathbf{B} = \langle -4, 3 \rangle$
2. $\mathbf{A} = \langle \frac{1}{3}, -\frac{1}{2} \rangle$; $\mathbf{B} = \langle \frac{5}{2}, \frac{4}{3} \rangle$
3. $\mathbf{A} = 2\mathbf{i} - \mathbf{j}$; $\mathbf{B} = \mathbf{i} + 3\mathbf{j}$
4. $\mathbf{A} = -2\mathbf{i}$; $\mathbf{B} = -\mathbf{i} + \mathbf{j}$
5. Show that $\mathbf{i} \cdot \mathbf{i} = 1$; $\mathbf{j} \cdot \mathbf{j} = 1$; $\mathbf{i} \cdot \mathbf{j} = 0$.
6. Prove Theorem 15.3.2(i).
7. Prove Theorem 15.3.2(ii).
8. Prove Theorem 15.3.3(i).
9. Prove Theorem 15.3.3(ii).
10. Prove Theorem 15.3.3(iii).

In Exercises 11 through 14, if α is the radian measure of the angle between $\mathbf{A}$ and $\mathbf{B}$, find $\cos \alpha$.

11. $\mathbf{A} = \langle 4, 3 \rangle$; $\mathbf{B} = \langle 1, -1 \rangle$
12. $\mathbf{A} = \langle -2, -3 \rangle$; $\mathbf{B} = \langle 3, 2 \rangle$
13. $\mathbf{A} = 5\mathbf{i} - 12\mathbf{j}$; $\mathbf{B} = 4\mathbf{i} + 3\mathbf{j}$
14. $\mathbf{A} = 2\mathbf{i} + 4\mathbf{j}$; $\mathbf{B} = -5\mathbf{j}$

15. Find k so that the radian measure of the angle between the vectors in Example 3 of this section is $\frac{1}{4}\pi$.

16. Given $\mathbf{A} = k\mathbf{i} - 2\mathbf{j}$ and $\mathbf{B} = k\mathbf{i} + 6\mathbf{j}$, where k is a scalar. Find k so that $\mathbf{A}$ and $\mathbf{B}$ are orthogonal.

17. Given $\mathbf{A} = 5\mathbf{i} - k\mathbf{j}$; $\mathbf{B} = k\mathbf{i} + 6\mathbf{j}$, where k is a scalar. Find (a) k so that $\mathbf{A}$ and $\mathbf{B}$ are orthogonal; (b) k so that $\mathbf{A}$ and $\mathbf{B}$ are parallel.

18. Find k so that the vectors given in Exercise 16 have opposite directions.

19. Given $\mathbf{A} = 5\mathbf{i} + 12\mathbf{j}$; $\mathbf{B} = \mathbf{i} + k\mathbf{j}$, where k is a scalar. Find k so that the radian measure of the angle between $\mathbf{A}$ and $\mathbf{B}$ is $\frac{1}{3}\pi$.

20. Find two unit vectors each having a representation whose initial point is $(2, 4)$ and which is tangent to the parabola $y = x^2$ there.

21. Find two unit vectors each having a representation whose initial point is $(2, 4)$ and which is normal to the parabola $y = x^2$ there.

22. If $\mathbf{A}$ is the vector $a_1\mathbf{i} + a_2\mathbf{j}$, find the unit vectors that are orthogonal to $\mathbf{A}$.

23. If $\mathbf{A} = -8\mathbf{i} + 4\mathbf{j}$ and $\mathbf{B} = 7\mathbf{i} - 6\mathbf{j}$, find the vector projection of $\mathbf{A}$ onto $\mathbf{B}$.

24. Find the vector projection of $\mathbf{B}$ onto $\mathbf{A}$ for the vectors of Exercise 23.

25. Find the component of the vector $\mathbf{A} = 5\mathbf{i} - 6\mathbf{j}$ in the direction of the vector $\mathbf{B} = 7\mathbf{i} + \mathbf{j}$.

26. For the vectors **A** and **B** of Exercise 25, find the component of the vector **B** in the direction of vector **A**.

27. A vector **F** represents a force which has a magnitude of 8 lb and $\frac{1}{3}\pi$ as the radian measure of the angle giving its direction. Find the work done by the force in moving an object (a) along the x axis from the origin to the point $(6, 0)$ and (b) along the y axis from the origin to the point $(0, 6)$. Distance is measured in feet.

28. Two forces represented by the vectors $\mathbf{F}_1$ and $\mathbf{F}_2$ act on a particle and cause it to move along a straight line from the point $(2, 5)$ to the point $(7, 3)$. If $\mathbf{F}_1 = 3\mathbf{i} - \mathbf{j}$ and $\mathbf{F}_2 = -4\mathbf{i} + 5\mathbf{j}$, the magnitudes of the forces are measured in pounds, and distance is measured in feet, find the work done by the two forces acting together.

29. If **A** and **B** are vectors, prove that

$$(\mathbf{A} + \mathbf{B}) \cdot (\mathbf{A} + \mathbf{B}) = \mathbf{A} \cdot \mathbf{A} + 2\mathbf{A} \cdot \mathbf{B} + \mathbf{B} \cdot \mathbf{B}$$

30. Prove by vector analysis that the medians of a triangle meet in a point.

31. Prove by vector analysis that the line segment joining the midpoints of two sides of a triangle is parallel to the third side and its length is one-half the length of the third side.

32. Prove by vector analysis that the line segment joining the midpoints of the nonparallel sides of a trapezoid is parallel to the parallel sides and its length is one-half the sum of the lengths of the parallel sides.

15.4 VECTOR-VALUED FUNCTIONS AND PARAMETRIC EQUATIONS

We now consider a function whose domain is a set of real numbers and whose range is a set of vectors. Such a function is called a *vector-valued function*. Following is the precise definition.

15.4.1 Definition   Let f and g be two real-valued functions of a real variable t. Then for every number t in the domain common to f and g, there is a vector **R** defined by

$$\mathbf{R}(t) = f(t)\mathbf{i} + g(t)\mathbf{j} \tag{1}$$

and **R** is called a *vector-valued function*.

EXAMPLE 1:   Given

$$\mathbf{R}(t) = \sqrt{t - 2}\,\mathbf{i} + (t - 3)^{-1}\mathbf{j}$$

find the domain of **R**.

SOLUTION: $f(t) = \sqrt{t - 2}$ and $g(t) = (t - 3)^{-1}$.

The domain of **R** is the set of values of t for which both $f(t)$ and $g(t)$ are defined. The function value $f(t)$ is defined for $t \geq 2$ and $g(t)$ is defined for all real numbers except 3. Therefore, the domain of **R** is given by $t \geq 2$, $t \neq 3$.

If **R** is the vector-valued function defined by (1), as t assumes all values in the domain of **R**, the endpoint of the position representation of the vector $\mathbf{R}(t)$ traces a curve C. For each such value of t, we obtain a point (x, y) on C for which

$$x = f(t) \quad \text{and} \quad y = g(t) \tag{2}$$

The curve C may be defined by Eq. (1) or Eqs. (2). Equation (1) is called a *vector equation* of C, and Eqs. (2) are called *parametric equations* of C. The variable t is a *parameter*. The curve C is also called a *graph*; that is, the set of all points (x, y) satisfying Eqs. (2) is the graph of the vector-valued function **R**.

A vector equation of a curve, as well as parametric equations of a curve, gives the curve a direction at each point. That is, if we think of the curve as being traced by a particle, we can consider the positive direction along a curve as the direction in which the particle moves as the parameter t increases. In such a case as this, t may be taken to be the measure of the time, and the vector $\mathbf{R}(t)$ is called the *position vector*. Sometimes $\mathbf{R}(t)$ is referred to as the *radius vector*.

If the parameter t is eliminated from the pair of Eqs. (2), we obtain one equation in x and y, which is called a *cartesian equation* of C. It may happen that elimination of the parameter leads to a cartesian equation whose graph contains more points than the graph defined by either the vector equation or the parametric equations. This situation occurs in Example 5.

EXAMPLE 2:   Given the vector equation

$$\mathbf{R}(t) = 2 \cos t\mathbf{i} + 2 \sin t\mathbf{j}$$

(a) draw a sketch of the graph of this equation, and (b) find a cartesian equation of the graph.

Figure 15.4.1

SOLUTION: The domain of $\mathbf{R}$ is the set of all real numbers. We could tabulate values of x and y for particular values of t. However, if we find the magnitude of the position vector, we have for every t

$$|\mathbf{R}(t)| = \sqrt{4 \cos^2 t + 4 \sin^2 t} = 2\sqrt{\cos^2 t + \sin^2 t} = 2$$

Therefore, the endpoint of the position representation of each vector $\mathbf{R}(t)$ is two units from the origin. By letting t take on all numbers in the closed interval $[0, 2\pi]$, we obtain a circle having its center at the origin and radius 2. This is the entire graph because any value of t will give a point on this circle. A sketch of the circle is shown in Fig. 15.4.1. Parametric equations of the graph are

$$x = 2 \cos t \quad \text{and} \quad y = 2 \sin t$$

A cartesian equation of the graph can be found by eliminating t from the two parametric equations, which when squaring on both sides of each equation and adding gives

$$x^2 + y^2 = 4$$

As previously stated, upon eliminating t from parametric equations (2) we obtain a cartesian equation. The cartesian equation either implicitly or explicitly defines y as one or more functions of x. That is, if $x = f(t)$ and $y = g(t)$, then $y = h(x)$. If h is a differentiable function of x and f is a differentiable function of t, it follows from the chain rule that

$$D_t y = (D_x y)(D_t x)$$

or

$$g'(t) = (h'(x))(f'(t))$$

or, by using differential notation,

$$\frac{dy}{dt} = \frac{dy}{dx}\frac{dx}{dt}$$

If $dx/dt \neq 0$, we can divide on both sides of the above equation by dx/dt and obtain

$$\frac{dy}{dx} = \frac{\dfrac{dy}{dt}}{\dfrac{dx}{dt}} \tag{3}$$

Equation (3) enables us to find the derivative of y with respect to x directly from the parametric equations.

EXAMPLE 3:   Given $x = 3t^2$ and $y = 4t^3$, find dy/dx and d^2y/dx^2 without eliminating t.

SOLUTION: Applying (3), we have

$$\frac{dy}{dx} = \frac{\dfrac{dy}{dt}}{\dfrac{dx}{dt}} = \frac{12t^2}{6t} = 2t$$

$$\frac{d^2y}{dx^2} = \frac{d(y')}{dx} = \frac{\dfrac{d(y')}{dt}}{\dfrac{dx}{dt}}$$

Because $y' = 2t$, $d(y')/dt = 2$; thus, we have from the above equation

$$\frac{d^2y}{dx^2} = \frac{2}{6t} = \frac{1}{3t}$$

EXAMPLE 4:   (a) Draw a sketch of the graph of the curve defined by the parametric equations of Example 3, and (b) find a cartesian equation of the graph in (a).

SOLUTION: Because $x = 3t^2$, we conclude that x is never negative. Table 15.4.1 gives values of x and y for particular values of t. Because $D_x y = 2t$, we see that when $t = 0$, $D_x y = 0$; hence, the tangent line is horizontal at the point $(0, 0)$. A sketch of the graph is shown in Fig. 15.4.2.

Figure 15.4.2

Table 15.4.1

t	x	y
0	0	0
$\frac{1}{2}$	$\frac{3}{4}$	$\frac{1}{2}$
1	3	4
2	12	32
$-\frac{1}{2}$	$\frac{3}{4}$	$-\frac{1}{2}$
-1	3	-4
-2	12	-32

From the two parametric equations $x = 3t^2$ and $y = 4t^3$, we get $x^3 = 27t^6$ and $y^2 = 16t^6$. Therefore,

$$\frac{x^3}{27} = \frac{y^2}{16}$$

or, equivalently,

$$16x^3 = 27y^2 \qquad (4)$$

which is the cartesian equation desired.

Differentiating implicitly in Eq. (4), we have

$$48x^2 = 54y\,\frac{dy}{dx}$$

and solving for dy/dx, we get

$$\frac{dy}{dx} = \frac{8x^2}{9y}$$

Substituting for x and y in terms of t from the given parametric equations, we obtain

$$\frac{dy}{dx} = \frac{8(3t^2)^2}{9(4t^3)} = 2t$$

which agrees with the value of dy/dx found in Example 3.

EXAMPLE 5: Draw a sketch of the graph of the curve defined by the parametric equations

$$x = \cosh t \quad \text{and} \quad y = \sinh t \qquad (5)$$

Also find a cartesian equation of the graph.

Figure 15.4.3

SOLUTION: Squaring on both sides of the given equations and subtracting, we have

$$x^2 - y^2 = \cosh^2 t - \sinh^2 t$$

From the identity $\cosh^2 t - \sinh^2 t = 1$, this equation becomes

$$x^2 - y^2 = 1 \qquad (6)$$

Equation (6) is an equation of an equilateral hyperbola. Note that for t any real number, $\cosh t$ is never less than 1. Thus, the curve defined by parametric equations (5) consists of only the points on the right branch of the hyperbola. A sketch of this curve is shown in Fig. 15.4.3. A cartesian equation is $x^2 - y^2 = 1$, where $x \geq 1$.

Figure 15.4.4

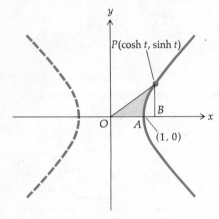

Figure 15.4.5

The results of Example 5 can be used to show how the function values of the hyperbolic sine and hyperbolic cosine functions have the same relationship to the equilateral hyperbola as the trigonometric sine and cosine functions have to the circle. The equations

$$x = \cos t \quad \text{and} \quad y = \sin t \tag{7}$$

are a set of parametric equations of the unit circle because if t is eliminated from them by squaring on both sides of each and adding, we obtain

$$x^2 + y^2 = \cos^2 t + \sin^2 t = 1$$

The parameter t in Eqs. (7) can be interpreted as the number of radians in the measure of the angle between the x axis and a line from the origin to $P(\cos t, \sin t)$ on the unit circle. See Fig. 15.4.4. Because the area of a circular sector of radius r units and a central angle of radian measure t is given by $\frac{1}{2}r^2t$ square units, the area of the circular sector in Fig. 15.4.4 is $\frac{1}{2}t$ square units because $r = 1$.

In Example 5 we showed that parametric equations (5) are a set of parametric equations of the right branch of the equilateral hyperbola $x^2 - y^2 = 1$. This hyperbola is called the *unit hyperbola*. Let $P(\cosh t, \sinh t)$ be a point on this curve, and let us calculate the area of the sector AOP shown in Fig. 15.4.5. The sector AOP is the region bounded by the x axis, the line OP, and the arc AP of the unit hyperbola. If A_1 square units is the area of sector AOP, A_2 square units is the area of triangle OBP, and A_3 square units is the area of region ABP, we have

$$A_1 = A_2 - A_3 \tag{8}$$

Using the formula for determining the area of a triangle, we get

$$A_2 = \tfrac{1}{2} \cosh t \sinh t \tag{9}$$

We find A_3 by integration:

$$A_3 = \int_0^t \sinh u \, d(\cosh u)$$

$$= \int_0^t \sinh^2 u \, du$$

$$= \tfrac{1}{2} \int_0^t (\cosh 2u - 1) \, du$$

$$= \tfrac{1}{4} \sinh 2u - \tfrac{1}{2} u \Big]_0^t$$

and so

$$A_3 = \tfrac{1}{2} \cosh t \sinh t - \tfrac{1}{2} t \tag{10}$$

Substituting from (9) and (10) into (8), we have

$$A_1 = \tfrac{1}{2} \cosh t \sinh t - (\tfrac{1}{2} \cosh t \sinh t - \tfrac{1}{2} t)$$

$$= \tfrac{1}{2} t$$

So we see that the number of square units in the area of circular sector *AOP* of Fig. 15.4.4 and the number of square units in the area of sector *AOP* of Fig. 15.4.5 is, in each case, one-half the value of the parameter associated with the point *P*. For the unit circle, the parameter *t* is the radian measure of the angle *AOP*. The parameter *t* for the unit hyperbola is not interpreted as the measure of an angle; however, sometimes the term *hyperbolic radian* is used in connection with *t*.

In Sec. 13.1, where Cauchy's mean-value theorem (13.1.3) was stated and proved, we indicated that a geometric interpretation would be given in this section because parametric equations are needed. Recall that the theorem states that if *f* and *g* are two functions such that (i) *f* and *g* are continuous on [*a*, *b*], (ii) *f* and *g* are differentiable on (*a*, *b*), and (iii) for all *x* in (*a*, *b*) $g'(x) \neq 0$, then there exists a number *z* in the open interval (*a*, *b*) such that

$$\frac{f(b) - f(a)}{g(b) - g(a)} = \frac{f'(z)}{g'(z)}$$

Figure 15.4.6

Figure 15.4.6 shows a curve having the parametric equations $x = g(t)$ and $y = f(t)$, where $a \leq t \leq b$. The slope of the curve in the figure at a particular point is given by

$$\frac{dy}{dx} = \frac{f'(t)}{g'(t)}$$

and the slope of the line segment through the points $A(g(a), f(a))$ and $B(g(b), f(b))$ is given by

$$\frac{f(b) - f(a)}{g(b) - g(a)}$$

Cauchy's mean-value theorem states that the slopes are equal for at least one value of *t* between *a* and *b*. For the curve shown in Fig. 15.4.6, there are

Figure 15.4.7

four values of t satisfying the conclusion of the theorem: $t = z_1$, $t = z_2$, $t = z_3$, and $t = z_4$.

We now show how parametric equations can be used to define a curve which is described by a physical motion. The curve we consider is a *cycloid*, which is the curve traced by a point on the circumference of a circle as the circle rolls along a straight line. Suppose the circle has radius a. Let the fixed straight line on which the circle rolls be the x axis, and let the origin be one of the points at which the given point P comes in contact with the x axis. See Fig. 15.4.7, which shows the circle after it has rolled through an angle of t radians.

We see from Fig. 15.4.7 that

$$\mathbf{V}(\overrightarrow{OT}) + \mathbf{V}(\overrightarrow{TA}) + \mathbf{V}(\overrightarrow{AP}) = \mathbf{V}(\overrightarrow{OP}) \tag{11}$$

$|\mathbf{V}(\overrightarrow{OT})| =$ length of the arc $PT = at$. Because the direction of $\mathbf{V}(\overrightarrow{OT})$ is along the positive x axis, we conclude that

$$\mathbf{V}(\overrightarrow{OT}) = at\mathbf{i} \tag{12}$$

Also, $|\mathbf{V}(\overrightarrow{TA})| = a - a \cos t$. And because the direction of $\mathbf{V}(\overrightarrow{TA})$ is the same as the direction of $\mathbf{j}$, we have

$$\mathbf{V}(\overrightarrow{TA}) = a(1 - \cos t)\mathbf{j} \tag{13}$$

$|\mathbf{V}(\overrightarrow{AP})| = a \sin t$, and the direction of $\mathbf{V}(\overrightarrow{AP})$ is the same as the direction of $-\mathbf{i}$; thus,

$$\mathbf{V}(\overrightarrow{AP}) = -a \sin t\mathbf{i} \tag{14}$$

Substituting from (12), (13), and (14) into (11), we obtain

$$at\mathbf{i} + a(1 - \cos t)\mathbf{j} - a \sin t\mathbf{i} = \mathbf{V}(\overrightarrow{OP})$$

or, equivalently,

$$\mathbf{V}(\overrightarrow{OP}) = a(t - \sin t)\mathbf{i} + a(1 - \cos t)\mathbf{j} \tag{15}$$

Equation (15) is a vector equation of the cycloid. So parametric equations of the cycloid are

$$x = a(t - \sin t) \quad \text{and} \quad y = a(1 - \cos t) \tag{16}$$

where t is any real number. A sketch of a portion of the cycloid is shown in Fig. 15.4.8.

Figure 15.4.8

Exercises 15.4

In Exercises 1 through 6, find the domain of the vector-valued function $\mathbf{R}$.

1. $\mathbf{R}(t) = (1/t)\mathbf{i} + \sqrt{4 - t}\,\mathbf{j}$
2. $\mathbf{R}(t) = (t^2 + 3)\mathbf{i} + (t - 1)\mathbf{j}$
3. $\mathbf{R}(t) = (\sin^{-1} t)\mathbf{i} + (\cos^{-1} t)\mathbf{j}$
4. $\mathbf{R}(t) = \ln(t + 1)\mathbf{i} + (\tan^{-1} t)\mathbf{j}$
5. $\mathbf{R}(t) = \sqrt{t^2 - 9}\,\mathbf{i} + \sqrt{t^2 + 2t - 8}\,\mathbf{j}$
6. $\mathbf{R}(t) = \sqrt{t - 4}\,\mathbf{i} + \sqrt{4 - t}\,\mathbf{j}$

In Exercises 7 through 12, find dy/dx and d^2y/dx^2 without eliminating the parameter.

7. $x = 3t, \; y = 2t^2$
8. $x = 1 - t^2, \; y = 1 + t$
9. $x = t^2 e^t, \; y = t \ln t$
10. $x = e^{2t}, \; y = 1 + \cos t$
11. $x = a \cos t, \; y = b \sin t$
12. $x = a \cosh t, \; y = b \sinh t$

In Exercises 13 through 16, draw a sketch of the graph of the given vector equation and find a cartesian equation of the graph.

13. $\mathbf{R}(t) = t^2 \mathbf{i} + (t + 1)\mathbf{j}$
14. $\mathbf{R}(t) = \dfrac{4}{t^2}\mathbf{i} + \dfrac{4}{t}\mathbf{j}$
15. $\mathbf{R}(t) = 3 \cosh t\,\mathbf{i} + 5 \sinh t\,\mathbf{j}$

16. $\mathbf{R}(t) = \cos t\,\mathbf{i} + \cos t\,\mathbf{j}$; t in $[0, \frac{1}{2}\pi]$

In Exercises 17 and 18, find equations of the horizontal tangent lines by finding the values of t for which $dy/dt = 0$, and find equations of the vertical tangent lines by finding the values of t for which $dx/dt = 0$. Then draw a sketch of the graph of the given pair of parameteric equations.

17. $x = 4t^2 - 4t, \; y = 1 - 4t^2$

18. $x = \dfrac{3at}{1 + t^3}, \; y = \dfrac{3at^2}{1 + t^3}$

19. Find an equation of the tangent line to the curve, $y = 5 \cos \theta, \; x = 2 \sin \theta$, at the point where $\theta = \frac{1}{3}\pi$.

20. A projectile moves so that the coordinates of its position at any time t are given by the equations $x = 60t$ and $y = 80t - 16t^2$. Draw a sketch of the path of the projectile.

21. Find dy/dx, d^2y/dx^2, and d^3y/dx^3 at the point on the cycloid having Eqs. (16) for which y has its largest value when x is in the closed interval $[0, 2\pi a]$.

22. Show that the slope of the tangent line at $t = t_1$ to the cycloid having Eqs. (16) is $\cot \frac{1}{2}t_1$. Deduce then that the tangent line is vertical when $t = 2n\pi$, where n is any integer.

23. A hypocycloid is the curve traced by a point P on a circle of radius b which is rolling inside a fixed circle of radius a, $a > b$. If the origin is at the center of the fixed circle, $A(a, 0)$ is one of the points at which the point P comes in contact with the fixed circle, B is the moving point of tangency of the two circles, and the parameter t is the number of radians in the angle AOB, prove that parametric equations of the hypocycloid are

$$x = (a - b) \cos t + b \cos \frac{a - b}{b}\,t$$

and

$$y = (a - b) \sin t - b \sin \frac{a - b}{b}\,t$$

24. If $a = 4b$ in Exercise 23, we have a *hypocycloid of four cusps*. Show that parametric equations of this curve are $x = a \cos^3 t$ and $y = a \sin^3 t$.

25. Use the parametric equations of Exercise 24 to find a cartesian equation of the hypocycloid of four cusps, and draw a sketch of the graph of the resulting equation.

26. Parametric equations for the *tractrix* are

$$x = t - a \tanh \frac{t}{a} \qquad y = a \operatorname{sech} \frac{t}{a}$$

Draw a sketch of the curve for $a = 4$.

27. Prove that the parameter t in the parametric equations of a tractrix (see Exercise 26) is the x intercept of the tangent line.

28. Show that the tractrix of Exercise 26 is a curve such that the length of the segment of every tangent line from the point of tangency to the point of intersection with the x axis is constant and equal to a.

29. Find the area of the region bounded by the x axis and one arch of the cycloid, having Eqs. (16).

30. Find the centroid of the region of Exercise 29.

15.5 CALCULUS OF VECTOR-VALUED FUNCTIONS

Let $\mathbf{R}$ be a vector-valued function whose function values are given by

$$\mathbf{R}(t) = f(t)\mathbf{i} + g(t)\mathbf{j}$$

15.5.1 Definition

Then *the limit of* $\mathbf{R}(t)$ *as t approaches t_1 is defined by*

$$\lim_{t \to t_1} \mathbf{R}(t) = \left[\lim_{t \to t_1} f(t)\right]\mathbf{i} + \left[\lim_{t \to t_1} g(t)\right]\mathbf{j}$$

if $\lim_{t \to t_1} f(t)$ *and* $\lim_{t \to t_1} g(t)$ *both exist.*

EXAMPLE 1: Given

$$\mathbf{R}(t) = \cos t\mathbf{i} + 2e^t\mathbf{j}$$

find $\lim_{t \to 0} \mathbf{R}(t)$ if it exists.

SOLUTION:

$$\lim_{t \to 0} \mathbf{R}(t) = (\lim_{t \to 0} \cos t)\mathbf{i} + (\lim_{t \to 0} 2e^t)\mathbf{j} = \mathbf{i} + 2\mathbf{j}$$

15.5.2 Definition

The vector-valued function $\mathbf{R}$ is *continuous* at t_1 if and only if the following three conditions are satisfied:

(i) $\mathbf{R}(t_1)$ exists;

(ii) $\lim_{t \to t_1} \mathbf{R}(t)$ exists;

(iii) $\lim_{t \to t_1} \mathbf{R}(t) = \mathbf{R}(t_1)$.

From Definitions 15.5.1 and 15.5.2, it follows that the vector-valued function $\mathbf{R}$, defined by $\mathbf{R}(t) = f(t)\mathbf{i} + g(t)\mathbf{j}$, is continuous at t_1 if and only if f and g are continuous there.

In the following definition the expression

$$\frac{\mathbf{R}(t + \Delta t) - \mathbf{R}(t)}{\Delta t}$$

is used. This is the division of a vector by a scalar which has not yet been defined. By this expression we mean

$$\frac{1}{\Delta t}[\mathbf{R}(t + \Delta t) - \mathbf{R}(t)]$$

15.5.3 Definition   If $\mathbf{R}$ is a vector-valued function, then the *derivative* of $\mathbf{R}$ is another vector-valued function, denoted by $\mathbf{R}'$ and defined by

$$\mathbf{R}'(t) = \lim_{\Delta t \to 0} \frac{\mathbf{R}(t + \Delta t) - \mathbf{R}(t)}{\Delta t}$$

if this limit exists.

The notation $D_t\mathbf{R}(t)$ is sometimes used in place of $\mathbf{R}'(t)$.
The following theorem follows from Definition 15.5.3 and the definition of the derivative of a real-valued function.

15.5.4 Theorem   If $\mathbf{R}$ is a vector-valued function defined by

$$\mathbf{R}(t) = f(t)\mathbf{i} + g(t)\mathbf{j} \tag{1}$$

then

$$\mathbf{R}'(t) = f'(t)\mathbf{i} + g'(t)\mathbf{j}$$

if $f'(t)$ and $g'(t)$ exist.

PROOF: From Definition 15.5.3

$$\mathbf{R}'(t) = \lim_{\Delta t \to 0} \frac{\mathbf{R}(t + \Delta t) - \mathbf{R}(t)}{\Delta t}$$

$$= \lim_{\Delta t \to 0} \frac{[f(t + \Delta t)\mathbf{i} + g(t + \Delta t)\mathbf{j}] - [f(t)\mathbf{i} + g(t)\mathbf{j}]}{\Delta t}$$

$$= \lim_{\Delta t \to 0} \frac{[f(t + \Delta t) - f(t)]}{\Delta t}\mathbf{i} + \lim_{\Delta t \to 0} \frac{[g(t + \Delta t) - g(t)]}{\Delta t}\mathbf{j}$$

$$= f'(t)\mathbf{i} + g'(t)\mathbf{j} \qquad \blacksquare$$

The direction of $\mathbf{R}'(t)$ is given by θ ($0 \le \theta < 2\pi$), where

$$\tan \theta = \frac{g'(t)}{f'(t)} = \frac{\dfrac{dy}{dt}}{\dfrac{dx}{dt}} = \frac{dy}{dx}$$

From the above equation, we see that the direction of $\mathbf{R}'(t)$ is along the tangent line to the curve having vector equation (1) at the point $(f(t), g(t))$.

A geometric interpretation of Definition 15.5.3 is obtained by considering representations of the vectors $\mathbf{R}(t), \mathbf{R}(t + \Delta t)$, and $\mathbf{R}'(t)$. Refer to Fig. 15.5.1. The curve C is traced by the endpoint of the position representation of $\mathbf{R}(t)$ as t assumes all values in the domain of $\mathbf{R}$. Let $\overrightarrow{OP}$ be the

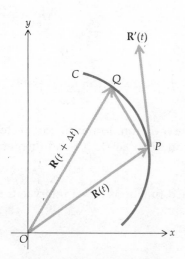

Figure 15.5.1

position representation of $\mathbf{R}(t)$ and OQ be the position representation of $\mathbf{R}(t + \Delta T)$. Then $\mathbf{R}(t + \Delta t) - \mathbf{R}(t)$ is a vector for which $\overrightarrow{PQ}$ is a representation. If the vector $\mathbf{R}(t + \Delta t) - \mathbf{R}(t)$ is multiplied by the scalar $1/\Delta t$, we obtain a vector having the same direction and whose magnitude is $1/|\Delta t|$ times the magnitude of $\mathbf{R}(t + \Delta t) - \mathbf{R}(t)$. As Δt approaches zero, the vector $[\mathbf{R}(t + \Delta t) - \mathbf{R}(t)]/\Delta t$ approaches a vector having one of its representations tangent to the curve C at the point P.

EXAMPLE 2:   Given

$$\mathbf{R}(t) = (2 + \sin t)\mathbf{i} + \cos t\mathbf{j}$$

find $\mathbf{R}'(t)$.

SOLUTION: $\mathbf{R}'(t) = \cos t\mathbf{i} - \sin t\mathbf{j}$.

Higher-order derivatives of vector-valued functions are defined as for higher-order derivatives of real-valued functions. So if $\mathbf{R}$ is a vector-valued function defined by $\mathbf{R}(t) = f(t)\mathbf{i} + g(t)\mathbf{j}$, the second derivative of $\mathbf{R}$, denoted by $\mathbf{R}''(t)$, is given by

$$\mathbf{R}''(t) = D_t[\mathbf{R}'(t)]$$

We also have the notation $D_t^2\mathbf{R}(t)$ in place of $\mathbf{R}''(t)$. By applying Theorem 15.5.4 to $\mathbf{R}'(t)$, we obtain

$$\mathbf{R}''(t) = f''(t)\mathbf{i} + g''(t)\mathbf{j}$$

if $f''(t)$ and $g''(t)$ exist.

EXAMPLE 3:   Given

$$\mathbf{R}(t) = (\ln t)\mathbf{i} + \left(\frac{1}{t}\right)\mathbf{j}$$

find $\mathbf{R}''(t)$.

SOLUTION:

$$\mathbf{R}'(t) = \frac{1}{t}\,\mathbf{i} - \frac{1}{t^2}\,\mathbf{j}$$

$$\mathbf{R}''(t) = -\frac{1}{t^2}\,\mathbf{i} + \frac{2}{t^3}\,\mathbf{j}$$

15.5.5 Definition   A vector-valued function $\mathbf{R}$ is said to be *differentiable* on an interval if $\mathbf{R}'(t)$ exists for all values of t in the interval.

The following theorems give differentiation formulas for vector-valued functions. The proofs are based on Theorem 15.5.4 and theorems on differentiation of real-valued functions.

15.5.6 Theorem   If $\mathbf{R}$ and $\mathbf{Q}$ are differentiable vector-valued functions on an interval, then $\mathbf{R} + \mathbf{Q}$ is differentiable on the interval, and

$$D_t[\mathbf{R}(t) + \mathbf{Q}(t)] = D_t\mathbf{R}(t) + D_t\mathbf{Q}(t)$$

The proof of this theorem is left for the reader (see Exercise 17).

EXAMPLE 4: If

$$\mathbf{R}(t) = t^2\mathbf{i} + (t-1)\mathbf{j}$$

and

$$\mathbf{Q}(t) = \sin t\mathbf{i} + \cos t\mathbf{j}$$

verify Theorem 15.5.6.

SOLUTION:

$$D_t[\mathbf{R}(t) + \mathbf{Q}(t)] = D_t([t^2\mathbf{i} + (t-1)\mathbf{j}] + [\sin t\mathbf{i} + \cos t\mathbf{j}])$$

$$= D_t[(t^2 + \sin t)\mathbf{i} + (t - 1 + \cos t)\mathbf{j}]$$

$$= (2t + \cos t)\mathbf{i} + (1 - \sin t)\mathbf{j}$$

$$D_t\mathbf{R}(t) + D_t\mathbf{Q}(t) = D_t[t^2\mathbf{i} + (t-1)\mathbf{j}] + D_t(\sin t\mathbf{i} + \cos t\mathbf{j})$$

$$= (2t\mathbf{i} + \mathbf{j}) + (\cos t\mathbf{i} - \sin t\mathbf{j})$$

$$= (2t + \cos t)\mathbf{i} + (1 - \sin t)\mathbf{j}$$

Hence, $D_t[\mathbf{R}(t) + \mathbf{Q}(t)] = D_t\mathbf{R}(t) + D_t\mathbf{Q}(t)$.

15.5.7 Theorem   If $\mathbf{R}$ and $\mathbf{Q}$ are differentiable vector-valued functions on an interval, then $\mathbf{R} \cdot \mathbf{Q}$ is differentiable on the interval, and

$$D_t[\mathbf{R}(t) \cdot \mathbf{Q}(t)] = [D_t\mathbf{R}(t)] \cdot \mathbf{Q}(t) + \mathbf{R}(t) \cdot [D_t\mathbf{Q}(t)]$$

PROOF: Let $\mathbf{R}(t) = f_1(t)\mathbf{i} + g_1(t)\mathbf{j}$ and $\mathbf{Q}(t) = f_2(t)\mathbf{i} + g_2(t)\mathbf{j}$. Then by Theorem 15.5.4

$$D_t\mathbf{R}(t) = f_1{}'(t)\mathbf{i} + g_1{}'(t)\mathbf{j} \quad \text{and} \quad D_t\mathbf{Q}(t) = f_2{}'(t)\mathbf{i} + g_2{}'(t)\mathbf{j}$$

$$\mathbf{R}(t) \cdot \mathbf{Q}(t) = [f_1(t)][f_2(t)] + [g_1(t)][g_2(t)]$$

So

$$D_t[\mathbf{R}(t) \cdot \mathbf{Q}(t)]$$

$$= [f_1{}'(t)][f_2(t)] + [f_1(t)][f_2{}'(t)] + [g_1{}'(t)][g_2(t)] + [g_1(t)][g_2{}'(t)]$$

$$= \{[f_1{}'(t)][f_2(t)] + [g_1{}'(t)][g_2(t)]\} + \{[f_1(t)][f_2{}'(t)] + [g_1(t)][g_2{}'(t)]\}$$

$$= [D_t\mathbf{R}(t)] \cdot \mathbf{Q}(t) + \mathbf{R}(t) \cdot [D_t\mathbf{Q}(t)]$$ ■

EXAMPLE 5: Verify Theorem 15.5.7 for the vectors given in Example 4.

SOLUTION: $\mathbf{R}(t) \cdot \mathbf{Q}(t) = t^2 \sin t + (t-1) \cos t$.

Therefore,

$$D_t[\mathbf{R}(t) \cdot \mathbf{Q}(t)] = 2t \sin t + t^2 \cos t + \cos t + (t-1)(-\sin t)$$

or

$$D_t[\mathbf{R}(t) \cdot \mathbf{Q}(t)] = (t+1) \sin t + (t^2 + 1) \cos t \qquad (2)$$

Because

$$D_t\mathbf{R}(t) = D_t[t^2\mathbf{i} + (t-1)\mathbf{j}] = 2t\mathbf{i} + \mathbf{j}$$

$$[D_t\mathbf{R}(t)] \cdot \mathbf{Q}(t) = (2t\mathbf{i} + \mathbf{j}) \cdot (\sin t\mathbf{i} + \cos t\mathbf{j})$$

$$= 2t \sin t + \cos t$$

Because

$$D_t\mathbf{Q}(t) = D_t[\sin t\mathbf{i} + \cos t\mathbf{j}] = \cos t\mathbf{i} - \sin t\mathbf{j}$$

$$\mathbf{R}(t) \cdot [D_t\mathbf{Q}(t)] = [t^2\mathbf{i} + (t-1)\mathbf{j}] \cdot (\cos t\mathbf{i} - \sin t\mathbf{j})$$

$$= t^2 \cos t - (t-1) \sin t$$

Therefore,

$$[D_t\mathbf{R}(t)] \cdot \mathbf{Q}(t) + \mathbf{R}(t) \cdot [D_t\mathbf{Q}(t)] = (2t \sin t + \cos t)$$
$$+ [t^2 \cos t - (t-1) \sin t]$$

or

$$[D_t\mathbf{R}(t)] \cdot \mathbf{Q}(t) + \mathbf{R}(t) \cdot [D_t\mathbf{Q}(t)] = (t+1) \sin t + (t^2+1) \cos t \qquad (3)$$

Comparing Eqs. (2) and (3), we see that Theorem 15.5.7 holds.

15.5.8 Theorem   If $\mathbf{R}$ is a differentiable vector-valued function on an interval and f is a differentiable real-valued function on the interval, then

$$D_t\{[f(t)][\mathbf{R}(t)]\} = [D_tf(t)]\mathbf{R}(t) + f(t) D_t\mathbf{R}(t)$$

The proof is left for the reader (see Exercise 18).

We now define an indefinite integral (or antiderivative) of a vector-valued function.

15.5.9 Definition   If $\mathbf{Q}$ is the vector-valued function given by

$$\mathbf{Q}(t) = f(t)\mathbf{i} + g(t)\mathbf{j}$$

then the *indefinite integral of* $\mathbf{Q}(t)$ is defined by

$$\int \mathbf{Q}(t) \, dt = \mathbf{i} \int f(t) \, dt + \mathbf{j} \int g(t) \, dt \qquad (4)$$

This definition is consistent with the definition of an indefinite integral of a real-valued function because if we take the derivative on both sides of (4) with respect to t, we have

$$D_t \int \mathbf{Q}(t) \, dt = \mathbf{i}D_t \int f(t) \, dt + \mathbf{j}D_t \int g(t) \, dt$$

which gives us

$$D_t \int \mathbf{Q}(t) \, dt = \mathbf{i}f(t) + \mathbf{j}g(t)$$

For each of the indefinite integrals on the right side of (4) there occurs an arbitrary scalar constant. When each of these scalars is multiplied by either $\mathbf{i}$ or $\mathbf{j}$, there occurs an arbitrary constant vector in the sum. So we have

$$\int \mathbf{Q}(t) \, dt = \mathbf{R}(t) + \mathbf{C}$$

where $D_t\mathbf{R}(t) = \mathbf{Q}(t)$ and $\mathbf{C}$ is an arbitrary constant vector.

EXAMPLE 6:   Find the most general vector-valued function whose derivative is

$$Q(t) = \sin t\mathbf{i} - 3 \cos t\mathbf{j}$$

SOLUTION: If $D_t\mathbf{R}(t) = \mathbf{Q}(t)$, then $\mathbf{R}(t) = \int\mathbf{Q}(t)\,dt$, or

$$\mathbf{R}(t) = \mathbf{i}\int \sin t\,dt - 3\mathbf{j}\int \cos t\,dt$$

$$= \mathbf{i}(-\cos t + C_1) - 3\mathbf{j}(\sin t + C_2)$$

$$= -\cos t\mathbf{i} - 3 \sin t\mathbf{j} + (C_1\mathbf{i} - 3C_2\mathbf{j})$$

$$= -\cos t\mathbf{i} - 3 \sin t\mathbf{j} + \mathbf{C}$$

EXAMPLE 7:   Find the vector $\mathbf{R}(t)$ for which

$$D_t\mathbf{R}(t) = e^{-t}\mathbf{i} + e^t\mathbf{j}$$

and for which $\mathbf{R}(0) = \mathbf{i} + \mathbf{j}$.

SOLUTION: $\mathbf{R}(t) = \mathbf{i}\int e^{-t}\,dt + \mathbf{j}\int e^t\,dt$

So

$$\mathbf{R}(t) = \mathbf{i}(-e^{-t} + C_1) + \mathbf{j}(e^t + C_2)$$

Because $\mathbf{R}(0) = \mathbf{i} + \mathbf{j}$, we have

$$\mathbf{i} + \mathbf{j} = \mathbf{i}(-1 + C_1) + \mathbf{j}(1 + C_2)$$

So

$$C_1 - 1 = 1 \quad \text{and} \quad C_2 + 1 = 1$$

Therefore,

$$C_1 = 2 \quad \text{and} \quad C_2 = 0$$

So

$$\mathbf{R}(t) = (-e^{-t} + 2)\mathbf{i} + e^t\mathbf{j}$$

The following theorem will be useful later.

15.5.10 Theorem   If $\mathbf{R}$ is a differentiable vector-valued function on an interval and $\mathbf{R}(t)$ is a nonzero vector of constant magnitude and variable direction for all t in the interval, then the vectors $\mathbf{R}(t)$ and $D_t\mathbf{R}(t)$ are orthogonal.

PROOF: Let the magnitude of $\mathbf{R}(t)$ be k, a constant. Then by Theorem 15.3.3(iii)

$$\mathbf{R}(t) \cdot \mathbf{R}(t) = k^2$$

Differentiating on both sides with respect to t and using Theorem 15.5.7, we obtain

$$[D_t\mathbf{R}(t)] \cdot \mathbf{R}(t) + \mathbf{R}(t) \cdot [D_t\mathbf{R}(t)] = 0$$

So

$$2\mathbf{R}(t) \cdot D_t\mathbf{R}(t) = 0$$

Because the dot product of $\mathbf{R}(t)$ and $D_t\mathbf{R}(t)$ is zero, either $\mathbf{R}(t)$ and $D_t\mathbf{R}(t)$ are orthogonal, or one of the vectors, $\mathbf{R}(t)$ or $D_t\mathbf{R}(t)$, is the zero

Figure 15.5.2

vector. By hypothesis, $\mathbf{R}(t)$ is not the zero vector. If $D_t\mathbf{R}(t)$ is the zero vector, then

$$\mathbf{R}(t) = \mathbf{i}\int 0\, dt + \mathbf{j}\int 0\, dt = C_1\mathbf{i} + C_2\mathbf{j}$$

that is, $\mathbf{R}(t)$ is constant. But $\mathbf{R}(t)$ is not constant because its direction changes even though its magnitude is constant. Therefore, $\mathbf{R}(t)$ and $D_t\mathbf{R}(t)$ are orthogonal.   ∎

The geometric interpretation of Theorem 15.5.10 is evident. If the vector $\mathbf{R}(t)$ has constant magnitude, then the position representation $\overrightarrow{OP}$ of $\mathbf{R}(t)$ has its terminal point P on the circle with its center at the origin and radius k. So the graph of $\mathbf{R}$ is this circle. Because $D_t\mathbf{R}(t)$ and $\mathbf{R}(t)$ are orthogonal, $\overrightarrow{OP}$ is perpendicular to a representation of $D_t\mathbf{R}(t)$. Figure 15.5.2 shows a sketch of a quarter circle, the position representation $\overrightarrow{OP}$ of $\mathbf{R}(t)$, and the representation $\overrightarrow{PB}$ of $D_t\mathbf{R}(t)$.

Exercises 15.5

In Exercises 1 through 4, find the indicated limit, if it exists.

1. $\mathbf{R}(t) = (t-2)\mathbf{i} + \dfrac{t^2-4}{t-2}\mathbf{j}$; $\lim\limits_{t\to 2} \mathbf{R}(t)$

2. $\mathbf{R}(t) = e^{t+1}\mathbf{i} + |t+1|\mathbf{j}$; $\lim\limits_{t\to -1} \mathbf{R}(t)$

3. $\mathbf{R}(t) = 2\sin t\mathbf{i} + \cos t\mathbf{j}$; $\lim\limits_{t\to \pi/2} \mathbf{R}(t)$

4. $\mathbf{R}(t) = \dfrac{t^2-2t-3}{t-3}\mathbf{i} + \dfrac{t^2-5t+6}{t-3}\mathbf{j}$; $\lim\limits_{t\to 3} \mathbf{R}(t)$

In Exercises 5 through 10, find $\mathbf{R}'(t)$ and $\mathbf{R}''(t)$.

5. $\mathbf{R}(t) = (t^2-3)\mathbf{i} + (2t+1)\mathbf{j}$

6. $\mathbf{R}(t) = \dfrac{t-1}{t+1}\mathbf{i} + \dfrac{t-2}{t}\mathbf{j}$

7. $\mathbf{R}(t) = e^{2t}\mathbf{i} + \ln t\mathbf{j}$

8. $\mathbf{R}(t) = \cos 2t\mathbf{i} + \tan t\mathbf{j}$

9. $\mathbf{R}(t) = \tan^{-1} t\mathbf{i} + 2^t\mathbf{j}$

10. $\mathbf{R}(t) = \sqrt{2t+1}\mathbf{i} + (t-1)^2\mathbf{j}$

In Exercises 11 and 12, find $D_t|\mathbf{R}(t)|$.

11. $\mathbf{R}(t) = (t-1)\mathbf{i} + (2-t)\mathbf{j}$

12. $\mathbf{R}(t) = (e^t+1)\mathbf{i} + (e^t-1)\mathbf{j}$

In Exercises 13 through 16, find $\mathbf{R}'(t) \cdot \mathbf{R}''(t)$.

13. $\mathbf{R}(t) = (2t^2-1)\mathbf{i} + (t^2+3)\mathbf{j}$

14. $\mathbf{R}(t) = -\cos 2t\mathbf{i} + \sin 2t\mathbf{j}$

15. $\mathbf{R}(t) = -\cos 2t\mathbf{i} + \cos 2t\mathbf{j}$

16. $\mathbf{R}(t) = e^{2t}\mathbf{i} + e^{-2t}\mathbf{j}$

17. Prove Theorem 15.5.6.

18. Prove Theorem 15.5.8.

In Exercises 19 through 22, find the most general vector whose derivative has the given function value.

19. $\tan t\mathbf{i} - \dfrac{1}{t}\mathbf{j}$

20. $\dfrac{1}{4+t^2}\mathbf{i} - \dfrac{4}{1-t^2}\mathbf{j}$

21. $\ln t\mathbf{i} + t^2\mathbf{j}$

22. $3^t\mathbf{i} - 2^t\mathbf{j}$

23. If $\mathbf{R}'(t) = \sin^2 t\mathbf{i} + 2\cos^2 t\mathbf{j}$, and $\mathbf{R}(\pi) = 0$, find $\mathbf{R}(t)$.

24. If $\mathbf{R}'(t) = e^t \sin t\mathbf{i} + e^t \cos t\mathbf{j}$, and $\mathbf{R}(0) = \mathbf{i} - \mathbf{j}$, find $\mathbf{R}(t)$.

25. Given the vector equation $\mathbf{R}(t) = \cos t\mathbf{i} + \sin t\mathbf{j}$. Find a cartesian equation of the curve which is traced by the endpoint of the position representation of $\mathbf{R}'(t)$. Find $\mathbf{R}(t) \cdot \mathbf{R}'(t)$. Interpret the result geometrically.

26. Given $\mathbf{R}(t) = 2t\mathbf{i} + (t^2-1)\mathbf{j}$ and $\mathbf{Q}(t) = 3t\mathbf{i}$. If $\alpha(t)$ is the radian measure of the angle between $\mathbf{R}(t)$ and $\mathbf{Q}(t)$, find $D_t\alpha(t)$.

27. Suppose **R** and **R**′ are vector-valued functions defined on an interval and **R**′ is differentiable on the interval. Prove

$$D_t[\mathbf{R}'(t) \cdot \mathbf{R}(t)] = |\mathbf{R}'(t)|^2 + \mathbf{R}(t) \cdot \mathbf{R}''(t)$$

28. If $|\mathbf{R}(t)| = h(t)$, prove that $\mathbf{R}(t) \cdot \mathbf{R}'(t) = [h(t)][h'(t)]$.

29. If the vector-valued function **R** and the real-valued function f are both differentiable on an interval and $f(t) \neq 0$ on the interval, prove that $\mathbf{R}/f$ is also differentiable on the interval and

$$D_t \left[\frac{\mathbf{R}(t)}{f(t)} \right] = \frac{f(t)\mathbf{R}'(t) - f'(t)\mathbf{R}(t)}{[f(t)]^2}$$

30. Prove that if **A** and **B** are constant vectors and f and g are integrable functions, then

$$\int [\mathbf{A}f(t) + \mathbf{B}g(t)] \, dt = \mathbf{A} \int f(t) \, dt + \mathbf{B} \int g(t) \, dt$$

(HINT: Express **A** and **B** in terms of **i** and **j**.)

15.6 LENGTH OF ARC   In Sec. 7.10 we obtained a formula for finding the length of arc of a curve having an equation of the form $y = f(x)$. This is a special kind of curve because the graph of a function f cannot be intersected by a vertical line in more than one point.

We now develop a method for finding the length of arc of some other kinds of curves. Let C be the curve having parametric equations

$$x = f(t) \quad \text{and} \quad y = g(t) \tag{1}$$

and suppose that f and g are continuous on the closed interval $[a, b]$. We wish to assign a number L to represent the number of units in the length of arc of C from $t = a$ to $t = b$. We proceed as in Sec. 7.10.

Let Δ be a partition of the closed interval $[a, b]$ formed by dividing the interval into n subintervals by choosing $n - 1$ numbers between a and b. Let $t_0 = a$ and $t_n = b$, and let $t_1, t_2, \ldots, t_{n-1}$ be intermediate numbers:

$$t_0 < t_1 < \cdots < t_{n-1} < t_n$$

The ith subinterval is $[t_{i-1}, t_i]$ and the number of units in its length, denoted by $\Delta_i t$, is $t_i - t_{i-1}$, where $i = 1, 2, \ldots, n$. Let $\|\Delta\|$ be the norm of the partition; so each $\Delta_i t \leq \|\Delta\|$.

Associated with each number t_i is a point $P_i(f(t_i), g(t_i))$ on C. From each point P_{i-1} draw a line segment to the next point P_i (see Fig. 15.6.1).

Figure 15.6.1

The number of units in the length of the line segment from P_{i-1} to P_i is denoted by $|\overline{P_{i-1}P_i}|$. From the distance formula we have

$$|\overline{P_{i-1}P_i}| = \sqrt{[f(t_i) - f(t_{i-1})]^2 + [g(t_i) - g(t_{i-1})]^2} \tag{2}$$

The sum of the numbers of units of lengths of the n line segments is

$$\sum_{i-1}^{n} |\overline{P_{i-1}P_i}| \tag{3}$$

Our intuitive notion of the length of the arc from $t = a$ to $t = b$ leads us to define the number of units of the length of arc as the limit of the sum in (3) as $\|\Delta\|$ approaches zero.

15.6.1 Definition Let the curve C have parametric equations $x = f(t)$ and $y = g(t)$. Then if there exists a number L having the property that for any $\epsilon > 0$ there is a $\delta > 0$ such that

$$\left| \sum_{i=1}^{n} |\overline{P_{i-1}P_i}| - L \right| < \epsilon$$

for every partition Δ of the interval $[a, b]$ for which $\|\Delta\| < \delta$, we write

$$L = \lim_{\|\Delta\| \to 0} \sum_{i=1}^{n} |\overline{P_{i-1}P_i}| \tag{4}$$

and L units is called the *length of arc* of the curve C from the point $(f(a), g(a))$ to the point $(f(b), g(b))$.

The arc of the curve is rectifiable if the limit in (4) exists.

If f' and g' are continuous on $[a, b]$, we can find a formula for evaluating the limit in (4). We proceed as follows.

Because f' and g' are continuous on $[a, b]$, they are continuous on each subinterval of the partition Δ. So the hypothesis of the mean-value theorem (Theorem 4.5.2) is satisfied by f and g on each $[t_{i-1}, t_i]$; therefore, there are numbers z_i and w_i in the open interval (t_{i-1}, t_i) such that

$$f(t_i) - f(t_{i-1}) = f'(z_i) \, \Delta_i t \tag{5}$$

and

$$g(t_i) - g(t_{i-1}) = g'(w_i) \, \Delta_i t \tag{6}$$

Substituting from (5) and (6) into (2), we obtain

$$|\overline{P_{i-1}P_i}| = \sqrt{[f'(z_i) \, \Delta_i t]^2 + [g'(w_i) \, \Delta_i t]^2}$$

or, equivalently,

$$|\overline{P_{i-1}P_i}| = \sqrt{[f'(z_i)]^2 + [g'(w_i)]^2} \, \Delta_i t \tag{7}$$

where z_i and w_i are in the open interval (t_{i-1}, t_i). Then from (4) and (7), if the limit exists,

$$L = \lim_{\|\Delta\| \to 0} \sum_{i=1}^{n} \sqrt{[f'(z_i)]^2 + [g'(w_i)]^2} \, \Delta_i t \tag{8}$$

The sum in (8) is not a Riemann sum because z_i and w_i are not necessarily the same numbers. So we cannot apply the definition of a definite integral to evaluate the limit in (8). However, there is a theorem which we can apply to evaluate this limit. We state the theorem, but a proof is not given because it is beyond the scope of this book. You can find a proof in most advanced calculus texts.

15.6.2 Theorem   If the functions F and G are continuous on the closed interval $[a, b]$, then the function $\sqrt{F^2 + G^2}$ is also continuous on $[a, b]$, and if Δ is a partition of the interval $[a, b]$ (Δ: $a = t_0 < t_i < \cdots < t_{i-1} < t_i < \cdots < t_n = b$), and z_i and w_i are any numbers in (t_{i-1}, t_i), then

$$\lim_{\|\Delta\| \to 0} \sum_{i=1}^{n} \sqrt{[F(z_i)]^2 + [G(w_i)]^2}\, \Delta_i t = \int_a^b \sqrt{[F(t)]^2 + [G(t)]^2}\ dt \quad (9)$$

Applying (9) to (8), where F is f' and G is g', we have

$$L = \int_a^b \sqrt{[f'(t)]^2 + [g'(t)]^2}\ dt$$

We state this result as a theorem.

15.6.3 Theorem   Let the curve C have parametric equations $x = f(t)$ and $y = g(t)$, and suppose that f' and g' are continuous on the closed interval $[a, b]$. Then the length of arc L units of the curve C from the point $(f(a), g(a))$ to the point $(f(b), g(b))$ is determined by

$$L = \int_a^b \sqrt{[f'(t)]^2 + [g'(t)]^2}\ dt \quad (10)$$

EXAMPLE 1:   Find the length of the arc of the curve having parametric equations $x = t^3$ and $y = 2t^2$ in each of the following cases: (a) from $t = 0$ to $t = 1$; (b) from $t = -2$ to $t = 0$.

Figure 15.6.2

SOLUTION: A sketch of the curve is shown in Fig. 15.6.2. (a) Letting $x = f(t)$, $f'(t) = D_t x = 3t^2$; and letting $y = g(t)$, $g'(t) = D_t y = 4t$. So from Theorem 15.6.3, if L units is the length of the arc of the curve from $t = 0$ to $t = 1$,

$x = t^3$
$y = 2t^2$

$$L = \int_0^1 \sqrt{9t^4 + 16t^2}\ dt$$

$$= \int_0^1 t\sqrt{9t^2 + 16}\ dt$$

$$= \tfrac{1}{18} \cdot \tfrac{2}{3}(9t^2 + 16)^{3/2}\Big]_0^1$$

$$= \tfrac{1}{27}[(25)^{3/2} - (16)^{3/2}]$$

$$= \tfrac{1}{27}(125 - 64)$$

$$= \tfrac{61}{27}$$

(b) If L units is the length of the arc of the curve from $t = -2$ to $t = 0$, we have from Theorem 15.6.3

$$L = \int_{-2}^{0} \sqrt{9t^4 + 16t^2}\ dt = \int_{-2}^{0} \sqrt{t^2}\ \sqrt{9t^2 + 16}\ dt$$

Because $-2 \le t \le 0$, $\sqrt{t^2} = -t$. So we have

$$L = \int_{-2}^{0} -t\sqrt{9t^2 + 16}\ dt$$

$$= -\tfrac{1}{27}(9t^2 + 16)^{3/2}\Big]_{-2}^{0}$$

$$= -\tfrac{1}{27}\left[(16)^{3/2} - (50)^{3/2}\right]$$

$$= \tfrac{1}{27}(250\sqrt{2} - 64)$$

$$\approx 10.7$$

The curve C has parametric equations (1). Let s units be the length of arc of C from the point $(f(t_0), g(t_0))$ to the point $(f(t), g(t))$, and let s increase as t increases. Then s is a function of t and is given by

$$s = \int_{t_0}^{t} \sqrt{[f'(u)]^2 + [g'(u)]^2}\ du \qquad (11)$$

From Theorem 6.6.1, we have

$$\frac{ds}{dt} = \sqrt{[f'(t)]^2 + [g'(t)]^2} \qquad (12)$$

A vector equation of C is

$$\mathbf{R}(t) = f(t)\mathbf{i} + g(t)\mathbf{j} \qquad (13)$$

Because

$$\mathbf{R}'(t) = f'(t)\mathbf{i} + g'(t)\mathbf{j}$$

we have

$$|\mathbf{R}'(t)| = \sqrt{[f'(t)]^2 + [g'(t)]^2} \qquad (14)$$

Substituting from (14) into (12), we obtain

$$|\mathbf{R}'(t)| = \frac{ds}{dt} \qquad (15)$$

From (15) we conclude that if s units is the length of arc of curve C having vector equation (13) measured from some fixed point to the point $(f(t), g(t))$ where s increases as t increases, then the derivative of s with respect to t is the magnitude of the derivative of the position vector at the point $(f(t), g(t))$.

If we substitute from (14) into (10), we obtain $L = \int_{a}^{b} |\mathbf{R}'(t)|\ dt$. So

Theorem 15.6.3 can be stated in terms of vectors in the following way.

15.6.4 Theorem   Let the curve C have the vector equation $\mathbf{R}(t) = f(t)\mathbf{i} + g(t)\mathbf{j}$, and suppose that f' and g' are continuous on the closed interval $[a, b]$. Then the length of arc of C, traced by the terminal point of the position representation of $\mathbf{R}(t)$ as t increases from a to b, is determined by

$$L = \int_a^b |\mathbf{R}'(t)|\, dt \tag{16}$$

EXAMPLE 2:   Find the length of the arc traced by the terminal point of the position representation of $\mathbf{R}(t)$ as t increases from 1 to 4 if

$$\mathbf{R}(t) = e^t \sin t\mathbf{i} + e^t \cos t\mathbf{j}$$

SOLUTION: $\mathbf{R}'(t) = (e^t \sin t + e^t \cos t)\mathbf{i} + (e^t \cos t - e^t \sin t)\mathbf{j}$.
Therefore,

$$|\mathbf{R}'(t)| = e^t \sqrt{\sin^2 t + 2\sin t \cos t + \cos^2 t + \cos^2 t - 2\sin t \cos t + \sin^2 t}$$

$$= e^t \sqrt{2}$$

From (16) we have

$$L = \int_1^4 \sqrt{2}\,e^t\, dt = \sqrt{2}\,e^t\Big]_1^4 = \sqrt{2}(e^4 - e)$$

An alternate form of formula (10) for the length of an arc of a curve C, having parametric equations $x = f(t)$ and $y = g(t)$, is obtained by replacing $f'(t)$ by dx/dt and $g'(t)$ by dy/dt. We have

$$L = \int_a^b \sqrt{\left(\frac{dx}{dt}\right)^2 + \left(\frac{dy}{dt}\right)^2}\, dt \tag{17}$$

Now suppose that we wish to find the length of arc of a curve C whose polar equation is $r = F(\theta)$. If (x, y) is the cartesian representation of a point P on C and (r, θ) is a polar representation of P, then

$$x = r \cos \theta \quad \text{and} \quad y = r \sin \theta \tag{18}$$

Replacing r by $F(\theta)$ in Eqs. (18), we have

$$x = \cos \theta F(\theta) \quad \text{and} \quad y = \sin \theta F(\theta) \tag{19}$$

Equations (19) can be considered as parametric equations of C where θ is the parameter instead of t. Therefore, if F' is continuous on the closed interval $[\alpha, \beta]$, the formula for the length of arc of the curve C whose polar equation is $r = F(\theta)$ is obtained from (17) by taking $t = \theta$. So we have

$$L = \int \sqrt{\left(\frac{dx}{d\theta}\right)^2 + \left(\frac{dy}{d\theta}\right)^2}\, d\theta \tag{20}$$

From (18) we have

$$\frac{dx}{d\theta} = \cos\theta \frac{dr}{d\theta} - r\sin\theta \quad \text{and} \quad \frac{dy}{d\theta} = \sin\theta \frac{dr}{d\theta} + r\cos\theta$$

Therefore,

$$\sqrt{\left(\frac{dx}{d\theta}\right)^2 + \left(\frac{dy}{d\theta}\right)^2} = \sqrt{\left(\cos\theta \frac{dr}{d\theta} - r\sin\theta\right)^2 + \left(\sin\theta \frac{dr}{d\theta} + r\cos\theta\right)^2}$$

$$= \sqrt{\cos^2\theta \left(\frac{dr}{d\theta}\right)^2 - 2r\sin\theta\cos\theta \frac{dr}{d\theta} + r^2\sin^2\theta + \sin^2\theta \left(\frac{dr}{d\theta}\right)^2 + 2r\sin\theta\cos\theta \frac{dr}{d\theta} + r^2\cos^2\theta}$$

$$= \sqrt{(\cos^2\theta + \sin^2\theta)\left(\frac{dr}{d\theta}\right)^2 + (\sin^2\theta + \cos^2\theta)r^2}$$

$$= \sqrt{\left(\frac{dr}{d\theta}\right)^2 + r^2}$$

Substituting this into (20), we obtain

$$L = \int_\alpha^\beta \sqrt{\left(\frac{dr}{d\theta}\right)^2 + r^2}\; d\theta \tag{21}$$

EXAMPLE 3: Find the length of the cardioid $r = 2(1 + \cos\theta)$.

Figure 15.6.3

SOLUTION: A sketch of the curve is shown in Fig. 15.6.3. To obtain the length of the entire curve, we can let θ take on values from 0 to 2π or we can make use of the symmetry of the curve and find half the length by letting θ take on values from 0 to π.

Because $r = 2(1 + \cos\theta)$, $dr/d\theta = -2\sin\theta$. Substituting into (21), integrating from 0 to π, and multiplying by 2, we have

$$L = 2\int_0^\pi \sqrt{(-2\sin\theta)^2 + 4(1 + \cos\theta)^2}\; d\theta$$

$$= 4\int_0^\pi \sqrt{\sin^2\theta + 1 + 2\cos\theta + \cos^2\theta}\; d\theta$$

$$= 4\sqrt{2}\int_0^\pi \sqrt{1 + \cos\theta}\; d\theta$$

To evaluate this integral, we use the identity $\cos^2\frac{1}{2}\theta = \frac{1}{2}(1 + \cos\theta)$, which gives $\sqrt{1 + \cos\theta} = \sqrt{2}\;|\cos\frac{1}{2}\theta|$. Because $0 \le \theta \le \pi$, $0 \le \frac{1}{2}\theta \le \frac{1}{2}\pi$; thus, $\cos\frac{1}{2}\theta \ge 0$. Therefore, $\sqrt{1 + \cos\theta} = \sqrt{2}\cos\frac{1}{2}\theta$. So we have

$$L = 4\sqrt{2}\int_0^\pi \sqrt{2}\cos\frac{1}{2}\theta\; d\theta = 16\sin\frac{1}{2}\theta\Big]_0^\pi = 16$$

Exercises 15.6

Find the length of arc in each of the following exercises.

1. $x = \frac{1}{2}t^2 + t$, $y = \frac{1}{2}t^2 - t$; from $t = 0$ to $t = 1$.

2. $x = t^3$, $y = 3t^2$; from $t = -2$ to $t = 0$.

3. $\mathbf{R}(t) = 2t^2\mathbf{i} + 2t^3\mathbf{j}$; from $t = 1$ to $t = 2$.

4. $\mathbf{R}(t) = a(\cos t + t \sin t)\mathbf{i} + a(\sin t - t \cos t)\mathbf{j}$; from $t = 0$ to $t = \frac{1}{3}\pi$.

5. The entire hypocycloid of four cusps: $x = a \cos^3 t$, $y = a \sin^3 t$.

6. $x = e^{-t} \cos t$, $y = e^{-t} \sin t$; from $t = 0$ to $t = \pi$.

7. The tractrix $x = t - a \tanh \dfrac{t}{a}$, $y = a \operatorname{sech} \dfrac{t}{a}$ from $t = -a$ to $t = 2a$.

8. One arch of the cycloid: $x = a(t - \sin t)$, $y = a(1 - \cos t)$.

9. The circumference of the circle: $\mathbf{R}(t) = a \cos t\mathbf{i} + a \sin t\mathbf{j}$.

10. The circumference of the circle: $r = a \sin \theta$.

11. The circumference of the circle: $r = a$.

12. The entire curve: $r = 1 - \sin \theta$.

13. The entire curve: $r = 3 \cos^2 \frac{1}{2}\theta$.

14. $r = a\theta$; from $\theta = 0$ to $\theta = 2\pi$.

15. $r = a \sin^3 \frac{1}{3}\theta$; from $\theta = 0$ to $\theta = \theta_1$.

16. $r = a\theta^2$; from $\theta = 0$ to $\theta = \pi$.

15.7 PLANE MOTION The previous discussion of the motion of a particle was confined to straight-line motion. In this connection, we defined the velocity and acceleration of a particle moving along a straight line. We now consider the motion of a particle along a curve in the plane.

Suppose that C is the plane curve having parametric equations $x = f(t)$, $y = g(t)$, where t units denotes time. Then

$$\mathbf{R}(t) = f(t)\mathbf{i} + g(t)\mathbf{j}$$

is a vector equation of C. As t varies, the endpoint $P(f(t), g(t))$ of $\overrightarrow{OP}$ moves along the curve C. The position at time t units of a particle moving along C is the point $P(f(t), g(t))$. The *velocity vector* of the particle at time t units is defined to be $\mathbf{R}'(t)$. We denote the velocity vector by the symbol $\mathbf{V}(t)$ instead of $\mathbf{R}'(t)$.

15.7.1 Definition Let C be the curve having parametric equations $x = f(t)$ and $y = g(t)$. If a particle is moving along C so that its position at any time t units is the point (x, y), then the *instantaneous velocity* of the particle at time t units is determined by the velocity vector

$$\mathbf{V}(t) = f'(t)\mathbf{i} + g'(t)\mathbf{j}$$

if $f'(t)$ and $g'(t)$ exist.

In Sec. 15.5 we saw that the direction of $\mathbf{R}'(t)$ at the point

THE INSTANTANEOUS VELOCITY IS THE DERIVATIVE OF THE VECTOR EQUATION

$P(f(t), g(t))$ is along the tangent line to the curve C at P. Therefore, the velocity vector $\mathbf{V}(t)$ has this direction at P.

The magnitude of the velocity vector is a measure of the *speed* of the particle at time t and is given by

$$|\mathbf{V}(t)| = \sqrt{[f'(t)]^2 + [g'(t)]^2} \qquad (1)$$

Note that the velocity is a vector and the speed is a scalar. As shown in Sec. 15.6, the expression on the right side of (1) is ds/dt. So the speed is the rate of change of s with respect to t, and we write

$$|\mathbf{V}(t)| = \frac{ds}{dt} \qquad (2)$$

The *acceleration vector* of the particle at time t units is defined to be the derivative of the velocity vector or, equivalently, the second derivative of the position vector. The acceleration vector is denoted by $\mathbf{A}(t)$.

15.7.2 Definition   The *instantaneous acceleration* at time t units of a particle moving along a curve C, having parametric equations $x = f(t)$ and $y = g(t)$, is determined by the acceleration vector

$$\mathbf{A}(t) = \mathbf{V}'(t) = \mathbf{R}''(t)$$

where $\mathbf{R}(t) = f(t)\mathbf{i} + g(t)\mathbf{j}$ and $\mathbf{R}''(t)$ exists.

Figure 15.7.1 shows the representations of the velocity vector and the acceleration vector whose initial point is the point P on C.

Figure 15.7.1

EXAMPLE 1:   A particle is moving along the curve having parametric equations $x = 4 \cos \frac{1}{2}t$ and $y = 4 \sin \frac{1}{2}t$. If t is the number of seconds in the time and x and y represent number of feet, find the speed and magnitude of the particle's acceleration vector at time t sec. Draw a sketch of the particle's path, and also draw the representations of the velocity and acceleration vectors having initial point where $t = \frac{1}{3}\pi$.

SOLUTION: A vector equation of C is

$$\mathbf{R}(t) = 4 \cos \tfrac{1}{2}t\,\mathbf{i} + 4 \sin \tfrac{1}{2}t\,\mathbf{j}$$

$$\mathbf{V}(t) = \mathbf{R}'(t) = -2 \sin \tfrac{1}{2}t\,\mathbf{i} + 2 \cos \tfrac{1}{2}t\,\mathbf{j}$$

$$\mathbf{A}(t) = \mathbf{V}'(t) = -\cos \tfrac{1}{2}t\,\mathbf{i} - \sin \tfrac{1}{2}t\,\mathbf{j}$$

$$|\mathbf{V}(t)| = \sqrt{(-2 \sin \tfrac{1}{2}t)^2 + (2 \cos \tfrac{1}{2}t)^2}$$

$$= \sqrt{4 \sin^2 \tfrac{1}{2}t + 4 \cos^2 \tfrac{1}{2}t}$$

$$= 2$$

$$|\mathbf{A}(t)| = \sqrt{(-\cos \tfrac{1}{2}t)^2 + (-\sin \tfrac{1}{2}t)^2} = 1$$

Therefore, the speed of the particle is constant and is 2 ft/sec. The magnitude of the acceleration vector is also constant and is 1 ft/sec².

Eliminating t between the parametric equations of C, we obtain the cartesian equation $x^2 + y^2 = 16$, which is a circle with its center at 0 and radius 4.

Figure 15.7.2

When $t = \frac{1}{3}\pi$, the direction of $\mathbf{V}(t)$ is given by

$$\tan \theta = -\frac{\cos \frac{1}{6}\pi}{\sin \frac{1}{6}\pi} = -\cot \frac{1}{6}\pi = -\sqrt{3}$$

and the direction of $\mathbf{A}(t)$ is given by

$$\tan \theta = \frac{\sin \frac{1}{6}\pi}{\cos \frac{1}{6}\pi} = \tan \frac{1}{6}\pi = \frac{1}{\sqrt{3}}$$

Figure 15.7.2 shows the representations of the velocity and acceleration vectors having initial point where $t = \frac{1}{3}\pi$.

EXAMPLE 2:   The position of a moving particle at time t units is given by the vector equation

$$\mathbf{R}(t) = e^{-2t}\mathbf{i} + 3e^t\mathbf{j}$$

Find $\mathbf{V}(t)$, $\mathbf{A}(t)$, $|\mathbf{V}(t)|$, $|\mathbf{A}(t)|$.

Draw a sketch of the path of the particle and the representations of the velocity and acceleration vectors having initial point where $t = \frac{1}{2}$.

Figure 15.7.3

SOLUTION:

$$\mathbf{V}(t) = \mathbf{R}'(t) = -2e^{-2t}\mathbf{i} + 3e^t\mathbf{j}$$

$$\mathbf{A}(t) = \mathbf{V}'(t) = 4e^{-2t}\mathbf{i} + 3e^t\mathbf{j}$$

$$|\mathbf{V}(t)| = \sqrt{4e^{-4t} + 9e^{2t}}$$

$$|\mathbf{A}(t)| = \sqrt{16e^{-4t} + 9e^{2t}} \qquad \triangledown \ \sqrt{.54 + 24.46} \approx \boxed{5}.$$

$$|\mathbf{V}(\tfrac{1}{2})| = \sqrt{4e^{-2} + 9e} \approx 5.01$$

$$|\mathbf{A}(\tfrac{1}{2})| = \sqrt{16e^{-2} + 9e} \approx 5.15$$

Parametric equations of the path of the particle are $x = e^{-2t}$ and $y = 3e^t$. Eliminating t between these two equations, we obtain

$$xy^2 = 9$$

Because $x > 0$ and $y > 0$, the path of the particle is the portion of the curve $xy^2 = 9$ in the first quadrant. Figure 15.7.3 shows the path of the particle and the velocity and acceleration vectors when $t = \frac{1}{2}$. The slope of $\mathbf{V}(\frac{1}{2})$ is $-\frac{3}{2}e^{3/2} \approx -6.7$, and the slope of $\mathbf{A}(\frac{1}{2})$ is $\frac{3}{4}e^{3/2} \approx 3.4$.

We now derive the equations of motion of a projectile by assuming that the projectile is moving in a vertical plane. We also assume that the only force acting on the projectile is its weight, which has a downward direction and a magnitude of mg lb, where m slugs is its mass and g ft/sec² is the constant of acceleration caused by gravity. We are neglecting the force attributed to air resistance (which for heavy bodies traveling at small

Figure 15.7.4

speeds has no noticeable effect). The positive direction is taken as vertically upward and horizontally to the right.

Suppose, then, that a projectile is shot from a gun having an angle of elevation of radian measure α. Let the number of feet per second in the initial speed, or *muzzle speed*, be denoted by v_0. We set up the coordinate axes so that the gun is located at the origin. Refer to Fig. 15.7.4. The initial velocity vector, $\mathbf{V}_0$, of the projectile is given by

$$\mathbf{V}_0 = v_0 \cos \alpha \mathbf{i} + v_0 \sin \alpha \mathbf{j} \tag{3}$$

Let $t =$ the number of seconds in the time that has elapsed since the gun was fired;
$\quad x =$ the number of feet in the horizontal distance of the projectile from the starting point at t sec;
$\quad y =$ the number of feet in the vertical distance of the projectile from the starting point at t sec;
$\mathbf{R}(t) =$ the position vector of the projectile at t sec;
$\mathbf{V}(t) =$ the velocity vector of the projectile at t sec;
$\mathbf{A}(t) =$ acceleration vector of the projectile at t sec.

x is a function of t; so we write $x(t)$. Similarly, y is a function of t; so we write $y(t)$. Then

$$\mathbf{R}(t) = x(t)\mathbf{i} + y(t)\mathbf{j} \tag{4}$$

$$\mathbf{V}(t) = \mathbf{R}'(t) \tag{5}$$

$$\mathbf{A}(t) = \mathbf{V}'(t) \tag{6}$$

Because the only force acting on the projectile has a magnitude of mg lb and is in the downward direction, then if $\mathbf{F}$ denotes this force we have

$$\mathbf{F} = -mg\mathbf{j} \tag{7}$$

Newton's second law of motion states that the net force which is acting on a body is its "mass times acceleration." So

$$\mathbf{F} = m\mathbf{A} \tag{8}$$

From (7) and (8) we obtain

$$m\mathbf{A} = -mg\mathbf{j}$$

Dividing by m, we have

$$\mathbf{A} = -g\mathbf{j} \tag{9}$$

Because $\mathbf{A}(t) = \mathbf{V}'(t)$, we have from (9)

$$\mathbf{V}'(t) = -g\mathbf{j} \tag{10}$$

Integrating on both sides of Eq. (10) with respect to t, we obtain

$$\mathbf{V}(t) = -gt\mathbf{j} + \mathbf{C}_1 \tag{11}$$

where $\mathbf{C}_1$ is a vector constant of integration.

When $t = 0$, $\mathbf{V} = \mathbf{V}_0$. So $\mathbf{C}_1 = \mathbf{V}_0$. Therefore, from (11) we have

$$\mathbf{V}(t) = -gt\mathbf{j} + \mathbf{V}_0$$

or, because $\mathbf{V}(t) = \mathbf{R}'(t)$, we have

$$\mathbf{R}'(t) = -gt\mathbf{j} + \mathbf{V}_0 \qquad (12)$$

Integrating on both sides of the vector equation (12) with respect to t, we obtain

$$\mathbf{R}(t) = -\tfrac{1}{2}gt^2\mathbf{j} + \mathbf{V}_0 t + \mathbf{C}_2$$

where $\mathbf{C}_2$ is a vector constant of integration.

When $t = 0$, $\mathbf{R} = \mathbf{0}$ because the projectile is at the origin at the start. So $\mathbf{C}_2 = \mathbf{0}$. Therefore,

$$\mathbf{R}(t) = -\tfrac{1}{2}gt^2\mathbf{j} + \mathbf{V}_0 t \qquad (13)$$

Substituting the value of $\mathbf{V}_0$ from Eq. (3) into (13), we obtain

$$\mathbf{R}(t) = -\tfrac{1}{2}gt^2\mathbf{j} + (v_0 \cos \alpha\mathbf{i} + v_0 \sin \alpha\mathbf{j})t$$

or, equivalently,

$$\mathbf{R}(t) = tv_0 \cos \alpha\mathbf{i} + (tv_0 \sin \alpha - \tfrac{1}{2}gt^2)\mathbf{j} \qquad (14)$$

Equation (14) gives the position vector of the projectile at time t sec. From this equation, we can discuss the motion of the projectile. We are usually concerned with the following questions:

1. What is the range of the projectile? The range is the distance $|\overline{OA}|$ along the x axis (see Fig. 15.7.4).
2. What is the total time of flight, that is, the time it takes the projectile to go from O to A?
3. What is the maximum height of the projectile?
4. What is a cartesian equation of the curve traveled by the projectile?
5. What is the velocity vector of the projectile at impact?

These questions are answered in the following example.

EXAMPLE 3: A projectile is shot from a gun at an angle of elevation of radian measure $\tfrac{1}{6}\pi$. Its muzzle speed is 480 ft/sec. Find (a) the position vector of the projectile at any time; (b) the time of flight; (c) the range; (d) the maximum height; (e) the velocity vector of the projectile at impact; (f) the position vector and the

SOLUTION: $v_0 = 480$ and $\alpha = \tfrac{1}{6}\pi$. So

$$\mathbf{V}_0 = 480 \cos \tfrac{1}{6}\pi\mathbf{i} + 480 \sin \tfrac{1}{6}\pi\mathbf{j}$$
$$= 240\sqrt{3}\,\mathbf{i} + 240\mathbf{j}$$

(a) The position vector at time t is given by Eq. (14), which in this case is

$$\mathbf{R}(t) = 240\sqrt{3}\,t\mathbf{i} + (240t - \tfrac{1}{2}gt^2)\mathbf{j} \qquad (15)$$

So if (x, y) is the position of the projectile at t sec, $x = 240\sqrt{3}\,t$ and $y = 240t - \tfrac{1}{2}gt^2$.

velocity vector at 2 sec; (g) the speed at 2 sec; (h) a cartesian equation of the curve traveled by the projectile.

(b) To find the time of flight, we find t when $y = 0$. From part (a), we get $y = 0$ and have

$$240t - \tfrac{1}{2}gt^2 = 0$$

$$t(240 - \tfrac{1}{2}gt) = 0$$

$$t = 0 \quad \text{and} \quad t = \frac{480}{g}$$

The value $t = 0$ is when the projectile is fired because then $y = 0$. If we take $g = 32$, the time of flight is determined by $t = 480/g = 480/32 = 15$. So the time of flight is 15 sec.

(c) To find the range, we must find x when $t = 15$. From part (a), $x = 240\sqrt{3}t$. So when $t = 15$, $x = 3600\sqrt{3}$. Therefore, the range is 6235 ft (approximately).

(d) The maximum height is attained when $D_t y = 0$, that is, when the vertical component of the velocity vector is 0. Because

$$y = 240t - \tfrac{1}{2}gt^2$$

$$D_t y = 240 - gt$$

So $D_t y = 0$ when $t = 240/g$. If we take $g = 32$, the maximum height is attained when $t = 7\tfrac{1}{2}$, which is half the total time of flight. When $t = 7\tfrac{1}{2}$, $y = 900$. So the maximum height attained is 900 ft.

(e) Because the time of flight is 15 sec, the velocity vector at impact is $\mathbf{V}(15)$. Finding $\mathbf{V}(t)$ by using (15), we have

$$\mathbf{V}(t) = D_t \mathbf{R}(t) = 240\sqrt{3}\,\mathbf{i} + (240 - gt)\mathbf{j}$$

Taking $g = 32$, we get

$$\mathbf{V}(15) = 240\sqrt{3}\,\mathbf{i} - 480\mathbf{j}$$

(f) Taking $t = 2$ in Eq. (15), we obtain

$$\mathbf{R}(2) = 480\sqrt{3}\,\mathbf{i} + 416\mathbf{j}$$

Because $\mathbf{V}(t) = \mathbf{R}'(t)$, we have

$$\mathbf{V}(t) = 240\sqrt{3}\,\mathbf{i} + (240 - gt)\mathbf{j}$$

So

$$\mathbf{V}(2) = 240\sqrt{3}\,\mathbf{i} + 176\mathbf{j}$$

(g) The speed when $t = 2$ is determined by

$$|\mathbf{V}(2)| = \sqrt{(240\sqrt{3})^2 + (176)^2}$$

$$= 16\sqrt{166}$$

So at 2 sec the speed is approximately 12.9 ft/sec.

(h) To find a cartesian equation, we eliminate t between the parametric equations

$$x = 240\sqrt{3}\,t$$

$$y = 240t - \tfrac{1}{2}gt^2$$

Solving the first equation for t and substituting into the second equation, we obtain

$$y = \frac{1}{\sqrt{3}}\,x - \frac{1}{21{,}600}\,x^2$$

which is an equation of a parabola.

Exercises 15.7

In Exercises 1 through 6, a particle is moving along the curve having the given parametric equations, where t sec is the time. Find: (a) the velocity vector $\mathbf{V}(t)$; (b) the acceleration vector $\mathbf{A}(t)$; (c) the speed at $t = t_1$; (d) the magnitude of the acceleration vector at $t = t_1$. Draw a sketch of the path of the particle and the representations of the velocity vector and the acceleration vector at $t = t_1$.

1. $x = t^2 + 4$, $y = t - 2$; $t_1 = 3$
2. $x = 2\cos t$, $y = 3\sin t$; $t_1 = \tfrac{1}{3}\pi$
3. $x = t$, $y = \ln\sec t$; $t_1 = \tfrac{1}{4}\pi$
4. $x = 2/t$, $y = -\tfrac{1}{4}t$; $t_1 = 4$
5. $x = \sin t$, $y = \tan t$; $t_1 = \tfrac{1}{6}\pi$
6. $x = e^{2t}$, $y = e^{3t}$; $t_1 = 0$

In Exercises 7 through 12, the position of a moving particle at t sec is determined from a vector equation. Find: (a) $\mathbf{V}(t_1)$; (b) $\mathbf{A}(t_1)$; (c) $|\mathbf{V}(t_1)|$; (d) $|\mathbf{A}(t_1)|$. Draw a sketch of a portion of the path of the particle containing the position of the particle at $t = t_1$, and draw the representations of $\mathbf{V}(t_1)$ and $\mathbf{A}(t_1)$ having initial point where $t = t_1$.

7. $\mathbf{R}(t) = (2t - 1)\mathbf{i} + (t^2 + 1)\mathbf{j}$; $t_1 = 3$
8. $\mathbf{R}(t) = (t^2 + 3t)\mathbf{i} + (1 - 3t^2)\mathbf{j}$; $t_1 = \tfrac{1}{2}$
9. $\mathbf{R}(t) = \cos 2t\mathbf{i} - 3\sin t\mathbf{j}$; $t_1 = \pi$
10. $\mathbf{R}(t) = e^{-t}\mathbf{i} + e^{2t}\mathbf{j}$; $t_1 = \ln 2$
11. $\mathbf{R}(t) = 2(1 - \cos t)\mathbf{i} + 2(1 - \sin t)\mathbf{j}$; $t_1 = \tfrac{5}{6}\pi$
12. $\mathbf{R}(t) = \ln(t + 2)\mathbf{i} + \tfrac{1}{3}t^2\mathbf{j}$; $t_1 = 1$

13. Find the position vector $\mathbf{R}(t)$ if the velocity vector

$$\mathbf{V}(t) = \frac{1}{(t-1)^2}\,\mathbf{i} - (t + 1)\mathbf{j} \quad \text{and} \quad \mathbf{R}(0) = 3\mathbf{i} + 2\mathbf{j}$$

14. Find the position vector $\mathbf{R}(t)$ if the acceleration vector

$$\mathbf{A}(t) = 2\cos 2t\mathbf{i} + 2\sin 2t\mathbf{j}$$

and $\mathbf{V}(0) = \mathbf{i} + \mathbf{j}$, and $\mathbf{R}(0) = \tfrac{1}{2}\mathbf{i} - \tfrac{1}{2}\mathbf{j}$.

15. A projectile is shot from a gun at an angle of elevation of $45°$ with a muzzle speed of 2500 ft/sec. Find (a) the range of the projectile, (b) the maximum height reached, and (c) the velocity at impact.

16. A projectile is shot from a gun at an angle of elevation of $60°$. The muzzle speed is 160 ft/sec. Find (a) the position vector of the projectile at t sec; (b) the time of flight; (c) the range; (d) the maximum height reached; (e) the velocity at impact; (f) the speed at 4 sec.

17. A projectile is shot from the top of a building 96 ft high from a gun at an angle of $30°$ with the horizontal. If the muzzle speed is 1600 ft/sec, find the time of flight and the distance from the base of the building to the point where the projectile lands.

18. A boy throws a ball horizontally from the top of a cliff 256 ft high with an initial speed of 50 ft/sec. Find the time of flight of the ball and the distance from the base of the cliff to the point where the ball lands.

19. A boy throws a ball with an initial speed of 60 ft/sec at an angle of elevation of 60° toward a tall building which is 25 ft from the boy. If the boy's hand is 5 ft from the ground, show that the ball hits the building, and find the direction of the ball when it hits the building.

20. The muzzle speed of a gun is 160 ft/sec. At what angle of elevation should the gun be fired so that a projectile will hit an object on the same level as the gun and a distance of 400 ft from it?

21. What is the muzzle speed of a gun if a projectile fired from it has a range of 2000 ft and reaches a maximum height of 1000 ft?

15.8 THE UNIT TANGENT AND UNIT NORMAL VECTORS AND ARC LENGTH AS A PARAMETER

We previously noted that a unit vector is a vector having a magnitude of 1, examples of which are the two unit vectors **i** and **j**. With each point on a curve in the plane we now associate two other unit vectors, the unit tangent vector and the unit normal vector.

15.8.1 Definition   If $\mathbf{R}(t)$ is the position vector of curve C at a point P on C, then the *unit tangent vector* of C at P, denoted by $\mathbf{T}(t)$, is the unit vector in the direction of $D_t\mathbf{R}(t)$ if $D_t\mathbf{R}(t) \neq 0$.

The unit vector in the direction of $D_t\mathbf{R}(t)$ is given by $D_t\mathbf{R}(t)/|D_t\mathbf{R}(t)|$; so we may write

$$\mathbf{T}(t) = \frac{D_t\mathbf{R}(t)}{|D_t\mathbf{R}(t)|} \tag{1}$$

Because $\mathbf{T}(t)$ is a unit vector, it follows from Theorem 15.5.10 that $D_t\mathbf{T}(t)$ must be orthogonal to $\mathbf{T}(t)$. $D_t\mathbf{T}(t)$ is not necessarily a unit vector. However, the vector $D_t\mathbf{T}(t)/|D_t\mathbf{T}(t)|$ is of unit magnitude and has the same direction as $D_t\mathbf{T}(t)$. Therefore, $D_t\mathbf{T}(t)/|D_t\mathbf{T}(t)|$ is a unit vector which is orthogonal to $\mathbf{T}(t)$, and it is called the unit normal vector.

15.8.2 Definition   If $\mathbf{T}(t)$ is the unit tangent vector of curve C at a point P on C, then the *unit normal vector*, denoted by $\mathbf{N}(t)$, is the unit vector in the direction of $D_t\mathbf{T}(t)$.

From Definition 15.8.2 and the previous discussion, we conclude that

$$\mathbf{N}(t) = \frac{D_t\mathbf{T}(t)}{|D_t\mathbf{T}(t)|} \tag{2}$$

EXAMPLE 1:   Given the curve having parametric equations $x = t^3 - 3t$ and $y = 3t^2$, find $\mathbf{T}(t)$ and $\mathbf{N}(t)$. Draw a sketch of a portion of the curve at $t = 2$ and draw the representations of $\mathbf{T}(2)$ and $\mathbf{N}(2)$ having their initial point at $t = 2$.

SOLUTION: A vector equation of the curve is

$$\mathbf{R}(t) = (t^3 - 3t)\mathbf{i} + 3t^2\mathbf{j}$$

So

$$D_t\mathbf{R}(t) = (3t^2 - 3)\mathbf{i} + 6t\mathbf{j}$$

Then

$$|D_t\mathbf{R}(t)| = \sqrt{(3t^2 - 3)^2 + 36t^2} = \sqrt{9(t^4 + 2t^2 + 1)} = 3(t^2 + 1)$$

Applying (1), we get

$$\mathbf{T}(t) = \frac{t^2 - 1}{t^2 + 1}\,\mathbf{i} + \frac{2t}{t^2 + 1}\,\mathbf{j}$$

Differentiating $\mathbf{T}(t)$ with respect to t, we obtain

$$D_t\mathbf{T}(t) = \frac{4t}{(t^2 + 1)^2}\,\mathbf{i} + \frac{2 - 2t^2}{(t^2 + 1)^2}\,\mathbf{j}$$

Therefore,

$$|D_t\mathbf{T}(t)| = \sqrt{\frac{16t^2}{(t^2 + 1)^4} + \frac{4 - 8t^2 + 4t^4}{(t^2 + 1)^4}}$$

$$= \sqrt{\frac{4 + 8t^2 + 4t^4}{(t^2 + 1)^4}}$$

$$= \sqrt{\frac{4(t^2 + 1)^2}{(t^2 + 1)^4}}$$

$$= \frac{2}{t^2 + 1}$$

Applying (2), we have

$$\mathbf{N}(t) = \frac{2t}{t^2 + 1}\,\mathbf{i} + \frac{1 - t^2}{t^2 + 1}\,\mathbf{j}$$

Finding $\mathbf{R}(t)$, $\mathbf{T}(t)$, and $\mathbf{N}(t)$, when $t = 2$, we obtain

$$\mathbf{R}(2) = 2\mathbf{i} + 12\mathbf{j} \qquad \mathbf{T}(2) = \tfrac{3}{5}\mathbf{i} + \tfrac{4}{5}\mathbf{j} \qquad \mathbf{N}(2) = \tfrac{4}{5}\mathbf{i} - \tfrac{3}{5}\mathbf{j}$$

The required sketch is shown in Fig. 15.8.1.

Figure 15.8.1

From Eq. (1) we obtain

$$D_t\mathbf{R}(t) = |D_t\mathbf{R}(t)|\mathbf{T}(t) \tag{3}$$

The right side of (3) is the product of a scalar and a vector. To differentiate this product, we apply Theorem 15.5.8, and we have

$$D_t^2\mathbf{R}(t) = [D_t|D_t\mathbf{R}(t)|]\mathbf{T}(t) + |D_t\mathbf{R}(t)|[D_t\mathbf{T}(t)] \tag{4}$$

From (2) we obtain

$$D_t\mathbf{T}(t) = |D_t\mathbf{T}(t)|\mathbf{N}(t) \tag{5}$$

Substituting from (5) into (4), we get

$$D_t^2\mathbf{R}(t) = [D_t|D_t\mathbf{R}(t)|]\mathbf{T}(t) + |D_t\mathbf{R}(t)||D_t\mathbf{T}(t)|\mathbf{N}(t) \tag{6}$$

Equation (3) expresses the vector $D_t\mathbf{R}(t)$ as a scalar times the unit tangent vector, and Eq. (6) expresses the vector $D_t^2\mathbf{R}(t)$ as a scalar times

Figure 15.8.2

the unit tangent vector plus a scalar times the unit normal vector. The coefficient of $\mathbf{T}(t)$ on the right side of (6) is the component of the vector $D_t^2\mathbf{R}(t)$ in the direction of the unit tangent vector. The coefficient of $\mathbf{N}(t)$ on the right side of (6) is the component of $D_t^2\mathbf{R}(t)$ in the direction of the unit normal vector. Figure 15.8.2 shows a portion of a curve C with the position representation of $\mathbf{R}(t)$ and the representations of $\mathbf{T}(t)$, $\mathbf{N}(t)$, $D_t\mathbf{R}(t)$, $D_t^2\mathbf{R}(t)$, $[D_t|D_t\mathbf{R}(t)|]\mathbf{T}(t)$, and $|D_t\mathbf{R}(t)||D_t\mathbf{T}(t)|\mathbf{N}(t)$, all of whose initial points are at the point P on C. Note that the representation of the unit normal vector $\mathbf{N}$ is on the concave side of the curve. This is proved in general in Sec. 15.9.

Sometimes instead of a parameter t, we wish to use as a parameter the number of units of arc length s from an arbitrarily chosen point $P_0(x_0, y_0)$ on curve C to the point $P(x, y)$ on C. Let s increase as t increases so that s is positive if the length of arc is measured in the direction of increasing t and s is negative if the length of arc is measured in the opposite direction. Therefore, s units is a directed distance. Also, $D_t s > 0$. To each value of s there corresponds a unique point P on the curve C. Consequently, the coordinates of P are functions of s, and s is a function of t. In Sec. 15.6 we showed that

$$|D_t\mathbf{R}(t)| = D_t s \tag{7}$$

Substituting from (7) into (1), we get

$$\mathbf{T}(t) = \frac{D_t\mathbf{R}(t)}{D_t s}$$

So

$$D_t\mathbf{R}(t) = D_t s\mathbf{T}(t)$$

If the parameter is s instead of t, we have from the above equation, by taking $t = s$ and noting that $D_t s = 1$,

$$D_s\mathbf{R}(s) = \mathbf{T}(s)$$

This result is stated as a theorem.

15.8.3 Theorem   If the vector equation of a curve C is $\mathbf{R}(s) = f(s)\mathbf{i} + g(s)\mathbf{j}$, where s units is the length of arc measured from a particular point P_0 on C to the point P, then the unit tangent vector of C at P is given by

$$\mathbf{T}(s) = D_s\mathbf{R}(s)$$

Now suppose that the parametric equations of a curve C involve a parameter t, and we wish to find parametric equations of C, with s, the number of units of arc length measured from some fixed point, as the parameter. Often the operations involved are quite complicated. However, the method used is illustrated in the following example.

EXAMPLE 2: Suppose that parametric equations of the curve C are $x = t^3$ and $y = t^2$, where $t \geq 0$. Find parametric equations of C having s as a parameter, where s is the number of units of arc length measured from the point where $t = 0$.

SOLUTION: If P_0 is the point where $t = 0$, P_0 is the origin. The vector equation of C is

$$\mathbf{R}(t) = t^3\mathbf{i} + t^2\mathbf{j}$$

Because $D_t S = |D_t \mathbf{R}(t)|$, we differentiate the above vector and obtain

$$D_t \mathbf{R}(t) = 3t^2\mathbf{i} + 2t\mathbf{j}$$

So

$$|D_t \mathbf{R}(t)| = \sqrt{9t^4 + 4t^2} = \sqrt{t^2}\ \sqrt{9t^2 + 4}$$

Because $t \geq 0$, $\sqrt{t^2} = t$. Thus, we have

$$|D_t \mathbf{R}(t)| = t\sqrt{9t^2 + 4}$$

Therefore,

$$D_t s = t\sqrt{9t^2 + 4}$$

and so

$$s = \int_0^t u\sqrt{9u^2 + 4}\ du$$

$$= \tfrac{1}{18} \int_0^t 18u\sqrt{9u^2 + 4}\ du$$

$$= \tfrac{1}{27} (9u^2 + 4)^{3/2} \Big]_0^t$$

We obtain

$$s = \tfrac{1}{27} (9t^2 + 4)^{3/2} - \tfrac{8}{27} \tag{8}$$

Solving Eq. (8) for t in terms of s, we have

$$(9t^2 + 4)^{3/2} = 27s + 8$$

$$9t^2 + 4 = (27s + 8)^{2/3}$$

Because $t \geq 0$, we get

$$t = \tfrac{1}{3}\sqrt{(27s + 8)^{2/3} - 4}$$

Substituting this value of t into the given parametric equations for C, we obtain

$$x = \tfrac{1}{27}[(27s + 8)^{2/3} - 4]^{3/2} \quad \text{and} \quad y = \tfrac{1}{9}[(27s + 8)^{2/3} - 4] \tag{9}$$

Now because $D_s \mathbf{R}(s) = \mathbf{T}(s)$, it follows that if $\mathbf{R}(s) = x(s)\mathbf{i} + y(s)\mathbf{j}$, then $\mathbf{T}(s) = (D_s x)\mathbf{i} + (D_s y)\mathbf{j}$. And because $\mathbf{T}(s)$ is a unit vector, we have

$$(D_s x)^2 + (D_s y)^2 = 1 \tag{10}$$

Equation (10) can be used to check Eqs. (9). This check is left for the reader (see Exercise 11).

Exercises 15.8

In Exercises 1 through 8, for the given curve, find $\mathbf{T}(t)$ and $\mathbf{N}(t)$, and at $t = t_1$ draw a sketch of a portion of the curve and draw the representations of $\mathbf{T}(t_1)$ and $\mathbf{N}(t_1)$ having initial point at $t = t_1$.

1. $x = \frac{1}{3}t^3 - t$, $y = t^2$; $t_1 = 2$

2. $x = \frac{1}{2}t^2$, $y = \frac{1}{3}t^3$; $t_1 = 1$

3. $\mathbf{R}(t) = e^t\mathbf{i} + e^{-t}\mathbf{j}$; $t_1 = 0$

4. $\mathbf{R}(t) = 3 \cos t\mathbf{i} + 3 \sin t\mathbf{j}$; $t_1 = \frac{1}{2}\pi$

5. $x = \cos kt$, $y = \sin kt$, $k > 0$; $t_1 = \pi/k$

6. $x = t - \sin t$, $y = 1 - \cos t$; $t_1 = \pi$

7. $\mathbf{R}(t) = \ln \cos t\mathbf{i} + \ln \sin t\mathbf{j}$, $0 < t < \frac{1}{2}\pi$; $t_1 = \frac{1}{4}\pi$

8. $\mathbf{R}(t) = t \cos t\mathbf{i} + t \sin t\mathbf{j}$; $t_1 = 0$

9. If the vector equation of curve C is $\mathbf{R}(t) = 3t^2\mathbf{i} + (t^3 - 3t)\mathbf{j}$, find the cosine of the measure of the angle between the vectors $\mathbf{R}(2)$ and $\mathbf{T}(2)$.

10. If the vector equation of curve C is $\mathbf{R}(t) = (4 - 3t^2)\mathbf{i} + (t^3 - 3t)\mathbf{j}$, find the radian measure of the angle between the vectors $\mathbf{N}(1)$ and $D_t^2\mathbf{R}(1)$.

11. Check Eqs. (9) of the solution of Example 2 by using Eq. (10).

In Exercises 12 through 15, find parametric equations of the curve having arc length s as a parameter, where s is measured from the point where $t = 0$. Check your result by using Eq. (10).

12. $x = a \cos t$, $y = a \sin t$

13. $x = 2 + \cos t$, $y = 3 + \sin t$

14. $x = 2(\cos t + t \sin t)$, $y = 2(\sin t - t \cos t)$

15. One cusp of the hypocycloid of four cusps: $\mathbf{R}(t) = a \cos^3 t\mathbf{i} + a \sin^3 t\mathbf{j}$, $0 \le t \le \frac{1}{2}\pi$.

16. Given the cycloid $x = 2(t - \sin t)$, $y = 2(1 - \cos t)$, express the arc length s as a function of t, where s is measured from the point where $t = 0$.

17. Prove that parametric equations of the catenary $y = a \cosh (x/a)$ where the parameter s is the number of units in the length of the arc from the point $(0, a)$ to the point (x, y) and $s \ge 0$ when $x \ge 0$ and $s < 0$ when $x < 0$, are

$$x = a \sinh^{-1}\frac{s}{a} \quad \text{and} \quad y = \sqrt{a^2 + s^2}$$

15.9 CURVATURE   Let ϕ be the radian measure of the angle giving the direction of the unit tangent vector associated with a curve C. Therefore, ϕ is the radian measure of the angle from the direction of the positive x axis counterclockwise to the direction of the unit tangent vector $\mathbf{T}(t)$. See Fig. 15.9.1.

Because $|\mathbf{T}(t)| = 1$, it follows from Eq. (1) in Sec. 15.2 that

$$\mathbf{T}(t) = \cos \phi\mathbf{i} + \sin \phi\mathbf{j} \tag{1}$$

Differentiating with respect to ϕ, we obtain

$$D_\phi\mathbf{T}(t) = -\sin \phi\mathbf{i} + \cos \phi\mathbf{j} \tag{2}$$

Figure 15.9.1

Because $|D_\phi \mathbf{T}(t)| = \sqrt{(-\sin \phi)^2 + (\cos \phi)^2} = 1$, $D_\phi \mathbf{T}(t)$ is a unit vector. Because $\mathbf{T}(t)$ has constant magnitude it follows from Theorem 15.5.10 that $D_\phi \mathbf{T}(t)$ is orthogonal to $\mathbf{T}(t)$.

Replacing $-\sin \phi$ by $\cos(\tfrac{1}{2}\pi + \phi)$ and $\cos \phi$ by $\sin(\tfrac{1}{2}\pi + \phi)$, we write (2) as

$$D_\phi \mathbf{T}(t) = \cos(\tfrac{1}{2}\pi + \phi)\mathbf{i} + \sin(\tfrac{1}{2}\pi + \phi)\mathbf{j} \tag{3}$$

From (3) and the previous discussion, the vector $D_\phi \mathbf{T}(t)$ is a unit vector orthogonal to $\mathbf{T}(t)$ in the direction $\tfrac{1}{2}\pi$ counterclockwise from the direction of $\mathbf{T}(t)$. The unit normal vector $\mathbf{N}(t)$ is also orthogonal to $\mathbf{T}(t)$. By the chain rule (which is valid for vector-valued functions, although we won't prove it here), we have

$$D_t \mathbf{T}(t) = [D_\phi \mathbf{T}(t)]D_t \phi \tag{4}$$

Because the direction of $\mathbf{N}(t)$ is the same as the direction of $D_t \mathbf{T}(t)$, we see from (4) that the direction of $\mathbf{N}(t)$ is the same as the direction of $D_\phi \mathbf{T}(t)$ if $D_t \phi > 0$ (i.e., if $\mathbf{T}(t)$ turns counterclockwise as t increases), and the direction of $\mathbf{N}(t)$ is opposite that of $D_\phi \mathbf{T}(t)$ if $D_t \phi < 0$ (i.e., if $\mathbf{T}(t)$ turns clockwise as t increases). Because both $D_\phi \mathbf{T}(t)$ and $\mathbf{N}(t)$ are unit vectors, we conclude that

$$D_\phi \mathbf{T}(t) = \begin{cases} \mathbf{N}(t) & \text{if } D_t \phi > 0 \\ -\mathbf{N}(t) & \text{if } D_t \phi < 0 \end{cases} \tag{5}$$

In Fig. 15.9.2a, b, c, and d various cases are illustrated; in a and b, $D_t \phi > 0$, and in c and d, $D_t \phi < 0$. The positive direction along the curve C is indicated by the tip of the arrow on C. In each figure are shown the angle of radian measure ϕ and representations of the vectors $\mathbf{T}(t), D_\phi \mathbf{T}(t)$, and $\mathbf{N}(t)$. *The representation of the unit normal vector $\mathbf{N}(t)$ is always on the concave side of the curve.*

(a)

(b)

(c)

(d)

Figure 15.9.2

Consider now $D_s\mathbf{T}(t)$, where s units is the arc length measured from an arbitrarily chosen point on C to point P and s increases as t increases. By the chain rule

$$D_s\mathbf{T}(t) = D_\phi\mathbf{T}(t)D_s\phi$$

Hence,

$$|D_s\mathbf{T}(t)| = |D_\phi\mathbf{T}(t)D_s\phi| = |D_\phi\mathbf{T}(t)||D_s\phi|$$

But because $D_\phi\mathbf{T}(t)$ is a unit vector, $|D_\phi\mathbf{T}(t)| = 1$; thus, we have

$$|D_s\mathbf{T}(t)| = |D_s\phi| \qquad (6)$$

The number $|D_s\phi|$ is the absolute value of the rate of change of the measure of the angle giving the direction of the unit tangent vector $\mathbf{T}(t)$ at a point on a curve with respect to the measure of arc length along the curve. This number is called the *curvature* of the curve at the point. Before giving the formal definition of curvature, let us see that taking it as this number is consistent with what we intuitively think of as the curvature. For example, at point P on C, ϕ is the radian measure of the angle giving the direction of the vector $\mathbf{T}(t)$, and s units is the arc length from a point P_0 on C to P. Let Q be a point on C for which the radian measure of the angle giving the direction of $\mathbf{T}(t + \Delta t)$ at Q is $\phi + \Delta\phi$ and $(s + \Delta s)$ units is the arc length from P_0 to Q. Then the arc length from P to Q is Δs units, and the ratio $\Delta\phi/\Delta s$ seems like a good measure of what we would intuitively think of as the *average curvature* along arc PQ. See Fig. 15.9.3a, b, c, and d: In a, $\Delta\phi > 0$ and $\Delta s > 0$; in b, $\Delta\phi > 0$ and $\Delta s < 0$; in c, $\Delta\phi < 0$ and $\Delta s > 0$; and in d, $\Delta\phi < 0$ and $\Delta s < 0$.

$\Delta\phi > 0 \qquad \Delta s > 0$

(a)

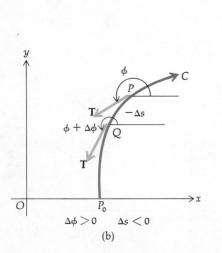

$\Delta\phi > 0 \qquad \Delta s < 0$

(b)

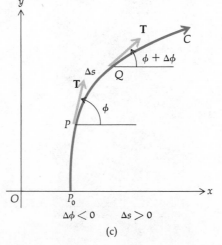

$\Delta\phi < 0 \qquad \Delta s > 0$

(c)

$\Delta\phi < 0 \qquad \Delta s < 0$

(d)

Figure 15.9.3

15.9.1 Definition If $\mathbf{T}(t)$ is the unit tangent vector to a curve C at a point P, s is the arc length measured from an arbitrarily chosen point on C to P, and s increases as t increases, then the *curvature vector* of C at P, denoted by $\mathbf{K}(t)$, is given by

$$\mathbf{K}(t) = D_s \mathbf{T}(t) \tag{7}$$

The *curvature* of C at P, denoted by $K(t)$, is the magnitude of the curvature vector.

To find the curvature vector and the curvature for a particular curve it is convenient to have a formula expressing the curvature vector in terms of derivatives with respect to t. By the chain rule

$$D_t \mathbf{T}(t) = [D_s \mathbf{T}(t)] D_t s$$

Replacing $D_t s$ by $|D_t \mathbf{R}(t)|$ and dividing by this, we obtain $D_s \mathbf{T}(t) = D_t \mathbf{T}(t)/|D_t \mathbf{R}(t)|$. So from (7) we have for the curvature vector

$$\mathbf{K}(t) = \frac{D_t \mathbf{T}(t)}{|D_t \mathbf{R}(t)|} \tag{8}$$

Because $K(t) = |\mathbf{K}(t)|$, the curvature is given by

$$K(t) = \left| \frac{D_t \mathbf{T}(t)}{|D_t \mathbf{R}(t)|} \right| \tag{9}$$

EXAMPLE 1: Given the circle

$$x = a \cos t, y = a \sin t \quad a > 0$$

find the curvature vector and the curvature at any t.

SOLUTION: The vector equation of the circle is

$$\mathbf{R}(t) = a \cos t\mathbf{i} + a \sin t\mathbf{j}$$

So

$$D_t \mathbf{R}(t) = -a \sin t\mathbf{i} + a \cos t\mathbf{j}$$

$$|D_t \mathbf{R}(t)| = \sqrt{(-a \sin t)^2 + (a \cos t)^2} = a$$

So

$$\mathbf{T}(t) = \frac{D_t \mathbf{R}(t)}{|D_t \mathbf{R}(t)|} = -\sin t\mathbf{i} + \cos t\mathbf{j}$$

$$D_t \mathbf{T}(t) = -\cos t\mathbf{i} - \sin t\mathbf{j}$$

$$\frac{D_t \mathbf{T}(t)}{|D_t \mathbf{R}(t)|} = -\frac{\cos t}{a}\mathbf{i} - \frac{\sin t}{a}\mathbf{j}$$

So the curvature vector

$$\mathbf{K}(t) = -\frac{1}{a} \cos t\mathbf{i} - \frac{1}{a} \sin t\mathbf{j}$$

and the curvature

$$K(t) = |\mathbf{K}(t)| = \frac{1}{a}$$

The result of Example 1 states that the curvature of a circle is constant and is the reciprocal of the radius.

Suppose that we are given a curve C and at a particular point P the curvature exists and is $K(t)$, where $K(t) \neq 0$. Furthermore, suppose that we wish to find the circle which is tangent to curve C at P and has curvature $K(t)$ at P. From Example 1, we know that the radius of this circle is $1/K(t)$ and that its center is on a line perpendicular to the tangent line in the direction of $\mathbf{N}(t)$. This circle is called the *circle of curvature*, and its radius is the *radius of curvature* of C at P. The circle of curvature is sometimes referred to as the *osculating circle*.

15.9.2 Definition   If $K(t)$ is the curvature of a curve C at point P and $K(t) \neq 0$, then the *radius of curvature* of C at P, denoted by $\rho(t)$, is defined by

$$\rho(t) = \frac{1}{K(t)}$$

EXAMPLE 2:   Given that a vector equation of a curve C is

$$\mathbf{R}(t) = 2t\mathbf{i} + (t^2 - 1)\mathbf{j}$$

find the curvature and the radius of curvature at $t = 1$. Draw a sketch of a portion of the curve, the unit tangent vector, and the circle of curvature at $t = 1$.

SOLUTION:

$$\mathbf{R}(t) = 2t\mathbf{i} + (t^2 - 1)\mathbf{j}$$

$$D_t\mathbf{R}(t) = 2\mathbf{i} + 2t\mathbf{j}$$

$$|D_t\mathbf{R}(t)| = 2\sqrt{1 + t^2}$$

$$\mathbf{T}(t) = \frac{D_t\mathbf{R}(t)}{|D_t\mathbf{R}(t)|} = \frac{1}{\sqrt{1 + t^2}}\mathbf{i} + \frac{t}{\sqrt{1 + t^2}}\mathbf{j}$$

$$D_t\mathbf{T}(t) = -\frac{t}{(1 + t^2)^{3/2}}\mathbf{i} + \frac{1}{(1 + t^2)^{3/2}}\mathbf{j}$$

$$\frac{D_t\mathbf{T}(t)}{|D_t\mathbf{R}(t)|} = -\frac{t}{2(1 + t^2)^2}\mathbf{i} + \frac{t}{2(1 + t^2)^2}\mathbf{j}$$

$$K(t) = \left|\frac{D_t\mathbf{T}(t)}{|D_t\mathbf{R}(t)|}\right| = \sqrt{\frac{t^2}{4(1 + t^2)^4} + \frac{1}{4(1 + t^2)^4}}$$

$$K(t) = \frac{1}{2(1 + t^2)^{3/2}}$$

So

$$K(1) = \frac{1}{4\sqrt{2}} \qquad \rho(1) = 4\sqrt{2}$$

and

$$\mathbf{T}(1) = \frac{1}{\sqrt{2}}\mathbf{i} + \frac{1}{\sqrt{2}}\mathbf{j}$$

Figure 15.9.4 shows the required sketch. The accompanying Table 15.9.1 gives corresponding values of x and y for $t = -2, -1, 0, 1,$ and 2.

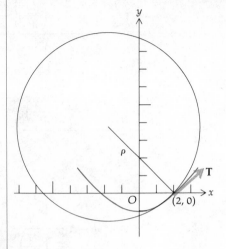

Table 15.9.1

t	x	y
-2	-4	3
-1	-2	0
0	0	-1
1	2	0
2	4	3

Figure 15.9.4

We now find a formula for computing the curvature directly from parametric equations of the curve, $x = f(t)$ and $y = g(t)$. From Eq. (6) $|D_s\mathbf{T}(t)| = |D_s\phi|$, and so

$$K(t) = |D_s\phi|$$

Assuming that s and t increase together, we have

$$D_s\phi = \frac{d\phi}{ds} = \frac{\dfrac{d\phi}{dt}}{\dfrac{ds}{dt}} = \frac{\dfrac{d\phi}{dt}}{\sqrt{[f'(t)]^2 + [g'(t)]^2}}$$

So

$$D_s\phi = \frac{\dfrac{d\phi}{dt}}{\sqrt{\left(\dfrac{dx}{dt}\right)^2 + \left(\dfrac{dy}{dt}\right)^2}} \tag{10}$$

To find $d\phi/dt$, we observe that because θ is the radian measure of the angle giving the direction of the unit tangent vector,

$$\tan \phi = \frac{dy}{dx} = \frac{\dfrac{dy}{dt}}{\dfrac{dx}{dt}} \tag{11}$$

Differentiating implicitly with respect to t the left and right members of (11), we obtain

$$\sec^2 \phi \, \frac{d\phi}{dt} = \frac{\left(\dfrac{dx}{dt}\right)\left(\dfrac{d^2y}{dt^2}\right) - \left(\dfrac{dy}{dt}\right)\left(\dfrac{d^2x}{dt^2}\right)}{\left(\dfrac{dx}{dt}\right)^2}$$

So

$$\frac{d\phi}{dt} = \frac{\left(\dfrac{dx}{dt}\right)\left(\dfrac{d^2y}{dt^2}\right) - \left(\dfrac{dy}{dt}\right)\left(\dfrac{d^2x}{dt^2}\right)}{\sec^2 \phi \left(\dfrac{dx}{dt}\right)^2} \tag{12}$$

But

$$\sec^2 \phi = 1 + \tan^2 \phi = 1 + \frac{\left(\dfrac{dy}{dt}\right)^2}{\left(\dfrac{dx}{dt}\right)^2}$$

Substituting this expression for $\sec^2 \phi$ in (12), we get

$$\frac{d\phi}{dt} = \frac{\left(\dfrac{dx}{dt}\right)\left(\dfrac{d^2y}{dt^2}\right) - \left(\dfrac{dy}{dt}\right)\left(\dfrac{d^2x}{dt^2}\right)}{\left(\dfrac{dx}{dt}\right)^2 + \left(\dfrac{dy}{dt}\right)^2} \tag{13}$$

Substituting from (13) into (10), and because $K(t) = |D_s\phi|$, we have

$$K(t) = \frac{\left|\left(\dfrac{dx}{dt}\right)\left(\dfrac{d^2y}{dt^2}\right) - \left(\dfrac{dy}{dt}\right)\left(\dfrac{d^2x}{dt^2}\right)\right|}{\left[\left(\dfrac{dx}{dt}\right)^2 + \left(\dfrac{dy}{dt}\right)^2\right]^{3/2}} \tag{14}$$

EXAMPLE 3:   Find the curvature of the curve in Example 2 by using formula (14).

SOLUTION: Parametric equations of C are $x = 2t$ and $y = t^2 - 1$. Hence,

$$\frac{dx}{dt} = 2 \qquad \frac{d^2x}{dt^2} = 0 \qquad \frac{dy}{dt} = 2t \qquad \frac{d^2y}{dt^2} = 2$$

From (14) we have, then,

$$K(t) = \frac{|2(2) - 2t(0)|}{[(2)^2 + (2t)^2]^{3/2}} = \frac{4}{(4 + 4t^2)^{3/2}} = \frac{1}{2(1 + t^2)^{3/2}}$$

Suppose that we are given a cartesian equation of a curve, either in the form $y = F(x)$ or $x = G(y)$. Special cases of formula (14) can be used to find the curvature of a curve in such situations.

If $y = F(x)$ is an equation of a curve C, a set of parametric equations of

C is $x = t$ and $y = F(t)$. Then $dx/dt = 1$, $d^2x/dt^2 = 0$, $dy/dt = dy/dx$, and $d^2y/dt^2 = d^2y/dx^2$. Substituting into (14), we obtain

$$K = \frac{\left|\dfrac{d^2y}{dx^2}\right|}{\left[1 + \left(\dfrac{dy}{dx}\right)^2\right]^{3/2}} \qquad (15)$$

Similarly, if an equation of a curve C is $x = G(y)$, we obtain

$$K = \frac{\left|\dfrac{d^2x}{dy^2}\right|}{\left[1 + \left(\dfrac{dx}{dy}\right)^2\right]^{3/2}} \qquad (16)$$

EXAMPLE 4: If the curve C has an equation $xy = 1$, find the radius of curvature of C at the point $(1, 1)$ and draw a sketch of the curve and the circle of curvature at $(1, 1)$.

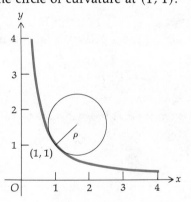

Figure 15.9.5

SOLUTION: Solving for y, we obtain $y = 1/x$. So $dy/dx = -1/x^2$ and $d^2y/dx^2 = 2/x^3$. Applying formula (15), we have

$$K = \frac{\left|\dfrac{2}{x^3}\right|}{\left[1 + \left(\dfrac{1}{x^4}\right)\right]^{3/2}} = \frac{2x^6}{|x^3|(x^4 + 1)^{3/2}} = \frac{2x^4}{|x|(x^4 + 1)^{3/2}}$$

Because $\rho = 1/K$, we have

$$\rho = \frac{|x|(x^4 + 1)^{3/2}}{2x^4}$$

So at $(1, 1)$, $\rho = \sqrt{2}$. The required sketch is shown in Fig. 15.9.5.

Exercises 15.9

In Exercises 1 through 4, find the curvature K and the radius of curvature ρ at the point where $t = t_1$. Use formula (9) to find K. Draw a sketch showing a portion of the curve, the unit tangent vector, and the circle of curvature at $t = t_1$.

1. $\mathbf{R}(t) = 2t\mathbf{i} + (t^2 - 1)\mathbf{j}$; $t_1 = 1$

2. $\mathbf{R}(t) = (t^2 - 2t)\mathbf{i} + (t^3 - t)\mathbf{j}$; $t_1 = 1$

3. $\mathbf{R}(t) = 2e^t\mathbf{i} + 2e^{-t}\mathbf{j}$; $t_1 = 0$

4. $\mathbf{R}(t) = \sin t\mathbf{i} + \sin 2t\mathbf{j}$; $t_1 = \frac{1}{2}\pi$

In Exercises 5 and 6, find the curvature K by using formula (14). Then find K and ρ at the point where $t = t_1$ and draw a sketch showing a portion of the curve, the unit tangent vector, and the circle of curvature at $t = t_1$.

5. $x = \dfrac{1}{1 + t}$, $y = \dfrac{1}{1 - t}$; $t_1 = 0$

6. $x = e^t + e^{-t}$, $y = e^t - e^{-t}$; $t_1 = 0$

In Exercises 7 through 12, find the curvature K and the radius of curvature ρ at the given point. Draw a sketch showing a portion of the curve, a piece of the tangent line, and the circle of curvature at the given point.

7. $y = 2\sqrt{x}$; $(0, 0)$ 8. $y^2 = x^3$; $(\frac{1}{4}, \frac{1}{8})$ 9. $y = e^x$; $(0, 1)$

10. $4x^2 + 9y^2 = 36$; $(0, 2)$ 11. $x = \sin y$; $(\frac{1}{2}, \frac{1}{6}\pi)$ 12. $x = \tan y$; $(1, \frac{1}{4}\pi)$

In Exercises 13 through 18, find the radius of curvature at any point on the given curve.

13. $y = \sin^{-1} x$ 14. $y = \ln \sec x$

15. $x^{1/2} + y^{1/2} = a^{1/2}$ 16. $\mathbf{R}(t) = e^t \sin t\mathbf{i} + e^t \cos t\mathbf{j}$

17. The cycloid $x = a(t - \sin t)$, $y = a(1 - \cos t)$ 18. The tractrix $x = t - a \tanh \dfrac{t}{a}$, $y = a \operatorname{sech} \dfrac{t}{a}$

19. Show that the curvature of the catenary $y = a \cosh (x/a)$ at any point (x, y) on the curve is a/y^2. Draw the circle of curvature at $(0, a)$. Show that the curvature K is an absolute maximum at the point $(0, a)$ without referring to $K'(x)$.

In Exercises 20 through 23, find a point on the given curve at which the curvature is an absolute maximum.

20. $y = e^x$ 21. $y = 6x - x^2$

22. $y = \sin x$ 23. $\mathbf{R}(t) = (2t - 3)\mathbf{i} + (t^2 - 1)\mathbf{j}$

24. If a polar equation of a curve is $r = F(\theta)$, prove that the curvature K is given by the formula

$$K = \frac{|r^2 + 2(dr/d\theta)^2 - r(d^2r/d\theta^2)|}{[r^2 + (dr/d\theta)^2]^{3/2}}$$

In Exercises 25 through 28, find the curvature K and the radius of curvature ρ at the indicated point. Use the formula of Exercise 24 to find K.

25. $r = 4 \cos 2\theta$; $\theta = \frac{1}{12}\pi$ 26. $r = 1 - \sin \theta$; $\theta = 0$

27. $r = a \sec^2 \frac{1}{2}\theta$; $\theta = \frac{2}{3}\pi$ 28. $r = a\theta$; $\theta = 1$

29. The center of the circle of curvature of a curve C at a point P is called the *center of curvature* at P. Prove that the coordinates of the center of curvature of a curve at $P(x, y)$ are given by

$$x_c = x - \frac{(dy/dx)[1 + (dy/dx)^2]}{d^2y/dx^2} \qquad y_c = y + \frac{(dy/dx)^2 + 1}{d^2y/dx^2}$$

In Exercises 30 through 32, find the curvature K, the radius of curvature ρ, and the center of curvature at the given point. Draw a sketch of the curve and the circle of curvature.

30. $y = \cos x$; $(\frac{1}{3}\pi, \frac{1}{2})$ 31. $y = x^4 - x^2$; $(0, 0)$ 32. $y = \ln x$; $(1, 0)$

In Exercises 33 through 36 find the coordinates of the center of curvature at any point.

33. $y^2 = 4px$ 34. $y^3 = a^2x$

35. $\mathbf{R}(t) = a \cos t\mathbf{i} + b \sin t\mathbf{j}$ 36. $\mathbf{R}(t) = a \cos^3 t\mathbf{i} + a \sin^3 t\mathbf{j}$

15.10 TANGENTIAL AND NORMAL COMPONENTS OF ACCELERATION

If a particle is moving along a curve C having the vector equation

$$\mathbf{R}(t) = f(t)\mathbf{i} + g(t)\mathbf{j} \tag{1}$$

from Definition 15.7.1, the velocity vector at P is given by

$$\mathbf{V}(t) = D_t\mathbf{R}(t) \tag{2}$$

From Sec. 15.8, if $\mathbf{T}(t)$ is the unit tangent vector at P, s is the length of arc of C from a fixed point P_0 to P, and s increases as t increases, we have

$$D_t\mathbf{R}(t) = D_t s[\mathbf{T}(t)] \tag{3}$$

Substituting from (3) into (2), we have

$$\mathbf{V}(t) = D_t s[\mathbf{T}(t)] \tag{4}$$

Equation (4) expresses the velocity vector at a point as a scalar times the unit tangent vector at the point. We now proceed to express the acceleration vector at a point in terms of the unit tangent and unit normal vectors at the point. From Definition 15.7.2 the acceleration vector at P is given by

$$\mathbf{A}(t) = D_t^2\mathbf{R}(t) \tag{5}$$

From Eq. (6) in Sec. 15.8 we have

$$D_t^2\mathbf{R}(t) = [D_t|D_t\mathbf{R}(t)|]\mathbf{T}(t) + |D_t\mathbf{R}(t)||D_t\mathbf{T}(t)|\mathbf{N}(t) \tag{6}$$

Because

$$D_t s = |D_t\mathbf{R}(t)| \tag{7}$$

if we differentiate with respect to t, we obtain

$$D_t^2 s = D_t|D_t\mathbf{R}(t)| \tag{8}$$

Furthermore,

$$|D_t\mathbf{R}(t)||D_t\mathbf{T}(t)| = |D_t\mathbf{R}(t)|^2 \left|\frac{D_t\mathbf{T}(t)}{|D_t\mathbf{R}(t)|}\right| \tag{9}$$

Applying (7) above and Eq. (9) of Sec. 15.9 to the right side of (9), we have

$$|D_t\mathbf{R}(t)||D_t\mathbf{T}(t)| = (D_t s)^2 K(t) \tag{10}$$

Substituting from (5), (8), and (10) into (6), we obtain

$$\mathbf{A}(t) = (D_t^2 s)\mathbf{T}(t) + (D_t s)^2 K(t)\mathbf{N}(t) \tag{11}$$

Equation (11) expresses the acceleration vector as the sum of a scalar times the unit tangent vector and a scalar times the unit normal vector. The coefficient of $\mathbf{T}(t)$ is called the *tangential component* of the acceleration vector and is denoted by $A_T(t)$, whereas the coefficient of $\mathbf{N}(t)$ is called the *normal component* of the acceleration vector and is denoted by $A_N(t)$. So

$$A_T(t) = D_t^2 s \tag{12}$$

and

$$A_N(t) = (D_t s)^2 K(t) \tag{13}$$

or, equivalently,

$$A_N(t) = \frac{(D_t s)^2}{\rho(t)} \tag{14}$$

Because the number of units in the speed of the particle at time t units is $|\mathbf{V}(t)| = D_t s$, $A_T(t)$ is the derivative of the measure of the speed of the particle and $A_N(t)$ is the square of the measure of the speed divided by the radius of curvature.

From Newton's second law of motion

$$\mathbf{F} = m\mathbf{A}$$

where $\mathbf{F}$ is the force vector applied to the moving object, m is the measure of the mass of the object, and $\mathbf{A}$ is the acceleration vector of the object. In curvilinear motion, the normal component of $\mathbf{F}$ is the force normal to the curve necessary to keep the object on the curve. For example, if an automobile is going around a curve at a high speed, then the normal force must have a large magnitude to keep the car on the road. Also, if the curve is sharp, the radius of curvature is a small number, and so the magnitude of the normal force must be a large number.

Equation (4) indicates that the tangential component of the velocity vector is $D_t s$ and that the normal component of the velocity vector is zero.

Substituting from (12) and (13) into (11), we have

$$\mathbf{A}(t) = A_T(t)\mathbf{T}(t) + A_N(t)\mathbf{N}(t) \tag{15}$$

from which it follows that

$$|\mathbf{A}(t)| = \sqrt{[A_T(t)]^2 + [A_N(t)]^2}$$

Solving for $A_N(t)$, noting from (13) that $A_N(t)$ is nonnegative, we have

$$A_N(t) = \sqrt{|A(t)|^2 - [A_T(t)]^2} \tag{16}$$

EXAMPLE 1:   A particle is moving along the curve having the vector equation

$$\mathbf{R}(t) = (t^2 - 1)\mathbf{i} + (\tfrac{1}{3}t^3 - t)\mathbf{j}$$

Find each of the following vectors: $\mathbf{V}(t), \mathbf{A}(t), \mathbf{T}(t)$, and $\mathbf{N}(t)$. Also, find the following scalars: $|\mathbf{V}(t)|$, $A_T(t), A_N(t)$, and $K(t)$. Find the particular values when $t = 2$. Draw a sketch showing a portion of the curve at the point where $t = 2$, and representations of $\mathbf{V}(2), \mathbf{A}(2), A_T(2)\mathbf{T}(2)$, and $A_N(2)\mathbf{N}(2)$, having their initial point at $t = 2$.

SOLUTION:

$$\mathbf{V}(t) = D_t\mathbf{R}(t) = 2t\mathbf{i} + (t^2 - 1)\mathbf{j}$$

$$\mathbf{A}(t) = D_t\mathbf{V}(t) = 2\mathbf{i} + 2t\mathbf{j}$$

$$|\mathbf{V}(t)| = \sqrt{4t^2 + t^4 - 2t^2 + 1} = \sqrt{t^4 + 2t^2 + 1} = t^2 + 1$$

$$|\mathbf{A}(t)| = \sqrt{4 + 4t^2} = 2\sqrt{1 + t^2}$$

$$D_t s = |\mathbf{V}(t)| = t^2 + 1$$

$$A_T(t) = D_t^2 s = 2t$$

From (16)

$$A_N(t) = \sqrt{|\mathbf{A}(t)|^2 - [A_T(t)]^2} = \sqrt{4 + 4t^2 - 4t^2} = 2$$

$$\mathbf{T}(t) = \frac{\mathbf{V}(t)}{|\mathbf{V}(t)|} = \frac{2t}{t^2 + 1}\mathbf{i} + \frac{t^2 - 1}{t^2 + 1}\mathbf{j}$$

To find $N(t)$, we use the following formula which comes from (11):

$$N(t) = \frac{1}{(D_t s)^2 K(t)} [A(t) - (D_t^2 s)T(t)] \qquad (17)$$

$$A(t) - (D_t^2 s)T(t) = 2i + 2tj - 2t \left(\frac{2t}{t^2+1} i + \frac{t^2-1}{t^2+1} j \right)$$

$$A(t) - (D_t^2 s)T(t) = \frac{2}{t^2+1} [(1-t^2)i + 2tj] \qquad (18)$$

From (17) we see that $N(t)$ is a scalar times the vector in (18). Because $N(t)$ is a unit vector, $N(t)$ can be obtained by dividing the vector in (18) by its magnitude. Thus, we have

$$N(t) = \frac{(1-t^2)i + 2tj}{\sqrt{(1-t^2)^2 + (2t)^2}} = \frac{1-t^2}{1+t^2} i + \frac{2t}{1+t^2} j$$

$K(t)$ is found from (13), and we have

$$K(t) = \frac{A_N(t)}{(D_t s)^2} = \frac{2}{(t^2+1)^2}$$

When $t = 2$, we obtain $V(2) = 4i + 3j$, $A(2) = 2i + 4j$, $|V(2)| = 5$, $A_T(2) = 4$, $A_N(2) = 2$, $T(2) = \frac{4}{5}i + \frac{3}{5}j$, $N(2) = -\frac{3}{5}i + \frac{4}{5}j$, $K(2) = \frac{2}{25}$. The required sketch is shown in Fig. 15.10.1.

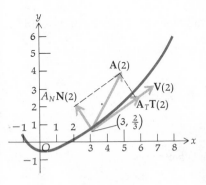

Figure 15.10.1

Exercises 15.10

In Exercises 1 through 6, a particle is moving along the curve having the given vector equation. In each problem, find the vectors $V(t)$, $A(t)$, $T(t)$, and $N(t)$, and the following scalars for an arbitrary value of t: $|V(t)|$, A_T, A_N, $K(t)$. Also find the particular values when $t = t_1$. At $t = t_1$, draw a sketch of a portion of the curve and representations of the vectors $V(t_1)$, $A(t_1)$, $A_T T(t_1)$, and $A_N N(t_1)$.

1. $R(t) = (2t + 3)i + (t^2 - 1)j$; $t_1 = 2$ 2. $R(t) = (t - 1)i + t^2 j$; $t_1 = 1$ 3. $R(t) = 5 \cos 3ti + 5 \sin 3tj$; $t_1 = \frac{1}{3}\pi$

4. $R(t) = \cos t^2 i + \sin t^2 j$; $t_1 = \frac{1}{2}\sqrt{\pi}$ 5. $R(t) = e^t i + e^{-t} j$; $t_1 = 0$ 6. $R(t) = 3t^2 i + 2t^3 j$; $t_1 = 1$

7. A particle is moving along the parabola $y^2 = 8x$ and its speed is constant. Find each of the following when the particle is at $(2, 4)$: the position vector, the velocity vector, the acceleration vector, the unit tangent vector, the unit normal vector, A_T, and A_N.

8. A particle is moving along the top branch of the hyperbola $y^2 - x^2 = 9$, such that $D_t x$ is a positive constant. Find each of the following when the particle is at $(4, 5)$: the position vector, the velocity vector, the acceleration vector, the unit tangent vector, the unit normal vector, A_T, and A_N.

Review Exercises (Chapter 15)

In Exercises 1 through 12, let $A = 4i - 6j$, $B = i + 7j$, and $C = 9i - 5j$.

1. Find $3B - 7A$ 2. Find $4A + B - 6C$ 3. Find $5B - 3C$

4. Find $|5B| - |3C|$ 5. Find $(A - B) \cdot C$ 6. Find $(A \cdot B)C$

7. Find a unit vector having the same direction as $2A + B$.

8. Find the unit vectors that are orthogonal to **B**.

9. Find scalars h and k such that $\mathbf{A} = h\mathbf{B} + k\mathbf{C}$.

10. Find the vector projection of **C** onto **A**.

11. Find the component of **A** in the direction of **B**.

12. Find $\cos \alpha$ if α is the radian measure of the angle between **A** and **C**.

In Exercises 13 and 14, for the vector-valued function, find (a) the domain of $\mathbf{R}$; (b) $\lim\limits_{t \to 1} \mathbf{R}(t)$; (c) $D_t \mathbf{R}(t)$

13. $\mathbf{R}(t) = \dfrac{1}{t+1}\mathbf{i} + \dfrac{\sqrt{t}-1}{t-1}\mathbf{j}$

14. $\mathbf{R}(t) = |t-1|\mathbf{i} + \ln t\mathbf{j}$

In Exercises 15 and 16, find equations of the horizontal and vertical tangent lines, and then draw a sketch of the graph of the given pair of parametric equations.

15. $x = 12 - t^2$, $y = 12t - t^3$

16. $x = \dfrac{2at^2}{1+t^2}$, $y = \dfrac{2at^3}{1+t^2}$, $a > 0$ (the cissoid of Diocles)

17. Find the length of the arc of the curve $\mathbf{R}(t) = (2-t)\mathbf{i} + t^2\mathbf{j}$ from $t = 0$ to $t = 3$.

18. Find the length of the arc of the curve $r = 3 \sec \theta$ from $\theta = 0$ to $\theta = \frac{1}{4}\pi$.

19. (a) Show that the curve defined by the parametric equations, $x = a \sin t$ and $y = b \cos t$, is an ellipse. (b) If s is the measure of the length of arc of the ellipse of part (a), show that

$$s = 4 \int_0^{\pi/2} a\sqrt{1 - k^2 \sin^2 t}\, dt$$

where $k^2 = (a^2 - b^2)/a^2 < 1$. This integral is called an *elliptic integral* and cannot be evaluated exactly in terms of elementary functions. There are tables available that give the value of the integral in terms of k.

20. Draw a sketch of the graph of the vector equation $\mathbf{R}(t) = e^t\mathbf{i} + e^{-t}\mathbf{j}$ and find a cartesian equation of the graph.

21. Show that the curvature of the curve $y = \ln x$ at any point (x, y) is $x/(x^2 + 1)^{3/2}$. Also show that the absolute maximum curvature is $2/3\sqrt{3}$ which occurs at the point $(\frac{1}{2}\sqrt{2}, -\frac{1}{2}\ln 2)$.

22. Find the curvature at any point of the branch of the hyperbola defined by $x = a \cosh t$, $y = b \sinh t$. Also show that the curvature is an absolute maximum at the vertex.

23. Find the radius of curvature at any point on the curve $x = a(\cos t + t \sin t)$, $y = a(\sin t - t \cos t)$.

24. Find the curvature, the radius of curvature, and the center of curvature of the curve $y = e^{-x}$ at the point $(0, 1)$.

25. For the hypocycloid of four cusps, $x = a \cos^3 t$ and $y = a \sin^3 t$, find dy/dx and d^2y/dx^2 without eliminating the parameter.

26. A particle is moving along a curve having the vector equation $\mathbf{R}(t) = 3t\mathbf{i} + (4t - t^2)\mathbf{j}$. Find a cartesian equation of the path of the particle. Also find the velocity vector and the acceleration vector at $t = 1$.

27. Find the tangential and normal components of the acceleration vector for the particle of Exercise 26.

28. If a particle is moving along a curve under what conditions will the acceleration vector and the unit tangent vector have the same or opposite directions?

In Exercises 29 and 30, for the given curve find $\mathbf{T}(t)$ and $\mathbf{N}(t)$, and at $t = t_1$ draw a sketch of a portion of the curve and draw the representations of $\mathbf{T}(t_1)$ and $\mathbf{N}(t_1)$ having initial point at $t = t_1$.

29. $\mathbf{R}(t) = (e^t + e^{-t})\mathbf{i} + 2t\mathbf{j}$; $t_1 = 2$

30. $\mathbf{R}(t) = 3(\cos t + t \sin t)\mathbf{i} + 3(\sin t - t \cos t)\mathbf{j}$, $t > 0$; $t_1 = \frac{1}{2}\pi$

31. Given the curve having parametric equations $x = 4t$, $y = \frac{1}{3}(2t + 1)^{3/2}$, $t > 0$, find parametric equations having the measure of arc length s as a parameter, where arc length is measured from the point where $t = 0$. Check your result by using Eq. (10) of Sec. 15.8.

32. Find the radian measure of the angle of elevation at which a gun should be fired in order to obtain the maximum range for a given muzzle speed.

33. Find a formula for obtaining the maximum height reached by a projectile fired from a gun having a given muzzle speed of v_0 ft/sec and an angle of elevation of radian measure α.

34. Find the position vector $\mathbf{R}(t)$ if the acceleration vector

$$\mathbf{A}(t) = t^2\mathbf{i} - \frac{1}{t^2}\mathbf{j}$$

and $\mathbf{V}(1) = \mathbf{j}$, and $\mathbf{R}(1) = -\frac{1}{4}\mathbf{i} + \frac{1}{2}\mathbf{j}$.

35. Prove by vector analysis that the diagonals of a parallelogram bisect each other.

36. Given triangle ABC, points D, E, and F are on sides AB, BC, and AC, respectively, and $\mathbf{V}(\overrightarrow{AD}) = \frac{1}{3}\mathbf{V}(\overrightarrow{AB})$; $\mathbf{V}(\overrightarrow{BE}) = \frac{1}{3}\mathbf{V}(\overrightarrow{BC})$; $\mathbf{V}(\overrightarrow{CF}) = \frac{1}{3}\mathbf{V}(\overrightarrow{CA})$. Prove $\mathbf{V}(\overrightarrow{AE}) + \mathbf{V}(\overrightarrow{BF}) + \mathbf{V}(\overrightarrow{CD}) = \mathbf{0}$.

In Exercises 37 and 38, find the velocity and acceleration vectors, the speed, and the tangential and normal components of acceleration.

37. $\mathbf{R}(t) = \cosh 2t\mathbf{i} + \sinh 2t\mathbf{j}$

38. $\mathbf{R}(t) = (2 \tan^{-1} t - t)\mathbf{i} + \ln(1 + t^2)\mathbf{j}$

39. An *epicycloid* is the curve traced by a point P on the circumference of a circle of radius b which is rolling externally on a fixed circle of radius a. If the origin is at the center of the fixed circle, $A(a, 0)$ is one of the points at which the given point P comes in contact with the fixed circle, B is the moving point of tangency of the two circles, and the parameter t is the radian measure of the angle AOB, prove that parametric equations of the epicycloid are

$$x = (a + b) \cos t - b \cos \frac{a + b}{b} t$$

and

$$y = (a + b) \sin t - b \sin \frac{a + b}{b} t$$

16

Vectors in Three-Dimensional Space and Solid Analytic Geometry

16.1 R_3, THE THREE-DIMENSIONAL NUMBER SPACE

In Chapter 1 we discussed the number line R_1 (the one-dimensional number space) and the number plane R_2 (the two-dimensional number space). We identified the real numbers in R_1 with points on a horizontal axis and the real number pairs in R_2 with points in a geometric plane. In an analogous fashion, we now introduce the set of all ordered triples of real numbers.

16.1.1 Definition

The set of all ordered triples of real numbers is called the *three-dimensional number space* and is denoted by R_3. Each ordered triple (x, y, z) is called a *point* in the three-dimensional number space.

To represent R_3 in a geometric three-dimensional space we consider the directed distances of a point from three mutually perpendicular planes. The planes are formed by first considering three mutually perpendicular lines which intersect at a point that we call the *origin* and denote by the letter O. These lines, called the coordinate axes, are designated as the x axis, the y axis, and the z axis. Usually the x axis and the y axis are taken in a horizontal plane, and the z axis is vertical. A positive direction is selected on each axis. If the positive directions are chosen as in Fig. 16.1.1, the coordinate system is called a *right-handed system*. This terminology follows from the fact that if the right hand is placed so the thumb is pointed in the positive direction of the x axis and the index finger is pointed in the positive direction of the y axis, then the middle finger is pointed in the positive direction of the z axis. If the middle finger is pointed in the negative direction of the z axis, then the coordinate system is called *left handed*. A

Figure 16.1.1

Figure 16.1.2

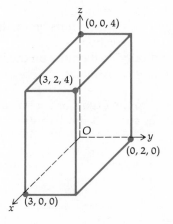

Figure 16.1.3

left-handed system is shown in Fig. 16.1.2. In general, we use a right-handed system. The three axes determine three coordinate planes: the xy plane containing the x and y axes, the xz plane containing the x and z axes, and the yz plane containing the y and z axes.

An ordered triple of real numbers (x, y, z) is associated with each point P in a geometric three-dimensional space. The directed distance of P from the yz plane is called the x coordinate, the directed distance of P from the xz plane is called the y coordinate, and the z coordinate is the directed distance of P from the xy plane. These three coordinates are called the *rectangular cartesian coordinates* of the point, and there is a one-to-one correspondence (called a *rectangular cartesian coordinate system*) between all such ordered triples of real numbers and the points in a geometric three-dimensional space. Hence, we identify R_3 with the geometric three-dimensional space, and we call an ordered triple (x, y, z) a point. The point $(3, 2, 4)$ is shown in Fig. 16.1.3, and the point $(4, -2, -5)$ is shown in Fig. 16.1.4.

The three coordinate planes divide the space into eight parts, called *octants*. The first octant is the one in which all three coordinates are positive. The other octants are usually numbered so the x coordinate is positive in the first four octants, with the numbering being in the counterclockwise direction. The remaining four octants are those for which the x coordinate is negative; the fifth octant is the one for which the y and z coordinates are positive. So the point $(4, -2, -5)$ shown in Fig. 16.1.4 is in the third octant, and the point $(-3, -1, 6)$ is in the sixth octant. The point $(-2, -4, -7)$ is in the seventh octant.

A line is parallel to a plane if and only if the distance from any point on the line to the plane is the same. A line parallel to the yz plane, one parallel to the xz plane, and one parallel to the xy plane are shown in Fig. 16.1.5a, b, and c, respectively. We consider all lines lying in a given plane as being parallel to the plane, in which case the distance from any point on the line to the plane is zero. The following theorem follows immediately.

Figure 16.1.4

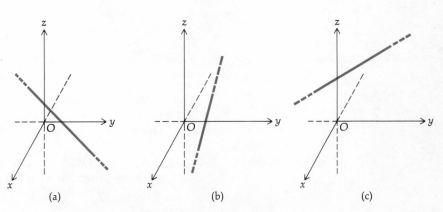

(a)   (b)   (c)

Figure 16.1.5

16.1.2 Theorem

(i) A line is parallel to the yz plane if and only if all points on the line have equal x coordinates.

(ii) A line is parallel to the xz plane if and only if all points on the line have equal y coordinates.

(iii) A line is parallel to the xy plane if and only if all points on the line have equal z coordinates.

In three-dimensional space, if a line is parallel to each of two intersecting planes, it is parallel to the line of intersection of the two planes. Also, if a given line is parallel to a second line, then the given line is parallel to any plane containing the second line. Theorem 16.1.3 follows from these two facts from solid geometry and from Theorem 16.1.2.

16.1.3 Theorem

(i) A line is parallel to the x axis if and only if all points on the line have equal y coordinates and equal z coordinates.

(ii) A line is parallel to the y axis if and only if all points on the line have equal x coordinates and equal z coordinates.

(iii) A line is parallel to the z axis if and only if all points on the line have equal x coordinates and equal y coordinates.

A line parallel to the x axis, a line parallel to the y axis, and a line parallel to the z axis are shown in Fig. 16.1.6a, b, and c, respectively.

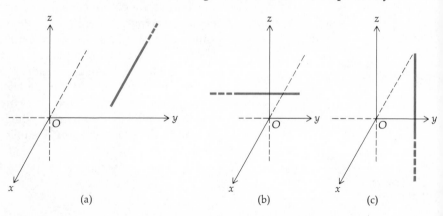

Figure 16.1.6

The formulas for finding the directed distance from one point to another on a line parallel to a coordinate axis follow from the definition of directed distance given in Sec. 1.4 and are stated in the following theorem.

16.1.4 Theorem

(i) If $A(x_1, y, z)$ and $B(x_2, y, z)$ are two points on a line parallel to the x axis, then the directed distance from A to B, denoted by $\overline{AB}$, is given by

$$\overline{AB} = x_2 - x_1$$

(ii) If $C(x, y_1, z)$ and $D(x, y_2, z)$ are two points on a line parallel to the y axis, then the directed distance from C to D, denoted by $\overline{CD}$, is given by

$$\overline{CD} = y_2 - y_1$$

(iii) If $E(x, y, z_1)$ and $F(x, y, z_2)$ are two points on a line parallel to the z axis, then the directed distance from E to F, denoted by $\overline{EF}$, is given by

$$\overline{EF} = z_2 - z_1$$

EXAMPLE 1:   Find the directed distance from the point $P(2, -5, -4)$ to the point $Q(2, -3, -4)$.

SOLUTION: From Theorem 16.1.4(ii), we have

$$\overline{PQ} = (-3) - (-5) = 2$$

The following theorem gives a formula for finding the undirected distance between any two points in three-dimensional space.

16.1.5 Theorem   The undirected distance between the two points $P_1(x_1, y_1, z_1)$ and $P_2(x_2, y_2, z_2)$ is given by

$$|\overline{P_1P_2}| = \sqrt{(x_2 - x_1)^2 + (y_2 - y_1)^2 + (z_2 - z_1)^2}$$

PROOF: Construct a rectangular parallelepiped having P_1 and P_2 as opposite vertices and faces parallel to the coordinate planes (see Fig. 16.1.7). By the Pythagorean theorem we have

$$|\overline{P_1P_2}| = |\overline{P_1A}|^2 + |\overline{AP_2}|^2 \tag{1}$$

Because

$$|\overline{P_1A}|^2 = |\overline{P_1B}|^2 + |\overline{BA}|^2 \tag{2}$$

we obtain, by substituting from (2) into (1),

$$|\overline{P_1P_2}|^2 = |\overline{P_1B}|^2 + |\overline{BA}|^2 + |\overline{AP_2}|^2 \tag{3}$$

Applying Theorem 16.1.4(i), (ii), and (iii) to the right side of (3), we obtain

$$|\overline{P_1P_2}|^2 = (x_2 - x_1)^2 + (y_2 - y_1)^2 + (z_2 - z_1)^2$$

So

$$|\overline{P_1P_2}| = \sqrt{(x_2 - x_1)^2 + (y_2 - y_1)^2 + (z_2 - z_1)^2}$$

and the theorem is proved.   ∎

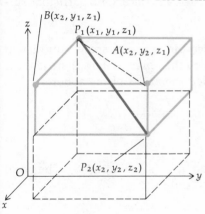

Figure 16.1.7

EXAMPLE 2:   Find the undirected distance between the points $P(-3, 4, -1)$ and $Q(2, 5, -4)$.

SOLUTION: From Theorem 16.1.5, we have

$$|\overline{PQ}| = \sqrt{(2+3)^2 + (5-4)^2 + (-4+1)^2} = \sqrt{25 + 1 + 9} = \sqrt{35}$$

Note that the formula for the distance between two points in R_3 is merely an extension of the corresponding formula for the distance between two points in R_2 given in Theorem 1.4.1. It is also noteworthy that the undirected distance between two points x_2 and x_1 in R_1 is given by

$$|x_2 - x_1| = \sqrt{(x_2 - x_1)^2}$$

The formulas for the coordinates of the midpoint of a line segment are derived by forming congruent triangles and proceeding in a manner analogous to the two-dimensional case. These formulas are given in Theorem 16.1.6, and the proof is left for the reader (see Exercise 15).

16.1.6 Theorem   The coordinates of the midpoint of the line segment having endpoints $P_1(x_1, y_1, z_1)$ and $P_2(x_2, y_2, z_2)$ are given by

$$\bar{x} = \frac{x_1 + x_2}{2} \qquad \bar{y} = \frac{y_1 + y_2}{2} \qquad \bar{z} = \frac{z_1 + z_2}{2}$$

16.1.7 Definition   The *graph of an equation* in R_3 is the set of all points (x, y, z) whose coordinates are numbers satisfying the equation.

The graph of an equation in R_3 is called a *surface*. One particular surface is the sphere, which is now defined.

16.1.8 Definition   A *sphere* is the set of all points in three-dimensional space equidistant from a fixed point. The fixed point is called the *center* of the sphere and the measure of the constant distance is called the *radius* of the sphere.

16.1.9 Theorem   An equation of the sphere of radius r and center at (h, k, l) is

$$(x - h)^2 + (y - k)^2 + (z - l)^2 = r^2 \tag{4}$$

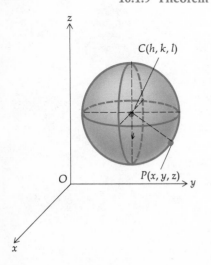

Figure 16.1.8

PROOF: Let the point (h, k, l) be denoted by C (see Fig. 16.1.8). The point $P(x, y, z)$ is a point on the sphere if and only if

$$|\overline{CP}| = r$$

or, equivalently,

$$\sqrt{(x - h)^2 + (y - k)^2 + (z - l)^2} = r$$

Squaring on both sides of the above equation, we obtain the desired result.   ∎

If the center of the sphere is at the origin, then $h = k = l = 0$, and so an equation of this sphere is

$$x^2 + y^2 + z^2 = r^2$$

If we expand the terms of Eq. (4) and regroup the terms, we have

$$x^2 + y^2 + z^2 - 2hx - 2ky - 2lz + (h^2 + k^2 + l^2 - r^2) = 0$$

This equation is of the form

$$x^2 + y^2 + z^2 + Gx + Hy + Iz + J = 0 \tag{5}$$

where G, H, I, and J are constants. Equation (5) is called the *general form* of an equation of a sphere, whereas Eq. (4) is called the *center-radius* form. Because every sphere has a center and a radius, its equation can be put in the center-radius form and hence the general form.

It can be shown that any equation of the form (5) can be put in the form

$$(x - h)^2 + (y - k)^2 + (z - l)^2 = K \tag{6}$$

where

$$h = -\tfrac{1}{2}G \qquad k = -\tfrac{1}{2}H \qquad l = -\tfrac{1}{2}I \qquad K = \tfrac{1}{4}(G^2 + H^2 + I^2 - 4J)$$

It is left as an exercise for the reader to show this (see Exercise 16).

If $K > 0$, then Eq. (6) is of the form of Eq. (4), and so the graph of the equation is a sphere having its center at (h, k, l) and radius $\sqrt{K}$. If $K = 0$, the graph of the equation is the point (h, k, l). This is called a *point-sphere*. If $K < 0$, there is no real locus because the sum of the squares of three real numbers is nonnegative. We state this result as a theorem.

16.1.10 Theorem   The graph of any second-degree equation in x, y, and z, of the form

$$x^2 + y^2 + z^2 + Gx + Hy + Iz + J = 0$$

is either a sphere, a point-sphere, or no real locus.

EXAMPLE 3:   Draw a sketch of the graph of the equation

$$x^2 + y^2 + z^2 - 6x - 4y + 2z = 2$$

(3, 2, −1)

Figure 16.1.9

SOLUTION: Regrouping terms and completing the squares, we have

$$x^2 - 6x + 9 + y^2 - 4y + 4 + z^2 + 2z + 1 = 2 + 9 + 4 + 1$$

or

$$(x - 3)^2 + (y - 2)^2 + (z + 1)^2 = 16$$

So the graph is a sphere having its center at $(3, 2, -1)$ and radius 4. A sketch of the graph is shown in Fig. 16.1.9.

EXAMPLE 4:   Find an equation of the sphere having the points $A(-5, 6, -2)$ and $B(9, -4, 0)$ as endpoints of a diameter.

SOLUTION: The center of the sphere will be the midpoint of the line segment AB. Let this point be $C(\bar{x}, \bar{y}, \bar{z})$. By Theorem 16.1.6, we get

$$\bar{x} = \frac{9 - 5}{2} = 2 \qquad \bar{y} = \frac{-4 + 6}{2} = 1 \qquad \bar{z} = \frac{0 - 2}{2} = -1$$

So C is the point $(2, 1, -1)$. The radius of the sphere is given by

$$r = |\overline{CB}| = \sqrt{(9 - 2)^2 + (-4 - 1)^2 + (0 + 1)^2} = \sqrt{75}$$

Therefore, from Theorem 16.1.9, an equation of the sphere is

$$(x-2)^2 + (y-1)^2 + (z+1)^2 = 75$$

or, equivalently,

$$x^2 + y^2 + z^2 - 4x - 2y + 2z - 69 = 0$$

Exercises 16.1

In Exercises 1 through 4, the given points A and B are opposite vertices of a rectangular parallelepiped, having its faces parallel to the coordinate planes. In each problem (a) draw a sketch of the figure, (b) find the coordinates of the other six vertices, (c) find the length of the diagonal AB.

1. $A(0, 0, 0)$; $B(7, 2, 3)$ 2. $A(1, 1, 1)$; $B(3, 4, 2)$

3. $A(-1, 1, 2)$; $B(2, 3, 5)$ 4. $A(2, -1, -3)$; $B(4, 0, -1)$

5. The vertex opposite one corner of a room is 18 ft east, 15 ft south, and 12 ft up from the first corner. (a) Draw a sketch of the figure, (b) determine the length of the diagonal joining two opposite vertices, (c) find the coordinates of all eight vertices of the room.

In Exercises 6 through 9, find (a) the undirected distance between the points A and B, and (b) the midpoint of the line segment joining A and B.

6. $A(3, 4, 2)$; $B(1, 6, 3)$ 7. $A(2, -4, 1)$; $B(\frac{1}{2}, 2, 3)$

8. $A(4, -3, 2)$; $B(-2, 3, -5)$ 9. $A(-2, -\frac{1}{2}, 5)$; $B(5, 1, -4)$

10. Prove that the three points $(1, -1, 3)$, $(2, 1, 7)$, and $(4, 2, 6)$ are the vertices of a right triangle, and find its area.

11. A line is drawn through the point $(6, 4, 2)$ perpendicular to the yz plane. Find the coordinates of the points on this line at a distance of 10 units from the point $(0, 4, 0)$.

12. Solve Exercise 11 if the line is drawn perpendicular to the xy plane.

13. Prove that the three points $(-3, 2, 4)$, $(6, 1, 2)$, and $(-12, 3, 6)$ are collinear by using the distance formula.

14. Find the vertices of the triangle whose sides have midpoints at $(3, 2, 3)$, $(-1, 1, 5)$, and $(0, 3, 4)$.

15. Prove Theorem 16.1.6.

16. Show that any equation of the form $x^2 + y^2 + z^2 + Gx + Hy + Iz + J = 0$ can be put in the form $(x-h)^2 + (y-k)^2 + (z-l)^2 = K$.

In Exercises 17 through 21, determine the graph of the given equation.

17. $x^2 + y^2 + z^2 - 8x + 4y + 2z - 4 = 0$ 18. $x^2 + y^2 + z^2 - 8y + 6z - 25 = 0$ 19. $x^2 + y^2 + z^2 - 6z + 9 = 0$

20. $x^2 + y^2 + z^2 - x - y - 3z + 2 = 0$ 21. $x^2 + y^2 + z^2 - 6x + 2y - 4z + 19 = 0$

In Exercises 22 through 24, find an equation of the sphere satisfying the given conditions.

22. A diameter is the line segment having endpoints at $(6, 2, -5)$ and $(-4, 0, 7)$.

23. It is concentric with the sphere having equation $x^2 + y^2 + z^2 - 2y + 8z - 9 = 0$.

24. It contains the points $(0, 0, 4)$, $(2, 1, 3)$, and $(0, 2, 6)$ and has its center in the yz plane.

25. Prove analytically that the four diagonals joining opposite vertices of a rectangular parallelepiped bisect each other.

26. If P, Q, R, and S are four points in three-dimensional space and A, B, C, and D are the midpoints of PQ, QR, RS, and SP, respectively, prove analytically that $ABCD$ is a parallelogram.

16.2 VECTORS IN THREE-DIMENSIONAL SPACE

The presentation of topics in solid analytic geometry is simplified by the use of vectors in three-dimensional space. The definitions and theorems given in Secs. 15.1 and 15.2 for vectors in the plane are easily extended.

16.2.1 Definition   A *vector in three-dimensional space* is an ordered triple of real numbers $\langle x, y, z \rangle$. The numbers x, y, and z are called the *components* of the vector $\langle x, y, z \rangle$.

We let V_3 be the set of all ordered triples $\langle x, y, z \rangle$ for which x, y, and z are real numbers. In this chapter, a vector is always in V_3 unless otherwise stated.

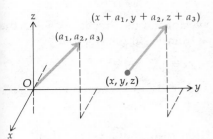

Figure 16.2.1

Just as for vectors in V_2, a vector in V_3 can be represented by a directed line segment. If $\mathbf{A} = \langle a_1, a_2, a_3 \rangle$, then the directed line segment having its initial point at the origin and its terminal point at the point (a_1, a_2, a_3) is called the *position representation* of $\mathbf{A}$. A directed line segment having its initial point at (x, y, z) and its terminal point at $(x + a_1, y + a_2, z + a_3)$ is also a representation of the vector $\mathbf{A}$. See Fig. 16.2.1.

The *zero vector* is the vector $\langle 0, 0, 0 \rangle$ and is denoted by $\mathbf{0}$. Any point is a representation of the zero vector.

The *magnitude* of a vector is the length of any of its representations. If the vector $\mathbf{A} = \langle a_1, a_2, a_3 \rangle$, the magnitude of $\mathbf{A}$ is denoted by $|\mathbf{A}|$, and it follows that

$$|\mathbf{A}| = \sqrt{a_1^2 + a_2^2 + a_3^2}$$

The *direction* of a nonzero vector in V_3 is given by three angles, called the *direction angles* of the vector.

16.2.2 Definition   The *direction angles* of a nonzero vector are the three angles that have the smallest nonnegative radian measures α, β, and γ measured from the positive x, y, and z axes, respectively, to the position representation of the vector.

Figure 16.2.2

The radian measure of each direction angle of a vector is greater than or equal to 0 and less than or equal to π. The direction angles having radian measures α, β, and γ of the vector $\mathbf{A} = \langle a_1, a_2, a_3 \rangle$ are shown in Fig. 16.2.2. In this figure the components of $\mathbf{A}$ are all positive numbers, and the direction angles of this vector all have positive radian measure less than $\frac{1}{2}\pi$. From the figure we see that triangle POR is a right triangle and

$$\cos \alpha = \frac{|\overrightarrow{OR}|}{|\overrightarrow{OP}|} = \frac{a_1}{|\mathbf{A}|}$$

It can be shown that the same formula holds if $\frac{1}{2}\pi \le \alpha \le \pi$. Similar formulas can be found for $\cos \beta$ and $\cos \gamma$, and we have

$$\cos \alpha = \frac{a_1}{|\mathbf{A}|} \qquad \cos \beta = \frac{a_2}{|\mathbf{A}|} \qquad \cos \gamma = \frac{a_3}{|\mathbf{A}|} \tag{1}$$

The three numbers $\cos \alpha$, $\cos \beta$, and $\cos \gamma$ are called the *direction cosines* of vector **A**. The zero vector has no direction angles and hence no direction cosines.

EXAMPLE 1:   Given $\mathbf{A} = \langle 3, 2, -6 \rangle$, find the magnitude and direction cosines of **A**.

SOLUTION:

$$|\mathbf{A}| = \sqrt{(3)^2 + (2)^2 + (-6)^2} = \sqrt{9 + 4 + 36} = \sqrt{49} = 7$$

From Eqs. (1) we get

$$\cos \alpha = \tfrac{3}{7} \qquad \cos \beta = \tfrac{2}{7} \qquad \cos \gamma = -\tfrac{6}{7}$$

If we are given the magnitude of a vector and its direction cosines, the vector is uniquely determined because from (1) it follows that

$$a_1 = |\mathbf{A}| \cos \alpha \qquad a_2 = |\mathbf{A}| \cos \beta \qquad a_3 = |\mathbf{A}| \cos \gamma \qquad (2)$$

The three direction cosines of a vector are not independent of each other, as we see by the following theorem.

16.2.3 Theorem   If $\cos \alpha$, $\cos \beta$, and $\cos \gamma$ are the direction cosines of a vector, then

$$\cos^2 \alpha + \cos^2 \beta + \cos^2 \gamma = 1$$

PROOF: If $\mathbf{A} = \langle a_1, a_2, a_3 \rangle$, then the direction cosines of **A** are given by (1) and we have

$$\cos^2 \alpha + \cos^2 \beta + \cos^2 \gamma = \frac{a_1^2}{|\mathbf{A}|^2} + \frac{a_2^2}{|\mathbf{A}|^2} + \frac{a_3^2}{|\mathbf{A}|^2}$$

$$= \frac{a_1^2 + a_2^2 + a_3^2}{|\mathbf{A}|^2}$$

$$= \frac{|\mathbf{A}|^2}{|\mathbf{A}|^2}$$

$$= 1 \qquad \blacksquare$$

EXAMPLE 2:   Verify Theorem 16.2.3 for the vector of Example 1.

SOLUTION: From the solution of Example 1 we have

$$\sqrt{\cos^2 \alpha + \cos^2 \beta + \cos^2 \gamma} = \sqrt{(\tfrac{3}{7})^2 + (\tfrac{2}{7})^2 + (-\tfrac{6}{7})^2}$$

$$= \sqrt{\tfrac{9}{49} + \tfrac{4}{49} + \tfrac{36}{49}}$$

$$= \sqrt{\tfrac{49}{49}}$$

$$= 1$$

The vector $\mathbf{A} = \langle a_1, a_2, a_3 \rangle$ is a unit vector if $|\mathbf{A}| = 1$, and from Eqs. (1) we see that the components of a unit vector are its direction cosines.

The operations of addition, subtraction, and scalar multiplication of vectors in V_3 are given definitions analogous to the corresponding definitions for vectors in V_2.

16.2.4 Definition If $\mathbf{A} = \langle a_1, a_2, a_3 \rangle$ and $\mathbf{B} = \langle b_1, b_2, b_3 \rangle$, then the sum of these vectors is given by

$$\mathbf{A} + \mathbf{B} = \langle a_1 + b_1, a_2 + b_2, a_3 + b_3 \rangle$$

EXAMPLE 3: Given $\mathbf{A} = \langle 5, -2, 6 \rangle$ and $\mathbf{B} = \langle 8, -5, -4 \rangle$, find $\mathbf{A} + \mathbf{B}$.

SOLUTION: $\mathbf{A} + \mathbf{B} = \langle 5 + 8, (-2) + (-5), 6 + (-4) \rangle = \langle 13, -7, 2 \rangle$.

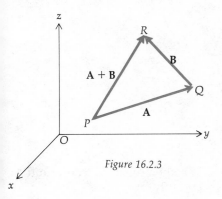

Figure 16.2.3

The geometric interpretation of the sum of two vectors in V_3 is similar to that for vectors in V_2. See Fig. 16.2.3. If P is the point (x, y, z), $\mathbf{A} = \langle a_1, a_2, a_3 \rangle$ and $\overrightarrow{PQ}$ is a representation of $\mathbf{A}$, then Q is the point $(x + a_1, y + a_2, z + a_3)$. Let $\mathbf{B} = \langle b_1, b_2, b_3 \rangle$ and let $\overrightarrow{QR}$ be a representation of $\mathbf{B}$. Then R is the point $(x + (a_1 + b_1), y + (a_2 + b_2), z + (a_3 + b_3))$. Therefore, $\overrightarrow{PR}$ is a representation of the vector $\mathbf{A} + \mathbf{B}$, and the parallelogram law holds.

16.2.5 Definition If $\mathbf{A} = \langle a_1, a_2, a_3 \rangle$, then the vector $\langle -a_1, -a_2, -a_3 \rangle$ is defined to be the *negative* of $\mathbf{A}$, denoted by $-\mathbf{A}$.

16.2.6 Definition The *difference* of the two vectors $\mathbf{A}$ and $\mathbf{B}$, denoted by $\mathbf{A} - \mathbf{B}$, is defined by

$$\mathbf{A} - \mathbf{B} = \mathbf{A} + (-\mathbf{B})$$

From Definitions 16.2.5 and 16.2.6 it follows that if $\mathbf{A} = \langle a_1, a_2, a_3 \rangle$ and $\mathbf{B} = \langle b_1, b_2, b_3 \rangle$, then $-\mathbf{B} = \langle -b_1, -b_2, -b_3 \rangle$ and

$$\mathbf{A} - \mathbf{B} = \langle a_1 - b_1, a_2 - b_2, a_3 - b_3 \rangle$$

EXAMPLE 4: For the vectors $\mathbf{A}$ and $\mathbf{B}$ of Example 3, find $\mathbf{A} - \mathbf{B}$.

SOLUTION:

$$\mathbf{A} - \mathbf{B} = \langle 5, -2, 6 \rangle - \langle 8, -5, -4 \rangle$$
$$= \langle 5, -2, 6 \rangle + \langle -8, 5, 4 \rangle$$
$$= \langle -3, 3, 10 \rangle$$

Figure 16.2.4

The difference of two vectors in V_3 is also interpreted geometrically as it is in V_2. See Fig. 16.2.4. A representation of the vector $\mathbf{A} - \mathbf{B}$ is obtained by choosing representations of $\mathbf{A}$ and $\mathbf{B}$ having the same initial point. Then a representation of the vector $\mathbf{A} - \mathbf{B}$ is the directed line segment from the terminal point of the representation of $\mathbf{B}$ to the terminal point of the representation of $\mathbf{A}$.

EXAMPLE 5:   Given the points $P(1,3,5)$ and $Q(2,-1,4)$, show the directed line segment $\overrightarrow{PQ}$ in a figure and find $\mathbf{V}(\overrightarrow{PQ})$.

SOLUTION: Figure 16.2.5 shows $\overrightarrow{PQ}$ as well as $\overrightarrow{OP}$ and $\overrightarrow{OQ}$. We see from the figure that $\mathbf{V}(\overrightarrow{PQ}) = \mathbf{V}(\overrightarrow{OQ}) - \mathbf{V}(\overrightarrow{OP})$. Hence,

$$\mathbf{V}(\overrightarrow{PQ}) = \langle 2, -1, 4 \rangle - \langle 1, 3, 5 \rangle = \langle 1, -4, -1 \rangle$$

Figure 16.2.5

16.2.7 Definition   If c is a scalar and $\mathbf{A}$ is the vector $\langle a_1, a_2, a_3 \rangle$, then the product of c and $\mathbf{A}$, denoted by $c\mathbf{A}$, is a vector and is given by

$$c\mathbf{A} = c\langle a_1, a_2, a_3 \rangle = \langle ca_1, ca_2, ca_3 \rangle$$

EXAMPLE 6:   Given $\mathbf{A} = \langle -4, 7, -2 \rangle$, find $3\mathbf{A}$ and $-5\mathbf{A}$.

SOLUTION:
$$3\mathbf{A} = 3\langle -4, 7, -2 \rangle = \langle -12, 21, -6 \rangle$$
and
$$-5\mathbf{A} = (-5)\langle -4, 7, -2 \rangle = \langle 20, -35, 10 \rangle$$

Suppose that $\mathbf{A} = \langle a_1, a_2, a_3 \rangle$ is a nonzero vector having direction cosines $\cos \alpha$, $\cos \beta$, and $\cos \gamma$, and c is any nonzero scalar. Then $c\mathbf{A} = \langle ca_1, ca_2, ca_3 \rangle$; and if $\cos \alpha_1$, $\cos \beta_1$, and $\cos \gamma_1$ are the direction cosines of $c\mathbf{A}$, we have from Eqs. (1)

$$\cos \alpha_1 = \frac{ca_1}{|c\mathbf{A}|} \qquad \cos \beta_1 = \frac{ca_2}{|c\mathbf{A}|} \qquad \cos \gamma_1 = \frac{ca_3}{|c\mathbf{A}|}$$

or, equivalently,

$$\cos \alpha_1 = \frac{c}{|c|} \frac{a_1}{|\mathbf{A}|} \qquad \cos \beta_1 = \frac{c}{|c|} \frac{a_2}{|\mathbf{A}|} \qquad \cos \gamma_1 = \frac{c}{|c|} \frac{a_3}{|\mathbf{A}|}$$

from which we get

$$\cos \alpha_1 = \frac{c}{|c|} \cos \alpha \qquad \cos \beta_1 = \frac{c}{|c|} \cos \beta \qquad \cos \gamma_1 = \frac{c}{|c|} \cos \gamma \qquad (3)$$

So if $c > 0$, it follows from Eqs. (3) that the direction cosines of vector $c\mathbf{A}$ are the same as the direction cosines of $\mathbf{A}$. And if $c < 0$, the direction cosines of $c\mathbf{A}$ are the negatives of the direction cosines of $\mathbf{A}$. Therefore, we conclude that if c is a nonzero scalar, then the vector $c\mathbf{A}$ is a vector whose magnitude is $|c|$ times the magnitude of **A**. If $c > 0$, c**A** has the same direction as **A**, whereas if $c < 0$, the direction of c**A** is opposite that of **A**.

The operations of vector addition and scalar multiplication of any vectors in V_3 satisfy properties identical with those given in Theorem 15.2.5. These are given in the following theorem, and the proofs are left for the reader (see Exercises 1 through 6).

16.2.8 Theorem   If **A**, **B**, and **C** are any vectors in V_3 and c and d are any scalars, then vector addition and scalar multiplication satisfy the following properties:

(i) $\mathbf{A} + \mathbf{B} = \mathbf{B} + \mathbf{A}$ (commutative law)

(ii) $\mathbf{A} + (\mathbf{B} + \mathbf{C}) = (\mathbf{A} + \mathbf{B}) + \mathbf{C}$ (associative law)

(iii) There is a vector **0** in V_3 for which

$$\mathbf{A} + \mathbf{0} = \mathbf{A} \qquad \text{(existence of additive identity)}$$

(iv) There is a vector $-\mathbf{A}$ in V_3 such that

$$\mathbf{A} + (-\mathbf{A}) = \mathbf{0} \qquad \text{(existence of negative)}$$

(v) $(cd)\mathbf{A} = c(d\mathbf{A})$ (associative law)

(vi) $c(\mathbf{A} + \mathbf{B}) = c\mathbf{A} + c\mathbf{B}$ (distributive law)

(vii) $(c + d)\mathbf{A} = c\mathbf{A} + d\mathbf{A}$ (distributive law)

(viii) $1(\mathbf{A}) = \mathbf{A}$ (existence of scalar multiplicative identity)

From Definition 15.2.6 and Theorem 16.2.8 it follows that V_3 is a set of vectors in a vector space. We use the same symbol, V_3, to denote this vector space. Furthermore, the three unit vectors

$$\mathbf{i} = \langle 1, 0, 0 \rangle \qquad \mathbf{j} = \langle 0, 1, 0 \rangle \qquad \mathbf{k} = \langle 0, 0, 1 \rangle$$

form a basis for the vector space V_3 because any vector $\langle a_1, a_2, a_3 \rangle$ can be written in terms of them as follows:

$$\langle a_1, a_2, a_3 \rangle = a_1 \langle 1, 0, 0 \rangle + a_2 \langle 0, 1, 0 \rangle + a_3 \langle 0, 0, 1 \rangle$$

Hence, if $\mathbf{A} = \langle a_1, a_2, a_3 \rangle$, we also can write

$$\mathbf{A} = a_1\mathbf{i} + a_2\mathbf{j} + a_3\mathbf{k} \tag{4}$$

Because there are three elements in a basis, V_3 is a three-dimensional vector space.

Substituting from Eqs. (2) into Eq. (4), we have

$$\mathbf{A} = |\mathbf{A}| \cos \alpha \mathbf{i} + |\mathbf{A}| \cos \beta \mathbf{j} + |\mathbf{A}| \cos \gamma \mathbf{k}$$

or, equivalently,

$$\mathbf{A} = |\mathbf{A}|(\cos \alpha \mathbf{i} + \cos \beta \mathbf{j} + \cos \gamma \mathbf{k}) \tag{5}$$

Equation (5) enables us to express any nonzero vector in terms of its magnitude and direction cosines.

EXAMPLE 7:   Express the vector of Example 1 in terms of its magnitude and direction cosines.

SOLUTION: In Example 1, $\mathbf{A} = \langle 3, 2, -6 \rangle$, $|\mathbf{A}| = 7$, $\cos \alpha = \frac{3}{7}$, $\cos \beta = \frac{2}{7}$, and $\cos \gamma = -\frac{6}{7}$. Hence, from Eq. (5) we have

$$\mathbf{A} = 7(\tfrac{3}{7}\mathbf{i} + \tfrac{2}{7}\mathbf{j} - \tfrac{6}{7}\mathbf{k})$$

16.2.9 Theorem   If the nonzero vector $\mathbf{A} = a_1\mathbf{i} + a_2\mathbf{j} + a_3\mathbf{k}$, then the unit vector $\mathbf{U}$ having the same direction as $\mathbf{A}$ is given by

$$\mathbf{U} = \frac{a_1}{|\mathbf{A}|}\mathbf{i} + \frac{a_2}{|\mathbf{A}|}\mathbf{j} + \frac{a_3}{|\mathbf{A}|}\mathbf{k}$$

The proof of Theorem 16.2.9 is analogous to the proof of Theorem 15.2.7 for a vector in V_2 and is left for the reader (see Exercise 30).

EXAMPLE 8:   Given the points $R(2, -1, 3)$ and $S(3, 4, 6)$, find the unit vector having the same direction as $\mathbf{V}(\overrightarrow{RS})$.

SOLUTION:

$$\mathbf{V}(\overrightarrow{RS}) = \langle 3, 4, 6 \rangle - \langle 2, -1, 3 \rangle = \langle 1, 5, 3 \rangle$$
$$= \mathbf{i} + 5\mathbf{j} + 3\mathbf{k}$$

So
$$|\mathbf{V}(\overrightarrow{RS})| = \sqrt{1^2 + 5^2 + 3^2} = \sqrt{35}$$

Therefore, by Theorem 16.2.9 the desired unit vector is

$$\mathbf{U} = \frac{1}{\sqrt{35}}\mathbf{i} + \frac{5}{\sqrt{35}}\mathbf{j} + \frac{3}{\sqrt{35}}\mathbf{k}$$

Exercises 16.2

1. Prove Theorem 16.2.8(i).

2. Prove Theorem 16.2.8(ii).

3. Prove Theorem 16.2.8(iii), (iv), and (viii).

4. Prove Theorem 16.2.8(v).

5. Prove Theorem 16.2.8(vi).

6. Prove Theorem 16.2.8(vii).

In Exercises 7 through 18, let $\mathbf{A} = \langle 1, 2, 3 \rangle$, $\mathbf{B} = \langle 4, -3, -1 \rangle$, $\mathbf{C} = \langle -5, -3, 5 \rangle$, $\mathbf{D} = \langle -2, 1, 6 \rangle$.

7. Find $\mathbf{A} + 5\mathbf{B}$

8. Find $2\mathbf{A} - \mathbf{C}$

9. Find $7\mathbf{C} - 5\mathbf{D}$

10. Find $4\mathbf{B} + 6\mathbf{C} - 2\mathbf{D}$

11. Find $|7\mathbf{C}| - |5\mathbf{D}|$

12. Find $|4\mathbf{B}| + |6\mathbf{C}| - |2\mathbf{D}|$

13. Find $\mathbf{C} + 3\mathbf{D} - 8\mathbf{A}$

14. Find $3\mathbf{A} - 2\mathbf{B} + \mathbf{C} - 12\mathbf{D}$

15. Find $|\mathbf{A}||\mathbf{B}|(\mathbf{C} - \mathbf{D})$

16. Find $|\mathbf{A}|\mathbf{C} - |\mathbf{B}|\mathbf{D}$

17. Find scalars a and b such that $a(\mathbf{A} + \mathbf{B}) + b(\mathbf{C} + \mathbf{D}) = 0$.

18. Find scalars a, b, and c such that $a\mathbf{A} + b\mathbf{B} + c\mathbf{C} = \mathbf{D}$.

In Exercises 19 through 22, find the direction cosines of the vector $\mathbf{V}(\overrightarrow{P_1 P_2})$ and check the answers by verifying that the sum of their squares is 1.

19. $P_1(3, -1, -4)$; $P_2(7, 2, 4)$

20. $P_1(1, 3, 5)$; $P_2(2, -1, 4)$

21. $P_1(4, -3, -1)$; $P_2(-2, -4, -8)$

22. $P_1(-2, 6, 5)$; $P_2(2, 4, 1)$

23. Using the points P_1 and P_2 of Exercise 19, find the point Q such that $\mathbf{V}(\overrightarrow{P_1P_2}) = 3\mathbf{V}(\overrightarrow{P_1Q})$.

24. Using the points P_1 and P_2 of Exercise 20, find the point R such that $\mathbf{V}(\overrightarrow{P_1R}) = -2\mathbf{V}(\overrightarrow{P_2R})$.

In Exercises 25 through 28, express the given vector in terms of its magnitude and direction cosines.

25. $-6\mathbf{i} + 2\mathbf{j} + 3\mathbf{k}$

26. $2\mathbf{i} - 2\mathbf{j} + \mathbf{k}$

27. $-2\mathbf{i} + \mathbf{j} - 3\mathbf{k}$

28. $3\mathbf{i} + 4\mathbf{j} - 5\mathbf{k}$

29. If the radian measure of each direction angle of a vector is the same, what is it?

30. Prove Theorem 16.2.9.

In Exercises 31 and 32 find the unit vector having the same direction as $\mathbf{V}(\overrightarrow{P_1P_2})$.

31. $P_1(4, -1, -6)$; $P_2(5, 7, -2)$

32. $P_1(-8, -5, 2)$; $P_2(-3, -9, 4)$

33. Three vectors in V_3 are said to be *independent* if and only if their position representations do not lie in a plane, and three vectors $\mathbf{E}_1$, $\mathbf{E}_2$, and $\mathbf{E}_3$ are said to form a *basis* for the vector space V_3 if and only if any vector in V_3 can be written as a linear combination of $\mathbf{E}_1$, $\mathbf{E}_2$, and $\mathbf{E}_3$. A theorem can be proved which states that three vectors form a basis for the vector space V_3 if they are independent. Show that this theorem holds for the three vectors $\langle 1, 0, 0 \rangle$, $\langle 1, 1, 0 \rangle$, and $\langle 1, 1, 1 \rangle$ by doing the following: (a) Verify that the vectors are independent by showing that their position representations are not coplanar; (b) verify that the vectors form a basis by showing that any vector $\mathbf{A}$ can be written

$$\mathbf{A} = r\langle 1, 0, 0 \rangle + s\langle 1, 1, 0 \rangle + t\langle 1, 1, 1 \rangle \tag{6}$$

where r, s, and t are scalars. (c) If $\mathbf{A} = \langle 6, -2, 5 \rangle$, find the particular values of r, s, and t so that equation (6) holds.

34. Refer to the first sentence of Exercise 33. A theorem can be proved which states that three vectors form a basis for the vector space V_3 only if they are independent. Show that this theorem holds for the three vectors $\mathbf{F}_1 = \langle 1, 0, 1 \rangle$, $\mathbf{F}_2 = \langle 1, 1, 1 \rangle$, and $\mathbf{F}_3 = \langle 2, 1, 2 \rangle$ by doing the following: (a) Verify that $\mathbf{F}_1$, $\mathbf{F}_2$, and $\mathbf{F}_3$ are not independent by showing that their position representations are coplanar; (b) verify that the vectors do not form a basis by showing that every vector in V_3 cannot be written as a linear combination of $\mathbf{F}_1$, $\mathbf{F}_2$, and $\mathbf{F}_3$.

16.3 THE DOT PRODUCT IN V_3

The definition of the dot product of two vectors in V_3 is an extension of the definition for vectors in V_2.

16.3.1 Definition   If $\mathbf{A} = \langle a_1, a_2, a_3 \rangle$ and $\mathbf{B} = \langle b_1, b_2, b_3 \rangle$, then the *dot product* of $\mathbf{A}$ and $\mathbf{B}$, denoted by $\mathbf{A} \cdot \mathbf{B}$, is given by

$$\mathbf{A} \cdot \mathbf{B} = \langle a_1, a_2, a_3 \rangle \cdot \langle b_1, b_2, b_3 \rangle = a_1b_1 + a_2b_2 + a_3b_3$$

EXAMPLE 1:   Given $\mathbf{A} = \langle 4, 2, -6 \rangle$ and $\mathbf{B} = \langle -5, 3, -2 \rangle$, find $\mathbf{A} \cdot \mathbf{B}$.

SOLUTION:

$$\begin{aligned}
\mathbf{A} \cdot \mathbf{B} &= \langle 4, 2, -6 \rangle \cdot \langle -5, 3, -2 \rangle \\
&= 4(-5) + (2)(3) + (-6)(-2) \\
&= -20 + 6 + 12 \\
&= -2
\end{aligned}$$

For the unit vectors $\mathbf{i}$, $\mathbf{j}$, and $\mathbf{k}$, we have

$$\mathbf{i} \cdot \mathbf{i} = \mathbf{j} \cdot \mathbf{j} = \mathbf{k} \cdot \mathbf{k} = 1$$

and

$$\mathbf{i} \cdot \mathbf{j} = \mathbf{i} \cdot \mathbf{k} = \mathbf{j} \cdot \mathbf{k} = 0$$

Laws of dot multiplication that are given in Theorem 16.3.2 are the same as those in Theorems 15.3.2 and 15.3.3 for vectors in V_2. The proofs are left for the reader (see Exercises 1 through 4).

16.3.2 Theorem   If $\mathbf{A}$, $\mathbf{B}$, and $\mathbf{C}$ are any vectors in V_3 and c is a scalar, then

    (i) $\mathbf{A} \cdot \mathbf{B} = \mathbf{B} \cdot \mathbf{A}$ (commutative law)
    (ii) $\mathbf{A} \cdot (\mathbf{B} + \mathbf{C}) = \mathbf{A} \cdot \mathbf{B} + \mathbf{A} \cdot \mathbf{C}$ (distributive law)
    (iii) $c(\mathbf{A} \cdot \mathbf{B}) = (c\mathbf{A}) \cdot \mathbf{B}$
    (iv) $\mathbf{0} \cdot \mathbf{A} = 0$
    (v) $\mathbf{A} \cdot \mathbf{A} = |\mathbf{A}|^2$

Before giving a geometric representation of the dot product for vectors in V_3, we do as we did with vectors in V_2. We define the angle between two vectors and then express the dot product in terms of the cosine of the radian measure of this angle.

16.3.3 Definition   Let $\mathbf{A}$ and $\mathbf{B}$ be two nonzero vectors in V_3 such that $\mathbf{A}$ is not a scalar multiple of $\mathbf{B}$. If $\overrightarrow{OP}$ is the position representation of $\mathbf{A}$ and $\overrightarrow{OQ}$ is the position representation of $\mathbf{B}$, then the angle between the vectors $\mathbf{A}$ and $\mathbf{B}$ is defined to be the angle of positive measure between $\overrightarrow{OP}$ and $\overrightarrow{OQ}$ interior to the triangle POQ. If $\mathbf{A} = c\mathbf{B}$, where c is a scalar, then if $c > 0$, the angle between the vectors has radian measure 0, and if $c < 0$, the angle between the vectors has radian measure π.

Figure 16.3.1

Figure 16.3.1 shows the angle of radian measure θ between the two vectors if $\mathbf{A}$ is not a scalar multiple of $\mathbf{B}$.

16.3.4 Theorem   If θ is the radian measure of the angle between the two nonzero vectors $\mathbf{A}$ and $\mathbf{B}$ in V_3, then

$$\mathbf{A} \cdot \mathbf{B} = |\mathbf{A}||\mathbf{B}| \cos \theta \tag{1}$$

The proof of Theorem 16.3.4 is analogous to the proof of Theorem 15.3.5 for vectors in V_2 and is left for the reader (see Exercise 15).

If $\mathbf{U}$ is a unit vector in the direction of $\mathbf{A}$, we have from (1)

$$\mathbf{U} \cdot \mathbf{B} = |\mathbf{U}||\mathbf{B}| \cos \theta = |\mathbf{B}| \cos \theta$$

As with vectors in V_2, $|\mathbf{B}| \cos \theta$ is the *scalar projection* of $\mathbf{B}$ on $\mathbf{A}$ and the *component* of $\mathbf{B}$ in the direction of $\mathbf{A}$. It follows from Theorem 16.3.4 that the dot product of two vectors $\mathbf{A}$ and $\mathbf{B}$ is the product of the magnitude, $|\mathbf{A}|$, of one vector by the scalar projection, $|\mathbf{B}| \cos \theta$, of the second vector on the first.

EXAMPLE 2: Given the vectors $A = 6i - 3j + 2k$ and $B = 2i + j - 3k$, find (a) the component of B in the direction of A, (b) the vector projection of B onto A; and (c) $\cos \theta$ if θ is the radian measure of the angle between A and B.

SOLUTION: $|A| = \sqrt{6^2 + (-3)^2 + 2^2} = \sqrt{36 + 9 + 4} = 7$. Hence, a unit vector in the direction of A is

$$U = \tfrac{6}{7}i - \tfrac{3}{7}j + \tfrac{2}{7}k$$

Because $U \cdot B = |B| \cos \theta$, the component of B in the direction of A is

$$U \cdot B = (\tfrac{6}{7}i - \tfrac{3}{7}j + \tfrac{2}{7}k) \cdot (2i + j - 3k)$$
$$= \tfrac{12}{7} - \tfrac{3}{7} - \tfrac{6}{7}$$
$$= \tfrac{3}{7}$$

The vector projection of B onto A is therefore

$$\tfrac{3}{7}U = \tfrac{18}{49}i - \tfrac{9}{49}j + \tfrac{6}{49}k$$

From Eq. (1)

$$\cos \theta = \frac{A \cdot B}{|A||B|} = \frac{U \cdot B}{|B|}$$

Because $U \cdot B = \tfrac{3}{7}$ and $|B| = \sqrt{2^2 + 1^2 + (-3)^2} = \sqrt{14}$

$$\cos \theta = \frac{3}{7\sqrt{14}} = \frac{3\sqrt{14}}{98}$$

EXAMPLE 3: Find the distance from the point $P(4, 1, 6)$ to the line through the points $A(8, 3, 2)$ and $B(2, -3, 5)$.

Figure 16.3.2

SOLUTION: Figure 16.3.2 shows the point P and a sketch of the line through A and B. The point M is the foot of the perpendicular line from P to the line through A and B. Let d units be the distance $|\overline{PM}|$. To find d we find $|\overline{AM}|$ and $|\overline{AP}|$ and use the Pythagorean theorem. $|\overline{AP}|$ is the magnitude of the vector $V(\overrightarrow{AP})$.

$$V(\overrightarrow{AP}) = V(\overrightarrow{OP}) - V(\overrightarrow{OA})$$
$$= \langle 4, 1, 6 \rangle - \langle 8, 3, 2 \rangle$$
$$= \langle -4, -2, 4 \rangle$$

Hence,

$$|\overline{AP}| = \sqrt{(-4)^2 + (-2)^2 + 4^2} = \sqrt{36} = 6$$

To find $|\overline{AM}|$ we find the scalar projection of $V(\overrightarrow{AP})$ on $V(\overrightarrow{AB})$

$$V(\overrightarrow{AB}) = V(\overrightarrow{OB}) - V(\overrightarrow{OA})$$
$$= \langle 2, -3, 5 \rangle - \langle 8, 3, 2 \rangle$$
$$= \langle -6, -6, 3 \rangle$$

The scalar projection of $V(\overrightarrow{AP})$ on $V(\overrightarrow{AB})$ is then

$$\frac{V(\overrightarrow{AP}) \cdot V(\overrightarrow{AB})}{|V(\overrightarrow{AB})|} = \frac{\langle -4, -2, 4 \rangle \cdot \langle -6, -6, 3 \rangle}{\sqrt{36 + 36 + 9}}$$

$$= \frac{24 + 12 + 12}{\sqrt{81}}$$

$$= \tfrac{48}{9}$$

Thus, $|\overline{AM}| = \tfrac{48}{9}$, and so

$$d = \sqrt{|\overline{AP}|^2 - |\overline{AM}|^2}$$

$$= \sqrt{36 - (\tfrac{48}{9})^2}$$

$$= 6\sqrt{1 - \tfrac{64}{81}}$$

$$= \tfrac{2}{3}\sqrt{17}$$

16.3.5 Definition   Two nonzero vectors in V_3 are said to be *parallel* if and only if the radian measure of the angle between them is zero or π.

16.3.6 Definition   Two nonzero vectors in V_3 are said to be *orthogonal* if and only if the radian measure of the angle between them is $\tfrac{1}{2}\pi$.

The following theorem can be proved by using Definition 16.3.6 and Theorem 16.3.4. The proof is similar to the proof of Theorem 15.3.8 and is left for the reader (see Exercise 16).

16.3.7 Theorem   If **A** and **B** are two nonzero vectors in V_3, **A** and **B** are orthogonal if and only if $\mathbf{A} \cdot \mathbf{B} = 0$.

EXAMPLE 4:   Prove by using vectors that the points $A(4, 9, 1)$, $B(-2, 6, 3)$, and $C(6, 3, -2)$ are the vertices of a right triangle.

Figure 16.3.3

SOLUTION: Triangle CAB is shown in Fig. 16.3.3. From the figure it looks as if the angle at A is the one that may be a right angle. We shall find $\mathbf{V}(\overrightarrow{AB})$ and $\mathbf{V}(\overrightarrow{AC})$, and if the dot product of these two vectors is zero, the angle will be a right angle.

$$\mathbf{V}(\overrightarrow{AB}) = \mathbf{V}(\overrightarrow{OB}) - \mathbf{V}(\overrightarrow{OA})$$

$$= \langle -2, 6, 3 \rangle - \langle 4, 9, 1 \rangle$$

$$= \langle -6, -3, 2 \rangle$$

$$\mathbf{V}(\overrightarrow{AC}) = \mathbf{V}(\overrightarrow{OC}) - \mathbf{V}(\overrightarrow{OA})$$

$$= \langle 6, 3, -2 \rangle - \langle 4, 9, 1 \rangle$$

$$= \langle 2, -6, -3 \rangle$$

$$\mathbf{V}(\overrightarrow{AB}) \cdot \mathbf{V}(\overrightarrow{AC}) = \langle -6, -3, 2 \rangle \cdot \langle 2, -6, -3 \rangle = -12 + 18 - 6 = 0$$

Therefore, $\mathbf{V}(\overrightarrow{AB})$ and $\mathbf{V}(\overrightarrow{AC})$ are orthogonal, and so the angle at A in triangle CAB is a right angle.

Exercises 16.3

1. Prove Theorem 16.3.2(i).   2. Prove Theorem 16.3.2(ii).

3. Prove Theorem 16.3.2(iii).   4. Prove Theorem 16.3.2(iv) and (v).

In Exercises 5 through 14, let $\mathbf{A} = \langle -4, -2, 4 \rangle$, $\mathbf{B} = \langle 2, 7, -1 \rangle$, $\mathbf{C} = \langle 6, -3, 0 \rangle$, and $\mathbf{D} = \langle 5, 4, -3 \rangle$.

5. Find $\mathbf{A} \cdot (\mathbf{B} + \mathbf{C})$ 6. Find $\mathbf{A} \cdot \mathbf{B} + \mathbf{A} \cdot \mathbf{C}$ 7. Find $(\mathbf{A} \cdot \mathbf{B})(\mathbf{C} \cdot \mathbf{D})$

8. Find $\mathbf{A} \cdot \mathbf{D} - \mathbf{B} \cdot \mathbf{C}$ 9. Find $(\mathbf{B} \cdot \mathbf{D})\mathbf{A} - (\mathbf{D} \cdot \mathbf{A})\mathbf{B}$ 10. Find $(2\mathbf{A} + 3\mathbf{B}) \cdot (4\mathbf{C} - \mathbf{D})$

11. Find the cosine of the measure of the angle between $\mathbf{A}$ and $\mathbf{B}$.

12. Find the cosine of the measure of the angle between $\mathbf{C}$ and $\mathbf{D}$.

13. Find (a) the component of $\mathbf{C}$ in the direction of $\mathbf{A}$ and (b) the vector projection of $\mathbf{C}$ onto $\mathbf{A}$.

14. Find (a) the component of $\mathbf{B}$ in the direction of $\mathbf{D}$ and (b) the vector projection of $\mathbf{B}$ onto $\mathbf{D}$.

15. Prove Theorem 16.3.4.   16. Prove Theorem 16.3.7.

17. Prove by using vectors that the points $(2, 2, 2)$, $(2, 0, 1)$, $(4, 1, -1)$, and $(4, 3, 0)$ are the vertices of a rectangle.

18. Prove by using vectors that the points $(2, 2, 2)$, $(0, 1, 2)$, $(-1, 3, 3)$, and $(3, 0, 1)$ are the vertices of a parallelogram.

19. Find the distance from the point $(2, -1, -4)$ to the line through the points $(3, -2, 2)$ and $(-9, -6, 6)$.

20. Find the distance from the point $(3, 2, 1)$ to the line through the points $(1, 2, 9)$ and $(-3, -6, -3)$.

21. Find the area of the triangle having vertices at $(-2, 3, 1)$, $(1, 2, 3)$, and $(3, -1, 2)$.

22. If a force has the vector representation $\mathbf{F} = 5\mathbf{i} - 3\mathbf{k}$, find the work done by the force in moving an object from the point $P_1(4, 1, 3)$ along a straight line to the point $P_2(-5, 6, 2)$. The magnitude of the force is measured in pounds and distance is measured in feet. (HINT: Review Sec. 15.3.)

23. A force is represented by the vector $\mathbf{F}$, has a magnitude of 10 lb, and direction cosines of $\mathbf{F}$ are $\cos \alpha = \frac{1}{6}\sqrt{6}$ and $\cos \beta = \frac{1}{3}\sqrt{6}$. If the force moves an object from the origin along a straight line to the point $(7, -4, 2)$, find the work done. Distance is measured in feet. (See hint for Exercise 22.)

24. If $\mathbf{A}$ and $\mathbf{B}$ are nonzero vectors, prove that the vector $\mathbf{A} - c\mathbf{B}$ is orthogonal to $\mathbf{B}$ if $c = \mathbf{A} \cdot \mathbf{B}/|\mathbf{B}|^2$.

25. If $\mathbf{A} = 12\mathbf{i} + 9\mathbf{j} - 5\mathbf{k}$ and $\mathbf{B} = 4\mathbf{i} + 3\mathbf{j} - 5\mathbf{k}$, use the result of Exercise 24 to find the value of the scalar c so that the vector $\mathbf{B} - c\mathbf{A}$ is orthogonal to $\mathbf{A}$.

26. For the vectors of Exercise 25, use the result of Exercise 24 to find the value of the scalar d so that the vector $\mathbf{A} - d\mathbf{B}$ is orthogonal to $\mathbf{B}$.

27. Prove that if $\mathbf{A}$ and $\mathbf{B}$ are any nonzero vectors, then the vectors $|\mathbf{B}|\mathbf{A} + |\mathbf{A}|\mathbf{B}$ and $|\mathbf{B}|\mathbf{A} - |\mathbf{A}|\mathbf{B}$ are orthogonal.

28. Prove that if $\mathbf{A}$ and $\mathbf{B}$ are any nonzero vectors and $\mathbf{C} = |\mathbf{B}|\mathbf{A} + |\mathbf{A}|\mathbf{B}$ then the angle between $\mathbf{A}$ and $\mathbf{C}$ has the same measure as the angle between $\mathbf{B}$ and $\mathbf{C}$.

16.4 PLANES   The graph of an equation in two variables, x and y, is a curve in the xy plane. The simplest kind of curve in two-dimensional space is a straight line, and the general equation of a straight line is of the form $Ax + By$

$+ C = 0$, which is an equation of the first degree. In three-dimensional space, the graph of an equation in three variables, x, y, and z, is a surface. The simplest kind of surface is a *plane*, and we shall see that an equation of a plane is an equation of the first degree in three variables.

16.4.1 Definition   If $\mathbf{N}$ is a given nonzero vector and P_0 is a given point, then the set of all points P for which $\mathbf{V}(\overrightarrow{P_0P})$ and $\mathbf{N}$ are orthogonal is defined to be a *plane* through P_0 having $\mathbf{N}$ as a *normal vector*.

Figure 16.4.1

Figure 16.4.1 shows a portion of a plane through the point $P_0(x_0, y_0, z_0)$ and the representation of the normal vector $\mathbf{N}$ having its initial point at P_0.

In plane analytic geometry we can obtain an equation of a line if we are given a point on the line and its direction (slope). In an analogous manner, in solid analytic geometry an equation of a plane can be determined by knowing a point in the plane and the direction of a normal vector.

16.4.2 Theorem   If $P_0(x_0, y_0, z_0)$ is a point in a plane and a normal vector to the plane is $\mathbf{N} = \langle a, b, c \rangle$, then an equation of the plane is

$$a(x - x_0) + b(y - y_0) + c(z - z_0) = 0 \tag{1}$$

PROOF: Refer to Fig. 16.4.1. Let $P(x, y, z)$ be any point in the plane. $\mathbf{V}(\overrightarrow{P_0P})$ is the vector having $\overrightarrow{P_0P}$ as a representation, and so

$$\mathbf{V}(\overrightarrow{P_0P}) = \langle x - x_0, y - y_0, z - z_0 \rangle \tag{2}$$

From Definition 16.4.1 and Theorem 16.3.7, it follows that

$$\mathbf{V}(\overrightarrow{P_0P}) \cdot \mathbf{N} = 0$$

Because $\mathbf{N} = \langle a, b, c \rangle$, from (2) and the above equation we obtain

$$a(x - x_0) + b(y - y_0) + c(z - z_0) = 0 \tag{3}$$

which is the desired equation.   ■

EXAMPLE 1:   Find an equation of the plane containing the point $(2, 1, 3)$ and having $3\mathbf{i} - 4\mathbf{j} + \mathbf{k}$ as a normal vector.

SOLUTION: Using (1) with the point $(x_0, y_0, z_0) = (2, 1, 3)$ and the vector $\langle a, b, c \rangle = \langle 3, -4, 1 \rangle$, we have as an equation of the required plane

$$3(x - 2) - 4(y - 1) + (z - 3) = 0$$

or, equivalently,

$$3x - 4y + z - 5 = 0$$

16.4.3 Theorem   If a, b, and c are not all zero, the graph of an equation of the form

$$ax + by + cz + d = 0 \tag{4}$$

is a plane and $\langle a, b, c \rangle$ is a normal vector to the plane.

PROOF: Suppose that $b \neq 0$. Then the point $(0, -d/b, 0)$ is on the graph of the equation because its coordinates satisfy the equation. The given equation can be written as

$$a(x - 0) + b \left(y + \frac{d}{b} \right) + c(z - 0) = 0$$

which from Theorem 16.4.2 is an equation of a plane through the point $(0, -d/b, 0)$ and for which $\langle a, b, c \rangle$ is a normal vector. This proves the theorem if $b \neq 0$. A similar argument holds if $b = 0$ and either $a \neq 0$ or $c \neq 0$.   ■

Equations (1) and (4) are called *cartesian equations* of a plane. Equation (1) is analogous to the point-slope form of an equation of a line in two dimensions. Equation (4) is the general first-degree equation in three variables and it is called a *linear equation*.

A plane is determined by three noncollinear points, by a line and a point not on the line, by two intersecting lines, or by two parallel lines. To draw a sketch of a plane from its equation, it is convenient to find the points at which the plane intersects each of the coordinate axes. The x coordinate of the point at which the plane intersects the x axis is called the *x intercept* of the plane; the y coordinate of the point at which the plane intersects the y axis is called the *y intercept* of the plane; and the *z intercept* of the plane is the z coordinate of the point at which the plane intersects the z axis.

EXAMPLE 2:   Draw a sketch of the plane having the equation

$$2x + 4y + 3z = 8$$

Figure 16.4.2

SOLUTION: By substituting zero for y and z, we obtain $x = 4$; so the x intercept of the plane is 4. In a similar manner we obtain the y intercept and the z intercept, which are 2 and $\frac{8}{3}$, respectively. Plotting the points corresponding to these intercepts and connecting them with lines, we have the sketch of the plane shown in Fig. 16.4.2. Note that only a portion of the plane is shown in the figure.

EXAMPLE 3:   Draw a sketch of the plane having the equation

$$3x + 2y - 6z = 0$$

Figure 16.4.3

SOLUTION: Because the equation is satisfied when x, y, and z are all zero, the plane intersects each of the axes at the origin. If we set $x = 0$ in the given equation, we obtain $y - 3z = 0$, which is a line in the yz plane; this is the line of intersection of the yz plane with the given plane. Similarly, the line of intersection of the xz plane with the given plane is obtained by setting $y = 0$, and we get $x - 2z = 0$. Drawing a sketch of each of these two lines and drawing a line segment from a point on one of the lines to a point on the other line, we obtain Fig. 16.4.3.

In Example 3 the line in the yz plane and the line in the xz plane used to draw the sketch of the plane are called the *traces* of the given plane in the yz plane and the xz plane, respectively. The equation $x = 0$ is an equation of the yz plane because the point (x, y, z) is in the yz plane if and only if $x = 0$. Similarly, the equations $y = 0$ and $z = 0$ are equations of the xz plane and the xy plane, respectively.

A plane parallel to the yz plane has an equation of the form $x = k$, where k is a constant. Figure 16.4.4 shows a sketch of the plane having the equation $x = 3$. A plane parallel to the xz plane has an equation of the form $y = k$, and a plane parallel to the xy plane has an equation of the form $z = k$. Figures 16.4.5 and 16.4.6 show sketches of the planes having the equations $y = -5$ and $z = 6$, respectively.

Figure 16.4.4

Figure 16.4.5

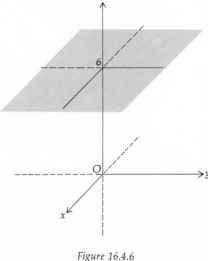

Figure 16.4.6

16.4.4 Definition   The *angle between two planes* is defined to be the angle between the normal vectors of the two planes.

EXAMPLE 4:   Find the radian measure of the angle between the two planes $5x - 2y + 5z - 12 = 0$ and $2x + y - 7z + 11 = 0$.

SOLUTION: Let $\mathbf{N}_1$ be a normal vector to the first plane and $\mathbf{N}_1 = 5\mathbf{i} - 2\mathbf{j} + 5\mathbf{k}$. Let $\mathbf{N}_2$ be a normal vector to the second plane and $\mathbf{N}_2 = 2\mathbf{i} + \mathbf{j} - 7\mathbf{k}$.

By Definition 16.4.4 the angle between the two planes is the angle between $\mathbf{N}_1$ and $\mathbf{N}_2$, and so by Theorem 16.3.4 if θ is the radian measure of this angle

$$\cos \theta = \frac{\mathbf{N}_1 \cdot \mathbf{N}_2}{|\mathbf{N}_1||\mathbf{N}_2|} = \frac{(5\mathbf{i} - 2\mathbf{j} + 5\mathbf{k}) \cdot (2\mathbf{i} + \mathbf{j} - 7\mathbf{k})}{\sqrt{25 + 4 + 25} \ \sqrt{4 + 1 + 49}} = \frac{-27}{54} = -\frac{1}{2}$$

Therefore,

$$\theta = \tfrac{2}{3}\pi$$

16.4.5 Definition   Two planes are *parallel* if and only if their normal vectors are parallel.

Figure 16.4.7

From Definitions 16.4.4 and 16.4.5, it follows that two planes are parallel if and only if the angle between their normal vectors has radian measure 0 or π or, equivalently, if and only if their normal vectors have the same or opposite direction. So if we have two planes with equations

$$a_1 x + b_1 y + c_1 z + d_1 = 0 \tag{5}$$

and

$$a_2 x + b_2 y + c_2 z + d_2 = 0 \tag{6}$$

and normal vectors $\mathbf{N}_1 = \langle a_1, b_1, c_1 \rangle$ and $\mathbf{N}_2 = \langle a_2, b_2, c_2 \rangle$, respectively, then the two planes are parallel if and only if

$$\mathbf{N}_1 = k\mathbf{N}_2 \qquad \text{where } k \text{ is a constant}$$

Figure 16.4.7 shows sketches of two parallel planes and representations of some of their normal vectors.

16.4.6 Definition   Two planes are *perpendicular* if and only if their normal vectors are orthogonal.

From Definition 16.4.6 and Theorem 16.3.7 it follows that two planes having normal vectors $\mathbf{N}_1$ and $\mathbf{N}_2$ are perpendicular if and only if

$$\mathbf{N}_1 \cdot \mathbf{N}_2 = 0 \tag{7}$$

EXAMPLE 5:   Find an equation of the plane perpendicular to each of the planes $x - y + z = 0$ and $2x + y - 4z - 5 = 0$ and containing the point $(4, 0, -2)$.

SOLUTION: Let M be the required plane and $\langle a, b, c \rangle$ be a normal vector of M. Let M_1 be the plane having equation $x - y + z = 0$. By Theorem 16.4.3 a normal vector of M_1 is $\langle 1, -1, 1 \rangle$. Because M and M_1 are perpendicular, it follows from Eq. (7) that

$$\langle a, b, c \rangle \cdot \langle 1, -1, 1 \rangle = 0$$

or, equivalently,

$$a - b + c = 0 \qquad (8)$$

Let M_2 be the plane having the equation $2x + y - 4z - 5 = 0$. A normal vector of M_2 is $\langle 2, 1, -4 \rangle$. Because M and M_2 are perpendicular, we have

$$\langle a, b, c \rangle \cdot \langle 2, 1, -4 \rangle = 0$$

or, equivalently,

$$2a + b - 4c = 0 \qquad (9)$$

Solving Eqs. (8) and (9) simultaneously for b and c in terms of a, we get $b = 2a$ and $c = a$. Therefore, a normal vector of M is $\langle a, 2a, a \rangle$. Because $(4, 0, -2)$ is a point in M, it follows from Theorem 16.4.2 that an equation of M is

$$a(x - 4) + 2a(y - 0) + a(z + 2) = 0$$

or, equivalently,

$$x + 2y + z - 2 = 0$$

Consider now the plane having the equation $ax + by + d = 0$ and the xy plane whose equation is $z = 0$. Normal vectors to these planes are $\langle a, b, 0 \rangle$ and $\langle 0, 0, 1 \rangle$, respectively. Because $\langle a, b, 0 \rangle \cdot \langle 0, 0, 1 \rangle = 0$, the two planes are perpendicular. This means that a plane having an equation with no z term is perpendicular to the xy plane. Figure 16.4.8 illustrates this. In a similar manner, we can conclude that a plane having an equation with no x term is perpendicular to the yz plane (see Fig. 16.4.9), and a plane having an equation with no y term is perpendicular to the xz plane (see Fig. 16.4.10).

An important application of the use of vectors is in finding the undirected distance from a plane to a point. The following example illustrates this.

Figure 16.4.8

Figure 16.4.9

Figure 16.4.10

EXAMPLE 6: Find the distance from the plane $2x - y + 2z + 10 = 0$ to the point $(1, 4, 6)$.

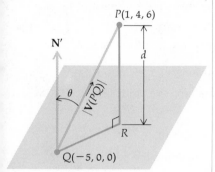

$P(1, 4, 6)$

N'

d

$|V(\overrightarrow{QP})|$

θ

R

$Q(-5, 0, 0)$

Figure 16.4.11

SOLUTION: Let P be the point $(1, 4, 6)$ and choose any point Q in the plane. For simplicity, choose the point Q as the point where the plane intersects the x axis, that is, the point $(-5, 0, 0)$. The vector having $\overrightarrow{QP}$ as a representation is given by

$$\mathbf{V}(\overrightarrow{QP}) = 6\mathbf{i} + 4\mathbf{j} + 6\mathbf{k}$$

A normal vector to the given plane is

$$\mathbf{N} = 2\mathbf{i} - \mathbf{j} + 2\mathbf{k}$$

The negative of $\mathbf{N}$ is also a normal vector to the given plane and

$$-\mathbf{N} = -2\mathbf{i} + \mathbf{j} - 2\mathbf{k}$$

We are not certain which of the two vectors, $\mathbf{N}$ or $-\mathbf{N}$, makes the smaller angle with vector $\mathbf{V}(\overrightarrow{QP})$. Let $\mathbf{N}'$ be the one of the two vectors $\mathbf{N}$ or $-\mathbf{N}$ which makes an angle of radian measure $\theta < \frac{1}{2}\pi$ with $\mathbf{V}(\overrightarrow{QP})$. In Fig. 16.4.11 we show a portion of the given plane containing the point $Q(-5, 0, 0)$, the representation of the vector $\mathbf{N}'$ having its initial point at Q, the point $P(1, 4, 6)$, the directed line segment $\overrightarrow{QP}$, and the point R, which is the foot of the perpendicular from P to the plane. For simplicity, we did not include the coordinate axes in this figure. The distance $|\overrightarrow{RP}|$ is the required distance, which we call d. We see from Fig. 16.4.11 that

$$d = |\mathbf{V}(\overrightarrow{QP})| \cos \theta \tag{10}$$

Because θ is the radian measure of the angle between $\mathbf{N}'$ and $\mathbf{V}(\overrightarrow{QP})$, we have

$$\cos \theta = \frac{\mathbf{N}' \cdot \mathbf{V}(\overrightarrow{QP})}{|\mathbf{N}'||\mathbf{V}(\overrightarrow{QP})|} \tag{11}$$

Substituting from (11) into (10) and replacing $|\mathbf{N}'|$ by $|\mathbf{N}|$, we obtain

$$d = \frac{|\mathbf{V}(\overrightarrow{QP})|(\mathbf{N}' \cdot \mathbf{V}(\overrightarrow{QP}))}{|\mathbf{N}||\mathbf{V}(\overrightarrow{QP})|} = \frac{\mathbf{N}' \cdot \mathbf{V}(\overrightarrow{QP})}{|\mathbf{N}|}$$

Because d is an undirected distance, it is nonnegative; hence, we can replace the numerator in the above expression by the absolute value of the dot product of $\mathbf{N}$ and $\mathbf{V}(\overrightarrow{QP})$. Therefore,

$$d = \frac{|\mathbf{N} \cdot \mathbf{V}(\overrightarrow{QP})|}{|\mathbf{N}|} = \frac{|(2\mathbf{i} - \mathbf{j} + 2\mathbf{k}) \cdot (6\mathbf{i} + 4\mathbf{j} + 6\mathbf{k})|}{\sqrt{4 + 1 + 4}} = \frac{20}{3}$$

Exercises 16.4

In Exercises 1 through 4, find an equation of the plane containing the given point P and having the given vector $\mathbf{N}$ as a normal vector.

1. $P(3, 1, 2)$; $\mathbf{N} = \langle 1, 2, -3 \rangle$ 2. $P(-1, 8, 3)$; $\mathbf{N} = \langle -7, -1, 1 \rangle$

3. $P(2, 1, -1)$; $\mathbf{N} = -\mathbf{i} + 3\mathbf{j} + 4\mathbf{k}$ 4. $P(1, 0, 0)$; $\mathbf{N} = \mathbf{i} + \mathbf{k}$

In Exercises 5 and 6, find an equation of the plane containing the given three points.

5. $(3, 4, 1)$, $(1, 7, 1)$, $(-1, -2, 5)$ 6. $(0, 0, 2)$, $(2, 4, 1)$, $(-2, 3, 3)$

In Exercises 7 through 12, draw a sketch of the given plane and find two unit vectors which are normal to the plane.

7. $2x - y + 2z - 6 = 0$ 8. $4x - 4y - 2z - 9 = 0$ 9. $4x + 3y - 12z = 0$

10. $y + 2z - 4 = 0$ 11. $3x + 2z - 6 = 0$ 12. $z = 5$

In Exercises 13 through 17, find an equation of the plane satisfying the given conditions.

13. Perpendicular to the line through the points $(2, 2, -4)$ and $(7, -1, 3)$ and containing the point $(-5, 1, 2)$.

14. Parallel to the plane $4x - 2y + z - 1 = 0$ and containing the point $(2, 6, -1)$.

15. Perpendicular to the plane $x + 3y - z - 7 = 0$ and containing the points $(2, 0, 5)$ and $(0, 2, -1)$.

16. Perpendicular to each of the planes $x - y + z = 0$ and $2x + y - 4z - 5 = 0$ and containing the point $(4, 0, -2)$.

17. Perpendicular to the yz plane, containing the point $(2, 1, 1)$, and making an angle of radian measure $\cos^{-1}(\frac{2}{3})$ with the plane $2x - y + 2z - 3 = 0$.

18. Find the cosine of the measure of the angle between the planes $2x - y - 2z - 5 = 0$ and $6x - 2y + 3z + 8 = 0$.

19. Find the cosine of the measure of the angle between the planes $3x + 4y = 0$ and $4x - 7y + 4z - 6 = 0$.

20. Find the distance from the plane $2x + 2y - z - 6 = 0$ to the point $(2, 2, -4)$.

21. Find the distance from the plane $5x + 11y + 2z - 30 = 0$ to the point $(-2, 6, 3)$.

22. Find the perpendicular distance between the parallel planes

$$4x - 8y - z + 9 = 0 \quad \text{and} \quad 4x - 8y - z - 6 = 0$$

23. Find the perpendicular distance between the parallel planes

$$4y - 3z - 6 = 0 \quad \text{and} \quad 8y - 6z - 27 = 0$$

24. Prove that the undirected distance from the plane $ax + by + cz + d = 0$ to the point (x_0, y_0, z_0) is given by

$$\frac{|ax_0 + by_0 + cz_0 + d|}{\sqrt{a^2 + b^2 + c^2}}$$

25. Prove that the perpendicular distance between the two parallel planes $ax + by + cz + d_1 = 0$ and $ax + by + cz + d_2 = 0$ is given by

$$\frac{|d_1 - d_2|}{\sqrt{a^2 + b^2 + c^2}}$$

26. If a, b, and c are nonzero and are the x intercept, y intercept, and z intercept, respectively, of a plane, prove that an equation of the plane is

$$\frac{x}{a} + \frac{y}{b} + \frac{z}{c} = 1$$

This is called the *intercept form* of an equation of a plane.

16.5 LINES IN R_3

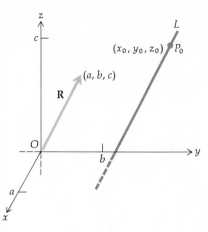

Figure 16.5.1

Let L be a line in R_3 such that it contains a given point $P_0(x_0, y_0, z_0)$ and is parallel to the representations of a given vector $\mathbf{R} = \langle a, b, c \rangle$. Figure 16.5.1 shows a sketch of line L and the position representation of vector $\mathbf{R}$. Line L is the set of points $P(x, y, z)$ such that $\mathbf{V}(\overrightarrow{P_0P})$ is parallel to the vector $\mathbf{R}$. So P is on the line L if and only if there is a nonzero scalar t such that

$$\mathbf{V}(\overrightarrow{P_0P}) = t\mathbf{R} \tag{1}$$

Because $\mathbf{V}(\overrightarrow{P_0P}) = \langle x - x_0, y - y_0, z - z_0 \rangle$ we obtain from (1)

$$\langle x - x_0, y - y_0, z - z_0 \rangle = t\langle a, b, c \rangle$$

from which it follows that

$$x - x_0 = ta \qquad y - y_0 = tb \qquad z - z_0 = tc$$

or, equivalently,

$$x = x_0 + ta \qquad y = y_0 + tb \qquad z = z_0 + tc \tag{2}$$

Letting the parameter t be any real number (i.e., t takes on all values in the interval $(-\infty, +\infty)$), the point P may be any point on the line L. Therefore, Eqs. (2) represent the line L, and we call these equations *parametric equations* of the line.

EXAMPLE 1:   Find parametric equations of the line that is parallel to the representations of the vector $\mathbf{R} = \langle 11, 8, 10 \rangle$ and contains the point $(8, 12, 6)$. Draw a sketch of the line and the position representation of $\mathbf{R}$.

SOLUTION: From Eqs. (2) we have as parametric equations of the line

$$x = 8 + 11t \qquad y = 12 + 8t \qquad z = 6 + 10t$$

Figure 16.5.2 shows the required sketch.

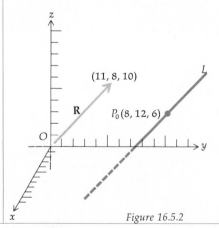

Figure 16.5.2

If none of the numbers a, b, or c is zero, we can eliminate t from Eqs. (2) and obtain

$$\frac{x - x_0}{a} = \frac{y - y_0}{b} = \frac{z - z_0}{c} \tag{3}$$

These equations are called *symmetric equations* of the line.

The vector $\mathbf{R} = \langle a, b, c \rangle$ determines the direction of the line, and the numbers a, b, and c are called *direction numbers* of the line. Any vector parallel to $\mathbf{R}$ has either the same or the opposite direction as $\mathbf{R}$; hence, such a vector can be used in place of $\mathbf{R}$ in the above discussion. Because the components of any vector parallel to $\mathbf{R}$ are proportional to the components of $\mathbf{R}$, we can conclude that any set of three numbers proportional to a, b, and c also can serve as a set of direction numbers of the line. So a line has an unlimited number of sets of direction numbers. We write a set of direction numbers of a line in brackets as $[a, b, c]$. In particular, if $[2, 3, -4]$ represents a set of direction numbers of a line, other sets of direction numbers of the same line can be represented as $[4, 6, -8]$, $[1, \frac{3}{2}, -2]$, and $[2/\sqrt{29}, 3/\sqrt{29}, -4/\sqrt{29}]$.

EXAMPLE 2: Find symmetric equations of the line of Example 1.

SOLUTION: A set of direction numbers of the line is $[11, 8, 10]$. Therefore, from (3) we have as symmetric equations of the line

$$\frac{x - 8}{11} = \frac{y - 12}{8} = \frac{z - 6}{10}$$

EXAMPLE 3: Find two sets of symmetric equations of the line through the two points $(-3, 2, 4)$ and $(6, 1, 2)$.

SOLUTION: Let P_1 be the point $(-3, 2, 4)$ and P_2 be the point $(6, 1, 2)$. Then the required line is parallel to the representations of the vector $\mathbf{V}(\overrightarrow{P_1P_2})$, and so the components of this vector constitute a set of direction numbers of the line. $\mathbf{V}(\overrightarrow{P_1P_2}) = \langle 9, -1, -2 \rangle$. Taking P_0 as the point $(-3, 2, 4)$, we have from (3) the equations

$$\frac{x + 3}{9} = \frac{y - 2}{-1} = \frac{z - 4}{-2}$$

Another set of symmetric equations of this line is obtained by taking P_0 as the point $(6, 1, 2)$, and we have

$$\frac{x - 6}{9} = \frac{y - 1}{-1} = \frac{z - 2}{-2}$$

Equations (3) are equivalent to the system of three equations

$$b(x - x_0) = a(y - y_0) \qquad c(x - x_0) = a(z - z_0) \qquad c(y - y_0) = b(z - z_0) \quad (4)$$

Actually, the three equations in (4) are not independent because any one of them can be derived from the other two. Each of the equations in (4) is an equation of a plane containing the line L represented by Eqs. (3). Any two of these planes have as their intersection the line L; hence, any two of the Eqs. (4) define the line. However, there is an unlimited number of planes which contain a given line and because any two of them will determine the line, we conclude that there is an unlimited number of pairs of equations which represent a line.

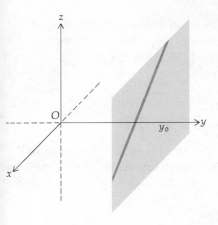

Figure 16.5.3

If one of the numbers a, b, or c is zero, we do not use symmetric equations (3). However, suppose for example that $b = 0$ and neither a nor c is zero. Then we can write as equations of the line

$$\frac{x - x_0}{a} = \frac{z - z_0}{c} \quad \text{and} \quad y = y_0 \tag{5}$$

A line having symmetric equations (5) lies in the plane $y = y_0$ and hence is parallel to the xz plane. Figure 16.5.3 shows such a line.

EXAMPLE 4:   Given the two planes

$$x + 3y - z - 9 = 0$$

and

$$2x - 3y + 4z + 3 = 0$$

For the line of intersection of these two planes, find (a) a set of symmetric equations and (b) a set of parametric equations.

SOLUTION: If we solve the two given equations for x and y in terms of z, we obtain

$$x = -z + 2 \qquad y = \tfrac{2}{3}z + \tfrac{7}{3}$$

from which we get

$$\frac{x - 2}{-1} = \frac{y - \tfrac{7}{3}}{\tfrac{2}{3}} = \frac{z - 0}{1}$$

or, equivalently,

$$\frac{x - 2}{-3} = \frac{y - \tfrac{7}{3}}{2} = \frac{z - 0}{3}$$

which is a set of symmetric equations of the line. A set of parametric equations can be obtained by setting each of the above ratios equal to t, and we have

$$x = 2 - 3t \qquad y = \tfrac{7}{3} + 2t \qquad z = 3t$$

EXAMPLE 5:   Find the direction cosines of a vector whose representations are parallel to the line of Example 4.

SOLUTION: From the symmetric equations of the line in Example 4, we see that a set of direction numbers of the line is $[-3, 2, 3]$. Therefore, the vector $\langle -3, 2, 3 \rangle$ is a vector whose representations are parallel to the line. The direction cosines of this vector are as follows: $\cos \alpha = -3/\sqrt{22}$, $\cos \beta = 2/\sqrt{22}$, $\cos \gamma = 3/\sqrt{22}$.

EXAMPLE 6:   Find equations of the line through the point $(1, -1, 1)$, perpendicular to the line

$$3x = 2y = z$$

and parallel to the plane

$$x + y - z = 0$$

SOLUTION: Let $[a, b, c]$ be a set of direction numbers of the required line. The equations $3x = 2y = z$ can be written as

$$\frac{x - 0}{\tfrac{1}{3}} = \frac{y - 0}{\tfrac{1}{2}} = \frac{z - 0}{1}$$

which are symmetric equations of a line. A set of direction numbers of this line is $[\frac{1}{3}, \frac{1}{2}, 1]$. Because the required line is perpendicular to this line, it follows that the vectors $\langle a, b, c \rangle$ and $\langle \frac{1}{3}, \frac{1}{2}, 1 \rangle$ are orthogonal. So

$$\langle a, b, c \rangle \cdot \langle \tfrac{1}{3}, \tfrac{1}{2}, 1 \rangle = 0$$

or, equivalently,

$$\tfrac{1}{3}a + \tfrac{1}{2}b + c = 0 \tag{6}$$

A normal vector to the plane $x + y - z = 0$ is $\langle 1, 1, -1 \rangle$. Because the required line is parallel to this plane, it is perpendicular to representations of the normal vector. Hence, the vectors $\langle a, b, c \rangle$ and $\langle 1, 1, -1 \rangle$ are orthogonal, and so

$$\langle a, b, c \rangle \cdot \langle 1, 1, -1 \rangle = 0$$

or, equivalently,

$$a + b - c = 0 \tag{7}$$

Solving Eqs. (6) and (7) simultaneously for a and b in terms of c we get $a = 9c$ and $b = -8c$. The required line then has the set of direction numbers $[9c, -8c, c]$ and contains the point $(1, -1, 1)$. Therefore, symmetric equations of the line are

$$\frac{x-1}{9c} = \frac{y+1}{-8c} = \frac{z-1}{c}$$

or, equivalently,

$$\frac{x-1}{9} = \frac{y+1}{-8} = \frac{z-1}{1}$$

EXAMPLE 7:   If l_1 is the line through $A(1, 2, 7)$ and $B(-2, 3, -4)$ and l_2 is the line through $C(2, -1, 4)$ and $D(5, 7, -3)$, prove that l_1 and l_2 are skew lines (i.e., they do not lie in one plane).

SOLUTION: To show that two lines do not lie in one plane we demonstrate that they do not intersect and are not parallel. Parametric equations of a line are

$$x = x_0 + ta \qquad y = y_0 + tb \qquad z = z_0 + tc$$

where $[a, b, c]$ is a set of direction numbers of the line and (x_0, y_0, z_0) is any point on the line. Because $\mathbf{V}(\overrightarrow{AB}) = \langle -3, 1, -11 \rangle$, a set of direction numbers of l_1 is $[-3, 1, -11]$. Taking A as the point P_0, we have as parametric equations of l_1

$$x = 1 - 3t \qquad y = 2 + t \qquad z = 7 - 11t \tag{8}$$

Because $\mathbf{V}(\overrightarrow{CD}) = \langle 3, 8, -7 \rangle$, and l_2 contains the point C, we have as parametric equations of l_2

$$x = 2 + 3s \qquad y = -1 + 8s \qquad z = 4 - 7s \tag{9}$$

Because the sets of direction numbers are not proportional, l_1 and l_2 are not parallel. For the lines to intersect, there have to be a value of t and a value of s which give the same point (x_1, y_1, z_1) in both sets of Eqs. (8) and (9). Therefore, we equate the right sides of the respective equations and obtain

$$1 - 3t = 2 + 3s$$

$$2 + t = -1 + 8s$$

$$7 - 11t = 4 - 7s$$

Solving the first two equations simultaneously, we obtain $s = \frac{8}{27}$ and $t = -\frac{17}{27}$. This set of values does not satisfy the third equation; hence, the two lines do not intersect. Thus, l_1 and l_2 are skew lines.

Exercises 16.5

In Exercises 1 through 6, find parametric and symmetric equations for the line satisfying the given conditions.

1. Through the two points $(1, 2, 1)$ and $(5, -1, 1)$.

2. Through the point $(5, 3, 2)$ with direction numbers $[4, 1, -1]$.

3. Through the point $(4, -5, 20)$ and perpendicular to the plane $x + 3y - 6z - 8 = 0$.

4. Through the origin and perpendicular to the lines having direction numbers $[4, 2, 1]$ and $[-3, -2, 1]$.

5. Through the origin and perpendicular to the line $\frac{1}{4}(x - 10) = \frac{1}{3}y = \frac{1}{2}z$ at their intersection.

6. Through the point $(2, 0, -4)$ and parallel to each of the planes $2x + y - z = 0$ and $x + 3y + 5z = 0$.

7. Show that the lines

$$\frac{x + 1}{2} = \frac{y + 4}{-5} = \frac{z - 2}{3} \quad \text{and} \quad \frac{x - 3}{-2} = \frac{y + 14}{5} = \frac{z - 8}{-3}$$

are coincident.

8. Prove that the line $x + 1 = -\frac{1}{2}(y - 6) = z$ lies in the plane $3x + y - z = 3$.

The planes through a line which are perpendicular to the coordinate planes are called the *projecting planes* of the line. In Exercises 9 through 12, find equations of the projecting planes of the given line and draw a sketch of the line.

9. $3x - 2y + 5z - 30 = 0$
   $2x + 3y - 10z - 6 = 0$

10. $x + y - 3z + 1 = 0$
    $2x - y - 3z + 14 = 0$

11. $x - 2y - 3z + 6 = 0$
    $x + y + z - 1 = 0$

12. $2x - y + z - 7 = 0$
    $4x - y + 3z - 13 = 0$

13. Find the cosine of the measure of the smallest angle between the two lines $x = 2y + 4$, $z = -y + 4$, and $x = y + 7$, $2z = y + 2$.

14. Find an equation of the plane containing the point $(6, 2, 4)$ and the line $\frac{1}{5}(x - 1) = \frac{1}{6}(y + 2) = \frac{1}{7}(z - 3)$.

In Exercises 15 and 16 find an equation of the plane containing the given intersecting lines.

15. $\dfrac{x - 2}{4} = \dfrac{y + 3}{-1} = \dfrac{z + 2}{3}$ and $\begin{cases} 3x + 2y + z + 2 = 0 \\ x - y + 2z - 1 = 0 \end{cases}$

16. $\dfrac{x}{2} = \dfrac{y - 2}{3} = \dfrac{z - 1}{1}$ and $\dfrac{x}{1} = \dfrac{y - 2}{-1} = \dfrac{z - 1}{1}$

17. Show that the lines

$$\begin{cases} 3x - y - z = 0 \\ 8x - 2y - 3z + 1 = 0 \end{cases} \quad \text{and} \quad \begin{cases} x - 3y + z + 3 = 0 \\ 3x - y - z + 5 = 0 \end{cases}$$

are parallel and find an equation of the plane determined by these lines.

18. Find equations of the line through the point $(1, -1, 1)$, perpendicular to the line $3x = 2y = z$, and parallel to the plane $x + y - z = 0$.

19. Find equations of the line through the point $(3, 6, 4)$, intersecting the z axis, and parallel to the plane $x - 3y + 5z - 6 = 0$.

20. Find equations of the line through the origin, perpendicular to the line $x = y - 5$, $z = 2y - 3$, and intersecting the line $y = 2x + 1$, $z = x + 2$.

21. Find the perpendicular distance from the point $(-1, 3, -1)$ to the line $x - 2z = 7$, $y = 1$.

22. Find the perpendicular distance from the origin to the line

$$x = -2 + \tfrac{6}{7}t \qquad y = 7 - \tfrac{2}{7}t \qquad z = 4 + \tfrac{3}{7}t$$

23. Prove that the lines

$$\frac{x-1}{5} = \frac{y-2}{-2} = \frac{z+1}{-3} \quad \text{and} \quad \frac{x-2}{1} = \frac{y+1}{-3} = \frac{z+3}{2}$$

are skew lines.

24. Find equations of the line through the point $(3, -4, -5)$ which intersects each of the skew lines of Exercise 23.

16.6 CROSS PRODUCT

Figure 16.6.1

Let **A** and **B** be two nonparallel vectors. Representations of these two vectors having the same initial point determine a plane as shown in Fig. 16.6.1. We show that a vector whose representations are perpendicular to this plane is given by the vector operation called the *cross product* of the two vectors **A** and **B**. The cross product is a vector operation for vectors in V_3 that we did not have for vectors in V_2. We first define this operation and then consider its algebraic and geometric properties.

16.6.1 Definition   If $\mathbf{A} = \langle a_1, a_2, a_3 \rangle$ and $\mathbf{B} = \langle b_1, b_2, b_3 \rangle$, then the *cross product of* **A** *and* **B**, denoted by $\mathbf{A} \times \mathbf{B}$, is given by

$$\mathbf{A} \times \mathbf{B} = \langle a_2 b_3 - a_3 b_2, \; a_3 b_1 - a_1 b_3, \; a_1 b_2 - a_2 b_1 \rangle \tag{1}$$

Because the cross product of two vectors is a vector, the cross product also is called the *vector product*. The operation of obtaining the cross product is called *vector multiplication*.

EXAMPLE 1:   Given $\mathbf{A} = \langle 2, 1, -3 \rangle$ and $\mathbf{B} = \langle 3, -1, 4 \rangle$, find $\mathbf{A} \times \mathbf{B}$.

SOLUTION: Using Definition 16.6.1, we have

$$\mathbf{A} \times \mathbf{B} = \langle 2, 1, -3 \rangle \times \langle 3, -1, 4 \rangle$$
$$= \langle (1)(4) - (-3)(-1), \; (-3)(3) - (2)(4), \; (2)(-1) - (1)(3) \rangle$$
$$= \langle 4 - 3, \; -9 - 8, \; -2 - 3 \rangle$$
$$= \langle 1, -17, -5 \rangle$$
$$= \mathbf{i} - 17\mathbf{j} - 5\mathbf{k}$$

There is a mnemomic device for remembering formula (1) that makes use of determinant notation. A second-order determinant is defined by the equation

$$\begin{vmatrix} a & b \\ c & d \end{vmatrix} = ad - bc$$

where a, b, and c are real numbers. For example,

$$\begin{vmatrix} 3 & 6 \\ -2 & 5 \end{vmatrix} = 3(5) - (6)(-2) = 27$$

Therefore, formula (1) can be written as

$$\mathbf{A} \times \mathbf{B} = \begin{vmatrix} a_2 & a_3 \\ b_2 & b_3 \end{vmatrix} \mathbf{i} - \begin{vmatrix} a_1 & a_3 \\ b_1 & b_3 \end{vmatrix} \mathbf{j} + \begin{vmatrix} a_1 & a_2 \\ b_1 & b_2 \end{vmatrix} \mathbf{k}$$

The right side of the above expression can be written symbolically as

$$\begin{vmatrix} \mathbf{i} & \mathbf{j} & \mathbf{k} \\ a_1 & a_2 & a_3 \\ b_1 & b_2 & b_3 \end{vmatrix}$$

which is the notation for a third-order determinant. However, observe that the first row contains vectors and not real numbers as is customary with determinant notation.

EXAMPLE 2: Use the mnemonic device employing determinant notation to find the cross product of the vectors of Example 1.

SOLUTION:

$$\mathbf{A} \times \mathbf{B} = \begin{vmatrix} \mathbf{i} & \mathbf{j} & \mathbf{k} \\ 2 & 1 & -3 \\ 3 & -1 & 4 \end{vmatrix}$$

$$= \begin{vmatrix} 1 & -3 \\ -1 & 4 \end{vmatrix} \mathbf{i} - \begin{vmatrix} 2 & -3 \\ 3 & 4 \end{vmatrix} \mathbf{j} + \begin{vmatrix} 2 & 1 \\ 3 & -1 \end{vmatrix} \mathbf{k}$$

$$= [(1)(4) - (-3)(-1)]\mathbf{i} - [(2)(4) - (-3)(3)]\mathbf{j}$$
$$+ [(2)(-1) - (1)(3)]\mathbf{k}$$

$$= \mathbf{i} - 17\mathbf{j} - 5\mathbf{k}$$

16.6.2 Theorem   If $\mathbf{A}$ is any vector in V_3, then

(i) $\mathbf{A} \times \mathbf{A} = \mathbf{0}$
(ii) $\mathbf{0} \times \mathbf{A} = \mathbf{0}$
(iii) $\mathbf{A} \times \mathbf{0} = \mathbf{0}$

PROOF OF (i): If $\mathbf{A} = \langle a_1, a_2, a_3 \rangle$, then by Definition 16.6.1 we have

$$\mathbf{A} \times \mathbf{A} = \langle a_2 a_3 - a_3 a_2, a_3 a_1 - a_1 a_3, a_1 a_2 - a_2 a_1 \rangle$$

$$= \langle 0, 0, 0 \rangle$$

$$= \mathbf{0}$$

The proofs of (ii) and (iii) are left for the reader (see Exercise 13).   ∎

By applying Definition 16.6.1 to pairs of unit vectors **i**, **j**, and **k**, we obtain the following:

$$\mathbf{i} \times \mathbf{i} = \mathbf{j} \times \mathbf{j} = \mathbf{k} \times \mathbf{k} = \mathbf{0}$$

$$\mathbf{i} \times \mathbf{j} = \mathbf{k} \qquad \mathbf{j} \times \mathbf{k} = \mathbf{i} \qquad \mathbf{k} \times \mathbf{i} = \mathbf{j}$$

$$\mathbf{j} \times \mathbf{i} = -\mathbf{k} \qquad \mathbf{k} \times \mathbf{j} = -\mathbf{i} \qquad \mathbf{i} \times \mathbf{k} = -\mathbf{j}$$

As an aid in remembering the above cross products, we first notice that the cross product of any one of the unit vectors **i**, **j**, or **k** with itself is the zero vector. The other six cross products can be obtained from Fig. 16.6.2 by applying the following rule: The cross product of two consecutive vectors, in the clockwise direction, is the next vector; and the cross product of two consecutive vectors, in the counterclockwise direction, is the negative of the next vector.

It can be easily seen that cross multiplication of two vectors is not commutative because in particular $\mathbf{i} \times \mathbf{j} \neq \mathbf{j} \times \mathbf{i}$. However, $\mathbf{i} \times \mathbf{j} = \mathbf{k}$ and $\mathbf{j} \times \mathbf{i} = -\mathbf{k}$; and so $\mathbf{i} \times \mathbf{j} = -(\mathbf{j} \times \mathbf{i})$. It is true in general that $\mathbf{A} \times \mathbf{B} = -(\mathbf{B} \times \mathbf{A})$, which we state and prove as a theorem.

Figure 16.6.2

16.6.3 Theorem   If **A** and **B** are any vectors in V_3,

$$\mathbf{A} \times \mathbf{B} = -(\mathbf{B} \times \mathbf{A})$$

PROOF: If $\mathbf{A} = \langle a_1, a_2, a_3 \rangle$ and $\mathbf{B} = \langle b_1, b_2, b_3 \rangle$, then by Definition 16.6.1 we have

$$\mathbf{A} \times \mathbf{B} = \langle a_2 b_3 - a_3 b_2, \ a_3 b_1 - a_1 b_3, \ a_1 b_2 - a_2 b_1 \rangle$$

$$= -1 \langle a_3 b_2 - a_2 b_3, \ a_1 b_3 - a_3 b_1, \ a_2 b_1 - a_1 b_2 \rangle$$

$$= -(\mathbf{B} \times \mathbf{A}) \qquad\qquad ∎$$

Cross multiplication of vectors is not associative. This is shown by the following example:

$$\mathbf{i} \times (\mathbf{i} \times \mathbf{j}) = \mathbf{i} \times \mathbf{k} = -\mathbf{j}$$

$$(\mathbf{i} \times \mathbf{i}) \times \mathbf{j} = \mathbf{0} \times \mathbf{j} = \mathbf{0}$$

So

$$\mathbf{i} \times (\mathbf{i} \times \mathbf{j}) \neq (\mathbf{i} \times \mathbf{i}) \times \mathbf{j}$$

Cross multiplication of vectors is distributive with respect to vector addition, as given by the following theorem.

16.6.4 Theorem   If **A**, **B**, and **C** are any vectors in V_3, then

$$\mathbf{A} \times (\mathbf{B} + \mathbf{C}) = \mathbf{A} \times \mathbf{B} + \mathbf{A} \times \mathbf{C} \tag{2}$$

Theorem 16.6.4 can be proved by letting $\mathbf{A} = \langle a_1, a_2, a_3 \rangle$, $\mathbf{B} = \langle b_1, b_2, b_3 \rangle$, and $\mathbf{C} = \langle c_1, c_2, c_3 \rangle$, and then showing that the components of the vector on the left side of (2) are the same as the components of the vector on the right side of (2). The details are left for the reader (see Exercise 14).

16.6.5 Theorem   If $\mathbf{A}$ and $\mathbf{B}$ are any two vectors in V_3 and c is a scalar, then

(i) $(c\mathbf{A}) \times \mathbf{B} = \mathbf{A} \times (c\mathbf{B})$;

(ii) $(c\mathbf{A}) \times \mathbf{B} = c(\mathbf{A} \times \mathbf{B})$.

The proof of Theorem 16.6.5 is left for the reader (see Exercises 15 and 16).

Repeated applications of Theorems 16.6.4 and 16.6.5 enable us to compute the cross product of two vectors by using laws of algebra, provided we do not change the order of the vectors in cross multiplication, which is prohibited by Theorem 16.6.3. The following example illustrates this.

EXAMPLE 3:   Find the cross product of the vectors in Example 1 by applying Theorems 16.6.4 and 16.6.5.

SOLUTION:

$$\mathbf{A} \times \mathbf{B} = (2\mathbf{i} + \mathbf{j} - 3\mathbf{k}) \times (3\mathbf{i} - \mathbf{j} + 4\mathbf{k})$$
$$= 6(\mathbf{i} \times \mathbf{i}) - 2(\mathbf{i} \times \mathbf{j}) + 8(\mathbf{i} \times \mathbf{k}) + 3(\mathbf{j} \times \mathbf{i}) - 1(\mathbf{j} \times \mathbf{j})$$
$$+ 4(\mathbf{j} \times \mathbf{k}) - 9(\mathbf{k} \times \mathbf{i}) + 3(\mathbf{k} \times \mathbf{j}) - 12(\mathbf{k} \times \mathbf{k})$$
$$= 6(\mathbf{0}) - 2(\mathbf{k}) + 8(-\mathbf{j}) + 3(-\mathbf{k}) - 1(\mathbf{0})$$
$$+ 4(\mathbf{i}) - 9(\mathbf{j}) + 3(-\mathbf{i}) - 12(\mathbf{0})$$
$$= -2\mathbf{k} - 8\mathbf{j} - 3\mathbf{k} + 4\mathbf{i} - 9\mathbf{j} - 3\mathbf{i}$$
$$= \mathbf{i} - 17\mathbf{j} - 5\mathbf{k}$$

The method used in the solution of Example 3 gives a way of finding the cross product without having to remember formula (1) or to use determinant notation. Actually all the steps shown in the solution need not be included because the various cross products of the unit vectors can be obtained immediately by using Fig. 16.6.2 and the corresponding rule.

EXAMPLE 4:   Prove that if $\mathbf{A}$ and $\mathbf{B}$ are any two vectors in V_3,

$$|\mathbf{A} \times \mathbf{B}|^2 = |\mathbf{A}|^2 |\mathbf{B}|^2 - (\mathbf{A} \cdot \mathbf{B})^2$$

SOLUTION: Let $\mathbf{A} = \langle a_1, a_2, a_3 \rangle$ and $\mathbf{B} = \langle b_1, b_2, b_3 \rangle$. Then

$$|\mathbf{A} \times \mathbf{B}|^2 = (a_2 b_3 - a_3 b_2)^2 + (a_3 b_1 - a_1 b_3)^2 + (a_1 b_2 - a_2 b_1)^2$$
$$= a_2^2 b_3^2 - 2a_2 a_3 b_2 b_3 + a_3^2 b_2^2 + a_3^2 b_1^2 - 2a_1 a_3 b_1 b_3$$
$$+ a_1^2 b_3^2 + a_1^2 b_2^2 - 2a_1 a_2 b_1 b_2 + a_2^2 b_1^2$$

$$|\mathbf{A}|^2 |\mathbf{B}|^2 - (\mathbf{A} \cdot \mathbf{B})^2 = (a_1^2 + a_2^2 + a_3^2)(b_1^2 + b_2^2 + b_3^2)$$
$$- (a_1 b_1 + a_2 b_2 + a_3 b_3)^2$$
$$= a_1^2 b_2^2 + a_1^2 b_3^2 + a_2^2 b_1^2 + a_2^2 b_3^2 + a_3^2 b_1^2$$
$$+ a_3^2 b_2^2 - 2a_1 a_3 b_1 b_3 - 2a_2 a_3 b_2 b_3 - 2a_1 a_2 b_1 b_2$$

Comparing the two expressions, we conclude that

$$|\mathbf{A} \times \mathbf{B}|^2 = |\mathbf{A}|^2|\mathbf{B}|^2 - (\mathbf{A} \cdot \mathbf{B})^2$$

The formula proved in Example 4 is useful to us in proving the following theorem from which we can obtain a geometric interpretation of the cross product.

16.6.6 Theorem   If $\mathbf{A}$ and $\mathbf{B}$ are two vectors in V_3 and θ is the radian measure of the angle between $\mathbf{A}$ and $\mathbf{B}$, then

$$|\mathbf{A} \times \mathbf{B}| = |\mathbf{A}||\mathbf{B}| \sin \theta \qquad (3)$$

PROOF: From Example 4 we have

$$|\mathbf{A} \times \mathbf{B}|^2 = |\mathbf{A}|^2|\mathbf{B}|^2 - (\mathbf{A} \cdot \mathbf{B})^2 \qquad (4)$$

From Theorem 16.3.4, if θ is the radian measure of the angle between $\mathbf{A}$ and $\mathbf{B}$, we have

$$\mathbf{A} \cdot \mathbf{B} = |\mathbf{A}||\mathbf{B}| \cos \theta \qquad (5)$$

Substituting from (5) into (4) we get

$$|\mathbf{A} \times \mathbf{B}|^2 = |\mathbf{A}|^2|\mathbf{B}|^2 - |\mathbf{A}|^2|\mathbf{B}|^2 \cos^2 \theta$$
$$= |\mathbf{A}|^2|\mathbf{B}|^2(1 - \cos^2 \theta)$$

So

$$|\mathbf{A} \times \mathbf{B}|^2 = |\mathbf{A}|^2|\mathbf{B}|^2 \sin^2 \theta \qquad (6)$$

Because $0 \le \theta \le \pi$, $\sin \theta \ge 0$. Therefore, from Eq. (6), we get

$$|\mathbf{A} \times \mathbf{B}| = |\mathbf{A}||\mathbf{B}| \sin \theta \qquad \blacksquare$$

We consider now a geometric interpretation of $|\mathbf{A} \times \mathbf{B}|$. Let $\overrightarrow{PR}$ be a representation of $\mathbf{A}$ and let $\overrightarrow{PQ}$ be a representation of $\mathbf{B}$. Then the angle between the vectors $\mathbf{A}$ and $\mathbf{B}$ is the angle at P in triangle RPQ (see Fig. 16.6.3). Let the radian measure of this angle be θ. Therefore, the number of square units in the area of the parallelogram having $\overrightarrow{PR}$ and $\overrightarrow{PQ}$ as adjacent sides is $|\mathbf{A}||\mathbf{B}| \sin \theta$ because the altitude of the parallelogram has length $|\mathbf{B}| \sin \theta$ units and the length of the base is $|\mathbf{A}|$ units. So from Eq. (3) it follows that $|\mathbf{A} \times \mathbf{B}|$ square units is the area of this parallelogram.

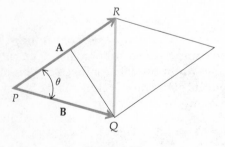

Figure 16.6.3

EXAMPLE 5:   Show that the quadrilateral having vertices at $P(1, -2, 3)$, $Q(4, 3, -1)$, $R(2, 2, 1)$, and $S(5, 7, -3)$ is a parallelogram and find its area.

SOLUTION: Figure 16.6.4 shows the quadrilateral $PQSR$.

$$\mathbf{V}(\overrightarrow{PQ}) = \langle 4 - 1, 3 - (-2), (-1) - 3 \rangle = \langle 3, 5, -4 \rangle$$
$$\mathbf{V}(\overrightarrow{PR}) = \langle 2 - 1, 2 - (-2), 1 - 3 \rangle = \langle 1, 4, -2 \rangle$$
$$\mathbf{V}(\overrightarrow{RS}) = \langle 5 - 2, 7 - 2, -3 - 1 \rangle = \langle 3, 5, -4 \rangle$$
$$\mathbf{V}(\overrightarrow{QS}) = \langle 5 - 4, 7 - 3, -3 - (-1) \rangle = \langle 1, 4, -2 \rangle$$

$P(1, -2, 3)$

O

$R(2, 2, 1)$

Q
$(4, 3, -1)$

$S(5, 7, -3)$

Figure 16.6.4

Because $\mathbf{V}(\overrightarrow{PQ}) = \mathbf{V}(\overrightarrow{RS})$ and $\mathbf{V}(\overrightarrow{PR}) = \mathbf{V}(\overrightarrow{QS})$, it follows that $\overrightarrow{PQ}$ is parallel to $\overrightarrow{RS}$ and $\overrightarrow{PR}$ is parallel to $\overrightarrow{QS}$. Therefore, $PQSR$ is a parallelogram. Let $\mathbf{A} = \mathbf{V}(\overrightarrow{PR})$ and $\mathbf{B} = \mathbf{V}(\overrightarrow{PQ})$, then

$$\mathbf{A} \times \mathbf{B} = (\mathbf{i} + 4\mathbf{j} - 2\mathbf{k}) \times (3\mathbf{i} + 5\mathbf{j} - 4\mathbf{k})$$
$$= 3(\mathbf{i} \times \mathbf{i}) + 5(\mathbf{i} \times \mathbf{j}) - 4(\mathbf{i} \times \mathbf{k}) + 12(\mathbf{j} \times \mathbf{i}) + 20(\mathbf{j} \times \mathbf{j})$$
$$- 16(\mathbf{j} \times \mathbf{k}) - 6(\mathbf{k} \times \mathbf{i}) - 10(\mathbf{k} \times \mathbf{j}) + 8(\mathbf{k} \times \mathbf{k})$$
$$= 3(\mathbf{0}) + 5(\mathbf{k}) - 4(-\mathbf{j}) + 12(-\mathbf{k}) + 20(\mathbf{0}) - 16(\mathbf{i})$$
$$- 6(\mathbf{j}) - 10(-\mathbf{i}) + 8(\mathbf{0})$$
$$= -6\mathbf{i} - 2\mathbf{j} - 7\mathbf{k}$$

Hence,

$$|\mathbf{A} \times \mathbf{B}| = \sqrt{36 + 4 + 49} = \sqrt{89}$$

The area of the parallelogram is therefore $\sqrt{89}$ square units.

The following theorem, which gives a method for determining if two vectors in V_3 are parallel, follows from Theorem 16.6.6.

16.6.7 Theorem   If $\mathbf{A}$ and $\mathbf{B}$ are two nonzero vectors in V_3, $\mathbf{A}$ and $\mathbf{B}$ are parallel if and only if $\mathbf{A} \times \mathbf{B} = \mathbf{0}$.

PROOF: Because neither $\mathbf{A}$ nor $\mathbf{B}$ is the zero vector, $|\mathbf{A}| \neq 0$ and $|\mathbf{B}| \neq 0$. Therefore, from Eq. (3), $|\mathbf{A} \times \mathbf{B}| = 0$ if and only if $\sin \theta = 0$. Because $|\mathbf{A} \times \mathbf{B}| = 0$ if and only if $\mathbf{A} \times \mathbf{B} = \mathbf{0}$ and $\sin \theta = 0$ $(0 \leq \theta \leq \pi)$ if and only if $\theta = 0$ or π, we can conclude that

$$\mathbf{A} \times \mathbf{B} = \mathbf{0} \quad \text{if and only if} \quad \theta = 0 \text{ or } \pi$$

However, from Definition 16.3.5 two vectors are parallel if and only if the radian measure of the angle between the two vectors is 0 or π, and so the theorem follows.   ∎

The product $\mathbf{A} \cdot (\mathbf{B} \times \mathbf{C})$ is called the *triple scalar product* of the vectors $\mathbf{A}$, $\mathbf{B}$, and $\mathbf{C}$. Actually, the parentheses are not needed because $\mathbf{A} \cdot \mathbf{B}$ is a scalar, and therefore $\mathbf{A} \cdot \mathbf{B} \times \mathbf{C}$ can be interpreted only in one way.

16.6.8 Theorem   If $\mathbf{A}$, $\mathbf{B}$, and $\mathbf{C}$ are vectors in V_3, then

$$\mathbf{A} \cdot \mathbf{B} \times \mathbf{C} = \mathbf{A} \times \mathbf{B} \cdot \mathbf{C} \tag{7}$$

Theorem 16.6.8 can be proved by letting $\mathbf{A} = \langle a_1, a_2, a_3 \rangle$, $\mathbf{B} = \langle b_1, b_2, b_3 \rangle$, and $\mathbf{C} = \langle c_1, c_2, c_3 \rangle$ and then by showing that the number on the left side of (7) is the same as the number on the right. The details are left for the reader (see Exercise 17).

EXAMPLE 6:   Verify Theorem 16.6.8 if $\mathbf{A} = \langle 1, -1, 2 \rangle$, $\mathbf{B} = \langle 3, 4, -2 \rangle$, and $\mathbf{C} = \langle -5, 1, -4 \rangle$.

SOLUTION:

$$\mathbf{B} \times \mathbf{C} = (3\mathbf{i} + 4\mathbf{j} - 2\mathbf{k}) \times (-5\mathbf{i} + \mathbf{j} - 4\mathbf{k})$$

$$= 3\mathbf{k} - 12(-\mathbf{j}) - 20(-\mathbf{k}) - 16\mathbf{i} + 10\mathbf{j} - 2(-\mathbf{i})$$

$$= -14\mathbf{i} + 22\mathbf{j} + 23\mathbf{k}$$

$$\mathbf{A} \cdot (\mathbf{B} \times \mathbf{C}) = \langle 1, -1, 2 \rangle \cdot \langle -14, 22, 23 \rangle = -14 - 22 + 46$$

$$= 10$$

$$\mathbf{A} \times \mathbf{B} = (\mathbf{i} - \mathbf{j} + 2\mathbf{k}) \times (3\mathbf{i} + 4\mathbf{j} - 2\mathbf{k})$$

$$= 4\mathbf{k} - 2(-\mathbf{j}) - 3(-\mathbf{k}) + 2\mathbf{i} + 6\mathbf{j} + 8 (-\mathbf{i})$$

$$= -6\mathbf{i} + 8\mathbf{j} + 7\mathbf{k}$$

$$(\mathbf{A} \times \mathbf{B}) \cdot \mathbf{C} = \langle -6, 8, 7 \rangle \cdot \langle -5, 1, -4 \rangle$$

$$= 30 + 8 - 28$$

$$= 10$$

This verifies the theorem for these three vectors.

16.6.9 Theorem   If $\mathbf{A}$ and $\mathbf{B}$ are two nonzero and nonparallel vectors in V_3, then the vector $\mathbf{A} \times \mathbf{B}$ is orthogonal to both $\mathbf{A}$ and $\mathbf{B}$.

PROOF: From Theorem 16.6.8 we have

$$\mathbf{A} \cdot \mathbf{A} \times \mathbf{B} = \mathbf{A} \times \mathbf{A} \cdot \mathbf{B}$$

From Theorem 16.6.2(i), $\mathbf{A} \times \mathbf{A} = \mathbf{0}$. Therefore, from the above equation we have

$$\mathbf{A} \cdot \mathbf{A} \times \mathbf{B} = \mathbf{0} \cdot \mathbf{B} = 0$$

Because the dot product of $\mathbf{A}$ and $\mathbf{A} \times \mathbf{B}$ is zero and neither $\mathbf{A}$ nor $\mathbf{A} \times \mathbf{B}$ is the zero vector, it follows from Theorem 16.3.7 that $\mathbf{A}$ and $\mathbf{A} \times \mathbf{B}$ are orthogonal.

We also have from Theorem 16.6.8 that

$$\mathbf{A} \times \mathbf{B} \cdot \mathbf{B} = \mathbf{A} \cdot \mathbf{B} \times \mathbf{B}$$

Again applying Theorem 16.6.2(i), we get $\mathbf{B} \times \mathbf{B} = \mathbf{0}$, and so from the above equation we have

$$\mathbf{A} \times \mathbf{B} \cdot \mathbf{B} = \mathbf{A} \cdot \mathbf{0} = 0$$

Therefore, since the dot product of $\mathbf{A} \times \mathbf{B}$ and $\mathbf{B}$ is zero and neither $\mathbf{A}$ nor $\mathbf{A} \times \mathbf{B}$ is $\mathbf{0}$, $\mathbf{A} \times \mathbf{B}$ and $\mathbf{B}$ are orthogonal and the theorem is proved.   ∎

From Theorem 16.6.9 we can conclude that if representations of the vectors **A**, **B**, and **A** × **B**, have the same initial point, then the representation of **A** × **B** is perpendicular to the plane formed by the representations of **A** and **B**.

EXAMPLE 7: Given the points $P(-1, -2, -3)$, $Q(-2, 1, 0)$, and $R(0, 5, 1)$, find a unit vector whose representations are perpendicular to the plane through the points P, Q, and R.

SOLUTION: Let $\mathbf{A} = \mathbf{V}(\vec{PQ})$ and $\mathbf{B} = \mathbf{V}(\vec{PR})$. Then

$$\mathbf{A} = \langle -2 - (-1), 1 - (-2), 0 - (-3) \rangle = \langle -1, 3, 3 \rangle$$

$$\mathbf{B} = \langle 0 - (-1), 5 - (-2), 1 - (-3) \rangle = \langle 1, 7, 4 \rangle$$

The plane through P, Q, and R is the plane formed by $\vec{PQ}$ and $\vec{PR}$, which are, respectively, representations of vectors **A** and **B**. Therefore, any representation of the vector **A** × **B** is perpendicular to this plane.

$$\mathbf{A} \times \mathbf{B} = (-\mathbf{i} + 3\mathbf{j} + 3\mathbf{k}) \times (\mathbf{i} + 7\mathbf{j} + 4\mathbf{k}) = -9\mathbf{i} + 7\mathbf{j} - 10\mathbf{k}$$

The desired vector is a unit vector parallel to **A** × **B**. To find this unit vector we apply Theorem 16.2.9 and divide **A** × **B** by $|\mathbf{A} \times \mathbf{B}|$, and we obtain

$$\frac{\mathbf{A} \times \mathbf{B}}{|\mathbf{A} \times \mathbf{B}|} = -\frac{9}{\sqrt{230}}\mathbf{i} + \frac{7}{\sqrt{230}}\mathbf{j} - \frac{10}{\sqrt{230}}\mathbf{k}$$

EXAMPLE 8: Find an equation of the plane through the points $P(1, 3, 2)$, $Q(3, -2, 2)$, and $R(2, 1, 3)$.

SOLUTION: $\mathbf{V}(\vec{QR}) = -\mathbf{i} + 3\mathbf{j} + \mathbf{k}$ and $\mathbf{V}(\vec{PR}) = \mathbf{i} - 2\mathbf{j} + \mathbf{k}$. A normal vector to the required plane is the cross product $\mathbf{V}(\vec{QR}) \times \mathbf{V}(\vec{PR})$, which is

$$(-\mathbf{i} + 3\mathbf{j} + \mathbf{k}) \times (\mathbf{i} - 2\mathbf{j} + \mathbf{k}) = 5\mathbf{i} + 2\mathbf{j} - \mathbf{k}$$

So if $P_0 = (1, 3, 2)$ and $\mathbf{N} = \langle 5, 2, -1 \rangle$, from Theorem 16.4.2 we have as an equation of the required plane

$$5(x - 1) + 2(y - 3) - (z - 2) = 0$$

or, equivalently,

$$5x + 2y - z - 9 = 0$$

N

S

θ

R

h C h

B

P A Q

Figure 16.6.5

A geometric interpretation of the triple scalar product is obtained by considering a parallelepiped having edges $\vec{PQ}$, $\vec{PR}$, and $\vec{PS}$, and letting $\mathbf{A} = \mathbf{V}(\vec{PQ})$, $\mathbf{B} = \mathbf{V}(\vec{PR})$, and $\mathbf{C} = \mathbf{V}(\vec{PS})$. See Fig. 16.6.5. The vector **A** × **B** is a normal vector to the plane of $\vec{PQ}$ and $\vec{PR}$. The vector $-(\mathbf{A} \times \mathbf{B})$ is also a normal vector to this plane. We are not certain which of the two vectors, $(\mathbf{A} \times \mathbf{B})$ or $-(\mathbf{A} \times \mathbf{B})$, makes the smaller angle with **C**. Let **N** be the one of the two vectors $(\mathbf{A} \times \mathbf{B})$ or $-(\mathbf{A} \times \mathbf{B})$ that makes an angle of radian measure $\theta < \frac{1}{2}\pi$ with **C**. Then the representations of **N** and **C** having their initial points at **P** are on the same side of the plane of $\vec{PQ}$ and $\vec{PR}$ as shown in Fig. 16.6.5. The area of the base of the parallelepiped is $|\mathbf{A} \times \mathbf{B}|$ square units. If h units is the length of the altitude of the parallelepiped, and if V cubic units is the volume of the parallelepiped,

$$V = |\mathbf{A} \times \mathbf{B}|h \tag{8}$$

Consider now the dot product $\mathbf{N} \cdot \mathbf{C}$. By Theorem 16.3.4, $\mathbf{N} \cdot \mathbf{C} = |\mathbf{N}||\mathbf{C}| \cos \theta$. But $h = |\mathbf{C}| \cos \theta$, and so $\mathbf{N} \cdot \mathbf{C} = |\mathbf{N}|h$. Because $\mathbf{N}$ is either $(\mathbf{A} \times \mathbf{B})$ or $-(\mathbf{A} \times \mathbf{B})$, it follows that $|\mathbf{N}| = |\mathbf{A} \times \mathbf{B}|$. Hence, we have

$$\mathbf{N} \cdot \mathbf{C} = |\mathbf{A} \times \mathbf{B}|h \qquad (9)$$

Comparing Eqs. (8) and (9) we have

$$\mathbf{N} \cdot \mathbf{C} = V$$

It follows that the measure of the volume of the parallelepiped is either $(\mathbf{A} \times \mathbf{B}) \cdot \mathbf{C}$ or $-(\mathbf{A} \times \mathbf{B}) \cdot \mathbf{C}$; that is, the measure of the volume of the parallelepiped is the absolute value of the triple scalar product $\mathbf{A} \times \mathbf{B} \cdot \mathbf{C}$.

EXAMPLE 9: Find the volume of the parallelepiped having vertices $P(5, 4, 5), Q(4, 10, 6), R(1, 8, 7)$, and $S(2, 6, 9)$ and edges $\overrightarrow{PQ}, \overrightarrow{PR}$, and $\overrightarrow{PS}$.

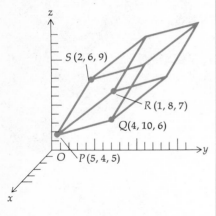

Figure 16.6.6

SOLUTION: Figure 16.6.6 shows the parallelepiped. Let $\mathbf{A} = \mathbf{V}(\overrightarrow{PQ}) = \langle -1, 6, 1 \rangle$, $\mathbf{B} = \mathbf{V}(\overrightarrow{PR}) = \langle -4 \ 4, 2 \rangle$, and $\mathbf{C} = \mathbf{V}(\overrightarrow{PS}) = \langle -3, 2, 4 \rangle$. Then

$$\mathbf{A} \times \mathbf{B} = (-\mathbf{i} + 6\mathbf{j} + \mathbf{k}) \times (-4\mathbf{i} + 4\mathbf{j} + 2\mathbf{k}) = 8\mathbf{i} - 2\mathbf{j} + 20\mathbf{k}$$

Therefore,

$$(\mathbf{A} \times \mathbf{B}) \cdot \mathbf{C} = \langle 8, -2, 20 \rangle \cdot \langle -3, 2, 4 \rangle = -24 - 4 + 80 = 52$$

Thus, the volume is 52 cubic units.

EXAMPLE 10: Find the distance between the two skew lines, l_1 and l_2, of Example 7 in Sec. 16.5.

SOLUTION: Because l_1 and l_2 are skew lines, there are parallel planes P_1 and P_2 containing the lines l_1 and l_2, respectively. See Fig. 16.6.7. Let d units be the distance between planes P_1 and P_2. The distance between l_1 and l_2 is also d units. A normal vector to the two planes is $\mathbf{N} = \mathbf{V}(\overrightarrow{AB}) \times \mathbf{V}(\overrightarrow{CD})$. Let $\mathbf{U}$ be a unit normal vector in the direction of $\mathbf{N}$ Then

$$\mathbf{U} = \frac{\mathbf{V}(\overrightarrow{AB}) \times \mathbf{V}(\overrightarrow{CB})}{|\mathbf{V}(\overrightarrow{AB}) \times \mathbf{V}(\overrightarrow{CD})|}$$

Now we take two points, one in each plane (e.g., B and C). Then the scalar projection of $\mathbf{V}(\overrightarrow{CB})$ on $\mathbf{N}$ is $\mathbf{V}(\overrightarrow{CB}) \cdot \mathbf{U}$, and

$$d = |\mathbf{V}(\overrightarrow{CB}) \cdot \mathbf{U}| = \left| \mathbf{V}(\overrightarrow{CB}) \cdot \frac{\mathbf{V}(\overrightarrow{AB}) \times \mathbf{V}(\overrightarrow{CD})}{|\mathbf{V}(\overrightarrow{AB}) \times \mathbf{V}(\overrightarrow{CD})|} \right|$$

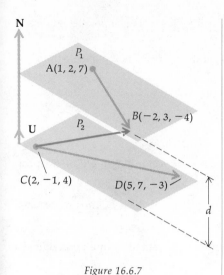

Figure 16.6.7

Performing the computations required, we have

$$\mathbf{V}(\overrightarrow{AB}) = -3\mathbf{i} + \mathbf{j} - 11\mathbf{k} \qquad \mathbf{V}(\overrightarrow{CD}) = 3\mathbf{i} + 8\mathbf{j} - 7\mathbf{k}$$

$$\mathbf{N} = \mathbf{V}(\overrightarrow{AB}) \times \mathbf{V}(\overrightarrow{CD}) = \begin{vmatrix} \mathbf{i} & \mathbf{j} & \mathbf{k} \\ -3 & 1 & -11 \\ 3 & 8 & -7 \end{vmatrix} = 27(3\mathbf{i} - 2\mathbf{j} - \mathbf{k})$$

$$\mathbf{U} = \frac{27(3\mathbf{i} - 2\mathbf{j} - \mathbf{k})}{\sqrt{27^2(3^2 + 2^2 + 1^2)}} = \frac{3\mathbf{i} - 2\mathbf{j} - \mathbf{k}}{\sqrt{14}}$$

Finally, $\mathbf{V}(\overrightarrow{CB}) = -4\mathbf{i} + 4\mathbf{j} - 8\mathbf{k}$, and so

$$d = |\mathbf{V}(\overrightarrow{CB}) \cdot \mathbf{U}| = \frac{1}{\sqrt{14}}|-12 - 8 + 8| = \frac{12}{\sqrt{14}} = \frac{6}{7}\sqrt{14}$$

Exercises 16.6

In Exercises 1 through 12, let $\mathbf{A} = \langle 1, 2, 3 \rangle$, $\mathbf{B} = \langle 4, -3, -1 \rangle$, $\mathbf{C} = \langle -5, -3, 5 \rangle$, $\mathbf{D} = \langle -2, 1, 6 \rangle$, $\mathbf{E} = \langle 4, 0, -7 \rangle$, and $\mathbf{F} = \langle 0, 2, 1 \rangle$.

1. Find $\mathbf{A} \times \mathbf{B}$

2. Find $\mathbf{D} \times \mathbf{E}$

3. Find $(\mathbf{C} \times \mathbf{D}) \cdot (\mathbf{E} \times \mathbf{F})$

4. Find $(\mathbf{C} \times \mathbf{E}) \cdot (\mathbf{D} \times \mathbf{F})$

5. Verify Theorem 16.6.3 for vectors $\mathbf{A}$ and $\mathbf{B}$.

6. Verify Theorem 16.6.4 for vectors $\mathbf{A}$, $\mathbf{B}$, and $\mathbf{C}$.

7. Verify Theorem 16.6.5(i) for vectors $\mathbf{A}$ and $\mathbf{B}$ and $c = 3$.

8. Verify Theorem 16.6.5(ii) for vectors $\mathbf{A}$ and $\mathbf{B}$ and $c = 3$.

9. Verify Theorem 16.6.8 for vectors $\mathbf{A}$, $\mathbf{B}$, and $\mathbf{C}$.

10. Find $(\mathbf{A} \times \mathbf{B}) \times \mathbf{C}$ and $\mathbf{A} \times (\mathbf{B} \times \mathbf{C})$.

11. Find $(\mathbf{A} + \mathbf{B}) \times (\mathbf{C} - \mathbf{D})$ and $(\mathbf{D} - \mathbf{C}) \times (\mathbf{A} + \mathbf{B})$ and verify they are equal.

12. Find $|\mathbf{A} \times \mathbf{B}||\mathbf{C} \times \mathbf{D}|$.

13. Prove Theorem 16.6.2(ii) and (iii).

14. Prove Theorem 16.6.4.

15. Prove Theorem 16.6.5(i).

16. Prove Theorem 16.6.5(ii).

17. Prove Theorem 16.6.8.

18. Given the two unit vectors

$$\mathbf{A} = \tfrac{4}{9}\mathbf{i} + \tfrac{7}{9}\mathbf{j} - \tfrac{4}{9}\mathbf{k} \quad \text{and} \quad \mathbf{B} = -\tfrac{2}{3}\mathbf{i} + \tfrac{2}{3}\mathbf{j} + \tfrac{1}{3}\mathbf{k}$$

If θ is the radian measure of the angle between $\mathbf{A}$ and $\mathbf{B}$, find $\sin \theta$ in two ways: (a) by using the cross product (formula (3) of this section); (b) by using the dot product and a trigonometric identity.

19. Follow the instructions of Exercise 18 for the two unit vectors:

$$\mathbf{A} = \frac{1}{\sqrt{3}}\mathbf{i} - \frac{1}{\sqrt{3}}\mathbf{j} + \frac{1}{\sqrt{3}}\mathbf{k} \quad \text{and} \quad \mathbf{B} = \frac{1}{3\sqrt{3}}\mathbf{i} + \frac{5}{3\sqrt{3}}\mathbf{j} + \frac{1}{3\sqrt{3}}\mathbf{k}$$

20. Show that the quadrilateral having vertices at $(1, 1, 3)$, $(-2, 1, -1)$, $(-5, 4, 0)$, and $(-8, 4, -4)$ is a parallelogram and find its area.

21. Show that the quadrilateral having vertices at $(1, -2, 3)$, $(4, 3, -1)$, $(2, 2, 1)$, and $(5, 7, -3)$ is a parallelogram and find its area.

22. Find the area of the parallelogram $PQRS$ if $\mathbf{V}(\overrightarrow{PQ}) = 3\mathbf{i} - 2\mathbf{j}$ and $\mathbf{V}(\overrightarrow{PS}) = 3\mathbf{j} + 4\mathbf{k}$.

23. Find the area of the triangle having vertices at $(0, 2, 2)$, $(8, 8, -2)$, and $(9, 12, 6)$.

24. Find the area of the triangle having vertices at $(4, 5, 6)$, $(4, 4, 5)$, and $(3, 5, 5)$.

25. Let $\overrightarrow{OP}$ be the position representation of vector $\mathbf{A}$, $\overrightarrow{OQ}$ be the position representation of vector $\mathbf{B}$, and $\overrightarrow{OR}$ be the position representation of vector $\mathbf{C}$. Prove that the area of triangle PQR is $\frac{1}{2}|(\mathbf{B} - \mathbf{A}) \times (\mathbf{C} - \mathbf{A})|$.

26. Find a unit vector whose representations are perpendicular to the plane containing $\overrightarrow{PQ}$ and $\overrightarrow{PR}$ if $\overrightarrow{PQ}$ is a representation of the vector $\mathbf{i} + 3\mathbf{j} - 2\mathbf{k}$ and $\overrightarrow{PR}$ is a representation of the vector $2\mathbf{i} - \mathbf{j} - \mathbf{k}$.

27. Given the points $P(5, 2, -1)$, $Q(2, 4, -2)$, and $R(11, 1, 4)$. Find a unit vector whose representations are perpendicular to the plane through points P, Q, and R.

28. Find the volume of the parallelepiped having edges $\overrightarrow{PQ}$, $\overrightarrow{PR}$, and $\overrightarrow{PS}$ if the points P, Q, R, and S are, respectively, $(1, 3, 4)$, $(3, 5, 3)$, $(2, 1, 6)$, and $(2, 2, 5)$.

29. Find the volume of the parallelepiped $PQRS$ if the vectors $\mathbf{V}(\overrightarrow{PQ})$, $\mathbf{V}(\overrightarrow{PR})$, and $\mathbf{V}(\overrightarrow{PS})$ are, respectively, $\mathbf{i} + 3\mathbf{j} + 2\mathbf{k}$, $2\mathbf{i} + \mathbf{j} - \mathbf{k}$, and $\mathbf{i} - 2\mathbf{j} + \mathbf{k}$.

30. If $\mathbf{A}$ and $\mathbf{B}$ are any two vectors in V_3, prove that $(\mathbf{A} - \mathbf{B}) \times (\mathbf{A} + \mathbf{B}) = 2(\mathbf{A} \times \mathbf{B})$.

In Exercises 31 and 32, use the cross product to find an equation of the plane containing the given three points.

31. $(-2, 2, 2)$, $(-8, 1, 6)$, $(3, 4, -1)$　　　　32. $(a, b, 0)$, $(a, 0, c)$, $(0, b, c)$

In Exercises 33 and 34, find the perpendicular distance between the two given skew lines.

33. $\dfrac{x-1}{5} = \dfrac{y-2}{3} = \dfrac{z+1}{2}$　and　$\dfrac{x+2}{4} = \dfrac{y+1}{2} = \dfrac{z-3}{-3}$　　34. $\dfrac{x+1}{2} = \dfrac{y+2}{-4} = \dfrac{z-1}{-3}$　and　$\dfrac{x-1}{5} = \dfrac{y-1}{3} = \dfrac{z+1}{2}$

35. Let P, Q, and R be three noncollinear points in R_3 and $\overrightarrow{OP}$, $\overrightarrow{OQ}$, and $\overrightarrow{OR}$ be the position representations of vectors $\mathbf{A}$, $\mathbf{B}$, and $\mathbf{C}$, respectively. Prove that the representations of the vector $\mathbf{A} \times \mathbf{B} + \mathbf{B} \times \mathbf{C} + \mathbf{C} \times \mathbf{A}$ are perpendicular to the plane containing the points P, Q, and R.

16.7 CYLINDERS AND SURFACES OF REVOLUTION

As mentioned previously, the graph of an equation in three variables is a *surface*. A surface is represented by an equation if the coordinates of every point on the surface satisfy the equation and if every point whose coordinates satisfy the equation lies on the surface. We have already discussed two kinds of surfaces, a plane and a sphere. Another kind of surface that is fairly simple is a cylinder. You are probably familiar with right-circular cylinders from previous experience. We now consider a more general cylindrical surface.

16.7.1 Definition　　A *cylinder* is a surface that is generated by a line moving along a given plane curve in such a way that it always remains parallel to a fixed line not lying in the plane of the given curve. The moving line is called a *generator* of the cylinder and the given plane curve is called a *directrix* of the cylinder. Any position of a generator is called a *ruling* of the cylinder.

We confine ourselves to cylinders having a directrix in a coordinate plane and rulings perpendicular to that plane. If the rulings of a cylinder are perpendicular to the plane of a directrix, the cylinder is said to be perpendicular to the plane.

The familiar right-circular cylinder is one for which a directrix is a circle in a plane perpendicular to the cylinder. In Fig. 16.7.1, we show a cylinder whose directrix is the parabola $y^2 = 8x$ in the xy plane and whose rulings are parallel to the z axis. This cylinder is called a *parabolic cylinder*. An *elliptic cylinder* is shown in Fig. 16.7.2; its directrix is the ellipse $9x^2 + 16y^2 = 144$ in the xy plane and its rulings are parallel to the z axis. Figure 16.7.3 shows a hyperbolic cylinder having as a directrix the hyperbola $25x^2 - 4y^2 = 100$ in the xy plane and rulings parallel to the z axis.

Let us consider the problem of finding an equation of a cylinder having a directrix in a coordinate plane and rulings parallel to the coordinate axis not in that plane. To be specific, we take the directrix in the xy plane and the rulings parallel to the z axis. Refer to Fig. 16.7.4. Suppose that an equation of the directrix in the xy plane is $y = f(x)$. If the point $(x_0, y_0, 0)$ in the xy plane satisfies this equation, any point (x_0, y_0, z) in three-dimensional space, where z is any real number, will satisfy the same equation because z does not appear in the equation. The points having representations (x_0, y_0, z) all lie on the line parallel to the z axis through the point $(x_0, y_0, 0)$. This line is a ruling of the cylinder. Hence, any point whose x and y coordinates satisfy the equation $y = f(x)$ lies on the cylinder. Conversely, if the point $P(x, y, z)$ lies on the cylinder (see Fig. 16.7.5), then the point $(x, y, 0)$ lies on the directrix of the cylinder in the xy plane, and hence the x and y coordinates of P satisfy the equation $y = f(x)$. Therefore, if $y = f(x)$ is considered as an equation of a graph in

Figure 16.7.1

Figure 16.7.2

Figure 16.7.3

① GENERATOR
② DIRECTRIX
③ RULING

$(x_0, y_0, 0)$ $y = f(x)$

Figure 16.7.4

(x, y, z)

$(x, y, 0)$ $y = f(x)$

Figure 16.7.5

three-dimensional space, the graph is a cylinder whose rulings are parallel to the z axis and which has as a directrix the curve $y = f(x)$ in the plane $z = 0$. A similar discussion pertains when the directrix is in either of the other coordinate planes. The results are summarized in the following theorem.

16.7.2 Theorem   In three-dimensional space, the graph of an equation in two of the three variables x, y, and z is a cylinder whose rulings are parallel to the axis associated with the missing variable and whose directrix is a curve in the plane associated with the two variables appearing in the equation.

It follows from Theorem 16.7.2 that an equation of the parabolic cylinder of Fig. 16.7.1 is $y^2 = 8x$, considered as an equation in R_3. Similarly, equations of the elliptic cylinder of Fig. 16.7.2 and the hyperbolic cylinder of Fig. 16.7.3 are, respectively, $9x^2 + 16y^2 = 144$ and $25x^2 - 4y^2 = 100$, both considered as equations in R_3.

A *cross section* of a surface in a plane is the set of all points of the surface which lie in the given plane. If a plane is parallel to the plane of the directrix of a cylinder, the cross section of the cylinder is the same as the directrix. For example, the cross section of the elliptic cylinder of Fig. 16.7.2 in any plane parallel to the xy plane is an ellipse.

EXAMPLE 1:   Draw a sketch of the graph of each of the following equations: (a) $y = \ln z$; (b) $z^2 = x^3$.

z	y
1	0
2	.7
3	.57
9	1

SOLUTION: (a) The graph is a cylinder whose directrix in the yz plane is the curve $y = \ln z$ and whose rulings are parallel to the x axis. A sketch of the graph is shown in Fig. 16.7.6.

(b) The graph is a cylinder whose directrix is in the xz plane and whose rulings are parallel to the y axis. An equation of the directrix is the curve $z^2 = x^3$ in the xz plane. A sketch of the graph is shown in Fig. 16.7.7.

Figure 16.7.6   Figure 16.7.7

16.7.3 Definition   If a plane curve is revolved about a fixed line lying in the plane of the curve, the surface generated is called a *surface of revolution*. The fixed line is called the *axis* of the surface of revolution, and the plane curve is called the *generating curve*.

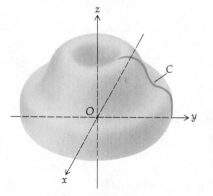

Figure 16.7.8

Figure 16.7.8 shows a surface of revolution whose generating curve is the curve C in the yz plane and whose axis is the z axis. A sphere is a particular example of a surface of revolution because a sphere can be generated by revolving a semicircle about a diameter. Figure 16.7.9 shows a sphere which can be generated by revolving the semicircle $y^2 + z^2 = r^2$, $z \geq 0$, about the y axis. Another example is a right-circular cylinder for which the generating curve and the axis are parallel straight lines. If the generating curve is the line $z = k$ in the xz plane and the axis is the x axis, we obtain the right-circular cylinder shown in Fig. 16.7.10.

We now find an equation of the surface generated by revolving about the y axis the curve in the yz plane having the two-dimensional equation

$$z = f(y) \tag{1}$$

Refer to Fig. 16.7.11. Let $P(x, y, z)$ be any point on the surface of revolution. Through P, pass a plane perpendicular to the y axis. Denote the point of intersection of this plane with the y axis by $Q(0, y, 0)$, and let $P_0(0, y, z)$ be the point of intersection of the plane with the generating curve. Because the cross section of the surface with the plane through P is a circle, P is on the surface if and only if

$$|\overline{QP}|^2 = |\overline{QP_0}|^2 \tag{2}$$

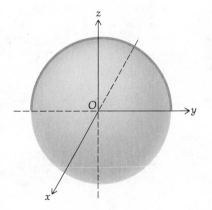

Figure 16.7.9

Because $|\overline{QP}| = \sqrt{x^2 + z^2}$ and $|\overline{QP_0}| = z_0$, we obtain from (2)

$$x^2 + z^2 = z_0^2 \tag{3}$$

The point P_0 is on the generating curve, and so its coordinates must satisfy Eq. (1). Therefore, we have

$$z_0 = f(y) \tag{4}$$

Figure 16.7.10

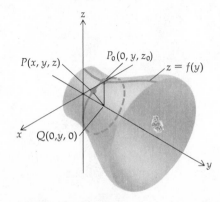

Figure 16.7.11

From Eqs. (3) and (4), we conclude that the point P is on the surface of revolution if and only if

$$x^2 + z^2 = [f(y)]^2 \qquad (5)$$

Equation (5) is the desired equation of the surface of revolution. Because (5) is equivalent to

$$\pm \sqrt{x^2 + z^2} = f(y)$$

we can obtain (5) by replacing z in (1) by $\pm \sqrt{x^2 + z^2}$.

In a similar manner we can show that if the curve in the yz plane having the two-dimensional equation

$$y = g(z) \qquad (6)$$

is revolved about the z axis, an equation of the surface of revolution generated is obtained by replacing y in (6) by $\pm \sqrt{x^2 + y^2}$. Analogous remarks hold when a curve in any coordinate plane is revolved about either one of the coordinate axes in that plane. In summary, the graphs of any of the following equations are surfaces of revolution having the indicated axis: $x^2 + y^2 = [F(z)]^2$—z axis; $x^2 + z^2 = [F(y)]^2$—y axis; $y^2 + z^2 = [F(x)]^2$—x axis. In each case, cross sections of the surface in planes perpendicular to the axis are circles having centers on the axis.

EXAMPLE 2:   Find an equation of the surface of revolution generated by revolving the parabola $y^2 = 4x$ in the xy plane about the x axis. Draw a sketch of the graph of the surface.

SOLUTION: In the equation of the parabola, we replace y by $\pm \sqrt{y^2 + z^2}$ and obtain

$$y^2 + z^2 = 4x$$

A sketch of the graph is shown in Fig. 16.7.12. Note that the same surface is generated if the parabola $z^2 = 4x$ in the xz plane is revolved about the x axis.

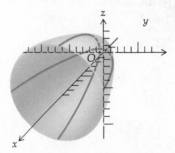

Figure 16.7.12

The surface obtained in Example 2 is called a *paraboloid of revolution*. If an ellipse is revolved about one of its axes, the surface obtained is called an *ellipsoid of revolution*. A *hyperboloid of revolution* is obtained when a hyperbola is revolved about an axis.

EXAMPLE 3:   Draw a sketch of the surface $x^2 + z^2 - 4y^2 = 0$.

SOLUTION: The given equation is of the form $x^2 + z^2 = [F(y)]^2$, and so its graph is a surface of revolution having the y axis as axis. If we solve the

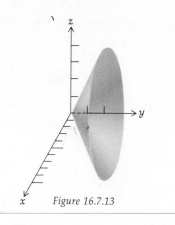

Figure 16.7.13

given equation for y, we obtain

$$2y = \pm \sqrt{x^2 + z^2}$$

Hence, the generating curve can be either the straight line $2y = x$ in the xy plane or the straight line $2y = z$ in the yz plane. By drawing sketches of the two possible generating curves and using the fact that cross sections of the surface in planes perpendicular to the y axis are circles having centers on the y axis, we obtain the surface shown in Fig. 16.7.13.

The surface obtained in Example 3 is called a *right-circular cone*.

Exercises 16.7

In Exercises 1 through 8, draw a sketch of the cylinder having the given equation.

1. $4x^2 + 9y^2 = 36$ 2. $x^2 - z^2 = 4$ 3. $y = |z|$ 4. $z = \sin y$
5. $z = 2x^2$ 6. $x^2 = y^3$ 7. $y = \cosh x$ 8. $z^2 = 4y^2$

In Exercises 9 through 14, find an equation of the surface of revolution generated by revolving the given plane curve about the indicated axis. Draw a sketch of the surface.

9. $x^2 = 4y$ in the xy plane, about the y axis.
10. $x^2 = 4y$ in the xy plane, about the x axis.
11. $x^2 + 4z^2 = 16$ in the xz plane, about the x axis.
12. $x^2 + 4z^2 = 16$ in the xz plane, about the z axis.
13. $y = \sin x$ in the xy plane, about the x axis.
14. $y^2 = z^3$ in the yz plane, about the z axis.

In Exercises 15 through 18, find the generating curve and the axis for the given surface of revolution. Draw a sketch of the surface.

15. $x^2 + y^2 - z^2 = 4$ 16. $y^2 + z^2 = e^{2x}$ 17. $x^2 + z^2 = |y|$ 18. $4x^2 + 9y^2 + 4z^2 = 36$
19. The tractrix

$$x = t - a \tanh \frac{t}{a} \qquad y = a \operatorname{sech} \frac{t}{a}$$

from $x = -a$ to $x = 2a$ is revolved about the x axis. Draw a sketch of the surface of revolution.

16.8 QUADRIC SURFACES

The graph of a second-degree equation in three variables x, y, and z is called a *quadric surface*. These surfaces correspond to the conics in the plane.

The simplest type of quadric surfaces are the parabolic, elliptic, and hyperbolic cylinders, which were discussed in the preceding section. There are six other types of quadric surfaces, which we now consider. We choose the coordinate axes so the equations are in their simplest form. In our discussion of each of these surfaces, we refer to the cross sections of the surfaces in planes parallel to the coordinate planes. These cross sections help to visualize the surface.

The ellipsoid

$$\frac{x^2}{a^2} + \frac{y^2}{b^2} + \frac{z^2}{c^2} = 1 \tag{1}$$

where a, b, and c are positive (see Fig. 16.8.1).

If in Eq. (1) we replace z by zero, we obtain the cross section of the ellipsoid in the xy plane, which is the ellipse $x^2/a^2 + y^2/b^2 = 1$. To obtain the cross sections of the surface with the planes $z = k$, we replace z by k in the equation of the ellipsoid and get

$$\frac{x^2}{a^2} + \frac{y^2}{b^2} = 1 - \frac{k^2}{c^2}$$

If $|k| < c$, the cross section is an ellipse and the lengths of the semiaxes decrease to zero as $|k|$ increases to the value c. If $|k| = c$, the intersection of a plane $z = k$ with the ellipsoid is the single point $(0, 0, k)$. If $|k| > c$, there is no intersection. We may have a similar discussion if we consider cross sections formed by planes parallel to either of the other coordinate planes.

The numbers a, b, and c are the lengths of the semiaxes of the ellipsoid. If any two of these three numbers are equal, we have an ellipsoid of revolution, which is also called a *spheroid*. If we have a spheroid and the third number is greater than the two equal numbers, the spheroid is said to be *prolate*. A prolate spheroid is shaped like a football. An *oblate* spheroid is obtained if the third number is less than the two equal numbers. If all three numbers a, b, and c in the equation of an ellipsoid are equal, the ellipsoid is a *sphere*.

The elliptic hyperboloid of one sheet

$$\frac{x^2}{a^2} + \frac{y^2}{b^2} - \frac{z^2}{c^2} = 1 \tag{2}$$

where a, b, and c are positive (see Fig. 16.8.2).

The cross sections in the planes $z = k$ are ellipses $x^2/a^2 + y^2/b^2 = 1 + k^2/c^2$. When $k = 0$, the lengths of the semiaxes of the ellipse are smallest, and these lengths increase as $|k|$ increases. The cross sections in the planes $x = k$ are hyperbolas $y^2/b^2 - z^2/c^2 = 1 - k^2/a^2$. If $|k| < a$, the transverse axis of the hyperbola is parallel to the y axis, and if $|k| > a$, the transverse axis is parallel to the z axis. If $k = a$, the hyperbola degenerates into two

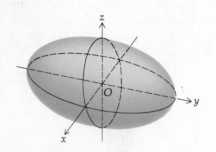

Figure 16.8.1

THE ELLIPSOID CAN BE:

① SPHEROID IF $a \neq b \neq c$

② PROLATE IF $a = b \neq c$

③ OBLATE IF $a = b \gtrless c$.

④

Figure 16.8.2

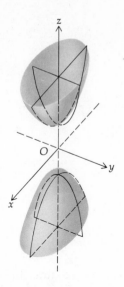

Figure 16.8.3

straight lines: $y/b - z/c = 0$ and $y/b + z/c = 0$. In an analogous manner, the cross sections in the planes $y = k$ are also hyperbolas. The axis of this hyperboloid is the z axis.

If $a = b$, the surface is a hyperboloid of revolution for which the axis is the line containing the conjugate axis.

The elliptic hyperboloid of two sheets

$$-\frac{x^2}{a^2} - \frac{y^2}{b^2} + \frac{z^2}{c^2} = 1 \tag{3}$$

where a, b, and c are positive (see Fig. 16.8.3).

Replacing z by k in Eq. (3), we obtain $x^2/a^2 + y^2/b^2 = k^2/c^2 - 1$. If $|k| < c$, there is no intersection of the plane $z = k$ with the surface; hence, there are no points of the surface between the planes $z = -c$ and $z = c$. If $|k| = c$, the intersection of the plane $z = k$ with the surface is the single point $(0, 0, k)$. When $|k| > c$, the cross section of the surface in the plane $z = k$ is an ellipse and the lengths of the semiaxes of the ellipse increase as $|k|$ increases.

The cross sections of the surface in the planes $x = k$ are the hyperbolas $z^2/c^2 - y^2/b^2 = 1 + k^2/a^2$ whose transverse axes are parallel to the z axis. In a similar fashion, the cross sections in the planes $y = k$ are the hyperbolas given by $z^2/c^2 - x^2/a^2 = 1 + k^2/b^2$ for which the transverse axes are also parallel to the z axis.

If $a = b$, the surface is a hyperboloid of revolution in which the axis is the line containing the transverse axis of the hyperbola.

Each of the above three quadric surfaces is symmetric with respect to each of the coordinate planes and symmetric with respect to the origin. Their graphs are called *central quadrics* and their center is at the origin. The graph of any equation of the form

$$\pm \frac{x^2}{a^2} \pm \frac{y^2}{b^2} \pm \frac{z^2}{c^2} = 1$$

where a, b, and c are positive, is a central quadric.

EXAMPLE 1:   Draw a sketch of the graph of the equation

$$4x^2 - y^2 + 25z^2 = 100$$

and name the surface.

SOLUTION: The given equation can be written as

$$\frac{x^2}{25} - \frac{y^2}{100} + \frac{z^2}{4} = 1$$

which is of the form of Eq. (2) with y and z interchanged. Hence, the surface is an elliptic hyperboloid of one sheet whose axis is the y axis. The cross sections in the planes $y = k$ are the ellipses $x^2/25 + z^2/4 = 1 + k^2/100$. The cross sections in the planes $x = k$ are the hyperbolas $z^2/4 - y^2/100 = 1 - k^2/25$, and the cross sections in the planes $z = k$ are the hyperbolas $x^2/25 - y^2/100 = 1 - k^2/4$. A sketch of the surface is shown in Fig. 16.8.4.

Figure 16.8.4

EXAMPLE 2: Draw a sketch of the graph of the equation

$$4x^2 - 25y^2 - z^2 = 100$$

and name the surface.

SOLUTION: The given equation can be written as

$$\frac{x^2}{25} - \frac{y^2}{4} - \frac{z^2}{100} = 1$$

which is of the form of Eq. (3) with x and z interchanged; thus, the surface is an elliptic hyperboloid of two sheets whose axis is the x axis. The cross sections in the planes $x = k$, where $|k| > 5$, are the ellipses $y^2/4 + z^2/100 = k^2/25 - 1$. The planes $x = k$, where $|k| < 5$, do not intersect the surface. The cross sections in the planes $y = k$ are the hyperbolas $x^2/25 - z^2/100 = 1 + k^2/4$, and the cross sections in the planes $z = k$ are the hyperbolas $x^2/25 - y^2/4 = 1 + k^2/100$. The required sketch is shown in Fig. 16.8.5.

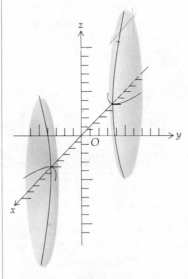

Figure 16.8.5

The following two quadrics are called noncentral quadrics.

The elliptic paraboloid

$$\left\{\ \frac{x^2}{a^2} + \frac{y^2}{b^2} = \frac{z}{c} \right. \tag{4}$$

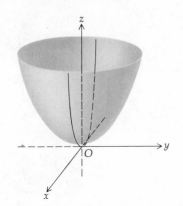

Figure 16.8.6

where a and b are positive and $c \neq 0$. Figure 16.8.6 shows the surface if $c > 0$.

Substituting k for z in Eq. (4), we obtain $x^2/a^2 + y^2/b^2 = k/c$. When $k = 0$, this equation becomes $x^2/a^2 + y^2/b^2 = 0$, which represents a single point, the origin. If $k \neq 0$ and k and c have the same sign, the equation is that of an ellipse. So we conclude that cross sections of the surface in the planes $z = k$, where k and c have the same sign, are ellipses and the lengths of the semiaxes increase as $|k|$ increases. If k and c have opposite signs, the planes $z = k$ do not intersect the surface. The cross sections of the surface with the planes $x = k$ and $y = k$ are parabolas. When $c > 0$, the parabolas open upward, as shown in Fig. 16.8.6; when $c < 0$, the parabolas open downward.

If $a = b$, the surface is a paraboloid of revolution.

The hyperbolic paraboloid

$$\frac{y^2}{b^2} - \frac{x^2}{a^2} = \frac{z}{c} \tag{5}$$

Figure 16.8.7

where a and b are positive and $c \neq 0$. The surface is shown in Fig. 16.8.7 for $c > 0$.

The cross sections of the surface in the planes $z = k$, where $k \neq 0$, are hyperbolas having their transverse axes parallel to the y axis if k and c have the same sign and parallel to the x axis if k and c have opposite signs. The cross section of the surface in the plane $z = 0$ consists of two straight lines through the origin. The cross sections in the planes $x = k$ are parabolas opening upward if $c > 0$ and opening downward if $c < 0$. The cross sections in the planes $y = k$ are parabolas opening downward if $c > 0$ and opening upward if $c < 0$.

EXAMPLE 3:   Draw a sketch of the graph of the equation

$$3y^2 + 12z^2 = 16x$$

and name the surface.

SOLUTION: The given equation can be written as

$$\frac{y^2}{16} + \frac{z^2}{4} = \frac{x}{3}$$

which is of the form of Eq. (4) with x and z interchanged. Hence, the graph of the equation is an elliptic paraboloid whose axis is the x axis. The cross sections in the planes $x = k > 0$ are the ellipses $y^2/16 + z^2/4 = k/3$, and the planes $x = k < 0$ do not intersect the surface. The cross sections in the planes $y = k$ are the parabolas $12z^2 = 16x - 3k^2$, and the cross sections in the planes $z = k$ are the parabolas $3y^2 = 16x - 12k^2$. A sketch of the elliptic paraboloid is shown in Fig. 16.8.8.

Figure 16.8.8

EXAMPLE 4: Draw a sketch of the graph of the equation

$$3y^2 - 12z^2 = 16x$$

and name the surface.

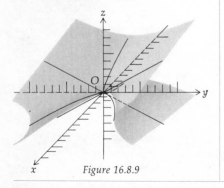

Figure 16.8.9

SOLUTION: Writing the given equation as

$$\frac{y^2}{16} - \frac{z^2}{4} = \frac{x}{3}$$

we see it is of the form of Eq. (5) with x and z interchanged. The surface is therefore a hyperbolic paraboloid. The cross sections in the planes $x = k \neq 0$ are the hyperbolas $y^2/16 - z^2/4 = k/3$. The cross section in the yz plane ($x = 0$) consists of the two lines $y = 2z$ and $y = -2z$. In the planes $z = k$, the cross sections are the parabolas $3y^2 = 16x + 12k^2$; in the planes $y = k$, the cross sections are the parabolas $12z^2 = 3k^2 - 16x$. Figure 16.8.9 shows a sketch of the hyperbolic paraboloid.

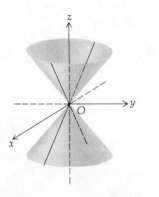

Figure 16.8.10

The elliptic cone

$$\frac{x^2}{a^2} + \frac{y^2}{b^2} - \frac{z^2}{c^2} = 0 \tag{6}$$

where a, b, and c are positive (see Fig. 16.8.10).

The intersection of the plane $z = 0$ with the surface is a single point, the origin. The cross sections of the surface in the planes $z = k$, where $k \neq 0$, are ellipses, and the lengths of the semiaxes increase as k increases. Cross sections in the planes $x = 0$ and $y = 0$ are pairs of intersecting lines. In the planes $x = k$ and $y = k$, where $k \neq 0$, the cross sections are hyperbolas.

EXAMPLE 5: Draw a sketch of the graph of the equation

$$4x^2 - y^2 + 25z^2 = 0$$

and name the surface.

SOLUTION: The given equation can be written as

$$\frac{x^2}{25} - \frac{y^2}{100} + \frac{z^2}{4} = 0$$

which is of the form of Eq. (6) with y and z interchanged. Therefore, the surface is an elliptic cone having the y axis as its axis. The surface intersects the xz plane $(y = 0)$ at the origin only. The intersection of the surface with the yz plane $(x = 0)$ is the pair of intersecting lines $y = \pm 5z$, and the intersection with the xy plane $(z = 0)$ is the pair of intersecting lines $y = \pm 2x$. The cross sections in the planes $y = k \neq 0$ are the ellipses $x^2/25 + z^2/4 = k^2/100$. In the planes $x = k \neq 0$ and $z = k \neq 0$, the cross sections are, respectively, the hyperbolas $y^2/100 - z^2/4 = k^2/25$ and $y^2/100 - x^2/25 = k^2/4$. A sketch of the surface is shown in Fig. 16.8.11.

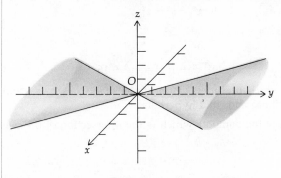

Figure 16.8.11

The general equation of the second degree in x, y, and z is of the form

$$ax^2 + by^2 + cz^2 + dxy + exz + fyz + gx + hy + iz + j = 0$$

where $a, b, \ldots , j$ are constants. It can be shown that by translation and rotation of the three-dimensional coordinate axes (the study of which is beyond the scope of this book) this equation can be reduced to one of the following two forms:

$$Ax^2 + By^2 + Cz^2 + J = 0 \qquad (7)$$

or

$$Ax^2 + By^2 + Iz = 0 \qquad (8)$$

Graphs of the equations of the second degree will either be one of the above six types of quadrics or else will degenerate into a cylinder, plane, line, point, or no real locus.

The nondegenerate curves associated with equations of the form (7) are the central quadrics and the elliptic cone, whereas those associated with equations of the form (8) are the noncentral quadrics. Following are examples of some degenerate cases:

$$x^2 - y^2 = 0; \text{ two planes, } x - y = 0 \text{ and } x + y = 0$$

$$z^2 = 0; \text{ one plane, the } xy \text{ plane}$$

$$x^2 + y^2 = 0; \text{ one line, the } z \text{ axis}$$

$$x^2 + y^2 + z^2 = 0; \text{ a single point, the origin}$$

$$x^2 + y^2 + z^2 + 1 = 0; \text{ no real locus}$$

Exercises 16.8

In Exercises 1 through 12 draw a sketch of the graph of the given equation and name the surface.

1. $4x^2 + 9y^2 + z^2 = 36$
2. $4x^2 - 9y^2 - z^2 = 36$
3. $4x^2 + 9y^2 - z^2 = 36$

4. $4x^2 - 9y^2 + z^2 = 36$
5. $x^2 = y^2 - z^2$
6. $x^2 = y^2 + z^2$

7. $\dfrac{x^2}{36} + \dfrac{z^2}{25} = 4y$
8. $\dfrac{y^2}{25} + \dfrac{x^2}{36} = 4$
9. $\dfrac{x^2}{36} - \dfrac{z^2}{25} = 9y$

10. $x^2 = 2y + 4z$
11. $x^2 + 16z^2 = 4y^2 - 16$
12. $9y^2 - 4z^2 + 18x = 0$

13. Find the values of k for which the intersection of the plane $x + ky = 1$ and the elliptic hyperboloid of two sheets $y^2 - x^2 - z^2 = 1$ is (a) an ellipse and (b) a hyperbola.

14. Find the vertex and focus of the parabola which is the intersection of the plane $y = 2$ with the hyperbolic paraboloid

$$\frac{y^2}{16} - \frac{x^2}{4} = \frac{z}{9}$$

15. Find the area of the plane section formed by the intersection of the plane $y = 3$ with the solid bounded by the ellipsoid

$$\frac{x^2}{9} + \frac{y^2}{25} + \frac{z^2}{4} = 1$$

16. Show that the intersection of the hyperbolic paraboloid $y^2/b^2 - x^2/a^2 = z/c$ and the plane $z = bx + ay$ consists of two intersecting straight lines and hence that a hyperbolic paraboloid may be thought of as being "composed entirely of straight lines."

17. Use the method of parallel plane sections to find the volume of the solid bounded by the ellipsoid $x^2/a^2 + y^2/b^2 + z^2/c^2 = 1$. (The measure of the area of the region enclosed by the ellipse having semiaxes a and b is πab.)

16.9 CURVES IN R_3

16.9.1 Definition Let f_1, f_2, and f_3 be three real-valued functions of a real variable t. Then for every number t in the domain common to f_1, f_2, and f_3 there is a vector $\mathbf{R}$ defined by

$$\mathbf{R}(t) = f_1(t)\mathbf{i} + f_2(t)\mathbf{j} + f_3(t)\mathbf{k} \tag{1}$$

and $\mathbf{R}$ is called a *vector-valued function*.

The graph of a vector-valued function in three-dimensional space is obtained analogously to the way we obtained the graph of a vector-valued function in two dimensions in Sec. 15.4. As t assumes all values in the domain of $\mathbf{R}$, the terminal point of the position representation of the vector $\mathbf{R}(t)$ traces a curve C, and this curve is called the graph of (1). A point on the curve C has the cartesian representation (x, y, z), where

$$x = f_1(t) \quad y = f_2(t) \quad z = f_3(t) \tag{2}$$

Equations (2) are called *parametric equations* of C, whereas Eq. (1) is called a *vector equation* of C. By eliminating t from Eqs. (2) we obtain two equations in x, y, and z. These equations are called *cartesian equations* of C. Each cartesian equation is an equation of a surface, and curve C is the intersection of the two surfaces. The equations of any two surfaces containing C may be taken as the cartesian equations defining C.

EXAMPLE 1: Draw a sketch of the curve having the vector equation

$$\mathbf{R}(t) = a \cos t\mathbf{i} + b \sin t\mathbf{j} + t\mathbf{k}$$

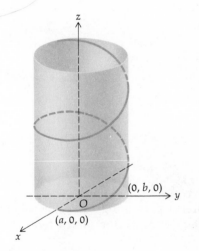

Figure 16.9.1

SOLUTION: Parametric equations of the given curve are

$$x = a \cos t \quad y = b \sin t \quad z = t$$

To eliminate t from the first two equations, we write them as

$$x^2 = a^2 \cos^2 t \quad \text{and} \quad y^2 = b^2 \sin^2 t$$

from which we get

$$\frac{x^2}{a^2} = \cos^2 t \quad \text{and} \quad \frac{y^2}{b^2} = \sin^2 t$$

Adding corresponding members of these two equations, we obtain

$$\frac{x^2}{a^2} + \frac{y^2}{b^2} = 1$$

Therefore, the curve lies entirely on the elliptical cylinder whose directrix is an ellipse in the xy plane and whose rulings are parallel to the z axis. Table 16.9.1 gives sets of values of x, y, and z for specific values of t. A sketch of the curve is shown in Fig. 16.9.1.

Table 16.9.1

t	x	y	z
0	a	0	0
$\frac{\pi}{4}$	$\frac{a}{\sqrt{2}}$	$\frac{b}{\sqrt{2}}$	$\frac{\pi}{4}$
$\frac{\pi}{2}$	0	b	$\frac{\pi}{2}$
$\frac{3\pi}{4}$	$-\frac{a}{\sqrt{2}}$	$\frac{b}{\sqrt{2}}$	$\frac{3\pi}{4}$
π	$-a$	0	π
$\frac{3\pi}{2}$	0	$-b$	$\frac{3\pi}{2}$

The curve of Example 1 is called a *helix*. If $a = b$, the helix is called a *circular helix* and it lies on the right-circular cylinder $x^2 + y^2 = a^2$.

EXAMPLE 2:   The curve having the vector equation

$$\mathbf{R}(t) = t\mathbf{i} + t^2\mathbf{j} + t^3\mathbf{k}$$

is called a *twisted cubic*. Show that this curve lies on the cylinder $y = x^2$ and draw a sketch of the portion of the curve from $t = 0$ to $t = 2$.

SOLUTION: Parametric equations of the twisted cubic are

$$x = t \qquad y = t^2 \qquad z = t^3$$

Eliminating t from the first two of these equations yields $y = x^2$, which is a cylinder whose directrix in the xy plane is a parabola. Figure 16.9.2 shows a sketch of the cylinder and the portion of the twisted cubic from $t = 0$ to $t = 2$.

Figure 16.9.2

Many of the definitions and theorems pertaining to vector-valued functions in two dimensions can be extended to vector-valued functions in three dimensions.

16.9.2 Definition   If $\mathbf{R}(t) = f_1(t)\mathbf{i} + f_2(t)\mathbf{j} + f_3(t)\mathbf{k}$, then

$$\lim_{t \to t_1} \mathbf{R}(t) = \lim_{t \to t_1} f_1(t)\mathbf{i} + \lim_{t \to t_1} f_2(t)\mathbf{j} + \lim_{t \to t_1} f_3(t)\mathbf{k}$$

if $\lim_{t \to t_1} f_1(t)$, $\lim_{t \to t_1} f_2(t)$, and $\lim_{t \to t_1} f_3(t)$ all exist.

16.9.3 Definition   The vector-valued function $\mathbf{R}$ is continuous at t_1 if and only if

(i) $\mathbf{R}(t_1)$ exists;

(ii) $\lim_{t \to t_1} \mathbf{R}(t)$ exists;

(iii) $\lim_{t \to t_1} \mathbf{R}(t) = \mathbf{R}(t_1)$.

16.9.4 Definition   The derivative of the vector-valued function **R** is a vector-valued function, denoted by **R**′ and defined by

$$\mathbf{R}'(t) = \lim_{\Delta t \to 0} \frac{\mathbf{R}(t + \Delta t) - \mathbf{R}(t)}{\Delta t}$$

if this limit exists.

16.9.5 Theorem   If **R** is the vector-valued function defined by

$$\mathbf{R}(t) = f_1(t)\mathbf{i} + f_2(t)\mathbf{j} + f_3(t)\mathbf{k}$$

and **R**′(t) exists, then

$$\mathbf{R}'(t) = f_1'(t)\mathbf{i} + f_2'(t)\mathbf{j} + f_3'(t)\mathbf{k}$$

The proof of Theorem 16.9.5 is left to the reader (see Exercise 9).

The geometric interpretation for the derivative of **R** is the same as that for the derivative of a vector-valued function in R_2. Figure 16.9.3 shows a portion of the curve C, which is the graph of **R**. In the figure $\overrightarrow{OP}$ is the position representation of **R**(t), $\overrightarrow{OQ}$ is the position representation of **R**$(t + \Delta t)$, and so $\overrightarrow{PQ}$ is a representation of the vector **R**$(t + \Delta t) -$ **R**(t). As Δt approaches zero, the vector [**R**$(t + \Delta t) -$ **R**(t)]/Δt has a representation approaching a directed line segment tangent to the curve C at P.

The definition of the unit tangent vector is analogous to Definition 15.8.1 for vectors in the plane. So if **T**(t) denotes the unit tangent vector to curve C having vector equation (1), then

$$\mathbf{T}(t) = \frac{D_t\mathbf{R}(t)}{|D_t\mathbf{R}(t)|} \tag{3}$$

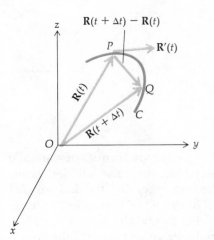

Figure 16.9.3

EXAMPLE 3:   Find the unit tangent vector for the twisted cubic of Example 2. Also, find $T(1)$ and show its representation at the point $(1, 1, 1)$ on the curve.

SOLUTION: Because $\mathbf{R}(t) = t\mathbf{i} + t^2\mathbf{j} + t^3\mathbf{k}$,

$$D_t\mathbf{R}(t) = \mathbf{i} + 2t\mathbf{j} + 3t^2\mathbf{k}$$

and

$$|D_t\mathbf{R}(t)| = \sqrt{1 + 4t^2 + 9t^4}$$

From Eq. (3), we have, then,

$$\mathbf{T}(t) = \frac{1}{\sqrt{1 + 4t^2 + 9t^4}} (\mathbf{i} + 2t\mathbf{j} + 3t^2\mathbf{k})$$

Therefore,

$$\mathbf{T}(1) = \frac{1}{\sqrt{14}} \mathbf{i} + \frac{2}{\sqrt{14}} \mathbf{j} + \frac{3}{\sqrt{14}} \mathbf{k}$$

Figure 16.9.4 shows the representation of $T(1)$ at the point $(1, 1, 1)$.

Figure 16.9.4

Theorems 15.5.6, 15.5.7, and 15.5.8 regarding derivatives of sums and products of two-dimensional vector-valued functions also hold for vectors in three dimensions. The following theorem regarding the derivative of the cross product of two vector-valued functions is similar to the corresponding formula for the derivative of the product of real-valued functions; however, it is important to maintain the correct order of the vector-valued functions because the cross product is not commutative.

16.9.6 Theorem   If **R** and **Q** are vector-valued functions, then

$$D_t[\mathbf{R}(t) \times \mathbf{Q}(t)] = \mathbf{R}(t) \times \mathbf{Q}'(t) + \mathbf{R}'(t) \times \mathbf{Q}(t)$$

for all values of t for which $\mathbf{R}'(t)$ and $\mathbf{Q}'(t)$ exist.

The proof of Theorem 16.9.6 is left for the reader (see Exercise 10).

We can define the length of an arc of a curve C in three-dimensional space in exactly the same way as we defined the length of an arc of a curve in the plane (see Definition 15.6.1). If C is the curve having parametric equations (2), f_1', f_2', f_3' are continuous on the closed interval $[a, b]$, and no two values of t give the same point (x, y, z) on C, then we can prove (as we did for the plane) a theorem similar to Theorem 15.6.3, which states that the length of arc, L units, of the curve C from the point $(f_1(a), f_2(a), f_3(a))$ to the point $(f_1(b), f_2(b), f_3(b))$ is determined by

$$L = \int_a^b \sqrt{[f_1'(t)]^2 + [f_2'(t)]^2 + [f_3'(t)]^2}\; dt \tag{4}$$

If s is the measure of the length of arc of C from the fixed point

$(f_1(t_0), f_2(t_0), f_3(t_0))$ to the variable point $(f_1(t), f_2(t), f_3(t))$ and s increases as t increases, then s is a function of t and is given by

$$s = \int_{t_0}^{t} \sqrt{[f_1'(u)]^2 + [f_2'(u)]^2 + [f_3'(u)]^2} \; du \tag{5}$$

As we showed in Sec. 15.6 for plane curves, we can show that if (1) is a vector equation of C, then

$$D_t s = |D_t \mathbf{R}(t)| \tag{6}$$

and the length of arc, L units, given by (4), also can be determined by

$$L = \int_a^b |D_t \mathbf{R}(t)| \; dt \tag{7}$$

EXAMPLE 4: Given the circular helix $\mathbf{R}(t) = a \cos t\mathbf{i} + a \sin t\mathbf{j} + t\mathbf{k}$, where $a > 0$, find the length of arc from $t = 0$ to $t = 2\pi$.

SOLUTION: $D_t \mathbf{R}(t) = -a \sin t\mathbf{i} + a \cos t\mathbf{j} + \mathbf{k}$. So from (7) we obtain

$$L = \int_0^{2\pi} \sqrt{(-a \sin t)^2 + (a \cos t)^2 + 1} \; dt$$

$$= \int_0^{2\pi} \sqrt{a^2 + 1} \; dt = 2\pi \sqrt{a^2 + 1}$$

Thus, the length of arc is $2\pi \sqrt{a^2 + 1}$ units.

The definitions of the *curvature vector* $\mathbf{K}(t)$ and the *curvature* $K(t)$ at a point P on a curve C in R_3 are the same as for plane curves given in Definition 15.9.1. Hence, if $\mathbf{T}(t)$ is the unit tangent vector to C at P and s is the measure of the arc length from an arbitrarily chosen point on C to P, where s increases as t increases, then

$$\mathbf{K}(t) = D_s \mathbf{T}(t)$$

or, equivalently,

$$\mathbf{K}(t) = \frac{D_t \mathbf{T}(t)}{|D_t \mathbf{R}(t)|} \tag{8}$$

and

$$K(t) = |D_s \mathbf{T}(t)|$$

or, equivalently,

$$K(t) = \left| \frac{D_t \mathbf{T}(t)}{|D_t \mathbf{R}(t)|} \right| \tag{9}$$

Taking the dot product of $\mathbf{K}(t)$ and $\mathbf{T}(t)$ and using (8), we get

$$\mathbf{K}(t) \cdot \mathbf{T}(t) = \frac{D_t \mathbf{T}(t)}{|D_t \mathbf{R}(t)|} \cdot \mathbf{T}(t) = \frac{1}{|D_t \mathbf{R}(t)|} D_t \mathbf{T}(t) \cdot \mathbf{T}(t) \tag{10}$$

Theorem 15.5.10 states that if a vector-valued function in a plane has a constant magnitude, it is orthogonal to its derivative. This theorem and its proof also hold for vectors in three dimensions. Therefore, because

$|\mathbf{T}(t)| = 1$, we can conclude from (10) that $\mathbf{K}(t) \cdot \mathbf{T}(t) = 0$. And so the curvature vector and the unit tangent vector of a curve at a point are orthogonal.

We define the *unit normal vector* as the unit vector having the same direction as the curvature vector, provided that the curvature vector is not the zero vector. So if $\mathbf{N}(t)$ denotes the unit normal vector to a curve C at a point P, then if $\mathbf{K}(t) \neq \mathbf{0}$,

$$\mathbf{N}(t) = \frac{\mathbf{K}(t)}{|\mathbf{K}(t)|} \tag{11}$$

From (11) and the previous discussion, it follows that the unit normal vector and the unit tangent vector are orthogonal. Thus, the angle between these two vectors has a radian measure of $\frac{1}{2}\pi$, and we have from Theorem 16.6.6,

$$|\mathbf{T}(t) \times \mathbf{N}(t)| = |\mathbf{T}(t)||\mathbf{N}(t)| \sin \tfrac{1}{2}\pi = (1)(1)(1) = 1$$

Therefore, the cross product of $\mathbf{T}(t)$ and $\mathbf{N}(t)$ is a unit vector. By Theorem 16.6.9 $\mathbf{T}(t) \times \mathbf{N}(t)$ is orthogonal to both $\mathbf{T}(t)$ and $\mathbf{N}(t)$; hence, the vector $\mathbf{B}(t)$, defined by

$$\mathbf{B}(t) = \mathbf{T}(t) \times \mathbf{N}(t) \tag{12}$$

is a unit vector orthogonal to $\mathbf{T}(t)$ and $\mathbf{N}(t)$ and is called the *unit binormal vector* to the curve C at P.

The three mutually orthogonal unit vectors, $\mathbf{T}(t)$, $\mathbf{N}(t)$, and $\mathbf{B}(t)$, of a curve C are called the *moving trihedral* of C (see Fig. 16.9.5).

Figure 16.9.5

EXAMPLE 5: Find the moving trihedral and the curvature at any point of the circular helix of Example 4.

SOLUTION: A vector equation of the circular helix is

$$\mathbf{R}(t) = a \cos t\mathbf{i} + a \sin t\mathbf{j} + t\mathbf{k}$$

So $D_t\mathbf{R}(t) = -a \sin t\mathbf{i} + a \cos t\mathbf{j} + \mathbf{k}$ and $|D_t\mathbf{R}(t)| = \sqrt{a^2 + 1}$. From (3) we get

$$\mathbf{T}(t) = \frac{1}{\sqrt{a^2 + 1}} \, (-a \sin t\mathbf{i} + a \cos t\mathbf{j} + \mathbf{k})$$

So

$$D_t\mathbf{T}(t) = \frac{1}{\sqrt{a^2 + 1}} \, (-a \cos t\mathbf{i} - a \sin t\mathbf{j})$$

Applying (8), we obtain

$$\mathbf{K}(t) = \frac{1}{a^2 + 1} \, (-a \cos t\mathbf{i} - a \sin t\mathbf{j})$$

The curvature, then, is given by

$$K(t) = |\mathbf{K}(t)| = \frac{a}{a^2 + 1}$$

and so the curvature of the circular helix is constant. From (11) we get

$$\mathbf{N}(t) = -\cos t\mathbf{i} - \sin t\mathbf{j}$$

Applying (12), we have

$$\mathbf{B}(t) = \frac{1}{\sqrt{a^2 + 1}} \, (-a \sin t\mathbf{i} + a \cos t\mathbf{j} + \mathbf{k}) \times (-\cos t\mathbf{i} - \sin t\mathbf{j})$$

$$= \frac{1}{\sqrt{a^2 + 1}} \, (\sin t\mathbf{i} - \cos t\mathbf{j} + a\mathbf{k})$$

A thorough study of curves and surfaces by means of calculus forms the subject of *differential geometry*. The use of the calculus of vectors further enhances this subject. The previous discussion has been but a short introduction.

We now consider briefly the motion of a particle along a curve in three-dimensional space. If the parameter t in the vector equation (1) measures time, then the position at t of a particle moving along the curve C, having vector equation (1), is the point $P(f_1(t), f_2(t), f_3(t))$. The *velocity vector*, $\mathbf{V}(t)$, and the *acceleration vector*, $\mathbf{A}(t)$, are defined as in the plane. The vector $\mathbf{R}(t)$ is called the *position vector*, and

$$\mathbf{V}(t) = D_t\mathbf{R}(t) \tag{13}$$

and

$$\mathbf{A}(t) = D_t\mathbf{V}(t) = D_t^2\mathbf{R}(t) \tag{14}$$

The *speed* of the particle at t is the magnitude of the velocity vector. By applying (6) we can write

$$|\mathbf{V}(t)| = D_t s$$

EXAMPLE 6:   A particle is moving along the curve having parametric equations $x = 3t$, $y = t^2$, and $z = \frac{2}{3}t^3$. Find the velocity and acceleration vectors and the speed of the particle at $t = 1$. Draw a sketch of a portion of the curve at $t = 1$, and draw representations of the velocity and acceleration vectors there.

SOLUTION: A vector equation of the curve is

$$\mathbf{R}(t) = 3t\mathbf{i} + t^2\mathbf{j} + \tfrac{2}{3}t^3\mathbf{k}$$

Therefore,

$$\mathbf{V}(t) = D_t\mathbf{R}(t) = 3\mathbf{i} + 2t\mathbf{j} + 2t^2\mathbf{k}$$

and

$$\mathbf{A}(t) = D_t\mathbf{V}(t) = 2\mathbf{j} + 4t\mathbf{k}$$

Also,

$$|\mathbf{V}(t)| = \sqrt{9 + 4t^2 + 4t^4}$$

So when $t = 1$, $\mathbf{V} = 3\mathbf{i} + 2\mathbf{j} + 2\mathbf{k}$, $\mathbf{A} = 2\mathbf{j} + 4\mathbf{k}$, and $|\mathbf{V}(1)| = \sqrt{17}$. The required sketch is shown in Fig. 16.9.6.

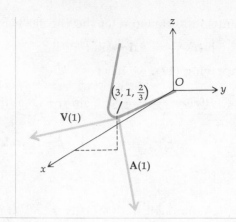

Figure 16.9.6

Exercises 16.9

In Exercises 1 through 4, find the unit tangent vector for the curve having the given vector equation.

1. $\mathbf{R}(t) = (t+1)\mathbf{i} - t^2\mathbf{j} + (1-2t)\mathbf{k}$

2. $\mathbf{R}(t) = \sin 2t\mathbf{i} + \cos 2t\mathbf{j} + 2t^{3/2}\mathbf{k}$

3. $\mathbf{R}(t) = e^t \cos t\mathbf{i} + e^t \sin t\mathbf{j} + e^t\mathbf{k}$

4. $\mathbf{R}(t) = t^2\mathbf{i} + (t + \frac{1}{3}t^3)\mathbf{j} + (t - \frac{1}{3}t^3)\mathbf{k}$

In Exercises 5 through 8, find the length of arc of the curve from t_1 to t_2.

5. The curve of Exercise 1; $t_1 = -1$; $t_2 = 2$.

6. The curve of Exercise 2; $t_1 = 0$; $t_2 = 1$.

7. The curve of Exercise 3; $t_1 = 0$; $t_2 = 3$.

8. The curve of Exercise 4; $t_1 = 0$; $t_2 = 1$.

9. Prove Theorem 16.9.5.

10. Prove Theorem 16.9.6.

11. Write a vector equation of the curve of intersection of the surfaces $y = e^x$ and $z = xy$.

12. Prove that the unit tangent vector of the circular helix of Example 2 makes an angle of constant radian measure with the unit vector $\mathbf{k}$.

13. Find the moving trihedral and the curvature at the point where $t = 1$ on the twisted cubic of Example 2.

14. Find the moving trihedral and the curvature at any point of the curve $\mathbf{R}(t) = \cosh t\mathbf{i} + \sinh t\mathbf{j} + t\mathbf{k}$.

In Exercises 15 through 18, find the moving trihedral and the curvature of the given curve at $t = t_1$, if they exist.

15. The curve of Exercise 1; $t_1 = -1$.

16. The curve of Exercise 2; $t_1 = 0$.

17. The curve of Exercise 3; $t_1 = 0$.

18. The curve of Exercise 4; $t_1 = 1$.

In Exercises 19 through 22, a particle is moving along the given curve. Find the velocity vector, the acceleration vector, and the speed at $t = t_1$. Draw a sketch of a portion of the curve at $t = t_1$ and draw the velocity and acceleration vectors there.

19. The circular helix of Example 4; $t_1 = \frac{1}{2}\pi$.

20. $x = t$, $y = \frac{1}{2}t^2$, $z = \frac{1}{3}t^3$; $t_1 = 2$.

21. $x = e^{2t}$, $y = e^{-2t}$, $z = te^{2t}$; $t_1 = 1$.

22. $x = 1/2(t^2 + 1)$; $y = \ln(1 + t^2)$, $z = \tan^{-1} t$; $t_1 = 1$.

23. Prove that if the speed of a moving particle is constant, its acceleration vector is always orthogonal to its velocity vector.

24. Prove that for the twisted cubic of Example 2, if $t \neq 0$, no two of the vectors $\mathbf{R}(t)$, $\mathbf{V}(t)$, and $\mathbf{A}(t)$ are orthogonal.

25. Prove that if $\mathbf{R}(t) = f_1(t)\mathbf{i} + f_2(t)\mathbf{j} + f_3(t)\mathbf{k}$ is a vector equation of curve C, and $K(t)$ is the curvature of C, then

$$K(t) = \frac{|D_t\mathbf{R}(t) \times D_t^2\mathbf{R}(t)|}{|D_t\mathbf{R}(t)|^3}$$

26. Use the formula of Exercise 25 to show that the curvature of the circular helix of Example 4 is $a/(a^2 + 1)$.

In Exercises 27 and 28, find the curvature of the given curve at the indicated point.

27. $x = t$, $y = t^2$, $z = t^3$; the origin.

28. $x = e^t$, $y = e^{-t}$, $z = t$; $t = 0$.

29. Prove that if $\mathbf{R}(t) = f_1(t)\mathbf{i} + f_2(t)\mathbf{j} + f_3(t)\mathbf{k}$ is a vector equation of curve C, $K(t)$ is the curvature of C at a point P, and s units is the arc length measured from an arbitrarily chosen point on C to P, then

$$D_s\mathbf{R}(t) \cdot D_s^3\mathbf{R}(t) = -[K(t)]^2$$

16.10 CYLINDRICAL AND SPHERICAL COORDINATES

Cylindrical and *spherical coordinates* are generalizations of polar coordinates to three-dimensional space. The cylindrical coordinate representation of a point P is (r, θ, z), where r and θ are the polar coordinates of the projection of P on a polar plane and z is the directed distance from this polar plane to P. See Fig. 16.10.1.

Figure 16.10.1

EXAMPLE 1: Draw a sketch of the graph of each of the following equations where c is a constant: (a) $r = c$; (b) $\theta = c$; (c) $z = c$.

SOLUTION: (a) For a point $P(r, \theta, z)$ on the graph of $r = c$, θ and z can have any values and r is a constant. The graph is a right-circular cylinder having radius $|c|$ and the z axis as its axis. A sketch of the graph is shown in Fig. 16.10.2.

Figure 16.10.2

Figure 16.10.3

Figure 16.10.4

(b) For all points $P(r, \theta, z)$ on the graph of $\theta = c$, r and z can assume any value while θ remains constant. The graph is a plane through the z axis. See Fig. 16.10.3 for a sketch of the graph.

(c) The graph of $z = c$ is a plane parallel to the polar plane at a directed distance of c units from it. Figure 16.10.4 shows a sketch of the graph.

Figure 16.10.5

The name "cylindrical coordinates" comes from the fact that the graph of $r = c$ is a right-circular cylinder as in Example 1(a). Cylindrical coordinates are often used in a physical problem when there is an axis of symmetry.

Suppose that a cartesian-coordinate system and a cylindrical-coordinate system are placed so the xy plane is the polar plane of the cylindrical-coordinate system and the positive side of the x axis is the polar axis as shown in Fig. 16.10.5. Then the point P has (x, y, z) and (r, θ, z) as two sets of coordinates which are related by the equations

$$x = r \cos \theta \qquad y = r \sin \theta \qquad z = z \tag{1}$$

and

$$r^2 = x^2 + y^2 \qquad \tan \theta = \frac{y}{x} \text{ if } x \neq 0 \qquad z = z \tag{2}$$

$$\theta = \tan^{-1} \frac{y}{x}$$

EXAMPLE 2: Find an equation in cartesian coordinates of the following surfaces whose equations are given in cylindrical coordinates and identify the surface:
(a) $r = 6 \sin \theta$;
(b) $r(3 \cos \theta + 2 \sin \theta) + 6z = 0$.

SOLUTION: (a) Multiplying on both sides of the equation by r, we get $r^2 = 6r \sin \theta$. Because $r^2 = x^2 + y^2$ and $r \sin \theta = y$, we have $x^2 + y^2 = 6y$. This equation can be written in the form $x^2 + (y - 3)^2 = 9$ which shows that its graph is a right-circular cylinder whose cross section in the xy plane is the circle with its center at $(0, 3)$ and radius 3.

(b) Replacing $r \cos \theta$ by x and $r \sin \theta$ by y, we get the equation $3x + 2y + 6z = 0$. Hence, the graph is a plane through the origin and has $\langle 3, 2, 6 \rangle$ as a normal vector.

EXAMPLE 3: Find an equation in cylindrical coordinates for each of the following surfaces whose equations are given in cartesian coordinates and identify the sur-

SOLUTION: (a) The equation is similar to Eq. (4) of Sec. 16.8, and so the graph is an elliptic paraboloid. If $x^2 + y^2$ is replaced by r^2, the equation becomes $r^2 = z$.

(b) The equation is similar to Eq. (5) of Sec. 16.8 with x and y interchanged. The graph is therefore a hyperbolic paraboloid having the z

face: (a) $x^2 + y^2 = z$;
(b) $x^2 - y^2 = z$.

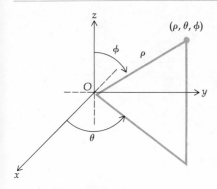

Figure 16.10.6

axis as its axis. When we replace x by $r \cos \theta$ and y by $r \sin \theta$, the equation becomes $r^2 \cos^2 \theta - r^2 \sin^2 \theta = z$; and because $\cos^2 \theta - \sin^2 \theta = \cos 2\theta$, we can write this as $z = r^2 \cos 2\theta$.

In a spherical-coordinate system there is a polar plane and an axis perpendicular to the polar plane, with the origin of the z axis at the pole of the polar plane. A point is located by three numbers, and the spherical-coordinate representation of a point P is (ρ, θ, ϕ), where $\rho = |OP|$, θ is the radian measure of the polar angle of the projection of P on the polar plane, and ϕ is the nonnegative radian measure of the smallest angle measured from the positive side of the z axis to the line OP. See Fig. 16.10.6. The origin has the spherical-coordinate representation $(0, \theta, \phi)$, where θ and ϕ may have any values. If the point $P(\rho, \theta, \phi)$ is not the origin, then $\rho > 0$ and $0 \leq \phi \leq \pi$, where $\phi = 0$ if P is on the positive side of the z axis and $\phi = \pi$ if P is on the negative side of the z axis.

EXAMPLE 4: Draw a sketch of the graph of each of the following equations where c is a constant:
(a) $\rho = c$, and $c > 0$; (b) $\theta = c$; (c) $\phi = c$, and $0 < c < \pi$.

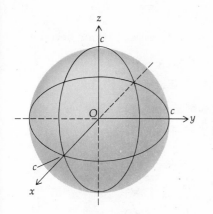

Figure 16.10.7

SOLUTION: (a) Every point $P(\rho, \theta, \phi)$ on the graph of $\rho = c$ has the same value of ρ, θ may be any number, and $0 \leq \phi \leq \pi$. It follows that the graph is a sphere of radius c and has its center at the pole. Figure 16.10.7 shows a sketch of the sphere.

(b) For any point $P(\rho, \theta, \phi)$ on the graph of $\theta = c$, ρ may be any nonnegative number, ϕ may be any number in the closed interval $[0, \pi]$, and θ is constant. The graph is a half plane containing the z axis and is obtained by rotating about the z axis through an angle of c radians that half of the xz plane for which $x \geq 0$. Figure 16.10.8 shows sketches of the half planes for $\theta = \frac{1}{4}\pi$, $\theta = \frac{2}{3}\pi$, $\theta = \frac{4}{3}\pi$, and $\theta = -\frac{1}{6}\pi$.

(c) The graph of $\phi = c$ contains all the points $P(\rho, \theta, \phi)$ for which ρ is any nonnegative number, θ is any number, and ϕ is the constant c. The graph is half of a cone having its vertex at the origin and the z axis as its axis. Figure 16.10.9a and b each show a sketch of the half cone for $0 < c < \frac{1}{2}\pi$ and $\frac{1}{2}\pi < c < \pi$, respectively.

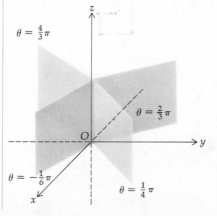

$\theta = \frac{4}{3}\pi$

$\theta = \frac{2}{3}\pi$

$\theta = -\frac{1}{6}\pi$

$\theta = \frac{1}{4}\pi$

Figure 16.10.8

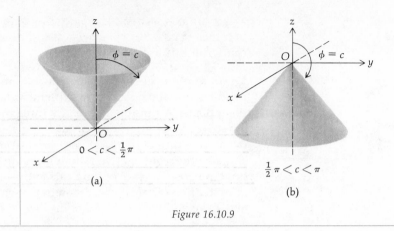

Figure 16.10.9

Because the graph of $\rho = c$ is a sphere as seen in Example 4(a), we have the name "spherical coordinates." In a physical problem when there is a point that is a center of symmetry, spherical coordinates are often used.

By placing a spherical-coordinate system and a cartesian-coordinate system together as shown in Fig. 16.10.10, we obtain relationships between the spherical coordinates and the cartesian coordinates of a point P from

$$x = |\overline{OQ}| \cos \theta \qquad y = |\overline{OQ}| \sin \theta \qquad z = |\overline{QP}|$$

Because $|\overline{OQ}| = \rho \sin \phi$ and $|\overline{QP}| = \rho \cos \phi$, these equations become

$$\left(\quad x = \rho \sin \phi \cos \theta \qquad y = \rho \sin \phi \sin \theta \qquad z = \rho \cos \phi \right. \tag{3}$$

By squaring each of the equations in (3) and adding, we have

$$x^2 + y^2 + z^2 = \rho^2 \sin^2 \phi \cos^2 \theta + \rho^2 \sin^2 \phi \sin^2 \theta + \rho^2 \cos^2 \phi$$
$$= \rho^2 \sin^2 \phi (\cos^2 \theta + \sin^2 \theta) + \rho^2 \cos^2 \phi$$
$$= \rho^2 (\sin^2 \phi + \cos^2 \phi)$$
$$= \rho^2$$

Figure 16.10.10

EXAMPLE 5:   Find an equation in cartesian coordinates of the following surfaces whose equations are given in spherical coordinates and identify the surface:
(a) $\rho \cos \phi = 4$; (b) $\rho \sin \phi = 4$.

SOLUTION: (a) Because $z = \rho \cos \phi$, the equation becomes $z = 4$. Hence, the graph is a plane parallel to the xy plane and 4 units above it.

(b) For spherical coordinates $\rho \geq 0$ and $\sin \phi \geq 0$ (because $0 \leq \phi \leq \pi$); therefore, if we square on both sides of the given equation, we obtain the equivalent equation $\rho^2 \sin^2 \phi = 16$, which in turn is equivalent to

$$\rho^2 (1 - \cos^2 \phi) = 16$$

or

$$\rho^2 - \rho^2 \cos^2 \phi = 16$$

Replacing ρ^2 by $x^2 + y^2 + z^2$ and $\rho \cos \phi$ by z, we get

$$x^2 + y^2 + z^2 - z^2 = 16$$

or, equivalently,

$$x^2 + y^2 = 16$$

Therefore, the graph is the right-circular cylinder having the z axis as its axis and radius 4.

EXAMPLE 6:   Find an equation in spherical coordinates for: (a) the elliptic paraboloid of Example 3(a); and (b) the plane of Example 2(b).

SOLUTION: (a) A cartesian equation of the elliptic paraboloid of Example 3(a) is $x^2 + y^2 = z$. Replacing x by $\rho \sin \phi \cos \theta$, y by $\rho \sin \phi \sin \theta$, and z by $\rho \cos \phi$, we get

$$\rho^2 \sin^2 \phi \cos^2 \theta + \rho^2 \sin^2 \phi \sin^2 \theta = \rho \cos \phi$$

or, equivalently,

$$\rho^2 \sin^2 \phi (\cos^2 \theta + \sin^2 \theta) = \rho \cos \phi$$

which is equivalent to the two equations

$$\rho = 0 \quad \text{and} \quad \rho \sin^2 \phi = \cos \phi$$

The origin is the only point whose coordinates satisfy $\rho = 0$. Because the origin $(0, \theta, \frac{1}{2}\pi)$ lies on $\rho \sin^2 \phi = \cos \phi$, we can disregard the equation $\rho = 0$. Furthermore, $\sin \phi \neq 0$ because there is no value of ϕ for which both $\sin \phi$ and $\cos \phi$ are 0. Therefore, the equation $\rho \sin^2 \phi = \cos \phi$ can be written as $\rho = \csc^2 \phi \cos \phi$, or, equivalently, $\rho = \csc \phi \cot \phi$.

(b) A cartesian equation of the plane of Example 2(b) is $3x + 2y + 6z = 0$. By using Eqs. (3) this equation becomes

$$3\rho \sin \phi \cos \theta + 2\rho \sin \phi \sin \theta + 6\rho \cos \phi = 0$$

Exercises 16.10

1. Find the cartesian coordinates of the point having the given cylindrical coordinates:
   (a) $(3, \frac{1}{2}\pi, 5)$ (b) $(7, \frac{2}{3}\pi, -4)$ (c) $(1, 1, 1)$

2. Find a set of cylindrical coordinates of the point having the given cartesian coordinates:
   (a) $(4, 4, -2)$ (b) $(-3\sqrt{3}, 3, 6)$ (c) $(1, 1, 1)$

3. Find the cartesian coordinates of the point having the given spherical coordinates:
   (a) $(4, \frac{1}{6}\pi, \frac{1}{4}\pi)$ (b) $(4, \frac{1}{2}\pi, \frac{1}{3}\pi)$ (c) $(\sqrt{6}, \frac{1}{3}\pi, \frac{3}{4}\pi)$

4. Find a set of spherical coordinates of the point having the given cartesian coordinates:
   (a) $(1, -1, -\sqrt{2})$ (b) $(-1, \sqrt{3}, 2)$ (c) $(2, 2, 2)$

5. Find a set of cylindrical coordinates of the point having the given spherical coordinates:

    (a) $(4, \frac{2}{3}\pi, \frac{5}{6}\pi)$ (b) $(\sqrt{2}, \frac{3}{4}\pi, \pi)$ (c) $(2\sqrt{3}, \frac{1}{3}\pi, \frac{1}{4}\pi)$

6. Find a set of spherical coordinates of the point having the given cylindrical coordinates:

    (a) $(3, \frac{1}{6}\pi, 3)$ (b) $(3, \frac{1}{2}\pi, 2)$ (c) $(2, \frac{5}{6}\pi, -4)$

In Exercises 7 through 10, find an equation in cylindrical coordinates of the given surface and identify the surface.

7. $x^2 + y^2 + 4z^2 = 16$ 8. $x^2 - y^2 = 9$

9. $x^2 - y^2 = 3z^2$ 10. $x^2 + y^2 = z^2$

In Exercises 11 through 14, find an equation in spherical coordinates of the given surface and identify the surface.

11. $x^2 + y^2 + z^2 - 9z = 0$ 12. $x^2 + y^2 = z^2$

13. $x^2 + y^2 = 9$ 14. $x^2 + y^2 = 2z$

In Exercises 15 through 18, find an equation in cartesian coordinates for the surface whose equation is given in cylindrical coordinates. In Exercises 15 and 16, identify the surface.

15. (a) $r = 4$; (b) $\theta = \frac{1}{4}\pi$ 16. $r = 3 \cos \theta$

17. $r^2 \cos 2\theta = z^3$ 18. $z^2 \sin^3 \theta = r^3$

In Exercises 19 through 22, find an equation in cartesian coordinates for the surface whose equation is given in spherical coordinates. In Exercises 19 and 20 identify the surface.

19. (a) $\rho = 9$; (b) $\theta = \frac{1}{4}\pi$; (c) $\phi = \frac{1}{4}\pi$ 20. $\rho = 9 \sec \phi$

21. $\rho = 2 \tan \theta$ 22. $\rho = 6 \sin \phi \sin \theta + 3 \cos \phi$

23. A curve C in R_3 has the following parametric equations in cylindrical coordinates:

$$r = F_1(t) \qquad \theta = F_2(t) \qquad z = F_3(t)$$

Use formula (4) of Sec. 16.9 and formulas (1) of this section to prove that if L units is the length of arc of C from the point where $t = a$ to the point where $t = b$, then

$$L = \int_a^b \sqrt{(D_t r)^2 + r^2 (D_t \theta)^2 + (D_t z)^2} \, dt$$

24. A curve C in R_3 has the following parametric equations in spherical coordinates:

$$\rho = G_1(t) \qquad \theta = G_2(t) \qquad \phi = G_3(t)$$

Use formula (4) of Sec. 16.9 and formulas (3) of this section to prove that if L units is the length of arc of C from the point where $t = a$ to the point where $t = b$, then

$$L = \int_a^b \sqrt{(D_t \rho)^2 + \rho^2 \sin^2 \phi (D_t \theta)^2 + \rho^2 (D_t \phi)^2} \, dt$$

25. (a) Show that parametric equations for the circular helix of Example 4, Sec. 16.9, are

$$r = a \qquad \theta = t \qquad z = t$$

(b) Use the formula of Exercise 23 to find the length of arc of the circular helix of part (a) from $t = 0$ to $t = 2\pi$. Check your result with that of Example 4, Sec. 16.9.

26. A *conical helix* winds around a cone in a way similar to that in which a circular helix winds around a cylinder. Use the formula of Exercise 24 to find the length of arc from $t = 0$ to $t = 2\pi$ of the conical helix having parametric equations

$$\rho = t \qquad \theta = t \qquad \phi = \frac{1}{4}\pi$$

Review Exercises (Chapter 16)

1. Draw a sketch of the graph of $x = 3$ in R_1, R_2, and R_3.

2. Draw a sketch of the set of points satisfying the simultaneous equations $x = 6$ and $y = 3$ in R_2 and R_3.

In Exercises 3 through 11, describe in words the set of points in R_3 satisfying the given equation or the given pair of equations. Draw a sketch of the graph.

3. $\begin{cases} y = 0 \\ z = 0 \end{cases}$

4. $\begin{cases} x = z \\ y = z \end{cases}$

5. $\begin{cases} x^2 + z^2 = 4 \\ y = 0 \end{cases}$

6. $x^2 + z^2 = 4$

7. $x = y$

8. $y^2 - z^2 = 0$

9. $x^2 + y^2 = 9z$

10. $x^2 + y^2 = z^2$

11. $x^2 - y^2 = z^2$

In Exercises 12 through 17, let $\mathbf{A} = -\mathbf{i} + 3\mathbf{j} + 2\mathbf{k}$, $\mathbf{B} = 2\mathbf{i} + \mathbf{j} - 4\mathbf{k}$, $\mathbf{C} = \mathbf{i} + 2\mathbf{j} - 2\mathbf{k}$, $\mathbf{D} = 3\mathbf{j} - \mathbf{k}$, $\mathbf{E} = 5\mathbf{i} - 2\mathbf{j}$, and find the indicated vector or scalar.

12. $3\mathbf{A} - 2\mathbf{B} + \mathbf{C}$

13. $6\mathbf{C} + 4\mathbf{D} - \mathbf{E}$

14. $2\mathbf{B} \cdot \mathbf{C} + 3\mathbf{D} \cdot \mathbf{E}$

15. $\mathbf{D} \cdot \mathbf{B} \times \mathbf{C}$

16. $(\mathbf{A} \times \mathbf{C}) - (\mathbf{D} \times \mathbf{E})$

17. $|\mathbf{A} \times \mathbf{B}||\mathbf{D} \times \mathbf{E}|$

In Exercises 18 through 23 there is only one way that a meaningful expression can be obtained by inserting parentheses. Insert the parentheses and find the indicated vector or scalar if $\mathbf{A} = \langle 3, -2, 4 \rangle$, $\mathbf{B} = \langle -5, 7, 2 \rangle$, and $\mathbf{C} = \langle 4, 6, -1 \rangle$.

18. $\mathbf{B} \cdot \mathbf{A} - \mathbf{C}$

19. $\mathbf{A} + \mathbf{B} \cdot \mathbf{C}$

20. $\mathbf{A} \cdot \mathbf{B} \, \mathbf{C}$

21. $\mathbf{A} \, \mathbf{B} \cdot \mathbf{C}$

22. $\mathbf{A} \times \mathbf{B} \cdot \mathbf{C} \times \mathbf{A}$

23. $\mathbf{A} \times \mathbf{B} \cdot \mathbf{A} + \mathbf{B} - \mathbf{C}$

24. If $\mathbf{A}$ is any vector, prove that $\mathbf{A} = (\mathbf{A} \cdot \mathbf{i})\mathbf{i} + (\mathbf{A} \cdot \mathbf{j})\mathbf{j} + (\mathbf{A} \cdot \mathbf{k})\mathbf{k}$.

25. Find an equation of the sphere concentric with the sphere $x^2 + y^2 + z^2 + 4x + 2y - 6z + 10 = 0$ and containing the point $(-4, 2, 5)$.

26. Find an equation of the surface of revolution generated by revolving the ellipse $9x^2 + 4z^2 = 36$ in the xz plane about the x axis. Draw a sketch of the surface.

27. Determine the value of c so that the vectors $3\mathbf{i} + c\mathbf{j} - 3\mathbf{k}$ and $5\mathbf{i} - 4\mathbf{j} + \mathbf{k}$ are orthogonal.

28. Show that there are representations of the three vectors $\mathbf{A} = 5\mathbf{i} + \mathbf{j} - 3\mathbf{k}$, $\mathbf{B} = \mathbf{i} + 3\mathbf{j} - 2\mathbf{k}$, and $\mathbf{C} = -4\mathbf{i} + 2\mathbf{j} + \mathbf{k}$ which form a triangle.

29. Find the distance from the origin to the plane through the point $(-6, 3, -2)$ and having $5\mathbf{i} - 3\mathbf{j} + 4\mathbf{k}$ as a normal vector.

30. Find an equation of the plane containing the points $(1, 7, -3)$ and $(3, 1, 2)$ and which does not intersect the x axis.

31. Find an equation of the plane through the three points $(-1, 2, 1)$, $(1, 4, 0)$, and $(1, -1, 3)$ by two methods: (a) using the cross product; (b) without using the cross product.

32. Find two unit vectors orthogonal to $\mathbf{i} - 3\mathbf{j} + 4\mathbf{k}$ and whose representations are parallel to the yz plane.

33. Find the distance from the point $P(4, 6, -4)$ to the line through the two points $A(2, 2, 1)$ and $B(4, 3, -1)$.

34. Find the distance from the plane $9x - 2y + 6z + 44 = 0$ to the point $(-3, 2, 0)$.

35. If θ is the radian measure of the angle between the vectors $\mathbf{A} = 2\mathbf{i} + \mathbf{j} + \mathbf{k}$ and $\mathbf{B} = 4\mathbf{i} - 3\mathbf{j} + 5\mathbf{k}$ find $\cos \theta$ in two ways: (a) by using the dot product; (b) by using the cross product and a trigonometric identity.

36. Prove that the lines

$$\frac{x-1}{1} = \frac{y+2}{2} = \frac{z-2}{2} \quad \text{and} \quad \frac{x-2}{2} = \frac{y-5}{3} = \frac{z-5}{1}$$

are skew lines and find the distance between them.

37. Find symmetric and parametric equations of the line through the origin and perpendicular to each of the lines of Exercise 36.

38. Find the area of the parallelogram two of whose sides are the position representations of the vectors $2\mathbf{j} - 3\mathbf{k}$ and $5\mathbf{i} + 4\mathbf{k}$.

39. Find the volume of the parallelepiped having vertices at $(1, 3, 0)$, $(2, -1, 3)$, $(-2, 2, -1)$, and $(-1, 1, 2)$.

40. Find the length of the arc of the curve

$$x = t \cos t \qquad y = t \sin t \qquad z = t$$

from $t = 0$ to $t = \frac{1}{2}\pi$.

41. A particle is moving along the curve of Exercise 40. Find the velocity vector, the acceleration vector, and the speed at $t = \frac{1}{2}\pi$. Draw a sketch of a portion of the curve at $t = \frac{1}{2}\pi$ and draw the representations of the velocity and acceleration vectors there.

42. Find the unit tangent vector and the curvature at any point on the curve having the vector equation

$$\mathbf{R}(t) = e^t\mathbf{i} + e^{-t}\mathbf{j} + 2t\mathbf{k}$$

43. Find an equation in cylindrical coordinates of the graph of each of the equations: (a) $(x + y)^2 + 1 = z$; (b) $25x^2 + 4y^2 = 100$.

44. Find an equation in spherical coordinates of the graph of each of the equations: (a) $x^2 + y^2 + 4z^2 = 4$; (b) $4x^2 - 4y^2 + 9z^2 = 36$.

45. If $\mathbf{R}$, $\mathbf{Q}$, and $\mathbf{W}$ are three vector-valued functions whose derivatives with respect to t exist, prove that

$$D_t[\mathbf{R}(t) \cdot \mathbf{Q}(t) \times \mathbf{W}(t)] = D_t\mathbf{R}(t) \cdot \mathbf{Q}(t) \times \mathbf{W}(t) + \mathbf{R}(t) \cdot D_t\mathbf{Q}(t) \times \mathbf{W}(t) + \mathbf{R}(t) \cdot \mathbf{Q}(t) \times D_t\mathbf{W}(t)$$

17

Differential Calculus of Functions of Several Variables

17.1 FUNCTIONS OF MORE THAN ONE VARIABLE

In this section we extend the concept of a function to functions of n variables, and in succeeding sections we extend to functions of n variables the concepts of the *limit* of a function, *continuity* of a function, and *derivative* of a function. A thorough treatment of these topics belongs to a course in advanced calculus. In this book we confine most of our discussion of functions of more than one variable to those of two and three variables; however, we make the definitions for functions of n variables and then show the applications of these definitions to functions of two and three variables. We also show that when each of these definitions is applied to a function of one variable we have the definition previously given.

To extend the concept of a function to functions of any number of variables, we must first consider points in n-dimensional number space. Just as we denoted a point in R_1 by a real number x, a point in R_2 by an ordered pair of real numbers (x, y), and a point in R_3 by an ordered triple of real numbers (x, y, z), we represent a point in n-dimensional number space, R_n, by an ordered n-tuple of real numbers customarily denoted by $P = (x_1, x_2, \ldots, x_n)$. In particular, if $n = 1$, we let $P = x$; if $n = 2$, $P = (x, y)$; if $n = 3$, $P = (x, y, z)$; if $n = 6$, $P = (x_1, x_2, x_3, x_4, x_5, x_6)$.

17.1.1 Definition

The set of all ordered n-tuples of real numbers is called the *n-dimensional number space* and is denoted by R_n. Each ordered n-tuple $(x_1, x_2, \ldots, x_n)$ is called a *point* in the n-dimensional number space.

17.1.2 Definition   A *function of n variables* is a set of ordered pairs of the form (P, w) in which no two distinct ordered pairs have the same first element. P is a point in n-dimensional number space and w is a real number. The totality of all possible values of P is called the *domain* of the function, and the totality of all possible values of w is called the *range* of the function.

From this definition, we see that the domain of a function of n variables is a set of points in R_n and that the range is a set of real numbers or, equivalently, a set of points in R_1. When $n = 1$, we have a function of one variable; thus, the domain is a set of points in R_1 or, equivalently, a set of real numbers, and the range is a set of real numbers. Hence, we see that Definition 2.1.1 is a special case of Definition 17.1.2. If $n = 2$, we have a function of two variables, and the domain is a set of points in R_2 or, equivalently, a set of ordered pairs of real numbers (x, y). The range is a set of real numbers.

EXAMPLE 1:   Let the function f of two variables x and y be the set of all ordered pairs of the form (P, z) such that

$$z = \sqrt{25 - x^2 - y^2}$$

Find the domain and range of f and draw a sketch showing as a shaded region in R_2 the set of points in the domain of f.

SOLUTION: The domain of f is the set of all ordered pairs (x, y) for which $25 - x^2 - y^2 \geq 0$. This is the set of all points in the xy plane on the circle $x^2 + y^2 = 25$ and in the interior region bounded by the circle.

Because $z = \sqrt{25 - (x^2 + y^2)}$, we see that $0 \leq z \leq 5$; therefore, the range of f is the set of all real numbers in the closed interval $[0, 5]$. The required sketch is shown in Fig. 17.1.1.

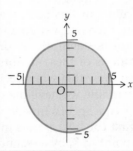

Figure 17.1.1

EXAMPLE 2:   The function g of two variables x and y is the set of all ordered pairs of the form (P, z) such that

$$z = \frac{\sqrt{x^2 + y^2 - 25}}{y}$$

SOLUTION: The domain of g consists of all ordered pairs (x, y) for which $x^2 + y^2 \geq 25$ and $y \neq 0$. This is the set of all points, not on the x axis, which are either on the circle $x^2 + y^2 = 25$ or in the exterior region bounded by the circle. The required sketch is shown in Fig. 17.1.2.

Find the domain of g and draw a sketch showing as a shaded region in R_2 the set of points in the domain of g.

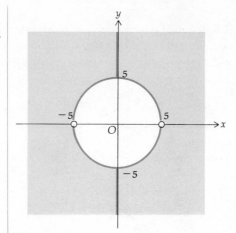

Figure 17.1.2

EXAMPLE 3:   The function F of two variables x and y is the set of all ordered pairs of the form (P, z) such that

$$z = y\sqrt{x^2 + y^2 - 25}$$

Find the domain of F and draw a sketch showing as a shaded region in R_2 the set of points in the domain of F.

SOLUTION: If $y = 0$, then $z = 0$ regardless of the value of x. However, if $y \neq 0$, then $x^2 + y^2 - 25$ must be nonnegative in order for z to be defined. Therefore, the domain of F consists of all ordered pairs (x, y) for which either $y = 0$ or $x^2 + y^2 - 25 \geq 0$. This is the set of all points on the circle $x^2 + y^2 = 25$, all points in the exterior region bounded by the circle, and all points on the x axis for which $-5 < x < 5$. The required sketch is shown in Fig. 17.1.3.

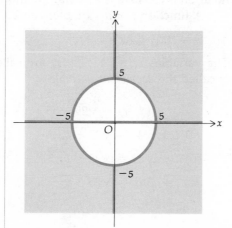

Figure 17.1.3

EXAMPLE 4:   The function G of two variables x and y is the set of all ordered pairs of the form (P, z) such that

$$z = \frac{y}{\sqrt{x^2 + y^2 - 25}}$$

SOLUTION: If $y = 0$, then $z = 0$ provided that $x^2 + y^2 - 25 \neq 0$. If $y \neq 0$, then $x^2 + y^2 - 25$ must be positive in order for z to be defined. Hence, the domain of G consists of all ordered pairs (x, y) for which $x^2 + y^2 - 25 > 0$ and those for which $y = 0$ and $x \neq \pm 5$. These are all the points in the exterior region bounded by the circle $x^2 + y^2 = 25$ and the points on the x axis for which $-5 < x < 5$. The required sketch is shown in Fig. 17.1.4.

Find the domain of G and draw a sketch showing as a shaded region in R_2 the set of points in the domain of G.

Figure 17.1.4

If f is a function of n variables, then according to Definition 17.1.2, f is a set of ordered pairs of the form (P, w), where $P = (x_1, x_2, \ldots, x_n)$ is a point in R_n and w is a real number. We denote the particular value of w, which corresponds to a point P, by the symbol $f(P)$ or $f(x_1, x_2, \ldots, x_n)$. In particular, if $n = 2$ and we let $P = (x, y)$, we can denote the function value by either $f(P)$ or $f(x, y)$. Similarly, if $n = 3$ and $P = (x, y, z)$, we denote the function value by either $f(P)$ or $f(x, y, z)$. Note that if $n = 1$, $P = x$; hence, if f is a function of one variable, $f(P) = f(x)$. Therefore, this notation is consistent with our notation for function values of one variable.

A function f of n variables can be defined by the equation

$$w = f(x_1, x_2, \ldots, x_n)$$

The variables $x_1, x_2, \ldots, x_n$ are called the *independent variables*, and w is called the *dependent variable*.

EXAMPLE 5:   If f is the function of Example 1, find (a) $f(3, -4)$; (b) $f(-2, 1)$; (c) $f(u, 3v)$.

SOLUTION: $f(x, y) = \sqrt{25 - x^2 - y^2}$, and, therefore,

(a) $f(3, -4) = \sqrt{25 - (3)^2 - (-4)^2} = \sqrt{25 - 9 - 16} = 0$

(b) $f(-2, 1) = \sqrt{25 - (-2)^2 - (1)^2} = \sqrt{25 - 4 - 1} = 2\sqrt{5}$

(c) $f(u, 3v) = \sqrt{25 - u^2 - (3v)^2} = \sqrt{25 - u^2 - 9v^2}$

EXAMPLE 6:   The domain of a function g is the set of all ordered triples of real numbers (x, y, z) such that $g(x, y, z) = x^2 - 5xz + yz^2$. Find (a) $g(1, 4, -2)$; (b) $g(2a, -b, 3c)$; (c) $g(x^2, y^2, z^2)$; (d) $g(y, z, -x)$.

SOLUTION:

(a) $g(1, 4, -2) = 1^2 - 5(1)(-2) + 4(-2)^2 = 1 + 10 + 16 = 27$

(b) $g(2a, -b, 3c) = (2a)^2 - 5(2a)(3c) + (-b)(3c)^2$
$$= 4a^2 - 30ac - 9bc^2$$

(c) $g(x^2, y^2, z^2) = (x^2)^2 - 5(x^2)(z^2) + (y^2)(z^2)^2 = x^4 - 5x^2z^2 + y^2z^4$

(d) $g(y, z, -x) = y^2 - 5y(-x) + z(-x)^2 = y^2 + 5xy + x^2z$

17.1.3 Definition

If f is a function of a single variable and g is a function of two variables, then the *composite function* $f \circ g$ is the function of two variables defined by

$$(f \circ g)(x, y) = f(g(x, y))$$

and the domain of $f \circ g$ is the set of all points (x, y) in the domain of g such that $g(x, y)$ is in the domain of f.

EXAMPLE 7:   Given $f(t) = \ln t$ and $g(x, y) = x^2 + y$, find $h(x, y)$ if $h = f \circ g$, and find the domain of h.

SOLUTION:

$$h(x, y) = (f \circ g)(x, y) = f(g(x, y))$$
$$= f(x^2 + y)$$
$$= \ln(x^2 + y)$$

The domain of g is the set of all points in R_2, and the domain of f is $(0, +\infty)$. Therefore, the domain of h is the set of all points (x, y) for which $x^2 + y > 0$.

Definition 17.1.3 can be extended to a composite function of n variables as follows.

17.1.4 Definition

If f is a function of a single variable and g is a function of n variables, then the *composite function* $f \circ g$ is the function of n variables defined by

$$(f \circ g)(x_1, x_2, \ldots, x_n) = f(g(x_1, x_2, \ldots, x_n))$$

and the domain of $f \circ g$ is the set of all points $(x_1, x_2, \ldots, x_n)$ in the domain of g such that $g(x_1, x_2, \ldots, x_n)$ is in the domain of f.

EXAMPLE 8:   Given $F(x) = \sin^{-1} x$ and $G(x, y, z) = \sqrt{x^2 + y^2 + z^2 - 4}$, find the function $F \circ G$ and its domain.

SOLUTION:

$$(F \circ G)(x, y, z) = F(G(x, y, z))$$
$$= F(\sqrt{x^2 + y^2 + z^2 - 4})$$
$$= \sin^{-1} \sqrt{x^2 + y^2 + z^2 - 4}$$

The domain of G is the set of all points (x, y, z) in R_3 such that $x^2 + y^2 + z^2 - 4 \geq 0$, and the domain of F is $[-1, 1]$. So the domain of $F \circ G$ is the set of all points (x, y, z) in R_3 such that $0 \leq x^2 + y^2 + z^2 - 4 \leq 1$ or, equivalently, $4 \leq x^2 + y^2 + z^2 \leq 5$.

A *polynomial function* of two variables x and y is a function f such that $f(x, y)$ is the sum of terms of the form $cx^n y^m$, where c is a real number and n and m are nonnegative integers. The *degree* of the polynomial function is determined by the largest sum of the exponents of x and y appearing in any one term. Hence, the function f defined by

$$f(x, y) = 6x^3 y^2 - 5xy^3 + 7x^2 y - 2x^2 + y$$

is a polynomial function of degree 5.

A *rational function* of two variables is a function h such that $h(x, y) =$

$f(x, y)/g(x, y)$, where f and g are two polynomial functions. For example, the function f defined by

$$f(x, y) = \frac{x^2 y^2}{x^2 + y^2}$$

is a rational function.

The graph of a function f of a single variable consists of the set of points (x, y) in R_2 for which $y = f(x)$. Similarly, the graph of a function of two variables is a set of points in R_3.

17.1.5 Definition   If f is a function of two variables, then the *graph* of f is the set of all points (x, y, z) in R_3 for which (x, y) is a point in the domain of f and $z = f(x, y)$.

Hence, the graph of a function f of two variables is a surface which is the set of all points in three-dimensional space whose cartesian coordinates are given by the ordered triples of real numbers (x, y, z). Because the domain of f is a set of points in the xy plane, and because for each ordered pair (x, y) in the domain of f there corresponds a unique value of z, no line perpendicular to the xy plane can intersect the graph of f in more than one point.

EXAMPLE 9:   Draw a sketch of the graph of the function of Example 1.

SOLUTION: The function of Example 1 is the function f which is the set of all ordered pairs of the form (P, z) such that

$$z = \sqrt{25 - x^2 - y^2}$$

So the graph of f is the hemisphere on and above the xy plane having a radius of 5 and its center at the origin. A sketch of the graph of this hemisphere is shown in Fig. 17.1.5.

Figure 17.1.5

EXAMPLE 10:   Draw a sketch of the graph of the function f having function values $f(x, y) = x^2 + y^2$.

SOLUTION: The graph of f is the surface having the equation $z = x^2 + y^2$. The trace of the surface in the xy plane is found by using the equation $z = 0$ simultaneously with the equation of the surface. We obtain $x^2 + y^2 = 0$, which is the origin. The traces in the xz and yz planes are found by using the equations $y = 0$ and $x = 0$, respectively, with the equation $z = x^2 + y^2$. We obtain the parabolas $z = x^2$ and $z = y^2$. The cross section of the surface in a plane $z = k$, parallel to the xy plane, is a circle with its

Figure 17.1.6

Figure 17.1.7

center on the z axis and radius $\sqrt{k}$. With this information we have the required sketch shown in Fig. 17.1.6.

There is another useful method of representing a function of two variables geometrically. It is a method similar to that of representing a three-dimensional landscape by a two-dimensional topographical map. Suppose that the surface $z = f(x, y)$ is intersected by the plane $z = k$, and the curve of intersection is projected onto the xy plane. This projected curve has $f(x, y) = k$ as an equation, and the curve is called the *level curve* (or *contour curve*) of the function f at k. Each point on the level curve corresponds to the unique point on the surface which is k units above it if k is positive, or k units below it if k is negative. By considering different values for the constant k, we obtain a set of level curves. This set of curves is called a *contour map*. The set of all possible values of k is the range of the function f, and each level curve, $f(x, y) = k$, in the contour map consists of the points (x, y) in the domain of f having equal function values of k. For example, for the function f of Example 10, the level curves are circles with the center at the origin. The particular level curves for $z = 1, 2, 3, 4, 5$, and 6 are shown in Fig. 17.1.7.

A contour map shows the variation of z with x and y. The level curves are usually shown for values of z at constant intervals, and the values of z are changing more rapidly when the level curves are close together than when they are far apart; that is, when the level curves are close together, the surface is steep, and when the level curves are far apart the elevation of the surface is changing slowly. On a two-dimensional topographical map of a landscape, a general notion of its steepness is obtained by considering the spacing of its level curves. Also on a topographical map if the path of a level curve is followed, the elevation remains constant.

To illustrate a use of level curves, suppose that the temperature at any point of a flat metal plate is given by the function f; that is, if t degrees is the temperature, then at the point (x, y), $t = f(x, y)$. Then the curves having equations of the form $f(x, y) = k$, where k is a constant, are curves on which the temperature is constant. These are the level curves of f and are called *isothermals*. Furthermore, if V volts gives the amount of electric potential at any point (x, y) of the xy plane, and $V = f(x, y)$, then the level curves of f are called *equipotential curves* because the electric potential at each point of such a curve is the same.

EXAMPLE 11:   Let f be the function for which $f(x, y) = 8 - x^2 - 2y$. Draw a sketch of the graph of f and a contour map of f showing the level curves of f at 10, 8, 6, 4, 2, 0, −2, −4, −6, and −8.

SOLUTION: A sketch of the graph of f is shown in Fig. 17.1.8. This is the surface $z = 8 - x^2 - 2y$. The trace in the xy plane is obtained by setting $z = 0$, which gives the parabola $x^2 = -2(y - 4)$. Setting $y = 0$ and $x = 0$, we obtain the traces in the xz and yz planes, which are, respectively, the parabola $x^2 = -(z - 8)$ and the line $2y + z = 8$. The cross section of the surface made by the plane $z = k$ is a parabola having its vertex on the line $2y + z = 8$ in the yz plane and opening to the left. The cross sections for $z = 8$, 6, 4, 2, −2, −4, −6, and −8 are shown in the figure.

   The level curves of f are the parabolas $x^2 = -2(y - 4 + \frac{1}{2}k)$. The contour map of f with sketches of the required level curves is shown in Fig. 17.1.9.

Figure 17.1.8   Figure 17.1.9

Extending the notion of the graph of a function to a function of n variables, we have the following definition.

17.1.6 Definition   If f is a function of n variables, then the *graph* of f is the set of all points $(x_1, x_2, \ldots, x_n, w)$ in R_{n+1} for which $(x_1, x_2, \ldots, x_n)$ is a point in the domain of f and $w = f(x_1, x_2, \ldots, x_n)$.

Analogous to level curves for a function of two variables is a similar situation for functions of three variables. If f is a function whose domain is a set of points in R_3, then if k is a number in the range of f, the graph of the equation $f(x, y, z) = k$ is a surface. This surface is called the *level surface* of f at k. Every surface in three-dimensional space can be considered as a level surface of some function of three variables. For example, if the function g is defined by the equation $g(x, y, z) = x^2 + y^2 - z$, then the surface shown in Fig. 17.1.6 is the level surface of g at 0. Similarly, the surface having equation $z - x^2 - y^2 + 5 = 0$ is the level surface of g at 5.

Exercises 17.1

1. Let the function f of two variables x and y be the set of all ordered pairs of the form (P, z) such that $z = (x + y)/(x - y)$. Find: (a) $f(-3, 4)$; (b) $f(x^2, y^2)$; (c) $[f(x, y)]^2$; (d) $f(-x, y) - f(x, -y)$; (e) the domain of f; (f) the range of f. Draw a sketch showing as a shaded region in R_2 the set of points not in the domain of f.

2. Let the function g of three variables, x, y, and z, be the set of all ordered pairs of the form (P, w) such that $w = \sqrt{4 - x^2 - y^2 - z^2}$. Find: (a) $g(1, -1, -1)$; (b) $g(-a, 2b, \frac{1}{2}c)$; (c) $g(y, -x, -y)$; (d) the domain of g; (e) the range of g; (f) $[g(x, y, z)]^2 - [g(x + 2, y + 2, z)]^2$. Draw a sketch showing as a shaded solid in R_3 the set of points in the domain of g.

In Exercises 3 through 11, find the domain and range of the function f and draw a sketch showing as a shaded region in R_2 the set of points in the domain of f.

3. $f(x, y) = \dfrac{\sqrt{25 - x^2 - y^2}}{x}$

4. $f(x, y) = x\sqrt{25 - x^2 - y^2}$

5. $f(x, y) = \dfrac{x}{\sqrt{25 - x^2 - y^2}}$

6. $f(x, y) = \sqrt{\dfrac{x - y}{x + y}}$

7. $f(x, y) = \dfrac{x^2 - y^2}{x - y}$

8. $f(x, y) = \dfrac{x + y}{xy}$

9. $f(x, y) = \dfrac{x}{|y|}$

10. $f(x, y) = \sin^{-1}(x + y)$

11. $f(x, y) = \ln(xy - 1)$

In Exercises 12 through 14, find the domain and range of the function f.

12. $f(x, y, z) = (x + y)\sqrt{z - 2}$

13. $f(x, y, z) = \sin^{-1} x + \cos^{-1} y + \tan^{-1} z$

14. $f(x, y, z) = |x|e^{y/z}$

In Exercises 15 through 20, find the domain and range of the function f and draw a sketch of the graph.

15. $f(x, y) = 4x^2 + 9y^2$

16. $f(x, y) = \sqrt{x + y}$

17. $f(x, y) = 16 - x^2 - y^2$

18. $f(x, y) = \sqrt{100 - 25x^2 - 4y^2}$

19. $f(x, y) = \sqrt{10 - x - y^2}$

20. $f(x, y) = \begin{cases} 2 & \text{if } x \neq y \\ 0 & \text{if } x = y \end{cases}$

In Exercises 21 through 26, draw a sketch of a contour map of the function f showing the level curves of f at the given numbers.

21. The function of Exercise 15 at 36, 25, 16, 9, 4, 1, and 0.

22. The function of Exercise 16 at 5, 4, 3, 2, 1, and 0.

23. The function of Exercise 17 at 8, 4, 0, -4, and -8.

24. The function of Exercise 18 at 10, 8, 6, 5, and 0.

25. The function f for which $f(x, y) = \frac{1}{2}(x^2 + y^2)$ at 8, 6, 4, 2, and 0.

26. The function f for which $f(x, y) = (x - 3)/(y + 2)$ at 4, 2, 1, $\frac{1}{2}$, $\frac{1}{4}$, 0, $-\frac{1}{4}$, $-\frac{1}{2}$, -1, -2, and -4.

In Exercises 27 and 28, a function f and a function g are defined. Find $h(x, y)$ if $h = f \circ g$, and also find the domain of h.

27. $f(t) = \sin^{-1} t; g(x, y) = \sqrt{1 - x^2 - y^2}$ 28. $f(t) = \tan^{-1} t; g(x, y) = \sqrt{x^2 - y^2}$

29. Given $f(x, y) = x - y, g(t) = \sqrt{t}, h(s) = s^2$. Find (a) $(g \circ f)(5, 1)$; (b) $f(h(3), g(9))$; (c) $f(g(x), h(y))$; (d) $g((h \circ f)(x, y))$; (e) $(g \circ h)(f(x, y))$.

30. Given $f(x, y) = x/y^2, g(x) = x^2, h(x) = \sqrt{x}$. Find (a) $(h \circ f)(2, 1)$; (b) $f(g(2), h(4))$; (c) $f(g(\sqrt{x}), h(x^2))$; (d) $h((g \circ f)(x, y))$; (e) $(h \circ g)(f(x, y))$.

31. The electric potential at a point (x, y) of the xy plane is V volts and $V = 4/\sqrt{9 - x^2 - y^2}$. Draw the equipotential curves for $V = 16, 12, 8, 4, 1, \frac{1}{2}$, and $\frac{1}{4}$.

32. The temperature at a point (x, y) of a flat metal plate is t degrees and $t = 4x^2 + 2y^2$. Draw the isothermals for $t = 12$, $8, 4, 1$, and 0.

33. For the production of a certain commodity, if x is the number of machines used and y is the number of man-hours, the number of units of the commodity produced is $f(x, y)$ and $f(x, y) = 6xy$. Such a function f is called a production function and the level curves of f are called constant product curves. Draw the constant product curves for this function f at 30, 24, 18, 12, 6, and 0.

In Exercises 34 and 35, draw sketches of the level surfaces of the function f at the given numbers.

34. $f(x, y, z) = x^2 + y^2 + z^2$ at 9, 4, 1, and 0.   35. $f(x, y, z) = x^2 + y^2 - 4z$ at 8, 4, 0, −4, and −8.

17.2 LIMITS OF FUNCTIONS OF MORE THAN ONE VARIABLE

In R_1 the distance between two points is the absolute value of the difference of two real numbers. That is, $|x - a|$ is the distance between the points x and a. In R_2 the distance between the two points $P(x, y)$ and $P_0(x_0, y_0)$ is given by $\sqrt{(x - x_0)^2 + (y - y_0)^2}$. In R_3 the distance between the two points $P(x, y, z)$ and $P_0(x_0, y_0, z_0)$ is given by

$$\sqrt{(x - x_0)^2 + (y - y_0)^2 + (z - z_0)^2}$$

In R_n we define the distance between two points analogously as follows.

17.2.1 Definition   If $P(x_1, x_2, \ldots, x_n)$ and $A(a_1, a_2, \ldots, a_n)$ are two points in R_n, then the distance between P and A, denoted by $\|P - A\|$, is given by

$$\|P - A\| = \sqrt{(x_1 - a_1)^2 + (x_2 - a_2)^2 + \cdots + (x_n - a_n)^2} \tag{1}$$

If in R_1 we take $P = x$ and $A = a$, (1) becomes

$$\|x - a\| = \sqrt{(x - a)^2} = |x - a| \tag{2}$$

If in R_2 we take $P = (x, y)$ and $A = (x_0, y_0)$, (1) becomes

$$\|(x, y) - (x_0, y_0)\| = \sqrt{(x - x_0)^2 + (y - y_0)^2} \tag{3}$$

And, if in R_3 we take $P = (x, y, z)$ and $A = (x_0, y_0, z_0)$, (1) becomes

$$\|(x, y, z) - (x_0, y_0, z_0)\| = \sqrt{(x - x_0)^2 + (y - y_0)^2 + (z - z_0)^2} \tag{4}$$

$\|P - A\|$ is read as "the distance between P and A." It is a nonnegative number.

17.2.2 Definition If A is a point in R_n and r is a positive number, then the *open ball* $B(A; r)$ is defined to be the set of all points P in R_n such that $\|P - A\| < r$.

17.2.3 Definition If A is a point in R_n and r is a positive number, then the *closed ball* $B[A; r]$ is defined to be the set of all points in R_n such that $\|P - A\| \leq r$.

To illustrate these definitions, we show what they mean in R_1, R_2, and R_3. First of all, if a is a point in R_1, then the open ball $B(a; r)$ is the set of all points x in R_1 such that

$$|x - a| < r \tag{5}$$

open ball $B(a; r)$ in R_1

Figure 17.2.1

The set of all points x satisfying (5) is the set of all points in the open interval $(a - r, a + r)$; so the open ball $B(a; r)$ in R_1 (see Fig. 17.2.1) is simply an open interval having its midpoint at a and its endpoints at $a - r$ and $a + r$. The closed ball $B[a; r]$ in R_1 (Fig. 17.2.2) is the closed interval $[a - r, a + r]$.

closed ball $B[a; r]$ in R_1

Figure 17.2.2

If (x_0, y_0) is a point in R_2, then the open ball $B((x_0, y_0); r)$ is the set of all points (x, y) in R_2 such that

$$\|(x, y) - (x_0, y_0)\| < r \tag{6}$$

From (3) we see that (6) is equivalent to

$$\sqrt{(x - x_0)^2 + (y - y_0)^2} < r$$

So the open ball $B((x_0, y_0); r)$ in R_2 (Fig. 17.2.3) consists of all points in the interior region bounded by the circle having its center at (x_0, y_0) and radius r. An open ball in R_2 is sometimes called an *open disk*. The closed ball, or closed disk, $B[(x_0, y_0); r]$ in R_2 (Fig. 17.2.4) is the set of all points in the open ball $B((x_0, y_0); r)$ and on the circle having its center at (x_0, y_0) and radius r.

open ball $B((x_0, y_0); r)$ in R_2

Figure 17.2.3

If (x_0, y_0, z_0) is a point in R_3, then the open ball $B((x_0, y_0, z_0); r)$ is the set of all points (x, y, z) in R_3 such that

$$\|(x, y, z) - (x_0, y_0, z_0)\| < r \tag{7}$$

From (4) and (7) we see that the open ball $B((x_0, y_0, z_0); r)$ in R_3 (Fig. 17.2.5) consists of all points in the interior region bounded by

closed ball $B[(x_0, y_0); r]$ in R_2

Figure 17.2.4

Figure 17.2.5   open ball $B((x_0, y_0, z_0); r)$ in R_3

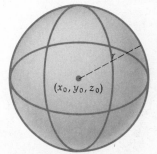

Figure 17.2.6   closed ball $B[(x_0, y_0, z_0); r]$ in R_3

the sphere having its center at P_0 and radius r. Similarly, the closed ball $B[(x_0, y_0, z_0); r]$ in R_3 (Fig. 17.2.6) consists of all points in the open ball $B((x_0, y_0, z_0); r)$ and on the sphere having its center at (x_0, y_0, z_0) and radius r. We are now in a position to define what is meant by the limit of a function of n variables.

17.2.4 Definition   Let f be a function of n variables which is defined on some open ball $B(A; r)$, except possibly at the point A itself. Then *the limit of $f(P)$ as P approaches A is L*, written as

$$\lim_{P \to A} f(P) = L \qquad (8)$$

if for any $\epsilon > 0$, however small, there exists a $\delta > 0$ such that

$$|f(P) - L| < \epsilon \quad \text{whenever} \quad 0 < \|P - A\| < \delta \qquad (9)$$

If f is a function of one variable and if in the above definition we take $A = a$ in R_1 and $P = x$, then (8) becomes

$$\lim_{x \to a} f(x) = L$$

and (9) becomes

$$|f(x) - L| < \epsilon \quad \text{whenever} \quad 0 < |x - a| < \delta$$

So we see that the definition (2.4.1) of the limit of a function of one variable is a special case of Definition 17.2.4.

We now state the definition of the limit of a function of two variables. It is the special case of Definition 17.2.4, where A is the point (x_0, y_0) and P is the point (x, y).

17.2.5 Definition   Let f be a function of two variables which is defined on some open disk $B((x_0, y_0); r)$, except possibly at the point (x_0, y_0) itself. Then

$$\lim_{(x,y) \to (x_0,y_0)} f(x, y) = L$$

if for any $\epsilon > 0$, however small, there exists a $\delta > 0$ such that

$$|f(x, y) - L| < \epsilon \quad \text{whenever} \quad 0 < \sqrt{(x - x_0)^2 + (y - y_0)^2} < \delta \qquad (10)$$

In words, Definition 17.2.5 states that the function values $f(x, y)$ approach a limit L as the point (x, y) approaches the point (x_0, y_0) if the absolute value of the difference between $f(x, y)$ and L can be made arbitrarily small by taking the point (x, y) sufficiently close to (x_0, y_0) but not equal to (x_0, y_0). Note that in Definition 17.2.5 nothing is said about the function value at the point (x_0, y_0); that is, it is not necessary that the function be defined at (x_0, y_0) in order for $\lim_{(x,y) \to (x_0,y_0)} f(x, y)$ to exist.

A geometric interpretation of Definition 17.2.5 is illustrated in Fig.

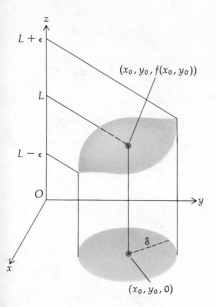

Figure 17.2.7

17.2.7. The portion above the open disk $B((x_0, y_0); r)$ of the surface having equation $z = f(x, y)$ is shown. We see that $f(x, y)$ on the z axis will lie between $L - \epsilon$ and $L + \epsilon$ whenever the point (x, y) in the xy plane is in the open disk $B((x_0, y_0); \delta)$. Another way of stating this is that $f(x, y)$ on the z axis can be restricted to lie between $L - \epsilon$ and $L + \epsilon$ by restricting the point (x, y) in the xy plane to be in the open disk $B((x_0, y_0); \delta)$.

EXAMPLE 1: Prove that

$$\lim_{(x,y)\to(1,3)} (2x + 3y) = 11$$

by applying Definition 17.2.5.

SOLUTION: We wish to show that for any $\epsilon > 0$ there exists a $\delta > 0$ such that

$$|(2x + 3y) - 11| < \epsilon \quad \text{whenever} \quad 0 < \sqrt{(x-1)^2 + (y-3)^2} < \delta$$

Applying the triangle inequality, we get

$$|2x + 3y - 11| = |2x - 2 + 3y - 9| \leq 2|x - 1| + 3|y - 3|$$

Because

$$|x - 1| \leq \sqrt{(x-1)^2 + (y-3)^2} \quad \text{and} \quad |y - 3| \leq \sqrt{(x-1)^2 + (y-3)^2}$$

we can conclude that

$$2|x - 1| + 3|y - 3| < 2\delta + 3\delta$$

whenever

$$0 < \sqrt{(x-1)^2 + (y-3)^2} < \delta$$

So if we take $\delta = \frac{1}{5}\epsilon$, we have

$$|2x + 3y - 11| \leq 2|x - 1| + 3|y - 3| < 5\delta = \epsilon$$

whenever

$$0 < \sqrt{(x-1)^2 + (y-3)^2} < \delta$$

This proves that $\lim_{(x,y)\to(1,3)} (2x + 3y) = 11$.

EXAMPLE 2:   Prove that

$$\lim_{(x,y)\to(1,2)} (3x^2 + y) = 5$$

by applying Definition 17.2.5.

SOLUTION: We wish to show that for any $\epsilon > 0$ there exists a $\delta > 0$ such that

$$|(3x^2 + y) - 5| < \epsilon \quad \text{whenever} \quad 0 < \sqrt{(x-1)^2 + (y-2)^2} < \delta$$

Applying the triangle inequality, we get

$$|3x^2 + y - 5| = |3x^2 - 3 + y - 2| \leq 3|x-1||x+1| + |y-2| \qquad (11)$$

If we require the δ, for which we are looking, to be less than or equal to 1, then $|x-1| < \delta \leq 1$ and $|y-2| < \delta \leq 1$ whenever

$$0 < \sqrt{(x-1)^2 + (y-2)^2} < \delta \leq 1$$

Furthermore, whenever $|x-1| < 1$, then $-1 < x-1 < 1$, and so $1 < x+1 < 3$. Hence,

$$3|x-1||x+1| + |y-2| < 3 \cdot \delta \cdot 3 + \delta = 10\delta \qquad (12)$$

whenever

$$0 < \sqrt{(x-1)^2 + (y-2)^2} < \delta \leq 1$$

So if for any $\epsilon > 0$ we take $\delta = \min(1, \tfrac{1}{10}\epsilon)$, we have from (11) and (12)

$$|3x^2 + y - 5| < 10\delta \leq \epsilon \quad \text{whenever} \quad 0 < \sqrt{(x-1)^2 + (y-2)^2} < \delta$$

This proves that $\displaystyle\lim_{(x,y)\to(1,2)} (3x^2 + y) = 5$.

We now introduce the concept of an *accumulation point*, which we need in order to continue the discussion of limits of functions of two variables.

17.2.6 Definition   A point P_0 is said to be an *accumulation point* of a set S of points in R_n if every open ball $B(P_0; r)$ contains infinitely many points of S.

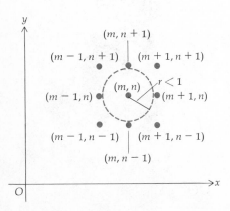

Figure 17.2.8

For example, if S is the set of all points in R_2 on the positive side of the x axis, the origin will be an accumulation point of S because no matter how small we take the value of r, every open disk having its center at the origin and radius r will contain infinitely many points of S. This is an example of a set having an accumulation point for which the accumulation point is not a point of the set. Any point of this set S also will be an accumulation point of S.

If S is the set of all points in R_2 for which the cartesian coordinates are positive integers, then this set has no accumulation point. This can be seen by considering the point (m, n), where m and n are positive integers. Then an open disk having its center at (m, n) and radius less than 1 will contain no points of S other than (m, n); therefore, Definition 17.2.6 will not be satisfied (see Fig. 17.2.8).

We now consider the limit of a function of two variables as a point

(x, y) approaches a point (x_0, y_0), where (x, y) is restricted to a specific set of points.

17.2.7 Definition Let f be a function defined on a set of points S in R_2, and let (x_0, y_0) be an accumulation point of S. Then *the limit of $f(x, y)$ as (x, y) approaches (x_0, y_0) in S is L*, written as

$$\lim_{\substack{(x,y)\to(x_0,y_0)\\(P \text{ in } S)}} f(x, y) = L \tag{13}$$

if for any $\epsilon > 0$, however small, there exists a $\delta > 0$ such that

$$|f(x, y) - L| < \epsilon \quad \text{whenever} \quad 0 < \|(x, y) - (x_0, y_0)\| < \delta$$

and (x, y) is in S.

A special case of (13) occurs when S is a set of points on a curve containing (x_0, y_0). In such cases the limit in (13) becomes the limit of a function of one variable. For example, consider $\lim_{(x,y)\to(0,0)} f(x, y)$. Then if S_1 is the set of all points on the positive side of the x axis, we have

$$\lim_{\substack{(x,y)\to(0,0)\\(P \text{ in } S_1)}} f(x, y) = \lim_{x\to 0^+} f(x, 0)$$

If S_2 is the set of all points on the negative side of the y axis,

$$\lim_{\substack{(x,y)\to(0,0)\\(P \text{ in } S_2)}} f(x, y) = \lim_{y\to 0^-} f(0, y)$$

If S_3 is the set of all points on the x axis,

$$\lim_{\substack{(x,y)\to(0,0)\\(P \text{ in } S_3)}} f(x, y) = \lim_{x\to 0} f(x, 0)$$

If S_4 is the set of all points on the parabola $y = x^2$,

$$\lim_{\substack{(x,y)\to(0,0)\\(P \text{ in } S_4)}} f(x, y) = \lim_{x\to 0} f(x, x^2)$$

17.2.8 Theorem Suppose that the function f is defined for all points on an open disk having its center at (x_0, y_0), except possibly at (x_0, y_0) itself, and

$$\lim_{(x,y)\to(x_0,y_0)} f(x, y) = L$$

Then if S is any set of points in R_2 having (x_0, y_0) as an accumulation point,

$$\lim_{\substack{(x,y)\to(x_0,y_0)\\(P \text{ in } S)}} f(x, y)$$

exists and always has the value L.

PROOF: Because $\lim\limits_{(x,y)\to(x_0,y_0)} f(x,y) = L$, then by Definition 17.2.5, for any $\epsilon > 0$ there exists a $\delta > 0$ such that

$$|f(x,y) - L| < \epsilon \quad \text{whenever} \quad 0 < \|(x,y) - (x_0,y_0)\| < \delta$$

The above will be true if we further restrict (x,y) by the requirement that (x,y) be in a set S, where S is any set of points having (x_0, y_0) as an accumulation point. Therefore, by Definition 17.2.7

$$\lim\limits_{\substack{(x,y)\to(x_0,y_0)\\(P \text{ in } S)}} f(x,y) = L$$

and L does not depend on the set S through which (x,y) is approaching (x_0, y_0). This proves the theorem. ∎

The following is an immediate consequence of Theorem 17.2.8.

17.2.9 Theorem   If the function f has different limits as (x,y) approaches (x_0, y_0) through two distinct sets of points having (x_0, y_0) as an accumulation point, then $\lim\limits_{(x,y)\to(x_0,y_0)} f(x,y)$ does not exist.

PROOF: Let S_1 and S_2 be two distinct sets of points in R_2 and let

$$\lim\limits_{\substack{(x,y)\to(x_0,y_0)\\(P \text{ in } S_1)}} f(x,y) = L_1 \quad \text{and} \quad \lim\limits_{\substack{(x,y)\to(x_0,y_0)\\(P \text{ in } S_2)}} f(x,y) = L_2$$

Now assume that $\lim\limits_{(x,y)\to(x_0,y_0)} f(x,y)$ exists. Then by Theorem 17.2.8 L_1 must equal L_2, but by hypothesis $L_1 \neq L_2$, and so we have a contradiction. Therefore, $\lim\limits_{(x,y)\to(x_0,y_0)} f(x,y)$ does not exist. ∎

EXAMPLE 3:   Given

$$f(x,y) = \frac{xy}{x^2 + y^2}$$

find $\lim\limits_{(x,y)\to(0,0)} f(x,y)$ if it exists.

SOLUTION: Let S_1 be the set of all points on the x axis. Then

$$\lim\limits_{\substack{(x,y)\to(0,0)\\(P \text{ in } S_1)}} f(x,y) = \lim\limits_{x\to 0} f(x,0) = \lim\limits_{x\to 0} \frac{0}{x^2 + 0} = 0$$

Let S_2 be the set of all points on the line $y = x$. Then

$$\lim\limits_{\substack{(x,y)\to(0,0)\\(P \text{ in } S_2)}} f(x,y) = \lim\limits_{x\to 0} \frac{x^2}{x^2 + x^2} = \lim\limits_{x\to 0} \frac{1}{2} = \frac{1}{2}$$

Because

$$\lim\limits_{\substack{(x,y)\to(0,0)\\(P \text{ in } S_1)}} f(x,y) \neq \lim\limits_{\substack{(x,y)\to(0,0)\\(P \text{ in } S_2)}} f(x,y)$$

it follows from Theorem 17.2.9 that $\lim\limits_{(x,y)\to(0,0)} f(x,y)$ does not exist.

In the solution of Example 3, instead of taking S_1 to be the set of all the points on the x axis, we could just as well have restricted the points of S_1 to be on the positive side of the x axis because the origin is an accumulation point of this set.

EXAMPLE 4:   Given

$$f(x, y) = \frac{3x^2y}{x^2 + y^2}$$

find $\lim\limits_{(x,y)\to(0,0)} f(x, y)$ if it exists.

SOLUTION: Let S_1 be the set of all points on the x axis. Then

$$\lim_{\substack{(x,y)\to(0,0)\\(P \text{ in } S_1)}} f(x, y) = \lim_{x\to 0} \frac{0}{x^2 + 0} = 0$$

Let S_2 be the set of all points on any line through the origin; that is, for any point (x, y) in S_2, $y = mx$.

$$\lim_{\substack{(x,y)\to(0,0)\\(P \text{ in } S_2)}} f(x, y) = \lim_{x\to 0} \frac{3x^2(mx)}{x^2 + m^2x^2} = \lim_{x\to 0} \frac{3mx}{1 + m^2} = 0$$

Even though we obtain the same limit of 0, if (x, y) approaches $(0, 0)$ through a set of points on any line through the origin, we cannot conclude that $\lim\limits_{(x,y)\to(0,0)} f(x, y)$ exists and is zero (see Example 5). However, let us attempt to prove that $\lim\limits_{(x,y)\to(0,0)} f(x, y) = 0$. From Definition 17.2.5, if we can show that for any $\epsilon > 0$ there exists a $\delta > 0$ such that

$$\left| \frac{3x^2y}{x^2 + y^2} \right| < \epsilon \quad \text{whenever} \quad 0 < \sqrt{x^2 + y^2} < \delta \tag{14}$$

then we have proved that $\lim\limits_{(x,y)\to(0,0)} f(x, y) = 0$.

Because $x^2 \leq x^2 + y^2$ and $|y| \leq \sqrt{x^2 + y^2}$, we have

$$\left| \frac{3x^2y}{x^2 + y^2} \right| = \frac{3x^2|y|}{x^2 + y^2} \leq \frac{3(x^2 + y^2)\sqrt{x^2 + y^2}}{x^2 + y^2} = 3\sqrt{x^2 + y^2}$$

So if $\delta = \frac{1}{3}\epsilon$, we can conclude that

$$\left| \frac{3x^2y}{x^2 + y^2} \right| < \epsilon \quad \text{whenever} \quad 0 < \sqrt{x^2 + y^2} < \delta$$

which is (14). Hence, we have proved that $\lim\limits_{(x,y)\to(0,0)} f(x, y) = 0$.

EXAMPLE 5:   Given

$$f(x, y) = \frac{x^2y}{x^4 + y^2}$$

find $\lim\limits_{(x,y)\to(0,0)} f(x, y)$ if it exists.

SOLUTION: Let S_1 be the set of all points on either the x axis or the y axis. So if (x, y) is in S_1, $xy = 0$. Therefore,

$$\lim_{\substack{(x,y)\to(0,0)\\(P \text{ in } S_1)}} f(x, y) = 0$$

Let S_2 be the set of all points on any line through the origin; so if (x, y) is a point in S_2, $y = mx$. We have, then,

$$\lim_{\substack{(x,y)\to(0,0)\\(P \text{ in } S_2)}} f(x, y) = \lim_{x\to 0} \frac{mx^3}{x^4 + m^2x^2} = \lim_{x\to 0} \frac{mx}{x^2 + m^2} = 0$$

Let S_3 be the set of all points on the parabola $y = x^2$. Then

$$\lim_{\substack{(x,y) \to (0,0) \\ (P \text{ in } S_3)}} f(x, y) = \lim_{x \to 0} \frac{x^4}{x^4 + x^4} = \lim_{x \to 0} \frac{1}{2} = \frac{1}{2}$$

Because

$$\lim_{\substack{(x,y) \to (0,0) \\ (P \text{ in } S_3)}} f(x, y) \neq \lim_{\substack{(x,y) \to (0,0) \\ (P \text{ in } S_1)}} f(x, y)$$

it follows that $\displaystyle\lim_{(x,y) \to (0,0)} f(x, y)$ does not exist.

EXAMPLE 6: Given

$$f(x, y) = \begin{cases} (x + y) \sin \dfrac{1}{x} & \text{if } x \neq 0 \\ 0 & \text{if } x = 0 \end{cases}$$

find $\displaystyle\lim_{(x,y) \to (0,0)} f(x, y)$ if it exists.

SOLUTION: Let S_1 be the set of all points on the y axis. Then

$$\lim_{\substack{(x,y) \to (0,0) \\ (P \text{ in } S_1)}} f(x, y) = \lim_{x \to 0} 0 = 0$$

Let S_2 be the set of all points on any line through the origin except points on the y axis; that is, if (x, y) is a point in S_2, $y = kx$, where $x \neq 0$. Then

$$\lim_{\substack{(x,y) \to (0,0) \\ (P \text{ in } S_2)}} f(x, y) = \lim_{x \to 0} (x + kx) \sin \frac{1}{x}$$

To find the above limit we make use of the fact that $\displaystyle\lim_{x \to 0} (x + kx) = 0$. Because $\displaystyle\lim_{x \to 0} \sin(1/x)$ does not exist, we cannot apply the theorem about the limit of a product. However, because $\displaystyle\lim_{x \to 0} (x + kx) = 0$, it follows that for any $\epsilon > 0$ there exists a $\delta > 0$ such that

$$|x + kx| < \epsilon \quad \text{whenever} \quad 0 < |x| < \delta$$

The δ is, in fact, $\epsilon/|1 + k|$. But

$$\left| (x + kx) \sin \frac{1}{x} \right| = |x + kx| \left| \sin \frac{1}{x} \right| \leq |x + kx| \cdot 1$$

Hence, for any $\epsilon > 0$ there exists a $\delta > 0$ such that

$$\left| (x + kx) \sin \frac{1}{x} \right| < \epsilon \quad \text{whenever} \quad 0 < |x| < \delta$$

Thus,

$$\lim_{\substack{(x,y) \to (0,0) \\ (P \text{ in } S_2)}} f(x, y) = 0 \tag{15}$$

Let S_3 be the set of all points (x, y) for which $y = kx^n$, where n is any positive integer and $x \neq 0$. Then by an argument similar to that used for proving (15) it follows that

$$\lim_{\substack{(x,y) \to (0,0) \\ (P \text{ in } S_3)}} f(x, y) = \lim_{x \to 0} (x + kx^n) \sin \frac{1}{x} = 0$$

We now attempt to find a $\delta > 0$ for any $\epsilon > 0$ such that

$$|f(x, y) - 0| < \epsilon \quad \text{whenever} \quad 0 < \|(x, y) - (0, 0)\| < \delta \qquad (16)$$

which will prove that $\lim\limits_{(x,y)\to(0,0)} f(x, y) = 0$. We distinguish two cases: $x = 0$ and $x \neq 0$.

Case 1: If $x = 0$, $|f(x, y) - 0| = |0 - 0| = 0$, which is less than ϵ for any $\delta > 0$.

Case 2: If $x \neq 0$, $|f(x, y) - 0| = |(x + y) \sin(1/x)|$.

$$\left|(x + y) \sin \frac{1}{x}\right| = |x + y| \left|\sin \frac{1}{x}\right|$$

$$\leq |x + y|(1)$$

$$\leq |x| + |y|$$

$$\leq \sqrt{x^2 + y^2} + \sqrt{x^2 + y^2}$$

$$= 2\sqrt{x^2 + y^2}$$

Then

$$\left|(x + y) \sin \frac{1}{x}\right| < 2 \cdot \tfrac{1}{2}\epsilon \quad \text{whenever} \quad 0 < \sqrt{x^2 + y^2} < \tfrac{1}{2}\epsilon$$

So take $\delta = \tfrac{1}{2}\epsilon$.

Therefore, in both cases we have found a $\delta > 0$ for any $\epsilon > 0$ such that (16) holds, and this proves that $\lim\limits_{(x,y)\to(0,0)} f(x, y) = 0$.

The limit theorems of Chapter 2 and their proofs, with minor modifications, apply to functions of several variables. We use these theorems without restating them and their proofs.

EXAMPLE 7: Find

$$\lim_{(x,y)\to(-2,1)} (x^3 + 2x^2y - y^2 + 2).$$

SOLUTION: By applying the limit theorems on sums and products, we have

$$\lim_{(x,y)\to(-2,1)} (x^3 + 2x^2y - y^2 + 2) = (-2)^3 + 2(-2)^2(1) - (1)^2 + 2 = 1$$

Analogous to Theorem 2.11.5 for functions of a single variable is the following theorem regarding the limit of a composite function of two variables.

17.2.10 Theorem   If g is a function of two variables and $\lim\limits_{(x,y)\to(x_0,y_0)} g(x, y) = b$, and f is a function of a single variable continuous at b, then

$$\lim_{(x,y)\to(x_0,y_0)} (f \circ g)(x, y) = f(b)$$

or, equivalently,

$$\lim_{(x,y)\to(x_0,y_0)} f(g(x, y)) = f\left(\lim_{(x,y)\to(x_0,y_0)} g(x, y)\right)$$

The proof of this theorem is similar to the proof of Theorem 2.11.5 and is left for the reader (see Exercise 20).

EXAMPLE 8: Use Theorem 17.2.10 to find $\lim\limits_{(x,y)\to(2,1)} \ln(xy - 1)$.

SOLUTION: Let g be the function such that $g(x, y) = xy - 1$, and f be the function such that $f(t) = \ln t$.

$$\lim_{(x,y)\to(2,1)} (xy - 1) = 1$$

and because f is continuous at 1, we use Theorem 17.2.10 and get

$$\lim_{(x,y)\to(2,1)} \ln(xy - 1) = \ln\left(\lim_{(x,y)\to(2,1)} (xy - 1)\right)$$

$$= \ln 1$$

$$= 0$$

Exercises 17.2

In Exercises 1 through 6, establish the limit by finding a $\delta > 0$ for any $\epsilon > 0$ so that Definition 17.2.5 holds.

1. $\lim\limits_{(x,y)\to(3,2)} (3x - 4y) = 1$

2. $\lim\limits_{(x,y)\to(2,4)} (5x - 3y) = -2$

3. $\lim\limits_{(x,y)\to(1,1)} (x^2 + y^2) = 2$

4. $\lim\limits_{(x,y)\to(2,3)} (2x^2 - y^2) = -1$

5. $\lim\limits_{(x,y)\to(2,4)} (x^2 + 2x - y) = 4$

6. $\lim\limits_{(x,y)\to(3,-1)} (x^2 + y^2 - 4x + 2y) = -4$

In Exercises 7 through 12, prove that for the given function f, $\lim\limits_{(x,y)\to(0,0)} f(x, y)$ does not exist.

7. $f(x, y) = \dfrac{x^2 - y^2}{x^2 + y^2}$

8. $f(x, y) = \dfrac{x^2}{x^2 + y^2}$

9. $f(x, y) = \dfrac{x^3 + y^3}{x^2 + y}$

10. $f(x, y) = \dfrac{x^4 + 3x^2y^2 + 2xy^3}{(x^2 + y^2)^2}$

11. $f(x, y) = \dfrac{x^4 y^4}{(x^2 + y^4)^3}$

12. $f(x, y) = \dfrac{x^2 y^2}{x^3 + y^3}$

In Exercises 13 through 16, prove that $\lim\limits_{(x,y)\to(0,0)} f(x, y)$ exists.

13. $f(x, y) = \dfrac{xy}{\sqrt{x^2 + y^2}}$

14. $f(x, y) = \dfrac{x^3 + y^3}{x^2 + y^2}$

15. $f(x, y) = \begin{cases} (x + y) \sin\dfrac{1}{x} \sin\dfrac{1}{y} & \text{if } x \neq 0 \text{ and } y \neq 0 \\ 0 & \text{if either } x = 0 \text{ or } y = 0 \end{cases}$

16. $f(x, y) = \begin{cases} \dfrac{1}{x} \sin (xy) & \text{if } x \neq 0 \\ y & \text{if } x = 0 \end{cases}$

In Exercises 17 through 19, evaluate the given limit by the use of limit theorems.

17. $\lim\limits_{(x,y)\to(2,3)} (3x^2 + xy - 2y^2)$

18. $\lim\limits_{(x,y)\to(-2,4)} y\sqrt{x^3 + 2y}$

19. $\lim\limits_{(x,y)\to(0,0)} \dfrac{e^x + e^y}{\cos x + \sin y}$

20. Prove Theorem 17.2.10

In Exercises 21 through 23, show the application of Theorem 17.2.10 to find the indicated limit.

21. $\lim\limits_{(x,y)\to(2,2)} \tan^{-1}\dfrac{y}{x}$ 22. $\lim\limits_{(x,y)\to(-2,3)} [\![5x + \tfrac{1}{2}y^2]\!]$ 23. $\lim\limits_{(x,y)\to(4,2)} \sqrt{\dfrac{1}{3x - 4y}}$

In Exercises 24 through 29 determine if the indicated limit exists.

24. $\lim\limits_{(x,y)\to(0,0)} \dfrac{x^2 y^2}{x^4 + y^4}$ 25. $\lim\limits_{(x,y)\to(0,0)} \dfrac{x^2 y^2}{x^2 + y^2}$ 26. $\lim\limits_{(x,y)\to(2,-2)} \dfrac{\sin(x + y)}{x + y}$ 27. $\lim\limits_{(x,y)\to(0,0)} \dfrac{x^2 + y}{x^2 + y^2}$

28. $f(x, y) = \begin{cases} \dfrac{xy}{x^2 + y^2} + y \sin\dfrac{1}{x} & \text{if } x \neq 0 \\ 0 & \text{if } x = 0 \end{cases}$ $\lim\limits_{(x,y)\to(0,0)} f(x, y)$

29. $f(x, y) = \begin{cases} x \sin\dfrac{1}{y} + y \sin\dfrac{1}{x} & \text{if } x \neq 0 \text{ and } y \neq 0 \\ 0 & \text{if either } x = 0 \text{ or } y = 0 \end{cases}$ $\lim\limits_{(x,y)\to(0,0)} f(x, y)$

30. (a) Give a definition, similar to Definition 17.2.5, of the limit of a function of three variables as a point (x, y, z) approaches a point (x_0, y_0, z_0). (b) Give a definition, similar to Definition 17.2.7, of the limit of a function of three variables as a point (x, y, z) approaches a point (x_0, y_0, z_0) in a specific set of points S in R_3.

31. (a) State and prove a theorem similar to Theorem 17.2.8 for a function f of three variables. (b) State and prove a theorem similar to Theorem 17.2.9 for a function f of three variables.

In Exercises 32 through 36, use the definitions and theorems of Exercises 30 and 31 to prove that $\lim\limits_{(x,y,z)\to(0,0,0)} f(x, y, z)$ does not exist.

32. $f(x, y, z) = \dfrac{x^4 + yx^3 + z^2 x^2}{x^4 + y^4 + z^4}$

33. $f(x, y, z) = \dfrac{x^2 + y^2 - z^2}{x^2 + y^2 + z^2}$

34. $f(x, y, z) = \dfrac{x^3 + yz^2}{x^4 + y^2 + z^4}$

35. $f(x, y, z) = \dfrac{x^2 y^2 z^2}{x^6 + y^6 + z^6}$

In Exercises 36 and 37, use the definition in Exercise 30(a) to prove that $\lim\limits_{(x,y,z)\to(0,0,0)} f(x, y, z)$ exists.

36. $f(x, y, z) = \dfrac{y^3 + xz^2}{x^2 + y^2 + z^2}$

37. $f(x, y, z) = \begin{cases} (x + y + z) \sin\dfrac{1}{x} \sin\dfrac{1}{y} & \text{if } x \neq 0 \text{ and } y \neq 0 \\ 0 & \text{if either } x = 0 \text{ or } y = 0 \end{cases}$

17.3 CONTINUITY OF FUNCTIONS OF MORE THAN ONE VARIABLE

17.3.1 Definition

Suppose that f is a function of n variables and A is a point in R_n. Then f is said to be *continuous* at the point A if and only if the following three conditions are satisfied:

$\begin{cases} \text{(i) } f(A) \text{ exists;} \\ \text{(ii) } \lim\limits_{P\to A} f(P) \text{ exists;} \\ \text{(iii) } \lim\limits_{P\to A} f(P) = f(A). \end{cases}$

If one or more of these three conditions fails to hold at the point A, then f is said to be *discontinuous* at A.

Definition 2.11.1 of continuity of a function of one variable at a number a is a special case of Definition 17.3.1.

If f is a function of two variables, A is the point (x_0, y_0), and P is a point (x, y), then Definition 17.3.1 becomes the following.

17.3.2 Definition   The function f of two variables x and y is said to be *continuous* at the point (x_0, y_0) if and only if the following three conditions are satisfied:

(i) $f(x_0, y_0)$ exists;

(ii) $\lim\limits_{(x,y) \to (x_0,y_0)} f(x, y)$ exists;

(iii) $\lim\limits_{(x,y) \to (x_0,y_0)} f(x, y) = f(x_0, y_0)$.

EXAMPLE 1:   Given

$$f(x, y) = \begin{cases} \dfrac{3x^2 y}{x^2 + y^2} & \text{if } (x, y) \neq (0, 0) \\ 0 & \text{if } (x, y) = (0, 0) \end{cases}$$

determine if f is continuous at $(0, 0)$.

SOLUTION: We check the three conditions of Definition 17.3.2 at the point $(0, 0)$.

(i) $f(0, 0) = 0$. Therefore, condition (i) holds.

(ii) $\lim\limits_{(x,y) \to (0,0)} f(x, y) = \lim\limits_{(x,y) \to (0,0)} \dfrac{3x^2 y}{x^2 + y^2} = 0$, which was proved in Example 4, Sec. 17.2.

(iii) $\lim\limits_{(x,y) \to (0,0)} f(x, y) = f(0, 0)$.

So we conclude that f is continuous at $(0, 0)$.

EXAMPLE 2:   Let the function f be defined by

$$f(x, y) = \begin{cases} \dfrac{xy}{x^2 + y^2} & \text{if } (x, y) \neq (0, 0) \\ 0 & \text{if } (x, y) = (0, 0) \end{cases}$$

Determine if f is continuous at $(0, 0)$.

SOLUTION: Checking the conditions of Definition 17.3.2, we have the following.

(i) $f(0, 0) = 0$ and so condition (i) holds.

(ii) When $(x, y) \neq (0, 0)$, $f(x, y) = xy/(x^2 + y^2)$. In Example 3, Sec. 17.2, we showed that $\lim\limits_{(x,y) \to (0,0)} xy/(x^2 + y^2)$ does not exist and so $\lim\limits_{(x,y) \to (0,0)} f(x, y)$ does not exist. Therefore, condition (ii) fails to hold.

We conclude that f is discontinuous at $(0, 0)$.

If a function f of two variables is discontinuous at the point (x_0, y_0) but $\lim\limits_{(x,y) \to (x_0,y_0)} f(x, y)$ exists, then f is said to have a *removable discontinuity* at (x_0, y_0) because if f is redefined at (x_0, y_0) so that $f(x_0, y_0) = \lim\limits_{(x,y) \to (x_0,y_0)} f(x, y)$, then f becomes continuous at (x_0, y_0). If the discontinuity is not removable, it is called an *essential discontinuity*.

EXAMPLE 3:   For each of the following functions, determine whether the discontinuity is

SOLUTION: (a) In Example 4, Sec. 17.2, we showed that

$$\lim\limits_{(x,y) \to (0,0)} 3x^2 y/(x^2 + y^2) = 0$$

removable or essential at the origin: (a) $g(x, y) = 3x^2y/(x^2 + y^2)$; (b) $h(x, y) = xy/(x^2 + y^2)$.

Therefore, the discontinuity is removable if $g(0, 0)$ is defined to be 0. (Refer to Example 1.)

(b) In Example 3, Sec. 17.2, we showed that $\lim\limits_{(x,y) \to (0,0)} xy/(x^2 + y^2)$ does not exist. Therefore, the discontinuity is essential. (Refer to Example 2.)

The theorems about continuity for functions of a single variable can be extended to functions of two variables.

17.3.3 Theorem   If f and g are two functions which are continuous at the point (x_0, y_0), then

(i) $f + g$ is continuous at (x_0, y_0);
(ii) $f - g$ is continuous at (x_0, y_0);
(iii) fg is continuous at (x_0, y_0);
(iv) f/g is continuous at (x_0, y_0), provided that $g(x_0, y_0) \neq 0$.

The proof of this theorem is analogous to the proof of the corresponding theorem (2.11.1) for functions of one variable, and hence it is omitted.

17.3.4 Theorem   A polynomial function of two variables is continuous at every point in R_2.

PROOF: Every polynomial function is the sum of products of the functions defined by $f(x, y) = x$, $g(x, y) = y$, and $h(x, y) = c$, where c is a real number. Because f, g, and h are continuous at every point in R_2, the theorem follows by repeated applications of Theorem 17.3.3, parts (i) and (iii).   ∎

17.3.5 Theorem   A rational function of two variables is continuous at every point in its domain.

PROOF: A rational function is the quotient of two polynomial functions f and g which are continuous at every point in R_2 by Theorem 17.3.4. If (x_0, y_0) is any point in the domain of f/g, then $g(x_0, y_0) \neq 0$; so by Theorem 17.3.3(iv) f/g is continuous there.   ∎

EXAMPLE 4:   Let the function f be defined by

$$f(x, y) = \begin{cases} x^2 + y^2 & \text{if } x^2 + y^2 \leq 1 \\ 0 & \text{if } x^2 + y^2 > 1 \end{cases}$$

Discuss the continuity of f. What is the region of continuity of f?

SOLUTION: The function f is defined at all points in R_2. Therefore, condition (i) of Definition 17.3.2 holds for every point (x_0, y_0).

Consider the points (x_0, y_0) if $x_0^2 + y_0^2 \neq 1$. If $x_0^2 + y_0^2 < 1$, then

$$\lim_{(x,y) \to (x_0,y_0)} f(x, y) = \lim_{(x,y) \to (x_0,y_0)} (x^2 + y^2) = x_0^2 + y_0^2 = f(x_0, y_0)$$

If $x_0^2 + y_0^2 > 1$, then

$$\lim_{(x,y) \to (x_0,y_0)} f(x, y) = \lim_{(x,y) \to (x_0,y_0)} 0 = 0 = f(x_0, y_0)$$

Thus, f is continuous at all points (x_0, y_0) for which $x_0^2 + y_0^2 \neq 1$.

To determine the continuity of f at points (x_0, y_0) for which $x_0^2 + y_0^2 = 1$, we determine if $\lim\limits_{(x,y)\to(x_0,y_0)} f(x, y)$ exists and equals 1.

Let S_1 be the set of all points (x, y) such that $x^2 + y^2 \leq 1$. Then

$$\lim_{\substack{(x,y)\to(x_0,y_0)\\(P \text{ in } S_1)}} f(x, y) = \lim_{\substack{(x,y)\to(x_0,y_0)\\(P \text{ in } S_1)}} (x^2 + y^2) = x_0^2 + y_0^2 = 1$$

Let S_2 be the set of all points (x, y) such that $x^2 + y^2 > 1$. Then

$$\lim_{\substack{(x,y)\to(x_0,y_0)\\(P \text{ in } S_2)}} f(x, y) = \lim_{\substack{(x,y)\to(x_0,y_0)\\(P \text{ in } S_2)}} 0 = 0$$

Because

$$\lim_{\substack{(x,y)\to(x_0,y_0)\\(P \text{ in } S_1)}} f(x, y) \neq \lim_{\substack{(x,y)\to(x_0,y_0)\\(P \text{ in } S_2)}} f(x, y)$$

we conclude that $\lim\limits_{(x,y)\to(x_0,y_0)} f(x, y)$ does not exist. Hence, f is discontinuous at all points (x_0, y_0) for which $x_0^2 + y_0^2 = 1$. The region of continuity of f consists of all points in the xy plane except those on the circle $x^2 + y^2 = 1$.

17.3.6 Definition   The function f of n variables is said to be *continuous on an open ball* if it is continuous at every point of the open ball.

As an illustration of the above definition, the function of Example 3 is continuous on every open disk that does not contain a point of the circle $x^2 + y^2 = 1$.

The following theorem states that a continuous function of a continuous function is continuous. It is analogous to Theorem 2.11.6.

17.3.7 Theorem   Suppose that f is a function of a single variable and g is a function of two variables. Suppose further that g is continuous at (x_0, y_0) and f is continuous at $g(x_0, y_0)$. Then the composite function $f \circ g$ is continuous at (x_0, y_0).

The proof of this theorem, which makes use of Theorem 17.2.10, is similar to the proof of Theorem 2.12.6 and is left for the reader (see Exercise 7).

EXAMPLE 5: Given

$$h(x, y) = \ln(xy - 1)$$

discuss the continuity of h. Draw a sketch showing as a shaded region in R_2 the region of continuity of f.

SOLUTION: If g is the function defined by $g(x, y) = xy - 1$, g is continuous at all points in R_2. The natural logarithmic function is continuous on its entire domain, which is the set of all positive numbers. So if f is the function defined by $f(t) = \ln t$, f is continuous for all $t > 0$. Then the function h is the composite function $f \circ g$ and, by Theorem 17.3.7, is continuous at all points (x, y) in R_2 for which $xy - 1 > 0$ or, equivalently, $xy > 1$. The shaded region of Fig. 17.3.1 is the region of continuity of h.

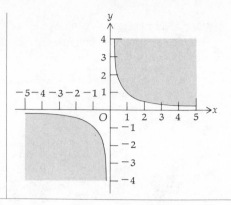

Figure 17.3.1

EXAMPLE 6: Given that

$$f(x, y) = \frac{y}{\sqrt{x^2 + y^2 - 25}}$$

discuss the continuity of f and draw a sketch showing as a shaded region in R_2 the region of continuity of f.

Figure 17.3.2

SOLUTION: This is the same function as the function G of Example 4 in Sec. 17.1. We saw there that the domain of this function is the set of all points in the exterior region bounded by the circle $x^2 + y^2 = 25$ and the points on the x axis for which $-5 < x < 5$.

The function f is the quotient of the functions g and h for which $g(x, y) = y$ and $h(x, y) = \sqrt{x^2 + y^2 - 25}$. The function g is a polynomial function and therefore is continuous everywhere. It follows from Theorem 17.3.7 that h is continuous at all points in R_2 for which $x^2 + y^2 > 25$. Therefore, by Theorem 17.3.3(iv) we conclude that f is continuous at all points in the exterior region bounded by the circle $x^2 + y^2 = 25$.

Now consider the points on the x axis for which $-5 < x < 5$, that is, the points $(a, 0)$ where $-5 < a < 5$. If S_1 is the set of points on the line $x = a$, $(a, 0)$ is an accumulation point of S_1, but

$$\lim_{\substack{(x,y)\to(a,0) \\ (P \text{ in } S_1)}} f(x, y) = \lim_{y\to 0} \frac{y}{\sqrt{a^2 + y^2 - 25}}$$

which does not exist because $y/\sqrt{a^2 + y^2 - 25}$ is not defined if $|y| \leq \sqrt{25 - a^2}$. Therefore, f is discontinuous at the points on the x axis for which $-5 < x < 5$. The shaded region of Fig. 17.3.2 is the region of continuity of f.

Exercises 17.3

In Exercises 1 through 6, discuss the continuity of f.

1. $f(x, y) = \begin{cases} \dfrac{xy}{\sqrt{x^2 + y^2}} & \text{if } (x, y) \neq (0, 0) \\ 0 & \text{if } (x, y) = (0, 0) \end{cases}$ (HINT: See Exercise 13, Exercises 17.2.)

2. $f(x, y) = \begin{cases} \dfrac{x^2 y}{x^4 + y^2} & \text{if } (x, y) \neq (0, 0) \\ 0 & \text{if } (x, y) = (0, 0) \end{cases}$ (HINT: See Example 5, Sec. 17.2.)

3. $f(x, y) = \begin{cases} \dfrac{x + y}{x^2 + y^2} & \text{if } (x, y) \neq (0, 0) \\ 0 & \text{if } (x, y) = (0, 0) \end{cases}$ 4. $f(x, y) = \begin{cases} \dfrac{x^3 + y^3}{x^2 + y^2} & \text{if } (x, y) \neq (0, 0) \\ 0 & \text{if } (x, y) = (0, 0) \end{cases}$

5. $f(x, y) = \begin{cases} \dfrac{xy}{|x| + |y|} & \text{if } (x, y) \neq (0, 0) \\ 0 & \text{if } (x, y) = (0, 0) \end{cases}$ 6. $f(x, y) = \begin{cases} \dfrac{x^2 y^2}{|x^3| + |y^3|} & \text{if } (x, y) \neq (0, 0) \\ 0 & \text{if } (x, y) = (0, 0) \end{cases}$

7. Prove Theorem 17.3.7

In Exercises 8 through 17, determine the region of continuity of f and draw a sketch showing as a shaded region in R_2 the region of continuity of f.

8. $f(x, y) = \dfrac{y}{\sqrt{x^2 - y^2 - 4}}$ 9. $f(x, y) = \dfrac{xy}{\sqrt{16 - x^2 - y^2}}$

10. $f(x, y) = \dfrac{x^2 + y^2}{\sqrt{9 - x^2 - y^2}}$ 11. $f(x, y) = \dfrac{x}{\sqrt{4x^2 + 9y^2 - 36}}$

12. $f(x, y) = \ln(x^2 + y^2 - 9) - \ln(1 - x^2 - y^2)$ 13. $f(x, y) = x \ln(xy)$

14. $f(x, y) = \sin^{-1}(xy)$ 15. $f(x, y) = \tan^{-1} \dfrac{x}{y} + \sec^{-1}(xy)$

16. $f(x, y) = \begin{cases} \dfrac{x^2 - y^2}{x - y} & \text{if } x \neq y \\ x - y & \text{if } x = y \end{cases}$ 17. $f(x, y) = \begin{cases} \dfrac{\sin(x + y)}{x + y} & \text{if } x + y \neq 0 \\ 1 & \text{if } x + y = 0 \end{cases}$

In Exercises 18 through 21, prove that the function is discontinuous at the origin. Then determine if the discontinuity is removable or essential. If the discontinuity is removable define $f(0, 0)$ so that the discontinuity is removed.

18. $f(x, y) = \dfrac{\sqrt{xy}}{x + y}$ 19. $f(x, y) = (x + y) \sin \dfrac{x}{y}$

20. $f(x, y) = \dfrac{x^2 y^2}{x^2 + y^2}$ 21. $f(x, y) = \dfrac{x^3 y^2}{x^6 + y^4}$

22. (a) Give a definition of continuity at a point for a function of three variables, similar to Definition 17.3.2. (b) State theorems for functions of three variables similar to Theorems 17.3.3 and 17.3.7. (c) Define a polynomial function of three variables and a rational function of three variables.

In Exercises 23 through 26, use the definitions and theorems of Exercise 22 to discuss the continuity of the given function.

23. $f(x, y, z) = \dfrac{xz}{\sqrt{x^2 + y^2 + z^2 - 1}}$ 24. $f(x, y, z) = \ln(36 - 4x^2 - y^2 - 9z^2)$

25. $f(x, y, z) = \begin{cases} \dfrac{3xyz}{x^2 + y^2 + z^2} & \text{if } (x, y, z) \neq (0, 0, 0) \\ 0 & \text{if } (x, y, z) = (0, 0, 0) \end{cases}$ 26. $f(x, y, z) = \begin{cases} \dfrac{xz - y^2}{x^2 + y^2 + z^2} & \text{if } (x, y, z) \neq (0, 0, 0) \\ 0 & \text{if } (x, y, z) = (0, 0, 0) \end{cases}$

17.4 PARTIAL DERIVATIVES

We now discuss differentiation of real-valued functions of n variables. The discussion is reduced to the one-dimensional case by treating a function of n variables as a function of one variable at a time and holding the others fixed. This leads to the concept of a *partial derivative*. We first define the partial derivative of a function of two variables.

17.4.1 Definition

Let f be a function of two variables, x and y. The *partial derivative of f with respect to x* is that function, denoted by D_1f, such that its function value at any point (x, y) in the domain of f is given by

$$D_1f(x, y) = \lim_{\Delta x \to 0} \frac{f(x + \Delta x, y) - f(x, y)}{\Delta x}$$ (1)

if this limit exists. Similarly, the *partial derivative of f with respect to y* is that function, denoted by D_2f, such that its function value at any point (x, y) in the domain of f is given by

$$D_2f(x, y) = \lim_{\Delta y \to 0} \frac{f(x, y + \Delta y) - f(x, y)}{\Delta y}$$ (2)

if this limit exists.

The process of finding a partial derivative is called *partial differentiation*.

D_1f is read as "D sub 1 of f," and this denotes the partial-derivative function. $D_1f(x, y)$ is read as "D sub 1 of f of x and y," and this denotes the partial-derivative function value at the point (x, y). Other notations for the partial-derivative function D_1f are $f_1, f_x,$ and $\partial f/\partial x$. Other notations for the partial-derivative function value $D_1f(x, y)$ are $f_1(x, y), f_x(x, y),$ and $\partial f(x, y)/\partial x$. Similarly, other notations for D_2f are $f_2, f_y,$ and $\partial f/\partial y$; other notations for $D_2f(x, y)$ are $f_2(x, y), f_y(x, y),$ and $\partial f(x, y)/\partial y$. If $z = f(x, y)$, we can write $\partial z/\partial x$ for $D_1f(x, y)$. A partial derivative cannot be thought of as a ratio of ∂z and ∂x because neither of these symbols has a separate meaning. The notation dy/dx can be regarded as the quotient of two differentials when y is a function of the single variable x, but there is not a similar interpretation for $\partial z/\partial x$.

EXAMPLE 1: Given

$$f(x, y) = 3x^2 - 2xy + y^2$$

find $D_1f(x, y)$ and $D_2f(x, y)$ by applying Definition 17.4.1.

SOLUTION:

$$D_1f(x, y) = \lim_{\Delta x \to 0} \frac{f(x + \Delta x, y) - f(x, y)}{\Delta x}$$

$$= \lim_{\Delta x \to 0} \frac{3(x + \Delta x)^2 - 2(x + \Delta x)y + y^2 - (3x^2 - 2xy + y^2)}{\Delta x}$$

$$= \lim_{\Delta x \to 0} \frac{3x^2 + 6x\,\Delta x + 3(\Delta x)^2 - 2xy - 2y\,\Delta x + y^2 - 3x^2 + 2xy - y^2}{\Delta x}$$

$$= \lim_{\Delta x \to 0} \frac{6x\,\Delta x + 3(\Delta x)^2 - 2y\,\Delta x}{\Delta x}$$

$$= \lim_{\Delta x \to 0} (6x + 3\,\Delta x - 2y)$$

$$= 6x - 2y$$

$$D_2 f(x, y) = \lim_{\Delta y \to 0} \frac{f(x, y + \Delta y) - f(x, y)}{\Delta y}$$

$$= \lim_{\Delta y \to 0} \frac{3x^2 - 2x(y + \Delta y) + (y + \Delta y)^2 - (3x^2 - 2xy + y^2)}{\Delta y}$$

$$= \lim_{\Delta y \to 0} \frac{3x^2 - 2xy - 2x\,\Delta y + y^2 + 2y\,\Delta y + (\Delta y)^2 - 3x^2 + 2xy - y^2}{\Delta y}$$

$$= \lim_{\Delta y \to 0} \frac{-2x\,\Delta y + 2y\,\Delta y + (\Delta y)^2}{\Delta y}$$

$$= \lim_{\Delta y \to 0} (-2x + 2y + \Delta y)$$

$$= -2x + 2y$$

If (x_0, y_0) is a particular point in the domain of f, then

$$D_1 f(x_0, y_0) = \lim_{\Delta x \to 0} \frac{f(x_0 + \Delta x, y_0) - f(x_0, y_0)}{\Delta x} \qquad (3)$$

if this limit exists, and

$$D_2 f(x_0, y_0) = \lim_{\Delta y \to 0} \frac{f(x_0, y_0 + \Delta y) - f(x_0, y_0)}{\Delta y} \qquad (4)$$

if this limit exists.

Alternate formulas to (3) and (4) for $D_1 f(x_0, y_0)$ and $D_2 f(x_0, y_0)$ are given by

$$D_1 f(x_0, y_0) = \lim_{x \to x_0} \frac{f(x, y_0) - f(x_0, y_0)}{x - x_0} \qquad (5)$$

if this limit exists, and

$$D_2 f(x_0, y_0) = \lim_{y \to y_0} \frac{f(x_0, y) - f(x_0, y_0)}{y - y_0} \qquad (6)$$

if this limit exists.

EXAMPLE 2:   For the function f of Example 1, find $D_1 f(3, -2)$ in three ways: (a) apply (3); (b) apply (5); (c) substitute $(3, -2)$ for (x, y) in the expression for $D_1 f(x, y)$ found in Example 1.

SOLUTION:

$$\text{(a) } D_1 f(3, -2) = \lim_{\Delta x \to 0} \frac{f(3 + \Delta x, -2) - f(3, -2)}{\Delta x}$$

$$= \lim_{\Delta x \to 0} \frac{3(3 + \Delta x)^2 - 2(3 + \Delta x)(-2) + (-2)^2 - (27 + 12 + 4)}{\Delta x}$$

$$= \lim_{\Delta x \to 0} \frac{27 + 18\,\Delta x + 3(\Delta x)^2 + 12 + 4\,\Delta x + 4 - 43}{\Delta x}$$

$$= \lim_{\Delta x \to 0} (18 + 3\,\Delta x + 4)$$

$$= 22$$

(b) $D_1 f(3, -2) = \lim_{x \to 3} \dfrac{f(x, -2) - f(3, -2)}{x - 3}$

$$= \lim_{x \to 3} \frac{3x^2 + 4x + 4 - 43}{x - 3}$$

$$= \lim_{x \to 3} \frac{3x^2 + 4x - 39}{x - 3}$$

$$= \lim_{x \to 3} \frac{(3x + 13)(x - 3)}{x - 3}$$

$$= \lim_{x \to 3} (3x + 13)$$

$$= 22$$

(c) From Example 1,

$$D_1 f(x, y) = 6x - 2y$$

Therefore,

$$D_1 f(3, -2) = 18 + 4 = 22$$

To distinguish derivatives of functions of more than one variable from derivatives of functions of one variable, we call the latter derivatives *ordinary derivatives*.

Comparing Definition 17.4.1 with the definition of an ordinary derivative (3.3.1), we see that $D_1 f(x, y)$ is the ordinary derivative of f if f is considered as a function of one variable x (i.e., y is held constant), and $D_2 f(x, y)$ is the ordinary derivative of f if f is considered as a function of one variable y (and x is held constant). So the results in Example 1 could have been obtained more easily by applying the theorems for ordinary differentiation if we consider y constant when finding $D_1 f(x, y)$ and if we consider x constant when finding $D_2 f(x, y)$. The following example illustrates this.

EXAMPLE 3:   Given $f(x, y) = 3x^3 - 4x^2 y + 3xy^2 + 7x - 8y$, find $D_1 f(x, y)$ and $D_2 f(x, y)$.

SOLUTION: Considering f as a function of x and holding y constant, we have

$$D_1 f(x, y) = 9x^2 - 8xy + 3y^2 + 7$$

Considering f as a function of y and holding x constant, we have

$$D_2 f(x, y) = -4x^2 + 6xy - 8$$

EXAMPLE 4:   Given

$$f(x, y) = \begin{cases} \dfrac{xy(x^2 - y^2)}{x^2 + y^2} & \text{if } (x, y) \neq (0, 0) \\ 0 & \text{if } (x, y) = (0, 0) \end{cases}$$

SOLUTION: (a) If $y \neq 0$, from (5) we have

$$f_1(0, y) = \lim_{x \to 0} \frac{f(x, y) - f(0, y)}{x - 0}$$

$$= \lim_{x \to 0} \frac{\dfrac{xy(x^2 - y^2)}{x^2 + y^2} - 0}{x}$$

$$= \lim_{x \to 0} \frac{y(x^2 - y^2)}{x^2 + y^2}$$

$$= -\frac{y^3}{y^2}$$

$$= -y$$

If $y = 0$, we have

$$f_1(0, 0) = \lim_{x \to 0} \frac{f(x, 0) - f(0, 0)}{x - 0} = \lim_{x \to 0} \frac{0 - 0}{x} = 0$$

Because $f_1(0, y) = -y$ if $y \neq 0$ and $f_1(0, 0) = 0$, we can conclude that $f_1(0, y) = -y$ for all y.

(b) If $x \neq 0$, from (6) we have

$$f_2(x, 0) = \lim_{y \to 0} \frac{f(x, y) - f(x, 0)}{y - 0}$$

$$= \lim_{y \to 0} \frac{\dfrac{xy(x^2 - y^2)}{x^2 + y^2} - 0}{y}$$

$$= \lim_{y \to 0} \frac{x(x^2 - y^2)}{x^2 + y^2}$$

$$= \frac{x^3}{x^2}$$

$$= x$$

If $x = 0$, we have

$$f_2(0, 0) = \lim_{y \to 0} \frac{f(0, y) - f(0, 0)}{y - 0} = \lim_{y \to 0} \frac{0 - 0}{y} = 0$$

Because $f_2(x, 0) = x$, if $x \neq 0$ and $f_2(0, 0) = 0$, we can conclude that $f_2(x, 0) = x$ for all x.

Geometric interpretations of the partial derivatives of a function of two variables are similar to those of a function of one variable. The graph of a function f of two variables is a surface having equation $z = f(x, y)$. If y is held constant (say, $y = y_0$), then $z = f(x, y_0)$ is the equation of the trace of this surface in the plane $y = y_0$. The curve can be represented by the two equations

$$y = y_0 \quad \text{and} \quad z = f(x, y) \tag{7}$$

because the curve is the intersection of these two surfaces.

Then $D_1f(x_0, y_0)$ is the slope of the tangent line to the curve given by Eqs. (7) at the point $P_0(x_0, y_0, f(x_0, y_0))$ in the plane $y = y_0$. In an analogous fashion, $D_2f(x_0, y_0)$ represents the slope of the tangent line to the curve having equations

$$x = x_0 \quad \text{and} \quad z = f(x, y)$$

at the point P_0 in the plane $x = x_0$. Figure 17.4.1a and b shows the portions of the curves and the tangent lines.

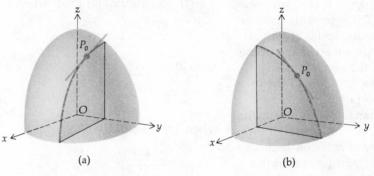

(a)   (b)

Figure 17.4.1

EXAMPLE 5: Find the slope of the tangent line to the curve of intersection of the surface $z = \frac{1}{2}\sqrt{24 - x^2 - 2y^2}$ with the plane $y = 2$ at the point $(2, 2, \sqrt{3})$.

SOLUTION: The required slope will be the value of $\partial z/\partial x$ at the point $(2, 2, \sqrt{3})$.

$$\frac{\partial z}{\partial x} = \frac{-x}{2\sqrt{24 - x^2 - 2y^2}}$$

So at $(2, 2, \sqrt{3})$,

$$\frac{\partial z}{\partial x} = \frac{-2}{2\sqrt{12}} = -\frac{1}{2\sqrt{3}}$$

A partial derivative can be interpreted as a rate of change. Actually, every derivative is a measure of a rate of change. If f is a function of the two variables x and y, the partial derivative of f with respect to x at the point $P_0(x_0, y_0)$ gives the instantaneous rate of change, at P_0, of $f(x, y)$ per unit change in x (x alone varies and y is held fixed at y_0). Similarly, the partial derivative of f with respect to y at P_0 gives the instantaneous rate of change, at P_0, of $f(x, y)$ per unit change in y.

EXAMPLE 6: According to the *ideal gas law* for a confined gas, if P pounds per square unit is the pressure, V cubic units is the volume, and T degrees is the temperature, we have the formula

$$PV = kT \qquad (8)$$

where k is a constant of proportionality. Suppose that the volume of gas in a certain container is 100 in.^{3} and the temperature is 90°, and $k = 8$.

(a) Find the instantaneous rate of change of P per unit change in T if V remains fixed at 100. (b) Use the result of part (a) to approximate the change in the pressure if the temperature is increased to 92°. (c) Find the instantaneous rate of change of V per unit change in P if T remains fixed at 90. (d) Suppose that the temperature is held constant. Use the result of part (c) to find the approximate change in the volume necessary to produce the same change in the pressure as obtained in part (b).

SOLUTION: Substituting $V = 100$, $T = 90$, and $k = 8$ in Eq. (8), we obtain $P = 7.2$. (a) Solving Eq. (8) for P when $k = 8$, we get

$$P = \frac{8T}{V}$$

Therefore,

$$\frac{\partial P}{\partial T} = \frac{8}{V}$$

When $T = 90$ and $V = 100$, $\partial P/\partial T = 0.08$, which is the answer required.

(b) From the result of part (a) when T is increased by 2 (and V remains fixed) an approximate increase in P is $2(0.08) = 0.16$. We conclude, then, that if the temperature is increased from 90° to 92°, the increase in the pressure is approximately 0.16 lb/in.^{2}.

(c) Solving Eq. (8) for V when $k = 8$, we obtain

$$V = \frac{8T}{P}$$

Therefore,

$$\frac{\partial V}{\partial P} = -\frac{8T}{P^2}$$

When $T = 90$ and $P = 7.2$,

$$\frac{\partial V}{\partial P} = -\frac{8(90)}{(7.2)^2} = -\frac{125}{9}$$

which is the instantaneous rate of change of V per unit change in P when $T = 90$ and $P = 7.2$ if T remains fixed at 90.

(d) If P is to be increased by 0.16 and T is held fixed, then from the result of part (c) the change in V should be approximately $(0.16)(-\frac{125}{9}) = -\frac{20}{9}$. Hence, the volume should be decreased by approximately $\frac{20}{9}$ in.^{3} if the pressure is to be increased from 7.2 lb/in.^{2} to 7.36 lb/in.^{2}.

We now extend the concept of partial derivative to functions of n variables.

17.4.2 Definition Let $P(x_1, x_2, \ldots, x_n)$ be a point in R_n, and let f be a function of the n variables $x_1, x_2, \ldots, x_n$. Then the partial derivative of f with respect to x_k is that function, denoted by $D_k f$, such that its function value at any point P in the domain of f is given by

$$D_k f(x_1, x_2, \ldots, x_n) =$$

$$\lim_{\Delta x_k \to 0} \frac{f(x_1, x_2, \ldots, x_{k-1}, x_k + \Delta x_k, x_{k+1}, \ldots, x_n) - f(x_1, x_2, \ldots, x_n)}{\Delta x_k}$$

if this limit exists.

In particular, if f is a function of the three variables x, y, and z, then the partial derivatives of f are given by

$$D_1f(x, y, z) = \lim_{\Delta x \to 0} \frac{f(x + \Delta x, y, z) - f(x, y, z)}{\Delta x}$$

$$D_2f(x, y, z) = \lim_{\Delta y \to 0} \frac{f(x, y + \Delta y, z) - f(x, y, z)}{\Delta y}$$

and

$$D_3f(x, y, z) = \lim_{\Delta z \to 0} \frac{f(x, y, z + \Delta z) - f(x, y, z)}{\Delta z}$$

if these limits exist.

EXAMPLE 7: Given

$$f(x, y, z) = x^2y + yz^2 + z^3$$

verify that $xf_1(x, y, z)$

$+ yf_2(x, y, z) + zf_3(x, y, z) =$

$3f(x, y, z)$.

SOLUTION: Holding y and z constant, we get

$$f_1(x, y, z) = 2xy$$

Holding x and z constant, we obtain

$$f_2(x, y, z) = x^2 + z^2$$

Holding x and y constant, we get

$$f_3(x, y, z) = 2yz + 3z^2$$

Therefore,

$$xf_1(x, y, z) + yf_2(x, y, z) + zf_3(x, y, z) = x(2xy) + y(x^2 + z^2) + z(2yz + 3z^2)$$

$$= 2x^2y + x^2y + yz^2 + 2yz^2 + 3z^3$$

$$= 3(x^2y + yz^2 + z^3)$$

$$= 3f(x, y, z)$$

Exercises 17.4

In Exercises 1 through 6, apply Definition 17.4.1 to find each of the partial derivatives.

1. $f(x, y) = 6x + 3y - 7$; $D_1f(x, y)$

2. $f(x, y) = 4x^2 - 3xy$; $D_1f(x, y)$

3. $f(x, y) = 3xy + 6x - y^2$; $D_2f(x, y)$

4. $f(x, y) = xy^2 - 5y + 6$; $D_2f(x, y)$

5. $f(x, y) = \sqrt{x^2 + y^2}$; $D_1f(x, y)$

6. $f(x, y) = \dfrac{x + 2y}{x^2 - y}$; $D_2f(x, y)$

In Exercises 7 through 10, apply Definition 17.4.2 to find each of the partial derivatives.

7. $f(x, y, z) = x^2y - 3xy^2 + 2yz$; $D_2f(x, y, z)$

8. $f(x, y, z) = x^2 + 4y^2 + 9z^2$; $D_1f(x, y, z)$

9. $f(x, y, z, r, t) = xyr + yzt + yrt + zrt$; $D_4f(x, y, z, r, t)$

10. $f(r, s, t, u, v, w) = 3r^2st + st^2v - 2tuv^2 - tvw + 3uw^2$; $D_5f(r, s, t, u, v, w)$

11. Given $f(x, y) = x^2 - 9y^2$. Find $D_1f(2, 1)$ by (a) applying formula (3); (b) applying formula (5); (c) applying formula (1) and then replacing x and y by 2 and 1, respectively.

12. For the function in Exercise 11, find $D_2f(2, 1)$ by (a) applying formula (4); (b) applying formula (6); (c) applying formula (2) and then replacing x and y by 2 and 1, respectively.

In Exercises 13 through 24, find the indicated partial derivatives by holding all but one of the variables constant and applying theorems for ordinary differentiation.

13. $f(x, y) = 4y^3 + \sqrt{x^2 + y^2}$; $D_1f(x, y)$

14. $f(x, y) = \dfrac{x + y}{\sqrt{y^2 - x^2}}$; $D_2f(x, y)$

15. $f(\theta, \phi) = \sin 3\theta \cos 2\phi$; $D_2f(\theta, \phi)$

16. $f(r, \theta) = r^2 \cos \theta - 2r \tan \theta$; $D_2f(r, \theta)$

17. $z = e^{y/x} \ln \dfrac{x^2}{y}$; $\dfrac{\partial z}{\partial y}$

18. $r = e^{-\theta} \cos(\theta + \phi)$; $\dfrac{\partial r}{\partial \theta}$

19. $u = (x^2 + y^2 + z^2)^{-1/2}$; $\dfrac{\partial u}{\partial z}$

20. $u = \tan^{-1}(xyzw)$; $\dfrac{\partial u}{\partial w}$

21. $f(x, y, z) = 4xyz + \ln(2xyz)$; $f_3(x, y, z)$

22. $f(x, y, z) = e^{xy} \sinh 2z - e^{xy} \cosh 2z$; $f_3(x, y, z)$

23. $f(x, y, z) = e^{xyz} + \tan^{-1} \dfrac{3xy}{z^2}$; $f_2(x, y, z)$

24. $f(r, \theta, \phi) = 4r^2 \sin \theta + 5e^r \cos \theta \sin \phi - 2 \cos \phi$; $f_2(r, \theta, \phi)$

In Exercises 25 and 26, find $f_x(x, y)$ and $f_y(x, y)$.

25. $f(x, y) = \displaystyle\int_x^y \ln \sin t \, dt$

26. $f(x, y) = \displaystyle\int_x^y e^{\cos t} \, dt$

27. Given $u = \sin \dfrac{r}{t} + \ln \dfrac{t}{r}$. Verify $t \dfrac{\partial u}{\partial t} + r \dfrac{\partial u}{\partial r} = 0$.

28. Given $w = x^2y + y^2z + z^2x$. Verify $\dfrac{\partial w}{\partial x} + \dfrac{\partial w}{\partial y} + \dfrac{\partial w}{\partial z} = (x + y + z)^2$.

29. Given $f(x, y) = \begin{cases} \dfrac{x^3 + y^3}{x^2 + y^2} & \text{if } (x, y) \neq (0, 0) \\ 0 & \text{if } (x, y) = (0, 0) \end{cases}$

Find (a) $f_1(0, 0)$; (b) $f_2(0, 0)$.

30. Given $f(x, y) = \begin{cases} \dfrac{x^2 - xy}{x + y} & \text{if } (x, y) \neq (0, 0) \\ 0 & \text{if } (x, y) = (0, 0) \end{cases}$

Find (a) $f_1(0, y)$ if $y \neq 0$; (b) $f_1(0, 0)$.

31. For the function of Exercise 30 find (a) $f_2(x, 0)$ if $x \neq 0$; (b) $f_2(0, 0)$.

32. Find the slope of the tangent line to the curve of intersection of the surface $36x^2 - 9y^2 + 4z^2 + 36 = 0$ with the plane $x = 1$ at the point $(1, \sqrt{12}, -3)$. Interpret this slope as a partial derivative.

33. Find the slope of the tangent line to the curve of intersection of the surface $z = x^2 + y^2$ with the plane $y = 1$ at the point $(2, 1, 5)$. Draw a sketch. Interpret this slope as a partial derivative.

34. Find equations of the tangent line to the curve of intersection of the surface $x^2 + y^2 + z^2 = 9$ with the plane $y = 2$ at the point $(1, 2, 2)$.

35. The temperature at any point (x, y) of a flat plate is T degrees and $T = 54 - \frac{2}{3}x^2 - 4y^2$. If distance is measured in feet find the rate of change of the temperature with respect to the distance moved along the plate in the directions of the positive x and y axes, respectively, at the point $(3, 1)$.

36. Use the ideal gas law for a confined gas (see Example 6) to show that

$$\dfrac{\partial V}{\partial T} \cdot \dfrac{\partial T}{\partial P} \cdot \dfrac{\partial P}{\partial V} = -1$$

37. If V dollars is the present value of an ordinary annuity of equal payments of $100 per year for t years at an interest rate of $100i$ percent per year, then

$$V = 100 \left[\dfrac{1 - (1 + i)^{-t}}{i} \right]$$

(a) Find the instantaneous rate of change of V per unit change in i if t remains fixed at 8. (b) Use the result of part (a) to find the approximate change in the present value if the interest rate changes from 6% to 7% and the time remains fixed at 8 years. (c) Find the instantaneous rate of change of V per unit change in t if i remains fixed at 0.06. (d) Use the result of part (c) to find the approximate change in the present value if the time is decreased from 8 to 7 years and the interest rate remains fixed at 6%.

17.5 DIFFERENTIABILITY AND THE TOTAL DIFFERENTIAL

In Sec. 3.6 in the proof of the chain rule we showed that if f is a differentiable function of the single variable x and $y = f(x)$, then the increment Δy of the dependent variable can be expressed as

$$\Delta y = f'(x)\,\Delta x + \eta\,\Delta x$$

where η is a function of Δx and $\eta \to 0$ as $\Delta x \to 0$.

From the above it follows that if the function f is differentiable at x_0, the increment of f at x_0, denoted by $\Delta f(x_0)$, is given by

$$\Delta f(x_0) = f'(x_0)\,\Delta x + \eta\,\Delta x \tag{1}$$

where $\lim\limits_{\Delta x \to 0} \eta = 0$.

For functions of two or more variables we use an equation corresponding to Eq. (1) to define *differentiability* of a function. And from the definition we determine criteria for a function to be differentiable at a point. We give the details for a function of two variables and begin by defining the increment of such a function.

17.5.1 Definition   If f is a function of two variables x and y, then the *increment of f* at the point (x_0, y_0), denoted by $\Delta f(x_0, y_0)$, is given by

$$\Delta f(x_0, y_0) = f(x_0 + \Delta x, y_0 + \Delta y) - f(x_0, y_0) \tag{2}$$

Figure 17.5.1 illustrates Eq. (2) for a function which is continuous on an open disk containing the points (x_0, y_0) and $(x_0 + \Delta x, y_0 + \Delta y)$. The figure shows a portion of the surface $z = f(x, y)$. $\Delta f(x_0, y_0) = \overline{QR}$, where Q is the point $(x_0 + \Delta x, y_0 + \Delta y, f(x_0, y_0))$ and R is the point $(x_0 + \Delta x, y_0 + \Delta y, f(x_0 + \Delta x, y_0 + \Delta y))$.

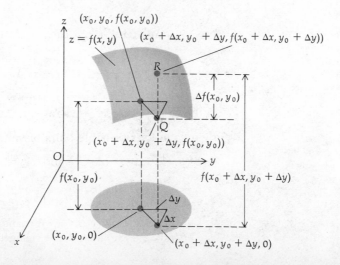

Figure 17.5.1

EXAMPLE 1:   Given

$$f(x, y) = 3x - xy^2$$

find the increment of f at any point (x_0, y_0).

SOLUTION:

$$\Delta f(x_0, y_0) = f(x_0 + \Delta x, y_0 + \Delta y) - f(x_0, y_0)$$

$$= 3(x_0 + \Delta x) - (x_0 + \Delta x)(y_0 + \Delta y)^2 - (3x_0 - x_0y_0^2)$$

$$= 3x_0 + 3\,\Delta x - x_0y_0^2 - y_0^2\,\Delta x - 2x_0y_0\,\Delta y - 2y_0\,\Delta x\,\Delta y$$

$$- x_0(\Delta y)^2 - \Delta x(\Delta y)^2 - 3x_0 + x_0y_0^2$$

$$= 3\,\Delta x - y_0^2\,\Delta x - 2x_0y_0\,\Delta y - 2y_0\,\Delta x\,\Delta y - x_0(\Delta y)^2 - \Delta x(\Delta y)^2$$

17.5.2 Definition

If f is a function of two variables x and y and the increment of f at (x_0, y_0) can be written as

$$\Delta f(x_0, y_0) = D_1 f(x_0, y_0)\,\Delta x + D_2 f(x_0, y_0)\,\Delta y + \epsilon_1\,\Delta x + \epsilon_2\,\Delta y \qquad (3)$$

where ϵ_1 and ϵ_2 are functions of Δx and Δy such that $\epsilon_1 \to 0$ and $\epsilon_2 \to 0$ as $(\Delta x, \Delta y) \to (0, 0)$, then f is said to be *differentiable* at (x_0, y_0).

EXAMPLE 2:   Prove that the function of Example 1 is differentiable at all points in R_2.

SOLUTION: From Definition 17.5.2, if for all points (x_0, y_0) in R_2 we can find an ϵ_1 and an ϵ_2 such that

$$\Delta f(x_0, y_0) - D_1 f(x_0, y_0)\,\Delta x - D_2 f(x_0, y_0)\,\Delta y = \epsilon_1\,\Delta x + \epsilon_2\,\Delta y$$

and $\epsilon_1 \to 0$ and $\epsilon_2 \to 0$ as $(\Delta x, \Delta y) \to (0, 0)$, we have proved that f is differentiable at all points in R_2.

Because $f(x, y) = 3x - xy^2$,

$$D_1 f(x_0, y_0) = 3 - y_0^2 \quad \text{and} \quad D_2 f(x_0, y_0) = -2x_0y_0$$

Using these values and the value of $\Delta f(x_0, y_0)$ from Example 1, we have

$$\Delta f(x_0, y_0) - D_1 f(x_0, y_0)\,\Delta x - D_2 f(x_0, y_0)\,\Delta y = -x_0(\Delta y)^2 - 2y_0\,\Delta x\,\Delta y - \Delta x(\Delta y)^2$$

The right side of the above equation can be written in the following ways:

$$[-2y_0\,\Delta y - (\Delta y)^2]\,\Delta x + (-x_0\,\Delta y)\,\Delta y$$

or

$$(-2y_0\,\Delta y)\,\Delta x + (-\Delta x\,\Delta y - x_0\,\Delta y)\,\Delta y$$

or

$$[-(\Delta y)^2]\,\Delta x + (-2y_0\,\Delta x - x_0\,\Delta y)\,\Delta y$$

or

$$0 \cdot \Delta x + [-2y_0\,\Delta x - \Delta x\,\Delta y - x_0\,\Delta y]\,\Delta y$$

So we have four possible pairs of values for ϵ_1 and ϵ_2:

$$\epsilon_1 = -2y_0\,\Delta y - (\Delta y)^2 \quad \text{and} \quad \epsilon_2 = -x_0\,\Delta y$$

or

$$\epsilon_1 = -2y_0\,\Delta y \qquad\qquad \text{and} \quad \epsilon_2 = -\Delta x\,\Delta y - x_0\,\Delta y$$

or

$$\epsilon_1 = -(\Delta y)^2 \qquad \text{and} \quad \epsilon_2 = -2y_0\,\Delta x - x_0\,\Delta y$$

or

$$\epsilon_1 = 0 \qquad \text{and} \quad \epsilon_2 = -2y_0\,\Delta x - \Delta x\,\Delta y - x_0\,\Delta y$$

For each pair, we see that

$$\lim_{(\Delta x, \Delta y)\to(0,0)} \epsilon_1 = 0 \quad \text{and} \quad \lim_{(\Delta x, \Delta y)\to(0,0)} \epsilon_2 = 0$$

It should be noted that in the solution of Example 2 it is only necessary to find one pair of values for ϵ_1 and ϵ_2.

17.5.3 Theorem   If a function f of two variables is differentiable at a point, it is continuous at that point.

PROOF: If f is differentiable at the point (x_0, y_0), it follows from Definition 17.5.2 that

$$f(x_0 + \Delta x, y_0 + y) - f(x_0, y_0) = D_1f(x_0, y_0)\,\Delta x + D_2f(x_0, y_0)\,\Delta y$$
$$+ \epsilon_1\,\Delta x + \epsilon_2\,\Delta y$$

where $\epsilon_1 \to 0$ and $\epsilon_2 \to 0$ as $(\Delta x, \Delta y) \to (0, 0)$. Therefore,

$$f(x_0 + \Delta x, y_0 + \Delta y) = f(x_0, y_0) + D_1f(x_0, y_0)\,\Delta x + D_2f(x_0, y_0)\,\Delta y$$
$$+ \epsilon_1\,\Delta x + \epsilon_2\,\Delta y$$

Taking the limit on both sides of the above as $(\Delta x, \Delta y) \to (0, 0)$, we obtain

$$\lim_{(\Delta x, \Delta y)\to(0,0)} f(x_0 + \Delta x, y_0 + \Delta y) = f(x_0, y_0) \tag{4}$$

If we let $x_0 + \Delta x = x$ and $y_0 + \Delta y = y$, "$(\Delta x, \Delta y) \to (0, 0)$" is equivalent to "$(x, y) \to (x_0, y_0)$." Thus, we have from (4)

$$\lim_{(x,y)\to(x_0,y_0)} f(x, y) = f(x_0, y_0)$$

which proves that f is continuous at (x_0, y_0).   ∎

Theorem 17.5.3 states that for a function of two variables *differentiability implies continuity*. However, the mere existence of the partial derivatives D_1f and D_2f at a point does not imply differentiability at that point. The following example illustrates this.

EXAMPLE 3:   Given

$$f(x, y) = \begin{cases} \dfrac{xy}{x^2 + y^2} & \text{if } (x, y) \neq (0, 0) \\ 0 & \text{if } (x, y) = (0, 0) \end{cases}$$

prove that $D_1f(0, 0)$ and $D_2f(0, 0)$

SOLUTION:

$$D_1f(0, 0) = \lim_{x\to 0} \frac{f(x, 0) - f(0, 0)}{x - 0} = \lim_{x\to 0} \frac{0 - 0}{x} = 0$$

$$D_2f(0, 0) = \lim_{y\to 0} \frac{f(0, y) - f(0, 0)}{y - 0} = \lim_{y\to 0} \frac{0 - 0}{y} = 0$$

exist but that f is not differentiable at $(0, 0)$.

Therefore, both $D_1f(0, 0)$ and $D_2f(0, 0)$ exist.

In Example 3 of Sec. 17.2 we showed that for this function

$$\lim_{(x,y)\to(0,0)} f(x, y)$$

does not exist; hence, f is not continuous at $(0, 0)$. Because f is not continuous at $(0, 0)$, it follows from Theorem 17.5.3 that f is not differentiable there.

So even though the existence of the derivative of a function of a single variable at a point implies differentiability and continuity of the function at that point, we see from Example 3 that this does not hold for functions of more than one variable.

Before stating a theorem that gives conditions for which a function will be differentiable at a point, we consider a theorem needed in its proof. It is the mean-value theorem for a function of a single variable applied to a function of two variables.

17.5.4 Theorem   Let f be a function of two variables defined for all x in the closed interval $[a, b]$ and all y in the closed interval $[c, d]$.

(i) If $D_1f(x, y_0)$ exists for some y_0 in $[c, d]$ and for all x in $[a, b]$, then there is a number ξ_1 in the open interval (a, b) such that

$$f(b, y_0) - f(a, y_0) = (b - a)D_1f(\xi_1, y_0) \tag{5}$$

(ii) If $D_2f(x_0, y)$ exists for some x_0 in $[a, b]$ and for all y in $[c, d]$, then there is a number ξ_2 in the open interval (c, d) such that

$$f(x_0, d) - f(x_0, c) = (d - c)D_2f(x_0, \xi_2) \tag{6}$$

Before proving this theorem, we interpret it geometrically. For part (i)

Figure 17.5.2

refer to Fig. 17.5.2, which shows the portion of the surface $z = f(x, y)$ above the rectangular region in the xy plane bounded by the lines $x = a$, $x = b$, $y = c$, and $y = d$. The plane $y = y_0$ intersects the surface in the curve represented by the two equations $y = y_0$ and $z = f(x, y)$. The slope of the line through the points $A(a, y_0, f(a, y_0))$ and $B(b, y_0, f(b, y_0))$ is

$$\frac{f(b, y_0) - f(a, y_0)}{b - a}$$

Theorem 17.5.4(i) states that there is some point $(\xi_i, y_0, f(\xi_i, y_0))$ on the curve between the points A and B where the tangent line is parallel to the secant line through A and B; that is, there is some number ξ_1 in (a, b) such that $D_1 f(\xi_1, y_0) = [f(b, y_0) - f(a, y_0)]/(b - a)$, and this is illustrated in the figure, for which $D_1 f(\xi_i, y_0) < 0$.

Figure 17.5.3 illustrates part (ii) of Theorem 17.5.4. The plane $x = x_0$ intersects the surface $z = f(x, y)$ in the curve represented by the two equations $x = x_0$ and $z = f(x, y)$. The slope of the line through the points $C(x_0, c, f(x_0, c))$ and $D(x_0, d, f(x_0, d))$ is $[f(x_0, d) - f(x_0, c)]/(d - c)$, and Theorem 17.5.4(ii) states that there is some point $(x_0, \xi_2, f(x_0, \xi_2))$ on the curve between the points C and D where the tangent line is parallel to the secant line through C and D; that is, there is some number ξ_2 in (c, d) such that $D_2 f(x_0, \xi_2) = [f(x_0, d) - f(x_0, c)]/(d - c)$.

Figure 17.5.3

PROOF OF THEOREM 17.5.4(i):   Let g be the function of one variable x defined by

$$g(x) = f(x, y_0)$$

Then

$$g'(x) = D_1 f(x, y_0)$$

Because $D_1f(x, y_0)$ exists for all x in $[a, b]$, it follows that $g'(x)$ exists for all x in $[a, b]$, and therefore g is continuous on $[a, b]$. So by the mean-value theorem (4.5.2) for ordinary derivatives there exists a number ξ_1 in (a, b) such that

$$g'(\xi_1) = \frac{g(b) - g(a)}{b - a}$$

or, equivalently,

$$D_1f(\xi_1, y_0) = \frac{f(b, y_0) - f(a, y_0)}{b - a}$$

from which we obtain

$$f(b, y_0) - f(a, y_0) = (b - a)D_1f(\xi_1, y_0)$$

The proof of part (ii) is similar to the proof of part (i) and is left for the reader (see Exercise 11). ∎

Equation (5) can be written in the form

$$f(x_0 + h, y_0) - f(x_0, y_0) = hD_1f(\xi_1, y_0) \tag{7}$$

where ξ_1 is between x_0 and $x_0 + h$ and h is either positive or negative (see Exercise 12).

Equation (6) can be written in the form

$$f(x_0, y_0 + k) - f(x_0, y_0) = kD_2f(x_0, \xi_2) \tag{8}$$

where ξ_2 is between y_0 and $y_0 + k$ and k is either positive or negative (see Exercise 13).

EXAMPLE 4:   Given

$$f(x, y) = \frac{2xy}{3 + x}$$

find a ξ_1 required by Theorem 17.5.4 if x is in $[2, 5]$ and $y = 4$.

SOLUTION: By Theorem 17.5.4, there is a number ξ_1 in the open interval $(2, 5)$ such that

$$f(5, 4) - f(2, 4) = (5 - 2)D_1f(\xi_1, 4)$$

So

$$5 - \frac{16}{5} = 3 \cdot \frac{24}{(3 + \xi_1)^2}$$

or

$$\frac{9}{5} = \frac{72}{(3 + \xi_1)^2}$$

or

$$(3 + \xi_1)^2 = 40$$

Therefore,

$$3 + \xi_1 = \pm 2\sqrt{10}$$

But because $2 < \xi_1 < 5$, we take only the "+" sign and obtain

$$\xi_1 = 2\sqrt{10} - 3$$

The following theorem states that a function having continuous partial derivatives at a point is necessarily differentiable at the point.

17.5.5 Theorem   Let f be a function of two variables x and y. Suppose that $D_1 f$ and $D_2 f$ exist on an open disk $B(P_0; r)$, where P_0 is the point (x_0, y_0). Then if $D_1 f$ and $D_2 f$ are continuous at P_0, f is differentiable at P_0.

PROOF: Choose the point $(x_0 + \Delta x, y_0 + \Delta y)$ so it is in $B(P_0; r)$. Then

$$\Delta f(x_0, y_0) = f(x_0 + \Delta x, y_0 + \Delta y) - f(x_0, y_0)$$

Subtracting and adding $f(x_0 + \Delta x, y_0)$ to the right side of the above, we get

$$\Delta f(x_0, y_0) = [f(x_0 + \Delta x, y_0 + \Delta y) - f(x_0 + \Delta x, y_0)]$$
$$+ [f(x_0 + \Delta x, y_0) - f(x_0, y_0)] \quad (9)$$

Because $D_1 f$ and $D_2 f$ exist on $B(P_0; r)$ and $(x_0 + \Delta x, y_0 + \Delta y)$ is in $B(P_0; r)$, it follows from (8) that

$$f(x_0 + \Delta x, y_0 + \Delta y) - f(x_0 + \Delta x, y_0) = (\Delta y)D_2 f(x_0 + \Delta x, \xi_2) \quad (10)$$

where ξ_2 is between y_0 and $y_0 + \Delta y$.
From (7) it follows that

$$f(x_0 + \Delta x, y_0) - f(x_0, y_0) = (\Delta x)D_1 f(\xi_1, y_0) \quad (11)$$

where ξ_1 is between x_0 and $x_0 + \Delta x$.
Substituting from (10) and (11) in (9), we obtain

$$\Delta f(x_0, y_0) = (\Delta y)D_2 f(x_0 + \Delta x, \xi_2) + (\Delta x)D_1 f(\xi_1, y_0) \quad (12)$$

Because $(x_0 + \Delta x, y_0 + \Delta y)$ is in $B(P_0; r)$, ξ_2 is between y_0 and $y_0 + \Delta y$, and $D_2 f$ is continuous at P_0, it follows that

$$\lim_{(\Delta x, \Delta y) \to (0,0)} D_2 f(x_0 + \Delta x, \xi_2) = D_2 f(x_0, y_0) \quad (13)$$

and, because ξ_1 is between x_0 and $x_0 + \Delta x$ and $D_1 f$ is continuous at P_0, it follows that

$$\lim_{(\Delta x, \Delta y) \to (0,0)} D_1 f(\xi_1, y_0) = D_1 f(x_0, y_0) \quad (14)$$

If we let

$$\epsilon_1 = D_1 f(\xi_1, y_0) - D_1 f(x_0, y_0) \quad (15)$$

it follows from Eq. (14) that

$$\lim_{(\Delta x, \Delta y) \to (0,0)} \epsilon_1 = 0 \quad (16)$$

and if we let

$$\epsilon_2 = D_2 f(x_0 + \Delta x, \xi_2) - D_2 f(x_0, y_0) \tag{17}$$

it follows from Eq. (13) that

$$\lim_{(\Delta x, \Delta y) \to (0,0)} \epsilon_2 = 0 \tag{18}$$

Substituting from Eqs. (15) and (17) into (12), we get

$$\Delta f(x_0, y_0) = \Delta y [D_2 f(x_0, y_0) + \epsilon_2] + \Delta x [D_1 f(x_0, y_0) + \epsilon_1]$$

from which we obtain

$$\Delta f(x_0, y_0) = D_1 f(x_0, y_0) \, \Delta x + D_2 f(x_0, y_0) \, \Delta y + \epsilon_1 \, \Delta x + \epsilon_2 \, \Delta y \tag{19}$$

From Eqs. (16), (18), and (19) we see that Definition 17.5.2 holds; so f is differentiable at (x_0, y_0). ∎

A function satisfying the hypothesis of Theorem 17.5.5 is said to be *continuously differentiable* at the point P_0.

EXAMPLE 5:   Given

$$f(x, y) = \begin{cases} \dfrac{x^2 y^2}{x^2 + y^2} & \text{if } (x, y) \neq (0, 0) \\ 0 & \text{if } (x, y) = (0, 0) \end{cases}$$

use Theorem 17.5.5 to prove that f is differentiable at $(0, 0)$.

SOLUTION: To find $D_1 f$ we consider two cases: $(x, y) = (0, 0)$ and $(x, y) \neq (0, 0)$. If $(x, y) = (0, 0)$, we have

$$D_1 f(0, 0) = \lim_{x \to 0} \frac{f(x, 0) - f(0, 0)}{x - 0} = \lim_{x \to 0} \frac{0 - 0}{x} = 0$$

If $(x, y) \neq (0, 0)$, $f(x, y) = x^2 y^2 / (x^2 + y^2)$. To find $D_1 f(x, y)$ we can use the theorem for the ordinary derivative of a quotient and consider y as a constant. We have

$$D_1 f(x, y) = \frac{2xy^2(x^2 + y^2) - 2x(x^2 y^2)}{(x^2 + y^2)^2}$$

$$= \frac{2xy^4}{(x^2 + y^2)^2}$$

The function $D_1 f$ is therefore defined by

$$D_1 f(x, y) = \begin{cases} \dfrac{2xy^4}{(x^2 + y^2)^2} & \text{if } (x, y) \neq (0, 0) \\ 0 & \text{if } (x, y) = (0, 0) \end{cases}$$

In the same manner we obtain the function $D_2 f$ defined by

$$D_2 f(x, y) = \begin{cases} \dfrac{2x^4 y}{(x^2 + y^2)^2} & \text{if } (x, y) \neq (0, 0) \\ 0 & \text{if } (x, y) = (0, 0) \end{cases}$$

Both $D_1 f$ and $D_2 f$ exist on every open disk having its center at the origin. It remains to show that $D_1 f$ and $D_2 f$ are continuous at $(0, 0)$.

Because $D_1 f(0, 0) = 0$, $D_1 f$ will be continuous at $(0, 0)$ if

$$\lim_{(x, y) \to (0, 0)} D_1 f(x, y) = 0$$

Therefore, we must show that for any $\epsilon > 0$ there exists a $\delta > 0$ such that

$$\left| \frac{2xy^4}{(x^2+y^2)^2} \right| < \epsilon \quad \text{whenever} \quad 0 < \sqrt{x^2+y^2} < \delta \tag{20}$$

$$\left| \frac{2xy^4}{(x^2+y^2)^2} \right| = \frac{2|x|y^4}{(x^2+y^2)^2} \le \frac{2\sqrt{x^2+y^2}\,(\sqrt{x^2+y^2})^4}{(x^2+y^2)^2} = 2\sqrt{x^2+y^2}$$

Therefore,

$$\left| \frac{2xy^4}{(x^2+y^2)^2} \right| < 2\delta \quad \text{whenever} \quad 0 < \sqrt{x^2+y^2} < \delta$$

So if we take $\delta = \frac{1}{2}\epsilon$, we have (20). Hence, D_1f is continuous at $(0,0)$. In the same way we show that D_2f is continuous at $(0,0)$. It follows from Theorem 17.5.5 that f is differentiable at $(0,0)$.

If we refer back to Eq. (3), the expression involving the first two terms on the right side, $D_1f(x_0, y_0)\,\Delta x + D_2f(x_0, y_0)\,\Delta y$, is called the *principal part* of $\Delta f(x_0, y_0)$ or the *total differential* of the function f at (x_0, y_0). We make this as a formal definition.

17.5.6 Definition   If f is a function of two variables x and y, and f is differentiable at (x, y), then the *total differential* of f is the function df having function values given by

$$df(x, y, \Delta x, \Delta y) = D_1f(x, y)\,\Delta x + D_2f(x, y)\,\Delta y \tag{21}$$

Note that df is a function of the four variables x, y, Δx, and Δy. If $z = f(x, y)$ we sometimes write dz in place of $df(x, y, \Delta x, \Delta y)$, and then Eq. (21) is written as

$$dz = D_1f(x, y)\,\Delta x + D_2f(x, y)\,\Delta y \tag{22}$$

If in particular $f(x, y) = x$, then $z = x$, $D_1f(x, y) = 1$, and $D_2f(x, y) = 0$, and so Eq. (22) gives $dz = \Delta x$. Because $z = x$, we have for this function $dx = \Delta x$. In a similar fashion, if we take $f(x, y) = y$, then $z = y$, $D_1f(x, y) = 0$, and $D_2f(x, y) = 1$, and so Eq. (22) gives $dz = \Delta y$. Because $z = y$, we have for this function $dy = \Delta y$. Hence, we define the differentials of the independent variables as $dx = \Delta x$ and $dy = \Delta y$. Then Eq. (22) can be written as

$$dz = D_1f(x, y)\,dx + D_2f(x, y)\,dy \tag{23}$$

and at the point (x_0, y_0), we have

$$dz = D_1f(x_0, y_0)\,dx + D_2f(x_0, y_0)\,dy \tag{24}$$

In Eq. (3), letting $\Delta z = \Delta f(x_0, y_0)$, $dx = \Delta x$, and $dy = \Delta y$, we have

$$\Delta z = D_1f(x_0, y_0)\,dx + D_2f(x_0, y_0)\,dy + \epsilon_1\,dx + \epsilon_2\,dy \tag{25}$$

Comparing Eqs. (24) and (25), we see that when dx (i.e., Δx) and dy (i.e.,

Δy) are close to zero, and because then ϵ_1 and ϵ_2 also will be close to zero, we can conclude that dz is an approximation to Δz. Because dz is often easier to calculate than Δz, we make use of the fact that $dz \approx \Delta z$ in certain situations. Before showing this in an example, we write Eq. (23) with the notation $\partial z/\partial x$ and $\partial z/\partial y$ instead of $D_1 f(x, y)$ and $D_2 f(x, y)$, respectively:

$$dz = \frac{\partial z}{\partial x}\, dx + \frac{\partial z}{\partial y}\, dy \tag{26}$$

EXAMPLE 6: A closed metal can in the shape of a right-circular cylinder is to have an inside height of 6 in., an inside radius of 2 in., and a thickness of 0.1 in. If the cost of the metal to be used is 10 cents per in.³, find by differentials the approximate cost of the metal to be used in the manufacture of the can.

SOLUTION: The formula for the volume of a right-circular cylinder, where the volume is V in.³, the radius is r in., and the height is h in., is

$$V = \pi r^2 h \tag{27}$$

The exact volume of metal in the can is the difference between the volumes of two right-circular cylinders for which $r = 2.1$, $h = 6.2$, and $r = 2$, $h = 6$, respectively.

ΔV would give us the exact volume of metal, but because we only want an approximate value, we find dV instead. Using (26), we have

$$dV = \frac{\partial V}{\partial r}\, dr + \frac{\partial V}{\partial h}\, dh \tag{28}$$

From Eq. (27) it follows that

$$\frac{\partial V}{\partial r} = 2\pi r h \quad \text{and} \quad \frac{\partial V}{\partial h} = \pi r^2$$

Substituting these values into Eq. (28) gives

$$dV = 2\pi r h\, dr + \pi r^2\, dh$$

Because $r = 2$, $h = 6$, $dr = 0.1$, and $dh = 0.2$, we have

$$dV = 2\pi(2)(6)(0.1) + \pi(2)^2(0.2)$$

$$= 3.2\pi$$

Hence, $\Delta V \approx 3.2\pi$, and so there is approximately 3.2π in.³ of metal in the can. Because the cost of the metal is 10 cents per in.³ and $10 \cdot 3.2\pi = 32\pi \approx 100.53$, the approximate cost of the metal to be used in the manufacture of the can is $1.

We conclude this section by extending the concepts of differentiability and the total differential to a function of n variables.

17.5.7 Definition If f is a function of the n variables $x_1, x_2, \ldots, x_n$, and $\bar{P}$ is the point $(\bar{x}_1, \bar{x}_2, \ldots, \bar{x}_n)$, then the *increment of f at $\bar{P}$* is given by

$$\Delta f(\bar{P}) = f(\bar{x}_1 + \Delta x_1, \bar{x}_2 + \Delta x_2, \ldots, \bar{x}_n + \Delta x_n) - f(\bar{P}) \tag{29}$$

17.5.8 Definition   If f is a function of the n variables $x_1, x_2, \ldots, x_n$, and the increment of f at the point $\bar{P}$ can be written as

$$\Delta f(\bar{P}) = D_1 f(\bar{P})\, \Delta x_1 + D_2 f(\bar{P})\, \Delta x_2 + \cdots + D_n f(\bar{P})\, \Delta x_n$$

$$+ \epsilon_1\, \Delta x_1 + \epsilon_2\, \Delta x_2 + \cdots + \epsilon_n\, \Delta x_n \quad (30)$$

where $\epsilon_1 \to 0, \epsilon_2 \to 0, \ldots, \epsilon_n \to 0$, as

$$(\Delta x_1, \Delta x_2, \ldots, \Delta x_n) \to (0, 0, \ldots, 0)$$

then f is said to be *differentiable* at $\bar{P}$.

Analogous to Theorem 17.5.5, it can be proved that sufficient conditions for a function f of n variables to be differentiable at a point $\bar{P}$ are that $D_1 f, D_2 f, \ldots, D_n f$ all exist on an open ball $B(\bar{P}; r)$ and that $D_1 f, D_2 f, \ldots, D_n f$ are all continuous at $\bar{P}$. As was the case for functions of two variables, it follows that for functions of n variables differentiability implies continuity. However, the existence of the partial derivatives $D_1 f, D_2 f, \ldots, D_n f$ at a point does not imply differentiability of the function at the point.

17.5.9 Definition   If f is a function of the n variables $x_1, x_2, \ldots, x_n$ and f is differentiable at P, then the *total differential* of f is the function df having function values given by

$$df(P, \Delta x_1, \Delta x_2, \ldots, \Delta x_n) = D_1 f(P)\, \Delta x_1 + D_2 f(P)\, \Delta x_2 + \cdots + D_n f(P)\, \Delta x_n \quad (31)$$

Letting $w = f(x_1, x_2, \ldots, x_n)$, defining $dx_1 = \Delta x_1, dx_2 = \Delta x_2, \ldots, dx_n = \Delta x_n$, and using the notation $\partial w / \partial x_i$ instead of $D_i f(P)$, we can write Eq. (31) as

$$dw = \frac{\partial w}{\partial x_1}\, dx_1 + \frac{\partial w}{\partial x_2}\, dx_2 + \cdots + \frac{\partial w}{\partial x_n}\, dx_n \quad (32)$$

EXAMPLE 7:   The dimensions of a box are measured to be 10 in., 12 in., and 15 in., and the measurements are correct to 0.02 in. Find approximately the greatest error if the volume of the box is calculated from the given measurements. Also find the approximate percent error.

SOLUTION: Letting V in.^{3} be the volume of a box whose dimensions are x in., y in., and z in., we have the formula

$$V = xyz$$

The exact value of the error would be found from ΔV; however, we use dV as an approximation to ΔV. Using Eq. (32) for three independent variables, we have

$$dV = \frac{\partial V}{\partial x}\, dx + \frac{\partial V}{\partial y}\, dy + \frac{\partial V}{\partial z}\, dz$$

and so

$$dV = yz\, dx + xz\, dy + xy\, dz \quad (33)$$

From the given information $|\Delta x| \le 0.02$, $|\Delta y| \le 0.02$, and $|\Delta z| \le 0.02$. To find the greatest error in the volume we take the greatest error in the measurements of the three dimensions. So taking $dx = 0.02$, $dy = 0.02$, $dz = 0.02$, and $x = 10$, $y = 12$, $z = 15$, we have from Eq. (33)

$$dV = (12)(15)(0.02) + (10)(15)(0.02) + (10)(12)(0.02)$$

$$= 9$$

So, $\Delta V \approx 9$, and therefore the greatest possible error in the calculation of the volume from the given measurements is approximately 9 in^3.

The relative error is found by dividing the error by the actual value. Hence, the relative error in computing the volume from the given measurements is $\Delta V/V \approx dV/V = \frac{9}{1800} = \frac{1}{200} = 0.005$. So the approximate percent error is 0.5%.

Exercises 17.5

1. If $f(x, y) = 3x^2 + 2xy - y^2$, $\Delta x = 0.03$, and $\Delta y = -0.02$, find (a) the increment of f at $(1, 4)$ and (b) the total differential of f at $(1, 4)$.

2. If $f(x, y) = xye^{xy}$, $\Delta x = -0.1$, and $\Delta y = 0.2$, find (a) the increment of f at $(2, -4)$ and (b) the total differential of f at $(2, -4)$.

3. If $f(x, y, z) = xy + \ln(yz)$, $\Delta x = 0.02$, $\Delta y = 0.04$, and $\Delta z = -0.03$, find (a) the increment of f at $(4, 1, 5)$ and (b) the total differential of f at $(4, 1, 5)$.

4. If $f(x, y, z) = x^2y + 2xyz - z^3$, $\Delta x = 0.01$, $\Delta y = 0.03$, and $\Delta z = -0.01$, find (a) the increment of f at $(-3, 0, 2)$ and (b) the total differential of f at $(-3, 0, 2)$.

In Exercises 5 through 8, prove that f is differentiable at all points in its domain by doing each of the following: (a) Find $\Delta f(x_0, y_0)$ for the given function; (b) find an ϵ_1 and an ϵ_2 so that Eq. (3) holds; (c) show that the ϵ_1 and the ϵ_2 found in part (b) both approach zero as $(\Delta x, \Delta y) \to (0, 0)$.

5. $f(x, y) = x^2y - 2xy$

6. $f(x, y) = 2x^2 + 3y^2$

7. $f(x, y) = \dfrac{x^2}{y}$

8. $f(x, y) = \dfrac{y}{x}$

9. Given $f(x, y) = \begin{cases} x + y - 2 & \text{if } x = 1 \text{ or } y = 1 \\ 2 & \text{if } x \ne 1 \text{ and } y \ne 1 \end{cases}$

Prove that $D_1 f(1, 1)$ and $D_2 f(1, 1)$ exist, but f is not differentiable at $(1, 1)$.

10. Given $f(x, y) = \begin{cases} \dfrac{3x^2y^2}{x^4 + y^4} & \text{if } (x, y) \ne (0, 0) \\ 0 & \text{if } (x, y) = (0, 0) \end{cases}$

Prove that $D_1 f(0, 0)$ and $D_2 f(0, 0)$ exist, but f is not differentiable at $(0, 0)$.

11. Prove Theorem 17.5.4(ii).

12. Show that Eq. (5) may be written in the form (7) where ξ_1 is between x_0 and $x_0 + h$.

13. Show that Eq. (6) may be written in the form (8) where ξ_2 is between y_0 and $y_0 + k$.

In Exercises 14 through 17, use Theorem 17.5.4 to find either a ξ_1 or a ξ_2, whichever applies.

14. $f(x, y) = x^2 + 3xy - y^2$; x is in $[1, 3]$; $y = 4$

15. $f(x, y) = x^3 - y^2$; x is in $[2, 6]$; $y = 3$

16. $f(x, y) = \dfrac{4x}{x + y}$; y is in $[-2, 2]$; $x = 4$

17. $f(x, y) = \dfrac{2x - y}{2y + x}$; y is in $[0, 4]$; $x = 2$

18. Given $f(x, y) = \begin{cases} \dfrac{3x^2 y}{x^2 + y^2} & \text{if } (x, y) \neq (0, 0) \\ 0 & \text{if } (x, y) = (0, 0) \end{cases}$

This function is continuous at $(0, 0)$ (see Example 4, Sec. 17.2, and Example 1, Sec. 17.3). Prove that $D_1 f(0, 0)$ and $D_2 f(0, 0)$ exist but $D_1 f$ and $D_2 f$ are not continuous at $(0, 0)$.

19. Given $f(x, y) = \begin{cases} \dfrac{xy(x^2 - y^2)}{x^2 + y^2} & \text{if } (x, y) \neq (0, 0) \\ 0 & \text{if } (x, y) = (0, 0) \end{cases}$

Prove that f is differentiable at $(0, 0)$ by using Theorem 17.5.5.

In Exercises 20 and 21 prove that f is differentiable at all points in R_3 by doing each of the following: (a) Find $\Delta f(x_0, y_0, z_0)$; (b) find an ϵ_1, ϵ_2, and ϵ_3, so that Eq. (30) holds; (c) show that the ϵ_1, ϵ_2, and ϵ_3 found in (b) all approach zero as $(\Delta x, \Delta y, \Delta z)$ approaches $(0, 0, 0)$.

20. $f(x, y, z) = 2x^2 z - 3yz^2$

21. $f(x, y, z) = xy - xz + z^2$

22. Given $f(x, y, z) = \begin{cases} \dfrac{xy^2 z}{x^4 + y^4 + z^4} & \text{if } (x, y, z) \neq (0, 0, 0) \\ 0 & \text{if } (x, y, z) = (0, 0, 0) \end{cases}$

(a) Show that $D_1 f(0, 0, 0)$, $D_2 f(0, 0, 0)$, and $D_3 f(0, 0, 0)$ exist; (b) make use of the fact that differentiability implies continuity to prove that f is not differentiable at $(0, 0, 0)$.

23. Given $f(x, y, z) = \begin{cases} \dfrac{xyz^2}{x^2 + y^2 + z^2} & \text{if } (x, y, z) \neq (0, 0, 0) \\ 0 & \text{if } (x, y, z) = (0, 0, 0) \end{cases}$

Prove that f is differentiable at $(0, 0, 0)$.

24. Use the total differential to find approximately the greatest error in calculating the area of a right triangle from the lengths of the legs if they are measured to be 6 in. and 8 in., respectively, with a possible error of 0.1 in. for each measurement. Also find the approximate percent error.

25. Find approximately, by using the total differential, the greatest error in calculating the length of the hypotenuse of the right triangle from the measurements of Exercise 24. Also find the approximate percent error.

26. If the ideal gas law (see Example 6, Sec. 17.4) is used to find P when T and V are given, but there is an error of 0.3% in measuring T and an error of 0.8% in measuring V, find approximately the greatest percent error in P.

27. The specific gravity s of an object is given by the formula

$$s = \frac{A}{A - W}$$

where A is the number of pounds in the weight of the object in air and W is the number of pounds in the weight of the object in water. If the weight of an object in air is read as 20 lb with a possible error of 0.01 lb and its weight in water is read as 12 lb with a possible error of 0.02 lb, find approximately the largest possible error in calculating s from these measurements. Also find the largest possible relative error.

28. A wooden box is to be made of lumber that is $\frac{2}{3}$ in. thick. The inside length is to be 6 ft, the inside width is to be 3 ft,

the inside depth is to be 4 ft, and the box is to have no top. Use the total differential to find the approximate amount of lumber to be used in the box.

29. A company has contracted to manufacture 10,000 closed wooden crates having dimensions 3 ft, 4 ft, and 5 ft. The cost of the wood to be used is 5¢ per square foot. If the machines that are used to cut the pieces of wood have a possible error of 0.05 ft in each dimension, find approximately, by using the total differential, the greatest possible error in the estimate of the cost of the wood.

In Exercises 30 through 33 we show that a function may be differentiable at a point even though it is not continuously differentiable there. Hence, the conditions of Theorem 17.5.5 are sufficient but not necessary for differentiability. The function f in these exercises is defined by

$$f(x, y) = \begin{cases} (x^2 + y^2) \sin \dfrac{1}{\sqrt{x^2 + y^2}} & \text{if } (x, y) \neq (0, 0) \\ 0 & \text{if } (x, y) = (0, 0) \end{cases}$$

30. Find $\Delta f(0, 0)$

31. Find $D_1 f(x, y)$ and $D_2 f(x, y)$

32. Prove that f is differentiable at $(0, 0)$ by using Definition 17.5.2 and the results of Exercises 30 and 31.

33. Prove that $D_1 f$ and $D_2 f$ are not continuous at $(0, 0)$.

17.6 THE CHAIN RULE

In Sec. 3.6 we had the following chain rule (Theorem 3.6.1) for functions of a single variable: If y is a function of u, defined by $y = f(u)$, and $D_u y$ exists; and u is a function of x, defined by $u = g(x)$, and $D_x u$ exists; then y is a function of x, and $D_x y$ exists and is given by

$$D_x y = D_u y \, D_x u$$

or, equivalently,

$$\frac{dy}{dx} = \frac{dy}{du} \frac{du}{dx} \tag{1}$$

We now consider the chain rule for a function of two variables, where each of these variables is also a function of two variables.

17.6.1 Theorem
The Chain Rule

If u is a differentiable function of x and y, defined by $u = f(x, y)$, and $x = F(r, s)$, $y = G(r, s)$, and $\partial x/\partial r$, $\partial x/\partial s$, $\partial y/\partial r$, and $\partial y/\partial s$ all exist, then u is a function of r and s and

$$\frac{\partial u}{\partial r} = \left(\frac{\partial u}{\partial x}\right)\left(\frac{\partial x}{\partial r}\right) + \left(\frac{\partial u}{\partial y}\right)\left(\frac{\partial y}{\partial r}\right) \tag{2}$$

$$\frac{\partial u}{\partial s} = \left(\frac{\partial u}{\partial x}\right)\left(\frac{\partial x}{\partial s}\right) + \left(\frac{\partial u}{\partial y}\right)\left(\frac{\partial y}{\partial s}\right) \tag{3}$$

PROOF: We prove (2). The proof of (3) is similar.

If s is held fixed and r is changed by an amount Δr, then x is changed by an amount Δx and y is changed by an amount Δy. So we have

$$\Delta x = F(r + \Delta r, s) - F(r, s) \tag{4}$$

and

$$\Delta y = G(r + \Delta r, s) - G(r, s) \tag{5}$$

Because f is differentiable,

$$\Delta f(x, y) = D_1 f(x, y) \, \Delta x + D_2 f(x, y) \, \Delta y + \epsilon_1 \, \Delta x + \epsilon_2 \, \Delta y \tag{6}$$

where ϵ_1 and ϵ_2 both approach zero as $(\Delta x, \Delta y)$ approaches $(0, 0)$. Furthermore, we require that $\epsilon_1 = 0$ and $\epsilon_2 = 0$ when $\Delta x = \Delta y = 0$. We make this requirement so that ϵ_1 and ϵ_2, which are functions of Δx and Δy, will be continuous at $(\Delta x, \Delta y) = (0, 0)$.

If in (6) we replace $\Delta f(x, y)$ by Δu, $D_1 f(x, y)$ by $\partial u / \partial x$, and $D_2 f(x, y)$ by $\partial u / \partial y$ and divide on both sides by Δr $(\Delta r \neq 0)$, we obtain

$$\frac{\Delta u}{\Delta r} = \frac{\partial u}{\partial x} \frac{\Delta x}{\Delta r} + \frac{\partial u}{\partial y} \frac{\Delta y}{\Delta r} + \epsilon_1 \frac{\Delta x}{\Delta r} + \epsilon_2 \frac{\Delta y}{\Delta r}$$

Taking the limit on both sides of the above as Δr approaches zero, we get

$$\lim_{\Delta r \to 0} \frac{\Delta u}{\Delta r} = \frac{\partial u}{\partial x} \lim_{\Delta r \to 0} \frac{\Delta x}{\Delta r} + \frac{\partial u}{\partial y} \lim_{\Delta r \to 0} \frac{\Delta y}{\Delta r} + (\lim_{\Delta r \to 0} \epsilon_1) \lim_{\Delta r \to 0} \frac{\Delta x}{\Delta r} + (\lim_{\Delta r \to 0} \epsilon_2) \lim_{\Delta r \to 0} \frac{\Delta y}{\Delta r} \tag{7}$$

Because u is a function of x and y and both x and y are functions of r and s, u is a function of r and s. Because s is held fixed and r is changed by an amount Δr, we have

$$\lim_{\Delta r \to 0} \frac{\Delta u}{\Delta r} = \lim_{\Delta r \to 0} \frac{u(r + \Delta r, s) - u(r, s)}{\Delta r} = \frac{\partial u}{\partial r} \tag{8}$$

Also,

$$\lim_{\Delta r \to 0} \frac{\Delta x}{\Delta r} = \lim_{\Delta r \to 0} \frac{F(r + \Delta r, s) - F(r, s)}{\Delta r} = \frac{\partial x}{\partial r} \tag{9}$$

and

$$\lim_{\Delta r \to 0} \frac{\Delta y}{\Delta r} = \lim_{\Delta r \to 0} \frac{G(r + \Delta r, s) - G(r, s)}{\Delta r} = \frac{\partial y}{\partial r} \tag{10}$$

Because $\partial x / \partial r$ and $\partial y / \partial r$ exist, F and G are each continuous with respect to the variable r. (NOTE: The existence of the partial derivatives of a function does not imply continuity with respect to all of the variables simultaneously, as we saw in the preceding section, but as with functions of a single variable it does imply continuity of the function with respect to each variable separately.) Hence, we have from (4)

$$\lim_{\Delta r \to 0} \Delta x = \lim_{\Delta r \to 0} [F(r + \Delta r, s) - F(r, s)]$$

$$= F(r, s) - F(r, s)$$

$$= 0$$

and from (5)

$$\lim_{\Delta r \to 0} \Delta y = \lim_{\Delta r \to 0} \left[G(r + \Delta r, s) - G(r, s) \right]$$

$$= G(r, s) - G(r, s)$$

$$= 0$$

Therefore, as Δr approaches zero, both Δx and Δy approach zero. And because both ϵ_1 and ϵ_2 approach zero as $(\Delta x, \Delta y)$ approaches $(0, 0)$, we can conclude that

$$\lim_{\Delta r \to 0} \epsilon_1 = 0 \quad \text{and} \quad \lim_{\Delta r \to 0} \epsilon_2 = 0 \tag{11}$$

Now it is possible that for certain values of Δr, $\Delta x = \Delta y = 0$. Because we required in such a case that $\epsilon_1 = \epsilon_2 = 0$, the limits in (11) are still zero. Substituting from (8), (9), (10), and (11) into (7), we obtain

$$\frac{\partial u}{\partial r} = \left(\frac{\partial u}{\partial x}\right)\left(\frac{\partial x}{\partial r}\right) + \left(\frac{\partial u}{\partial y}\right)\left(\frac{\partial y}{\partial r}\right)$$

which proves (2). ∎

EXAMPLE 1: Given

$$u = \ln \sqrt{x^2 + y^2}$$

$x = re^s$, and $y = re^{-s}$, find $\partial u/\partial r$ and $\partial u/\partial s$.

SOLUTION:

$$\frac{\partial u}{\partial x} = \frac{x}{x^2 + y^2} \qquad \frac{\partial u}{\partial y} = \frac{y}{x^2 + y^2} \qquad \frac{\partial x}{\partial r} = e^s$$

$$\frac{\partial x}{\partial s} = re^s \qquad \frac{\partial y}{\partial r} = e^{-s} \qquad \frac{\partial y}{\partial s} = -re^{-s}$$

From (2) we get

$$\frac{\partial u}{\partial r} = \frac{x}{x^2 + y^2}\,(e^s) + \frac{y}{x^2 + y^2}\,(e^{-s}) = \frac{xe^s + ye^{-s}}{x^2 + y^2}$$

From (3) we get

$$\frac{\partial u}{\partial s} = \frac{x}{x^2 + y^2}\,(re^s) + \frac{y}{x^2 + y^2}\,(-re^{-s}) = \frac{r(xe^s - ye^{-s})}{x^2 + y^2}$$

As mentioned earlier the symbols $\partial u/\partial r$, $\partial u/\partial s$, $\partial u/\partial x$, $\partial u/\partial y$, and so forth must not be considered as fractions. The symbols ∂u, ∂x, and so on have no meaning by themselves. For functions of one variable, the chain rule, given by Eq. (1), is easily remembered by thinking of an ordinary derivative as the quotient of two differentials, but there is no similar interpretation for partial derivatives.

Another troublesome notational problem arises when considering u as a function of x and y and then as a function of r and s. If $u = f(x, y)$, $x = F(r, s)$, and $y = G(r, s)$, then $u = f(F(r, s), G(r, s))$. [Note that it is incorrect to write $u = f(r, s)$.] For instance, in Example 1

$$u = f(x, y) = \ln \sqrt{x^2 + y^2}$$

$$x = F(r, s) = re^s$$

$$y = G(r, s) = re^{-s}$$

and so

$$u = f(F(r, s), G(r, s)) = \ln \sqrt{r^2 e^{2s} + r^2 e^{-2s}}$$

$[f(r, s) = \ln \sqrt{r^2 + s^2} \neq u.]$

If we let $f(F(r, s), G(r, s)) = h(r, s)$, then Eqs. (2) and (3) can be written respectively as

$$h_1(r, s) = f_1(x, y)F_1(r, s) + f_2(x, y)G_1(r, s)$$

and

$$h_2(r, s) = f_1(x, y)F_2(r, s) + f_2(x, y)G_2(r, s)$$

In the statement of Theorem 17.6.1, the independent variables are r and s, and u is the dependent variable. The variables x and y can be called the intermediate variables. We now extend the chain rule to n intermediate variables and m independent variables.

17.6.2 Theorem
The General Chain Rule

Suppose that u is a differentiable function of the n variables $x_1, x_2, \ldots, x_n$, and each of these variables is in turn a function of the m variables $y_1, y_2, \ldots, y_m$. Suppose further that each of the partial derivatives $\partial x_i / \partial y_j$ $(i = 1, 2, \ldots, n; j = 1, 2, \ldots, m)$ exist. Then u is a function of $y_1, y_2, \ldots, y_m$, and

$$\frac{\partial u}{\partial y_1} = \left(\frac{\partial u}{\partial x_1}\right)\left(\frac{\partial x_1}{\partial y_1}\right) + \left(\frac{\partial u}{\partial x_2}\right)\left(\frac{\partial x_2}{\partial y_1}\right) + \cdots + \left(\frac{\partial u}{\partial x_n}\right)\left(\frac{\partial x_n}{\partial y_1}\right)$$

$$\frac{\partial u}{\partial y_2} = \left(\frac{\partial u}{\partial x_1}\right)\left(\frac{\partial x_1}{\partial y_2}\right) + \left(\frac{\partial u}{\partial x_2}\right)\left(\frac{\partial x_2}{\partial y_2}\right) + \cdots + \left(\frac{\partial u}{\partial x_n}\right)\left(\frac{\partial x_n}{\partial y_2}\right)$$

$$\vdots$$

$$\frac{\partial u}{\partial y_m} = \left(\frac{\partial u}{\partial x_1}\right)\left(\frac{\partial x_1}{\partial y_m}\right) + \left(\frac{\partial u}{\partial x_2}\right)\left(\frac{\partial x_2}{\partial y_m}\right) + \cdots + \left(\frac{\partial u}{\partial x_n}\right)\left(\frac{\partial x_n}{\partial y_m}\right)$$

The proof is an extension of the proof of Theorem 17.6.1.

Note that in the general chain rule, there are as many terms on the right side of each equation as there are intermediate variables.

EXAMPLE 2:   Given

$$u = xy + xz + yz$$

$x = r$, $y = r \cos t$, and $z = r \sin t$, find $\partial u/\partial r$ and $\partial u/\partial t$.

SOLUTION: By applying the chain rule, we obtain

$$\frac{\partial u}{\partial r} = \left(\frac{\partial u}{\partial x}\right)\left(\frac{\partial x}{\partial r}\right) + \left(\frac{\partial u}{\partial y}\right)\left(\frac{\partial y}{\partial r}\right) + \left(\frac{\partial u}{\partial z}\right)\left(\frac{\partial z}{\partial r}\right)$$

$$= (y + z)(1) + (x + z)(\cos t) + (x + y)(\sin t)$$

$$= y + z + x \cos t + z \cos t + x \sin t + y \sin t$$

$$= r \cos t + r \sin t + r \cos t + (r \sin t)(\cos t) + r \sin t + (r \cos t)(\sin t)$$

$$= 2r(\cos t + \sin t) + r(2 \sin t \cos t)$$

$$= 2r(\cos t + \sin t) + r \sin 2t$$

$$\frac{\partial u}{\partial t} = \left(\frac{\partial u}{\partial x}\right)\left(\frac{\partial x}{\partial t}\right) + \left(\frac{\partial u}{\partial y}\right)\left(\frac{\partial y}{\partial t}\right) + \left(\frac{\partial u}{\partial z}\right)\left(\frac{\partial z}{\partial t}\right)$$

$$= (y + z)(0) + (x + z)(-r \sin t) + (s + y)(r \cos t)$$

$$= (r + r \sin t)(-r \sin t) + (r + r \cos t)(r \cos t)$$

$$= -r^2 \sin t - r^2 \sin^2 t + r^2 \cos t + r^2 \cos^2 t$$

$$= r^2(\cos t - \sin t) + r^2(\cos^2 t - \sin^2 t)$$

$$= r^2(\cos t - \sin t) + r^2 \cos 2t$$

Now suppose that u is a differentiable function of the two variables x and y, and both x and y are differentiable functions of the single variable t. Then u is a function of the single variable t, and so instead of the partial derivative of u with respect to t, we have the ordinary derivative of u with respect to t, which is given by

$$\frac{du}{dt} = \left(\frac{\partial u}{\partial x}\right)\left(\frac{dx}{dt}\right) + \left(\frac{\partial u}{\partial y}\right)\left(\frac{dy}{dt}\right) \tag{12}$$

We call du/dt given by Eq. (12) the *total derivative* of u with respect to t. If u is a differentiable function of the n variables $x_1, x_2, \ldots, x_n$ and each x_i is a differentiable function of the single variable t, then u is a function of t and the total derivative of u with respect to t is given by

$$\frac{du}{dt} = \left(\frac{\partial u}{\partial x_1}\right)\left(\frac{dx_1}{dt}\right) + \left(\frac{\partial u}{\partial x_2}\right)\left(\frac{dx_2}{dt}\right) + \cdots + \left(\frac{\partial u}{\partial x_n}\right)\left(\frac{dx_n}{dt}\right)$$

EXAMPLE 3:   Given

$$u = x^2 + 2xy + y^2$$

$x = t \cos t$, and $y = t \sin t$, find du/dt by two methods: (a) using the chain rule; (b) expressing u in terms of t before differentiating.

SOLUTION: (a) $\partial u/\partial x = 2x + 2y$; $\partial u/\partial y = 2x + 2y$; $dx/dt = \cos t - t \sin t$; $dy/dt = \sin t + t \cos t$. So from (12) we have

$$\frac{du}{dt} = (2x + 2y)(\cos t - t \sin t) + (2x + 2y)(\sin t + t \cos t)$$

$$= 2(x + y)(\cos t - t \sin t + \sin t + t \cos t)$$

$$= 2(t \cos t + t \sin t)(\cos t - t \sin t + \sin t + t \cos t)$$

$$= 2t(\cos^2 t - t \sin t \cos t + \sin t \cos t + t \cos^2 t + \sin t \cos t$$

$$\qquad\qquad - t \sin^2 t + \sin^2 t + t \sin t \cos t)$$

$$= 2t[1 + 2 \sin t \cos t + t(\cos^2 t - \sin^2 t)]$$

$$= 2t(1 + \sin 2t + t \cos 2t)$$

(b) $u = (t \cos t)^2 + 2(t \cos t)(t \sin t) + (t \sin t)^2$

$$= t^2 \cos^2 t + t^2(2 \sin t \cos t) + t^2 \sin^2 t$$

$$= t^2 + t^2 \sin 2t$$

So

$$\frac{du}{dt} = 2t + 2t \sin 2t + 2t^2 \cos 2t$$

EXAMPLE 4: If f is a differentiable function and a and b are constants, prove that $z = f(\frac{1}{2}bx^2 - \frac{1}{3}ay^3)$ satisfies the partial differential equation

$$ay^2 \frac{\partial z}{\partial x} + bx \frac{\partial z}{\partial y} = 0$$

SOLUTION: Let $u = \frac{1}{2}bx^2 - \frac{1}{3}ay^3$. We wish to show that $z = f(u)$ satisfies the given equation. By the chain rule we get

$$\frac{\partial z}{\partial x} = \frac{dz}{du}\frac{\partial u}{\partial x} = f'(u)(bx) \quad \text{and} \quad \frac{\partial z}{\partial y} = \frac{dz}{du}\frac{\partial u}{\partial y} = f'(u)(-ay^2)$$

Therefore,

$$ay^2 \frac{\partial z}{\partial x} + bx \frac{\partial z}{\partial y} = ay^2[f'(u)(bx)] + bx[f'(u)(-ay^2)] = 0$$

which is what we wished to prove.

EXAMPLE 5: Use the ideal gas law (see Example 6, Sec. 17.4) with $k = 10$ to find the rate at which the temperature is changing at the instant when the volume of the gas is 120 in.^{3} and the gas is under a pressure of 8 lb/in.^{2} if the volume is increasing at the rate of 2 in.^{3}/sec and the pressure is decreasing at the rate of 0.1 lb/in.^{2} per sec.

SOLUTION: Let $t =$ the number of seconds in the time that has elapsed since the volume of the gas started to increase;
$T =$ the number of degrees in the temperature at t sec;
$P =$ the number of pounds per square inch in the pressure at t sec;
$V =$ the number of cubic inches in the volume of the gas at t sec.

$$PV = 10T \quad \text{and so} \quad T = \frac{PV}{10}$$

At the given instant, $P = 8$, $V = 120$, $dP/dt = -0.1$, and $dV/dt = 2$. Using the chain rule, we obtain

$$\frac{dT}{dt} = \frac{\partial T}{\partial P}\frac{dP}{dt} + \frac{\partial T}{\partial V}\frac{dV}{dt}$$

$$= \frac{V}{10}\frac{dP}{dt} + \frac{P}{10}\frac{dV}{dt}$$

$$= \frac{120}{10}(-0.1) + \frac{8}{10}(2)$$

$$= -1.2 + 1.6$$

$$= 0.4$$

Therefore the temperature is increasing at the rate of 0.4 degrees per second at the given instant.

Exercises 17.6

In Exercises 1 through 4, find the indicated partial derivative by two methods: (a) Use the chain rule; (b) make the substitutions for x and y before differentiating.

1. $u = x^2 - y^2$; $x = 3r - s$; $y = r + 2s$; $\dfrac{\partial u}{\partial r}$, $\dfrac{\partial u}{\partial s}$

2. $u = 3x^2 + xy - 2y^2 + 3x - y$; $x = 2r - 3s$; $y = r + s$; $\dfrac{\partial u}{\partial r}$, $\dfrac{\partial u}{\partial s}$

3. $u = e^{y/x}$; $x = 2r \cos t$; $y = 4r \sin t$; $\dfrac{\partial u}{\partial r}$, $\dfrac{\partial u}{\partial t}$

4. $u = x^2 + y^2$; $x = \cosh r \cos t$; $y = \sinh r \sin t$; $\dfrac{\partial u}{\partial r}$, $\dfrac{\partial u}{\partial t}$

In Exercises 5 through 10, find the indicated partial derivative by using the chain rule.

5. $u = \sin^{-1}(3x + y)$; $x = r^2 e^s$; $y = \sin rs$; $\dfrac{\partial u}{\partial r}$, $\dfrac{\partial u}{\partial s}$

6. $u = xe^{-y}$; $x = \tan^{-1}(rst)$; $y = \ln(3rs + 5st)$; $\dfrac{\partial u}{\partial r}$, $\dfrac{\partial u}{\partial s}$, $\dfrac{\partial u}{\partial t}$

7. $u = \cosh \dfrac{y}{x}$; $x = 3r^2 s$; $y = 6se^r$; $\dfrac{\partial u}{\partial r}$, $\dfrac{\partial u}{\partial s}$

8. $u = xy + xz + yz$; $x = rs$; $y = r^2 - s^2$; $z = (r - s)^2$; $\dfrac{\partial u}{\partial r}$, $\dfrac{\partial u}{\partial s}$

9. $u = x^2 + y^2 + z^2$; $x = r \sin \phi \cos \theta$; $y = r \sin \phi \sin \theta$; $z = r \cos \phi$; $\dfrac{\partial u}{\partial r}$, $\dfrac{\partial u}{\partial \phi}$, $\dfrac{\partial u}{\partial \theta}$

10. $u = x^2 yz$; $x = \dfrac{r}{s}$; $y = re^s$; $z = re^{-s}$; $\dfrac{\partial u}{\partial r}$, $\dfrac{\partial u}{\partial s}$

In Exercises 11 through 14, find the total derivative du/dt by two methods: (a) Use the chain rule; (b) make the substitutions for x and y or for x, y, and z before differentiating.

11. $u = ye^x + xe^y$; $x = \cos t$; $y = \sin t$

12. $u = \ln xy + y^2$; $x = e^t$; $y = e^{-t}$

13. $u = \sqrt{x^2 + y^2 + z^2}$; $x = \tan t$; $y = \cos t$; $z = \sin t$; $0 < t < \tfrac{1}{2}\pi$

14. $u = \dfrac{t + e^x}{y - e^t}$; $x = 3 \sin t$; $y = \ln t$

In Exercises 15 through 18, find the total derivative du/dt by using the chain rule; do not express u as a function of t before differentiating.

15. $u = \tan^{-1}\left(\dfrac{y}{x}\right)$; $x = \ln t$; $y = e^t$

16. $u = xy + xz + yz$; $x = t \cos t$; $y = t \sin t$; $z = t$

17. $u = \dfrac{x + t}{y + t}$; $x = \ln t$; $y = \ln \dfrac{1}{t}$

18. $u = \ln(x^2 + y^2 + t^2)$; $x = t \sin t$; $y = \cos t$

In Exercises 19 through 22, assume that the given equation defines z as a function of x and y. Differentiate implicitly to find $\partial z/\partial x$ and $\partial z/\partial y$.

19. $3x^2 + y^2 + z^2 - 3xy + 4xz - 15 = 0$

20. $z = (x^2 + y^2) \sin xz$

21. $ye^{xyz} \cos 3xz = 5$

22. $ze^{yz} + 2xe^{xz} - 4e^{xy} = 3$

23. If f is a differentiable function of the variable u, let $u = bx - ay$ and prove that $z = f(bx - ay)$ satisfies the equation $a(\partial z/\partial x) + b(\partial z/\partial y) = 0$, where a and b are constants.

24. If f is a differentiable function of two variables u and v, let $u = x - y$ and $v = y - x$ and prove that $z = f(x - y, y - x)$ satisfies the equation $\partial z/\partial x + \partial z/\partial y = 0$.

25. If f is a differentiable function of x and y and $u = f(x, y)$, $x = r \cos \theta$, and $y = r \sin \theta$, show that

$$\frac{\partial u}{\partial x} = \frac{\partial u}{\partial r} \cos \theta - \frac{\partial u}{\partial \theta} \frac{\sin \theta}{r}$$

$$\frac{\partial u}{\partial y} = \frac{\partial u}{\partial r} \sin \theta + \frac{\partial u}{\partial \theta} \frac{\cos \theta}{r}$$

26. If f and g are differentiable functions of x and y and $u = f(x, y)$ and $v = g(x, y)$, such that $\partial u/\partial x = \partial v/\partial y$ and $\partial u/\partial y = -\partial v/\partial x$, then if $x = r \cos \theta$ and $y = r \sin \theta$, show that

$$\frac{\partial u}{\partial r} = \frac{1}{r}\frac{\partial v}{\partial \theta} \quad \text{and} \quad \frac{\partial v}{\partial r} = -\frac{1}{r}\frac{\partial u}{\partial \theta}$$

27. Suppose f is a differentiable function of x and y and $u = f(x, y)$. Then if $x = \cosh v \cos w$ and $y = \sinh v \sin w$, express $\partial u/\partial v$ and $\partial u/\partial w$ in terms of $\partial u/\partial x$ and $\partial u/\partial y$.

28. Suppose f is a differentiable function of x, y, and z and $u = f(x, y, z)$. Then if $x = r \sin \phi \cos \theta$, $y = r \sin \phi \sin \theta$, and $z = r \cos \phi$, express $\partial u/\partial r$, $\partial u/\partial \phi$, and $\partial u/\partial \theta$ in terms of $\partial u/\partial x$, $\partial u/\partial y$, and $\partial u/\partial z$.

29. At a given instant, the length of one leg of a right triangle is 10 ft and it is increasing at the rate of 1 ft/min and the length of the other leg of the right triangle is 12 ft and it is decreasing at the rate of 2 ft/min. Find the rate of change of the measure of the acute angle opposite the leg of length 12 ft at the given instant.

30. A vertical wall makes an angle of radian measure $\frac{2}{3}\pi$ with the ground. A ladder of length 20 ft is leaning against the wall and its top is sliding down the wall at the rate of 3 ft/sec. How fast is the area of the triangle formed by the ladder, the wall, and the ground changing when the ladder makes an angle of $\frac{1}{6}\pi$ radians with the ground?

31. A quantity of gas obeys the ideal gas law (see Example 6, Sec. 17.4) with $k = 12$, and the gas is in a container which is being heated at a rate of 3° per second. If at the instant when the temperature is 300°, the pressure is 6 lb/in.^{2} and is decreasing at the rate of 0.1 lb/in.^{2} per second, find the rate of change of the volume at that instant.

32. Water is flowing into a tank in the form of a right-circular cylinder at the rate of $\frac{4}{5}\pi$ ft^3/min. The tank is stretching in such a way that even though it remains cylindrical, its radius is increasing at the rate of 0.002 ft/min. How fast is the depth of the water rising when the radius is 2 ft and the volume of water in the tank is 20π ft^3?

17.7 DIRECTIONAL DERIVATIVES AND THE GRADIENT

We now generalize the definition of a partial derivative to obtain the rate of change of a function with respect to distance in any direction. This leads to the concept of a *directional derivative*.

Let f be a function of the two variables x and y and let $P(x, y)$ be a point in the xy plane. Suppose that $\mathbf{U}$ is the unit vector making an angle of radian measure θ with the positive side of the x axis. Then

$$\mathbf{U} = \cos \theta \mathbf{i} + \sin \theta \mathbf{j}$$

Figure 17.7.1 shows the representation of $\mathbf{U}$ having its initial point at the point $P(x, y)$.

17.7.1 Definition

Let f be a function of two variables x and y. If $\mathbf{U}$ is the unit vector $\cos \theta \mathbf{i} + \sin \theta \mathbf{j}$, then the *directional derivative* of f in the direction of $\mathbf{U}$, denoted by $D_{\mathbf{U}}f$, is given by

$$D_{\mathbf{U}}f(x, y) = \lim_{h \to 0} \frac{f(x + h \cos \theta, y + h \sin \theta) - f(x, y)}{h}$$

if this limit exists.

Figure 17.7.1

The directional derivative gives the rate of change of the function values $f(x, y)$ with respect to distance in the xy plane measured in the

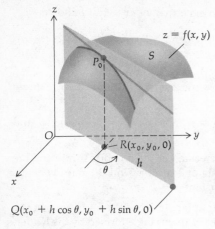

Figure 17.72

direction of the unit vector **U**. This is illustrated in Fig. 17.7.2. The equation of the surface S in the figure is $z = f(x, y)$. $P_0(x_0, y_0, z_0)$ is a point on the surface, and the points $R(x_0, y_0, 0)$ and $Q(x_0 + h \cos \theta, y_0 + h \sin \theta, 0)$ are points in the xy plane. The plane through R and Q, parallel to the z axis, makes an angle of θ radians with the positive direction on the x axis. This plane intersects the surface S in the curve C. The directional derivative $D_U f$, evaluated at P_0, is the slope of the tangent line to the curve C at P_0 in the plane of R, Q, and P_0.

If $\mathbf{U} = \mathbf{i}$, then $\cos \theta = 1$ and $\sin \theta = 0$, and we have from Definition 17.7.1

$$D_i f(x, y) = \lim_{h \to 0} \frac{f(x + h, y) - f(x, y)}{h}$$

which is the partial derivative of f with respect to x.

If $\mathbf{U} = \mathbf{j}$, then $\cos \theta = 0$ and $\sin \theta = 1$, and we have

$$D_j f(x, y) = \lim_{h \to 0} \frac{f(x, y + h) - f(x, y)}{h}$$

which is the partial derivative of f with respect to y.

So we see that f_x and f_y are special cases of the directional derivative in the directions of the unit vectors $\mathbf{i}$ and $\mathbf{j}$, respectively.

EXAMPLE 1: Given

$$f(x, y) = 3x^2 - y^2 + 4x$$

and **U** is the unit vector in the direction $\frac{1}{6}\pi$, find $D_U f$ by applying Definition 17.7.1.

SOLUTION: $\mathbf{U} = \cos \frac{1}{6}\pi \mathbf{i} + \sin \frac{1}{6}\pi \mathbf{j} = \frac{1}{2}\sqrt{3}\mathbf{i} + \frac{1}{2}\mathbf{j}$. So from Definition 17.7.1 we have

$$D_U f(x, y) = \lim_{h \to 0} \frac{f(x + \frac{1}{2}\sqrt{3}h, y + \frac{1}{2}h) - f(x, y)}{h}$$

$$= \lim_{h \to 0} \frac{3(x + \frac{1}{2}\sqrt{3}h)^2 - (y + \frac{1}{2}h)^2 + 4(x + \frac{1}{2}\sqrt{3}h) - (3x^2 - y^2 + 4x)}{h}$$

$$= \lim_{h \to 0} \frac{3x^2 + 3\sqrt{3}hx + \frac{9}{4}h^2 - y^2 - hy - \frac{1}{4}h^2 + 4x + 2\sqrt{3}h - 3x^2 + y^2 - 4x}{h}$$

$$= \lim_{h \to 0} \frac{3\sqrt{3}hx + \frac{9}{4}h^2 - hy - \frac{1}{4}h^2 + 2\sqrt{3}h}{h}$$

$$= \lim_{h \to 0} (3\sqrt{3}x + \frac{9}{4}h - y - \frac{1}{4}h + 2\sqrt{3})$$

$$= 3\sqrt{3}x - y + 2\sqrt{3}$$

We now proceed to obtain a formula that will enable us to calculate a directional derivative in a way that is shorter than if we used the definition. We define g as the function of the single variable t, keeping x, y, and θ fixed such that

$$g(t) = f(x + t \cos \theta, y + t \sin \theta) \tag{1}$$

and let $\mathbf{U} = \cos \theta \mathbf{i} + \sin \theta \mathbf{j}$. Then by the definition of an ordinary derivative we have

$$g'(0) = \lim_{h \to 0} \frac{f(x + (0 + h) \cos \theta, y + (0 + h) \sin \theta) - f(x + 0 \cos \theta, y + 0 \sin \theta)}{h}$$

or

$$g'(0) = \lim_{h \to 0} \frac{f(x + h \cos \theta, y + h \sin \theta) - f(x, y)}{h}$$

Because the right side of the above is $D_{\mathbf{U}} f(x, y)$, it follows that

$$g'(0) = D_{\mathbf{U}} f(x, y) \tag{2}$$

We now find $g'(t)$ by applying the chain rule to the right side of (1), which gives

$$g'(t) = f_1(x + t \cos \theta, y + t \sin \theta) \frac{\partial(x + t \cos \theta)}{\partial t}$$

$$+ f_2(x + t \cos \theta, y + t \sin \theta) \frac{\partial(y + t \sin \theta)}{\partial t}$$

$$= f_1(x + t \cos \theta, y + t \sin \theta) \cos \theta$$

$$+ f_2(x + t \cos \theta, y + t \sin \theta) \sin \theta$$

Therefore,

$$g'(0) = f_x(x, y) \cos \theta + f_y(x, y) \sin \theta \tag{3}$$

From (2) and (3) the following theorem is obtained.

17.7.2 Theorem   If f is a differentiable function of x and y, and $\mathbf{U} = \cos \theta \mathbf{i} + \sin \theta \mathbf{j}$, then

$$D_{\mathbf{U}} f(x, y) = f_x(x, y) \cos \theta + f_y(x, y) \sin \theta$$

EXAMPLE 2: For the function f and the unit vector $\mathbf{U}$ of Example 1, find $D_{\mathbf{U}} f$ by Theorem 17.7.2.

SOLUTION: Because $f(x, y) = 3x^2 - y^2 + 4x$, $f_x(x, y) = 6x + 4$ and $f_y(x, y) = -2y$. Because $\mathbf{U} = \cos \frac{1}{6}\pi \mathbf{i} + \sin \frac{1}{6}\pi \mathbf{j}$, we have from Theorem 17.7.2

$$D_{\mathbf{U}} f(x, y) = (6x + 4)\tfrac{1}{2}\sqrt{3} + (-2y)\tfrac{1}{2} = 3\sqrt{3}x + 2\sqrt{3} - y$$

which agrees with the answer in Example 1.

The directional derivative can be written as the dot product of two vectors. Because

$$f_x(x, y) \cos \theta + f_y(x, y) \sin \theta = (\cos \theta \mathbf{i} + \sin \theta \mathbf{j}) \cdot [f_x(x, y)\mathbf{i} + f_y(x, y)\mathbf{j}]$$

it follows from Theorem 17.7.2 that

$$D_{\mathbf{U}} f(x, y) = (\cos \theta \mathbf{i} + \sin \theta \mathbf{j}) \cdot [f_x(x, y)\mathbf{i} + f_y(x, y)\mathbf{j}] \tag{4}$$

The second vector on the right side of Eq. (4) is a very important one, and it is called the *gradient* of the function f. The symbol that we use for the gradient of f is ∇f, where ∇ is an inverted capital delta and is read "del." Sometimes the abbreviation *grad f* is used.

17.7.3 Definition   If f is a function of two variables x and y and f_x and f_y exist, then the *gradient* of f, denoted by ∇f (read: "del f"), is defined by

$$\nabla f(x, y) = f_x(x, y)\mathbf{i} + f_y(x, y)\mathbf{j}$$

Using Definition 17.7.3, Eq. (4) can be written as

$$D_\mathbf{U} f(x, y) = \mathbf{U} \cdot \nabla f(x, y) \tag{5}$$

Therefore, any directional derivative of a function can be obtained by dot-multiplying the gradient by a unit vector in the desired direction.

EXAMPLE 3:   If

$$f(x, y) = \frac{x^2}{16} + \frac{y^2}{9}$$

find the gradient of f at the point $(4, 3)$. Also find the rate of change of $f(x, y)$ in the direction $\frac{1}{4}\pi$ at $(4, 3)$.

SOLUTION: Because $f_x(x, y) = \frac{1}{8}x$ and $f_y(x, y) = \frac{2}{9}y$, we have

$$\nabla f(x, y) = \frac{1}{8}x\mathbf{i} + \frac{2}{9}y\mathbf{j}$$

Therefore,

$$\nabla f(4, 3) = \frac{1}{2}\mathbf{i} + \frac{2}{3}\mathbf{j}$$

The rate of change of $f(x, y)$ in the direction $\frac{1}{4}\pi$ at $(4, 3)$ is $D_\mathbf{U} f(4, 3)$, where $\mathbf{U}$ is the unit vector

$$\frac{1}{\sqrt{2}}\mathbf{i} + \frac{1}{\sqrt{2}}\mathbf{j}$$

This is found by dot-multiplying $\nabla f(4, 3)$ by $\mathbf{U}$. We have, then,

$$D_\mathbf{U} f(4, 3) = \left(\frac{1}{\sqrt{2}}\mathbf{i} + \frac{1}{\sqrt{2}}\mathbf{j}\right) \cdot \left(\frac{1}{2}\mathbf{i} + \frac{2}{3}\mathbf{j}\right) = \frac{7}{12}\sqrt{2}$$

If α is the radian measure of the angle between the two vectors $\mathbf{U}$ and ∇f, then

$$\mathbf{U} \cdot \nabla f = |\mathbf{U}||\nabla f| \cos \alpha \tag{6}$$

From Eqs. (5) and (6) it follows that

$$D_\mathbf{U} f = |\mathbf{U}||\nabla f| \cos \alpha \tag{7}$$

We see from Eq. (7) that $D_\mathbf{U} f$ will be a maximum when $\cos \alpha = 1$, or when $\mathbf{U}$ is in the direction of ∇f; and in this case, $D_\mathbf{U} f = |\nabla f|$. Hence, the gradient of a function is in the direction in which the function has its maximum rate of change. In particular, on a two-dimensional topographical map of a landscape where z units is the elevation at a point (x, y) and $z = f(x, y)$, the direction in which the rate of change of z is the greatest is given by $\nabla f(x, y)$, that is, $\nabla f(x, y)$ points in the direction of steepest ascent. This accounts for the name "gradient" (the grade is steepest in the direction of the gradient).

EXAMPLE 4:   Draw a contour map showing the level curves of the function of Example 3 at 1, 2, and 3. Also show the representation of $\nabla f(4, 3)$ having its initial point at $(4, 3)$.

SOLUTION: The level curves are ellipses and are shown in Fig. 17.7.3 along with the representation of $\nabla f(4, 3)$.

Figure 17.7.3

EXAMPLE 5:   Given

$$f(x, y) = 2x^2 - y^2 + 3x - y$$

find the maximum value of $D_U f$ at the point where $x = 1$ and $y = -2$.

SOLUTION: $f_x(x, y) = 4x + 3$ and $f_y(x, y) = -2y - 1$. So,

$$\nabla f(x, y) = (4x + 3)\mathbf{i} + (-2y - 1)\mathbf{j}$$

Therefore,

$$\nabla f(1, -2) = 7\mathbf{i} + 3\mathbf{j}$$

So the maximum value of $D_U f$ at the point $(2, -1)$ is

$$|\nabla f(1, -2)| = \sqrt{49 + 9} = \sqrt{58}$$

EXAMPLE 6:   The temperature at any point (x, y) of a rectangular plate lying in the xy plane is determined by $T(x, y) = x^2 + y^2$. (a) Find the rate of change of the temperature at the point $(3, 4)$ in the direction making an angle of radian measure $\frac{1}{3}\pi$ with the positive x direction; (b) find the direction for which the rate of change of the temperature at the point $(-3, 1)$ is a maximum.

SOLUTION: We wish to find $D_U T(x, y)$, where

$$\mathbf{U} = \cos \tfrac{1}{3}\pi\mathbf{i} + \sin \tfrac{1}{3}\pi\mathbf{j} = \tfrac{1}{2}\mathbf{i} + \tfrac{1}{2}\sqrt{3}\mathbf{j}$$

Because $T(x, y) = x^2 + y^2$, $T_x(x, y) = 2x$, and $T_y(x, y) = 2y$. Hence,

$$\nabla T(x, y) = T_x(x, y)\mathbf{i} + T_y(x, y)\mathbf{j} = 2x\mathbf{i} + 2y\mathbf{j}$$

Therefore,

$$D_U T(x, y) = \mathbf{U} \cdot \nabla T(x, y)$$
$$= (\tfrac{1}{2}\mathbf{i} + \tfrac{1}{2}\sqrt{3}\mathbf{j}) \cdot (2x\mathbf{i} + 2y\mathbf{j})$$
$$= x + \sqrt{3}y$$

Hence,

$$D_U T(3, 4) = 3 + 4\sqrt{3} \approx 3 + 4(1.732) = 9.93$$

So at $(3, 4)$ the temperature is increasing at the rate of 9.93 units per unit change in the distance measured in the direction of $\mathbf{U}$.

(b) $D_U T(-3, 1)$ is a maximum when $\mathbf{U}$ is in the direction of $\nabla T(-3, 1)$. Because $\nabla T(-3, 1) = -6\mathbf{i} + 2\mathbf{j}$, the radian measure of the angle giving the direction of $\nabla T(-3, 1)$ is θ, where $\tan \theta = -\frac{1}{3}$. So $\theta = \pi - \tan^{-1} \frac{1}{3}$. Therefore, the rate of change of the temperature at the point $(-3, 1)$ is a maximum in the direction making an angle of radian measure $\pi - \tan^{-1} \frac{1}{3}$ with the positive side of the x axis.

We extend the definition of a directional derivative to a function of three variables. In three-dimensional space the direction of a vector is determined by its direction cosines. So we let $\cos \alpha$, $\cos \beta$, and $\cos \gamma$ be the direction cosines of the unit vector $\mathbf{U}$; therefore, $\mathbf{U} = \cos \alpha \mathbf{i} + \cos \beta \mathbf{j} + \cos \gamma \mathbf{k}$.

17.7.4 Definition   Suppose that f is a function of three variables x, y, and z. If $\mathbf{U}$ is the unit vector $\cos \alpha \mathbf{i} + \cos \beta \mathbf{j} + \cos \gamma \mathbf{k}$, then the directional derivative of f in the direction of $\mathbf{U}$, denoted by $D_{\mathbf{U}} f$, is given by

$$D_{\mathbf{U}} f(x, y, z) = \lim_{h \to 0} \frac{f(x + h \cos \alpha, y + h \cos \beta, z + h \cos \gamma) - f(x, y, z)}{h}$$

if this limit exists.

The directional derivative of a function of three variables gives the rate of change of the function values $f(x, y, z)$ with respect to distance in three-dimensional space measured in the direction of the unit vector $\mathbf{U}$.

The following theorem, which gives a method for calculating a directional derivative for a function of three variables, is proved in a manner similar to the proof of Theorem 17.7.2.

17.7.5 Theorem   If f is a differentiable function of x, y, and z and

$$\mathbf{U} = \cos \alpha \mathbf{i} + \cos \beta \mathbf{j} + \cos \gamma \mathbf{k}$$

then

$$D_{\mathbf{U}} f(x, y, z) = f_x(x, y, z) \cos \alpha + f_y(x, y, z) \cos \beta + f_z(x, y, z) \cos \gamma \quad (8)$$

EXAMPLE 7:   Given $f(x, y, z) = 3x^2 + xy - 2y^2 - yz + z^2$, find the rate of change of $f(x, y, z)$ at $(1, -2, -1)$ in the direction of the vector $2\mathbf{i} - 2\mathbf{j} - \mathbf{k}$.

SOLUTION: The unit vector in the direction of $2\mathbf{i} - 2\mathbf{j} - \mathbf{k}$ is given by

$$\mathbf{U} = \tfrac{2}{3}\mathbf{i} - \tfrac{2}{3}\mathbf{j} - \tfrac{1}{3}\mathbf{k}$$

Also,

$$f(x, y, z) = 3x^2 + xy - 2y^2 - yz + z^2$$

So from (8)

$$D_{\mathbf{U}} f(x, y, z) = \tfrac{2}{3}(6x + y) - \tfrac{2}{3}(x - 4y - z) - \tfrac{1}{3}(-y + 2z)$$

Therefore, the rate of change of $f(x, y, z)$ at $(1, -2, -1)$ in the direction of $\mathbf{U}$ is given by

$$D_{\mathbf{U}} f(1, -2, -1) = \tfrac{2}{3}(4) - \tfrac{2}{3}(10) - \tfrac{1}{3}(0) = -4$$

17.7.6 Definition   If f is a function of three variables x, y, and z and the first partial derivatives f_x, f_y, and f_z exist, then the *gradient* of f, denoted by ∇f, is defined by

$$\nabla f(x, y, z) = f_x(x, y, z)\mathbf{i} + f_y(x, y, z)\mathbf{j} + f_z(x, y, z)\mathbf{k}$$

Just as for functions of two variables, it follows from Theorem 17.7.5 and Definition 17.7.6 that if $\mathbf{U} = \cos \alpha \mathbf{i} + \cos \beta \mathbf{j} + \cos \gamma \mathbf{k}$, then

$$D_{\mathbf{U}}f(x, y, z) = \mathbf{U} \cdot \nabla f(x, y, z) \tag{9}$$

Also, the directional derivative is a maximum when $\mathbf{U}$ is in the direction of the gradient, and the maximum directional derivative is the magnitude of the gradient.

Applications of the gradient occur in physics in problems in heat conduction and electricity. Suppose that $w = f(x, y, z)$. A level surface of this function f at k is given by

$$f(x, y, z) = k \tag{10}$$

If w is the number of degrees in the temperature at point (x, y, z), then all points on the surface of Eq. (10) have the same temperature of k degrees, and the surface is called an *isothermal surface*. If w is the number of volts in the electric potential at point (x, y, z), then all points on the surface are at the same potential, and the surface is called an *equipotential surface*. The gradient vector at a point gives the direction of greatest rate of change of w. So if the level surface of Eq. (10) is an isothermal surface, $\nabla f(x, y, z)$ gives the direction of the greatest rate of change of temperature at (x, y, z). If Eq. (10) is an equation of an equipotential surface, then $\nabla f(x, y, z)$ gives the direction of the greatest rate of change of potential at (x, y, z).

EXAMPLE 8: If V volts is the electric potential at any point (x, y, z) in three-dimensional space and $V = 1/\sqrt{x^2 + y^2 + z^2}$, find: (a) the rate of change of V at the point $(2, 2, -1)$ in the direction of the vector $2\mathbf{i} - 3\mathbf{j} + 6\mathbf{k}$; and (b) the direction of the greatest rate of change of V at $(2, 2, -1)$.

SOLUTION: Let $f(x, y, z) = 1/\sqrt{x^2 + y^2 + z^2}$.
(a) A unit vector in the direction of $2\mathbf{i} - 3\mathbf{j} + 6\mathbf{k}$ is

$$\mathbf{U} = \tfrac{2}{7}\mathbf{i} - \tfrac{3}{7}\mathbf{j} + \tfrac{6}{7}\mathbf{k}$$

We wish to find $D_{\mathbf{U}}f(2, 2, -1)$.

$$\nabla f(x, y, z) = f_x(x, y, z)\mathbf{i} + f_y(x, y, z)\mathbf{j} + f_z(x, y, z)\mathbf{k}$$

$$= \frac{-x}{(x^2 + y^2 + z^2)^{3/2}}\mathbf{i} + \frac{-y}{(x^2 + y^2 + z^2)^{3/2}}\mathbf{j} + \frac{-z}{(x^2 + y^2 + z^2)^{3/2}}\mathbf{k}$$

Then we have

$$D_{\mathbf{U}}f(2, 2, -1) = \mathbf{U} \cdot \nabla f(2, 2, -1)$$

$$= (\tfrac{2}{7}\mathbf{i} - \tfrac{3}{7}\mathbf{j} + \tfrac{6}{7}\mathbf{k}) \cdot (-\tfrac{2}{27}\mathbf{i} - \tfrac{2}{27}\mathbf{j} + \tfrac{1}{27}\mathbf{k})$$

$$= -\tfrac{4}{189} + \tfrac{6}{189} + \tfrac{6}{189}$$

$$= \tfrac{8}{189}$$

$$\approx 0.042$$

Therefore, at $(2, 2, -1)$ the potential is increasing at the rate of 0.042 volts per unit change in the distance measured in the direction of $\mathbf{U}$.

(b) $\nabla f(2, 2, -1) = -\frac{2}{27}\mathbf{i} - \frac{2}{27}\mathbf{j} + \frac{1}{27}\mathbf{k}$. A unit vector in the direction of $\nabla f(2, 2, -1)$ is

$$\frac{\nabla f(2, 2, -1)}{|\nabla f(2, 2, -1)|} = \frac{-\frac{2}{27}\mathbf{i} - \frac{2}{27}\mathbf{j} + \frac{1}{27}\mathbf{k}}{\frac{3}{27}} = -\frac{2}{3}\mathbf{i} - \frac{2}{3}\mathbf{j} + \frac{1}{3}\mathbf{k}$$

The direction cosines of this vector are $-\frac{2}{3}, -\frac{2}{3}$, and $\frac{1}{3}$, which give the direction of the greatest rate of change of V at $(2, 2, -1)$.

Exercises 17.7

In Exercises 1 through 4, find the directional derivative of the given function in the direction of the given unit vector $\mathbf{U}$ by using either Definition 17.7.1 or Definition 17.7.4, and then verify your result by applying either Theorem 17.7.2 or Theorem 17.7.5, whichever one applies.

1. $f(x, y) = 2x^2 + 5y^2$; $\mathbf{U} = \cos \frac{1}{4}\pi \mathbf{i} + \sin \frac{1}{4}\pi \mathbf{j}$

2. $g(x, y) = \dfrac{1}{x^2 + y^2}$; $\mathbf{U} = \frac{3}{5}\mathbf{i} - \frac{4}{5}\mathbf{j}$

3. $h(x, y, z) = 3x^2 + y^2 - 4z^2$; $\mathbf{U} = \cos \frac{1}{3}\pi \mathbf{i} + \cos \frac{1}{4}\pi \mathbf{j} + \cos \frac{2}{3}\pi \mathbf{k}$

4. $f(x, y, z) = 6x^2 - 2xy + yz$; $\mathbf{U} = \frac{3}{7}\mathbf{i} + \frac{2}{7}\mathbf{j} + \frac{6}{7}\mathbf{k}$

In Exercises 5 through 10, find the value of the directional derivative at the particular point P_0 for the given function in the direction of $\mathbf{U}$.

5. $g(x, y) = y^2 \tan^2 x$; $\mathbf{U} = -\frac{1}{2}\sqrt{3}\mathbf{i} + \frac{1}{2}\mathbf{j}$; $P_0 = (\frac{1}{3}\pi, 2)$

6. $f(x, y) = xe^{2y}$; $\mathbf{U} = \frac{1}{2}\mathbf{i} + \frac{1}{2}\sqrt{3}\mathbf{j}$; $P_0 = (2, 0)$

7. $h(x, y, z) = \cos(xy) + \sin(yz)$; $\mathbf{U} = -\frac{1}{3}\mathbf{i} + \frac{2}{3}\mathbf{j} + \frac{2}{3}\mathbf{k}$; $P_0 = (2, 0, -3)$

8. $f(x, y, z) = \ln(x^2 + y^2 + z^2)$; $\mathbf{U} = \dfrac{1}{\sqrt{3}}\mathbf{i} - \dfrac{1}{\sqrt{3}}\mathbf{j} - \dfrac{1}{\sqrt{3}}\mathbf{k}$; $P_0 = (1, 3, 2)$

9. $f(x, y) = e^{-3x} \cos 3y$; $\mathbf{U} = \cos(-\frac{1}{12}\pi)\mathbf{i} + \sin(-\frac{1}{12}\pi)\mathbf{j}$; $P_0 = (-\frac{1}{12}\pi, 0)$

10. $g(x, y, z) = \cos 2x \cos 3y \sinh 4z$; $\mathbf{U} = \dfrac{1}{\sqrt{3}}\mathbf{i} - \dfrac{1}{\sqrt{3}}\mathbf{j} + \dfrac{1}{\sqrt{3}}\mathbf{k}$; $P_0 = (\frac{1}{2}\pi, 0, 0)$.

In Exercises 11 through 14, a function f, a point P, and a unit vector $\mathbf{U}$ are given. Find (a) the gradient of f at P, and (b) the rate of change of the function value in the direction of $\mathbf{U}$ at P.

11. $f(x, y) = x^2 - 4y$; $P = (-2, 2)$; $\mathbf{U} = \cos \frac{1}{3}\pi \mathbf{i} + \sin \frac{1}{3}\pi \mathbf{j}$

12. $f(x, y) = e^{2xy}$; $P = (2, 1)$; $\mathbf{U} = \frac{4}{5}\mathbf{i} - \frac{3}{5}\mathbf{j}$

13. $f(x, y, z) = y^2 + z^2 - 4xz$; $P = (-2, 1, 3)$; $\mathbf{U} = \frac{2}{7}\mathbf{i} - \frac{6}{7}\mathbf{j} + \frac{3}{7}\mathbf{k}$

14. $f(x, y, z) = 2x^3 + xy^2 + xz^2$; $P = (1, 1, 1)$; $\mathbf{U} = \frac{1}{7}\sqrt{21}\mathbf{j} - \frac{2}{7}\sqrt{7}\mathbf{k}$

15. Draw a contour map showing the level curves of the function of Exercise 11 at $8, 4, 0, -4$, and -8. Also show the representation of $\nabla f(-2, 2)$ having its initial point at $(-2, 2)$.

16. Draw a contour map showing the level curves of the function of Exercise 12 at $e^8, e^4, 1, e^{-4}$, and e^{-8}. Also show the representation of $\nabla f(2, 1)$ having its initial point at $(2, 1)$.

In Exercises 17 through 20, find $D_U f$ at the given point P for which $\mathbf{U}$ is a unit vector in the direction of $\overrightarrow{PQ}$. Also at P find $D_U f$, if $\mathbf{U}$ is a unit vector for which $D_U f$ is a maximum.

17. $f(x, y) = e^x \tan^{-1} y$; $P(0, 1)$, $Q(3, 5)$

18. $f(x, y) = e^x \cos y + e^y \sin x$; $P(1, 0)$, $Q(-3, 3)$

19. $f(x, y, z) = x - 2y + z^2$; $P(3, 1, -2)$, $Q(10, 7, 4)$

20. $f(x, y, z) = x^2 + y^2 - 4xz$; $P(3, 1, -2)$, $Q(-6, 3, 4)$

21. Find the direction from the point $(1, 3)$ for which the value of f does not change if $f(x, y) = e^{2y} \tan^{-1}(y/3x)$.

22. The density is ρ slugs/ft^2 at any point (x, y) of a rectangular plate in the xy plane and $\rho = 1/\sqrt{x^2 + y^2 + 3}$. (a) Find the rate of change of the density at the point $(3, 2)$ in the direction of the unit vector $\cos \frac{2}{3}\pi \mathbf{i} + \sin \frac{2}{3}\pi \mathbf{j}$. (b) Find the direction and magnitude of the greatest rate of change of ρ at $(3, 2)$.

23. The electric potential is V volts at any point (x, y) in the xy plane and $V = e^{-2x} \cos 2y$. Distance is measured in feet. (a) Find the rate of change of the potential at the point $(0, \frac{1}{4}\pi)$ in the direction of the unit vector $\cos \frac{1}{6}\pi \mathbf{i} + \sin \frac{1}{6}\pi \mathbf{j}$. (b) Find the direction and magnitude of the greatest rate of change of V at $(0, \frac{1}{4}\pi)$.

24. The temperature is T degrees at any point (x, y, z) in three-dimensional space and $T = 60/(x^2 + y^2 + z^2 + 3)$. Distance is measured in inches. (a) Find the rate of change of the temperature at the point $(3, -2, 2)$ in the direction of the vector $-2\mathbf{i} + 3\mathbf{j} - 6\mathbf{k}$. (b) Find the direction and magnitude of the greatest rate of change of T at $(3, -2, 2)$.

25. An equation of the surface of a mountain is $z = 1200 - 3x^2 - 2y^2$, where distance is measured in feet, the x axis points to the east, and the y axis points to the north. A mountain climber is at the point corresponding to $(-10, 5, 850)$. (a) What is the direction of steepest ascent? (b) If the climber moves in the east direction, is he ascending or descending, and what is his rate? (c) If the climber moves in the southwest direction, is he ascending or descending, and what is his rate? (d) In what direction is he traveling a level path?

17.8 TANGENT PLANES AND NORMALS TO SURFACES

Let S be the surface having the equation

$$F(x, y, z) = 0 \tag{1}$$

and suppose that $P_0(x_0, y_0, z_0)$ is a point on S. Then $F(x_0, y_0, z_0) = 0$. Suppose further that C is a curve on S through P_0 and a set of parametric equations of C is

$$x = f(t) \qquad y = g(t) \qquad z = h(t) \tag{2}$$

Let the value of the parameter t at the point P_0 be t_0. A vector equation of C is

$$\mathbf{R}(t) = f(t)\mathbf{i} + g(t)\mathbf{j} + h(t)\mathbf{k} \tag{3}$$

Because curve C is on surface S, we have, upon substituting from (2) in (1),

$$F(f(t), g(t), h(t)) = 0 \tag{4}$$

Let $G(t) = F(f(t), g(t), h(t))$. If F_x, F_y, and F_z are continuous and not all zero at P_0, and if $f'(t_0)$, $g'(t_0)$, and $h'(t_0)$ exist, then the total derivative of F with respect to t at P_0 is given by

$$G'(t_0) = F_x(x_0, y_0, z_0)f'(t_0) + F_y(x_0, y_0, z_0)g'(t_0) + F_z(x_0, y_0, z_0)h'(t_0)$$

which also can be written as

$$G'(t_0) = \nabla F(x_0, y_0, z_0) \cdot D_t \mathbf{R}(t_0)$$

Because $G'(t) = 0$ for all t under consideration (because of (4)) $G'(t_0) = 0$; so it follows from the above that

$$\nabla F(x_0, y_0, z_0) \cdot D_t \mathbf{R}(t_0) = 0 \qquad (5)$$

From Sec. 16.9, we know that $D_t \mathbf{R}(t_0)$ has the same direction as the unit tangent vector to curve C at P_0. Therefore, from (5) we can conclude that the gradient vector of F at P_0 is orthogonal to the unit tangent vector of every curve C on S through the point P_0. We are led, then, to the following definition.

17.8.1 Definition   A vector which is orthogonal to the unit tangent vector of every curve C through a point P_0 on a surface S is called a *normal vector* to S at P_0.

From this definition and the preceding discussion we have the following theorem.

17.8.2 Theorem   If an equation of a surface S is $F(x, y, z) = 0$, and F_x, F_y, and F_z are continuous and not all zero at the point $P_0(x_0, y_0, z_0)$ on S, then a normal vector to S at P_0 is $\nabla F(x_0, y_0, z_0)$.

We now can define the *tangent plane* to a surface at a point.

17.8.3 Definition   If an equation of a surface S is $F(x, y, z) = 0$, then the *tangent plane* of S at a point $P_0(x_0, y_0, z_0)$ is the plane through P_0 having as a normal vector $\nabla F(x_0, y_0, z_0)$.

An equation of the tangent plane of the above definition is

$$F_x(x_0, y_0, z_0)(x - x_0) + F_y(x_0, y_0, z_0)(y - y_0) + F_z(x_0, y_0, z_0)(z - z_0) = 0 \qquad (6)$$

Refer to Fig. 17.8.1, which shows the tangent plane to the surface S at P_0 and the representation of the gradient vector having its initial point at P_0.

A vector equation of the tangent plane given by (6) is

$$\nabla F(x_0, y_0, z_0) \cdot [(x - x_0)\mathbf{i} + (y - y_0)\mathbf{j} + (z - z_0)\mathbf{k}] = 0 \qquad (7)$$

Figure 17.8.1

EXAMPLE 1:   Find an equation of the tangent plane to the elliptic paraboloid $4x^2 + y^2 - 16z = 0$ at the point $(2, 4, 2)$.

SOLUTION: Let $F(x, y, z) = 4x^2 + y^2 - 16z$. Then $\nabla F(x, y, z) = 8x\mathbf{i} + 2y\mathbf{j} - 16\mathbf{k}$, and so $\nabla F(2, 4, 2) = 16\mathbf{i} + 8\mathbf{j} - 16\mathbf{k}$. From (7) it follows that an equation of the tangent plane is

$$16(x - 2) + 8(y - 4) - 16(z - 2) = 0$$

or

$$2x + y - 2z - 4 = 0$$

17.8.4 Definition   The *normal line* to a surface S at a point P_0 on S is the line through P_0 having as a set of direction numbers the components of any normal vector to S at P_0.

If an equation of a surface S is $F(x, y, z) = 0$, symmetric equations of the normal line to S at $P_0(x_0, y_0, z_0)$ are

$$\frac{x - x_0}{F_x(x_0, y_0, z_0)} = \frac{y - y_0}{F_y(x_0, y_0, z_0)} = \frac{z - z_0}{F_z(x_0, y_0, z_0)} \tag{8}$$

The denominators in (8) are components of $\nabla F(x_0, y_0, z_0)$, which is a normal vector to S at P_0; thus, (8) follows from Definition 17.8.4. The normal line at a point on a surface is perpendicular to the tangent plane there.

EXAMPLE 2: Find symmetric equations of the normal line to the surface of Example 1 at $(2, 4, 2)$.	SOLUTION: Because $\nabla F(2, 4, 2) = 16\mathbf{i} + 8\mathbf{j} - 16\mathbf{k}$, it follows that symmetric equations of the required normal line are $\dfrac{x - 2}{2} = \dfrac{y - 4}{1} = \dfrac{z - 2}{-2}$

17.8.5 Definition   The *tangent line* to a curve C at a point P_0 is the line through P_0 having as a set of direction numbers the components of the unit tangent vector to C at P_0.

From Definitions 17.8.3 and 17.8.5 we see that all the tangent lines at the point P_0 to the curves lying on a given surface lie in the tangent plane to the surface at P_0. Refer to Fig. 17.8.2 showing sketches of a surface and the tangent plane at P_0. Some of the curves through P_0 and their tangent lines are also sketched in the figure.

Figure 17.8.2

Consider a curve C which is the intersection of two surfaces having equations

$$F(x, y, z) = 0 \tag{9}$$

and

$$G(x, y, z) = 0 \tag{10}$$

respectively. We shall show how to obtain equations of the tangent line to C at a point $P_0(x_0, y_0, z_0)$. Because this tangent line lies in each of the tangent planes to the given surfaces at P_0, it is the line of intersection of the two tangent planes. A normal vector at P_0 to the surface having Eq. (9) is given by

$$\mathbf{N}_1 = \nabla F(x_0, y_0, z_0) = F_x(x_0, y_0, z_0)\mathbf{i} + F_y(x_0, y_0, z_0)\mathbf{j} + F_z(x_0, y_0, z_0)\mathbf{k}$$

and a normal vector at P_0 to the surface having Eq. (10) is given by

$$\mathbf{N}_2 = \nabla G(x_0, y_0, z_0) = G_x(x_0, y_0, z_0)\mathbf{i} + G_y(x_0, y_0, z_0)\mathbf{j} + G_z(x_0, y_0, z_0)\mathbf{k}$$

Both $\mathbf{N}_1$ and $\mathbf{N}_2$ are orthogonal to the unit tangent vector to C at P_0; so if $\mathbf{N}_1$ and $\mathbf{N}_2$ are not parallel, it follows from Theorem 16.6.9 that the unit tangent vector has the direction which is the same as, or opposite to, the direction of $\mathbf{N}_1 \times \mathbf{N}_2$. Therefore, the components of $\mathbf{N}_1 \times \mathbf{N}_2$ serve as a set of direction numbers of the tangent line. From this set of direction numbers and the coordinates of P_0 we can obtain symmetric equations of the required tangent line. This is illustrated in the following example.

EXAMPLE 3:   Find symmetric equations of the tangent line to the curve of intersection of the surfaces $3x^2 + 2y^2 + z^2 = 49$ and $x^2 + y^2 - 2z^2 = 10$ at the point $(3, -3, 2)$.

SOLUTION: Let $F(x, y, z) = 3x^2 + 2y^2 + z^2 - 49$ and

$$G(x, y, z) = x^2 + y^2 - 2z^2 - 10$$

Then $\nabla F(x, y, z) = 6x\mathbf{i} + 4y\mathbf{j} + 2z\mathbf{k}$ and $\nabla G(x, y, z) = 2x\mathbf{i} + 2y\mathbf{j} - 4z\mathbf{k}$. So

$$\mathbf{N}_1 = \nabla F(3, -3, 2) = 18\mathbf{i} - 12\mathbf{j} + 4\mathbf{k} = 2(9\mathbf{i} - 6\mathbf{j} + 2\mathbf{k})$$

and

$$\mathbf{N}_2 = \nabla G(3, -3, 2) = 6\mathbf{i} - 6\mathbf{j} - 8\mathbf{k} = 2(3\mathbf{i} - 3\mathbf{j} - 4\mathbf{k})$$

$$\mathbf{N}_1 \times \mathbf{N}_2 = 4(9\mathbf{i} - 6\mathbf{j} + 2\mathbf{k}) \times (3\mathbf{i} - 3\mathbf{j} - 4\mathbf{k})$$

$$= 4(30\mathbf{i} + 42\mathbf{j} - 9\mathbf{k})$$

$$= 12(10\mathbf{i} + 14\mathbf{j} - 3\mathbf{k})$$

Therefore, a set of direction numbers of the required tangent line is $[10, 14, -3]$. Symmetric equations of the line are, then,

$$\frac{x-3}{10} = \frac{y+3}{14} = \frac{z-2}{-3}$$

If two surfaces have a common tangent plane at a point, the two surfaces are said to be *tangent* at that point.

Exercises 17.8

In Exercises 1 through 12, find an equation of the tangent plane and equations of the normal line to the given surface at the indicated point.

1. $x^2 + y^2 + z^2 = 17$; $(2, -2, 3)$

2. $4x^2 + y^2 + 2z^2 = 26$; $(1, -2, 3)$

3. $x^2 + y^2 - 3z = 2$; $(-2, -4, 6)$

4. $x^2 + y^2 - z^2 = 6$; $(3, -1, 2)$

5. $y = e^x \cos z$; $(1, e, 0)$

6. $z = e^{3x} \sin 3y$; $(0, \frac{1}{6}\pi, 1)$

7. $x^2 = 12y$; $(6, 3, 3)$ 8. $z = x^{1/2} + y^{1/2}$; $(1, 1, 2)$ 9. $x^{1/2} + y^{1/2} + z^{1/2} = 4$; $(4, 1, 1)$

10. $zx^2 - xy^2 - yz^2 = 18$; $(0, -2, 3)$ 11. $x^{2/3} + y^{2/3} + z^{2/3} = 14$; $(-8, 27, 1)$ 12. $x^{1/2} + z^{1/2} = 8$; $(25, 2, 9)$

In Exercises 13 through 18, if the two given surfaces intersect in a curve, find equations of the tangent line to the curve of intersection at the given point; if the two given surfaces are tangent at the given point, prove it.

13. $x^2 + y^2 - z = 8$, $x - y^2 + z^2 = -2$; $(2, -2, 0)$ 14. $x^2 + y^2 - 2z + 1 = 0$, $x^2 + y^2 - z^2 = 0$; $(0, 1, 1)$

15. $y = x^2$, $y = 16 - z^2$; $(4, 16, 0)$ 16. $x = 2 + \cos \pi yz$, $y = 1 + \sin \pi xz$; $(3, 1, 2)$

17. $x^2 + z^2 + 4y = 0$, $x^2 + y^2 + z^2 - 6z + 7 = 0$; $(0, -1, 2)$ 18. $x^2 + y^2 + z^2 = 8$, $yz = 4$; $(0, 2, 2)$

19. Prove that every normal line to the sphere $x^2 + y^2 + z^2 = a^2$ passes through the center of the sphere.

17.9 HIGHER-ORDER PARTIAL DERIVATIVES

If f is a function of two variables, then in general $D_1 f$ and $D_2 f$ are also functions of two variables. And if the partial derivatives of these functions exist, they are called second partial derivatives of f. In contrast, $D_1 f$ and $D_2 f$ are called first partial derivatives of f. There are four second partial derivatives of a function of two variables. If f is a function of the two variables x and y, the notations

$$D_2(D_1 f) \qquad D_{12} f \qquad f_{12} \qquad f_{xy} \qquad \frac{\partial^2 f}{\partial y\, \partial x}$$

all denote the second partial derivative of f, which we obtain by first partial-differentiating f with respect to x and then partial-differentiating the result with respect to y. This second partial derivative is defined by

$$f_{12}(x, y) = \lim_{\Delta y \to 0} \frac{f_1(x, y + \Delta y) - f_1(x, y)}{\Delta y} \qquad (1)$$

if this limit exists. The notations

$$D_1(D_1 f) \qquad D_{11} f \qquad f_{11} \qquad f_{xx} \qquad \frac{\partial^2 f}{\partial x^2}$$

all denote the second partial derivative of f, which is obtained by partial-differentiating twice with respect to x. We have the definition

$$f_{11}(x, y) = \lim_{\Delta x \to 0} \frac{f_1(x + \Delta x, y) - f_1(x, y)}{\Delta x} \qquad (2)$$

if this limit exists. We define the other two second partial derivatives in an analogous way and obtain

$$f_{21}(x, y) = \lim_{\Delta x \to 0} \frac{f_2(x + \Delta x, y) - f_2(x, y)}{\Delta x} \qquad (3)$$

and

$$f_{22}(x, y) = \lim_{\Delta y \to 0} \frac{f_2(x, y + \Delta y) - f_2(x, y)}{\Delta y} \qquad (4)$$

if these limits exist.

The definitions of higher-order partial derivatives are similar. Again we have various notations for a specific derivative. For example,

$$D_{112}f \qquad f_{112} \qquad f_{xxy} \qquad \frac{\partial^3 f}{\partial y\, \partial x\, \partial x} \qquad \frac{\partial^3 f}{\partial y\, \partial x^2}$$

all stand for the third partial derivative of f, which is obtained by partial-differentiating twice with respect to x and then once with respect to y. Note that in the subscript notation, the order of partial differentiation is from left to right; in the notation $\partial^3 f / \partial y\, \partial x\, \partial x$, the order is from right to left.

EXAMPLE 1: Given

$$f(x, y) = e^x \sin y + \ln xy$$

find: (a) $D_{11}f(x, y)$; (b) $D_{12}f(x, y)$;
(c) $\partial^3 f / \partial x\, \partial y^2$.

SOLUTION:

$$D_1 f(x, y) = e^x \sin y + \frac{1}{xy}\, y = e^x \sin y + \frac{1}{x}$$

So (a) $D_{11}f(x, y) = e^x \sin y - 1/x^2$; and (b) $D_{12}f(x, y) = e^x \cos y$. (c) To find $\partial^3 f / \partial x\, \partial y^2$, we partial-differentiate twice with respect to y and then once with respect to x. This gives us

$$\frac{\partial f}{\partial y} = e^x \cos y + \frac{1}{y} \qquad \frac{\partial^2 f}{\partial y^2} = -e^x \sin y - \frac{1}{y^2} \qquad \frac{\partial^3 f}{\partial x\, \partial y^2} = -e^x \sin y$$

Higher-order partial derivatives of a function of n variables have definitions which are analogous to the definitions of higher-order partial derivatives of a function of two variables. If f is a function of n variables, there may be n^2 second partial derivatives of f at a particular point. That is, for a function of three variables, if all the second-order partial derivatives exist, there are nine of them: $f_{11}, f_{12}, f_{13}, f_{21}, f_{22}, f_{23}, f_{31}, f_{32}$, and f_{33}.

EXAMPLE 2: Given

$$f(x, y, z) = \sin(xy + 2z)$$

find $D_{132}f(x, y, z)$.

SOLUTION:

$$D_1 f(x, y, z) = y \cos(xy + 2z)$$

$$D_{13}f(x, y, z) = -2y \sin(xy + 2z)$$

$$D_{132}f(x, y, z) = -2 \sin(xy + 2z) - 2xy \cos(xy + 2z)$$

EXAMPLE 3: Given

$$f(x, y) = x^3 y - y \cosh xy$$

find: (a) $D_{12}f(x, y)$; (b) $D_{21}f(x, y)$

SOLUTION:

(a) $D_1 f(x, y) = 3x^2 y - y^2 \sinh xy$

$\quad D_{12}f(x, y) = 3x^2 - 2y \sinh xy - xy^2 \cosh xy$

(b) $D_2 f(x, y) = x^3 - \cosh xy - xy \sinh xy$

$\quad D_{21}f(x, y) = 3x^2 - y \sinh xy - y \sinh xy - xy^2 \cosh xy$

$\qquad\qquad\quad = 3x^2 - 2y \sinh xy - xy^2 \cosh xy$

We see from the above results that for the function of Example 3 the "mixed" partial derivatives $D_{12}f(x, y)$ and $D_{21}f(x, y)$ are equal. So for this particular function, when finding the second partial derivative with respect to x and then y, the order of differentiation is immaterial. This condition holds for many functions. However, the following example shows that it is not always true.

EXAMPLE 4: Let f be the function defined by

$$f(x, y) = \begin{cases} (xy)\dfrac{x^2 - y^2}{x^2 + y^2} & \text{if } (x, y) \neq (0, 0) \\ 0 & \text{if } (x, y) = (0, 0) \end{cases}$$

Find $f_{12}(0, 0)$ and $f_{21}(0, 0)$.

SOLUTION: In Example 4, Sec. 17.4, we showed that for this function

$$f_1(0, y) = -y \qquad \text{for all } y \tag{5}$$

and

$$f_2(x, 0) = x \qquad \text{for all } x \tag{6}$$

From formula (1) we obtain

$$f_{12}(0, 0) = \lim_{\Delta y \to 0} \frac{f_1(0, 0 + \Delta y) - f_1(0, 0)}{\Delta y}$$

But from (5), $f_1(0, \Delta y) = -\Delta y$ and $f_1(0, 0) = 0$, and so we have

$$f_{12}(0, 0) = \lim_{\Delta y \to 0} \frac{-\Delta y - 0}{\Delta y} = \lim_{\Delta y \to 0} (-1) = -1$$

From formula (3), we get

$$f_{21}(0, 0) = \lim_{\Delta x \to 0} \frac{f_2(0 + \Delta x, 0) - f_2(0, 0)}{\Delta x}$$

From (6), $f_2(\Delta x, 0) = \Delta x$ and $f_2(0, 0) = 0$. Therefore,

$$f_{21}(0, 0) = \lim_{\Delta x \to 0} \frac{\Delta x - 0}{\Delta x} = \lim_{\Delta x \to 0} 1 = 1$$

For the function in Example 4 we see that the mixed partial derivatives $f_{12}(x, y)$ and $f_{21}(x, y)$ are not equal at $(0, 0)$. A set of conditions for which $f_{12}(x_0, y_0) = f_{21}(x_0, y_0)$ is given by Theorem 17.9.1 which follows. The function of Example 4 does not satisfy the hypothesis of this theorem because both f_{12} and f_{21} are discontinuous at $(0, 0)$. It is left for the reader to show this (see Exercise 20).

17.9.1 Theorem Suppose that f is a function of two variables x and y defined on an open disk $B((x_0, y_0); r)$ and f_x, f_y, f_{xy}, and f_{yx} also are defined on B. Furthermore, suppose that f_{xy} and f_{yx} are continuous on B. Then

$$f_{xy}(x_0, y_0) = f_{yx}(x_0, y_0)$$

PROOF: Consider a square having its center at (x_0, y_0) and the length of its side $2|h|$ such that $0 < \sqrt{2}|h| < r$. Then all the points in the interior of the square and on the sides of the square are in the open disk B (see Fig. 17.9.1). So the points $(x_0 + h, y_0 + h)$, $(x_0 + h, y_0)$, and $(x_0, y_0 + h)$ are in B. Let Δ be defined by

$$\Delta = f(x_0 + h, y_0 + h) - f(x_0 + h, y_0) - f(x_0, y_0 + h) + f(x_0, y_0) \tag{7}$$

Figure 17.9.1

Consider the function G defined by

$$G(x) = f(x, y_0 + h) - f(x, y_0) \tag{8}$$

Then

$$G(x + h) = f(x + h, y_0 + h) - f(x + h, y_0)$$

So (7) can be written as

$$\Delta = G(x_0 + h) - G(x_0) \tag{9}$$

From (8) we obtain

$$G'(x) = f_x(x, y_0 + h) - f_x(x, y_0) \tag{10}$$

Now, because $f_x(x, y_0 + h)$ and $f_x(x, y_0)$ are defined on B, $G'(x)$ exists if x is in the closed interval having endpoints at x_0 and $x_0 + h$. Hence, G is continuous if x is in this closed interval. By the mean-value theorem (4.5.2) there is a number c_1 between x_0 and $x_0 + h$ such that

$$G(x_0 + h) - G(x_0) = hG'(c_1) \tag{11}$$

Substituting from (11) into (9), we get

$$\Delta = hG'(c_1) \tag{12}$$

From (12) and (10) we obtain

$$\Delta = h[f_x(c_1, y_0 + h) - f_x(c_1, y_0)] \tag{13}$$

Now if g is the function defined by

$$g(y) = f_x(c_1, y) \tag{14}$$

we can write (13) as

$$\Delta = h[g(y_0 + h) - g(y_0)] \tag{15}$$

From (14) we obtain

$$g'(y) = f_{xy}(c_1, y) \tag{16}$$

Because $f_{xy}(c_1, y)$ is defined on B, $g'(y)$ exists if y is in the closed interval having endpoints at y_0 and $y_0 + h$; hence, g is continuous if y is in this closed interval. Therefore, by the mean-value theorem there is a number d_1 between y_0 and $y_0 + h$ such that

$$g(y_0 + h) - g(y_0) = hg'(d_1) \tag{17}$$

Substituting from (17) into (15), we get $\Delta = h^2 g'(d_1)$; so from (16) it follows that

$$\Delta = h^2 f_{xy}(c_1, d_1) \tag{18}$$

for some point (c_1, d_1) in the open disk B.

We now define a function ϕ by

$$\phi(y) = f(x_0 + h, y) - f(x_0, y) \tag{19}$$

and so $\phi(y + h) = f(x_0 + h, y + h) - f(x_0, y + h)$. Therefore, (7) can be written as

$$\Delta = \phi(y_0 + h) - \phi(y_0) \tag{20}$$

From (19) we get

$$\phi'(y) = f_y(x_0 + h, y) - f_y(x_0, y) \tag{21}$$

ϕ' exists if y is in the closed interval having y_0 and $y_0 + h$ as endpoints because by hypothesis each term on the right side of (21) exists on B. Therefore, ϕ is continuous on this closed interval. So by the mean-value theorem there is a number d_2 between y_0 and $y_0 + h$ such that

$$\phi(y_0 + h) - \phi(y_0) = h\phi'(d_2) \tag{22}$$

From (20), (21), and (22) it follows that

$$\Delta = h[f_y(x_0 + h, d_2) - f_y(x_0, d_2)] \tag{23}$$

Define the function χ by

$$\chi(x) = f_y(x, d_2) \tag{24}$$

and write (23) as

$$\Delta = h[\chi(x_0 + h) - \chi(x_0)] \tag{25}$$

From (24) we get

$$\chi'(x) = f_{yx}(x, d_2) \tag{26}$$

and by the mean-value theorem we conclude that there is a number c_2 between x_0 and $x_0 + h$ such that

$$\chi(x_0 + h) - \chi(x_0) = h\chi'(c_2) \tag{27}$$

From (25), (26), and (27) we obtain

$$\Delta = h^2 f_{yx}(c_2, d_2) \tag{28}$$

Equating the right sides of (18) and (28), we get

$$h^2 f_{xy}(c_1, d_1) = h^2 f_{yx}(c_2, d_2)$$

and because $h \neq 0$, we can divide by h^2, which gives

$$f_{xy}(c_1, d_1) = f_{yx}(c_2, d_2) \tag{29}$$

where (c_1, d_1) and (c_2, d_2) are in B.

Because c_1 and c_2 are each between x_0 and $x_0 + h$, we can write $c_1 = x_0 + \epsilon_1 h$, where $0 < \epsilon_1 < 1$, and $c_2 = x_0 + \epsilon_2 h$, where $0 < \epsilon_2 < 1$. Similarly, because both d_1 and d_2 are between y_0 and $y_0 + h$, we can write $d_1 = y_0 + \epsilon_3 h$, where $0 < \epsilon_3 < 1$, and $d_2 = y_0 + \epsilon_4 h$, where $0 < \epsilon_4 < 1$. Making these substitutions in (29) gives

$$f_{xy}(x_0 + \epsilon_1 h, y_0 + \epsilon_3 h) = f_{yx}(x_0 + \epsilon_2 h, y_0 + \epsilon_4 h) \tag{30}$$

Because f_{xy} and f_{yx} are continuous on B, upon taking the limit on both sides of (30) as h approaches zero, we obtain

$$f_{xy}(x_0, y_0) = f_{yx}(x_0, y_0)$$

As a result of the above theorem, if the function f of two variables has continuous partial derivatives on some open disk, then the order of partial differentiation can be changed without affecting the result; that is,

$$D_{112}f = D_{121}f = D_{211}f$$

$$D_{1122}f = D_{1212}f = D_{1221}f = D_{2112}f = D_{2121}f = D_{2211}f$$

and so forth. In particular, assuming that all of the partial derivatives are continuous on some open disk, we can prove that $D_{211}f = D_{112}f$ by applying Theorem 17.9.1 repeatedly. Doing this, we have

$$D_{211}f = D_1(D_{21}f) = D_1(D_{12}f) = D_1[D_2(D_1f)] = D_2[D_1(D_1f)]$$

$$= D_2(D_{11}f) = D_{112}f$$

EXAMPLE 5: Given that $u = f(x, y)$, $x = F(r, s)$, and $y = G(r, s)$, and assuming that $f_{xy} = f_{yx}$, prove by using the chain rule that

$$\frac{\partial^2 u}{\partial r^2} = f_{xx}(x, y)[F_r(r, s)]^2$$

$$+ 2f_{xy}(x, y)F_r(r, s)G_r(r, s)$$

$$+ f_{yy}(x, y)[G_r(r, s)]^2$$

$$+ f_x(x, y)F_{rr}(r, s)$$

$$+ f_y(x, y)G_{rr}(r, s)$$

SOLUTION: From the chain rule (Theorem 17.6.1) we have

$$\frac{\partial u}{\partial r} = f_x(x, y)F_r(r, s) + f_y(x, y)G_r(r, s)$$

Taking the partial derivative again with respect to r, and using the formula for the derivative of a product and the chain rule, we obtain

$$\frac{\partial^2 u}{\partial r^2} = [f_{xx}(x, y)F_r(r, s) + f_{xy}(x, y)G_r(r, s)]F_r(r, s) + f_x(x, y)F_{rr}(r, s)$$

$$+ [f_{yx}(x, y)F_r(r, s) + f_{yy}(x, y)G_r(r, s)]G_r(r, s) + f_y(x, y)G_{rr}(r, s)$$

Multiplying and combining terms, and using the fact that $f_{xy}(x, y) = f_{yx}(x, y)$, we get

$$\frac{\partial^2 u}{\partial r^2} = f_{xx}(x, y)[F_r(r, s)]^2 + 2f_{xy}(x, y)F_r(r, s)G_r(r, s)$$

$$+ f_{yy}(x, y)[G_r(r, s)]^2 + f_x(x, y)F_{rr}(r, s) + f_y(x, y)G_{rr}(r, s)$$

which is what we wished to prove.

Exercises 17.9

In Exercises 1 through 8, do each of the following: (a) Find $D_{11}f(x, y)$; (b) find $D_{22}f(x, y)$; (c) show that $D_{12}f(x, y) = D_{21}f(x, y)$.

1. $f(x, y) = \dfrac{x^2}{y} - \dfrac{y}{x^2}$

2. $f(x, y) = 2x^3 - 3x^2y + xy^2$

3. $f(x, y) = e^{2x} \sin y$

4. $f(x, y) = e^{-x/y} + \ln \dfrac{y}{x}$

5. $f(x, y) = (x^2 + y^2) \tan^{-1} \dfrac{y}{x}$

6. $f(x, y) = \sin^{-1} \dfrac{3y}{x^2}$

7. $f(x, y) = 4x \sinh y + 3y \cosh x$

8. $f(x, y) = x \cos y - ye^x$

In Exercises 9 through 14, find the indicated partial derivatives.

9. $f(x, y, z) = ye^x + ze^y + e^z$; (a) $f_{xz}(x, y, z)$; (b) $f_{yz}(x, y, z)$

10. $g(x, y, z) = \sin(xyz)$; (a) $g_{23}(x, y, z)$; (b) $g_{12}(x, y, z)$

11. $f(r, s) = 2r^3s + r^2s^2 - 5rs^3$; (a) $f_{121}(r, s)$; (b) $f_{221}(r, s)$

12. $f(u, v) = \ln \cos(u - v)$; (a) $f_{uuv}(u, v)$; (b) $f_{vuv}(u, v)$

13. $g(r, s, t) = \ln(r^2 + 4s^2 - 5t^2)$; (a) $g_{132}(r, s, t)$; (b) $g_{122}(r, s, t)$

14. $f(x, y, z) = \tan^{-1}(3xyz)$; (a) $f_{113}(x, y, z)$; (b) $f_{123}(x, y, z)$

In Exercises 15 through 18, show that $u(x, y)$ satisfies the equation

$$\frac{\partial^2 u}{\partial x^2} + \frac{\partial^2 u}{\partial y^2} = 0$$

which is known as *Laplace's equation* in R_2.

15. $u(x, y) = \ln(x^2 + y^2)$

16. $u(x, y) = e^x \sin y + e^y \cos x$

17. $u(x, y) = \tan^{-1} \dfrac{y}{x} + \dfrac{x}{x^2 + y^2}$

18. $u(x, y) = \tan^{-1} \dfrac{2xy}{x^2 - y^2}$

19. Laplace's equation in R_3 is

$$\frac{\partial^2 u}{\partial x^2} + \frac{\partial^2 u}{\partial y^2} + \frac{\partial^2 u}{\partial z^2} = 0$$

Show that $u(x, y, z) = (x^2 + y^2 + z^2)^{-1/2}$ satisfies this equation.

20. For the function of Example 4, show that f_{12} is discontinuous at $(0, 0)$ and hence that the hypothesis of Theorem 17.9.1 is not satisfied if $(x_0, y_0) = (0, 0)$.

In Exercises 21 through 23, find $f_{12}(0, 0)$ and $f_{21}(0, 0)$, if they exist.

21. $f(x, y) = \begin{cases} \dfrac{2xy}{x^2 + y^2} & \text{if } (x, y) \neq (0, 0) \\ 0 & \text{if } (x, y) = (0, 0) \end{cases}$

22. $f(x, y) = \begin{cases} \dfrac{x^2y^2}{x^4 + y^4} & \text{if } (x, y) \neq (0, 0) \\ 0 & \text{if } (x, y) = (0, 0) \end{cases}$

23. $f(x, y) = \begin{cases} x^2 \tan^{-1} \dfrac{y}{x} - y^2 \tan^{-1} \dfrac{x}{y} & \text{if } x \neq 0 \text{ and } y \neq 0 \\ 0 & \text{if either } x = 0 \text{ or } y = 0 \end{cases}$

24. Given that $u = f(x, y)$, $x = F(t)$, and $y = G(t)$, and assuming that $f_{xy} = f_{yx}$, prove by using the chain rule that

$$\frac{d^2u}{dt^2} = f_{xx}(x, y)[F'(t)]^2 + 2f_{xy}(x, y)F'(t)G'(t) + f_{yy}(x, y)[G'(t)]^2 + f_x(x, y)F''(t) + f_y(x, y)G''(t)$$

25. Given that $u = f(x, y)$, $x = F(r, s)$, and $y = G(r, s)$, and assuming that $f_{xy} = f_{yx}$, prove by using the chain rule that

$$\frac{\partial^2 u}{\partial r \, \partial s} = f_{xx}(x, y)F_r(r, s)F_s(r, s) + f_{xy}(x, y)[F_s(r, s)G_r(r, s) + F_r(r, s)G_s(r, s)]$$
$$+ f_{yy}(x, y)G_r(r, s)G_s(r, s) + f_x(x, y)F_{sr}(r, s) + f_y(x, y)G_{sr}(r, s)$$

26. Given $u = e^y \cos x$, $x = 2t$, $y = t^2$. Find d^2u/dt^2 in three ways: (a) by first expressing u in terms of t; (b) by using the formula of Exercise 24; (c) by using the chain rule.

27. Given $u = 3xy - 4y^2$, $x = 2se^r$, $y = re^{-s}$. Find $\partial^2u/\partial r^2$ in three ways: (a) by first expressing u in terms of r and s; (b) by using the formula of Example 5; (c) by using the chain rule.

28. For u, x, and y as given in Exercise 27, find $\partial^2u/\partial s \, \partial r$ in three ways: (a) by first expressing u in terms of r and s; (b) by using the formula of Exercise 25; (c) by using the chain rule.

29. Given $u = 9x^2 + 4y^2$, $x = r \cos \theta$, $y = r \sin \theta$. Find $\partial^2u/\partial r^2$ in three ways: (a) by first expressing u in terms of r and θ; (b) by using the formula of Example 5; (c) by using the chain rule.

30. For u, x, and y as given in Exercise 29, find $\partial^2u/\partial\theta^2$ in three ways: (a) by first expressing u in terms of r and θ; (b) by using the formula of Example 5; (c) by using the chain rule.

31. For u, x, and y as given in Exercise 29, find $\partial^2 u/\partial r\,\partial\theta$ in three ways: (a) by first expressing u in terms of r and θ; (b) by using the formula of Exercise 25; (c) by using the chain rule.

32. If $u = f(x, y)$ and $v = g(x, y)$, then the equations

$$\frac{\partial u}{\partial x} = \frac{\partial v}{\partial y} \quad \text{and} \quad \frac{\partial v}{\partial x} = -\frac{\partial u}{\partial y}$$

are called the *Cauchy-Riemann equations*. If f and g and their first and second partial derivatives are continuous, prove that if u and v satisfy the Cauchy-Riemann equations, they also satisfy Laplace's equation (see Exercises 15 through 18).

33. The one-dimensional heat-conduction partial differential equation is

$$\frac{\partial u}{\partial t} = k^2 \frac{\partial^2 u}{\partial x^2}$$

Show that if f is a function of x satisfying the equation

$$\frac{d^2 f}{dx^2} + \lambda^2 f(x) = 0$$

and g is a function of t satisfying the equation $dg/dt + k^2\lambda^2 g(t) = 0$, then if $u = f(x)g(t)$, the partial differential equation is satisfied. k and λ are constants.

34. The partial differential equation for a vibrating string is

$$\frac{\partial^2 u}{\partial t^2} = a^2 \frac{\partial^2 u}{\partial x^2}$$

Show that if f is a function of x satisfying the equation $d^2 f/dx^2 + \lambda^2 f(x) = 0$ and g is a function of t satisfying the equation $d^2 g/dt^2 + a^2\lambda^2 g(t) = 0$, then if $u = f(x)g(t)$, the partial differential equation is satisfied. a and λ are constants.

35. Prove that if f and g are two arbitrary functions of a real variable having continuous second derivatives and $u = f(x + at) + g(x - at)$, then u satisfies the partial differential equation of the vibrating string given in Exercise 34. (HINT: Let $v = x + at$ and $w = x - at$; then u is a function of v and w, and v and w are in turn functions of x and t.)

36. Prove that if f is a function of two variables and all the partial derivatives of f up to the fourth order are continuous on some open disk, then

$$D_{1122}f = D_{2121}f$$

17.10 EXTREMA OF FUNCTIONS OF TWO VARIABLES

An important application of the derivatives of a function of a single variable is in the study of extreme values of a function, which leads to a variety of problems involving maximum and minimum. We discussed this thoroughly in Chapter 4, where we proved theorems involving the first and second derivatives, which enabled us to determine relative maximum and minimum values of a function of one variable. In extending the theory to functions of two variables, we see that it is similar to the one-variable case; however, more complications arise.

17.10.1 Definition

The function f of two variables is said to have an *absolute maximum value* on a disk B in the xy plane if there is some point (x_0, y_0) in B such that $f(x_0, y_0) \geq f(x, y)$ for all points (x, y) in B. In such a case, $f(x_0, y_0)$ is the absolute maximum value of f on B.

17.10.2 Definition   The function f of two variables is said to have an *absolute minimum value* on a disk B in the xy plane if there is some point (x_0, y_0) in B such that $f(x_0, y_0) \le f(x, y)$ for all points (x, y) in B. In such a case, $f(x_0, y_0)$ is the absolute minimum value of f on B.

17.10.3 Theorem   Let B be a closed disk in the xy plane, and let f be a function of two vari-
The Extreme-Value Theorem   ables which is continuous on B. Then there is at least one point in B where
for Functions of Two Variables f has an absolute maximum value and at least one point in B where f has an absolute minimum value.

The proof of Theorem 17.10.3 is omitted because it is beyond the scope of this book.

17.10.4 Definition   The function f of two variables is said to have a *relative maximum value* at the point (x_0, y_0) if there exists an open disk $B((x_0, y_0); r)$ such that $f(x, y) \le f(x_0, y_0)$ for all (x, y) in the open disk.

17.10.5 Definition   The function f of two variables is said to have a *relative minimum value* at the point (x_0, y_0) if there exists an open disk $B((x_0, y_0); r)$ such that $f(x, y) \ge f(x_0, y_0)$ for all (x, y) in the open disk.

17.10.6 Theorem   If $f(x, y)$ exists at all points in some open disk $B((x_0, y_0); r)$ and if f has a relative extremum at (x_0, y_0), then if $f_x(x_0, y_0)$ and $f_y(x_0, y_0)$ exist,

$$f_x(x_0, y_0) = f_y(x_0, y_0) = 0$$

PROOF: We prove that if f has a relative maximum value at (x_0, y_0) and if $f_x(x_0, y_0)$ exists, then $f_x(x_0, y_0) = 0$. By the definition of a partial derivative,

$$f_x(x_0, y_0) = \lim_{\Delta x \to 0} \frac{f(x_0 + \Delta x, y_0) - f(x_0, y_0)}{\Delta x}$$

Because f has a relative maximum value at (x_0, y_0), by Definition 17.10.4 it follows that

$$f(x_0 + \Delta x, y_0) - f(x_0, y_0) \le 0$$

whenever Δx is sufficiently small so that $(x_0 + \Delta x, y_0)$ is in B. If Δx approaches zero from the right, $\Delta x > 0$; therefore,

$$\frac{f(x_0 + \Delta x, y_0) - f(x_0, y_0)}{\Delta x} \le 0$$

Hence, by Theorem 2.10.6, if $f_x(x_0, y_0)$ exists, $f_x(x_0, y_0) \le 0$.
Similarly, if Δx approaches zero from the left, $\Delta x < 0$; so

$$\frac{f(x_0 + \Delta x, y_0) - f(x_0, y_0)}{\Delta x} \ge 0$$

Therefore, by Theorem 2.10.7, if $f_x(x_0, y_0)$ exists, $f_x(x_0, y_0) \geq 0$. We conclude, then, that because $f_x(x_0, y_0)$ exists, both inequalities, $f_x(x_0, y_0) \leq 0$ and $f_x(x_0, y_0) \geq 0$, must hold. Consequently, $f_x(x_0, y_0) = 0$.

The proof that $f_y(x_0, y_0) = 0$ if $f_y(x_0, y_0)$ exists and f has a relative maximum value at (x_0, y_0) is analogous and is left for the reader (see Exercise 13). The proof of the theorem when $f(x_0, y_0)$ is a relative minimum value is also left for the reader (see Exercise 14). ■

17.10.7 Definition   A point (x_0, y_0) for which both $f_x(x_0, y_0) = 0$ and $f_y(x_0, y_0) = 0$ is called a *critical point*.

Theorem 17.10.6 states that a necessary condition for a function of two variables to have a relative extremum at a point, where its first partial derivatives exist, is that this point be a critical point. It is possible for a function of two variables to have a relative extremum at a point at which the partial derivatives do not exist, but we do not consider this situation in this book. Furthermore, the vanishing of the first partial derivatives of a function of two variables is not a sufficient condition for the function to have a relative extremum at the point. Such a situation occurs at a point called a *saddle point*. A simple example of a function which has a saddle point is the one defined by

$$f(x, y) = y^2 - x^2$$

For this function we see that $f_x(x, y) = -2x$ and $f_y(x, y) = 2y$. Both $f_x(0, 0)$ and $f_y(0, 0)$ equal zero. A sketch of the graph of the function is shown in Fig. 17.10.1, and we see that it is saddle shaped at points close to the origin. It is apparent that this function f does not satisfy either Definition 17.10.4 or 17.10.5 when $(x_0, y_0) = (0, 0)$.

We have a second-derivative test which gives conditions that guarantee a function to have a relative extremum at a point where the first partial derivatives vanish. However, sometimes it is possible to determine relative extrema of a function by Definitions 17.10.4 and 17.10.5. This is illustrated in the following example.

Figure 17.10.1

EXAMPLE 1:   Given the function f, defined by

$$f(x, y) = 6x - 4y - x^2 - 2y^2$$

determine if f has any relative extrema.

SOLUTION: Because f and its first partial derivatives exist at all (x, y) in R_2, Theorem 17.10.6 is applicable. Differentiating, we get

$$f_x(x, y) = 6 - 2x \quad \text{and} \quad f_y(x, y) = -4 - 4y$$

Setting $f_x(x, y)$ and $f_y(x, y)$ equal to zero, we get $x = 3$ and $y = -1$. The graph (see Fig. 17.10.2 for a sketch) of the equation

$$z = 6x - 4y - x^2 - 2y^2$$

is a paraboloid having a vertical axis, with vertex at $(3, -1, 11)$ and opening downward. We can conclude that $f(x, y) < f(3, -1)$ for all $(x, y) \neq$

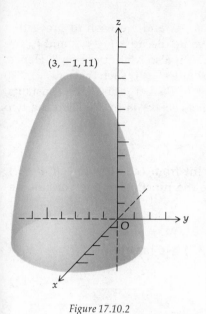

Figure 17.10.2

$(3, -1)$; hence, by Definition 17.10.4, $f(3, -1) = 11$ is a relative maximum function value. It follows from Definition 17.10.1 that 11 is the absolute maximum function value of f on R_2.

The basic test for determining relative maxima and minima for functions of two variables is the second-derivative test, which is given in the next theorem.

17.10.8 Theorem
Second-Derivative Test

Let f be a function of two variables such that f and its first- and second-order partial derivatives are continuous on some open disk $B((a, b); r)$. Suppose further that $f_x(a, b) = f_y(a, b) = 0$. Then

(i) f has a relative minimum value at (a, b) if
$$f_{xx}(a, b)f_{yy}(a, b) - f_{xy}^2(a, b) > 0 \quad \text{and} \quad f_{xx}(a, b) > 0$$

(ii) f has a relative maximum value at (a, b) if
$$f_{xx}(a, b)f_{yy}(a, b) - f_{xy}^2(a, b) > 0 \quad \text{and} \quad f_{xx}(a, b) < 0$$

(iii) $f(a, b)$ is not a relative extremum if
$$f_{xx}(a, b)f_{yy}(a, b) - f_{xy}^2(a, b) < 0$$

(iv) We can make no conclusion if
$$f_{xx}(a, b)f_{yy}(a, b) - f_{xy}^2(a, b) = 0$$

PROOF OF (i):   For simplicity of notation, let us define
$$\phi(x, y) = f_{xx}(x, y)f_{yy}(x, y) - f_{xy}^2(x, y)$$

We are given $\phi(a, b) > 0$ and $f_{xx}(a, b) > 0$, and we wish to prove that $f(a, b)$ is a relative minimum function value. Because f_{xx}, f_{xy}, and f_{yy} are continuous on $B((a, b); r)$, it follows that ϕ is also continuous on B. Hence, there exists an open disk $B'((a, b); r')$, where $r' \leq r$, such that $\phi(x, y) > 0$ and $f_{xx}(x, y) > 0$ for every point (x, y) in B'. Let h and k be constants, not both zero, such that the point $(a + h, b + k)$ is in B'. Then the two equations

$$x = a + ht \quad \text{and} \quad y = b + kt \qquad 0 \leq t \leq 1$$

define all the points on the line segment from (a, b) to $(a + h, b + k)$, and all these points are in B'. Let F be the function of one variable defined by

$$F(t) = f(a + ht, b + kt) \tag{1}$$

By Taylor's formula (formula (9), Sec. 13.5), we have

$$F(t) = F(0) + F'(0)t + \frac{F''(\xi)}{2!} t^2 \tag{2}$$

where ξ is between 0 and t. If $t = 1$ in Eq. (2), we get

$$F(1) = F(0) + F'(0) + \tfrac{1}{2}F''(\xi) \tag{3}$$

where $0 < \xi < 1$. Because $F(0) = f(a, b)$ and $F(1) = f(a + h, b + k)$, it follows from Eq. (3) that

$$f(a + h, b + k) = f(a, b) + F'(0) + \tfrac{1}{2}F''(\xi) \tag{4}$$

where $0 < \xi < 1$.

To find $F'(t)$ and $F''(t)$ from (1), we use the chain rule and obtain

$$F'(t) = hf_x(a + ht, b + kt) + kf_y(a + ht, b + kt) \tag{5}$$

and

$$F''(t) = h^2 f_{xx} + hkf_{yx} + hkf_{xy} + k^2 f_{yy}$$

where each second partial derivative is evaluated at $(a + ht, b + kt)$. From Theorem 17.9.1, it follows that $f_{xy}(x, y) = f_{yx}(x, y)$ for all (x, y) in B'. So

$$F''(t) = h^2 f_{xx} + 2hkf_{xy} + k^2 f_{yy} \tag{6}$$

where each second partial derivative is evaluated at $(a + ht, b + kt)$. Substituting 0 for t in Eq. (5) and ξ for t in Eq. (6), we get

$$F'(0) = hf_x(a, b) + kf_y(a, b) = 0 \tag{7}$$

and

$$F''(\xi) = h^2 f_{xx} + 2hkf_{xy} + k^2 f_{yy} \tag{8}$$

where each second partial derivative is evaluated at $(a + h\xi, b + k\xi)$, where $0 < \xi < 1$. Substituting from (7) and (8) into (4), we obtain

$$f(a + h, b + k) - f(a, b) = \tfrac{1}{2}(h^2 f_{xx} + 2hkf_{xy} + k^2 f_{yy}) \tag{9}$$

The terms in parentheses on the right side of Eq. (9) can be written as

$$h^2 f_{xx} + 2hk f_{xy} + k^2 f_{yy} = f_{xx}\left[h^2 + 2hk\frac{f_{xy}}{f_{xx}} + \left(k\frac{f_{xy}}{f_{xx}}\right)^2 - \left(k\frac{f_{xy}}{f_{xx}}\right)^2 + k^2\frac{f_{yy}}{f_{xx}}\right]$$

So from (9) we have

$$f(a+h, b+k) - f(a, b) = \frac{f_{xx}}{2}\left[\left(h + \frac{f_{xy}}{f_{xx}}k\right)^2 + \frac{f_{xx}f_{yy} - f_{xy}^2}{f_{xx}^2}k^2\right] \quad (10)$$

Because $f_{xx}f_{yy} - f_{xy}^2$ evaluated at $(a + h\xi, b + k\xi)$ equals

$$\phi(a + h\xi, b + k\xi) > 0$$

it follows that the expression in brackets on the right side of Eq. (10) is positive. Furthermore, because $f_{xx}(a + h\xi, b + k\xi) > 0$, it follows from Eq. (10) that $f(a + h, b + k) - f(a, b) > 0$. Hence, we have proved that

$$f(a+h, b+k) > f(a, b)$$

for every point $(a + h, b + k) \neq (a, b)$ in B'. Therefore, by Definition 17.10.5, $f(a, b)$ is a relative minimum value of f.

The proof of part (ii) is similar and is left for the reader (see Exercise 15). The proof of part (iii) is also left for the reader (see Exercise 16). Part (iv) is included to cover all possible cases. ■

EXAMPLE 2:   Given that f is the function defined by

$$f(x, y) = 2x^4 + y^2 - x^2 - 2y$$

determine the relative extrema of f if there are any.

SOLUTION:

$$f_x(x, y) = 8x^3 - 2x \qquad f_y(x, y) = 2y - 2$$

Setting $f_x(x, y) = 0$, we get $x = -\frac{1}{2}$, $x = 0$, and $x = \frac{1}{2}$. Setting $f_y(x, y) = 0$, we get $y = 1$. Therefore, f_x and f_y both vanish at the points $(-\frac{1}{2}, 1)$, $(0, 1)$, and $(\frac{1}{2}, 1)$.

To apply the second-derivative test, we find the second partial derivatives of f and get

$$f_{xx}(x, y) = 24x^2 - 2 \qquad f_{yy}(x, y) = 2 \qquad f_{xy}(x, y) = 0$$

$$f_{xx}(-\tfrac{1}{2}, 1) = 4 > 0$$

and

$$f_{xx}(-\tfrac{1}{2}, 1)f_{yy}(-\tfrac{1}{2}, 1) - f_{xy}^2(-\tfrac{1}{2}, 1) = 4 \cdot 2 - 0 = 8 > 0$$

Hence, by Theorem 17.10.8(i), f has a relative minimum value at $(-\frac{1}{2}, 1)$.

$$f_{xx}(0, 1)f_{yy}(0, 1) - f_{xy}^2(0, 1) = (-2)(2) - 0 = -4 < 0$$

and so by Theorem 17.10.8(iii), f does not have a relative extremum at $(0, 1)$.

$$f_{xx}(\tfrac{1}{2}, 1) = 4 > 0$$

and

$$f_{xx}(\tfrac{1}{2}, 1)f_{yy}(\tfrac{1}{2}, 1) - f_{xy}^2(\tfrac{1}{2}, 1) = 4 \cdot 2 - 0 = 8 > 0$$

Therefore, by Theorem 17.10.8(i) f has a relative minimum value at $(\frac{1}{2}, 1)$. Hence, we conclude that f has a relative minimum value of $-\frac{9}{8}$ at each of the points $(-\frac{1}{2}, 1)$ and $(\frac{1}{2}, 1)$.

EXAMPLE 3:   Determine the relative dimensions of a rectangular box, without a top and having a specific volume, if the least amount of material is to be used in its manufacture.

SOLUTION: Let $x =$ the number of units in the length of the base of the box;

$y =$ the number of units in the width of the base of the box;

$z =$ the number of units in the depth of the box;

$S =$ the number of square units in the surface area of the box;

$V =$ the number of cubic units in the volume of the box (V is constant).

x, y, and z are in the interval $(0, +\infty)$. Hence, the absolute minimum value of S will be among the relative minimum values of S. We have the equations

$$S = xy + 2xz + 2yz \quad \text{and} \quad V = xyz$$

Solving the second equation for z in terms of the variables x and y and the constant V, we get $z = V/xy$. And substituting this into the first equation gives us

$$S = xy + \frac{2V}{y} + \frac{2V}{x}$$

Differentiating, we get

$$\frac{\partial S}{\partial x} = y - \frac{2V}{x^2} \qquad \frac{\partial S}{\partial y} = x - \frac{2V}{y^2}$$

$$\frac{\partial^2 S}{\partial x^2} = \frac{4V}{x^3} \qquad \frac{\partial^2 S}{\partial y \, \partial x} = 1 \qquad \frac{\partial^2 S}{\partial y^2} = \frac{4V}{y^3}$$

Setting $\partial S/\partial x = 0$ and $\partial S/\partial y = 0$, and solving simultaneously, we get

$$x^2 y - 2V = 0$$

$$xy^2 - 2V = 0$$

from which it follows that $x = \sqrt[3]{2V}$, and $y = \sqrt[3]{2V}$. For these values of x and y, we have

$$\frac{\partial^2 S}{\partial x^2} = \frac{4V}{(\sqrt[3]{2V})^3} = \frac{4V}{2V} = 2 > 0$$

and

$$\frac{\partial^2 S}{\partial x^2} \frac{\partial^2 S}{\partial y^2} - \left(\frac{\partial^2 S}{\partial y \, \partial x}\right)^2 = \frac{4V}{(\sqrt[3]{2V})^3} \cdot \frac{4V}{(\sqrt[3]{2V})^3} - 1 = 3 > 0$$

From Theorem 17.10.8(i), it follows that S has a relative minimum value and hence an absolute minimum value when $x = \sqrt[3]{2V}$ and $y = \sqrt[3]{2V}$. From these values of x and y we get

$$z = \frac{V}{xy} = \frac{V}{\sqrt[3]{4V^2}} = \frac{\sqrt[3]{2V}}{2}$$

We therefore conclude that the box should have a square base and a depth which is one-half that of the length of a side of the base.

Our discussion of the extrema of functions of two variables can be extended to functions of three or more variables. The definitions of relative extrema and critical point are easily made. For example, if f is a function of the three variables x, y, and z, and $f_x(x_0, y_0, z_0) = f_y(x_0, y_0, z_0) = f_z(x_0, y_0, z_0) = 0$, then (x_0, y_0, z_0) is a critical point of f. Such a point is obtained by solving simultaneously three equations in three unknowns. For a function of n variables, the critical points are found by setting all the n first partial derivatives equal to zero and solving simultaneously the n equations in n unknowns. The extension of Theorem 17.10.8 to functions of three or more variables is given in advanced calculus texts.

In the solution of Example 3 we minimized the function having function values $xy + 2xz + 2yz$, subject to the condition that x, y, and z satisfy the equation $xyz = V$. Compare this with Example 2, in which we found the relative extrema of the function f for which $f(x, y) = 2x^4 + y^2 - x^2 - 2y$. These are essentially two different kinds of problems because in the first case we had an additional condition, called a *constraint* (or *side condition*). Such a problem is called one in *constrained extrema*, whereas that of the second type is called a problem in *free extrema*.

The solution of Example 3 involved obtaining a function of the two variables x and y by replacing z in the first equation by its value from the second equation. Another method that can be used to solve this example is due to Joseph Lagrange, and it is known as the method of *Lagrange multipliers*. The theory behind this method involves theorems known as implicit function theorems, which are studied in advanced calculus. Hence, a proof is not given here. The procedure is outlined and illustrated by examples.

Suppose that we wish to find the critical points of a function f of the three variables x, y, and z, subject to the constraint $g(x, y, z) = 0$. We introduce a new variable, usually denoted by λ, and form the auxiliary function F for which

$$F(x, y, z, \lambda) = f(x, y, z) + \lambda g(x, y, z)$$

The problem then becomes one of finding the critical points of the function F of the four variables x, y, z, and λ. The method is used in the following example.

EXAMPLE 4: Solve Example 3 by the method of Lagrange multipliers.

SOLUTION: Using the variables x, y, and z and the constant V as defined in the solution of Example 3, let

$$S = f(x, y, z) = xy + 2xz + 2yz$$

and

$$g(x, y, z) = xyz - V$$

We wish to minimize the function f subject to the constraint that

$$g(x, y, z) = 0$$

Let

$$F(x, y, z, \lambda) = f(x, y, z) + \lambda g(x, y, z)$$
$$= xy + 2xz + 2yz + \lambda(xyz - V)$$

Finding the four partial derivatives F_x, F_y, F_z, and F_λ and setting the function values equal to zero, we have

$$F_x(x, y, z, \lambda) = y + 2z + \lambda yz = 0 \qquad (11)$$

$$F_y(x, y, z, \lambda) = x + 2z + \lambda xz = 0 \qquad (12)$$

$$F_z(x, y, z, \lambda) = 2x + 2y + \lambda xy = 0 \qquad (13)$$

$$F_\lambda(x, y, z, \lambda) = xyz - V = 0 \qquad (14)$$

Subtracting corresponding members of Eq. (12) from those of Eq. (11) we obtain

$$y - x + \lambda z(y - x) = 0$$

from which we get

$$(y - x)(1 + \lambda z) = 0$$

giving us the two equations

$$y = x \qquad (15)$$

and

$$\lambda = -\frac{1}{z} \qquad (16)$$

Substituting from Eq. (16) into Eq. (12) we get $x + 2z - x = 0$, giving $z = 0$, which is impossible because z is in the interval $(0, +\infty)$. Substituting from Eq. (15) into Eq. (13) gives

$$2x + 2x + \lambda x^2 = 0$$

$$x(4 + \lambda x) = 0$$

and because $x \neq 0$, we get

$$\lambda = -\frac{4}{x}$$

If in Eq. (12) we take $\lambda = -4/x$, we have

$$x + 2z - \frac{4}{x}(xz) = 0$$

$$x + 2z - 4z = 0$$

$$z = \frac{x}{2} \tag{17}$$

Substituting from Eqs. (15) and (17) into Eq. (14), we get $\frac{1}{2}x^3 - V = 0$, from which it follows that $x = \sqrt[3]{2V}$. From Eqs. (15) and (17) it follows that $y = \sqrt[3]{2V}$ and $z = \frac{1}{2}\sqrt[3]{2V}$. These results agree with those found in the solution of Example 3.

Note in the solution that the equation $F_\lambda(x, y, z, \lambda) = 0$ is the same as the constraint given by the equation $V = xyz$.

If several constraints are imposed, the method used in Example 4 can be extended by using several multipliers. In particular, if we wish to find critical points of the function having function values $f(x, y, z)$ subject to the two side conditions $g(x, y, z) = 0$ and $h(x, y, z) = 0$, we find the critical points of the function F of the five variables x, y, z, λ, and μ for which

$$F(x, y, z, \lambda, \mu) = f(x, y, z) + \lambda g(x, y, z) + \mu h(x, y, z)$$

The following example illustrates the method.

EXAMPLE 5: Find the relative extrema of the function f if $f(x, y, z) = xz + yz$ and the point (x, y, z) lies on the intersection of the surfaces $x^2 + z^2 = 2$ and $yz = 2$.

SOLUTION: We form the function F for which

$$F(x, y, z, \lambda, \mu) = xz + yz + \lambda(x^2 + z^2 - 2) + \mu(yz - 2)$$

Finding the five partial derivatives and setting them equal to zero, we have

$$F_x(x, y, z, \lambda, \mu) = z + 2\lambda x = 0 \tag{18}$$

$$F_y(x, y, z, \lambda, \mu) = z + \mu z = 0 \tag{19}$$

$$F_z(x, y, z, \lambda, \mu) = x + y + 2\lambda z + \mu y = 0 \tag{20}$$

$$F_\lambda(x, y, z, \lambda, \mu) = x^2 + z^2 - 2 = 0 \tag{21}$$

$$F_\mu(x, y, z, \lambda, \mu) = yz - 2 = 0 \tag{22}$$

From Eq. (19) we obtain $\mu = -1$ and $z = 0$. We reject $z = 0$ because this contradicts Eq. (22). From Eq. (18) we obtain

$$\lambda = -\frac{z}{2x} \tag{23}$$

Substituting from (23) and $\mu = -1$ into Eq. (20), we get

$$x + y - \frac{z^2}{x} - y = 0$$

and so

$$x^2 = z^2 \tag{24}$$

Substituting from Eq. (24) into (21), we have $2x^2 - 2 = 0$, or $x^2 = 1$. This gives two values for x, namely 1 and -1; and for each of these values of x we get, from Eq. (24), the two values 1 and -1 for z. Obtaining the corresponding values for y from Eq. (22), we have four sets of solutions for the five Eqs. (18) through (22). These solutions are

$$
\begin{array}{llllll}
x = & 1 & y = & 2 & z = & 1 & \lambda = -\tfrac{1}{2} & \mu = -1 \\
x = & 1 & y = -2 & z = -1 & \lambda = \tfrac{1}{2} & \mu = -1 \\
x = -1 & y = & 2 & z = & 1 & \lambda = \tfrac{1}{2} & \mu = -1 \\
x = -1 & y = -2 & z = -1 & \lambda = -\tfrac{1}{2} & \mu = -1
\end{array}
$$

The first and fourth sets of solutions give $f(x, y, z) = 3$, and the second and third sets of solutions give $f(x, y, z) = 1$. Hence, f has a relative maximum function value of 3 and a relative minimum function value of 1.

Exercises 17.10

In Exercises 1 through 6, determine the relative extrema of f, if there are any.

1. $f(x, y) = 18x^2 - 32y^2 - 36x - 128y - 110$

2. $f(x, y) = \dfrac{1}{x} - \dfrac{64}{y} + xy$

3. $f(x, y) = \sin(x + y) + \sin x + \sin y$

4. $f(x, y) = x^3 + y^3 - 18xy$

5. $f(x, y) = 4xy^2 - 2x^2y - x$

6. $f(x, y) = \dfrac{2x + 2y + 1}{x^2 + y^2 + 1}$

In Exercises 7 through 12 use the method of Lagrange multipliers to find the critical points of the given function subject to the indicated constraint.

7. $f(x, y) = x^2 + 2xy + y^2$ with constraint $x - y = 3$

8. $f(x, y) = x^2 + xy + 2y^2 - 2x$ with constraint $x - 2y + 1 = 0$

9. $f(x, y) = 25 - x^2 - y^2$ with constraint $x^2 + y^2 - 4y = 0$

10. $f(x, y) = 4x^2 + 2y^2 + 5$ with constraint $x^2 + y^2 - 2y = 0$

11. $f(x, y, z) = x^2 + y^2 + z^2$ with constraint $3x - 2y + z - 4 = 0$

12. $f(x, y, z) = x^2 + y^2 + z^2$ with constraint $y^2 - x^2 = 1$

13. Prove that $f_y(x_0, y_0) = 0$ if $f_y(x_0, y_0)$ exists and f has a relative maximum value at (x_0, y_0).

14. Prove Theorem 17.10.6 when $f(x_0, y_0)$ is a relative minimum value.

15. Prove Theorem 17.10.8(ii).　　　　16. Prove Theorem 17.10.8(iii).

17. Find three numbers whose sum is N ($N > 0$) such that their product is as great as possible.

18. Prove that the box having the largest volume that can be placed inside a sphere is in the shape of a cube.

19. Determine the relative dimensions of a rectangular box, without a top, to be made from a given amount of material in order for the box to have the greatest possible volume.

20. A clothing store sells two kinds of overcoats which are similar but are made by different manufacturers. The cost to the store of the first kind is $40, and the cost of the second kind is $50. It has been determined by experience that if the selling price of the first kind is x dollars and the selling price of the second kind is y dollars, then the total monthly sales of the first kind is $(3200 - 50x + 25y)$ overcoats and the total monthly sales of the second kind is $(25x - 25y)$ overcoats. What should be the selling price of each kind of overcoat for the greatest profit?

21. A circular disk is in the shape of the region bounded by the circle $x^2 + y^2 = 1$. If T degrees is the temperature at any point (x, y) of the disk and $T = 2x^2 + y^2 - y$, find the hottest and coldest points on the disk.

22. Find the points on the surface $y^2 - xz = 4$ that are closest to the origin and find the minimum distance.

23. Find the points on the curve of intersection of the ellipsoid $x^2 + 4y^2 + 4z^2 = 4$ and the plane $x - 4y - z = 0$ that are closest to the origin and find the minimum distance.

24. A rectangular box without a top is to be made at a cost of $10 for the material. If the material for the bottom of the box costs 15¢ per square foot and the material for the sides costs 30¢ per square foot, find the dimensions of the box of greatest volume that can be made.

25. A closed rectangular box to contain 16 ft³ is to be made of three kinds of material. The cost of the material for the top and the bottom is 9¢ per ft², the cost of the material for the front and the back is 8¢ per ft², and the cost of the material for the other two sides is 6¢ per ft². Find the dimensions of the box so that the cost of the materials is a minimum.

26. Suppose that T degrees is the temperature at any point (x, y, z) on the sphere $x^2 + y^2 + z^2 = 4$, and $T = 100xy^2z$. Find the points on the sphere where the temperature is the greatest and also the points where the temperature is the least. Also find the temperature at these points.

27. Find the absolute maximum function value of f if $f(x, y, z) = x^2 + y^2 + z^2$ with the two constraints $x - y + z = 0$ and $25x^2 + 4y^2 + 20z^2 = 100$. Use Lagrange multipliers.

28. Find the absolute minimum function value of f if $f(x, y, z) = x^2 + 3y^2 + 2z^2$ with the two constraints $x - 2y - z = 6$ and $x - 3y + 2z = 4$. Use Lagrange multipliers.

17.11 SOME APPLICATIONS OF PARTIAL DERIVATIVES TO ECONOMICS

In Sec. 4.12 we discussed a demand equation giving the relationship between x and p, where p dollars is the price of one unit of a commodity when x units are demanded. In addition to the price of the given commodity, the demand often will depend on the prices of other commodities related to the given one. In particular, let us consider two related commodities for which p dollars is the price per unit of x units of the first commodity and q dollars is the price per unit of y units of the second commodity. Then the demand equations for these two commodities can be written, respectively, as

$$\alpha(x, p, q) = 0 \quad \text{and} \quad \beta(y, p, q) = 0$$

or, solving the first equation for x and the second equation for y, as

$$x = f(p, q) \tag{1}$$

and

$$y = g(p, q) \tag{2}$$

Figure 17.11.1

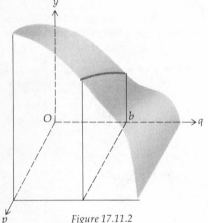

Figure 17.11.2

The functions f and g in Eqs. (1) and (2) are the demand functions and the graphs of these functions are surfaces. Under normal circumstances x, y, p, and q are nonnegative, and so the surfaces are restricted to the first octant. These surfaces are called *demand surfaces*. Recalling that p dollars is the price of one unit of x units of the first commodity, we note that if the variable q is held constant, then x decreases as p increases and x increases as p decreases. This is illustrated in Fig. 17.11.1, which is a sketch of the demand surface for an equation of type (1) under normal circumstances. The plane $q = b$ intersects the surface in section RST. For any point on the curve RT, q is the constant b. Referring to the points $M(p_1, b, x_1)$ and $N(p_2, b, x_2)$, we see that $x_2 > x_1$ if and only if $p_2 < p_1$; that is, x decreases as p increases and x increases as p decreases.

When q is constant, therefore, as p increases, x decreases; but y may either increase or decrease. If y increases, then a decrease in the demand for one commodity corresponds to an increase in the demand for the other, and the two commodities are said to be *substitutes* (for example, butter and margarine). Now if, when q is constant, y decreases as p increases, then a decrease in the demand for one commodity corresponds to a decrease in the demand for the other, and the two commodities are said to be *complementary* (for example, tires and gasoline). Figures 17.11.2 and 17.11.3 each show a sketch of a demand surface for an equation of type (2). In Fig. 17.11.2, we see that when q is constant, y increases as p increases, and so the two commodities are substitutes. In Fig. 17.11.3 the two commodities are complementary because when q is constant, y decreases as p increases. Note that in Figs. 17.11.1 and 17.11 2, which show the demand surfaces for equations of types (1) and (2), respectively, the p and q axes are interchanged and that the vertical axis in Fig. 17.11.1 is labeled x and in Fig. 17.11.2 it is labeled y.

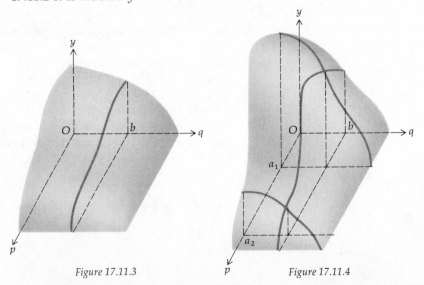

Figure 17.11.3

Figure 17.11.4

It is possible that for a fixed value of q, y may increase for some values of p and decrease for other values of p. For example, if the demand surface of Eq. (2) is that shown in Fig. 17.11.4, then for $q = b$, when $p = a_1$, y is increasing, and when $p = a_2$, y is decreasing. This of course means that if the price of the second commodity is held constant, then for some prices of the first commodity the two commodities will be substitutes and for other prices of the first commodity the two commodities will be complementary. These relationships between the two commodities that are determined by the demand surface having equation $y = g(p, q)$ will correspond to similar relationships determined by the demand surface having equation $x = f(p, q)$ for the same fixed values of p and q. An economic example might be one in which investors allocate funds between the stock market and real estate. As stock prices climb, they invest in real estate. Yet once stock prices seem to reach a crash level, investors begin to decrease the amount of real estate purchases with any increase in stock prices in anticipation of a collapse that will affect the real estate market and its values.

The demand functions are now used to define the (partial) *marginal demand*.

17.11.1 Definition Let p dollars be the price of one unit of x units of a first commodity and q dollars be the price of one unit of y units of a second commodity. Suppose that f and g are the respective demand functions for these two commodities so that

$$x = f(p, q) \quad \text{and} \quad y = g(p, q)$$

Then

(i) $\dfrac{\partial x}{\partial p}$ gives the (partial) *marginal demand of x with respect to p*;

(ii) $\dfrac{\partial x}{\partial q}$ gives the (partial) *marginal demand of x with respect to q*;

(iii) $\dfrac{\partial y}{\partial p}$ gives the (partial) *marginal demand of y with respect to p*;

(iv) $\dfrac{\partial y}{\partial q}$ gives the (partial) *marginal demand of y with respect to q*.

Because in normal circumstances if the variable q is held constant, x decreases as p increases and x increases as p decreases, we conclude that $\partial x/\partial p$ is negative. Similarly, $\partial y/\partial q$ is negative in normal circumstances. Two commodities are said to be complementary when a decrease in the demand for one commodity as a result of an increase in its price leads to a decrease in the demand for the other. So when the goods are complementary and q is held constant, both $\partial x/\partial p < 0$ and $\partial y/\partial p < 0$; and when p is held constant, then $\partial x/\partial q < 0$ as well as $\partial y/\partial q < 0$. Therefore, we can conclude that the two commodities are complementary if and only if both $\partial x/\partial q$ and $\partial y/\partial p$ are negative.

When a decrease in the demand for one commodity as a result of an increase in its price leads to an increase in the demand for the other commodity, the goods are substitutes. Hence, when the goods are substitutes, because $\partial x/\partial p$ is always negative, we conclude that $\partial y/\partial p$ is positive; and because $\partial y/\partial q$ is always negative, it follows that $\partial x/\partial q$ is positive. Consequently, the two commodities are substitutes if and only if $\partial x/\partial q$ and $\partial y/\partial p$ are both positive.

If $\partial x/\partial q$ and $\partial y/\partial p$ have opposite signs, the commodities are neither complementary nor substitutes. For example, if $\partial x/\partial q < 0$ and $\partial y/\partial p > 0$, and because $\partial x/\partial p$ and $\partial y/\partial q$ are always negative (in normal circumstances), we have both $\partial x/\partial q < 0$ and $\partial y/\partial q < 0$. Thus, a decrease in the price of the second commodity causes an increase in the demands of both commodities. Because $\partial x/\partial p < 0$ and $\partial y/\partial p > 0$, a decrease in the price of the first commodity causes an increase in the demand of the first commodity and a decrease in the demand of the second commodity.

EXAMPLE 1: Suppose that p dollars is the price per unit of x units of one commodity and q dollars is the price per unit of y units of a second commodity. The demand equations are

$$x = -2p + 3q + 12 \qquad (3)$$

and

$$y = -4q + p + 8 \qquad (4)$$

Find the four marginal demands and determine if the commodities are substitutes or complementary. Also draw sketches of the two demand surfaces.

SOLUTION: If we use Definition 17.11.1, the four marginal demands are given by

$$\frac{\partial x}{\partial p} = -2 \qquad \frac{\partial x}{\partial q} = 3 \qquad \frac{\partial y}{\partial p} = 1 \qquad \frac{\partial y}{\partial q} = -4$$

Because $\partial x/\partial q > 0$ and $\partial y/\partial p > 0$, the two commodities are substitutes.

A sketch of the demand surface of Eq. (3) is shown in Fig. 17.11.5. To draw this sketch we first determine from both equations the permissible values of p and q. Because x and y must be positive or zero, p and q must satisfy the inequalities $-2p + 3q + 12 \geq 0$ and $-4q + p + 8 \geq 0$. Also, p and q are each nonnegative. Hence, the values of p and q are restricted to the quadrilateral $AOBC$. The required demand surface then is the portion in the first octant of the plane defined by Eq. (3) which is above $AOBC$. This

Figure 17.11.5

Figure 17.11.6

is the shaded quadrilateral *ADEC* in the figure. In Fig. 17.11.6 we have a sketch of the demand surface defined by Eq. (4). This demand surface is the shaded quadrilateral *BFGC*, that is, the portion in the first octant of the plane defined by Eq. (4) which is above the quadrilateral *AOBC*.

For nonlinear demand functions of two variables, it is often more convenient to represent them geometrically by means of contour maps than by surfaces. The following example is such a case.

EXAMPLE 2: If *p* dollars is the price of one unit of *x* units of a first commodity and *q* dollars is the price of one unit of *y* units of a second commodity, and the demand equations are given by

$$x = \frac{8}{pq} \quad \text{and} \quad y = \frac{12}{pq}$$

draw sketches of the contour maps of the two demand functions showing the level curves of each function at 6, 4, 2, 1, and $\frac{1}{2}$. Are the commodities substitutes or complementary?

SOLUTION: Let the two demand functions be *f* and *g* so that $x = f(p, q) = 8/pq$ and $y = g(p, q) = 12/pq$. Sketches of the contour maps of *f* and *g* showing the level curves of these functions at the required numbers are shown in Figs. 17.11.7 and 17.11.8, respectively.

$$\frac{\partial x}{\partial q} = -\frac{8}{pq^2} \quad \text{and} \quad \frac{\partial y}{\partial p} = -\frac{12}{p^2q}$$

Because $\partial x/\partial q < 0$ and $\partial y/\partial p < 0$, the commodities are complementary.

Figure 17.11.7   Figure 17.11.8

EXAMPLE 3:   The demand equations for two related commodities are

$$x = 4e^{-pq} \quad \text{and} \quad y = 8e^{p-q}$$

Determine if the commodities are complementary, substitutes, or neither.

SOLUTION:

$$\frac{\partial x}{\partial q} = -4pe^{-pq} \quad \text{and} \quad \frac{\partial y}{\partial p} = 8e^{p-q}$$

Because $\partial x/\partial q < 0$ and $\partial y/\partial p > 0$, the commodities are neither complementary nor substitutes.

If the cost of producing *x* units of one commodity and *y* units of another commodity is given by $C(x, y)$, then *C* is called a *joint-cost function*. The partial derivatives of *C* are called *marginal cost functions*.

Suppose that a monopolist produces two related commodities whose demand equations are $x = f(p, q)$ and $y = g(p, q)$ and the joint-cost function is C. Because the revenue from the two commodities is given by $px + qy$, then if S is the number of dollars in the profit, we have

$$S = px + qy - C(x, y)$$

To determine the greatest profit that can be earned, we use the demand equations to express S in terms of either p and q or x and y alone and then apply the methods of the preceding section. The following example illustrates the procedure.

EXAMPLE 4: A monopolist produces two commodities which are substitutes having demand equations

$$x = 8 - p + q$$

and

$$y = 9 + p - 5q$$

where $1000x$ units of the first commodity are demanded if the price is p dollars per unit and $1000y$ units of the second commodity are demanded if the price is q dollars per unit. It costs \$4 to produce each unit of the first commodity and \$2 to produce each unit of the second commodity. Find the demands and prices of the two commodities in order to have the greatest profit.

SOLUTION: When $1000x$ units of the first commodity and $1000y$ units of the second commodity are produced and sold, the number of dollars in the total revenue is $1000px + 1000qy$, and the number of dollars in the total cost of production is $4000x + 2000y$. Hence, if S dollars is the profit, we have

$$S = 1000px + 1000qy - (4000x + 2000y)$$
$$S = 1000p(8 - p + q) + 1000q(9 + p - 5q)$$
$$\qquad\qquad - 4000(8 - p + q) - 2000(9 + p - 5q)$$
$$S = 1000(-p^2 + 2pq - 5q^2 + 10p + 15q - 50)$$

$$\frac{\partial S}{\partial p} = 1000(-2p + 2q + 10) \qquad \frac{\partial S}{\partial q} = 1000(2p - 10q + 15)$$

Setting $\partial S/\partial p = 0$ and $\partial S/\partial q = 0$, we have

$$-2p + 2q + 10 = 0 \quad \text{and} \quad 2p - 10q + 15 = 0$$

from which it follows that

$$p = \tfrac{65}{8} \quad \text{and} \quad q = \tfrac{25}{8}$$

Hence, $\left(\tfrac{65}{8}, \tfrac{25}{8}\right)$ is a critical point. Because

$$\frac{\partial^2 S}{\partial p^2} = -2000 \qquad \frac{\partial^2 S}{\partial q^2} = -10{,}000 \qquad \frac{\partial^2 S}{\partial q\, \partial p} = 2000$$

we have

$$\frac{\partial^2 S}{\partial p^2} \frac{\partial^2 S}{\partial q^2} - \left(\frac{\partial^2 S}{\partial q\, \partial p}\right)^2 = (-2000)(-10{,}000) - (2000)^2 > 0$$

Also, $\partial^2 S/\partial p^2 < 0$, and so from Theorem 17.10.8(ii) we conclude that S has a relative maximum value at $\left(\tfrac{65}{8}, \tfrac{25}{8}\right)$.

Because x, y, p, and q must be nonnegative, we know that

$$8 - p + q \geq 0 \qquad 9 + p - 5q \geq 0 \qquad p \geq 0 \qquad q \geq 0$$

From these inequalities we determine that the region of permissible values is that shaded in Fig. 17.11.9. It follows that S has an absolute maximum value at the point $\left(\tfrac{65}{8}, \tfrac{25}{8}\right)$, and the absolute maximum value of S is

Figure 17.11.9

14,062.5. From the demand equations we find that when $p = \frac{65}{8}$ and $q = \frac{25}{8}$, $x = 3$ and $y = \frac{3}{2}$.

We therefore conclude that the greatest profit of \$14,062.50 is attained when 3000 units of the first commodity are produced and sold at \$8.12$\frac{1}{2}$ per unit and 1500 units of the second commodity are produced and sold at \$3.12$\frac{1}{2}$ per unit.

Figure 17.11.10

In the preceding example, if the demand equations are solved for p and q in terms of x and y, we obtain

$$p = \tfrac{1}{4}(49 - 5x - y) \quad \text{and} \quad q = \tfrac{1}{4}(17 - x - y)$$

Because q and p must be nonnegative as well as x and y, we know that $17 - x - y \geq 0, 49 - 5x - y \geq 0, x \geq 0$, and $y \geq 0$. From these four inequalities we determine that the region of permissible values is that shaded in Fig. 17.11.10. The problem can be solved by considering x and y as the independent variables. You are asked to do this in Exercise 12.

Suppose that in the production of a certain commodity, x is the number of machines, y is the number of man-hours, and z is the number of units of the commodity produced, where z depends on x and y, and $z = f(x, y)$. Such a function f is called a *production function*. Other factors of production may be working capital, materials, and land.

Let us now consider, in general, a commodity involving two factors of production; that is, we have a production function f of two variables. If the amounts of the inputs are given by x and y, and z gives the amount of the output, then $z = f(x, y)$. Suppose that the prices of the two inputs are a dollars and b dollars per unit, respectively, and that the price of the output is c dollars (a, b, and c are constants). This situation could occur if there were so many producers in the market that a change in the output of any particular producer would not affect the price of the commodity. Such a market is called a *perfectly competitive market*. Now if P dollars is the total profit, and because the total profit is obtained by subtracting the total cost from the total revenue, we have

$$P = cz - (ax + by)$$

and because $z = f(x, y)$,

$$P = cf(x, y) - ax - by$$

It is, of course, desired to maximize P. This is illustrated by an example.

EXAMPLE 5: Suppose that the production of a certain commodity depends on two inputs. The

SOLUTION: If P dollars is the profit,

$$P = 9(100z) - 4(100x) - 100y \tag{5}$$

y, 50, 25, $5x + y = 49$, $(8, 9)$, $x + y = 17$, O, x

amounts of these are given by $100x$ and $100y$, whose prices per unit are, respectively, $4 and $1. The amount of the output is given by $100z$, the price per unit of which is $9. Furthermore, the production function f has the function values $f(x, y) = 5 - 1/x - 1/y$. Determine the greatest profit.

Letting $z = f(x, y)$, we get

$$P = 900 \left(5 - \frac{1}{x} - \frac{1}{y} \right) - 400x - 100y$$

x and y are both in the interval $(0, +\infty)$. Hence,

$$\frac{\partial P}{\partial x} = \frac{900}{x^2} - 400 \quad \text{and} \quad \frac{\partial P}{\partial y} = \frac{900}{y^2} - 100$$

Also,

$$\frac{\partial^2 P}{\partial x^2} = -\frac{1800}{x^3} \qquad \frac{\partial^2 P}{\partial y^2} = -\frac{1800}{y^3} \qquad \frac{\partial^2 P}{\partial y \, \partial x} = 0$$

Setting $\partial P/\partial x = 0$ and $\partial P/\partial y = 0$, we have

$$\frac{900}{x^2} - 400 = 0 \quad \text{and} \quad \frac{900}{y^2} - 100 = 0$$

from which we obtain $x = \frac{3}{2}$ and $y = 3$ (we reject the negative result because x and y must be positive). At $(\frac{3}{2}, 3)$

$$\frac{\partial^2 P}{\partial x^2} \cdot \frac{\partial^2 P}{\partial y^2} - \left(\frac{\partial^2 P}{\partial y \, \partial x} \right)^2 = -\left(\frac{1800}{\frac{27}{8}} \right) \cdot \left(-\frac{1800}{27} \right) - (0)^2 > 0$$

From the above and the fact that at $(\frac{3}{2}, 3)$ $\partial^2 P/\partial x^2 < 0$, it follows from Theorem 17.10.8(ii) that P has a relative maximum value at $(\frac{3}{2}, 3)$. Because x and y are both in the interval $(0, +\infty)$, and P is a negative number when x and y are either close to zero or very large, we conclude that the relative maximum value of P is an absolute maximum value. Because $z = f(x, y)$, the value of z at $(\frac{3}{2}, 3)$ is $f(\frac{3}{2}, 3) = 5 - \frac{2}{3} - \frac{1}{3} = 4$. Hence, from Eq. (5)

$$P_{\max} = 900 \cdot 4 - 400 \cdot \frac{3}{2} - 100 \cdot 3 = 2700$$

The greatest profit then is $2700.

EXAMPLE 6: Solve Example 5 by the method of Lagrange multipliers.

SOLUTION: We wish to maximize the function P defined by Eq. (5) subject to the constraint given by the equation $z = 5 - 1/x - 1/y$, which we can write as

$$g(x, y, z) = \frac{1}{x} + \frac{1}{y} + z - 5 = 0 \tag{6}$$

Let

$$F(x, y, z, \lambda) = P(x, y, z) + \lambda g(x, y, z)$$

$$= 900z - 400x - 100y + \lambda \left(\frac{1}{x} + \frac{1}{y} + z - 5 \right)$$

We find the four partial derivatives F_x, F_y, F_z, and F_λ and set them equal to zero.

$$F_x(x, y, z, \lambda) = -400 - \frac{\lambda}{x^2} = 0 \qquad F_y(x, y, z, \lambda) = -100 - \frac{\lambda}{y^2} = 0$$

$$F_z(x, y, z, \lambda) = 900 + \lambda = 0 \qquad F_\lambda(x, y, z, \lambda) = \frac{1}{x} + \frac{1}{y} + z - 5 = 0$$

Solving these equations simultaneously, we obtain

$$\lambda = -900 \qquad x = \tfrac{3}{2} \qquad y = 3 \qquad z = 4$$

The values of x, y, and z agree with those found previously, and P is shown to have an absolute maximum value in the same way as before.

In some applications of functions of several variables to problems in economics, the Lagrange multiplier λ is related to marginal concepts, in particular marginal cost and marginal utility of money (for details of this you should consult references in mathematical economics).

Exercises 17.11

In Exercises 1 through 9, demand equations for two related commodities are given. In each exercise, determine the four partial marginal demands. Determine if the commodities are complementary, substitutes, or neither. In Exercises 1 through 6 draw sketches of the two demand surfaces.

1. $x = 14 - p - 2q$, $y = 17 - 2p - q$

2. $x = 5 - 2p + q$, $y = 6 + p - q$

3. $x = -3p + 5q + 15$, $y = 2p - 4q + 10$

4. $x = 9 - 3p + q$, $y = 10 - 2p - 5q$

5. $x = 6 - 3p - 2q$, $y = 2 + p - 2q$

6. $x = -p - 3q + 6$, $y = -2q - p + 8$

7. $x = p^{-0.4}q^{0.5}$, $y = p^{0.4}q^{-1.5}$

8. $pqx = 4$, $p^2qy = 16$

9. $px = q$, $qy = p^2$

10. From the demand equations of Exercise 8, find the two demand functions and draw sketches of the contour maps of these functions showing the level curves of each function at 5, 4, 3, 2, 1, $\tfrac{1}{2}$, $\tfrac{1}{4}$.

11. Follow the instructions of Exercise 10 for the demand equations of Exercise 9.

12. Solve Example 4 of this section by considering x and y as the independent variables.

13. The demand equations for two commodities that are produced by a monopolist are

$$x = 6 - 2p + q \quad \text{and} \quad y = 7 + p - q$$

where $100x$ is the quantity of the first commodity demanded if the price is p dollars per unit and $100y$ is the quantity of the second commodity demanded if the price is q dollars per unit. Show that the two commodities are substitutes. If it costs \$2 to produce each unit of the first commodity and \$3 to produce each unit of the second commodity, find the quantities demanded and the prices of the two commodities in order to have the greatest profit. Take p and q as the independent variables.

14. A monopolist produces two commodities, and their demand equations are

$$x = 16 - 3p - 2q \quad \text{and} \quad y = 11 - 2p - 2q$$

where x, y, p, and q are defined as in Exercise 13. Show that the two commodities are complementary. If the cost of production of each unit of the first commodity is $1 and the cost of production of each unit of the second commodity is $3, find the quantities demanded and the price of each commodity in order to have the greatest profit.

15. Solve Exercise 13 by considering x and y as the independent variables.

16. The production function f for a certain commodity has function values

$$f(x, y) = 4 - \frac{8}{xy}$$

The amounts of the two inputs are given by $100x$ and $100y$, whose prices per unit are, respectively, $10 and $5, and the amount of the output is given by $100z$, whose price per unit is $20. Determine the greatest profit by two methods: (a) without using Lagrange multipliers; (b) using Lagrange multipliers.

17. Solve Exercise 16 if

$$f(x, y) = x + \tfrac{3}{2}y - \tfrac{1}{8}x^2 - \tfrac{1}{4}y^2 - \tfrac{9}{8}$$

the prices per unit of the two inputs are $4 and $8 (instead of $10 and $5, respectively), and the price per unit of the output is $16.

Review Exercises (Chapter 17)

In Exercises 1 through 6, find the indicated partial derivatives.

1. $f(x, y) = \dfrac{x^2 - y}{3y^2}$; $D_1 f(x, y)$, $D_2 f(x, y)$, $D_{12} f(x, y)$

2. $F(x, y, z) = 2xy^2 + 3yz^2 - 5xz^3$; $D_1 f(x, y, z)$, $D_3 f(x, y, z)$, $D_{13} f(x, y, z)$

3. $g(s, t) = \sin(st^2) + te^s$; $D_1 g(s, t)$, $D_2 g(s, t)$, $D_{21} g(s, t)$

4. $h(x, y) = \tan^{-1} \dfrac{x^3}{y^2}$; $D_1 h(x, y)$, $D_2 h(x, y)$, $D_{11} h(x, y)$

5. $f(u, v, w) = \dfrac{\ln 4uv}{w^2}$; $D_1 f(u, v, w)$, $D_{13} f(u, v, w)$, $D_{131} f(u, v, w)$

6. $f(u, v, w) = w \cos 2v + 3v \sin u - 2uv \tan w$; $D_2 f(u, v, w)$, $D_1 f(u, v, w)$, $D_{131} f(u, v, w)$

In Exercises 7 and 8 find $\partial u/\partial t$ and $\partial u/\partial s$ by two methods.

7. $u = y \ln(x^2 + y^2)$, $x = 2s + 3t$, $y = 3t - 2s$

8. $u = e^{2x+y} \cos(2y - x)$, $x = 2s^2 - t^2$, $y = s^2 + 2t^2$

9. If $u = xy + x^2$, $x = 4 \cos t$, and $y = 3 \sin t$, find the value of the total derivative du/dt at $t = \tfrac{1}{4}\pi$ by two methods: (a) Do not express u in terms of t before differentiating; (b) express u in terms of t before differentiating.

10. If $f(x, y, z) = 3xy^2 - 5xz^2 - 2xyz$, $\Delta x = 0.02$, $\Delta y = -0.01$, and $\Delta z = -0.02$, find (a) the increment of f at $(-1, 3, 2)$ and (b) the total differential of f at $(-1, 3, 2)$.

11. Find the gradient of f at $(-1, 3, 2)$ for the function of Exercise 10.

12. If $f(x, y, z) = \sinh(x + z) \cosh y$, find the rate of change of $f(x, y, z)$ with respect to distance in R_3 at the point $P(1, 1, 0)$ in the direction $\overrightarrow{PQ}$ if Q is the point $(-1, 0, 2)$.

In Exercises 13 through 16, find the domain and range of the function f and draw a sketch showing as a shaded region in R_2 the set of points in the domain of f.

13. $f(x, y) = \sqrt{4x^2 - y}$

14. $f(x, y) = \sin^{-1}\sqrt{1 - x^2 - y^2}$

15. $f(x, y) = \tan^{-1}\sqrt{x^2 - y^2}$

16. $f(x, y) = [\![x]\!] + [\![\sqrt{1 - y^2}]\!]$

In Exercises 17 through 19, find the domain and range of the function f.

17. $f(x, y, z) = \dfrac{xy}{\sqrt{z}}$

18. $f(x, y, z) = \dfrac{xy + xz + yz}{xyz}$

19. $f(x, y, z) = \dfrac{x}{|y| - |z|}$

In Exercises 20 through 22, establish the limit by finding a $\delta > 0$ for any $\epsilon > 0$ so that Definition 17.2.5 holds.

20. $\lim\limits_{(x,y)\to(4,-1)} (4x - 5y) = 21$

21. $\lim\limits_{(x,y)\to(2,-2)} (3x^2 - 4y^2) = -4$

22. $\lim\limits_{(x,y)\to(3,1)} (x^2 - y^2 + 2x - 4y) = 10$

In Exercises 23 and 24, determine if the indicated limit exists.

23. $\lim\limits_{(x,y)\to(0,0)} \dfrac{x^3 y^3}{x^2 + y^2}$

24. $\lim\limits_{(x,y)\to(0,0)} \dfrac{x^4 - y^4}{x^4 + y^4}$

In Exercises 25 through 29, discuss the continuity of f.

25. $f(x, y) = \begin{cases} \dfrac{x^3 y^3}{x^2 + y^2} & \text{if } (x, y) \neq (0, 0) \\ 0 & \text{if } (x, y) = (0, 0) \end{cases}$ (HINT: See Exercise 23.)

26. $f(x, y) = \begin{cases} \dfrac{x^4 - y^4}{x^4 + y^4} & \text{if } (x, y) \neq (0, 0) \\ 0 & \text{if } (x, y) = (0, 0) \end{cases}$ (HINT: See Exercise 24.)

27. $f(x, y) = \dfrac{x^2 + 4y^2}{x^2 - 4y^2}$

28. $f(x, y) = \dfrac{1}{\cos \frac{1}{2}\pi x} + \dfrac{1}{\cos \frac{1}{2}\pi y}$

29. $f(x, y) = \dfrac{1}{\cos^2 \frac{1}{2}\pi x + \cos^2 \frac{1}{2}\pi y}$

In Exercises 30 and 31, prove that the function f is differentiable at all points in its domain by showing that Definition 17.5.2 holds.

30. $f(x, y) = 3xy^2 - 4x^2 + y^2$

31. $f(x, y) = \dfrac{2x + y}{y^2}$

32. Find equations of the tangent line to the curve of intersection of the surface $z = 3x^2 + y^2 + 1$ with the plane $x = 2$ at the point $(2, -1, 14)$.

33. Find equations of the tangent plane and normal line to the surface $z^2 + 2y + z = 8$ at the point $(2, 1, 2)$.

34. The temperature is T degrees at any point on a heated circular plate and

$$T = \frac{44}{x^2 + y^2 + 9}$$

where distance is measured in inches from the origin at the center of the plate. (a) Find the rate of change of the temperature at the point $(3, 2)$ in the direction of the vector $\cos \frac{1}{6}\pi \mathbf{i} + \sin \frac{1}{6}\pi \mathbf{j}$. (b) Find the direction and magnitude of the greatest rate of change of T at the point $(3, 2)$.

35. The temperature is T degrees at any point (x, y) of the curve $4x^2 + 12y^2 = 1$ and $T = 4x^2 + 24y^2 - 2x$. Find the points on the curve where the temperature is the greatest and where it is the least. Also find the temperature at these points.

36. In order to mail a package by parcel post, the sum of the length and girth (the perimeter of a cross section) must not be greater than 100 in. If a package is to be in the shape of a rectangular box, find the dimensions of the package having the greatest possible volume that can be sent by parcel post.

37. A manufacturing plant has two classifications for its workers, A and B. Class A workers earn $14 per run, and class B

workers earn $13 per run. For a certain production run, it is determined that in addition to the salaries of the workers, if x class A workers and y class B workers are used, the number of dollars in the cost of the run is

$$y^3 + x^2 - 8xy + 600$$

How many workers of each class should be used so that the cost of the run is a minimum if at least three workers of each class are required for a run?

38. Suppose α is the radian measure of an acute angle of a right triangle and $\sin \alpha$ is determined by a/c, where a in. is the length of the side opposite the angle and c in. is the length of the hypotenuse. If by measurement a is found to be 3.52 and c is found to be 7.14, and there is a possible error of 0.01 in each, find the possible error in the computation of $\sin \alpha$ from these measurements.

39. A painting contractor charges 12¢ per square foot for painting the four walls and ceiling of a room. If the dimensions of the ceiling are measured to be 12 ft and 15 ft, the height of the room is measured to be 10 ft, and these measurements are correct to 0.05 ft, find approximately, by using the total differential, the greatest error in estimating the cost of the job from these measurements.

40. At a given instant, the length of one side of a rectangle is 6 ft and it is increasing at the rate of 1 ft/sec and the length of another side of the rectangle is 10 ft and it is decreasing at the rate of 2 ft/sec. Find the rate of change of the area of the rectangle at the given instant.

41. If f is a differentiable function of the variable u, let $u = x^2 + y^2$ and prove that $z = xy + f(x^2 + y^2)$ satisfies the equation

$$y \frac{\partial z}{\partial x} - x \frac{\partial z}{\partial y} = y^2 - x^2$$

42. Verify that $u(x, y) = (\sinh x)(\sin y)$ satisfies Laplace's equation in R_2:

$$\frac{\partial^2 u}{\partial x^2} + \frac{\partial^2 u}{\partial y^2} = 0$$

43. Verify that

$$u(x, t) = \sin \frac{n\pi x}{L} \, e^{(-n^2\pi^2 k^2/L^2)t}$$

satisfies the one-dimensional heat-conduction partial differential equation:

$$\frac{\partial u}{\partial t} = k^2 \frac{\partial^2 u}{\partial x^2}$$

44. Verify that $u(x, t) = A \cos(kat) \sin(kx)$, where A and k are arbitrary constants, satisfies the partial differential equation for a vibrating string:

$$\frac{\partial^2 u}{\partial t^2} = a^2 \frac{\partial^2 u}{\partial x^2}$$

45. If f is a differentiable function of x and y and $u = f(x, y)$, $x = r \cos \theta$, and $y = r \sin \theta$, show that

$$\left(\frac{\partial u}{\partial r}\right)^2 + \frac{1}{r^2} \left(\frac{\partial u}{\partial \theta}\right)^2 = \left(\frac{\partial u}{\partial x}\right)^2 + \left(\frac{\partial u}{\partial y}\right)^2$$

46. In parts (a), (b), and (c) demand equations of two related commodities are given. In each part, determine if the commodities are complementary, substitutes, or neither: (a) $x = -4p + 2q + 6$, $y = 5p - q + 10$; (b) $x = 6 - 3p - 2q$, $y = 4 + 2p - q$; (c) $x = -7q - p + 7$, $y = 18 - 3q - 9p$.

47. Use the method of Lagrange multipliers to find the critical points of the function f for which $f(x, y, z) = y + xz - 2x^2 - y^2 - z^2$ subject to the constraint $z = 35 - x - y$. Determine if the function has a relative maximum or a relative minimum value at any critical point.

48. Given

$$f(x, y) = \begin{cases} \dfrac{x^2 y}{x^4 + y^2} & \text{if } (x, y) \neq (0, 0) \\ 0 & \text{if } (x, y) = (0, 0) \end{cases}$$

Prove that $D_1 f(0, 0)$ and $D_2 f(0, 0)$ exist but that f is not differentiable at $(0, 0)$. (HINT: See Example 5, Sec. 17.2, and Exercise 2 in Exercises 17.3.)

49. Given

$$f(x, y, z) = \begin{cases} \dfrac{x^2 y^2 z^2}{(x^2 + y^2 + z^2)^2} & \text{if } (x, y, z) \neq (0, 0, 0) \\ 0 & \text{if } (x, y, z) = (0, 0, 0) \end{cases}$$

Prove that f is differentiable at $(0, 0, 0)$.

50. Let f be the function defined by

$$f(x, y) = \begin{cases} \dfrac{e^{-1/x^2} y}{e^{-2/x^2} + y^2} & \text{if } x \neq 0 \\ 0 & \text{if } x = 0 \end{cases}$$

Prove that f is discontinuous at the origin.

51. For the function of Exercise 50, prove that $D_1 f(0, 0)$ and $D_2 f(0, 0)$ both exist.

18

Multiple Integration

18.1 THE DOUBLE INTEGRAL

The definite integral of a function of a single variable can be extended to a function of several variables. We call an integral of a function of a single variable a *single integral* to distinguish it from a multiple integral, which involves a function of several variables. The physical and geometric applications of multiple integrals are analogous to those given in Chapter 7 for single integrals.

In the discussion of a single integral we required that the function be defined on a closed interval in R_1. For the double integral of a function of two variables, we require that the function be defined on a closed region in R_2. By a closed region we mean that the region includes its boundary. In this chapter, when we refer to a region, it is assumed to be closed. The simplest kind of closed region in R_2 is a closed rectangle, which we now proceed to define. Consider two distinct points $A(a_1, a_2)$ and $B(b_1, b_2)$ such that $a_1 \leq b_1$ and $a_2 \leq b_2$. These two points determine a rectangle having sides parallel to the coordinate axes. Refer to Fig. 18.1.1. The two points, together with the points (b_1, a_2) and (a_1, b_2), are called the *vertices* of the rectangle. The line segments joining consecutive vertices are called the *edges* of the rectangle. The set of all points interior to the rectangle is called an *open rectangle*, and the set of all points in the open rectangle, together with the points on the edges of the rectangle, is called a *closed rectangle*.

Let the closed rectangular region of Fig. 18.1.1 be denoted by R and let f be a function defined on R. The region R can be considered as a *region of integration* (it corresponds to the interval of integration for a function defined in R_1). Our first step is to define a *partition*, Δ, of R. We draw lines parallel to the coordinate axes and obtain a network of rectangular sub-regions which cover R. The *norm* of this partition, denoted by $\|\Delta\|$, is de-

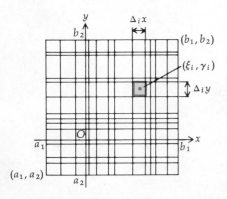

Figure 18.1.1

termined by the length of the longest diagonal of a rectangular subregion of the partition. We number the subregions in some arbitrary way (such as by starting in the upper left corner of R) and let the total be n. We denote the width of the ith subregion by $\Delta_i x$ units and its height by $\Delta_i y$ units. Then if $\Delta_i A$ square units is the area of the ith rectangular subregion,

$$\Delta_i A = \Delta_i x \, \Delta_i y$$

Let (ξ_i, γ_i) be an arbitrary point in the ith subregion and $f(\xi_i, \gamma_i)$ be the function value there. Consider the product $f(\xi_i, \gamma_i) \, \Delta_i A$. Associated with each of the n subregions is such a product, and their sum is

$$\sum_{i=1}^{n} f(\xi_i, \gamma_i) \, \Delta_i A \tag{1}$$

There are many sums of the form (1) because the norm of the partition can be any positive number and each point (ξ_i, γ_i) can be any point in the ith subregion. If all such sums can be made arbitrarily close to one number L by taking partitions with sufficiently small norms, then L is defined to be the limit of these sums as the norm of the partition of R approaches zero. We have the following definition.

18.1.1 Definition Let f be a function defined on a closed rectangular region R. The number L is said to be the *limit* of sums of the form $\sum_{i=1}^{n} f(\xi_i, \gamma_i) \, \Delta_i A$ if L satisfies the property that for any $\epsilon > 0$, there exists a $\delta > 0$ such that

$$\left| \sum_{i=1}^{n} f(\xi_i, \gamma_i) \, \Delta_i A - L \right| < \epsilon$$

for every partition Δ for which $\|\Delta\| < \delta$ and for all possible selections of the point (ξ_i, γ_i) in the ith rectangle, $i = 1, 2, \ldots, n$. If such a number L exists we write

$$\lim_{\|\Delta\| \to 0} \sum_{i=1}^{n} f(\xi_i, \gamma_i) \, \Delta_i A = L$$

If there is a number L satisfying Definition 18.1.1, it can be shown that it is unique. The proof is similar to the proof of the theorem (2.4.2) regarding the uniqueness of the limit of a function.

18.1.2 Definition A function f of two variables is said to be *integrable* on a rectangular region R if f is defined on R and the number L of Definition 18.1.1 exists. This number L is called the *double integral* of f on R, and we write

$$\lim_{\|\Delta\| \to 0} \sum_{i=1}^{n} f(\xi_i, \gamma_i) \, \Delta_i A = \iint_R f(x, y) \, dA \tag{2}$$

Other symbols for the double integral in (2) are

$$\iint_R f(x, y) \, dx \, dy \quad \text{and} \quad \iint_R f(x, y) \, dy \, dx$$

The following theorem, which is stated without proof, gives us a condition under which a function of two variables is integrable.

18.1.3 Theorem   If a function f of two variables is continuous on a closed rectangular region R, then f is integrable on R.

The approximation of the value of a double integral by using Definition 18.1.3 is shown in the following example.

EXAMPLE 1:   Find an approximate value of the double integral

$$\int_R\int (2x^2 - 3y)\, dA$$

where R is the rectangular region having vertices $(-1, 1)$ and $(2, 3)$. Take a partition of R formed by the lines $x = 0$, $x = 1$, and $y = 2$, and take (ξ_i, γ_i) at the center of the ith subregion.

SOLUTION: Refer to Fig. 18.1.2, which shows the region R partitioned into six subregions which are squares having sides one unit in length. So for each i, $\Delta_i A = 1$. In each of the subregions the point (ξ_i, γ_i) is at the center of the square. Therefore, an approximation to the given double integral is given by

$$\int_R\int (2x^2 - 3y)\, dA = f(-\tfrac{1}{2}, \tfrac{3}{2}) \cdot 1 + f(\tfrac{1}{2}, \tfrac{3}{2}) \cdot 1 + f(\tfrac{3}{2}, \tfrac{3}{2}) \cdot 1$$
$$+ f(\tfrac{3}{2}, \tfrac{5}{2}) \cdot 1 + f(\tfrac{1}{2}, \tfrac{5}{2}) \cdot 1 + f(-\tfrac{1}{2}, \tfrac{5}{2}) \cdot 1$$
$$= -4 \cdot 1 - 4 \cdot 1 + 0 \cdot 1 - 3 \cdot 1 - 7 \cdot 1 - 7 \cdot 1$$
$$= -25$$

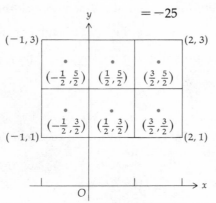

Figure 18.1.2

The exact value of the double integral in Example 1 is -24, as will be shown in Example 1 of Sec. 18.2.

We now consider the double integral of a function over a more general region. First we must define some terms. By a *smooth function* of a single variable we mean one that has a continuous derivative, and a *smooth curve* is a curve that consists of a finite number of arcs of graphs of smooth functions. Examples of smooth curves are straight lines, ellipses, and parabolas. Let R be a closed region whose boundary consists of a finite number of arcs of smooth curves that are joined together to form a closed curve. As we did with a rectangular region, we draw lines parallel to the coordinate axes, which gives us a rectangular partition of the region R. We discard the subregions which contain points not in R and consider only those which lie entirely in R (these are shaded in Fig. 18.1.3). Letting

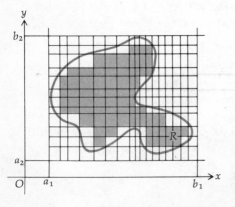

Figure 18.1.3

the number of these shaded subregions be n, we proceed in a manner analogous to the procedure we used for a rectangular region. Definitions 18.1.1 and 18.1.2 apply when the region R is the more general one described above. You should intuitively realize that as the norm of the partition approaches zero, n increases without bound, and the area of the region omitted (i.e., the discarded rectangles) approaches zero. Actually, in advanced calculus it can be proved that if a function is integrable on a region R, the limit of the approximating sums of the form (1) is the same no matter how we subdivide R, so long as each subregion has a shape to which an area can be assigned.

Just as the integral of a function of a single variable is interpreted geometrically as the measure of the area of a plane region, the double integral can be interpreted geometrically as the measure of the volume of a three-dimensional solid. Suppose that the function f is continuous on a closed region R in R_2. Furthermore, for simplicity in this discussion, assume that $f(x, y)$ is nonnegative on R. The graph of the equation $z = f(x, y)$ is a surface lying above the xy plane as shown in Fig. 18.1.4. The figure shows a particular rectangular subregion of R, having dimensions of measures $\Delta_i x$ and $\Delta_i y$. The figure also shows a rectangular solid having this subregion as a base and $f(\xi_i, \gamma_i)$ as the measure of the altitude where (ξ_i, γ_i) is a point in the ith subregion. The volume of the rectangular solid is determined by

Figure 18.1.4

$$\Delta_i V = f(\xi_i, \gamma_i) \; \Delta_i A = f(\xi_i, \gamma_i) \; \Delta_i x \; \Delta_i y \qquad (3)$$

The number given in (3) is the measure of the volume of the thin rectangular solid shown in Fig. 18.1.4; thus, the sum given in (1) is the sum of the measures of the volumes of n such solids. This sum approximates the measure of the volume of the three-dimensional solid shown in Fig. 18.1.4 which is bounded above by the graph of f and below by the region R in the xy plane. The sum in (1) also approximates the number given by the double integral

$$\int_R \int f(x, y) \; dA$$

It can be proved that the volume of the three-dimensional solid of Fig. 18.1.4 is the value of the double integral. We state this in the following theorem for which a formal proof is not given.

18.1.4 Theorem   Let f be a function of two variables that is continuous on a closed region R in the xy plane and $f(x, y) \geq 0$ for all (x, y) in R. If $V(S)$ is the measure of the volume of the solid S having the region R as its base and having an altitude of measure $f(x, y)$ at the point (x, y) in R, then

$$V(S) = \lim_{||\Delta|| \to 0} \sum_{i=1}^{n} f(\xi_i, \gamma_i) \; \Delta_i A = \int_R \int f(x, y) \; dA$$

EXAMPLE 2: Approximate the volume of the solid bounded by the surface

$$f(x, y) = 4 - \tfrac{1}{9}x^2 - \tfrac{1}{16}y^2$$

the planes $x = 3$ and $y = 2$, and the three coordinate planes. To find an approximate value of the double integral take a partition of the region in the xy plane by drawing the lines $x = 1$, $x = 2$, and $y = 1$, and take (ξ_i, γ_i) at the center of the ith subregion.

Figure 18.1.5

SOLUTION: The solid is shown in Fig. 18.1.5. The rectangular region R is the rectangle in the xy plane bounded by the coordinate axes and the lines $x = 3$ and $y = 2$. From Theorem 18.1.4, if V cubic units is the volume of the solid

$$V = \int\!\!\int_R (4 - \tfrac{1}{9}x^2 - \tfrac{1}{16}y^2) \, dA$$

Figure 18.1.5 shows R partitioned into six subregions which are squares having sides of length one unit. Therefore, for each i, $\Delta_i A = 1$. The point (ξ_i, γ_i) in each subregion is at the center of the square. Then an approximation of V is given by an approximation of the double integral, and we have

$$V \approx f(\tfrac{1}{2}, \tfrac{1}{2}) \cdot 1 + f(\tfrac{3}{2}, \tfrac{1}{2}) \cdot 1 + f(\tfrac{5}{2}, \tfrac{1}{2}) \cdot 1 + f(\tfrac{1}{2}, \tfrac{3}{2}) \cdot 1 + f(\tfrac{3}{2}, \tfrac{3}{2}) \cdot 1 + f(\tfrac{5}{2}, \tfrac{3}{2}) \cdot$$

$$= (4 - \tfrac{25}{576}) + (4 - \tfrac{17}{64}) + (4 - \tfrac{409}{576}) + (4 - \tfrac{97}{576}) + (4 - \tfrac{25}{64}) + (4 - \tfrac{481}{576})$$

$$= 24 - \tfrac{695}{288}$$

$$\approx 21.59$$

Thus, the volume is approximately 21.59 cubic units.

The exact value of the volume in Example 2 is shown to be 21.5 cubic units in Example 2 of Sec. 18.2.

Analogous to properties of the definite integral of a function of a single variable are several properties of the double integral, and the most important ones are given in the following theorems.

18.1.5 Theorem If c is a constant and the function f is integrable on a closed region R, then cf is integrable on R and

$$\int\!\!\int_R cf(x, y) \, dA = c \int\!\!\int_R f(x, y) \, dA$$

18.1.6 Theorem If the functions f and g are integrable on a closed region R, then the function $f + g$ is integrable on R and

$$\int\!\!\int_R [f(x, y) + g(x, y)] \, dA = \int\!\!\int_R f(x, y) \, dA + \int\!\!\int_R g(x, y) \, dA$$

The result of Theorem 18.1.6 can be extended to any finite number of functions which are integrable. The proofs of Theorems 18.1.5 and 18.1.6 follow directly from the definition of a double integral. These proofs are left for the reader (see Exercises 13 and 14).

18.1.7 Theorem   If the functions f and g are integrable on the closed region R and $f(x, y) \geq g(x, y)$ for all (x, y) in R, then

$$\int_R \int f(x, y) \, dA \geq \int_R \int g(x, y) \, dA$$

Theorem 18.1.7 is analogous to Theorem 6.4.8 for the definite integral of a function of a single variable. The proof is similar and is left for the reader (see Exercise 15).

18.1.8 Theorem   Let the function f be integrable on a closed region R, and suppose that m and M are two numbers such that $m \leq f(x, y) \leq M$ for all (x, y) in R. Then if A is the measure of the area of region R, we have

$$mA \leq \int_R \int f(x, y) \, dA \leq MA$$

The proof of Theorem 18.1.8 is left for the reader (see Exercise 16). The proof is similar to that of Theorem 6.5.2 and is based on Theorem 18.1.7.

18.1.9 Theorem   Suppose that the function f is continuous on the closed region R and that region R is composed of the two subregions R_1 and R_2 which have no points in common except for points on parts of their boundaries. Then

$$\int_R \int f(x, y) \, dA = \int_{R_1} \int f(x, y) \, dA + \int_{R_2} \int f(x, y) \, dA$$

The proof of Theorem 18.1.9 is also left for the reader and depends on the definition of a double integral and limit theorems (see Exercise 17).

Exercises 18.1

In Exercises 1 through 6, find an approximate value of the given double integral where R is the rectangular region having the vertices P and Q, Δ is a regular partition of R, and (ξ_i, γ_i) is the midpoint of each subregion.

1. $\displaystyle\int_R \int (x^2 + y) \, dA$; $P(0, 0)$; $Q(4, 2)$; Δ: $x_1 = 0$, $x_2 = 1$, $x_3 = 2$, $x_4 = 3$, $y_1 = 0$, $y_2 = 1$.

2. $\displaystyle\int_R \int (2 - x - y) \, dA$; $P(0, 0)$; $Q(6, 4)$; Δ: $x_1 = 0$, $x_2 = 2$, $x_3 = 4$, $y_1 = 0$, $y_2 = 2$.

3. $\displaystyle\int_R \int (xy + 3y^2) \, dA$; $P(-2, 0)$; $Q(4, 6)$; Δ: $x_1 = -2$, $x_2 = 0$, $x_3 = 2$, $y_1 = 0$, $y_2 = 2$, $y_3 = 4$.

4. $\displaystyle\int_R \int (xy + 3y^2) \, dA$; $P(0, -2)$; $Q(6, 4)$; Δ: $x_1 = 0$, $x_2 = 2$, $x_3 = 4$, $y_1 = -2$, $y_2 = 0$, $y_3 = 2$.

5. $\displaystyle\int_R \int (x^2 y - 2xy^2) \, dA$; $P(-3, -2)$; $Q(1, 6)$; Δ: $x_1 = -3$, $x_2 = -1$, $y_1 = -2$, $y_2 = 0$, $y_3 = 2$, $y_4 = 4$.

6. $\int\int_R (x^2y - 2xy^2) \, dA$; $P(-3, -2)$; $Q(1, 6)$; Δ: $x_1 = -3$, $x_2 = -2$, $x_3 = -1$, $x_4 = 0$, $y_1 = -2$, $y_2 = -1$, $y_3 = 0$, $y_4 = 1$, $y_5 = 2$, $y_6 = 3$, $y_7 = 4$, $y_8 = 5$.

In Exercises 7 through 10, find an approximate value of the given double integral where R is the rectangular region having the vertices P and Q, Δ is a regular partition of R, and (ξ_i, γ_i) is an arbitrary point in each subregion.

7. The double integral, P, Q, and Δ are the same as in Exercise 1; $(\xi_1, \gamma_1) = (\frac{1}{4}, \frac{1}{2})$; $(\xi_2, \gamma_2) = (\frac{7}{4}, 0)$; $(\xi_3, \gamma_3) = (\frac{5}{2}, \frac{1}{4})$; $(\xi_4, \gamma_4) = (4, 1)$; $(\xi_5, \gamma_5) = (\frac{3}{4}, \frac{7}{4})$; $(\xi_6, \gamma_6) = (\frac{5}{4}, \frac{3}{2})$; $(\xi_7, \gamma_7) = (\frac{5}{2}, 2)$; $(\xi_8, \gamma_8) = (3, 1)$.

8. The double integral, P, Q, and Δ are the same as in Exercise 2; $(\xi_1, \gamma_1) = (\frac{1}{2}, \frac{3}{2})$; $(\xi_2, \gamma_2) = (3, 1)$; $(\xi_3, \gamma_3) = (\frac{11}{2}, \frac{1}{2})$; $(\xi_4, \gamma_4) = (2, 2)$; $(\xi_5, \gamma_5) = (2, 2)$; $(\xi_6, \gamma_6) = (5, 3)$.

9. The double integral, P, Q, and Δ are the same as in Exercise 3; $(\xi_1, \gamma_1) = (-\frac{1}{2}, \frac{1}{2})$; $(\xi_2, \gamma_2) = (1, \frac{3}{2})$; $(\xi_3, \gamma_3) = (\frac{5}{2}, 2)$; $(\xi_4, \gamma_4) = (-\frac{3}{2}, \frac{7}{2})$; $(\xi_5, \gamma_5) = (0, 3)$; $(\xi_6, \gamma_6) = (4, 4)$; $(\xi_7, \gamma_7) = (-1, \frac{9}{2})$; $(\xi_8, \gamma_8) = (1, \frac{9}{2})$; $(\xi_9, \gamma_9) = (3, \frac{9}{2})$.

10. The double integral, P, Q, and Δ are the same as in Exercise 3; $(\xi_1, \gamma_1) = (-2, 0)$; $(\xi_2, \gamma_2) = (0, 0)$; $(\xi_3, \gamma_3) = (2, 0)$; $(\xi_4, \gamma_4) = (-2, 2)$; $(\xi_5, \gamma_5) = (0, 2)$; $(\xi_6, \gamma_6) = (2, 2)$; $(\xi_7, \gamma_7) = (-2, 4)$; $(\xi_8, \gamma_8) = (0, 4)$; $(\xi_9, \gamma_9) = (2, 4)$.

11. Approximate the volume of the solid in the first octant bounded by the sphere $x^2 + y^2 + z^2 = 64$, the planes $x = 3$ and $y = 3$, and the three coordinate planes. To find an approximate value of the double integral take a partition of the region in the xy plane by drawing the lines $x = 1$, $x = 2$, $y = 1$, and $y = 2$, and take (ξ_i, γ_i) at the center of the ith subregion.

12. Approximate the volume of the solid bounded by the surface $100z = 300 - 25x^2 - 4y^2$, the planes $x = -1$, $x = 3$, $y = -3$, and $y = 5$, and the xy plane. To find an approximate value of the double integral take a partition of the region in the xy plane by drawing the lines $x = 1$, $y = -1$, $y = 1$, and $y = 3$, and take (ξ_i, γ_i) at the center of the ith subregion.

13. Prove Theorem 18.1.5.   14. Prove Theorem 18.1.6.   15. Prove Theorem 18.1.7.

16. Prove Theorem 18.1.8.   17. Prove Theorem 18.1.9.

18.2 EVALUATION OF DOUBLE INTEGRALS AND ITERATED INTEGRALS

For functions of a single variable, the fundamental theorem of calculus provides a method for evaluating a definite integral by finding an antiderivative (or indefinite integral) of the integrand. We have a corresponding method for evaluating a double integral which involves performing successive single integrations. A rigorous development of this method belongs to a course in advanced calculus. Our discussion is an intuitive one, and we use the geometric interpretation of the double integral as the measure of a volume. We first develop the method for the double integral on a rectangular region.

Let f be a given function which is integrable on a closed rectangular region R in the xy plane bounded by the lines $x = a_1$, $x = b_1$, $y = a_2$, and $y = b_2$. We assume that $f(x, y) \geq 0$ for all (x, y) in R. Refer to Fig. 18.2.1, which shows a sketch of the graph of the equation $z = f(x, y)$ when (x, y) is in R. The number that represents the value of the double integral

$$\left(\int\int_R f(x, y) \, dA \right.$$

is the measure of the volume of the solid between the surface and the region R. We find this number by the method of parallel plane sections, which we discussed in Sec. 7.4.

Let y be a number in $[a_2, b_2]$. Consider the plane which is parallel to

Figure 18.2.1

the xz plane through the point $(0, y, 0)$. Let $A(y)$ be the measure of the area of the plane region of intersection of this plane with the solid. By the method of parallel plane sections, as discussed in Sec. 7.4, we express the measure of the volume of the solid by

$$\int_{a_2}^{b_2} A(y) \, dy$$

Because the volume of the solid also is determined by the double integral, we have

$$\int\!\!\int_R f(x, y) \, dA = \int_{a_2}^{b_2} A(y) \, dy \tag{1}$$

By using Eq. (1) we can find the value of the double integral of the function f on R by evaluating a single integral of $A(y)$. We now must find $A(y)$ when y is given. Because $A(y)$ is the measure of the area of a plane region, we can find it by integration. In Fig. 18.2.1, notice that the upper boundary of the plane region is the graph of the equation $z = f(x, y)$ when x is in $[a_1, b_1]$. Therefore, $A(y) = \int_{a_1}^{b_1} f(x, y) \, dx$. If we substitute from this equation into Eq. (1), we obtain

$$\left(\;\int\!\!\int_R f(x, y) \, dA = \int_{a_2}^{b_2} \left[\int_{a_1}^{b_1} f(x, y) \, dx\right] dy \tag{2}\right.$$

The integral on the right side of Eq. (2) is called an *iterated integral*. Usually the brackets are omitted when writing an iterated integral. So we write Eq. (2) as

$$\int\!\!\int_R f(x, y) \, dA = \int_{a_2}^{b_2} \int_{a_1}^{b_1} f(x, y) \, dx \, dy \tag{3}$$

When evaluating the "inner integral" in Eq. (3), remember that x is the variable of integration and y is considered a constant. This is analogous to considering y as a constant when finding the partial derivative of $f(x, y)$ with respect to x.

By considering plane sections parallel to the yz plane, we can develop the following formula, which interchanges the order of integration.

$$\left(\;\int\!\!\int_R f(x, y) \, dA = \int_{a_1}^{b_1} \int_{a_2}^{b_2} f(x, y) \, dy \, dx \tag{4}\right.$$

A sufficient condition for formulas (3) and (4) to be valid is that the function be continuous on the rectangular region R.

EXAMPLE 1: Evaluate the double integral

$$\int\!\!\int_R (2x^2 - 3y) \, dA$$

SOLUTION: $a_1 = -1, b_1 = 2, a_2 = 1$, and $b_2 = 3$. So we have from formula (3)

$$\int\!\!\int_R (2x^2 - 3y) \, dA = \int_1^3 \int_{-1}^2 (2x^2 - 3y) \, dx \, dy$$

$$= \int_1^3 \left[\int_{-1}^2 (2x^2 - 3y) \, dx\right] dy$$

if R is the region consisting of all points (x, y) for which $-1 \le x \le 2$ and $1 \le y \le 3$.

$$= \int_1^3 \left[\tfrac{2}{3}x^3 - 3xy \right]_{-1}^2 \, dy$$

$$= \int_1^3 (6 - 9y) \, dy$$

$$= -24$$

In Example 1 of Sec. 18.1 we found an approximate value of the double integral in the above example to be -25.

EXAMPLE 2:   Find the volume of the solid bounded by the surface

$$f(x, y) = 4 - \tfrac{1}{9}x^2 - \tfrac{1}{16}y^2$$

the planes $x = 3$ and $y = 2$, and the three coordinate planes.

SOLUTION: Figure 18.2.2 shows the graph of the equation $z = f(x, y)$ in the first octant and the given solid. If V cubic units is the volume of the solid, we have from Theorem 18.1.4

$$V = \lim_{\|\Delta\| \to 0} \sum_{i=1}^n f(\xi_i, \gamma_i) \, \Delta_i A = \iint_R f(x, y) \, dA$$

$$= \int_0^3 \int_0^2 (4 - \tfrac{1}{9}x^2 - \tfrac{1}{16}y^2) \, dy \, dx$$

$$= \int_0^3 \left[4y - \tfrac{1}{9}x^2 y - \tfrac{1}{48}y^3 \right]_0^2 \, dx$$

$$= \int_0^3 \left(\tfrac{47}{6} - \tfrac{2}{9}x^2 \right) \, dx$$

$$= \tfrac{47}{6}x - \tfrac{2}{27}x^3 \Big]_0^3$$

$$= 21.5$$

The volume is therefore 21.5 cubic units.

Figure 18.2.2

In Example 2 of Sec. 18.1 an approximate value of the volume in Example 2 was found to be 21.59 cubic units.

Figure 18.2.3

Figure 18.2.4

Suppose now that R is a region in the xy plane which is bounded by the lines $x = a$ and $x = b$, where $a < b$, and by the curves $y = \phi_1(x)$ and $y = \phi_2(x)$, where ϕ_1 and ϕ_2 are two functions which are continuous on the closed interval $[a, b]$; furthermore, $\phi_1(x) \leq \phi_2(x)$ whenever $a \leq x \leq b$ (see Fig. 18.2.3). Let Δ be a partition of the interval $[a, b]$ defined by Δ: $a = x_0 < x_1 < \cdots < x_n = b$. Consider the region R of Fig. 18.2.3 to be divided into vertical strips with widths of measure $\Delta_i x$. A particular strip is shown in the figure. The intersection of the surface $z = f(x, y)$ and a plane $x = \xi_i$, where $x_{i-1} \leq \xi_i \leq x_i$, is a curve. A segment of this curve is over the ith vertical strip. The region under this curve segment and above the xy plane is shown in Fig. 18.2.4, and the measure of the area of this region is given by

$$\int_{\phi_1(\xi_i)}^{\phi_2(\xi_i)} f(\xi_i, y)\, dy$$

The measure of the volume of the solid bounded above by the surface $z = f(x, y)$ and below by the ith vertical strip is approximately equal to

$$\left[\int_{\phi_1(\xi_i)}^{\phi_2(\xi_i)} f(\xi_i, y)\, dy \right] \Delta_i x$$

If we take the limit, as the norm of Δ approaches zero, of the sum of these measures of volume for n vertical strips of R from $x = a$ to $x = b$, we obtain the measure of the volume of the solid bounded above by the surface $z = f(x, y)$ and below by the region R in the xy plane. (See Fig. 18.2.5.) This is the double integral of f on R; that is,

$$\lim_{\|\Delta\| \to 0} \sum_{i=1}^{n} \left[\int_{\phi_1(\xi_i)}^{\phi_2(\xi_i)} f(\xi_i, y)\, dy \right] \Delta_i x = \int_a^b \int_{\phi_1(x)}^{\phi_2(x)} f(x, y)\, dy\, dx$$

$$= \iint_R f(x, y)\, dy\, dx \tag{5}$$

Figure 18.2.5

Sufficient conditions for formula (5) to be valid are that f be continuous on the closed region R and that ϕ_1 and ϕ_2 be smooth functions.

EXAMPLE 3: Express as both a double integral and an iterated integral the measure of the volume of the solid above the xy plane bounded by the elliptic paraboloid $z = x^2 + 4y^2$ and the cylinder $x^2 + 4y^2 = 4$. Evaluate the iterated integral to find the volume of the solid.

SOLUTION: The solid is shown in Fig. 18.2.6. Using properties of symmetry, we find the volume of the portion of the solid in the first octant which is one-fourth of the required volume. Then the region R in the xy plane is that bounded by the x and y axes and the ellipse $x^2 + 4y^2 = 4$. This region is shown in Fig. 18.2.7, which also shows the ith subregion of a rectangular partition of R, where (ξ_i, γ_i) is any point in this ith subregion. If V cubic units is the volume of the given solid, then by Theorem 18.1.4 we have

$$V = 4 \lim_{||\Delta|| \to 0} \sum_{i=1}^{n} (\xi_i^2 + 4\gamma_i^2)\, \Delta_i A = 4 \int_R \int (x^2 + 4y^2)\, dA$$

To express the measure of the volume as an iterated integral we divide the region R into n vertical strips. Figure 18.2.8 shows the region R and the ith vertical strip having width of $\Delta_i x$ units and length of $\frac{1}{2}\sqrt{4 - \xi_i^2}$ units, where $x_{i-1} \le \xi_i \le x_i$. Using formula (5) we have

$$V = 4 \lim_{||\Delta|| \to 0} \sum_{i=1}^{n} \left[\int_0^{\sqrt{4-\xi_i^2}/2} (\xi_i^2 + 4y^2)\, dy \right] \Delta_i x$$

$$= 4 \int_0^2 \int_0^{\sqrt{4-x^2}/2} (x^2 + 4y^2)\, dy\, dx$$

Evaluating the iterated integral, we have

$$V = 4 \int_0^2 \left[x^2 y + \tfrac{4}{3}y^3 \right]_0^{\sqrt{4-x^2}/2} dx$$

$$= 4 \int_0^2 \left[\tfrac{1}{2}x^2 \sqrt{4 - x^2} + \tfrac{1}{6}(4 - x^2)^{3/2} \right] dx$$

$$= \tfrac{4}{3} \int_0^2 (x^2 + 2)\sqrt{4 - x^2}\, dx$$

$$= -\tfrac{1}{3}x(4 - x^2)^{3/2} + 2x\sqrt{4 - x^2} + 2\sin^{-1}\tfrac{1}{2}x \Big]_0^2$$

$$= 4\pi$$

Therefore, the volume is 4π cubic units.

$x^2 + 4y^2 = 4$
$4y^2 = 4 - x^2$
$y = \dfrac{\sqrt{4 - x^2}}{2}$

Figure 18.2.6

Figure 18.2.7

Figure 18.2.8

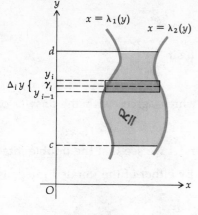

Figure 18.2.9

If the region R is bounded by the curves $x = \lambda_1(y)$ and $x = \lambda_2(y)$ and the lines $y = c$ and $y = d$, where $c < d$, and λ_1 and λ_2 are two functions which are continuous on the closed interval $[c, d]$ for which $\lambda_1(y) \leq \lambda_2(y)$ whenever $c \leq y \leq d$, then consider a partition Δ of the interval $[c, d]$ and divide the region into horizontal strips, the measures of whose widths are $\Delta_i y$. See Fig. 18.2.9, which shows the ith horizontal strip. The intersection of the surface $z = f(x, y)$ and a plane $y = \gamma_i$, where $y_{i-1} \leq \gamma_i \leq y_i$, is a curve, and a segment of this curve is over the ith horizontal strip. Then, as in the derivation of formula (5), the measure of the volume of the solid bounded above by the surface $z = f(x, y)$ and below by the ith vertical strip is approximately equal to

$$\left[\int_{\lambda_1(\gamma_i)}^{\lambda_2(\gamma_i)} f(x, \gamma_i) \, dx \right] \Delta_i y$$

Taking the limit, as $\|\Delta\|$ approaches zero, of the sum of these measures of volume for n horizontal strips of R from $y = c$ to $y = d$, we obtain the measure of the volume of the solid bounded above by the surface $z = f(x, y)$ and below by the region R in the xy plane. This measure of volume is the double integral of f on R. Hence, we have

$$\lim_{\|\Delta\| \to 0} \sum_{i=1}^{n} \left[\int_{\lambda_1(\gamma_i)}^{\lambda_2(\gamma_i)} f(x, \gamma_i) \, dx \right] \Delta_i y = \int_c^d \int_{\lambda_1(y)}^{\lambda_2(y)} f(x, y) \, dx \, dy$$

$$= \int \int_R f(x, y) \, dx \, dy$$

(6)

Sufficient conditions for formula (6) to be valid are that λ_1 and λ_2 be smooth functions and f be continuous on R. In applying both formula (5) and formula (6) sometimes it may be necessary to subdivide a region R into subregions on which these sufficient conditions hold.

EXAMPLE 4: Express the volume of the solid of Example 3 by an iterated integral in which the order of integration is the reverse of that of Example 3. Compute the volume.

Figure 18.2.10

SOLUTION: Again we find the volume of the solid in the first octant and multiply the result by 4. Figure 18.2.10 shows the region R in the xy plane and the ith horizontal strip whose width has a measure of $\Delta_i y$, and whose length has a measure of $2\sqrt{1 - \gamma_i^2}$. Then by formula (6) we have

$$V = 4 \lim_{\|\Delta\| \to 0} \sum_{i=1}^{n} \left[\int_0^{2\sqrt{1-\gamma_i^2}} (x^2 + 4\gamma_i^2) \, dx \right] \Delta_i y$$

$$= 4 \int_0^1 \int_0^{2\sqrt{1-y^2}} (x^2 + 4y^2) \, dx \, dy$$

$$= 4 \int_0^1 \left[\tfrac{1}{3}x^3 + 4y^2 x \right]_0^{2\sqrt{1-y^2}} dy$$

$$= 4 \int_0^1 \left[\tfrac{8}{3}(1 - y^2)^{3/2} + 8y^2 \sqrt{1 - y^2} \right] dy$$

$$\frac{32}{3} \int_0^1 \sqrt{1-y^2}\,(1-y^2) + 3y^2 \, dy = \frac{32}{3} \int_0^1 \sqrt{1-y^2} \; 2y^2 + 1 \, dy.$$

$$= \tfrac{32}{3} \int_0^1 (2y^2 + 1) \sqrt{1 - y^2} \, dy$$

$$= -\tfrac{16}{3} y (1 - y^2)^{3/2} + 8y \sqrt{1 - y^2} + 8 \sin^{-1} y \Big]_0^1$$

$$= 4\pi$$

Hence, the volume is 4π cubic units, which agrees with the answer of Example 3.

From the solutions of Examples 3 and 4 we see that the double integral $\int\!\!\int_R (x^2 + 4y^2) \, dA$ can be evaluated by either of the iterated integrals

$$\int_0^2 \int_0^{\sqrt{4-x^2}/2} (x^2 + 4y^2) \, dy \, dx \quad \text{or} \quad \int_0^1 \int_0^{2\sqrt{1-y^2}} (x^2 + 4y^2) \, dx \, dy$$

If in either formula (5) or (6), $f(x, y) = 1$ for all x and y, then we obtain a formula that expresses the measure A of the area of a region R as a double integral. We have

$$A = \int_R\!\!\int dy \, dx = \int_R\!\!\int dx \, dy \qquad (7)$$

EXAMPLE 5:   Find by double integration the area of the region in the xy plane bounded by the curves $y = x^2$ and $y = 4x - x^2$.

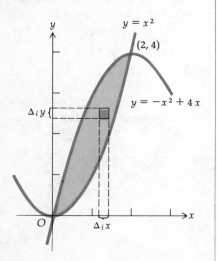

Figure 18.2.11

SOLUTION: The region is shown in Fig. 18.2.11. Applying formula (7), we have

$$A = \int_R\!\!\int dy \, dx = \int_0^2 \int_{x^2}^{4x-x^2} dy \, dx$$

$$= \int_0^2 (4x - x^2 - x^2) \, dx = 2x^2 - \tfrac{2}{3}x^3 \Big]_0^2$$

$$= \tfrac{8}{3}$$

Hence, the area of the region is $\tfrac{8}{3}$ square units.

Exercises 18.2

In Exercises 1 through 8, evaluate the given iterated integral.

(1) $\displaystyle\int_1^2 \int_0^{2x} xy^3 \, dy \, dx$ 2. $\displaystyle\int_0^4 \int_0^y dx \, dy$ 3. $\displaystyle\int_0^1 \int_0^{y^2} e^{x/y} \, dx \, dy$ 4. $\displaystyle\int_{-1}^1 \int_1^{e^x} \frac{1}{xy} \, dy \, dx$

(5) $\displaystyle\int_0^1 \int_{y^2}^y \sqrt{\frac{y}{x}} \, dx \, dy$ 6. $\displaystyle\int_0^1 \int_{x^2}^x \sqrt{\frac{y}{x}} \, dy \, dx$ 7. $\displaystyle\int_0^1 \int_0^1 |x - y| \, dy \, dx$ (8) $\displaystyle\int_0^\pi \int_0^{y^2} \sin\frac{x}{y} \, dx \, dy$

In Exercises 9 through 14, find the exact value of the double integral.

9. The double integral is the same as in Exercise 1 in Exercises 18.1.

10. The double integral is the same as in Exercise 4 in Exercises 18.1.

(11) $\displaystyle\iint_R \sin x \, dA$; R is the region bounded by the lines $y = 2x$, $y = \frac{1}{2}x$, and $x = \pi$.

12. $\displaystyle\iint_R \cos(x + y) \, dA$; R is the region bounded by the lines $y = x$ and $x = \pi$, and the x axis.

(13) $\displaystyle\iint_R x^2 \sqrt{9 - y^2} \, dA$; R is the region bounded by the circle $x^2 + y^2 = 9$.

(14) $\displaystyle\iint_R \frac{y^2}{x^2} \, dA$; R is the region bounded by the lines $y = x$ and $y = 2$, and the hyperbola $xy = 1$.

15. Find the volume of the solid under the plane $z = 4x$ and above the circle $x^2 + y^2 = 16$ in the xy plane. Draw a sketch of the solid.

16. Find the volume of the solid bounded by the planes $x = y + 2z + 1$, $x = 0$, $y = 0$, $z = 0$, and $3y + z - 3 = 0$. Draw a sketch of the solid.

17. Find the volume of the solid in the first octant bounded by the two cylinders $x^2 + y^2 = 4$ and $x^2 + z^2 = 4$. Draw a sketch of the solid.

18. Find the volume of the solid in the first octant bounded by the paraboloid $z = 9 - x^2 - 3y^2$. Draw a sketch of the solid.

19. Find the volume of the solid in the first octant bounded by the surfaces $x + z^2 = 1$, $x = y$, and $x = y^2$. Draw a sketch of the solid.

20. Find by double integration the volume of the portion of the solid bounded by the sphere $x^2 + y^2 + z^2 = 16$ which lies in the first octant. Draw a sketch of the solid.

In Exercises 21 through 24, use double integrals to find the area of the region bounded by the given curves in the xy plane. Draw a sketch of the region.

21. $y = x^3$ and $y = x^2$ (22) $y^2 = 4x$ and $x^2 = 4y$ 23. $y = x^2 - 9$ and $y = 9 - x^2$ 24. $x^2 + y^2 = 16$ and $y^2 = 6x$

25. Express as an iterated integral the measure of the volume of the solid bounded by the ellipsoid

$$\frac{x^2}{a^2} + \frac{y^2}{b^2} + \frac{z^2}{c^2} = 1$$

(26) Given the iterated integral

$$\int_0^a \int_0^x \sqrt{a^2 - x^2} \, dy \, dx$$

(a) Draw a sketch of the solid the measure of whose volume is represented by the given iterated integral; (b) evaluate the iterated integral; (c) write the iterated integral which gives the measure of the volume of the same solid with the order of integration reversed.

27. Given the iterated integral

$$\frac{2}{3} \int_0^a \int_0^{\sqrt{a^2-x^2}} (2x + y) \, dy \, dx$$

The instructions are the same as for Exercise 26.

28. Use double integration to find the area of the region in the first quadrant bounded by the parabola $y^2 = 4x$, the circle $x^2 + y^2 = 5$, and the x axis by two methods: (a) Integrate first with respect to x; (b) integrate first with respect to y. Compare the two methods of solution.

29. Find, by two methods, the volume of the solid below the plane $3x + 8y + 6z = 24$ and above the region in the xy plane bounded by the parabola $y^2 = 2x$, the line $2x + 3y = 10$, and the x axis: (a) Integrate first with respect to x; (b) integrate first with respect to y. Compare the two methods of solution.

In Exercises 30 and 31, the iterated integral cannot be evaluated exactly in terms of elementary functions by the given order of integration. Reverse the order of integration and perform the computation.

30. $\displaystyle\int_0^1 \int_y^1 e^{x^2} \, dx \, dy$

31. $\displaystyle\int_0^1 \int_x^1 \frac{\sin y}{y} \, dy \, dx$

32. Use double integration to find the volume of the solid common to two right-circular cylinders of radius r units, whose axes intersect at right angles. (See Exercise 8 in Exercises 7.4.)

18.3 CENTER OF MASS AND MOMENTS OF INERTIA

In Chapter 7 we used single integrals to find the center of mass of a homogeneous lamina. In using single integrals we can consider only laminae of constant area density (except in special cases); however, with double integrals we can find the center of mass of either a homogeneous or a nonhomogeneous lamina.

Suppose that we are given a lamina which has the shape of a closed region R in the xy plane. Let $\rho(x, y)$ be the measure of the area density of the lamina at any point (x, y) of R where ρ is continuous on R. To find the total mass of the lamina we proceed as follows. Let Δ be a partition of R into n rectangles. If (ξ_i, γ_i) is any point in the ith rectangle having an area of measure $\Delta_i A$, then an approximation to the measure of the mass of the ith rectangle is given by $\rho(\xi_i, \gamma_i) \, \Delta_i A$, and the measure of the total mass of the lamina is approximated by

$$\sum_{i=1}^{n} \rho(\xi_i, \gamma_i) \, \Delta_i A$$

Taking the limit of the above sum as the norm of Δ approaches zero, we express the measure M of the mass of the lamina by

$$M = \lim_{||\Delta|| \to 0} \sum_{i=1}^{n} \rho(\xi_i, \gamma_i) \, \Delta_i A = \iint_R \rho(x, y) \, dA \tag{1}$$

The measure of the moment of mass of the ith rectangle with respect to the x axis is approximated by $\gamma_i \rho(\xi_i, \gamma_i) \, \Delta_i A$. The sum of the measures of the moments of mass of the n rectangles with respect to the x axis is then approximated by the sum of n such terms. The measure M_x of the moment of mass with respect to the x axis of the entire lamina is given by

$$M_x = \lim_{||\Delta|| \to 0} \sum_{i=1}^{n} \gamma_i \rho(\xi_i, \gamma_i)\ \Delta_i A = \int\int_R y\rho(x, y)\ dA \tag{2}$$

Analogously, the measure M_y of its moment of mass with respect to the y axis is given by

$$M_y = \lim_{||\Delta|| \to 0} \sum_{i=1}^{n} \xi_i \rho(\xi_i, \gamma_i)\ \Delta_i A = \int\int_R x\rho(x, y)\ dA \tag{3}$$

The center of mass of the lamina is denoted by the point $(\bar{x}, \bar{y})$ and

$$\bar{x} = \frac{M_y}{M} \quad \text{and} \quad \bar{y} = \frac{M_x}{M}$$

EXAMPLE 1: A lamina in the shape of an isosceles right triangle has an area density which varies as the square of the distance from the vertex of the right angle. If mass is measured in slugs and distance is measured in feet, find the mass and the center of mass of the lamina.

Figure 18.3.1

SOLUTION: Choose the coordinate axes so that the vertex of the right triangle is at the origin and the sides of length a ft of the triangle are along the coordinate axes (see Fig. 18.3.1). Let $\rho(x, y)$ be the number of slugs/ft^2 in the area density of the lamina at the point (x, y). Then $\rho(x, y) = k(x^2 + y^2)$ where k is a constant. Therefore, if M slugs is the mass of the lamina, we have from formula (1)

$$M = \lim_{||\Delta|| \to 0} \sum_{i=1}^{n} k(\xi_i^2 + \gamma_i^2)\ \Delta_i A$$

$$= k \int\int_R (x^2 + y^2)\ dA$$

$$= \int_0^a \int_0^{a-x} (x^2 + y^2)\ dy\ dx$$

$$= k \int_0^a \left[yx^2 + \tfrac{1}{3}y^3 \right]_0^{a-x} dx$$

$$= k \int_0^a (\tfrac{1}{3}a^3 - a^2x + 2ax^2 - \tfrac{4}{3}x^3)\ dx$$

$$= k(\tfrac{1}{3}a^4 - \tfrac{1}{2}a^4 + \tfrac{2}{3}a^4 - \tfrac{1}{3}a^4)$$

$$= \tfrac{1}{6}ka^4$$

To find the center of mass, we observe that because of symmetry it must lie on the line $y = x$. Therefore, if we find $\bar{x}$, we also have $\bar{y}$. Using formula (3), we have

$$M_y = \lim_{||\Delta|| \to 0} \sum_{i=1}^{n} k\xi_i(\xi_i^2 + \gamma_i^2)\ \Delta_i A$$

$$= k \int\int_R x(x^2 + y^2)\ dA$$

$$= k \int_0^a \int_0^{a-x} x(x^2 + y^2) \, dy \, dx$$

$$= k \int_0^a \left[x^3 y + \tfrac{1}{3} x y^3 \right]_0^{a-x} dx$$

$$= k \int_0^a \left(\tfrac{1}{3} a^3 x - a^2 x^2 + 2 a x^3 - \tfrac{4}{3} x^4 \right) dx$$

$$= k(\tfrac{1}{6} a^5 - \tfrac{1}{3} a^5 + \tfrac{1}{2} a^5 - \tfrac{4}{15} a^5)$$

$$= \tfrac{1}{15} k a^5$$

Because $M\bar{x} = M_y$, we have $M\bar{x} = \tfrac{1}{15} k a^5$; and because $M = \tfrac{1}{6} k a^4$, we get $\bar{x} = \tfrac{2}{5} a$. Therefore, the center of mass is at the point $(\tfrac{2}{5}a, \tfrac{2}{5}a)$.

18.3.1 Definition   The *moment of inertia* of a particle, whose mass is m slugs, about an axis is defined to be mr^2 slug-ft^2, where r ft is the perpendicular distance from the particle to the axis.

If we have a system of n particles, the moment of inertia of the system is defined as the sum of the moments of inertia of all the particles. That is, if the ith particle has a mass of m_i slugs and is at a distance of r_i ft from the axis, then I slug-ft^2 is the moment of inertia of the system where

$$I = \sum_{i=1}^n m_i r_i^2 \tag{4}$$

Extending this concept of moment of inertia to a continuous distribution of mass in a plane such as rods or laminae by processes similar to those previously used, we have the following definition.

18.3.2 Definition   Suppose that we are given a continuous distribution of mass occupying a region R in the xy plane, and suppose that the measure of area density of this distribution at the point (x, y) is $\rho(x, y)$ slugs/ft^2, where ρ is continuous on R. Then the moment of inertia I_x slug-ft^2 about the x axis of this distribution of mass is determined by

$$I_x = \lim_{\|\Delta\| \to 0} \sum_{i=1}^n \gamma_i^2 \rho(\xi_i, \gamma_i) \, \Delta_i A = \iint_R y^2 \rho(x, y) \, dA \tag{5}$$

Similarly, the measure I_y of the moment of inertia about the y axis is given by

$$I_y = \lim_{\|\Delta\| \to 0} \sum_{i=1}^n \xi_i^2 \rho(\xi_i, \gamma_i) \, \Delta_i A = \iint_R x^2 \rho(x, y) \, dA \tag{6}$$

and the measure I_0 of the moment of inertia about the origin, or the z axis, is given by

$$I_0 = \lim_{\|\Delta\| \to 0} \sum_{i=1}^n (\xi_i^2 + \gamma_i^2) \rho(\xi_i, \gamma_i) \, \Delta_i A = \iint_R (x^2 + y^2) \rho(x, y) \, dA \tag{7}$$

The number I_0 of formula (7) is the measure of what is called the *polar moment of inertia*.

EXAMPLE 2:   A homogeneous straight wire has a constant linear density of ρ slugs/ft. Find the moment of inertia of the wire about an axis perpendicular to the wire and passing through one end.

SOLUTION: Let the wire be of length a ft, and suppose that it extends along the x axis from the origin. We find its moment of inertia about the y axis. Divide the wire into n segments; the length of the ith segment is $\Delta_i x$ ft. The mass of the ith segment is then $\rho \, \Delta_i x$ slugs. Assume that the mass of the ith segment is concentrated at a single point ξ_i, where $x_{i-1} \leq \xi_i \leq x_i$. The moment of inertia of the ith segment about the y axis lies between $\rho x_{i-1}{}^2 \, \Delta_i x$ slug-ft^2 and $\rho x_i{}^2 \, \Delta_i x$ slug-ft^2 and is approximated by $\rho \xi_i{}^2 \, \Delta_i x$ slug-ft^2, where $x_{i-1} \leq \xi_i \leq x_i$. If the moment of inertia of the wire about the y axis is I_y slug-ft^2, then

$$I_y = \lim_{||\Delta|| \to 0} \sum_{i=1}^{n} \rho \xi_i{}^2 \, \Delta_i x = \int_0^a \rho x^2 \, dx = \tfrac{1}{3}\rho a^3$$

Therefore, the moment of inertia is $\tfrac{1}{3}\rho a^3$ slug-ft^2.

EXAMPLE 3:   A homogeneous rectangular lamina has constant area density of ρ slugs/ft^2. Find the moment of inertia of the lamina about one corner.

Figure 18.3.2

SOLUTION: Suppose that the lamina is bounded by the lines $x = a$, $y = b$, the x axis, and the y axis. See Fig. 18.3.2. If I_0 slug-ft^2 is the moment of inertia about the origin, then

$$I_0 = \lim_{||\Delta|| \to 0} \sum_{i=1}^{n} \rho(\xi_i{}^2 + \gamma_i{}^2) \, \Delta_i A$$

$$= \int\!\!\int_R \rho(x^2 + y^2) \, dA$$

$$= \rho \int_0^b \int_0^a (x^2 + y^2) \, dx \, dy$$

$$= \rho \int_0^b \left[\tfrac{1}{3}x^3 + xy^2 \right]_0^a dy$$

$$= \rho \int_0^b (\tfrac{1}{3}a^3 + ay^2) \, dy$$

$$= \tfrac{1}{3}\rho ab(a^2 + b^2)$$

The moment of inertia is therefore $\tfrac{1}{3}\rho ab(a^2 + b^2)$ slug-ft^2.

Let us imagine the total mass M slugs of a lamina as being concentrated at one point; that is, suppose that a particle at this point has the same mass M slugs as the lamina. Then if this particle is at a distance r ft from a given axis L, the moment of inertia about L of this particle is Mr^2 slug-ft^2. The number r is the measure of the *radius of gyration* of the given lamina about L. We have the following definition.

18.3.3 Definition   If I is the measure of the moment of inertia about an axis L of a distribution of mass in a plane and M is the measure of the total mass of the distribution, then the *radius of gyration* of the distribution about L has measure r, where

$$r^2 = \frac{I}{M}$$

EXAMPLE 4:   Suppose that a lamina is in the shape of a semicircle and the measure of the area density of the lamina at any point is proportional to the measure of the distance of the point from the diameter. If mass is measured in slugs and distance is measured in feet, find the radius of gyration of the lamina about the x axis.

SOLUTION: Choose the x and y axes so that the semicircle is the top half of the circle $x^2 + y^2 = a^2$. See Fig. 18.3.3. The area density of the lamina at the point (x, y) is then ky slugs/ft². So if M slugs is the mass of the lamina, we have

$$M = \lim_{||\Delta|| \to 0} \sum_{i=1}^{n} k\gamma_i \, \Delta_i A$$

$$= \int\int_{R} ky \, dA$$

$$= \int_0^a \int_{-\sqrt{a^2-y^2}}^{\sqrt{a^2-y^2}} ky \, dx \, dy$$

$$= k \int_0^a \Big[yx \Big]_{-\sqrt{a^2-y^2}}^{\sqrt{a^2-y^2}} dy$$

$$= 2k \int_0^a y \sqrt{a^2 - y^2} \, dy$$

$$= -\tfrac{2}{3}k(a^2 - y^2)^{3/2} \Big]_0^a$$

$$= \tfrac{2}{3}ka^3$$

If I_x slug-ft² is the moment of inertia of the lamina about the x axis, then

$$I_x = \lim_{||\Delta|| \to 0} \sum_{i=1}^{n} \gamma_i^2 (k\gamma_i) \, \Delta_i A$$

$$= \int\int_{R} ky^3 \, dy \, dx$$

$$= \int_{-a}^{a} \int_0^{\sqrt{a^2-x^2}} ky^3 \, dy \, dx$$

$$= k \int_{-a}^{a} \Big[\tfrac{1}{4}y^4 \Big]_0^{\sqrt{a^2-x^2}} dx$$

$$= \tfrac{1}{4}k \int_{-a}^{a} (a^4 - 2a^2x^2 + x^4) \, dx$$

$$= \tfrac{1}{4}k(2a^5 - \tfrac{4}{3}a^5 + \tfrac{2}{5}a^5)$$

$$= \tfrac{4}{15}ka^5$$

Figure 18.3.3

Therefore, if r ft is the radius of gyration

$$r^2 = \frac{\frac{4}{15}ka^5}{\frac{2}{3}ka^3} = \frac{2}{5}a^2$$

and so $r = \frac{1}{5}\sqrt{10}a$. The radius of gyration is therefore $\frac{1}{5}\sqrt{10}a$ ft.

Exercises 18.3

In Exercises 1 through 10, find the mass and center of mass of the given lamina if the area density is as indicated. Mass is measured in slugs and distance is measured in feet.

1. A lamina in the shape of the rectangular region bounded by the lines $x = 3$ and $y = 2$, and the coordinate axes. The area density at any point is xy^2 slugs/ft².

2. A lamina in the shape of the region in the first quadrant bounded by the parabola $y = x^2$, the line $y = 1$, and the y axis. The area density at any point is $(x + y)$ slugs/ft².

3. A lamina in the shape of the region bounded by the parabola $x^2 = 8y$, the line $y = 2$, and the y axis. The area density varies as the distance from the line $y = -1$.

4. A lamina in the shape of the region bounded by the curve $y = e^x$, the line $x = 1$, and the coordinate axes. The area density varies as the distance from the x axis.

5. A lamina in the shape of the region in the first quadrant bounded by the circle $x^2 + y^2 = a^2$ and the coordinate axes. The area density varies as the sum of the distances from the two straight edges.

6. A lamina in the shape of the region bounded by the triangle whose sides are segments of the coordinate axes and the line $3x + 2y = 18$. The area density varies as the product of the distances from the coordinate axes.

7. A lamina in the shape of the region bounded by the curve $y = \sin x$ and the x axis from $x = 0$ to $x = \pi$. The area density varies as the distance from the x axis.

8. A lamina in the shape of the region bounded by the curve $y = \sqrt{x}$ and the line $y = x$. The area density varies as the distance from the y axis.

9. A lamina in the shape of the region in the first quadrant bounded by the circle $x^2 + y^2 = 4$ and the line $x + y = 2$. The area density at any point is xy slugs/ft².

10. A lamina in the shape of the region bounded by the circle $x^2 + y^2 = 1$ and the lines $x = 1$ and $y = 1$. The area density at any point is xy slugs/ft².

In Exercises 11 through 16 find the moment of inertia of the given homogeneous lamina about the indicated axis if the area density is ρ slugs/ft², and distance is measured in feet.

11. A lamina in the shape of the region bounded by $4y = 3x$, $x = 4$, and the x axis; about the x axis.

12. The lamina of Exercise 11; about the line $x = 4$.

13. A lamina in the shape of the region bounded by a circle of radius a units; about its center.

14. A lamina in the shape of the region bounded by the parabola $x^2 = 4 - 4y$ and the x axis; about the x axis.

15. The lamina of Exercise 14; about the origin.

16. A lamina in the shape of the region bounded by a triangle of sides of lengths a ft, b ft, and c ft; about the side of length a ft.

In Exercises 17 through 20, find for the given lamina each of the following: (a) the moment of inertia about the x axis; (b) the moment of inertia about the y axis; (c) the radius of gyration about the x axis; (d) the polar moment of inertia.

17. The lamina of Exercise 1.   18. The lamina of Exercise 2.   19. The lamina of Exercise 7.   20. The lamina of Exercise 8.

21. A homogeneous lamina of area density ρ slugs/ft^2 is in the shape of the region bounded by an isosceles triangle having a base of length b ft and an altitude of length h ft. Find the radius of gyration of the lamina about its line of symmetry.

22. A lamina is in the shape of the region enclosed by the parabola $y = 2x - x^2$ and the x axis. Find the moment of inertia of the lamina about the line $y = 4$ if the area density varies as its distance from the line $y = 4$. Mass is measured in slugs and distance is measured in feet.

18.4 THE DOUBLE INTEGRAL IN POLAR COORDINATES

Figure 18.4.1

We now show how the double integral of a function on a closed region in the polar coordinate plane can be defined. We begin by considering the simplest kind of region. Let R be the region bounded by the lines $\theta = \alpha$ and $\theta = \beta$ and by the circles $r = a$ and $r = b$. Then let Δ be a *partition* of this region which is obtained by drawing lines through the pole and circles having centers at the pole. This is shown in Fig. 18.4.1. We obtain a network of subregions which we call "curved" rectangles. The norm $\|\Delta\|$ of the partition is the length of the longest of the diagonals of the "curved" rectangles. Let the number of subregions be n, and let $\Delta_i A$ be the measure of area of the ith "curved" rectangle. Because the area of the ith subregion is the difference of the areas of two circular sectors, we have

$$\Delta_i A = \tfrac{1}{2} r_i^2 (\theta_i - \theta_{i-1}) - \tfrac{1}{2} r_{i-1}^2 (\theta_i - \theta_{i-1})$$

$$= \tfrac{1}{2}(r_i - r_{i-1})(r_i + r_{i-1})(\theta_i - \theta_{i-1})$$

Letting $\bar{r}_i = \tfrac{1}{2}(r_i + r_{i-1})$, $\Delta_i r = r_i - r_{i-1}$, and $\Delta_i \theta = \theta_i - \theta_{i-1}$, we have

$$\Delta_i A = \bar{r}_i \, \Delta_i r \, \Delta_i \theta$$

Take the point $(\bar{r}_i, \bar{\theta}_i)$ in the ith subregion, where $\theta_{i-1} \le \bar{\theta}_i \le \theta_i$ and form the sum

$$\sum_{i=1}^{n} f(\bar{r}_i, \bar{\theta}_i) \, \Delta_i A = \sum_{i=1}^{n} f(\bar{r}_i, \bar{\theta}_i) \bar{r}_i \, \Delta_i r \, \Delta_i \theta \tag{1}$$

It can be shown that if f is continuous on the region R, then the limit of the sum in (1), as $\|\Delta\|$ approaches zero, exists and that this limit will be the double integral of f on R. We write either

$$\lim_{\|\Delta\| \to 0} \sum_{i=1}^{n} f(\bar{r}_i, \bar{\theta}_i) \, \Delta_i A = \int\int_R f(r, \theta) \, dA \tag{2}$$

or

$$\lim_{\|\Delta\| \to 0} \sum_{i=1}^{n} f(\bar{r}_i, \bar{\theta}_i) \bar{r}_i \, \Delta_i r \, \Delta_i \theta = \int\int_R f(r, \theta) r \, dr \, d\theta \tag{3}$$

Figure 18.4.2

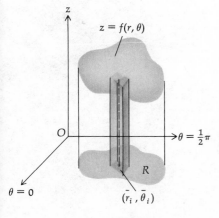

Figure 18.4.3

The double integral can be shown to be equal to an iterated integral having one of two possible forms:

$$\int\!\!\int_R f(r, \theta)\,dA = \int_\alpha^\beta \int_a^b f(r, \theta) r\,dr\,d\theta = \int_a^b \int_\alpha^\beta f(r, \theta)\,r\,d\theta\,dr \tag{4}$$

We can define the double integral of a continuous function f of two variables on closed regions of the polar coordinate plane other than the one previously considered. For example, consider the region R bounded by $r = \phi_1(\theta)$ and $r = \phi_2(\theta)$, where ϕ_1 and ϕ_2 are smooth functions, and by the lines $\theta = \alpha$ and $\theta = \beta$. See Fig. 18.4.2. In the figure, $\phi_1(\theta) \le \phi_2(\theta)$ for all θ in the closed interval $[\alpha, \beta]$. Then it can be shown that the double integral of f on R exists and equals an iterated integral, and we have

$$\int\!\!\int_R f(r, \theta)\,dA = \int_\alpha^\beta \int_{\phi_1(\theta)}^{\phi_2(\theta)} f(r, \theta) r\,dr\,d\theta \tag{5}$$

If the region R is bounded by the curves $\theta = \chi_1(r)$ and $\theta = \chi_2(r)$, where χ_1 and χ_2 are smooth functions, and by the circles $r = a$ and $r = b$, as shown in Fig. 18.4.3, where $\chi_1(r) \le \chi_2(r)$ for all r in the closed interval $[a, b]$, then

$$\int\!\!\int_R f(r, \theta)\,dA = \int_a^b \int_{\chi_1(r)}^{\chi_2(r)} f(r, \theta) r\,d\theta\,dr \tag{6}$$

We can interpret the double integral of a function on a closed region in the polar coordinate plane as the measure of the volume of a solid by using cylindrical coodinates. Figure 18.4.4 shows a solid having as its base a region R in the polar coordinate plane and bounded above by the surface $z = f(r, \theta)$ where f is continuous on R and $f(x, y) \ge 0$ on R. Take a partition of R giving a network of n "curved" rectangles. Construct the n solids for which the ith solid has as its base the ith "curved" rectangle and as the measure of its altitude $f(\bar{r}_i, \bar{\theta}_i)$ where $(\bar{r}_i, \bar{\theta}_i)$ is in the ith subregion. Figure 18.4.4 shows the ith solid. The measure of the volume of the ith solid is

$$f(\bar{r}_i, \bar{\theta}_i)\,\Delta_i A = f(\bar{r}_i, \bar{\theta}_i) \bar{r}_i\,\Delta_i r\,\Delta_i \theta$$

The sum of the measures of the volumes of the n solids is

$$\sum_{i=1}^n f(\bar{r}_i, \bar{\theta}_i) \bar{r}_i\,\Delta_i r\,\Delta_i \theta$$

If V is the measure of the volume of the given solid, then

$$V = \lim_{\|\Delta\| \to 0} \sum_{i=1}^n f(\bar{r}_i, \bar{\theta}_i) \bar{r}_i\,\Delta_i r\,\Delta_i \theta = \int\!\!\int_R f(r, \theta) r\,dr\,d\theta \tag{7}$$

Figure 18.4.4

EXAMPLE 1: Find the volume of the solid in the first octant

SOLUTION: The solid and the ith element are shown in Fig. 18.4.5. Using formula (7) with $f(r, \theta) = r$, we have, where V cubic units is the volume bounded by the cone $z = r$ and the cylinder $r = 3 \sin \theta$.

Figure 18.4.5

of the given solid,

$$V = \lim_{\|\Delta\| \to 0} \sum_{i=1}^{n} \bar{r}_i \cdot \bar{r}_i \, \Delta_i r \, \Delta_i \theta$$

$$= \int_R \int r^2 \, dr \, d\theta$$

$$= \int_0^{\pi/2} \int_0^{3 \sin \theta} r^2 \, dr \, d\theta$$

$$= \int_0^{\pi/2} \left[\tfrac{1}{3} r^3 \right]_0^{3 \sin \theta} d\theta$$

$$= 9 \int_0^{\pi/2} \sin^3 \theta \, d\theta$$

$$= -9 \cos \theta + 3 \cos^3 \theta \Big]_0^{\pi/2}$$

$$= 6$$

The volume is therefore 6 cubic units.

EXAMPLE 2: Find the mass of the lamina in the shape of the region inside the semicircle $r = a \cos \theta$, $0 \le \theta \le \tfrac{1}{2}\pi$, and whose measure of area density at any point is proportional to the measure of its distance from the pole. The mass is measured in slugs and distance is measured in feet.

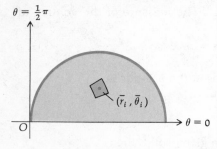

Figure 18.4.6

SOLUTION: Figure 18.4.6 shows a sketch of the lamina and the ith "curved" rectangle. The area density at the point (r, θ) is kr slugs/ft^2, where k is a constant. If M slugs is the mass of the lamina, then

$$M = \lim_{\|\Delta\| \to 0} \sum_{i=1}^{n} (k\bar{r}_i) \bar{r}_i \, \Delta_i r \, \Delta_i \theta$$

$$= \int_R \int kr^2 \, dr \, d\theta$$

$$= k \int_0^{\pi/2} \int_0^{a \cos \theta} r^2 \, dr \, d\theta$$

$$= \tfrac{1}{3} ka^3 \int_0^{\pi/2} \cos^3 \theta \, d\theta$$

$$= \tfrac{1}{3} ka^3 \left[\sin \theta - \tfrac{1}{3} \sin^3 \theta \right]_0^{\pi/2}$$

$$= \tfrac{2}{9} ka^3$$

Therefore, the mass is $\tfrac{2}{9} ka^3$ slugs.

EXAMPLE 3: Find the center of mass of the lamina in Example 2.

SOLUTION: Let the cartesian coordinates of the center of mass of the lamina be $\bar{x}$ and $\bar{y}$, where, as is customary, the x axis is along the polar axis and the y axis along the $\tfrac{1}{2}\pi$ axis. Let the cartesian coordinate representation of the point $(\bar{r}_i, \bar{\theta}_i)$ be $(\bar{x}_i, \bar{y}_i)$. Then if M_x slug-ft is the moment of mass of the lamina with respect to the x axis,

$$M_x = \lim_{||\Delta|| \to 0} \sum_{i=1}^{n} \bar{y}_i (k\bar{r}_i) \bar{r}_i \, \Delta_i r \, \Delta_i \theta$$

Replacing $\bar{y}_i$ by $\bar{r}_i \sin \bar{\theta}_i$, we get

$$M_x = \lim_{||\Delta|| \to 0} \sum_{i=1}^{n} k\bar{r}_i^3 \sin \bar{\theta}_i \, \Delta_i r \, \Delta_i \theta$$

$$= \int_R \int kr^3 \sin \theta \, dr \, d\theta$$

$$= k \int_0^{\pi/2} \int_0^{a \cos \theta} r^3 \sin \theta \, dr \, d\theta$$

$$= \tfrac{1}{4} ka^4 \int_0^{\pi/2} \cos^4 \theta \sin \theta \, d\theta$$

$$= -\tfrac{1}{20} ka^4 \cos^5 \theta \Big]_0^{\pi/2}$$

$$= \tfrac{1}{20} ka^4$$

If M_y slug-ft is the moment of mass of the lamina with respect to the y axis, then

$$M_y = \lim_{||\Delta|| \to 0} \sum_{i=1}^{n} \bar{x}_i (k\bar{r}_i) \bar{r}_i \, \Delta_i r \, \Delta_i \theta$$

Replacing $\bar{x}_i$ by $\bar{r}_i \cos \bar{\theta}_i$, we have

$$M_y = \lim_{||\Delta|| \to 0} \sum_{i=1}^{n} k\bar{r}_i^3 \cos \bar{\theta}_i \, \Delta_i r \, \Delta_i \theta$$

$$= \int_R \int kr^3 \cos \theta \, dr \, d\theta$$

$$= k \int_0^{\pi/2} \int_0^{a \cos \theta} r^3 \cos \theta \, dr \, d\theta$$

$$= \tfrac{1}{4} ka^4 \int_0^{\pi/2} \cos^5 \theta \, d\theta$$

$$= \tfrac{1}{4} ka^4 \left[\sin \theta - \tfrac{2}{3} \sin^3 \theta + \tfrac{1}{5} \sin^5 \theta \right]_0^{\pi/2}$$

$$= \tfrac{2}{15} ka^4$$

Therefore,

$$\bar{x} = \frac{M_y}{M} = \frac{\tfrac{2}{15} ka^4}{\tfrac{2}{9} ka^3} = \frac{3}{5} a$$

and

$$\bar{y} = \frac{M_x}{M} = \frac{\frac{1}{20}ka^4}{\frac{2}{9}ka^3} = \frac{9}{40}a$$

Hence, the center of mass is at the point $(\frac{3}{5}a, \frac{9}{40}a)$.

The area of a region in the polar plane can be found by double integration. The following example illustrates the method.

EXAMPLE 4: Find by double integration the area of the region enclosed by one leaf of the rose $r = \sin 3\theta$.

SOLUTION: Figure 18.4.7 shows the region and the ith "curved" rectangle. If A square units is the area of the region, then

$$A = \lim_{||\Delta|| \to 0} \sum_{i=1}^{n} \Delta_i A$$

$$= \lim_{||\Delta|| \to 0} \sum_{i=1}^{n} \bar{r}_i \, \Delta_i r \, \Delta_i \theta$$

$$= \int_R \int r \, dr \, d\theta$$

$$= \int_0^{\pi/3} \int_0^{\sin 3\theta} r \, dr \, d\theta$$

$$= \frac{1}{2} \int_0^{\pi/3} \sin^2 3\theta \, d\theta$$

$$= \frac{1}{4}\theta - \frac{1}{24} \sin 6\theta \Big]_0^{\pi/3}$$

$$= \frac{1}{12}\pi$$

Hence, the area is $\frac{1}{12}\pi$ square units.

Figure 18.4.7

Sometimes it is easier to evaluate a double integral by using polar coordinates instead of cartesian coordinates. Such a situation is shown in the following example.

EXAMPLE 5: Evaluate the double integral

$$\int_R \int e^{-(x^2+y^2)} \, dA$$

where the region R is in the first quadrant and bounded by the circle $x^2 + y^2 = a^2$ and the coordinate axes.

SOLUTION: Because $x^2 + y^2 = r^2$, and $dA = r \, dr \, d\theta$, we have

$$\int_R \int e^{-(x^2+y^2)} \, dA = \int_R \int e^{-r^2} r \, dr \, d\theta$$

$$= \int_0^{\pi/2} \int_0^a e^{-r^2} r \, dr \, d\theta$$

$$= -\frac{1}{2} \int_0^{\pi/2} \left[e^{-r^2} \right]_0^a \, d\theta$$

$$= -\frac{1}{2} \int_0^{\pi/2} (e^{-a^2} - 1) \, d\theta$$

$$= \frac{1}{4}\pi(1 - e^{-a^2})$$

Exercises 18.4

In Exercises 1 through 6, use double integrals to find the area of the given region.

1. The region inside the cardioid $r = 2(1 + \sin \theta)$.   2. One leaf of the rose $r = a \cos 2\theta$.

3. The region inside the cardioid $r = a(1 + \cos \theta)$ and outside the circle $r = a$.

4. The region inside the circle $r = 1$ and outside the lemniscate $r^2 = \cos 2\theta$.

5. The region inside the large loop of the limaçon $r = 2 - 4 \sin \theta$ and outside the small loop.

6. The region inside the limaçon $r = 3 - \cos \theta$ and outside the circle $r = 5 \cos \theta$.

In Exercises 7 through 12, find the volume of the given solid.

7. The solid bounded by the ellipsoid $z^2 + 9r^2 = 9$.

8. The solid cut out of the sphere $z^2 + r^2 = 4$ by the cylinder $r = 1$.

9. The solid cut out of the sphere $z^2 + r^2 = 16$ by the cylinder $r = 4 \cos \theta$.

10. The solid above the polar plane bounded by the cone $z = 2r$ and the cylinder $r = 1 - \cos \theta$.

11. The solid bounded by the paraboloid $z = 4 - r^2$, the cylinder $r = 1$, and the polar plane.

12. The solid above the paraboloid $z = r^2$ and below the plane $z = 2r \sin \theta$.

In Exercises 13 through 19 find the mass and center of mass of the given lamina if the area density is as indicated. Mass is measured in slugs and distance is measured in feet.

13. A lamina in the shape of the region of Exercise 1. The area density varies as the distance from the pole.

14. A lamina in the shape of the region of Exercise 2. The area density varies as the distance from the pole.

15. A lamina in the shape of the region inside the limaçon $r = 2 - \cos \theta$. The area density varies as the distance from the pole.

16. A lamina in the shape of the region bounded by the limaçon $r = 2 + \cos \theta$, $0 \le \theta \le \pi$, and the polar axis. The area density at any point is $k \sin \theta$ slugs/ft².

17. The lamina of Exercise 16. The area density at any point is $kr \sin \theta$ slugs/ft².

18. A lamina in the shape of the region of Exercise 6. The area density varies as the distance from the pole.

19. A lamina in the shape of the region of Exercise 5. The area density varies as the distance from the pole.

In Exercises 20 through 25, find the moment of inertia of the given lamina about the indicated axis or point, if the area density is as indicated. Mass is measured in slugs and distance is measured in feet.

20. A lamina in the shape of the region enclosed by the circle $r = \sin \theta$; about the $\frac{1}{2}\pi$ axis. The area density at any point is k slugs/ft².

21. The lamina of Exercise 20; about the polar axis. The area density at any point is k slugs/ft².

22. A lamina in the shape of the region bounded by the cardioid $r = a(1 - \cos \theta)$; about the pole. The area density at any point is k slugs/ft².

23. A lamina in the shape of the region bounded by the cardioid $r = a(1 + \cos \theta)$ and the circle $r = 2a \cos \theta$; about the pole. The area density at any point is k slugs/ft².

24. A lamina in the shape of the region enclosed by the lemniscate $r^2 = a^2 \cos 2\theta$; about the polar axis. The area density varies as the distance from the pole.

25. A homogeneous lamina is in the shape of the region enclosed by one loop of the lemniscate $r^2 = \cos 2\theta$. Find the radius of gyration of the lamina about an axis perpendicular to the polar plane at the pole.

26. A lamina is in the shape of the region enclosed by the circle $r = 4$, and the area density varies as the distance from the pole. Find the radius of gyration of the lamina about an axis perpendicular to the polar plane at the pole.

27. Evaluate by polar coordinates the double integral

$$\int_R \int e^{x^2 + y^2} \, dA$$

where R is the region bounded by the circles $x^2 + y^2 = 1$ and $x^2 + y^2 = 9$.

28. Evaluate by polar coordinates the double integral

$$\int_R \int \frac{x}{\sqrt{x^2 + y^2}} \, dA$$

where R is the region in the first quadrant bounded by the circle $x^2 + y^2 = 1$ and the coordinate axes.

29. In advanced calculus, improper double integrals are discussed, and $\int_0^{+\infty} \int_0^{+\infty} f(x, y) \, dx \, dy$ is defined to be

$$\lim_{h \to +\infty} \int_0^h \int_0^h f(x, y) \, dx \, dy$$

Use this definition to prove that $\int_0^{+\infty} e^{-x^2} \, dx = \frac{1}{2}\sqrt{\pi}$ by doing the following: (a) Show that the double integral in Example 5 can be expressed as $\left[\int_0^a e^{-x^2} \, dx \right]^2$; (b) because $\left[\int_0^{+\infty} e^{-x^2} \, dx \right]^2 = \lim_{a \to +\infty} \left[\int_0^a e^{-x^2} \, dx \right]^2$ use the result of Example 5 to obtain the desired result.

18.5 AREA OF A SURFACE

Figure 18.5.1

The double integral can be used to determine the area of the portion of the surface $z = f(x, y)$ that lies over a closed region R in the xy plane. To show this we must first define what we mean by the measure of this area and then obtain a formula for computing it. We assume that f and its first partial derivatives are continuous on R and suppose further that $f(x, y) > 0$ on R. Let Δ be a partition of R into n rectangular subregions. The ith rectangle has dimensions of measures $\Delta_i x$ and $\Delta_i y$ and an area of measure $\Delta_i A$. Let (ξ_i, γ_i) be any point in the ith rectangle, and at the point $Q(\xi_i, \gamma_i, f(\xi_i, \gamma_i))$ on the surface consider the tangent plane to the surface. Project vertically upward the ith rectangle onto the tangent plane and let $\Delta_i \sigma$ be the measure of the area of this projection. Figure 18.5.1 shows the region R, the portion of the surface above R, the ith rectangular subregion of R, and the projection of the ith rectangle onto the tangent plane to the surface at Q. The number $\Delta_i \sigma$ is an approximation to the measure of the area of the piece of the surface that lies above the ith rectangle. Because we have n such pieces, the summation

$$\sum_{i=1}^n \Delta_i \sigma$$

is an approximation to the measure σ of the area of the portion of the surface that lies above R. This leads to defining σ as follows:

$$\sigma = \lim_{\|\Delta\| \to 0} \sum_{i=1}^n \Delta_i \sigma \tag{1}$$

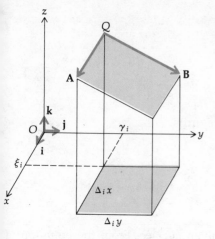

Figure 18.5.2

We now need to obtain a formula for computing the limit in Eq. (1). To do this we find a formula for computing $\Delta_i\sigma$ as the measure of the area of a parallelogram. For simplicity in computation we take the point (ξ_i, γ_i) in the ith rectangle at the corner (x_{i-1}, y_{i-1}). Let $\mathbf{A}$ and $\mathbf{B}$ be vectors having as representations the directed line segments having initial points at Q and forming the two adjacent sides of the parallelogram whose area has measure $\Delta_i\sigma$. See Fig. 18.5.2. Then $\Delta_i\sigma = |\mathbf{A} \times \mathbf{B}|$. Because

$$\mathbf{A} = \Delta_i x\mathbf{i} + f_x(\xi_i, \gamma_i)\ \Delta_i x\mathbf{k}$$

and

$$\mathbf{B} = \Delta_i y\mathbf{j} + f_y(\xi_i, \gamma_i)\ \Delta_i y\mathbf{k}$$

it follows that

$$\mathbf{A} \times \mathbf{B} = \begin{vmatrix} \mathbf{i} & \mathbf{j} & \mathbf{k} \\ \Delta_i x & 0 & f_x(\xi_i, \gamma_i)\ \Delta_i x \\ 0 & \Delta_i y & f_y(\xi_i, \gamma_i)\ \Delta_i y \end{vmatrix}$$

$$= -\Delta_i x\ \Delta_i y f_x(\xi_i, \gamma_i)\mathbf{i} - \Delta_i x\ \Delta_i y f_y(\xi_i, \gamma_i)\mathbf{j} + \Delta_i x\ \Delta_i y\mathbf{k}$$

Therefore,

$$\Delta_i\sigma = |\mathbf{A} \times \mathbf{B}| = \sqrt{f_x{}^2(\xi_i, \gamma_i) + f_y{}^2(\xi_i, \gamma_i) + 1}\ \Delta_i x\ \Delta_i y \tag{2}$$

Substituting from Eq. (2) into Eq. (1), we get

$$\sigma = \lim_{\|\Delta\| \to 0} \sum_{i=1}^{n} \sqrt{f_x{}^2(\xi_i, \gamma_i) + f_y{}^2(\xi_i, \gamma_i) + 1}\ \Delta_i x\ \Delta_i y$$

This limit is a double integral which exists on R because of the continuity of f_x and f_y on R. We have, then, the following theorem.

18.5.1 Theorem   Suppose that f and its first partial derivatives are continuous on the closed region R in the xy plane. Then if σ is the measure of the area of the surface $z = f(x, y)$ which lies over R,

$$\sigma = \int_R\int \sqrt{f_x{}^2(x, y) + f_y{}^2(x, y) + 1}\ dx\ dy \tag{3}$$

EXAMPLE 1:   Find the area of the surface that is cut from the cylinder $x^2 + z^2 = 16$ by the planes $x = 0$, $x = 2$, $y = 0$, and $y = 3$.

SOLUTION: The given surface is shown in Fig. 18.5.3. The region R is the rectangle in the first quadrant of the xy plane bounded by the lines $x = 2$ and $y = 3$. The surface has the equation $x^2 + z^2 = 16$. Solving for z, we get $z = \sqrt{16 - x^2}$. Hence, $f(x, y) = \sqrt{16 - x^2}$. So if σ is the measure of the area of the surface, we have from Theorem 18.5.1

$$\sigma = \int_R\int \sqrt{f_x{}^2(x, y) + f_y{}^2(x, y) + 1}\ dx\ dy$$

$$= \int_0^3\int_0^2 \sqrt{\left(\frac{-x}{\sqrt{16 - x^2}}\right)^2 + 0 + 1}\ dx\ dy$$

$$= \int_0^3\int_0^2 \frac{4}{\sqrt{16 - x^2}}\ dx\ dy$$

Figure 18.5.3

$$= 4 \int_0^3 \left[\sin^{-1} \tfrac{1}{4} x \right]_0^2 dy$$

$$= 4 \int_0^3 \tfrac{1}{6} \pi \, dy$$

$$= 2\pi$$

The surface area is therefore 2π square units.

EXAMPLE 2:   Find the area of the paraboloid $z = x^2 + y^2$ below the plane $z = 4$.

Figure 18.5.4

SOLUTION: Figure 18.5.4 shows the given surface. From the equation of the paraboloid we see that $f(x, y) = x^2 + y^2$. The closed region in the xy plane bounded by the circle $x^2 + y^2 = 4$ is the region R. If σ square units is the required surface area, we have from Theorem 18.5.1

$$\sigma = \int\int_R \sqrt{f_x{}^2(x, y) + f_y{}^2(x, y) + 1} \, dx \, dy$$

$$= \int\int_R \sqrt{4(x^2 + y^2) + 1} \, dx \, dy$$

Because the integrand contains the terms $4(x^2 + y^2)$, the evaluation of the double integral is simplified by using polar coordinates. Then $x^2 + y^2 = r^2$, and $dx \, dy = dA = r \, dr \, d\theta$. Furthermore, the limits for r are from 0 to 2 and the limits for θ are from 0 to 2π. We have then

$$\sigma = \int\int_R \sqrt{4r^2 + 1} \, r \, dr \, d\theta$$

$$= \int_0^{2\pi} \int_0^2 \sqrt{4r^2 + 1} \, r \, dr \, d\theta$$

$$= \int_0^{2\pi} \left[\tfrac{1}{12}(4r^2 + 1)^{3/2} \right]_0^2 d\theta$$

$$= \tfrac{1}{6}\pi(17\sqrt{17} - 1)$$

Hence, the area of the paraboloid below the given plane is $\tfrac{1}{6}\pi(17\sqrt{17} - 1)$ square units.

EXAMPLE 3:   Find the area of the top half of the sphere $x^2 + y^2 + z^2 = a^2$.

SOLUTION: The hemisphere is shown in Fig. 18.5.5. Solving the equation of the sphere for z and setting this equal to $f(x, y)$, we get

$$f(x, y) = \sqrt{a^2 - x^2 - y^2}$$

Because $f_x(x, y) = -x/\sqrt{a^2 - x^2 - y^2}$, and $f_y(x, y) = -y/\sqrt{a^2 - x^2 - y^2}$, we note that f_x and f_y are not defined on the circle $x^2 + y^2 = a^2$ which is the boundary of the region R in the xy plane. Furthermore, the double integral obtained from Eq. (3) is

$$\iint_R \frac{a}{\sqrt{a^2 - x^2 - y^2}} \, dx \, dy$$

which is improper because the integrand has an infinite discontinuity at each point of the boundary of R. We can take care of this situation by considering the region R' as that bounded by the circle $x^2 + y^2 = b^2$, where $b < a$, and then take the limit as $b \to a^-$. Furthermore, the computation is simplified if the double integral is evaluated by an iterated integral using polar coordinates. Then we have

$$\sigma = \lim_{b \to a^-} \int_0^b \int_0^{2\pi} \frac{a}{\sqrt{a^2 - r^2}} \, r \, d\theta \, dr$$

$$= 2\pi a \lim_{b \to a^-} \int_0^b \frac{r}{\sqrt{a^2 - r^2}} \, dr$$

$$= 2\pi a \lim_{b \to a^-} \left[-\sqrt{a^2 - r^2} \right]_0^b$$

$$= 2\pi a \lim_{b \to a^-} \left[-\sqrt{a^2 - b^2} + a \right]$$

$$= 2\pi a^2$$

The area of the hemisphere is therefore $2\pi a^2$ square units.

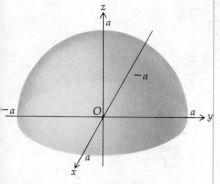

Figure 18.5.5

Consider now the curve $y = F(x)$ with $a \le x \le b$, F positive on $[a, b]$ and F' continuous on $[a, b]$. If this curve is rotated about the x axis, we obtain a surface of revolution. From Sec. 16.7 an equation of this surface is

$$y^2 + z^2 = [F(x)]^2 \tag{4}$$

Figure 18.5.6 shows the surface of revolution. In the figure we have taken the xy plane in the plane of the paper; however, we still have a right-handed system. We wish to obtain a formula for finding the measure of the area of this surface of revolution by using Theorem 18.5.1. From properties of symmetry, the measure of the area of the surface above the xz plane and in front of the xy plane is one-fourth of the measure of the area of the entire surface. Solving Eq. (4) for z (neglecting the negative square root because $z \ge 0$), we get $f(x, y) = \sqrt{[F(x)]^2 - y^2}$. The region R in the xy plane is that bounded by the x axis, the curve $y = F(x)$, and the lines $x = a$ and $x = b$. Computing the partial derivatives of f, we obtain

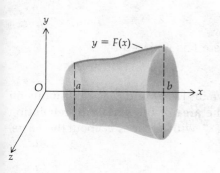

Figure 18.5.6

$$f_x(x, y) = \frac{F(x)F'(x)}{\sqrt{[F(x)]^2 - y^2}} \qquad f_y(x, y) = \frac{-y}{\sqrt{[F(x)]^2 - y^2}}$$

We see that $f_x(x, y)$ and $f_y(x, y)$ do not exist on part of the boundary of

R (when $y = -F(x)$ and when $y = F(x)$). The double integral obtained from Eq. (3) is

$$\iint_R \sqrt{\frac{[F(x)]^2[F'(x)]^2}{[F(x)]^2 - y^2} + \frac{y^2}{[F(x)]^2 - y^2} + 1} \; dy \; dx$$

$$= \iint_R \frac{F(x) \sqrt{[F'(x)]^2 + 1}}{\sqrt{[F(x)]^2 - y^2}} \; dy \; dx$$

This double integral is improper because the integrand has an infinite discontinuity at each point of the boundary of R where $y = -F(x)$ and $y = F(x)$. Hence, we evaluate the double integral by an iterated integral for which the inner integral is improper.

$$\sigma = 4 \int_a^b \left[F(x) \sqrt{F'(x)^2 + 1} \int_0^{F(x)} \frac{dy}{\sqrt{[F(x)]^2 - y^2}} \right] dx \qquad (5)$$

where

$$\int_0^{F(x)} \frac{dy}{\sqrt{[F(x)]^2 - y^2}} = \lim_{\epsilon \to 0^+} \int_0^{F(x) - \epsilon} \frac{dy}{\sqrt{[F(x)]^2 - y^2}}$$

$$= \lim_{\epsilon \to 0^+} \left[\sin^{-1} \frac{y}{F(x)} \right]_0^{F(x) - \epsilon}$$

$$= \lim_{\epsilon \to 0^+} \sin^{-1} \left(1 - \frac{\epsilon}{F(x)} \right)$$

$$= \tfrac{1}{2} \pi$$

Therefore, from Eq. (5) we have

$$\sigma = 2\pi \int_a^b F(x) \sqrt{[F'(x)]^2 + 1} \; dx$$

We state this result as a theorem, where F is replaced by f.

18.5.2 Theorem   Suppose that the function f is positive on $[a, b]$ and f' is continuous on $[a, b]$. Then if σ is the measure of the area of the surface of revolution obtained by revolving the curve $y = f(x)$, with $a \le x \le b$, about the x axis,

$$\sigma = 2\pi \int_a^b f(x) \sqrt{[f'(x)]^2 + 1} \; dx$$

EXAMPLE 4:   Find the area of the paraboloid of revolution generated by revolving the top half of the parabola $y^2 = 4px$, with $0 \le x \le h$, about the x axis.

SOLUTION: The paraboloid of revolution is shown in Fig. 18.5.7. Solving the equation of the parabola for y ($y \ge 0$), we obtain $y = 2p^{1/2}x^{1/2}$. So if σ square units is the area of the surface, from Theorem 18.5.2, with $f(x) = 2p^{1/2}x^{1/2}$, we have

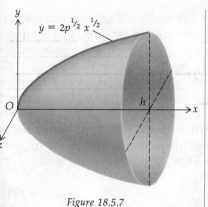

$y = 2p^{1/2} x^{1/2}$

Figure 18.5.7

$$\sigma = 2\pi \int_0^h 2p^{1/2}x^{1/2} \sqrt{\frac{p}{x} + 1} \; dx$$

$$= 4\pi p^{1/2} \int_0^h \sqrt{p + x} \; dx$$

$$= \tfrac{8}{3}\pi p^{1/2}(p + x)^{3/2} \Big]_0^h$$

$$= \tfrac{8}{3}\pi \left(\sqrt{p(p+h)^3} - p^2 \right)$$

The area of the paraboloid of revolution is therefore $\tfrac{8}{3}\pi\left(\sqrt{p(p+h)^3} - p^2 \right)$ square units.

Exercises 18.5

1. Find the area of the surface which is cut from the plane $2x + y + z = 4$ by the planes $x = 0$, $x = 1$, $y = 0$, and $y = 1$.

2. Find the area of the portion of the surface of the plane $36x + 16y + 9z = 144$ which is cut by the coordinate planes.

3. Find the area of the surface in the first octant which is cut from the cylinder $x^2 + y^2 = 9$ by the plane $x = z$.

4. Find the area of the surface in the first octant which is cut from the cone $x^2 + y^2 = z^2$ by the plane $x + y = 4$.

5. Find the area of the portion of the surface of the sphere $x^2 + y^2 + z^2 = 4x$ which is cut out by one nappe of the cone $y^2 + z^2 = x^2$.

6. Find the area of the portion of the surface of the sphere $x^2 + y^2 + z^2 = 36$ which lies within the cylinder $x^2 + y^2 = 9$.

7. Find the area of the portion of the surface of the sphere $x^2 + y^2 + z^2 = 4z$ which lies within the paraboloid $x^2 + y^2 = 3z$.

8. For the sphere and paraboloid of Exercise 7, find the area of the portion of the surface of the paraboloid which lies within the sphere.

9. The line segment from the origin to the point (a, b) is revolved about the x axis. Find the area of the surface of the cone generated.

10. Derive the formula for the area of the surface of a sphere by revolving a semicircle about its diameter.

11. Find the area of the surface of revolution obtained by revolving the arc of the catenary $y = a \cosh(x/a)$ from $x = 0$ to $x = a$ about the y axis.

12. Find the area of the surface of revolution obtained by revolving the catenary of Exercise 11 about the x axis.

13. The loop of the curve $18y^2 = x(6 - x)^2$ is revolved about the x axis. Find the area of the surface of revolution generated.

14. Find the area of the surface of revolution generated by revolving the arc of the curve $y = \ln x$ from $x = 1$ to $x = 2$ about the y axis.

15. Find the area of the portion of the plane $x = z$ which lies between the planes $y = 0$ and $y = 6$ and within the hyperboloid $9x^2 - 4y^2 + 16z^2 = 144$.

16. Find the area of the surface cut from the hyperbolic paraboloid $y^2 - x^2 = 6z$ by the cylinder $x^2 + y^2 = 36$.

18.6 THE TRIPLE INTEGRAL

The extension of the double integral to the triple integral is analogous to the extension of the single integral to the double integral. The simplest type of region in R_3 is a rectangular parallelepiped which is bounded by six planes: $x = a_1$, $x = a_2$, $y = b_1$, $y = b_2$, $z = c_1$, and $z = c_2$, with $a_1 < a_2$, $b_1 < b_2$, and $c_1 < c_2$. Let f be a function of three variables and suppose that f is continuous on such a region S. A partition of this region is formed by dividing S into rectangular boxes by drawing planes parallel to the coordinate planes. Denote such a partition by Δ and suppose that n is the number of boxes. Let $\Delta_i V$ be the measure of the volume of the ith box. Choose an arbitrary point (ξ_i, γ_i, μ_i) in the ith box. Form the sum

$$\sum_{i=1}^{n} f(\xi_i, \gamma_i, \mu_i)\, \Delta_i V \qquad (1)$$

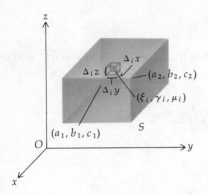

Figure 18.6.1

Refer to Fig. 18.6.1, which shows the rectangular parallelepiped together with the ith box. The *norm* $\|\Delta\|$ of the partition is the length of the longest diagonal of the boxes. The sums of the form (1) will approach a limit as the norm of the partition approaches zero for any choices of the points (ξ_i, γ_i, μ_i) if f is continuous on S. Then we call this limit the *triple integral* of f on R and write

$$\left(\lim_{\|\Delta\|\to 0} \sum_{i=1}^{n} f(\xi_i, \gamma_i, \mu_i)\, \Delta_i V = \iiint\limits_{S} f(x, y, z)\, dV \right.$$

Analogous to a double integral being equal to a twice-iterated integral, the triple integral is equal to a thrice-iterated integral. When S is the rectangular parallelepiped described above, and f is continuous on S, we have

$$\iiint\limits_{S} f(x, y, z)\, dV = \int_{a_1}^{a_2} \int_{b_1}^{b_2} \int_{c_1}^{c_2} f(x, y, z)\, dz\, dy\, dx$$

EXAMPLE 1:   Evaluate the triple integral

$$\iiint\limits_{S} xy \sin yz\, dV$$

if S is the rectangular parallelepiped bounded by the planes $x = \pi$, $y = \frac{1}{2}\pi$, $z = \frac{1}{3}\pi$, and the coordinate planes.

SOLUTION:

$$\iiint\limits_{S} xy \sin yz\, dV = \int_0^\pi \int_0^{\pi/2} \int_0^{\pi/3} xy \sin yz\, dz\, dy\, dx$$

$$= \int_0^\pi \int_0^{\pi/2} \Big[-x \cos yz \Big]_0^{\pi/3} dy\, dx$$

$$= \int_0^\pi \int_0^{\pi/2} x(1 - \cos \tfrac{1}{3}\pi y)\, dy\, dx$$

$$= \int_0^\pi x \left(y - \frac{3}{\pi} \sin \frac{1}{3}\pi y \right)\Big]_0^{\pi/2} dx$$

$$= \int_0^\pi x \left(\frac{\pi}{2} - \frac{3}{\pi} \sin \frac{\pi^2}{6} \right) dx$$

$$= \frac{x^2}{2} \left(\frac{\pi}{2} - \frac{3}{\pi} \sin \frac{\pi^2}{6} \right) \Big]_0^\pi$$

$$= \frac{\pi}{4} \left(\pi^2 - 6 \sin \frac{\pi^2}{6} \right)$$

We now discuss how to define the triple integral of a continuous function of three variables on a region in R_3 other than a rectangular parallelepiped. Let S be the closed three-dimensional region which is bounded by the planes $x = a$ and $x = b$, the cylinders $y = \phi_1(x)$ and $y = \phi_2(x)$, and the surfaces $z = F_1(x, y)$ and $z = F_2(x, y)$, where the functions ϕ_1, ϕ_2, F_1, and F_2 are smooth (i.e., they have continuous derivatives or partial derivatives). See Fig. 18.6.2. Construct planes parallel to the coordinate planes, thereby forming a set of rectangular parallelepipeds that completely cover S. The parallelepipeds which are entirely inside S or on the boundary of S form a *partition* Δ of S. Choose some system of numbering so that they are numbered from 1 to n. The norm $\|\Delta\|$ of this partition of S is the length of the longest diagonal of any parallelepiped belonging to the partition. Let the measure of the volume of the ith parallelepiped be $\Delta_i V$. Let f be a function of three variables which is continuous on S and let (ξ_i, γ_i, μ_i) be an arbitrary point in the ith parallelepiped. Form the sum

$$\sum_{i=1}^n f(\xi_i, \gamma_i, \mu_i)\, \Delta_i V \tag{2}$$

If the sums of form (2) have a limit as $\|\Delta\|$ approaches zero, and if this limit is independent of the choice of the partitioning planes and the choices of the arbitrary points (ξ_i, γ_i, μ_i) in each parallelepiped, then this limit is called the *triple integral* of f on S, and we write

$$\lim_{\|\Delta\| \to 0} \sum_{i=1}^n f(\xi_i, \gamma_i, \mu_i)\, \Delta_i V = \iiint_S f(x, y, z)\, dV \tag{3}$$

It can be proved in advanced calculus that a sufficient condition for the limit in (3) to exist is that f be continuous on S. Furthermore, under the condition imposed upon the functions ϕ_1, ϕ_2, F_1, and F_2 that they be smooth, it can also be proved that the triple integral can be evaluated by the iterated integral

$$\int_a^b \int_{\phi_1(x)}^{\phi_2(x)} \int_{F_1(x,y)}^{F_2(x,y)} f(x, y, z)\, dz\, dy\, dx$$

Just as the double integral can be interpreted as the measure of the area of a plane region when $f(x, y) = 1$ on R_1, the triple integral can be interpreted as the measure of the volume of a three-dimensional region. If

$f(x, y, z) = 1$ on S, then Eq. (3) becomes

$$\lim_{||\Delta|| \to 0} \sum_{i=1}^{n} \Delta_i V = \iiint_S dV$$

and the triple integral is the measure of the volume of the region S.

EXAMPLE 2: Find by triple integration the volume of the solid of Example 3 in Sec. 18.2.

SOLUTION: If V cubic units is the volume of the solid, then

$$V = \lim_{||\Delta|| \to 0} \sum_{i=1}^{n} \Delta_i V = \iiint_S dV \tag{4}$$

where S is the region bounded by the solid. The z limits are from 0 (the value of z on the xy plane) to $x^2 + 4y^2$ (the value of z on the elliptic paraboloid). The y limits for one-fourth of the volume are from 0 (the value of y on the xz plane) to $\frac{1}{2}\sqrt{4 - x^2}$ (the value of y on the cylinder). The x limits for the first octant are from 0 to 2. We evaluate the triple integral in (4) by an iterated integral and obtain

$$V = 4 \int_0^2 \int_0^{\sqrt{4-x^2}/2} \int_0^{x^2+4y^2} dz \, dy \, dx$$

Hence,

$$V = 4 \int_0^2 \int_0^{\sqrt{4-x^2}/2} (x^2 + 4y^2) \, dy \, dx \tag{5}$$

The right side of Eq. (5) is the same twice-iterated integral that we obtained in Example 3 in Sec. 18.2, and so the remainder of the solution is the same.

EXAMPLE 3: Find the volume of the solid bounded by the cylinder $x^2 + y^2 = 25$, the plane $x + y + z = 8$ and the xy plane.

SOLUTION: The solid is shown in Fig. 18.6.3. The z limits for the iterated integral are from 0 to $8 - x - y$ (the value of z on the plane). The y limits are obtained from the boundary region in the xy plane which is the circle $x^2 + y^2 = 25$. Hence, the y limits are from $-\sqrt{25 - x^2}$ to $\sqrt{25 - x^2}$. The x limits are from -5 to 5. If V cubic units is the required volume, we have

$$V = \lim_{||\Delta|| \to 0} \sum_{i=1}^{n} \Delta_i V = \iiint_S dV$$

$$= \int_{-5}^{5} \int_{-\sqrt{25-x^2}}^{\sqrt{25-x^2}} \int_0^{8-x-y} dz \, dy \, dx$$

$$= \int_{-5}^{5} \int_{-\sqrt{25-x^2}}^{\sqrt{25-x^2}} (8 - x - y) \, dy \, dx$$

$$= \int_{-5}^{5} \left[(8 - x)y - \tfrac{1}{2}y^2 \right]_{-\sqrt{25-x^2}}^{\sqrt{25-x^2}} dx$$

$$= 2 \int_{-5}^{5} (8 - x) \sqrt{25 - x^2} \, dx$$

Figure 18.6.3

$$= 16 \int_{-5}^{5} \sqrt{25 - x^2} \, dx + \int_{-5}^{5} \sqrt{25 - x^2}(-2x) \, dx$$

$$= 16\left(\tfrac{1}{2}x\sqrt{25 - x^2} + \tfrac{25}{2}\sin^{-1}\tfrac{1}{5}x\right) + \tfrac{2}{3}(25 - x^2)^{3/2}\Big]_{-5}^{5}$$

$$= 200\pi$$

The volume is therefore 200π cubic units.

EXAMPLE 4: Find the mass of the solid above the xy plane bounded by the cone $9x^2 + z^2 = y^2$ and the plane $y = 9$ if the measure of the volume density at any point (x, y, z) in the solid is proportional to the measure of the distance of the point from the xy plane.

Figure 18.6.4

SOLUTION: Figure 18.6.4 shows the solid. Let M slugs be the mass of the solid, and let the distance be measured in feet. Then the volume density at any point (x, y, z) in the solid is kz slugs/ft³, where k is a constant. Then if (ξ_i, γ_i, μ_i) is any point in the ith rectangular parallelepiped of the partition, we have

$$M = \lim_{\|\Delta\| \to 0} \sum_{i=1}^{n} k\mu_i \, \Delta_i V = \iiint\limits_{S} kz \, dV$$

$$= 2k \int_{0}^{9}\int_{0}^{y/3}\int_{0}^{\sqrt{y^2 - 9x^2}} z \, dz \, dx \, dy$$

$$= 2k \int_{0}^{9}\int_{0}^{y/3} \left[\tfrac{1}{2}z^2\right]_{0}^{\sqrt{y^2 - 9x^2}} dx \, dy$$

$$= k \int_{0}^{9}\int_{0}^{y/3} (y^2 - 9x^2) \, dx \, dy$$

$$= \tfrac{2}{9}k \int_{0}^{9} y^3 \, dy = \tfrac{729}{2}k$$

The mass is therefore $\tfrac{729}{2}k$ slugs.

Exercises 18.6

In Exercises 1 through 4, evaluate the iterated integral.

1. $\int_0^1 \int_0^{1-x} \int_{2y}^{1+y^2} x \, dz \, dy \, dx$ 2. $\int_1^2 \int_y^{y^2} \int_0^{\ln x} y e^z \, dz \, dx \, dy$ 3. $\int_0^{\pi/2} \int_z^{\pi/2} \int_0^{xz} \cos \frac{y}{z} \, dy \, dx \, dz$ 4. $\int_1^2 \int_0^y \int_0^{\sqrt{3z}} \frac{z}{x^2 + z^2} \, dx \, dz \, dy$

In Exercises 5 through 10, evaluate the triple integral.

5. $\iiint_S y \, dV$ if S is the region bounded by the tetrahedron formed by the plane $12x + 20y + 15z = 60$ and the coordinate planes.

6. $\iiint_S (x^2 + z^2) \, dV$ if S is the same region as in Exercise 5.

7. $\iiint_S z \, dV$ if S is the region bounded by the tetrahedron having vertices $(0, 0, 0)$, $(1, 1, 0)$, $(1, 0, 0)$, and $(1, 0, 1)$.

8. $\iiint_S yz \, dV$ if S is the same region as in Exercise 7.

9. $\iiint_S (xz + 3z) \, dV$ if S is the region bounded by the cylinder $x^2 + z^2 = 9$ and the planes $x + y = 3$, $z = 0$, and $y = 0$, above the xy plane.

10. $\iiint_S xyz \, dV$, if S is the region bounded by the cylinders $x^2 + y^2 = 4$ and $x^2 + z^2 = 4$.

In Exercises 11 through 21, use triple integration.

11. Find the volume of the solid in the first octant bounded below by the xy plane, above by the plane $z = y$, and laterally by the cylinder $y^2 = x$ and the plane $x = 1$.

12. Find the volume of the solid in the first octant bounded by the cylinder $x^2 + z^2 = 16$, the plane $x + y = 2$, and the three coordinate planes.

13. Find the volume of the solid in the first octant bounded by the cylinders $x^2 + y^2 = 4$ and $x^2 + 2z = 4$, and the three coordinate planes.

14. Find the volume of the solid bounded by the elliptic cone $4x^2 + 9y^2 - 36z^2 = 0$ and the plane $z = 1$.

15. Find the volume of the solid above the elliptic paraboloid $3x^2 + y^2 = z$ and below the cylinder $x^2 + z = 4$.

16. Find the volume of the solid enclosed by the sphere $x^2 + y^2 + z^2 = a^2$.

17. Find the volume of the solid enclosed by the ellipsoid

$$\frac{x^2}{a^2} + \frac{y^2}{b^2} + \frac{z^2}{c^2} = 1$$

18. Find the mass of the solid enclosed by the tetrahedron formed by the plane $100x + 25y + 16z = 400$ and the coordinate planes if the volume density varies as the distance from the yz plane. The volume density is measured in slugs/ft³.

19. Find the mass of the solid bounded by the cylinders $x = z^2$ and $y = x^2$, and the planes $x = 1$, $y = 0$, and $z = 0$. The volume density varies as the product of the distances from the three coordinate planes, and it is measured in slugs/ft³.

20. Find the mass of the solid bounded by the surface $z = 4 - 4x^2 - y^2$ and the xy plane. The volume density at any point of the solid is ρ slugs/ft³ and $\rho = 3z|x|$.

21. Find the mass of the solid bounded by the surface $z = xy$, and the planes $x = 1$, $y = 1$, and $z = 0$. The volume density at any point of the solid is ρ slugs/ft³ and $\rho = 3\sqrt{x^2 + y^2}$.

18.7 THE TRIPLE INTEGRAL IN CYLINDRICAL AND SPHERICAL COORDINATES

If a region S in R_3 has an axis of symmetry, triple integrals on S are easier to evaluate if cylindrical coordinates are used. If there is symmetry with respect to a point, it is often convenient to choose that point as the origin and to use spherical coordinates. In this section we discuss the triple integral in these coordinates and apply them to physical problems.

To define the triple integral in cylindrical coordinates we construct a partition of the region S by drawing planes through the z axis, planes perpendicular to the z axis, and right-circular cylinders having the z axis as axis. A typical subregion is shown in Fig. 18.7.1. The elements of the constructed partition lie entirely in S. We call this partition a *cylindrical partition*. The measure of the length of the longest "diagonal" of any of the subregions is the *norm* of the partition. Let n be the number of subregions of the partition and $\Delta_i V$ be the measure of the volume of the ith subregion. The measure of the area of the base is $\bar{r}_i \Delta_i r \Delta_i \theta$, where $\bar{r}_i = \frac{1}{2}(r_i + r_{i-1})$. Hence, if $\Delta_i z$ is the measure of the altitude of the ith subregion, $\Delta_i V = \bar{r}_i \Delta_i r \Delta_i \theta \Delta_i z$. Let f be a function of r, θ, and z, and suppose that f is continuous on S. Choose a point $(\bar{r}_i, \bar{\theta}_i, \bar{z}_i)$ in the ith subregion such that $\theta_{i-1} \le \bar{\theta}_i \le \theta_i$ and $z_{i-1} \le \bar{z}_i \le z_i$. Form the sum

$$\sum_{i=1}^{n} f(\bar{r}_i, \bar{\theta}_i, \bar{z}_i)\, \Delta_i V = \sum_{i=1}^{n} f(\bar{r}_i, \bar{\theta}_i, \bar{z}_i)\bar{r}_i\, \Delta_i r\, \Delta_i \theta\, \Delta_i z \qquad (1)$$

Figure 18.7.1

As the norm of Δ approaches zero, it can be shown, under suitable conditions on S, that the limit of the sums of form (1) exist. This limit is called the *triple integral in cylindrical coordinates* of the function f on S, and we write

$$\lim_{\|\Delta\| \to 0} \sum_{i=1}^{n} f(\bar{r}_i, \bar{\theta}_i, \bar{z}_i)\, \Delta_i V = \iiint\limits_{S} f(r, \theta, z)\, dV \qquad (2)$$

or

$$\lim_{\|\Delta\| \to 0} \sum_{i=1}^{n} f(\bar{r}_i, \bar{\theta}_i, \bar{z}_i)\bar{r}_i\, \Delta_i r\, \Delta_i \theta\, \Delta_i z = \iiint\limits_{S} f(r, \theta, z) r\, dr\, d\theta\, dz \qquad (3)$$

We can evaluate the triple integral in (2) and (3) by an iterated integral. For instance, suppose that the region S in R_3 is bounded by the planes $\theta = \alpha$ and $\theta = \beta$, with $\alpha < \beta$, by the cylinders $r = \lambda_1(\theta)$ and $r = \lambda_2(\theta)$, where λ_1 and λ_2 are smooth on $[\alpha, \beta]$ and $\lambda_1(\theta) \le \lambda_2(\theta)$ for $\alpha \le \theta \le \beta$, and by the surfaces $z = F_1(r, \theta)$ and $z = F_2(r, \theta)$, where F_1 and F_2 are functions of two variables that are smooth on some region R in the polar plane bounded by the curves $r = \lambda_1(\theta)$, $r = \lambda_2(\theta)$, $\theta = \alpha$, and $\theta = \beta$. Furthermore, suppose that $F_1(r, \theta) \le F_2(r, \theta)$ for every point (r, θ) in R.

Then the triple integral can be evaluated by an iterated integral by the formula

$$\iiint\limits_{S} f(r,\,\theta,\,z)r\,dr\,d\theta\,dz = \int_{\alpha}^{\beta}\int_{\lambda_1(\theta)}^{\lambda_2(\theta)}\int_{F_1(r,\theta)}^{F_2(r,\theta)} f(r,\,\theta,\,z)r\,dz\,dr\,d\theta \qquad (4)$$

There are five other iterated integrals that can be used to evaluate the triple integral in (4) because there are six possible permutations of the three variables r, θ, and z.

Triple integrals and cylindrical coordinates are especially useful in finding the moment of inertia of a solid with respect to the z axis because the distance from the z axis to a point in the solid is determined by the coordinate r.

EXAMPLE 1: A homogeneous solid in the shape of a right-circular cylinder has a radius of 2 ft and an altitude of 4 ft. Find the moment of inertia of the solid with respect to its axis.

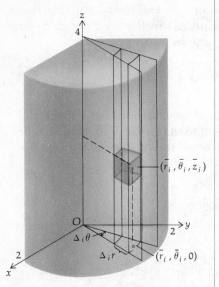

Figure 18.7.2

SOLUTION: Choose the coordinate planes so that the xy plane is the plane of the base of the solid and the z axis is the axis of the solid. Figure 18.7.2 shows the portion of the solid in the first octant together with the ith subregion of a cylindrical partition. Using cylindrical coordinates and taking the point $(\bar{r}_i,\,\bar{\theta}_i,\,\bar{z}_i)$ in the ith subregion with k slugs/ft^3 as the volume density at any point, then if I_z slug-ft^2 is the moment of inertia of the solid with respect to the z axis, we have

$$I_z = \lim_{\|\Delta\|\to 0} \sum_{i=1}^{n} \bar{r}_i^2 k\,\Delta_i V = \iiint\limits_{S} kr^2\,dV$$

There are six different possible orders of integration. Figure 18.7.2 shows the order $dz\,dr\,d\theta$. Using this order, we have

$$I_z = \iiint\limits_{S} kr^2\,dz\,r\,dr\,d\theta = 4k\int_0^{\pi/2}\int_0^2\int_0^4 r^3\,dz\,dr\,d\theta$$

In the first integration, the blocks are summed from $z=0$ to $z=4$; the blocks become a column. In the second integration, the columns are summed from $r=0$ to $r=2$; the columns become a wedge-shaped slice of the cylinder. In the third integration, the wedge-shaped slice is rotated from $\theta=0$ to $\theta=\frac{1}{2}\pi$; this sweeps the wedge about the entire three-dimensional region in the first octant. We multiply by 4 to obtain the entire volume. Performing the integration, we obtain

$$I_z = 16k\int_0^{\pi/2}\int_0^2 r^3\,dr\,d\theta = 64k\int_0^{\pi/2} d\theta = 32k\pi$$

Hence, the moment of inertia is $32k\pi$ slug-ft^2.

EXAMPLE 2: Solve Example 1 by taking the order of integration as (a) $dr\,dz\,d\theta$; (b) $d\theta\,dr\,dz$.

SOLUTION: (a) Figure 18.7.3 represents the order $dr\,dz\,d\theta$. It shows the block summed from $r=0$ to $r=2$ to give a wedge-shaped sector. We then sum from $z=0$ to $z=4$ to give a wedge-shaped slice. The slice is rotated from $\theta=0$ to $\theta=\frac{1}{2}\pi$ to cover the first octant. We have, then,

$$I_z = 4k\int_0^{\pi/2}\int_0^4\int_0^2 r^3\,dr\,dz\,d\theta = 32k\pi$$

(b) Figure 18.7.4 represents the order $d\theta\,dr\,dz$. It shows the blocks summed from $\theta = 0$ to $\theta = \frac{1}{2}\pi$ to give a hollow ring inside the cylinder. These hollow rings are summed from $r = 0$ to $r = 2$ to give a horizontal slice of the cylinder. The horizontal slices are summed from $z = 0$ to $z = 4$. Therefore, we have

$$I_z = 4k \int_0^4 \int_0^2 \int_0^{\pi/2} r^3\,d\theta\,dr\,dz = 32k\pi$$

Figure 18.7.3   *Figure 18.7.4*

EXAMPLE 3: Find the mass of a solid hemisphere of radius a ft if the volume density at any point is proportional to the distance of the point from the axis of the solid.

Figure 18.7.5

SOLUTION: If we choose the coordinate planes so that the origin is at the center of the sphere and the z axis is the axis of the solid, then an equation of the hemispherical surface above the xy plane is $z = \sqrt{a^2 - x^2 - y^2}$. Figure 18.7.5 shows this surface and the solid together with the ith subregion of a cylindrical partition. An equation of the hemisphere in cylindrical coordinates is $z = \sqrt{a^2 - r^2}$. If $(\bar{r}_i, \bar{\theta}_i, \bar{z}_i)$ is a point in the ith subregion, the volume density at this point is $k\bar{r}_i$ slugs/ft³, where k is a constant; and if M slugs is the mass of the solid, then

$$M = \lim_{||\Delta|| \to 0} \sum_{i=1}^{n} k\bar{r}_i\,\Delta_i V$$

$$= \iiint_S kr\,dV$$

$$= k \int_0^{2\pi} \int_0^a \int_0^{\sqrt{a^2-r^2}} r^2\,dz\,dr\,d\theta$$

$$= k \int_0^{2\pi} \int_0^a r^2 \sqrt{a^2 - r^2}\,dr\,d\theta$$

$$= k \int_0^{2\pi} \left[-\tfrac{1}{4}r(a^2 - r^2)^{3/2} + \tfrac{1}{8}a^2 r \sqrt{a^2 - r^2} + \tfrac{1}{8}a^4 \sin^{-1} \frac{r}{a} \right]_0^a d\theta$$

$$= \tfrac{1}{16} ka^4 \pi \int_0^{2\pi} d\theta$$

$$= \tfrac{1}{8} ka^4 \pi^2$$

The mass of the solid hemisphere is therefore $\tfrac{1}{8}ka^4\pi^2$ slugs.

EXAMPLE 4: Find the center of mass of the solid of Example 3.

SOLUTION: Let the cartesian-coordinate representation of the center of mass be $(\bar{x}, \bar{y}, \bar{z})$. Because of symmetry, $\bar{x} = \bar{y} = 0$. We need to calculate $\bar{z}$. If M_{xy} slug-ft is the moment of mass of the solid with respect to the xy plane, we have

$$M_{xy} = \lim_{||\Delta|| \to 0} \sum_{i=1}^n \bar{z}_i(k\bar{r}_i)\, \Delta_i V$$

$$= \iiint_S kzr\, dV$$

$$= k \int_0^{2\pi} \int_0^a \int_0^{\sqrt{a^2-r^2}} zr^2\, dz\, dr\, d\theta$$

$$= \tfrac{1}{2} k \int_0^{2\pi} \int_0^a (a^2 - r^2) r^2\, dr\, d\theta$$

$$= \tfrac{1}{15} ka^5 \int_0^{2\pi} d\theta$$

$$= \tfrac{2}{15} ka^5 \pi$$

Because $M\bar{z} = M_{xy}$, we get

$$\bar{z} = \frac{M_{xy}}{M} = \frac{\tfrac{2}{15} ka^5 \pi}{\tfrac{1}{8} ka^4 \pi^2} = \frac{16}{15\pi} a$$

The center of mass is therefore on the axis of the solid at a distance of $16a/15\pi$ ft from the plane of the base.

We now proceed to define the triple integral in spherical coordinates. A spherical partition of the three-dimensional region S is formed by planes containing the z axis, spheres with centers at the origin, and circular cones having vertices at the origin and the z axis as the axis. A typical subregion of the partition is shown in Fig. 18.7.6. If $\Delta_i V$ is the measure of the volume of the ith subregion, and $(\bar{\rho}_i, \bar{\theta}_i, \bar{\phi}_i)$ is a point in it, we can get an approximation to $\Delta_i V$ by considering the region as if it were a rectangular parallelepiped and taking the product of the measures of the three dimensions. These measures are $\bar{\rho}_i \sin \bar{\phi}_i\, \Delta_i \theta$, $\bar{\rho}_i\, \Delta_i \phi$, and $\Delta_i \rho$. Figures 18.7.7 and 18.7.8 show how the first two measures are obtained, and Figure 18.7.6 shows the dimension of measure $\Delta_i\rho$. Hence,

$$\Delta_i V = \bar{\rho}_i^2 \sin \bar{\phi}_i \, \Delta_i\rho \, \Delta_i\theta \, \Delta_i\phi$$

The *triple integral in spherical coordinates* of a function f on S is given by

$$\lim_{\|\Delta\|\to 0} \sum_{i=1}^n f(\bar{\rho}_i, \bar{\theta}_i, \bar{\phi}_i) \, \Delta_i V = \iiint_S f(\rho, \theta, \phi) \, dV \qquad (5)$$

or

$$\lim_{\|\Delta\|\to 0} \sum_{i=1}^n f(\bar{\rho}_i, \bar{\theta}_i, \bar{\phi}_i) \bar{\rho}_i^2 \sin \bar{\phi}_i \, \Delta_i\rho \, \Delta_i\theta \, \Delta_i\phi$$

$$= \iiint_S f(\rho, \theta, \phi) \rho^2 \sin \phi \, d\rho \, d\theta \, d\phi \qquad (6)$$

The triple integral in (5) or (6) can be evaluated by an iterated integral. Spherical coordinates are especially useful in some problems involving spheres, as illustrated in the following example.

Figure 18.7.6

Figure 18.7.7   *Figure 18.7.8*

EXAMPLE 5: Find the mass of the solid hemisphere of Example 3 if the volume density at any point is proportional to the distance of the point from the center of the base.

SOLUTION: If $(\bar{\rho}_i, \bar{\theta}_i, \bar{\phi}_i)$ is a point in the ith subregion of a spherical partition, the volume density at this point is $k\bar{\rho}_i$ slugs/ft³, where k is a constant. If M slugs is the mass of the solid, then

$$M = \lim_{\|\Delta\|\to 0} \sum_{i=1}^n k\bar{\rho}_i \, \Delta_i V$$

$$= \iiint_S k\rho \, dV$$

$$= 4k \int_0^{\pi/2} \int_0^{\pi/2} \int_0^a \rho^3 \sin\phi \, d\rho \, d\phi \, d\theta$$

$$= a^4 k \int_0^{\pi/2} \int_0^{\pi/2} \sin\phi \, d\phi \, d\theta$$

$$= a^4 k \int_0^{\pi/2} \left[-\cos\phi \right]_0^{\pi/2} d\theta$$

$$= a^4 k \int_0^{\pi/2} d\theta$$

$$= \tfrac{1}{2} a^4 k \pi$$

Hence, the mass of the solid hemisphere is $\tfrac{1}{2}a^4k\pi$ slugs.

It is interesting to compare the solution of Example 5 which uses spherical coordinates with what is entailed when using cartesian coordinates. By the latter method, a partition of S is formed by dividing S into rectangular boxes by drawing planes parallel to the coordinate planes. If (ξ_i, γ_i, μ_i) is any point in the ith subregion, and because $\rho = \sqrt{x^2 + y^2 + z^2}$, then

$$M = \lim_{\|\Delta\| \to 0} \sum_{i=1}^n k \sqrt{\xi_i^2 + \gamma_i^2 + \mu_i^2} \, \Delta_i V$$

$$= \iiint_S k \sqrt{x^2 + y^2 + z^2} \, dV$$

$$= 4k \int_0^a \int_0^{\sqrt{a^2-z^2}} \int_0^{\sqrt{a^2-y^2-z^2}} \sqrt{x^2 + y^2 + z^2} \, dx \, dy \, dz$$

The computation involved in evaluating this integral is obviously much more complicated than that using spherical coordinates.

EXAMPLE 6:   A homogeneous solid is bounded above by the sphere $\rho = a$ and below by the cone $\phi = \alpha$, where $0 < \alpha < \tfrac{1}{2}\pi$. Find the moment of inertia of the solid about the z axis.

SOLUTION: The solid is shown in Fig. 18.7.9. Let k slugs/ft^3 be the constant volume density at any point of the solid. Form a spherical partition of the solid and let $(\bar\rho_i, \bar\theta_i, \bar\phi_i)$ be a point in the ith subregion. The measure of the distance of the point $(\bar\rho_i, \bar\theta_i, \bar\phi_i)$ from the z axis is $\bar\rho_i \sin\bar\phi_i$. Hence, if I_z slug-ft^2 is the moment of inertia of the given solid about the z axis, then

$$I_z = \lim_{\|\Delta\| \to 0} \sum_{i=1}^n (\bar\rho_i \sin\bar\phi_i)^2 k \, \Delta_i V$$

$$= \iiint_S k\rho^2 \sin^2\phi \, dV$$

$$= k \int_0^\alpha \int_0^{2\pi} \int_0^a (\rho^2 \sin^2\phi)\rho^2 \sin\phi \, d\rho \, d\theta \, d\phi$$

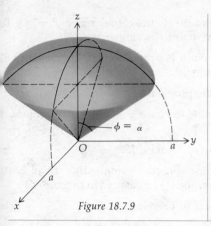

Figure 18.7.9

$$= \tfrac{1}{5} ka^5 \int_0^\alpha \int_0^{2\pi} \sin^3 \phi \, d\theta \, d\phi$$

$$= \tfrac{2}{5} ka^5 \pi \int_0^\alpha \sin^3 \phi \, d\phi$$

$$= \tfrac{2}{5} ka^5 \pi \left[-\cos \phi + \tfrac{1}{3} \cos^3 \phi \right]_0^\alpha$$

$$= \tfrac{2}{15} ka^5 \pi (\cos^3 \alpha - 3 \cos \alpha + 2)$$

The moment of inertia of the solid about the z axis is therefore

$$\tfrac{2}{15} ka^5 \pi (\cos^3 \alpha - 3 \cos \alpha + 2) \text{ slug-ft}^2$$

Exercises 18.7

In Exercises 1 through 4, evaluate the iterated integral.

1. $\displaystyle\int_0^{\pi/4} \int_0^a \int_0^{r \cos \theta} r \sec^3 \theta \, dz \, dr \, d\theta$

2. $\displaystyle\int_0^{\pi/4} \int_{2 \sin \theta}^{2 \cos \theta} \int_0^{r \sin \theta} r^2 \cos \theta \, dz \, dr \, d\theta$

3. $\displaystyle\int_0^{\pi/4} \int_0^{2a \cos \phi} \int_0^{2\pi} \rho^2 \sin \phi \, d\theta \, d\rho \, d\phi$

4. $\displaystyle\int_{\pi/4}^{\pi/2} \int_{\pi/4}^{\phi} \int_0^{a \csc \theta} \rho^3 \sin^2 \theta \sin \phi \, d\rho \, d\theta \, d\phi$

5. Find the volume of the solid enclosed by the sphere $x^2 + y^2 + z^2 = a^2$ by using (a) cylindrical coordinates and (b) spherical coordinates.

6. If S is the solid in the first octant bounded by the sphere $x^2 + y^2 + z^2 = 16$ and the coordinate planes evaluate the triple integral $\iiint\limits_S xyz \, dV$ by three methods: (a) using spherical coordinates; (b) using rectangular coordinates; (c) using cylindrical coordinates.

In Exercises 7 through 10, use cylindrical coordinates.

7. Find the mass of the solid bounded by a sphere of radius a ft if the volume density varies as the square of the distance from the center. The volume density is measured in slugs/ft³.

8. Find the mass of the solid in the first octant inside the cylinder $x^2 + y^2 = 4x$ and under the sphere $x^2 + y^2 + z^2 = 16$. The volume density varies as the distance from the xy plane, and it is measured in slugs/ft³.

9. Find the moment of inertia with respect to the z axis of the homogeneous solid bounded by the cylinder $r = 5$, the cone $z = r$, and the xy plane. The volume density at any point is k slugs/ft³.

10. Find the moment of inertia of the solid, bounded by a right-circular cylinder of altitude h ft and radius a ft, with respect to the axis of the cylinder. The volume density varies as the distance from the axis of the cylinder, and it is measured in slugs/ft³.

In Exercises 11 through 14, use spherical coordinates.

11. Find the center of mass of the solid bounded by the hemisphere of Example 5. The volume density is the same as that in Example 5.

12. Find the moment of inertia with respect to the z axis of the homogeneous solid bounded by the sphere $x^2 + y^2 + z^2 = 4$. The volume density at any point is k slugs/ft³.

13. Find the moment of inertia with respect to the z axis of the homogeneous solid inside the cylinder $x^2 + y^2 - 2x = 0$ below the cone $x^2 + y^2 = z^2$, and above the xy plane. The volume density at any point is k slugs/ft³.

14. Find the mass of a spherical solid of radius a ft if the volume density at each point is proportional to the distance of the point from the center of the sphere. The volume density is measured in slugs/ft³.

In Exercises 15 through 18, use the coordinate system that you decide is best for the problem.

15. Find the center of mass of the solid inside the paraboloid $x^2 + y^2 = z$ and outside the cone $x^2 + y^2 = z^2$. The constant volume density is k slugs/ft³.

16. Find the moment of inertia with respect to the z axis of the homogeneous solid of Exercise 15.

17. Find the moment of inertia about a diameter of the solid between two concentric spheres having radii a ft and $2a$ ft. The volume density varies inversely as the square of the distance from the center, and it is measured in slugs/ft³.

18. Find the mass of the solid of Exercise 17. The volume density is the same as that in Exercise 17.

In Exercises 19 through 22, evaluate the iterated integral by using either cylindrical or spherical coordinates.

19. $\displaystyle\int_0^4 \int_0^3 \int_0^{\sqrt{9-x^2}} \sqrt{x^2 + y^2}\, dy\, dx\, dz$

20. $\displaystyle\int_0^2 \int_0^{\sqrt{4-y^2}} \int_0^{\sqrt{4-x^2-y^2}} \frac{1}{x^2 + y^2 + z^2}\, dz\, dx\, dy$

21. $\displaystyle\int_0^1 \int_0^{\sqrt{1-y^2}} \int_{\sqrt{x^2+y^2}}^{\sqrt{2-x^2-y^2}} z^2\, dz\, dx\, dy$

22. $\displaystyle\int_0^1 \int_0^{\sqrt{1-x^2}} \int_0^{\sqrt{1-x^2-y^2}} \frac{z}{\sqrt{x^2 + y^2}}\, dz\, dy\, dx$

Review Exercises (Chapter 18)

In Exercises 1 through 8, evaluate the given iterated integral.

1. $\displaystyle\int_0^1 \int_x^{\sqrt{x}} x^2 y\, dy\, dx$

2. $\displaystyle\int_{-2}^2 \int_{-\sqrt{4-y^2}}^{\sqrt{4-y^2}} xy\, dx\, dy$

3. $\displaystyle\int_0^{\pi/2} \int_0^{2\sin\theta} r\cos^2\theta\, dr\, d\theta$

4. $\displaystyle\int_0^\pi \int_0^{3(1+\cos\theta)} r^2\sin\theta\, dr\, d\theta$

5. $\displaystyle\int_0^1 \int_0^z \int_0^{y+z} e^x e^y e^z\, dx\, dy\, dz$

6. $\displaystyle\int_1^2 \int_0^x \int_0^{\sqrt{3y}} \frac{y}{y^2 + z^2}\, dz\, dy\, dx$

7. $\displaystyle\int_0^{\pi/2} \int_{\pi/6}^{\pi/2} \int_0^2 \rho^3 \sin\phi \cos\phi\, d\rho\, d\phi\, d\theta$

8. $\displaystyle\int_0^{\pi/2} \int_0^a \int_0^{\sqrt{a^2-z^2}} zre^{-r^2}\, dr\, d\theta\, dz$

In Exercises 9 through 12, evaluate the multiple integral.

9. $\displaystyle\iint_R xy\, dA$; R is the region in the first quadrant bounded by the circle $x^2 + y^2 = 1$ and the coordinate axes.

10. $\displaystyle\iint_R (x + y)\, dA$; R is the region bounded by the curve $y = \cos x$ and the x axis from $x = -\tfrac{1}{2}\pi$ to $x = \tfrac{1}{2}\pi$.

11. $\displaystyle\iiint_S z^2\, dV$; S is the region bounded by the cylinders $x^2 + z = 1$ and $y^2 + z = 1$, and the xy plane.

12. $\displaystyle\iiint_S y\cos(x + z)\, dV$; S is the region bounded by the cylinder $x = y^2$, and the planes $x + z = \tfrac{1}{2}\pi$, $y = 0$, and $z = 0$.

13. Evaluate by polar coordinates the double integral

$$\iint_R \frac{1}{x^2 + y^2}\, dA$$

where R is the region in the first quadrant bounded by the two circles $x^2 + y^2 = 1$ and $x^2 + y^2 = 4$.

4. Evaluate by polar coordinates the iterated integral $\int_0^1 \int_{\sqrt{3}y}^{\sqrt{4-y^2}} \ln(x^2 + y^2) \, dx \, dy$.

In Exercises 15 and 16, evaluate the iterated integral by reversing the order of integration.

15. $\int_0^1 \int_x^1 \sin y^2 \, dy \, dx$

16. $\int_0^1 \int_0^{\cos^{-1}y} e^{\sin x} \, dx \, dy$

In Exercises 17 and 18, evaluate the iterated integral by changing to either cylindrical or spherical coordinates.

17. $\int_0^3 \int_0^{\sqrt{9-x^2}} \int_0^2 \frac{1}{\sqrt{x^2 + y^2}} \, dz \, dy \, dx$

18. $\int_0^2 \int_0^{\sqrt{4-x^2}} \int_0^{\sqrt{4-x^2-y^2}} z\sqrt{4 - x^2 - y^2} \, dz \, dy \, dx$

19. Use double integration to find the area of the region in the first quadrant bounded by the parabolas $x^2 = 4y$ and $x^2 = 8 - 4y$ by two methods: (a) Integrate first with respect to x; (b) integrate first with respect to y.

20. Use double integration to find the volume of the solid above the xy plane bounded by the cylinder $x^2 + y^2 = 16$ and the plane $z = 2y$ by two methods: (a) Integrate first with respect to x; (b) integrate first with respect to y.

21. Find the volume of the solid bounded by the surfaces $x^2 = 4y$, $y^2 = 4x$, and $x^2 = z - y$.

22. Find the mass of the lamina in the shape of the region bounded by the parabola $y = x^2$ and the line $x - y + 2 = 0$ if the area density at any point is x^2y^2 slugs/ft².

23. Find the area of the surface of the cylinder $x^2 + y^2 = 9$ lying in the first octant and between the planes $x = z$ and $3x = z$.

24. Find the area of the surface of the part of the cylinder $x^2 + y^2 = a^2$ that lies inside the cylinder $y^2 + z^2 = a^2$.

25. Use double integration to find the area of the region inside the circle $r = 1$ and to the right of the parabola $r(1 + \cos \theta) = 1$.

26. Find the mass of the lamina in the shape of the region exterior to the limaçon $r = 3 - \cos \theta$ and interior to the circle $r = 5 \cos \theta$ if the area density at any point is $2|\sin \theta|$ slugs/ft².

27. Find the center of mass of the rectangular lamina bounded by the lines $x = 3$ and $y = 2$ and the coordinate axes if the area density at any point is xy^2 slugs/ft².

28. Find the center of mass of the lamina in the shape of the region bounded by the parabolas $x^2 = 4 + 4y$ and $x^2 = 4 - 8y$ if the area density at any point is kx^2 slugs/ft².

29. Find the mass of the lamina in the shape of the region bounded by the polar axis and the curve $r = \cos 2\theta$, where $0 \le \theta \le \frac{1}{4}\pi$. The area density at any point is $r\theta$ slugs/ft.

30. Find the moment of inertia about the x axis of the lamina in the shape of the region bounded by the circle $x^2 + y^2 = a^2$ if the area density at any point is $k\sqrt{x^2 + y^2}$ slugs/ft².

31. Find the moment of inertia about the x axis of the lamina in the shape of the region bounded by the curve $y = e^x$, the line $x = 2$, and the coordinate axes if the area density at any point is xy slugs/ft².

32. Find the moment of inertia of the lamina of Exercise 31 about the y axis.

33. Find the moment of inertia with respect to the $\frac{1}{2}\pi$ axis of the homogeneous lamina in the shape of the region bounded by the curve $r^2 = 4 \cos 2\theta$ if the area density at any point is k slugs/ft².

34. Find the mass of the lamina of Exercise 33.

35. Find the polar moment of inertia and the corresponding radius of gyration of the lamina of Exercise 33.

36. Find the moment of inertia about the y axis of the lamina in the shape of the region bounded by the parabola $y = x - x^2$ and the line $x + y = 0$ if the area density at any point is $(x + y)$ slugs/ft².

37. Find the mass of the solid bounded by the spheres $x^2 + y^2 + z^2 = 4$ and $x^2 + y^2 + z^2 = 9$ if the volume density at any point is $k\sqrt{x^2 + y^2 + z^2}$ slugs/ft³.

38. Find the moment of inertia about the z axis of the solid of Exercise 37.

39. The homogeneous solid bounded by the cone $z^2 = 4x^2 + 4y^2$ between the planes $z = 0$ and $z = 4$ has a volume density at any point of k slugs/ft³. Find the moment of inertia about the z axis for this solid.

40. Find the center of mass of the solid bounded by the sphere $x^2 + y^2 + z^2 - 6z = 0$ and the cone $x^2 + y^2 = z^2$, and above the cone, if the volume density at any point is kz slugs/ft³.

Appendix

Table 1 *Powers and roots*

n	n^2	$\sqrt{n}$	n^3	$\sqrt[3]{n}$	n	n^2	$\sqrt{n}$	n^3	$\sqrt[3]{n}$
1	1	1.000	1	1.000	51	2,601	7.141	132,651	3.7
2	4	1.414	8	1.260	52	2,704	7.211	140,608	3.7
3	9	1.732	27	1.442	53	2,809	7.280	148,877	3.7
4	16	2.000	64	1.587	54	2,916	7.348	157,464	3.7
5	25	2.236	125	1.710	55	3,025	7.416	166,375	3.8
6	36	2.449	216	1.817	56	3,136	7.483	175,616	3.8
7	49	2.646	343	1.913	57	3,249	7.550	185,193	3.8
8	64	2.828	512	2.000	58	3,364	7.616	195,112	3.8
9	81	3.000	729	2.080	59	3,481	7.681	205,379	3.8
10	100	3.162	1,000	2.154	60	3,600	7.746	216,000	3.9
11	121	3.317	1,331	2.224	61	3,721	7.810	226,981	3.9
12	144	3.464	1,728	2.289	62	3,844	7.874	238,328	3.9
13	169	3.606	2,197	2.351	63	3,969	7.937	250,047	3.9
14	196	3.742	2,744	2.410	64	4,096	8.000	262,144	4.0
15	225	3.873	3,375	2.466	65	4,225	8.062	274,625	4.0
16	256	4.000	4,096	2.520	66	4,356	8.124	287,496	4.0
17	289	4.123	4,913	2.571	67	4,489	8.185	300,763	4.0
18	324	4.243	5,832	2.621	68	4,624	8.246	314,432	4.0
19	361	4.359	6,859	2.668	69	4,761	8.307	328,509	4.1
20	400	4.472	8,000	2.714	70	4,900	8.367	343,000	4.1
21	441	4.583	9,261	2.759	71	5,041	8.426	357,911	4.1
22	484	4.690	10,648	2.802	72	5,184	8.485	373,248	4.1
23	529	4.796	12,167	2.844	73	5,329	8.544	389,017	4.1
24	576	4.899	13,824	2.884	74	5,476	8.602	405,224	4.1
25	625	5.000	15,625	2.924	75	5,625	8.660	421,875	4.2
26	676	5.099	17,576	2.962	76	5,776	8.718	438,976	4.2
27	729	5.196	19,683	3.000	77	5,929	8.775	456,533	4.2
28	784	5.291	21,952	3.037	78	6,084	8.832	474,552	4.2
29	841	5.385	24,389	3.072	79	6,241	8.888	493,039	4.2
30	900	5.477	27,000	3.107	80	6,400	8.944	512,000	4.3
31	961	5.568	29,791	3.141	81	6,561	9.000	531,441	4.3
32	1,024	5.657	32,768	3.175	82	6,724	9.055	551,368	4.3
33	1,089	5.745	35,937	3.208	83	6,889	9.110	571,787	4.3
34	1,156	5.831	39,304	3.240	84	7,056	9.165	592,704	4.3
35	1,225	5.916	42,875	3.271	85	7,225	9.220	614,125	4.3
36	1,296	6.000	46,656	3.302	86	7,396	9.274	636,056	4.4
37	1,369	6.083	50,653	3.332	87	7,569	9.327	658,503	4.4
38	1,444	6.164	54,872	3.362	88	7,744	9.381	681,472	4.4
39	1,521	6.245	59,319	3.391	89	7,921	9.434	704,969	4.4
40	1,600	6.325	64,000	3.420	90	8,100	9.487	729,000	4.4
41	1,681	6.403	68,921	3.448	91	8,281	9.539	753,571	4.4
42	1,764	6.481	74,088	3.476	92	8,464	9.592	778,688	4.5
43	1,849	6.557	79,507	3.503	93	8,649	9.643	804,357	4.5
44	1,936	6.633	85,184	3.530	94	8,836	9.695	830,584	4.5
45	2,025	6.708	91,125	3.557	95	9,025	9.747	857,375	4.5
46	2,116	6.782	97,336	3.583	96	9,216	9.798	884,736	4.5
47	2,209	6.856	103,823	3.609	97	9,409	9.849	912,673	4.5
48	2,304	6.928	110,592	3.634	98	9,604	9.899	941,192	4.6
49	2,401	7.000	117,649	3.659	99	9,801	9.950	970,299	4.6
50	2,500	7.071	125,000	3.684	100	10,000	10.000	1,000,000	4.6

Table 2   Natural logarithms

N	0	1	2	3	4	5	6	7	8	9
1.0	0000	0100	0198	0296	0392	0488	0583	0677	0770	0862
1.1	0953	1044	1133	1222	1310	1398	1484	1570	1655	1740
1.2	1823	1906	1989	2070	2151	2231	2311	2390	2469	2546
1.3	2624	2700	2776	2852	2927	3001	3075	3148	3221	3293
1.4	3365	3436	3507	3577	3646	3716	3784	3853	3920	3988
1.5	4055	4121	4187	4253	4318	4383	4447	4511	4574	4637
1.6	4700	4762	4824	4886	4947	5008	5068	5128	5188	5247
1.7	5306	5365	5423	5481	5539	5596	5653	5710	5766	5822
1.8	5878	5933	5988	6043	6098	6152	6206	6259	6313	6366
1.9	6419	6471	6523	6575	6627	6678	6729	6780	6831	6881
2.0	6931	6981	7031	7080	7129	7178	7227	7275	7324	7372
2.1	7419	7467	7514	7561	7608	7655	7701	7747	7793	7839
2.2	7885	7930	7975	8020	8065	8109	8154	8198	8242	8286
2.3	8329	8372	8416	8459	8502	8544	8587	8629	8671	8713
2.4	8755	8796	8838	8879	8920	8961	9002	9042	9083	9123
2.5	9163	9203	9243	9282	9322	9361	9400	9439	9478	9517
2.6	9555	9594	9632	9670	9708	9746	9783	9821	9858	9895
2.7	9933	9969	*0006	*0043	*0080	*0116	*0152	*0188	*0225	*0260
2.8	1.0296	0332	0367	0403	0438	0473	0508	0543	0578	0613
2.9	0647	0682	0716	0750	0784	0818	0852	0886	0919	0953
3.0	1.0986	1019	1053	1086	1119	1151	1184	1217	1249	1282
3.1	1314	1346	1378	1410	1442	1474	1506	1537	1569	1600
3.2	1632	1663	1694	1725	1756	1787	1817	1848	1878	1909
3.3	1939	1969	2000	2030	2060	2090	2119	2149	2179	2208
3.4	2238	2267	2296	2326	2355	2384	2413	2442	2470	2499
3.5	1.2528	2556	2585	2613	2641	2669	2698	2726	2754	2782
3.6	2809	2837	2865	2892	2920	2947	2975	3002	3029	3056
3.7	3083	3110	3137	3164	3191	3218	3244	3271	3297	3324
3.8	3350	3376	3403	3429	3455	3481	3507	3533	3558	3584
3.9	3610	3635	3661	3686	3712	3737	3762	3788	3813	3838
4.0	1.3863	3888	3913	3938	3962	3987	4012	4036	4061	4085
4.1	4110	4134	4159	4183	4207	4231	4255	4279	4303	4327
4.2	4351	4375	4398	4422	4446	4469	4493	4516	4540	4563
4.3	4586	4609	4633	4656	4679	4702	4725	4748	4770	4793
4.4	4816	4839	4861	4884	4907	4929	4951	4974	4996	5019
4.5	1.5041	5063	5085	5107	5129	5151	5173	5195	5217	5239
4.6	5261	5282	5304	5326	5347	5369	5390	5412	5433	5454
4.7	5476	5497	5518	5539	5560	5581	5602	5623	5644	5665
4.8	5686	5707	5728	5748	5769	5790	5810	5831	5851	5872
4.9	5892	5913	5933	5953	5974	5994	6014	6034	6054	6074
5.0	1.6094	6114	6134	6154	6174	6194	6214	6233	6253	6273
5.1	6292	6312	6332	6351	6371	6390	6409	6429	6448	6467
5.2	6487	6506	6525	6544	6563	6582	6601	6620	6639	6658
5.3	6677	6696	6715	6734	6752	6771	6790	6808	6827	6845
5.4	6864	6882	6901	6919	6938	6956	6974	6993	7011	7029

Table 2   (*Continued*)

N	0	1	2	3	4	5	6	7	8	9
5.5	1.7047	7066	7084	7102	7120	7138	7156	7174	7192	72
5.6	7228	7246	7263	7281	7299	7317	7334	7352	7370	73
5.7	7405	7422	7440	7457	7475	7492	7509	7527	7544	75
5.8	7579	7596	7613	7630	7647	7664	7681	7699	7716	77
5.9	7750	7766	7783	7800	7817	7834	7851	7867	7884	79
6.0	1.7918	7934	7951	7967	7984	8001	8017	8034	8050	80
6.1	8083	8099	8116	8132	8148	8165	8181	8197	8213	82
6.2	8245	8262	8278	8294	8310	8326	8342	8358	8374	83
6.3	8405	8421	8437	8453	8469	8485	8500	8516	8532	85
6.4	8563	8579	8594	8610	8625	8641	8656	8672	8687	87
6.5	1.8718	8733	8749	8764	8779	8795	8810	8825	8840	88
6.6	8871	8886	8901	8916	8931	8946	8961	8976	8991	90
6.7	9021	9036	9051	9066	9081	9095	9110	9125	9140	91
6.8	9169	9184	9199	9213	9228	9242	9257	9272	9286	93
6.9	9315	9330	9344	9359	9373	9387	9402	9416	9430	94
7.0	1.9459	9473	9488	9502	9516	9530	9544	9559	9573	95
7.1	9601	9615	9629	9643	9657	9671	9685	9699	9713	97
7.2	9741	9755	9769	9782	9796	9810	9824	9838	9851	98
7.3	9879	9892	9906	9920	9933	9947	9961	9974	9988	*00
7.4	2.0015	0028	0042	0055	0069	0082	0096	0109	0122	01
7.5	2.0149	0162	0176	0189	0202	0215	0229	0242	0255	02
7.6	0281	0295	0308	0321	0334	0347	0360	0373	0386	03
7.7	0412	0425	0438	0451	0464	0477	0490	0503	0516	05
7.8	0541	0554	0567	0580	0592	0605	0618	0630	0643	06
7.9	0669	0681	0694	0707	0719	0732	0744	0757	0769	07
8.0	2.0794	0807	0819	0832	0844	0857	0869	0882	0894	09
8.1	0919	0931	0943	0956	0968	0980	0992	1005	1017	10
8.2	1041	1054	1066	1078	1090	1102	1114	1126	1138	11
8.3	1163	1175	1187	1199	1211	1223	1235	1247	1258	12
8.4	1282	1294	1306	1318	1330	1342	1353	1365	1377	13
8.5	2.1401	1412	1424	1436	1448	1459	1471	1483	1494	15
8.6	1518	1529	1541	1552	1564	1576	1587	1599	1610	16
8.7	1633	1645	1656	1668	1679	1691	1702	1713	1725	17
8.8	1748	1759	1770	1782	1793	1804	1815	1827	1838	18
8.9	1861	1872	1883	1894	1905	1917	1928	1939	1950	19
9.0	2.1972	1983	1994	2006	2017	2028	2039	2050	2061	20
9.1	2083	2094	2105	2116	2127	2138	2148	2159	2170	21
9.2	2192	2203	2214	2225	2235	2246	2257	2268	2279	22
9.3	2300	2311	2322	2332	2343	2354	2364	2375	2386	23
9.4	2407	2418	2428	2439	2450	2460	2471	2481	2492	25
9.5	2.2513	2523	2534	2544	2555	2565	2576	2586	2597	26
9.6	2618	2628	2638	2649	2659	2670	2680	2690	2701	27
9.7	2721	2732	2742	2752	2762	2773	2783	2793	2803	28
9.8	2824	2834	2844	2854	2865	2875	2885	2895	2905	29
9.9	2925	2935	2946	2956	2966	2976	2986	2996	3006	30

Use ln 10 = 2.30259 to find logarithms of numbers greater than 10 or less than 1. *Exam*
ln 220 = ln 2.2 + 2 ln 10 = 0.7885 + 2(2.30259) = 5.3937.

Table 3 *Exponential functions*

x	e^x	$\log_{10}(e^x)$	e^{-x}	x	e^x	$\log_{10}(e^x)$	e^{-x}
0.00	1.0000	0.00000	1.000000	**0.50**	1.6487	0.21715	0.606531
0.01	1.0101	.00434	0.990050	0.51	1.6653	.22149	.600496
0.02	1.0202	.00869	0.980199	0.52	1.6820	.22583	.594521
0.03	1.0305	.01303	0.970446	0.53	1.6989	.23018	.588605
0.04	1.0408	.01737	0.960789	0.54	1.7160	.23452	.582748
0.05	1.0513	0.02171	0.951229	**0.55**	1.7333	0.23886	0.576950
0.06	1.0618	.02606	0.941765	0.56	1.7507	.24320	.571209
0.07	1.0725	.03040	0.932394	0.57	1.7683	.24755	.565525
0.08	1.0833	.03474	0.923116	0.58	1.7860	.25189	.559898
0.09	1.0942	.03909	0.913931	0.59	1.8040	.35623	.554327
0.10	1.1052	0.04343	0.904837	**0.60**	1.8221	0.26058	0.548812
0.11	1.1163	.04777	0.895834	0.61	1.8404	.26492	.543351
0.12	1.1275	.05212	0.886920	0.62	1.8589	.26926	.537944
0.13	1.1388	.05646	0.878095	0.63	1.8776	.27361	.532592
0.14	1.1503	.06080	0.869358	0.64	1.8965	.27795	.527292
0.15	1.1618	0.06514	0.860708	**0.65**	1.9155	0.28229	0.522046
0.16	1.1735	.06949	0.852144	0.66	1.9348	.28663	.516851
0.17	1.1853	.07383	0.843665	0.67	1.9542	.29098	.511709
0.18	1.1972	.07817	0.835270	0.68	1.9739	.29532	.506617
0.19	1.2092	.08252	0.826959	0.69	1.9937	.29966	.501576
0.20	1.2214	0.08686	0.818731	**0.70**	2.0138	0.30401	0.496585
0.21	1.2337	.09120	0.810584	0.71	2.0340	.30835	.491644
0.22	1.2461	.09554	0.802519	0.72	2.0544	.31269	.486752
0.23	1.2586	.09989	0.794534	0.73	2.0751	.31703	.481909
0.24	1.2712	.10423	0.786628	0.74	2.0959	.32138	.477114
0.25	1.2840	0.10857	0.778801	**0.75**	2.1170	0.32572	0.472367
0.26	1.2969	.11292	0.771052	0.76	2.1383	.33006	.467666
0.27	1.3100	.11726	0.763379	0.77	2.1598	.33441	.463013
0.28	1.3231	.12160	0.755784	0.78	2.1815	.33875	.458406
0.29	1.3364	.12595	0.748264	0.79	2.2034	.34309	.453845
0.30	1.3499	0.13029	0.740818	**0.80**	2.2255	0.34744	0.449329
0.31	1.3634	.13463	0.733447	0.81	2.2479	.35178	.444858
0.32	1.3771	.13897	0.726149	0.82	2.2705	.35612	.440432
0.33	1.3910	.14332	0.718924	0.83	2.2933	.36046	.436049
0.34	1.4049	.14766	0.711770	0.84	2.3164	.36481	.431711
0.35	1.4191	0.15200	0.704688	**0.85**	2.3396	0.36915	0.427415
0.36	1.4333	.15635	0.697676	0.86	2.3632	.37349	.423162
0.37	1.4477	.16069	0.690734	0.87	2.3869	.37784	.418952
0.38	1.4623	.16503	0.683861	0.88	2.4109	.38218	.414783
0.39	1.4770	.16937	0.677057	0.89	2.4351	.38652	.410656
0.40	1.4918	0.17372	0.670320	**0.90**	2.4596	0.39087	0.406570
0.41	1.5068	.17806	0.663650	0.91	2.4843	.39521	.402524
0.42	1.5220	.18240	0.657047	0.92	2.5093	.39955	.398519
0.43	1.5373	.18675	0.650509	0.93	2.5345	.40389	.394554
0.44	1.5527	.19109	0.644036	0.94	2.5600	.40824	.390628
0.45	1.5683	0.19543	0.637628	**0.95**	2.5857	0.41258	0.386741
0.46	1.5841	.19978	0.631284	0.96	2.6117	.41692	.382893
0.47	1.6000	.20412	0.625002	0.97	2.6379	.42127	.379083
0.48	1.6161	.20846	0.618783	0.98	2.6645	.42561	.375311
0.49	1.6323	.21280	0.612626	0.99	2.6912	.42995	.371577
0.50	1.6487	0.21715	0.606531	**1.00**	2.7183	0.43429	0.367879

Table 3 (*Continued*)

x	e^x	$\log_{10}(e^x)$	e^{-x}	x	e^x	$\log_{10}(e^x)$	e^{-x}
1.00	2.7183	0.43429	0.367879	**1.50**	4.4817	0.65144	0.22313
1.01	2.7456	.43864	.364219	1.51	4.5267	.65578	.22091
1.02	2.7732	.44298	.360595	1.52	4.5722	.66013	.21871
1.03	2.8011	.44732	.357007	1.53	4.6182	.66447	.21654
1.04	2.8292	.45167	.353455	1.54	4.6646	.66881	.21438
1.05	2.8577	0.45601	0.349938	**1.55**	4.7115	0.67316	0.21224
1.06	2.8864	.46035	.346456	1.56	4.7588	.67750	.21013
1.07	2.9154	.46470	.343009	1.57	4.8066	.68184	.20804
1.08	2.9447	.46904	.339596	1.58	4.8550	.68619	.20597
1.09	2.9743	.47338	.336216	1.59	4.9037	.69053	.20393
1.10	3.0042	0.47772	0.332871	**1.60**	4.9530	0.69487	0.20190
1.11	3.0344	.48207	.329559	1.61	5.0028	.69921	.19988
1.12	3.0649	.48641	.326280	1.62	5.0531	.70356	.19789
1.13	3.0957	.49075	.323033	1.63	5.1039	.70790	.19593
1.14	3.1268	.49510	.319819	1.64	5.1552	.71224	.19398
1.15	3.1582	0.49944	0.316637	**1.65**	5.2070	0.71659	0.19205
1.16	3.1899	.50378	.313486	1.66	5.2593	.72093	.19013
1.17	3.2220	.50812	.310367	1.67	5.3122	.72527	.18824
1.18	3.2544	.51247	.307279	1.68	5.3656	.72961	.18637
1.19	3.2871	.51681	.304221	1.69	5.4195	.73396	.18452
1.20	3.3201	0.52115	0.301194	**1.70**	5.4739	0.73830	0.18268
1.21	3.3535	.52550	.298197	1.71	5.5290	.74264	.18086
1.22	3.3872	.52984	.295230	1.72	5.5845	.74699	.17906
1.23	3.4212	.53418	.292293	1.73	5.6407	.75133	.17728
1.24	3.4556	.53853	.289384	1.74	5.6973	.75567	.17552
1.25	3.4903	0.54287	0.286505	**1.75**	5.7546	0.76002	0.17377
1.26	3.5254	.54721	.283654	1.76	5.8124	.76436	.17204
1.27	3.5609	.55155	.280832	1.77	5.8709	.76870	.17033
1.28	3.5966	.55590	.278037	1.78	5.9299	.77304	.16863
1.29	3.6328	.56024	.275271	1.79	5.9895	.77739	.16696
1.30	3.6693	0.56458	0.272532	**1.80**	6.0496	0.78173	0.16529
1.31	3.7062	.56893	.269820	1.81	6.1104	.78607	.16365
1.32	3.7434	.57327	.267135	1.82	6.1719	.79042	.16202
1.33	3.7810	.57761	.264477	1.83	6.2339	.79476	.16041
1.34	3.8190	.58195	.261846	1.84	6.2965	.79910	.15881
1.35	3.8574	0.58630	0.259240	**1.85**	6.3598	0.80344	0.15723
1.36	3.8962	.59064	.256661	1.86	6.4237	.80779	.15567
1.37	3.9354	.59498	.254107	1.87	6.4483	.81213	.15412
1.38	3.9749	.59933	.251579	1.88	6.5535	.81647	.15259
1.39	4.0149	.60367	.249075	1.89	6.6194	.82082	.15107
1.40	4.0552	0.60801	0.246597	**1.90**	6.6859	0.82516	0.14956
1.41	4.0960	.61236	.244143	1.91	6.7531	.82950	.14808
1.42	4.1371	.61670	.241714	1.92	6.8210	.83385	.14660
1.43	4.1787	.62104	.239309	1.93	6.8895	.83819	.14514
1.44	4.2207	.62538	.236928	1.94	6.9588	.84253	.14370
1.45	4.2631	0.62973	0.234570	**1.95**	7.0287	0.84687	0.14227
1.46	4.3060	.63407	.232236	1.96	7.0993	.85122	.14085
1.47	4.3492	.63841	.229925	1.97	7.1707	.85556	.13945
1.48	4.3929	.64276	.227638	1.98	7.2427	.85990	.13806
1.49	4.4371	.64710	.225373	1.99	7.3155	.86425	.13669
1.50	4.4817	0.65144	0.223130	**2.00**	7.3891	0.86859	0.13533

Table 3   (Continued)

x	e^x	$\log_{10}(e^x)$	e^{-x}	x	e^x	$\log_{10}(e^x)$	e^{-x}
2.00	7.3891	0.86859	0.135335	**2.50**	12.182	1.08574	0.082085
2.01	7.4633	.87293	.133989	2.51	12.305	1.09008	.081268
2.02	7.5383	.87727	.132655	2.52	12.429	1.09442	.080460
2.03	7.6141	.88162	.131336	2.53	12.554	1.09877	.079659
2.04	7.6906	.88596	.130029	2.54	12.680	1.10311	.078866
2.05	7.7679	0.89030	0.128735	**2.55**	12.807	1.10745	0.078082
2.06	7.8460	.89465	.127454	2.56	12.936	1.11179	.077305
2.07	7.9248	.89899	.126186	2.57	13.066	1.11614	.076536
2.08	8.0045	.90333	.124930	2.58	13.197	1.12048	.075774
2.09	8.0849	.90756	.123687	2.59	13.330	1.12482	.075020
2.10	8.1662	0.91202	0.122456	**2.60**	13.464	1.12917	0.074274
2.11	8.2482	.91636	.121238	2.61	13.599	1.13351	.073535
2.12	8.3311	.92070	.120032	2.62	13.736	1.13785	.072803
2.13	8.4149	.92505	.118837	2.63	13.874	1.14219	.072078
2.14	8.4994	.92939	.117655	2.64	14.013	1.14654	.071361
2.15	8.5849	0.93373	0.116484	**2.65**	14.154	1.15088	0.070651
2.16	8.6711	.93808	.115325	2.66	14.296	1.15522	.069948
2.17	8.7583	.94242	.114178	2.67	14.440	1.15957	.069252
2.18	8.8463	.94676	.113042	2.68	14.585	1.16391	.068563
2.19	8.9352	.95110	.111917	2.69	14.732	1.16825	.067881
2.20	9.0250	0.95545	0.110803	**2.70**	14.880	1.17260	0.067206
2.21	9.1157	.95979	.109701	2.71	15.029	1.17694	.066537
2.22	9.2073	.96413	.108609	2.72	15.180	1.18128	.065875
2.23	9.2999	.96848	.107528	2.73	15.333	1.18562	.065219
2.24	9.3933	.97282	.106459	2.74	15.487	1.18997	.064570
2.25	9.4877	0.97716	0.105399	**2.75**	15.643	1.19431	0.063928
2.26	9.5831	.98151	.104350	2.76	15.800	1.19865	.063292
2.27	9.6794	.98585	.103312	2.77	15.959	1.20300	.062662
2.28	9.7767	.99019	.102284	2.78	16.119	1.20734	.062039
2.29	9.8749	.99453	.101266	2.79	16.281	1.21168	.061421
2.30	9.9742	0.99888	0.100259	**2.80**	16.445	1.21602	0.060810
2.31	10.074	1.00322	.099261	2.81	16.610	1.22037	.060205
2.32	10.176	1.00756	.098274	2.82	16.777	1.22471	.059606
2.33	10.278	1.01191	.097296	2.83	16.945	1.22905	.059013
2.34	10.381	1.01625	.096328	2.84	17.116	1.23340	.058426
2.35	10.486	1.02059	0.095369	**2.85**	17.288	1.23774	0.057844
2.36	10.591	1.02493	.094420	2.86	17.462	1.24208	.057269
2.37	10.697	1.02928	.093481	2.87	17.637	1.24643	.056699
2.38	10.805	1.03362	.092551	2.88	17.814	1.25077	.056135
2.39	10.913	1.03796	.091630	2.89	17.993	1.25511	.055576
2.40	11.023	1.04231	0.090718	**2.90**	18.174	1.25945	0.055023
2.41	11.134	1.04665	.089815	2.91	18.357	1.26380	.054476
2.42	11.246	1.05099	.088922	2.92	18.541	1.26814	.053934
2.43	11.359	1.05534	.088037	2.93	18.728	1.27248	.053397
2.44	11.473	1.05968	.087161	2.94	18.916	1.27683	.052866
2.45	11.588	1.06402	0.086294	**2.95**	19.106	1.28117	0.052340
2.46	11.705	1.06836	.085435	2.96	19.298	1.28551	.051819
2.47	11.822	1.07271	.084585	2.97	19.492	1.28985	.051303
2.48	11.941	1.07705	.083743	2.98	19.688	1.29420	.050793
2.49	12.061	1.08139	.082910	2.99	19.886	1.29854	.050287
2.50	12.182	1.08574	0.082085	**3.00**	20.086	1.30288	0.049787

Table 3   (Continued)

x	e^x	$\log_{10}(e^x)$	e^{-x}	x	e^x	$\log_{10}(e^x)$	e^{-x}
3.00	20.086	1.30288	0.049787	**3.50**	33.115	1.52003	0.030197
3.01	20.287	1.30723	.049292	3.51	33.448	1.52437	.029897
3.02	20.491	1.31157	.048801	3.52	33.784	1.52872	.029599
3.03	20.697	1.31591	.048316	3.53	34.124	1.53306	.029305
3.04	20.905	1.32026	.047835	3.54	34.467	1.53740	.029013
3.05	21.115	1.32460	0.047359	**3.55**	34.813	1.54175	0.028725
3.06	21.328	1.32894	.046888	3.56	35.163	1.54609	.028439
3.07	21.542	1.33328	.046421	3.57	35.517	1.55043	.028156
3.08	21.758	1.33763	.045959	3.58	35.874	1.55477	.027876
3.09	21.977	1.34197	.045502	3.59	36.234	1.55912	.027598
3.10	22.198	1.34631	0.045049	**3.60**	36.598	1.56346	0.027324
3.11	22.421	1.35066	.044601	3.61	36.966	1.56780	.027052
3.12	22.646	1.35500	.044157	3.62	37.338	1.57215	.026783
3.13	22.874	1.35934	.043718	3.63	37.713	1.57649	.026516
3.14	23.104	1.36368	.043283	3.64	38.092	1.58083	.026252
3.15	23.336	1.36803	0.042852	**3.65**	38.475	1.58517	0.025991
3.16	23.571	1.37237	.042426	3.66	38.861	1.58952	.025733
3.17	23.807	1.36671	.042004	3.67	39.252	1.59386	.025476
3.18	24.047	1.38106	.041586	3.68	39.646	1.59820	.025223
3.19	24.288	1.38540	.041172	3.69	40.045	1.60255	.024972
3.20	24.533	1.38974	0.040764	**3.70**	40.447	1.60689	0.024724
3.21	24.779	1.39409	.040357	3.71	40.854	1.61123	.024478
3.22	25.028	1.39843	.039955	3.72	41.264	1.61558	.024234
3.23	25.280	1.40277	.039557	3.73	41.679	1.61992	.023993
3.24	25.534	1.40711	.039164	3.74	42.098	1.62426	.023754
3.25	25.790	1.41146	0.038774	**3.75**	42.521	1.62860	0.023518
3.26	26.050	1.41580	.038388	3.76	42.948	1.63295	.023284
3.27	26.311	1.42014	.038006	3.77	43.380	1.63729	.023052
3.28	26.576	1.42449	.037628	3.78	43.816	1.64163	.022823
3.29	26.843	1.42883	.037254	3.79	44.256	1.64598	.022596
3.30	27.113	1.44317	0.036883	**3.80**	44.701	1.65032	0.022371
3.31	27.385	1.43751	.036516	3.81	45.150	1.65466	.022148
3.32	27.660	1.44186	.036153	3.82	45.604	1.65900	.021928
3.33	27.938	1.44620	.035793	3.83	46.063	1.66335	.021710
3.34	28.219	1.45054	.035437	3.84	46.525	1.66769	.021494
3.35	28.503	1.45489	0.035084	**3.85**	46.993	1.67203	0.021280
3.36	28.789	1.45923	.034735	3.86	47.465	1.67638	.021068
3.37	29.079	1.46357	.034390	3.87	47.942	1.68072	.020858
3.38	29.371	1.46792	.034047	3.88	48.424	1.68506	.020651
3.39	29.666	1.47226	.033709	3.89	48.911	1.68941	.020445
3.40	29.964	1.47660	0.033373	**3.90**	49.402	1.69375	0.020242
3.41	30.265	1.48094	.033041	3.91	49.899	1.69809	.020041
3.42	30.569	1.48529	.032712	3.92	50.400	1.70243	.019840
3.43	30.877	1.48963	.032387	3.93	50.907	1.70678	.019644
3.44	31.187	1.49397	.032065	3.94	51.419	1.71112	.019448
3.45	31.500	1.49832	0.031746	**3.95**	51.935	1.71546	0.019255
3.46	31.817	1.50266	.031430	3.96	52.457	1.71981	.019063
3.47	32.137	1.50700	.031117	3.97	52.985	1.72415	.018873
3.48	32.460	1.51134	.030807	3.98	53.517	1.72849	.018686
3.49	32.786	1.51569	.030501	3.99	54.055	1.73283	.018500
3.50	33.115	1.52003	0.030197	**4.00**	54.598	1.73718	0.018316

Table 3 (*Continued*)

x	e^x	$\log_{10}(e^x)$	e^{-x}	x	e^x	$\log_{10}(e^x)$	e^{-x}
4.00	54.598	1.73718	0.018316	**4.50**	90.017	1.95433	0.011109
4.01	55.147	1.74152	.018133	4.51	90.922	1.95867	.010998
4.02	55.701	1.74586	.017953	4.52	91.836	1.96301	.010889
4.03	56.261	1.75021	.017774	4.53	92.759	1.96735	.010781
4.04	56.826	1.75455	.017597	4.54	93.691	1.97170	.010673
4.05	57.397	1.75889	0.017422	**4.55**	94.632	1.97604	0.010567
4.06	57.974	1.76324	.017249	4.56	95.583	1.98038	.010462
4.07	58.577	1.76758	.017077	4.57	96.544	1.98473	.010358
4.08	59.145	1.77192	.016907	4.58	97.514	1.98907	.010255
4.09	59.740	1.77626	.016739	4.59	98.494	1.99341	.010153
4.10	60.340	1.78061	0.016573	**4.60**	99.484	1.99775	0.010052
4.11	60.947	1.78495	.016408	4.61	100.48	2.00210	.009952
4.12	61.559	1.78929	.016245	4.62	101.49	2.00644	.009853
4.13	62.178	1.79364	.016083	4.63	102.51	2.01078	.009755
4.14	62.803	1.79798	.015923	4.64	103.54	2.01513	.009658
4.15	63.434	1.80232	0.015764	**4.65**	104.58	2.01947	0.009562
4.16	64.072	1.80667	.015608	4.66	105.64	2.02381	.009466
4.17	64.715	1.81101	.015452	4.67	106.70	2.02816	.009372
4.18	65.366	1.81535	.015299	4.68	107.77	2.03250	.009279
4.19	66.023	1.81969	.015146	4.69	108.85	2.03684	.009187
4.20	66.686	1.82404	0.014996	**4.70**	109.95	2.04118	0.009095
4.21	67.357	1.82838	.014846	4.71	111.05	2.04553	.009005
4.22	68.033	1.83272	.014699	4.72	112.17	2.04987	.008915
4.23	68.717	1.83707	.014552	4.73	113.30	2.05421	.008826
4.24	69.408	1.84141	.014408	4.74	114.43	2.05856	.008739
4.25	70.105	1.84575	0.014264	**4.75**	115.58	2.06290	0.008652
4.26	70.810	1.85009	.014122	4.76	116.75	2.06724	.008566
4.27	71.522	1.85444	.013982	4.77	117.92	2.07158	.008480
4.28	72.240	1.85878	.013843	4.78	119.10	2.07593	.008396
4.29	72.966	1.86312	.013705	4.79	120.30	2.08027	.008312
4.30	73.700	1.86747	0.013569	**4.80**	121.51	2.08461	0.008230
4.31	74.440	1.87181	.013434	4.81	122.73	2.08896	.008148
4.32	75.189	1.87615	.013300	4.82	123.97	2.09330	.008067
4.33	75.944	1.88050	.013168	4.83	125.21	2.09764	.007987
4.34	76.708	1.88484	.013037	4.84	126.47	2.10199	.007907
4.35	77.478	1.88918	0.012907	**4.85**	127.74	2.10633	0.007828
4.36	78.257	1.89352	.012778	4.86	129.02	2.11067	.007750
4.37	79.044	1.89787	.012651	4.87	130.32	2.11501	.007673
4.38	79.838	1.90221	.012525	4.88	131.63	2.11936	.007597
4.39	80.640	1.90655	.012401	4.89	132.95	2.12370	.007521
4.40	81.451	1.91090	0.012277	**4.90**	134.29	2.12804	0.007477
4.41	82.269	1.91524	.012155	4.91	135.64	2.13239	.007372
4.42	83.096	1.91958	.012034	4.92	137.00	2.13673	.007299
4.43	83.931	1.92392	.011914	4.93	138.38	2.14107	.007227
4.44	84.775	1.92827	.011796	4.94	139.77	2.14541	.007155
4.45	85.627	1.93261	0.011679	**4.95**	141.17	2.14976	0.007083
4.46	86.488	1.93695	.011562	4.96	142.59	2.15410	.007013
4.47	87.357	1.94130	.011447	4.97	144.03	2.15844	.006943
4.48	88.235	1.94564	.011333	4.98	145.47	2.16279	.006874
4.49	89.121	1.94998	.011221	4.99	146.94	2.16713	.006806
4.50	90.017	1.95433	0.011109	**5.00**	148.41	2.17147	0.006738

Table 3 (Continued)

x	e^x	$\log_{10}(e^x)$	e^{-x}	x	e^x	$\log_{10}(e^x)$	e^{-x}
5.00	148.41	2.17147	0.006738	**5.50**	244.69	2.38862	0.0040868
5.01	149.90	2.17582	.006671	5.55	257.24	2.41033	.0038875
5.02	151.41	2.18016	.006605	5.60	270.43	2.43205	.0036979
5.03	152.93	2.18450	.006539	5.65	284.29	2.45376	.0035175
5.04	154.47	2.18884	.006474	5.70	298.87	2.47548	.0033460
5.05	156.02	2.19319	0.006409	**5.75**	314.19	2.49719	0.0031828
5.06	157.59	2.19753	.006346	5.80	330.30	2.51891	.0030276
5.07	159.17	2.20187	.006282	5.85	347.23	2.54062	.0028799
5.08	160.77	2.20622	.006220	5.90	365.04	2.56234	.0027394
5.09	162.39	2.21056	.006158	5.95	383.75	2.58405	.0026058
5.10	164.02	2.21490	0.006097	**6.00**	403.43	2.60577	0.0024788
5.11	165.67	2.21924	.006036	6.05	424.11	2.62748	.0023579
5.12	167.34	2.22359	.005976	6.10	445.86	2.64920	.0022429
5.13	169.02	2.22793	.005917	6.15	468.72	2.67091	.0021335
5.14	170.72	2.23227	.005858	6.20	492.75	2.69263	.0020294
5.15	172.43	2.23662	0.005799	**6.25**	518.01	2.71434	0.0019305
5.16	174.16	2.24096	.005742	6.30	544.57	2.73606	.0018363
5.17	175.91	2.24530	.005685	6.35	572.49	2.75777	.0017467
5.18	177.68	2.24965	.005628	6.40	601.85	2.77948	.0016616
5.19	179.47	2.25399	.005572	6.45	632.70	2.80120	.0015805
5.20	181.27	2.25833	0.005517	**6.50**	665.14	2.82291	0.0015034
5.21	183.09	2.26267	.005462	6.55	699.24	2.84463	.0014301
5.22	184.93	2.26702	.005407	6.60	735.10	2.86634	.0013604
5.23	186.79	2.27136	.005354	6.65	772.78	2.88806	.0012940
5.24	188.67	2.27570	.005300	6.70	812.41	2.90977	.0012309
5.25	190.57	2.28005	0.005248	**6.75**	854.06	2.93149	0.0011709
5.26	192.48	2.28439	.005195	6.80	897.85	2.95320	.0011138
5.27	194.42	2.28873	.005144	6.85	943.88	2.97492	.0010595
5.28	196.37	2.29307	.005092	6.90	992.27	2.99663	.0010078
5.29	198.34	2.29742	.005042	6.95	1043.1	3.01835	.0009586
5.30	200.34	2.30176	0.004992	**7.00**	1096.6	3.04006	0.0009119
5.31	202.35	2.30610	.004942	7.05	1152.9	3.06178	.0008674
5.32	204.38	2.31045	.004893	7.10	1212.0	3.08349	.0008251
5.33	206.44	2.31479	.004844	7.15	1274.1	3.10521	.0007849
5.34	208.51	2.31913	.004796	7.20	1339.4	3.12692	.0007466
5.35	210.61	2.32348	0.004748	**7.25**	1408.1	3.14863	0.0007102
5.36	212.72	2.32782	.004701	7.30	1480.3	3.17035	.0006755
5.37	214.86	2.33216	.004654	7.35	1556.2	3.19206	.0006426
5.38	217.02	2.33650	.004608	7.40	1636.0	3.21378	.0006113
5.39	219.20	2.34085	.004562	7.45	1719.9	3.23549	.0005814
5.40	221.41	2.34519	0.004517	**7.50**	1808.0	3.25721	0.0005531
5.41	223.63	2.34953	.004472	7.55	1900.7	3.27892	.0005261
5.42	225.88	2.35388	.004427	7.60	1998.2	3.30064	.0005005
5.43	228.15	2.35822	.004383	7.65	2100.6	3.32235	.0004760
5.44	230.44	2.36256	.004339	7.70	2208.3	3.34407	.0004528
5.45	232.76	2.36690	0.004296	**7.75**	2321.6	3.36578	0.0004307
5.46	235.10	2.37125	.004254	7.80	2440.6	3.38750	.0004097
5.47	237.46	2.37559	.004211	7.85	2565.7	3.40921	.0003898
5.48	239.85	2.37993	.004169	7.90	2697.3	3.43093	.0003707
5.49	242.26	2.38428	.004128	7.95	2835.6	3.45264	.0003527
5.50	244.69	2.38862	0.004087	**8.00**	2981.0	3.47436	0.0003355

Table 3   (Continued)

x	e^x	$\log_{10}(e^x)$	e^{-x}	x	e^x	$\log_{10}(e^x)$	e^{-x}
8.00	2981.0	3.47436	0.0003355	**9.00**	8103.1	3.90865	0.0001234
8.05	3133.8	3.49607	.0003191	9.05	8518.5	3.93037	.0001174
8.10	3294.5	3.51779	.0003035	9.10	8955.3	3.95208	.0001117
8.15	3463.4	3.53950	.0002887	9.15	9414.4	3.97379	.0001062
8.20	3641.0	3.56121	.0002747	9.20	9897.1	3.99551	.0001010
8.25	3827.6	3.58293	0.0002613	**9.25**	10405	4.01722	0.0000961
8.30	4023.9	3.60464	.0002485	9.30	10938	4.03894	.0000914
8.35	4230.2	3.62636	.0002364	9.35	11499	4.06065	.0000870
8.40	4447.1	3.64807	.0002249	9.40	12088	4.08237	.0000827
8.45	4675.1	3.66979	.0002139	9.45	12708	4.10408	.0000787
8.50	4914.8	3.69150	0.0002036	**9.50**	13360	4.12580	0.0000749
8.55	5166.8	3.71322	.0001935	9.55	14045	4.14751	.0000712
8.60	5431.7	3.73493	.0001841	9.60	14765	4.16923	.0000677
8.65	5710.0	3.75665	.0001751	9.65	15522	4.19094	.0000644
8.70	6002.9	3.77836	.0001666	9.70	16318	4.21266	.0000613
8.75	6310.7	3.80008	0.0001585	**9.75**	17154	4.23437	0.0000583
8.80	6634.2	3.82179	.0001507	9.80	18034	4.25609	.0000555
8.85	6974.4	3.84351	.0001434	9.85	18958	4.27780	.0000527
8.90	7332.0	3.86522	.0001364	9.90	19930	4.29952	.0000502
8.95	7707.9	3.88694	.0001297	9.95	20952	4.32123	0.0000477
9.00	8103.1	3.90865	0.0001234	**10.00**	22026	4.34294	0.0000454

Table 4   Hyperbolic functions

x	sinh x	cosh x	tanh x
0	.00000	1.0000	.00000
0.1	.10017	1.0050	.09967
0.2	.20134	1.0201	.19738
0.3	.30452	1.0453	.29131
0.4	.41075	1.0811	.37995
0.5	.52110	1.1276	.46212
0.6	.63665	1.1855	.53705
0.7	.75858	1.2552	.60437
0.8	.88811	1.3374	.66404
0.9	1.0265	1.4331	.71630
1.0	1.1752	1.5431	.76159
1.1	1.3356	1.6685	.80050
1.2	1.5095	1.8107	.83365
1.3	1.6984	1.9709	.86172
1.4	1.9043	2.1509	.88535
1.5	2.1293	2.3524	.90515
1.6	2.3756	2.5775	.92167
1.7	2.6456	2.8283	.93541
1.8	2.9422	3.1075	.94681
1.9	3.2682	3.4177	.95624
2.0	3.6269	3.7622	.96403
2.1	4.0219	4.1443	.97045
2.2	4.4571	4.5679	.97574
2.3	4.9370	5.0372	.98010
2.4	5.4662	5.5569	.98367
2.5	6.0502	6.1323	.98661
2.6	6.6947	6.7690	.98903
2.7	7.4063	7.4735	.99101
2.8	8.1919	8.2527	.99263
2.9	9.0596	9.1146	.99396
3.0	10.018	10.068	.99505
3.1	11.076	11.122	.99595
3.2	12.246	12.287	.99668
3.3	13.538	13.575	.99728
3.4	14.965	14.999	.99777
3.5	16.543	16.573	.99818
3.6	18.285	18.313	.99851
3.7	20.211	20.236	.99878
3.8	22.339	22.362	.99900
3.9	24.691	24.711	.99918
4.0	27.290	27.308	.99933
4.1	30.162	30.178	.99945
4.2	33.336	33.351	.99955
4.3	36.843	36.857	.99963
4.4	40.719	40.732	.99970
4.5	45.003	45.014	.99975
4.6	49.737	49.747	.99980
4.7	54.969	54.978	.99983
4.8	60.751	60.759	.99986
4.9	67.141	67.149	.99989
5.0	74.203	74.210	.99991

Table 5 *Trigonometric functions*

Degrees	Radians	Sin	Cos	Tan	Cot		
0	0.0000	0.0000	1.0000	0.0000		1.5708	90
1	0.0175	0.0175	0.9998	0.0175	57.290	1.5533	89
2	0.0349	0.0349	0.9994	0.0349	28.636	1.5359	88
3	0.0524	0.0523	0.9986	0.0524	19.081	1.5184	87
4	0.0698	0.0698	0.9976	0.0699	14.301	1.5010	86
5	0.0873	0.0872	0.9962	0.0875	11.430	1.4835	85
6	0.1047	0.1045	0.9945	0.1051	9.5144	1.4661	84
7	0.1222	0.1219	0.9925	0.1228	8.1443	1.4486	83
8	0.1396	0.1392	0.9903	0.1405	7.1154	1.4312	82
9	0.1571	0.1564	0.9877	0.1584	6.3138	1.4137	81
10	0.1745	0.1736	0.9848	0.1763	5.6713	1.3963	80
11	0.1920	0.1908	0.9816	0.1944	5.1446	1.3788	79
12	0.2094	0.2079	0.9781	0.2126	4.7046	1.3614	78
13	0.2269	0.2250	0.9744	0.2309	4.3315	1.3439	77
14	0.2443	0.2419	0.9703	0.2493	4.0108	1.3265	76
15	0.2618	0.2588	0.9659	0.2679	3.7321	1.3090	75
16	0.2793	0.2756	0.9613	0.2867	3.4874	1.2915	74
17	0.2967	0.2924	0.9563	0.3057	3.2709	1.2741	73
18	0.3142	0.3090	0.9511	0.3249	3.0777	1.2566	72
19	0.3316	0.3256	0.9455	0.3443	2.9042	1.2392	71
20	0.3491	0.3420	0.9397	0.3640	2.7475	1.2217	70
21	0.3665	0.3584	0.9336	0.3839	2.6051	1.2043	69
22	0.3840	0.3746	0.9272	0.4040	2.4751	1.1868	68
23	0.4014	0.3907	0.9205	0.4245	2.3559	1.1694	67
24	0.4189	0.4067	0.9135	0.4452	2.2460	1.1519	66
25	0.4363	0.4226	0.9063	0.4663	2.1445	1.1345	65
26	0.4538	0.4384	0.8988	0.4877	2.0503	1.1170	64
27	0.4712	0.4540	0.8910	0.5095	1.9626	1.0996	63
28	0.4887	0.4695	0.8829	0.5317	1.8807	1.0821	62
29	0.5061	0.4848	0.8746	0.5543	1.8040	1.0647	61
30	0.5236	0.5000	0.8660	0.5774	1.7321	1.0472	60
31	0.5411	0.5150	0.8572	0.6009	1.6643	1.0297	59
32	0.5585	0.5299	0.8480	0.6249	1.6003	1.0123	58
33	0.5760	0.5446	0.8387	0.6494	1.5399	0.9948	57
34	0.5934	0.5592	0.8290	0.6745	1.4826	0.9774	56
35	0.6109	0.5736	0.8192	0.7002	1.4281	0.9599	55
36	0.6283	0.5878	0.8090	0.7265	1.3764	0.9425	54
37	0.6458	0.6018	0.7986	0.7536	1.3270	0.9250	53
38	0.6632	0.6157	0.7880	0.7813	1.2799	0.9076	52
39	0.6807	0.6293	0.7771	0.8098	1.2349	0.8901	51
40	0.6981	0.6428	0.7660	0.8391	1.1918	0.8727	50
41	0.7156	0.6561	0.7547	0.8693	1.1504	0.8552	49
42	0.7330	0.6691	0.7431	0.9004	1.1106	0.8378	48
43	0.7505	0.6820	0.7314	0.9325	1.0724	0.8203	47
44	0.7679	0.6947	0.7193	0.9657	1.0355	0.8029	46
45	0.7854	0.7071	0.7071	1.0000	1.0000	0.7854	45
		Cos	Sin	Cot	Tan	Radians	Degrees

Table 6   Common logarithms

N	0	1	2	3	4	5	6	7	8	9
10	0000	0043	0086	0128	0170	0212	0253	0294	0334	0374
11	0414	0453	0492	0531	0569	0607	0645	0682	0719	0755
12	0792	0828	0864	0899	0934	0969	1004	1038	1072	1106
13	1139	1173	1206	1239	1271	1303	1335	1367	1399	1430
14	1461	1492	1523	1553	1584	1614	1644	1673	1703	1732
15	1761	1790	1818	1847	1875	1903	1931	1959	1987	2014
16	2041	2068	2095	2122	2148	2175	2201	2227	2253	2279
17	2304	2330	2355	2380	2405	2430	2455	2480	2504	2529
18	2553	2577	2601	2625	2648	2672	2695	2718	2742	2765
19	2788	2810	2833	2856	2878	2900	2923	2945	2967	2989
20	3010	3032	3054	3075	3096	3118	3139	3160	3181	3201
21	3222	3243	3263	3284	3304	3324	3345	3365	3385	3404
22	3424	3444	3464	3483	3502	3522	3541	3560	3579	3598
23	3617	3636	3655	3674	3692	3711	3729	3747	3766	3784
24	3802	3820	3838	3856	3874	3892	3909	3927	3945	3962
25	3979	3997	4014	4031	4048	4065	4082	4099	4116	4133
26	4150	4166	4183	4200	4216	4232	4249	4265	4281	4298
27	4314	4330	4346	4362	4378	4393	4409	4425	4440	4456
28	4472	4487	4502	4518	4533	4548	4564	4579	4594	4609
29	4624	4639	4654	4669	4683	4698	4713	4728	4742	4757
30	4771	4786	4800	4814	4829	4843	4857	4871	4886	4900
31	4914	4928	4942	4955	4969	4983	4997	5011	5024	5038
32	5051	5065	5079	5092	5105	5119	5132	5145	5159	5172
33	5185	5198	5211	5224	5237	5250	5263	5276	5289	5302
34	5315	5328	5340	5353	5366	5378	5391	5403	5416	5428
35	5441	5453	5465	5478	5490	5502	5514	5527	5539	5551
36	5563	5575	5587	5599	5611	5623	5635	5647	5658	5670
37	5682	5694	5705	5717	5729	5740	5752	5763	5775	5786
38	5798	5809	5821	5832	5843	5855	5866	5877	5888	5899
39	5911	5922	5933	5944	5955	5966	5977	5988	5999	6010
40	6021	6031	6042	6053	6064	6075	6085	6096	6107	6117
41	6128	6138	6149	6160	6170	6180	6191	6201	6212	6222
42	6232	6243	6253	6263	6274	6284	6294	6304	6314	6325
43	6335	6345	6355	6365	6375	6385	6395	6405	6415	6425
44	6435	6444	6454	6464	6474	6484	6493	6503	6513	6522
45	6532	6542	6551	6561	6571	6580	6590	6599	6609	6618
46	6628	6637	6646	6656	6665	6675	6684	6693	6702	6712
47	6721	6730	6739	6749	6758	6767	6776	6785	6794	6803
48	6812	6821	6830	6839	6848	6857	6866	6875	6884	6893
49	6902	6911	6920	6928	6937	6946	6955	6964	6972	6981
50	6990	6998	7007	7016	7024	7033	7042	7050	7059	7067
51	7076	7084	7093	7101	7110	7118	7126	7135	7143	7152
52	7160	7168	7177	7185	7193	7202	7210	7218	7226	7235
53	7243	7251	7259	7267	7275	7284	7292	7300	7308	7316
54	7324	7332	7340	7348	7356	7364	7372	7380	7388	7396

Table 6 (*Continued*)

N	0	1	2	3	4	5	6	7	8	9
55	7404	7412	7419	7427	7435	7443	7451	7459	7466	7474
56	7482	7490	7497	7505	7513	7520	7528	7536	7543	7551
57	7559	7566	7574	7582	7589	7597	7604	7612	7619	7627
58	7634	7642	7649	7657	7664	7672	7679	7686	7694	7701
59	7709	7716	7723	7731	7738	7745	7752	7760	7767	7774
60	7782	7789	7796	7803	7810	7818	7825	7832	7839	7846
61	7853	7860	7868	7875	7882	7889	7896	7903	7910	7917
62	7924	7931	7938	7945	7952	7959	7966	7973	7980	7987
63	7993	8000	8007	8014	8021	8028	8035	8041	8048	8055
64	8062	8069	8075	8082	8089	8096	8102	8109	8116	8122
65	8129	8136	8142	8149	8156	8162	8169	8176	8182	8189
66	8195	8202	8209	8215	8222	8228	8235	8241	8248	8254
67	8261	8267	8274	8280	8287	8293	8299	8306	8312	8319
68	8325	8331	8338	8344	8351	8357	8363	8370	8376	8382
69	8388	8395	8401	8407	8414	8420	8426	8432	8439	8445
70	8451	8457	8463	8470	8476	8482	8488	8494	8500	8506
71	8513	8519	8525	8531	8537	8543	8549	8555	8561	8567
72	8573	8579	8585	8591	8597	8603	8609	8615	8621	8627
73	8633	8639	8645	8651	8657	8663	8669	8675	8681	8686
74	8692	8698	8704	·8710	8716	8722	8727	8733	8739	8745
75	8751	8756	8762	8768	8774	8779	8785	8791	8797	8802
76	8808	8814	8820	8825	8831	8837	8842	8848	8854	8859
77	8865	8871	8876	8882	8887	8893	8899	8904	8910	8915
78	8921	8927	8932	8938	8943	8949	8954	8960	8965	8971
79	8976	8982	8987	8993	8998	9004	9009	9015	9020	9025
80	9031	9036	9042	9047	9053	9058	9063	9069	9074	9079
81	9085	9090	9096	9101	9106	9112	9117	9122	9128	9133
82	9138	9143	9149	9154	9159	9165	9170	9175	9180	9186
83	9191	9196	9201	9206	9212	9217	9222	9227	9232	9238
84	9243	9248	9253	9258	9263	9269	9274	9279	9284	9289
85	9294	9299	9304	9309	9315	9320	9325	9330	9335	9340
86	9345	9350	9355	9360	9365	9370	9375	9380	9385	9390
87	9395	9400	9405	9410	9415	9420	9425	9430	9435	9440
88	9445	9450	9455	9460	9465	9469	9474	9479	9484	9489
89	9494	9499	9504	9509	9513	9518	9523	9528	9533	9538
90	9542	9547	9552	9557	9562	9566	9571	9576	9581	9586
91	9590	9595	9600	9605	9609	9614	9619	9624	9628	9633
92	9638	9643	9647	9652	9657	9661	9666	9671	9675	9680
93	9685	9689	9694	9699	9703	9708	9713	9717	9722	9727
94	9731	9736	9741	9745	9750	9754	9759	9763	9768	9773
95	9777	9782	9786	9791	9795	9800	9805	9809	9814	9818
96	9823	9827	9832	9836	9841	9845	9850	9854	9859	9863
97	9868	9872	9877	9881	9886	9890	9894	9899	9903	9908
98	9912	9917	9921	9926	9930	9934	9939	9943	9948	9952
99	9956	9961	9965	9969	9974	9978	9983	9987	9991	9996

Table 7   The Greek alphabet

α	alpha	ν	nu
β	beta	ξ	xi
γ	gamma	o	omicron
δ	delta	π	pi
ϵ	epsilon	ρ	rho
ζ	zeta	σ	sigma
η	eta	τ	tau
θ	theta	υ	upsilon
ι	iota	ϕ	phi
κ	kappa	χ	chi
λ	lambda	ψ	psi
μ	mu	ω	omega

Answers to Odd-Numbered Exercises

Exercises 1.1 (Page 9)

1. $(-2, +\infty)$ 3. $(-\infty, \frac{3}{4})$ 5. $[4, 8]$ 7. $(-\frac{5}{3}, \frac{4}{3}]$ 9. all x not in $[-\frac{1}{2}, 0]$ 11. all x not in $[-2, 2]$ 13. all x not in $[-5, 3]$
15. $[-1, \frac{1}{2}]$ 17. $(-3, \frac{3}{4})$ 19. $(-\infty, -1)$ and $(\frac{1}{3}, 3)$ 21. $(\frac{3}{2}, \frac{31}{14})$ and $(\frac{7}{3}, +\infty)$

Exercises 1.2 (Page 16)

1. $1, -\frac{5}{2}$ 3. $-3, 8$ 5. $-\frac{1}{4}, 4$ 7. $-\frac{2}{3}, \frac{1}{2}$ 9. $\frac{4}{3}, 3$ 11. $[\frac{5}{8}, +\infty)$ 13. all x not in $(1, 4)$ 15. $(-11, 3)$ 17. $[\frac{2}{3}, 2]$
19. all x not in $[1, 4]$ 21. all x not in $(\frac{2}{3}, 10)$ 23. $[-\frac{9}{2}, \frac{3}{2}]$ 25. all x not in $[\frac{10}{9}, 2]$ 29. $|x| > |a|$ 31. $|x - 2| > 2$

Exercises 1.3 (Page 23)

1. (a) $(1, 2)$; (b) $(-1, -2)$; (c) $(-1, 2)$; (d) $(-2, 1)$ 3. (a) $(2, -2)$; (b) $(-2, 2)$; (c) $(-2, -2)$; (d) does not apply   5. (a) $(-2, 1)$;
(b) $(1, -3)$; (c) $(1, 3)$; (d) $(-3, -1)$

Exercises 1.4 (Page 28)

5. $\frac{1}{2}\sqrt{53}$; $\frac{1}{2}\sqrt{89}$; $\sqrt{26}$ 7. $\frac{41}{2}$ 11. $-2, 8$ 13. $(-2 + \frac{3}{2}\sqrt{3}, \frac{3}{2} + 2\sqrt{3})$ and $(-2 - \frac{3}{2}\sqrt{3}, \frac{3}{2} - 2\sqrt{3})$ 15. $77x^2 + 90xy + 21y^2 - 122x$
$- 66y - 55 = 0$ 17. $(-\frac{9}{4}, \frac{17}{4})$; $(\frac{1}{2}, \frac{11}{2})$; $(\frac{13}{4}, \frac{27}{4})$ 19. $(\frac{9}{4}, \frac{11}{4})$ 21. $(-\frac{3}{2}, \frac{7}{2})$ 23. $(5, -7)$ 25. (a) $2x + y = 5$

Exercises 1.5 (Page 37)

1. -1 3. $-\frac{1}{7}$ 5. $4x - y - 11 = 0$ 7. $x = -3$ 9. $4x - 3y + 12 = 0$ 11. $\sqrt{3}x - y + (2\sqrt{3} - 5) = 0$ 13. $x + y = 0$
15. $\frac{x}{\frac{8}{5}} + \frac{y}{8} = 1$ 19. (a) yes; (b) yes; (c) no; (d) no   21. $2x + 3y + 7 = 0$; $\sqrt{13}$ 23. (a) $-\frac{A}{B}$; (b) $-\frac{C}{B}$; (c) $-\frac{C}{A}$; (d) $Bx - Ay = 0$
25. $y = 1$; $9x - 4y - 11 = 0$; $9x + 4y - 19 = 0$ 27. $2x + 3y - 12 = 0$; $(2 + 2\sqrt{2})x + (3 - 3\sqrt{2})y - 12 = 0$; $(2 - 2\sqrt{2})x + (3 + 3\sqrt{2})y$
$- 12 = 0$ 29. (a) $x = 1$; (b) $y = 1$; (c) $x = 1$; (d) $2x + y - 3 = 0$; (e) $x - 2y + 1 = 0$; (f) $x + y - 2 = 0$

Exercises 1.6 (Page 43)

1. $(x - 4)^2 + (y + 3)^2 = 25$; $x^2 + y^2 - 8x + 6y = 0$ 3. $(x + 5)^2 + (y + 12)^2 = 9$; $x^2 + y^2 + 10x + 24y + 160 = 0$ 5. $x^2 + y^2 - 2x - 4y$
$- 8 = 0$ 7. $x^2 + y^2 + 6x + 10y + 9 = 0$ 9. $x^2 + y^2 - 4x - 4y - 2 = 0$ 11. $(3, 4)$; 4 13. $(0, -\frac{2}{3})$; $\frac{5}{3}$ 15. circle   17. no real
locus   19. circle   21. $x + y + 5 = 0$ 23. $3x + 4y - 19 = 0$

Exercises 1.7   (Page 47)

1. $(0, 1)$; $y = -1$; 4   3. $(-2, 0)$; $x = 2$; 8   5. $(0, -\frac{1}{4})$; $y = \frac{1}{4}$; 1   7. $(\frac{9}{8}, 0)$; $x = -\frac{9}{8}$; $\frac{9}{2}$ 9. $y^2 = 20x$ 11. $x^2 = -8y$ 13. $y^2 = 2x$
15. $y^2 = -6x$ 19. $x^2 = -y$ 21. 166 ft   23. $\frac{32}{45}$ in.   25. $y^2 - 10x - 10y + 20 = 0$ 27. $x^2 + y^2 + 10y = 0$

Exercises 1.8   (Page 52)

1. $x'^2 + y'^2 = 13$ 3. $y'^2 = 6x'$ 5. $x'^2 + 4y'^2 = 4$ 7. $y' = 2x'^3$ 9. $x'^2 + 4y'^2 = 16$ 11. $3x'^2 - 2y'^2 = 6$ 13. $(-3, \frac{1}{4})$;
$(-3, -\frac{3}{4})$; $x = -3$; $y = \frac{5}{4}$ 15. $(1, -5)$; $(-\frac{1}{2}, -5)$; $y = -5$; $x = \frac{5}{2}$ 17. $(\frac{2}{3}, 1)$; $(\frac{7}{24}, 1)$; $y = 1$; $x = \frac{25}{24}$ 19. $y^2 + 20x - 8y - 24 = 0$
21. $x^2 + 2x - 8y + 41 = 0$ 23. $x^2 - 6x - 6y - 3 = 0$; $x^2 - 6x + 6y + 21 = 0$ 25. $y^2 - 4x - 4y - 12 = 0$ 27. $y^2 - 2x - 8y + 25 = 0$;
$y^2 - 18x - 8y + 169 = 0$ 29. $\left(-\dfrac{b}{2a}, \dfrac{4ac - b^2}{4a}\right)$ 31. $x^2 - 2x + 4y + 1 = 0$; $x^2 - 2x - 16y - 79 = 0$; $x^2 - 2x - 4y - 31 = 0$; $x^2 - 2x + 16y$
$+ 49 = 0$ 33. $x'^3 - y'^2 = 0$

Exercises 1.9   (Page 59)

39. $3x - 4y + 5 \leq 0$ 41. $4x - y \geq 6$; $x + 2y \geq 6$; $5x + y \leq 21$ 43. $-21 < x^2 + y^2 + 6x - 8y < 11$

Review Exercises for Chapter 1   (Page 60)

1. $(\frac{4}{3}, \frac{6}{5}]$ 3. $(-\frac{3}{2}, 1)$ 5. $[-\frac{12}{5}, \frac{6}{5}]$ 7. (a) $(x - 3)^2 + (y + 5)^2 = 0$; (b) $(x - 3)^2 + (y + 5)^2 < 16$; (c) $(x - 3)^2 + (y + 5)^2 \geq 25$
9. $x = 0$, $3x + 4y = 0$ 11. $k = -\frac{3}{5}$; $h = \frac{10}{3}$ 13. $(3, -6)$; $(-2, -5)$ 15. $0 \leq k \leq 2$.   17. $7x^2 + 7y^2 + 11x - 19y - 6 = 0$
19. $(x - 5)^2 = 8(y - 1)$ 21. 9π in.   23. $9x + 11y - 80 = 0$; $3x + 13y - 70 = 0$ 31. $(\frac{13}{3}, \frac{13}{3})$; $(9, 7)$; $(2, 3)$ 33. $(x - p)^2$
$+ y^2 = 4p^2$; $(p, 2p)$; $(p - 2p)$

Exercises 2.1   (Page 69)

1. domain: $(-\infty, +\infty)$; range: $(-\infty, +\infty)$ 3. domain: $(-\infty, +\infty)$; range: $[-6, +\infty)$ 5. domain: $[\frac{4}{3}, +\infty)$; range: $[0, +\infty)$
7. domain: all x not in $(-2, 2)$; range: $[0, +\infty)$ 9. domain: $(-\infty, +\infty)$; range: $[0, +\infty)$ 11. domain: $(-\infty, +\infty)$; range: -2 and 2
13. domain: $(-\infty, +\infty)$; range: all real numbers except 3   15. domain: $(-\infty, +\infty)$; range: $[-4, +\infty)$ 17. domain: all real numbers
except -5 and -1; range: all real numbers except -7 and -3 19. domain: all x not in $(-1, 4)$; range: $[0, +\infty)$ 21. domain: all real
numbers except 2; range: $[0, +\infty)$ 23. domain: all real numbers except -5; range: $[3, +\infty)$

Exercises 2.2   (Page 73)

1. (a) -5; (b) -6; (c) -3; (d) 30; (e) $2h^2 + 9h + 4$; (f) $8x^4 + 10x^2 - 3$; (g) $2x^4 - 7x^2$; (h) $2x^2 + 4hx + 5x + 2h^2 + 5h - 3$; (i) $2x^2 + 5x + 2h^2$
$+ 5h - 6$; (j) $4x + 2h + 5$ 3. (a) 1; (b) $\sqrt{11}$; (c) 2; (d) $3\sqrt{7}$; (e) $\sqrt{4x + 9}$; (f) $\dfrac{2}{(\sqrt{2x + 2h + 3} + \sqrt{2x + 3})}$ 5. (a) 1; (b) -1; (c) 1; (d) -1;
(e) -1 if $x > 0$, 1 if $x \leq 0$; (f) 1 if $x \geq -1$, -1 if $x < -1$; (g) 1; (h) -1 7. (a) $x^2 + x - 6$, domain: $(-\infty, +\infty)$; (b) $-x^2 + x - 4$, domain:
$(-\infty, +\infty)$; (c) $x^3 - 5x^2 - x + 5$, domain: $(-\infty, +\infty)$; (d) $(x - 5)/(x^2 - 1)$, domain: all real numbers except -1 and 1; (e) $(x^2 - 1)/(x - 5)$,
domain: all real numbers except 5; (f) $x^2 - 6$, domain: $(-\infty, +\infty)$; (g) $x^2 - 10x + 24$, domain: $(-\infty, +\infty)$ 9. (a) $\dfrac{x^2 + 2x - 1}{x^2 - x}$, domain: all
real numbers except 0 and 1; (b) $\dfrac{x^2 + 1}{x^2 - x}$, domain: all real numbers except 0 and 1; (c) $\dfrac{x + 1}{x^2 - x}$, domain: all real numbers except 0 and 1;
(d) $\dfrac{x^2 + x}{x - 1}$, domain: all real numbers except 0 and 1; (e) $\dfrac{x - 1}{x^2 + x}$, domain: all real numbers except -1, 0, and 1; (f) $\dfrac{1 + x}{1 - x}$, domain: all real
numbers except 0 and 1; (g) $\dfrac{x - 1}{x + 1}$, domain: all real numbers except -1 and 1   11. (a) $\sqrt{x^2 - 1} + \sqrt{x - 1}$, domain: $[1, +\infty)$;
(b) $\sqrt{x^2 - 1} - \sqrt{x - 1}$, domain: $[1, +\infty)$; (c) $(x - 1)\sqrt{x + 1}$, domain: $[1, +\infty)$; (d) $\sqrt{x + 1}$, domain: $(1, +\infty)$; (e) $\dfrac{1}{\sqrt{x + 1}}$, domain: $(1, +\infty)$;
(f) $\sqrt{x - 2}$, domain: $[2, +\infty)$; (g) $\sqrt{\sqrt{x^2 - 1} - 1}$, domain: $(-\infty, -\sqrt{2}]$ and $[\sqrt{2}, +\infty)$
13. (a) even; (b) odd; (c) neither; (d) even; (e) neither; (f) even; (g) odd; (h) neither   17. (a) $[x^2 + 2] + [0]$;
(b) $[-1] + [x^3]$; (c) $[x^4 + 3] + [x^3 - x]$; (d) $[0] + \left[\dfrac{1}{x}\right]$; (e) $\left[\dfrac{x^2 + 1}{x^2 - 1}\right] + \left[\dfrac{-2x}{x^2 - 1}\right]$; (f) $\frac{1}{2}[|2x| + |x - 1| + |x + 1|] + \frac{1}{2}[|x - 1| - |x + 1|]$

19. (a) even; (b) odd; (c) even; (d) even   21. $(f \circ g)(x) = \begin{cases} 2 & \text{if } x < 0 \\ x & \text{if } 0 \le x \le 1 \\ 2 & \text{if } x > 1 \end{cases}$; domain: $(-\infty, +\infty)$; range: $[0, 1]$ and 2

23. $(f \circ g)(x) = \begin{cases} 1 & \text{if } x < 0 \\ 4x^2 & \text{if } 0 \le x \le \frac{1}{2} \\ 0 & \text{if } \frac{1}{2} < x \le 1 \\ 1 & \text{if } x > 1 \end{cases}$; domain: $(-\infty, +\infty)$; range: $[0, 1]$ 25. $g(x) = x - 3$; $g(x) = 1 - x$

Exercises 2.3   *(Page 77)*

1. domain: $(-\infty, +\infty)$; range: 0 and 1   3. domain: $(-\infty, +\infty)$; range: 0 and 1   5. domain: $(-\infty, +\infty)$; range: 0, 1, and 2
7. domain: $(-\infty, +\infty)$; range: $[0, +\infty]$ 9. domain: $(-\infty, +\infty)$; range: $[0, 1]$ 11. domain: $(-\infty, +\infty)$; range: $(-\infty, +\infty)$
13. domain: $(-\infty, +\infty)$; range: $-1, 0$, and 1   15. domain: $(-\infty, +\infty)$; range: $[1, +\infty)$ 17. domain: $(-\infty, +\infty)$; range: $[0, 1)$
19. domain: $(-\infty, +\infty)$; range: the nonnegative integers   21. domain: all real numbers except 0; range: $(-\infty, -1]$, 0, and $(\frac{1}{2}, 1]$
23. domain: $(-\infty, +\infty)$; range: 1 and 3

Exercises 2.4   *(Page 84)*

1. 0.005   3. 0.005   5. $\frac{1}{1400}$ 7. 0.01   9. $\delta = \frac{\epsilon}{5}$ 11. $\delta = \epsilon$ 13. $\delta = \min(1, \frac{1}{3}\epsilon)$ 15. $\delta = \min(1, \frac{1}{2}\epsilon)$ 17. $\delta = \min(\frac{1}{2}, \frac{1}{11}\epsilon)$
19. $\delta = \min(1, \frac{1}{8}\epsilon)$ 21. $\delta = \min(1, \frac{1}{6}\epsilon)$ 23. $\delta = \min(1, (2\sqrt{2} + 3)\epsilon)$

Exercises 2.5   *(Page 91)*

1. 7   3. $-\frac{1}{22}$ 5. 12   7. $\frac{4}{7}$ 9. $\frac{3}{2}$ 11. $\frac{1}{5}\sqrt{30}$ 13. $\frac{1}{4}\sqrt{2}$ 15. $\frac{1}{3}$ 17. $\frac{11}{7}$ 23. (a) 0

Exercises 2.6   *(Page 94)*

1. (a) -3; (b) 2; (c) does not exist   3. (a) 7; (b) 7; (c) 7   5. (a) 5; (b) 5; (c) 5   7. (a) 0; (b) 0; (c) 0   9. (a) 1; (b) -1; (c) does not
exist   11. (a) -2; (b) 2; (c) does not exist   13. (a) 2; (b) 1; (c) does not exist

Exercises 2.7   *(Page 100)*

1. $\frac{2}{5}$ 3. 0   5. 1   7. $\frac{1}{2}$ 9. 0   11. $-\infty$

Exercises 2.8   *(Page 109)*

1. ∞ 3. $+\infty$ 5. ∞ 7. $-\infty$ 9. $+\infty$ 11. $+\infty$ 13. $-\infty$ 15. $-\infty$

Exercises 2.9   *(Page 113)*

1. $x = 5$; $y = 0$ 3. $x = -2$; $y = 0$ 5. $x = -6, x = 1$; $y = 0$ 7. $x = 3, x = -3$; $y = 4$ 9. $x = -2, x = 2$; $y = 0$
11. $y = -3, y = 3$ 13. $x = -\sqrt{2}, x = \sqrt{2}$ 15. $x = \frac{4}{3}$; $y = \frac{2}{3}$ 17. $y = -1, y = +1$ 19. $x = 3$; $y = -1, y = +1$ 21. $x = -3$; $y = 1$

Exercises 2.11   *(Page 122)*

1. 4; $\lim\limits_{x \to 4} f(x)$ does not exist.   3. -3; $F(-3)$ does not exist.   5. -3; $\lim\limits_{x \to -3} g(x) \ne g(-3)$ 7. $-3, 2$; $h(-3)$ and $h(2)$ do not exist.
9. 0; $\lim\limits_{x \to 0} f(x)$ does not exist.   11. continuous everywhere   13. 3; $f(3)$ does not exist.   15. 2; $\lim\limits_{x \to 2} g(x) \ne g(2)$ 17. all integers;
$\lim\limits_{x \to n} f(x)$ does not exist if n is any integer.   19. 0; $\lim\limits_{x \to 0} f(x)$ does not exist.   21. $-1, 0$; $\lim\limits_{x \to -1} f(x)$ does not exist, $\lim\limits_{x \to 0} f(x)$ does not
exist.   23. removable; 4   25. removable; 0   27. removable; $\frac{1}{48}$ 29. essential   31. f is continuous everywhere.

Exercises 2.12   *(Page 129)*

5. $\frac{1}{5}$ 7. -2 9. 15   11. all real numbers   13. all real numbers except 2 and -2 15. all real numbers except 1, -3, and -4
17. all x not in $[-4, 4]$ 19. all x not in $[-4, 4]$ 21. all real numbers   23. all x in $(0, +\infty)$ 25. all x in $(-1, 0)$ and $(0, 1)$

Exercises 2.13   *(Page 132)*

1. continuous; discontinuous; discontinuous; continuous; discontinuous; continuous   3. continuous; continuous; continuous;
continuous; discontinuous   5. continuous; discontinuous; discontinuous; discontinuous; continuous   7. continuous; continuous;

continuous; continuous; discontinuous; discontinuous   9. continuous; discontinuous; discontinuous; discontinuous
11. discontinuous; continuous; continuous; continuous; discontinuous; discontinuous; discontinuous; continuous   13. $(-\infty, -2)$;
$(-2, 2)$; $(2, +\infty)$ 15. $(-\infty, -3]$; $[4, +\infty)$ 17. $(-\infty, -1)$; $(-1, 1)$; $(1, +\infty)$ 19. continuous on all intervals $[n, n+1)$ where n is
any integer   21. $\sqrt{x^3}$; continuous at all x in $(0, +\infty)$ 23. $\dfrac{1}{\sqrt{x-2}}$; continuous at all x in $(2, +\infty)$ 25. $\dfrac{1}{\sqrt{x-2}}$; continuous at all x
in $(0, 4)$ and $(4, +\infty)$ 27. $\dfrac{\sqrt{x}+1}{\sqrt{x}-1}$; continuous at all x in $(0, 1)$ and $(1, +\infty)$ 29. 5   31. $c = -3$ and $k = 4$ 33. no; f will be
continuous on $[a, c]$ if $\lim\limits_{x \to b^-} g(x)$ exists and is equal to $h(b)$.

Review Exercises for Chapter 2   (Page 134)

1. (a) $x^2 + 4x - 7$, domain: $(-\infty, +\infty)$; (b) $x^2 - 4x - 1$, domain: $(-\infty, +\infty)$; (c) $(x^2 - 4)(4x - 3)$, domain: $(-\infty, +\infty)$; (d) $\dfrac{x^2 - 4}{4x - 3}$, domain:
all real numbers except $\dfrac{3}{4}$; (e) $\dfrac{4x - 3}{x^2 - 4}$, domain: all real numbers except -2 and 2; (f) $16x^2 - 24x + 5$, domain: $(-\infty, +\infty)$; (g) $4x^2 - 19$,
domain: $(-\infty, +\infty)$ 3. (a) $\dfrac{x^2 - 2x + 1}{(x-3)(x+1)}$, domain: all real numbers except -1 and 3; (b) $\dfrac{-x^2 + 4x + 1}{(x-3)(x+1)}$, domain: all real numbers
except -1 and 3; (c) $\dfrac{x}{(x-3)(x+1)}$, domain: all real numbers except -1 and 3; (d) $\dfrac{x+1}{x^2 - 3x}$, domain: all real numbers except 0 and 3;
(e) $\dfrac{x^2 - 3x}{x+1}$, domain: all real numbers except -1; (f) $-\dfrac{x+1}{2x+3}$, domain: all real numbers except $-\dfrac{3}{2}$; (g) $\dfrac{1}{x-2}$, domain: all real numbers
except 2   5. 9   7. $-\frac{1}{6}$ 9. 4   11. continuous on $(-\infty, -\frac{3}{2}]$ and $[\frac{3}{2}, +\infty)$ 13. continuous on $[3, 4]$ 15. continuous
everywhere   17. $\delta = \frac{1}{3}\epsilon$ 19. $\delta = \min(1, \epsilon)$ 21. $\delta = \min(1, 5\epsilon)$ 25. (a) -2; (b) 0; (c) does not exist   27. $\frac{1}{3}$ 29. $\dfrac{2}{3\sqrt[3]{a}}$
31. $-\frac{1}{2}$ 33. 0   35. (a) yes; (b) yes   37. (a) $f(x) = \operatorname{sgn} x$; (b) $f(x) = \begin{cases} x & \text{if } x < 0 \\ \frac{1}{2} & \text{if } 0 \le x \le 1; \text{ (c) } f(x) = \begin{cases} x & \text{if } x \le 1 \\ x+1 & \text{if } 1 < x \end{cases} \\ x & \text{if } 1 < x \end{cases}$ 39. (b) all real
numbers; (c) any number which is not an integer   41. $y = 2, y = -2$; $x = 7, x = -1$

Exercises 3.1   (Page 140)

1. $-2x_1$ 3. $-6 - 2x_1$ 5. $3x_1^2 - 3$ 7. $12x_1^2 - 26x_1 + 4$ 9. $8x + y + 9 = 0$; $x - 8y + 58 = 0$ 11. $6x - y - 16 = 0$;
$x + 6y - 52 = 0$ 13. $2x + 5y - 17 = 0$; $5x - 2y + 30 = 0$ 15. $2x + 3y - 12 = 0$; $3x - 2y - 5 = 0$ 17. $x - 12y + 16 = 0$;
$12x + y - 98 = 0$ 19. $8x - y - 5 = 0$ 21. $2x - y - 2 = 0$ 23. $(12 - 2\sqrt{30})x - y - 30 + 4\sqrt{30} = 0$; $(12 + 2\sqrt{30})x - y - 30$
$- 4\sqrt{30} = 0$

Exercises 3.2   (Page 146)

1. $6t_1^2 - 8t_1 + 2$ 3. $6t_1$; 18   5. $\dfrac{1}{2\sqrt{t_1 + 1}}$; $\dfrac{1}{4}$ 7. $\dfrac{-5}{(5t_1 + 6)^{3/2}}$; $-\dfrac{5}{64}$ 9. $t < -3$, moving to right; $-3 < t < 1$, moving to left; $t > 1$,
moving to right; changes direction when $t = -3$ and $t = 1$ 11. $t < -1 - \sqrt{5}$, moving to left; $-1 - \sqrt{5} < t < -1 + \sqrt{5}$, moving to
right; $t > -1 + \sqrt{5}$, moving to left; changes direction when $t = -1 \pm \sqrt{5}$ 13. (a) -32 ft/sec; (b) -64 ft/sec; (c) 4 sec; (d) -128 ft/sec
15. (a) $(20t_1 + 24)$ ft/sec; (b) $\frac{6}{5}$ sec

Exercises 3.3   (Page 151)

1. $8x + 5$ 3. $\dfrac{1}{2\sqrt{x}}$ 5. $-\dfrac{1}{(x+1)^2}$ 7. $-\dfrac{2}{x^3} - 1$ 9. $-\dfrac{1}{2\sqrt{(x+1)^3}}$ 11. -6 13. $-\frac{1}{216}$ 15. $\frac{5}{4}$ 17. 3   19. -12
21. $-\frac{1}{27}$ 23. $\dfrac{1}{3\sqrt[3]{(x-1)^2}}$; no   25. $g(a)$

Exercises 3.4   (Page 155)

1. (b) yes; (c) $+1, -1$; (d) no   3. (b) yes; (c) $-1, +1$; (d) no   5. (b) yes; (c) 0, 1; (d) no   7. (b) yes; (c) 0, 0; (d) yes   9. (b) yes;

(c) does not exist, 0; (d) no   11. (b) yes; (c) neither exist; (d) no   13. (b) yes; (c) $-6, -6$; (d) yes   17. $f'_+(0) = 0$ 19. $a = 2$ and $b = -1$ 21. (a) 0; (b) 1; (c) does not exist

Exercises 3.5 (Page 162)

1. $3x^2 - 6x + 5$ 3. $x^7 - 4x^3$ 5. $t^3 - t$ 7. $4\pi r^2$ 9. $2x + 3 - \dfrac{2}{x^3}$ 11. $-\dfrac{6}{x^3} - \dfrac{20}{x^5}$ 13. $3\sqrt{3}s^2 - 2\sqrt{3}s$ 15. $70x^6 + 60x^4$

$- 15x^2 - 6$ 17. $-\dfrac{4(x+1)}{(x-1)^3}$ 19. $-\dfrac{1}{(x-1)^2}$ 21. $\dfrac{5(1-2x^2)}{(1+2x^2)^2}$ 23. $\dfrac{48x^2}{(x^3+8)^2}$ 25. $\dfrac{6(x^2+10x+1)}{(x+5)^2}$ 29. $2(3x+2)(6x^2+2x-3)$

31. $3(2x^2 + x + 1)^2(4x + 1)$ 33. $x + (4\sqrt{6} - 10)y - 8\sqrt{6} + 21 = 0$; $x - (4\sqrt{6} + 10)y + 8\sqrt{6} + 21 = 0$ 35. $x + 8y + 2 = 0$; $x + 8y - 2 = 0$

Exercises 3.6 (Page 167)

1. $6(x+2)(x^2+4x+5)^2$ 3. $2(8t^3 - 21t^2 + 2)(2t^4 - 7t^3 + 2t - 1)$ 5. $-2(x+4)^{-3}$ 7. $6(3u-1)(3u^2+5)^2(12u^2-3u+5)$
9. $2(-12x + 17)(2x-5)^{-2}(4x+3)^{-3}$ 11. $18(y-7)(y+2)^{-3}$ 13. $-2(14x+3)(7x^2+3x-1)^{-2}$
15. $2(r^2+1)^2(2r+5)(8r^2+15r+2)$ 17. $2z(z^2-5)^2(z^2+22)(z^2+4)^{-3}$
19. $4(4x-1)^2(x^2+2)^3(21x^4 - 3x^3 + 49x^2 - 4x + 30)(3x^2+5)^{-3}$ 21. $\dfrac{8t_1(t_1^2-1)}{(t_1^2+1)^3}$ ft/sec; 0 ft/sec; $\dfrac{960}{2197}$ ft/sec   23. $x + 16y - 35 = 0$
25. (a) $3x^4$; (b) $6x^5$

Exercises 3.7 (Page 171)

1. $2(3x+5)^{-1/3}$ 3. $\dfrac{17}{2\sqrt{2x-5}\sqrt{(3x+1)^3}}$ 5. $2x^{-1/2} - \tfrac{3}{2}x^{-3/2}$ 7. $\dfrac{6x^2 - 10x + 1}{3\sqrt[3]{(2x^3 - 5x^2 + x)^2}}$ 9. $\dfrac{1}{\sqrt{2t}}\left(1 - \dfrac{1}{t}\right)$ 11. $\dfrac{1}{x^2\sqrt{x^2-1}}$

13. $\dfrac{x+5}{6\sqrt{x-1}\sqrt[3]{(x+1)^4}}$ 15. $\dfrac{x(5x^2-1)}{3\sqrt{x^2-5}\sqrt[3]{(x^2+3)^2}}$ 17. $-\dfrac{1}{4\sqrt{9+\sqrt{9-x}}\sqrt{9-x}}$ 19. $4x - 5y + 9 = 0$ 21. $x + 4y = 0$

23. (a) 0; (b) $\tfrac{1}{2}$; (c) no value of t 25. $2x\left(\dfrac{x^2-4}{|x^2-4|}\right)$ 27. $3x|x|$ 33. $\tfrac{4}{3}(3x+2)^3(x^2-1)^{-1/3}(12x^2+2x-9)$

35. $\tfrac{1}{6}(t^3 - 2t + 1)^{1/2}(t^2 + t + 5)^{-2/3}(31t^4 + 29t^3 + 109t^2 - 18t - 88)$

Exercises 3.8 (Page 176)

1. $-\dfrac{x}{y}$ 3. $\dfrac{8y - 3x^2}{3y^2 - 8x}$ 5. $-\dfrac{y^2}{x^2}$ 7. $-y^{1/2}x^{-1/2}$ 9. $\dfrac{x - xy^2}{x^2y - y}$ 11. $\dfrac{3x^2 - 4y}{4x - 3y^2}$ 13. $\dfrac{y + 2x(x-y)^2}{x}$ 15. $\dfrac{y + 4\sqrt{xy}}{\sqrt{x} - x}$ 17. $\dfrac{3x^2 - y^3}{x^3 - 6xy}$

19. $-\dfrac{x^3 + 8y^3}{3x^2y - 4x^3}$ 21. $2x + y = 4$ 25. (a) $f_1(x) = 2\sqrt{x-2}$, domain: $x \geq 2$; $f_2(x) = -2\sqrt{x-2}$, domain: $x \geq 2$; (d) $f'_1(x) = (x-2)^{-1/2}$,

domain: $x > 2$; $f'_2(x) = -(x-2)^{-1/2}$, domain: $x > 2$; (e) $\dfrac{2}{y'}$; (f) $x - y - 1 = 0$; $x + y - 1 = 0$ 27. (a) $f_1(x) = \sqrt{x^2 - 9}$, domain: $|x| \geq 3$;

$f_2(x) = -\sqrt{x^2 - 9}$, domain: $|x| \geq 3$; (d) $f'_1(x) = x(x^2 - 9)^{-1/2}$, domain: $|x| > 3$; $f'_2(x) = -x(x^2 - 9)^{-1/2}$, domain: $|x| > 3$; (e) $\dfrac{x}{y}$;

(f) $5x + 4y + 9 = 0$; $5x - 4y + 9 = 0$ 29. (a) $f_1(x) = \sqrt{8 - x^2 + 2x} + 2$, domain: $-2 \leq x \leq 4$; $f_2(x) = -\sqrt{8 - x^2 + 2x} + 2$, domain:

$-2 \leq x \leq 4$; (d) $(1-x)(8 - x^2 + 2x)^{-1/2}$, domain: $-2 < x < 4$; $(x-1)(8 - x^2 + 2x)^{-1/2}$, domain: $-2 < x < 4$; (e) $\dfrac{1-x}{y-2}$; (f) $y - 5 = 0$,

$y + 1 = 0$

Review Exercises for Chapter 3 (Page 176)

1. $\dfrac{x(2a^3 - x^3)}{(x^3 + a^3)^2}$ 3. $\dfrac{8x}{y(3y - 8)}$ 5. $\dfrac{3}{2}\left(\sqrt{x} + \dfrac{1}{\sqrt{x}}\right)^2\left(\dfrac{x-1}{x\sqrt{x}}\right)$ 7. $\dfrac{1 - 2x^3}{3x^{2/3}(x^3 + 1)^{4/3}}$ 9. $\dfrac{1}{\sqrt{x^2 - 1}(x - \sqrt{x^2 - 1})}$ 11. $\dfrac{x(4x^2 - 13)\sqrt{x^2 - 1}}{\sqrt{x^2 - 4}}$

13. $2x + 3[x^3 + (x^4 + x)^2]^2[3x^2 + 2(x^4 + x)(4x^3 + 1)]$ 15. (a) $t = 3$ and $t = 8$; (b) when $t = 3$, $v = -15$, and particle is moving to the

left; when $t = 8$, $v = 40$, and particle is moving to the right   17. $5x - 4y - 6 = 0$; $4x + 5y - 3 = 0$ 19. $\dfrac{2}{\sqrt{4x - 3}}$

21. $2(|x+1| - |x|)\left(\dfrac{x+1}{|x+1|} - \dfrac{x}{|x|}\right)$ 23. (b) 0; (c) 0   25. -1 27. $(-1, 0)$ 29. (a) 32 ft/sec; (b) 256 ft; (c) 7 sec; (d) -128 ft/sec

31. $a = -\tfrac{1}{2}$; $b = \tfrac{3}{2}$ 33. $(f \circ g)'(0) = 2$ 35. $f(x) = |x|$, $g(x) = x^2$ 39. $P'(r)$

Exercises 4.1   *(Page 182)*

1. (a) 8.6; (b) 8.3; (c) 8.1; (d) 8   3. (a) $-\frac{1}{16}, -\frac{1}{4}$; (b) $-\frac{1}{100}, -\frac{1}{10}$ 5. (a) 18,750 gal/min; (b) 17,500 gal/min   7. (a) profitable;

(b) not profitable   9. $D_I R = -\frac{E}{I^2}$ 11. 2.7 mi/min

Exercises 4.2   *(Page 185)*

1. $\frac{9}{5}$ ft/sec   3. $\frac{1}{2\pi}$ ft/min   5. $\frac{5}{8\pi}$ ft/min   7. $\frac{25}{3}$ ft/sec   9. $\frac{6}{25\pi}$ ft/min   11. 1800 lb/ft² per min   13. 14 ft/sec

15. $\frac{1}{184}(3\sqrt{97} + 97)$ ft/sec ≈ 0.65 ft/sec   17. 22 ft³/min

Exercises 4.3   *(Page 194)*

1. $-5, \frac{1}{3}$ 3. $-3, -1, 1$ 5. $0, 2$ 7. $-2, 0, 2$ 9. no critical numbers   11. abs min: $f(2) = -2$ 13. no absolute extrema
15. abs min: $f(-3) = 0$ 17. abs min: $f(5) = 1$ 19. abs min: $f(4) = 1$ 21. abs max: $f(5) = 2$ 23. abs min: $f(2) = 0$
25. abs min: $f(-3) = -46$; abs max: $f(-1) = -10$ 27. abs min: $f(-2) = 0$; abs max: $f(-4) = 144$ 29. abs min: $f(2) = 0$; abs max:
$f(3) = 25$ 31. abs min: $f(-1) = -1$; abs max: $f(2) = \frac{1}{2}$ 33. abs min: $f(-1) = 0$; abs max: $f(1) = \sqrt[3]{4}$ 35. abs min: $f(-3) = -13$;
abs max: $f(3) = 7$

Exercises 4.4   *(Page 200)*

1. 2500 ft²   3. $\frac{5}{3}$ in.   5. From A to P to C, where P is 4 miles down the river from B.   7. 8 mi   9. radius $= 3\sqrt{2}$ in.,
height $= 6\sqrt{2}$ in.   11. (a) 3.4 units; (b) 9.4 units   13. 225   15. 400   17. (a) radius of circle $= \frac{5}{(\pi + 4)}$ ft and length of side of
square $= \frac{10}{(\pi + 4)}$ ft; (b) radius of circle $= \frac{5}{\pi}$ ft and there is no square.

Exercises 4.5   *(Page 206)*

1. 2   3. $\frac{1}{3}(2 + \sqrt{7})$ or $\frac{1}{3}(2 - \sqrt{7})$ 5. $(-3, -\frac{1}{2}), c = -1 - \frac{1}{6}\sqrt{39}$; $(-3, \frac{1}{2}), c = -1 + \frac{1}{6}\sqrt{39}$ or $c = -1 - \frac{1}{6}\sqrt{39}$; $(-\frac{1}{2}, \frac{1}{2}), c = -1 + \frac{1}{6}\sqrt{39}$
7. $\frac{1}{2}$ 9. $\frac{8}{27}$ 11. $\frac{1}{2}(3 + 4\sqrt{3})$ 13. 1   15. (i), (ii), (iii) satisfied; (c) $(\frac{3}{4}, -\frac{8}{9}\sqrt[3]{6})$ 17. (b) (ii) not satisfied   19. (b) (i) not
satisfied   21. (b) (ii) not satisfied   23. (b) (i), (ii), (iii) satisfied; (c) $(0, 9)$ 25. 4   27. $3 + \frac{1}{16}\sqrt{2}$ 29. $\pm\frac{1}{3}\sqrt{39}$ 31. (ii) not
satisfied   33. (ii) not satisfied

Exercises 4.6   *(Page 213)*

1. (a) and (b) $f(2) = -5$, rel min;   (c) $[2, +\infty)$; (d) $(-\infty, 2]$ 3. (a) and (b) no relative extrema; (c) $(-\infty, +\infty)$; (d) nowhere   5. (a) and
(b) $f(2) = -50$, rel min; $f(-2) = 46$, rel max; (c) $(-\infty, -2], [2, +\infty)$; (d) $[-2, 2]$ 7. (a) and (b) no relative extrema; (c) $(0, +\infty)$;
(d) nowhere   9. (a) and (b) $f(2) = 4$, rel max; (c) $(-\infty, 2]$; (d) $[2, 3]$ 11. (a) and (b) $f(\frac{1}{5}) = \frac{3456}{3125}$, rel max; $f(1) = 0$, rel min;
(c) $(-\infty, \frac{1}{5}], [1, +\infty)$; (d) $[\frac{1}{5}, 1]$ 13. (a) and (b) $f(4) = 2$, rel max; (c) $(-\infty, 4]$; (d) $[4, +\infty)$ 15. (a) and (b) $f(4) = 9$, rel max;
(c) $(-\infty, 4]$; (d) $[4, +\infty)$ 17. (a) and (b) $f(-2) = 5$, rel max; $f(0) = 1$, rel min; (c) $(-\infty, -2], [0, +\infty)$; (d) $[-2, 0]$ 19. (a) and (b)
$f(2) = -3$, rel min; (c) $[2, +\infty)$; (d) $(-\infty, 2]$ 21. (a) and (b) $f(-1) = 2$, rel max; $f(0) = 1$, rel min; $f(2) = 5$, rel max; (c) $(-\infty, -1]$,
$[0, 2]$; (d) $[-1, 0], [2, +\infty)$ 23. (a) and (b) $f(-9) = -8$, rel min; $f(-4) = -5$, rel min; $f(2) = -7$, rel min; $f(-7) = -4$, rel max;
$f(0) = -3$, rel max; (c) $[-9, -7], [-4, 0], [2, +\infty)$; (d) $(-\infty, -9], [-7, -4], [0, 2]$ 25. (a) and (b) no relative extrema; (c) $[0, +\infty)$;
(d) nowhere   27. (a) and (b) $f(-1) = 0$, rel max; $f(1) = -\sqrt[3]{4}$, rel min; (c) $(-\infty, -1], [1, +\infty)$; (d) $[-1, 1]$ 29. (a) and (b) $f(4) = \frac{1}{4}\sqrt[3]{4}$,
rel max; (c) $(-4, 4]$; (d) $(-\infty, -4), [4, +\infty)$ 31. $a = -3, b = 7$ 33. $a = -2, b = 9, c = -12, d = 7$

Exercises 4.7   *(Page 217)*

1. $f'(x) = 5x^4 - 6x^2 + 1$; $f''(x) = 20x^3 - 12x$ 3. $g'(s) = 8s^3 - 12s^2 + 7$; $g''(s) = 24s^2 - 24s$ 5. $f'(x) = x(x^2 + 1)^{-1/2}$;
$f''(x) = (x^2 + 1)^{-3/2}$ 7. $F'(x) = \frac{5}{2}x^{3/2} - 5$; $F''(x) = \frac{15}{4}x^{1/2}$ 9. $G'(x) = -2x(3 + 2x^2)^{-3/2}$; $G''(x) = (8x^2 - 6)(3 + 2x^2)^{-5/2}$
11. $D_x^3 y = 24x$ 13. $D_x^3 f(x) = 6(3 + x)(1 - x)^{-5}$ 15. $D_x^4 y = \frac{5}{8}(\frac{21}{2}x^{-1/2} + 3x^{-3/2} - \frac{3}{2}x^{-7/2})$ 19. $D_x^2 y = -3a^4 x^2 y^{-7}$ 21. $-\frac{7}{4}; 5$
23. $v = t^3 - 6t^2 + 8t$; $a = 3t^2 - 12t + 8$; the velocity has no abs. max. value; toward the origin: $2 < t < 4$; away from the origin: $0 < t < 2$
and $t > 4$ 25. $\frac{1}{2}; \frac{243}{80}; -\frac{11}{8}$ 27. $\frac{3}{2}; \frac{1}{3}\sqrt[4]{6}; \frac{2}{3}\sqrt[4]{6}$ 29. $f'(x) = 2|x|$, domain: $(-\infty, +\infty)$; $f''(x) = 2\frac{|x|}{x}$; domain: $(-\infty, 0)$ and $(0, +\infty)$
31. $f'(x) = 4|x^3|$, domain: $(-\infty, +\infty)$; $f''(x) = 12x|x|$, domain: $(-\infty, +\infty)$ 33. $f'''(x) = 24|x|$ 35. $h''(x) = (f'' \circ g)(x)(g'(x))^2$
$+ (f' \circ g)(x)g''(x)$

Exercises 4.8 (*Page 220*)

1. $f(\frac{1}{3}) = \frac{2}{3}$, rel min 3. $f(\frac{3}{2}) = \frac{81}{4}$, rel max; $f(-1) = -11$, rel min 5. $f(4) = 0$, rel min 7. $G(3) = 0$, rel min 9. $h(-2) = -2$, rel min 11. $f(1) = 8$, rel min 13. $F(27) = 9$, rel max

Exercises 4.9 (*Page 226*)

1. $f(0) = 0$, abs min 3. no absolute extrema 5. $g(\frac{1}{4}) = \frac{3}{4}$, abs min 7. $f(0) = 0$, abs min; $f(\sqrt{2}) = \frac{1}{18}\sqrt{3}$, abs max 9. 45 yd by 60 yd 11. Depth is one-half the length of the base. 13. $\sqrt{2}$ 15. Ratio of height of rectangle to radius of semicircle is $\frac{1}{4}(4 + \pi)$. 17. If R is the radius of the cylinder, breadth $= R$; depth $= \sqrt{3}R$. 19. $30(\sqrt{10} + 1)$ ft by $44(\sqrt{10} + 1)$ ft 21. $R = r$ 23. $2\sqrt{2}$

Exercises 4.10 (*Page 233*)

1. concave downward for $x < 0$; concave upward for $x > 0$; $(0, 0)$ pt. of infl. 3. concave upward everywhere 5. concave downward for $x < -1$ and $0 < x < 1$; concave upward for $-1 < x < 0$ and $x > 1$; $(0, 0)$ pt. of infl. 7. concave upward for $x < 2$; concave downward for $x > 2$; $(2, 0)$, pt. of infl. 9. concave upward for $x < 0$; concave downward for $x > 0$; $(0, 0)$ pt. of infl. 11. $a = -1, b = 3$ 13. $a = 2, b = -6, c = 0, d = 3$

Exercises 4.11 (*Page 236*)

1. $f(-1) = 5$, rel max; $f(1) = -3$, rel min; $(0', 1)$, pt. of infl; f increasing on $(-\infty, -1]$ and $[1, +\infty)$; f decreasing on $[-1, 1]$; graph concave downward for $x < 0$; graph concave upward for $x > 0$. 3. $f(\frac{2}{3}) = -\frac{27}{16}$, rel min; $(0, 0)$, $(1, -1)$, pts. of infl.; f increasing on $[\frac{2}{3}, +\infty)$; f decreasing on $(-\infty, \frac{2}{3}]$; graph concave upward for $x < 0$ and $x > 1$; graph concave downward for $0 < x < 1$ 5. $f(-3) = 5$, rel max; $f(-\frac{1}{3}) = -\frac{121}{27}$, rel min; $(-\frac{5}{3}, \frac{7}{27})$, pt. of infl.; f increasing on $(-\infty, -3]$ and $[-\frac{1}{3}, +\infty)$; f decreasing on $[-3, -\frac{1}{3}]$; graph concave downward for $x < -\frac{5}{3}$; graph concave upward for $x > -\frac{5}{3}$ 7. $f(0) = 1$, rel min; $(\frac{1}{2}, \frac{23}{16})$, $(1, 2)$, pts. of infl.; f decreasing on $(-\infty, 0]$; f increasing on $[0, +\infty)$; graph concave upward for $x < \frac{1}{2}$ and $x > 1$; graph concave downward for $\frac{1}{2} < x < 1$ 9. $f(-1) = \frac{7}{12}$, rel min; $f(0) = 1$, rel max; $f(2) = -\frac{5}{3}$, rel min; pts. of infl. at $x = \frac{1}{3}(1 \pm \sqrt{7})$; f decreasing on $(-\infty, -1]$ and $[0, 2]$; f increasing on $[-1, 0]$ and $[2, +\infty)$; graph concave upward for $x < \frac{1}{3}(1 - \sqrt{7})$ and $x > \frac{1}{3}(1 + \sqrt{7})$; graph concave downward for $\frac{1}{3}(1 - \sqrt{7}) < x < \frac{1}{3}(1 + \sqrt{7})$ 11. $f(0) = 0$, rel min; no pts. of infl.; f decreasing on $(-\infty, 0]$; f increasing on $[0, +\infty)$; graph concave upward everywhere 13. no relative extrema; $(0, 0)$ pt. of infl. with horizontal tangent; f increasing on $(-\infty, +\infty)$; graph concave downward on $(-\infty, 0)$; graph concave upward on $(0, +\infty)$ 15. $f\left(\frac{4}{5}\right) = \frac{26,244}{3,125}$, rel max; $f(2) = 0$, rel min; pts. of infl. at $(-1, 0)$ and $x = \frac{1}{10}(8 \pm 3\sqrt{6})$; f increasing on $(-\infty, \frac{4}{5}]$ and $[2, +\infty)$; f decreasing on $[\frac{4}{5}, 2]$; graph concave downward for $x < -1$ and $\frac{1}{10}(8 - 3\sqrt{6}) < x < \frac{1}{10}(8 + 3\sqrt{6})$; graph concave upward for $-1 < x < \frac{1}{10}(8 - 3\sqrt{6})$ and $x > \frac{1}{10}(8 + 3\sqrt{6})$ 17. $f(-\frac{4}{3}) = \frac{256}{81}$, rel max; $f(0) = 0$, rel. min; $(-1, 2)$, pt. of infl.; f increasing on $(-\infty, -\frac{4}{3}]$ and $[0, +\infty)$; f decreasing on $[-\frac{4}{3}, 0]$; graph concave downward for $x < -1$; graph concave upward for $x > -1$ 19. $f(0) = 0$, rel min; $f(1) = 1$, rel max; f decreasing on $(-\infty, 0)$ and $[1, +\infty)$; f increasing on $(0, 1]$; graph concave downward for $x < 0$ and $x > 0$ 21. $f(-\frac{1}{8}) = -\frac{3}{8}$, rel min; $(0, 0)$, $(\frac{1}{4}, \frac{3}{4}\sqrt[3]{2})$, pts. of infl.; f decreasing on $(-\infty, -\frac{1}{8}]$; f increasing on $[-\frac{1}{8}, +\infty)$; graph concave upward for $x < 0$ and $x > \frac{1}{4}$; graph concave downward for $0 < x < \frac{1}{4}$ 23. no relative extrema; $(3, 2)$, pt. of infl.; f increasing on $(-\infty, +\infty)$; graph concave downward for $x > 3$; graph concave upward for $x < 3$ 25. no relative extrema; $(3, 2)$, pt. of infl. with horizontal tangent; f increasing on $(-\infty, +\infty)$; graph concave downward for $x < 3$; graph concave upward for $x > 3$ 27. $f(-1) = 3$, rel min; f decreasing on $(-\infty, -1]$; f increasing on $[-1, +\infty)$; graph concave upward for all x 29. $f(0) = 0$, rel min; $f(\frac{16}{5}) = \frac{512}{125}\sqrt{5}$, rel max; pt. of infl. at $x = \frac{1}{15}(48 - 8\sqrt{6})$; f decreasing on $(-\infty, 0]$ and $[\frac{16}{5}, 4]$; f increasing on $[0, \frac{16}{5}]$; graph concave upward for $x < \frac{1}{15}(48 - 8\sqrt{6})$; graph concave downward for $\frac{1}{15}(48 - 8\sqrt{6}) < x < 4$ 31. $f(-1) = 0$, rel min; $f(1) = 2$, rel max; pts. of infl. at $x = 0$ and $x = \pm\sqrt{3}$; f decreasing on $(-\infty, -1]$ and $[1, +\infty)$; f increasing on $[-1, 1]$; graph concave upward for $-\sqrt{3} < x < 0$ and $x > \sqrt{3}$; graph concave downward for $x < -\sqrt{3}$ and $0 < x < \sqrt{3}$ 33. $f(-\frac{2}{3}) = \frac{4}{9}\sqrt{6}$, rel max; f increasing on $(-\infty, -\frac{2}{3}]$; f decreasing on $[-\frac{2}{3}, 0]$; graph concave downward for $x < 0$

Exercises 4.12 (*Page 245*)

1. (a) $30 - \frac{20}{x^2}$; (b) \$29.99; (c) \$29.9878 3. (a) 50 cents per gallon; (b) 25 5. (a) $Q(x) = x + 4 + \frac{8}{x}$; (b) $C'(x) = 2x + 4$; (c) $Q'(x) = 1 - \frac{8}{x^2}$; (d) \$9.66 7. (a) $[2, +\infty)$; (b) $C'(x) = x^2 - 4x + 5$; (c) decreasing on $[0, 2]$ and increasing on $[2, +\infty)$; (d) graph concave downward for $0 < x < 2$, graph concave upward for $x > 2$, pt. of infl. at $(2, \frac{20}{3})$, infl. tangent: $3x - 3y + 14 = 0$ 9. (a) $C(x) = 3x + 400$;

(b) $Q(x) = 3 + \dfrac{400}{x}$; (c) $C'(x) = 3$; (e) 953   11. (a) $3 - \frac{3}{4}x$; (b) $3x - \frac{3}{4}x^2$; (c) $3 - \frac{3}{2}x$ 13. (a) $P(x) = \sqrt{36 - x^2}$; (b) $R(x) = 100x\sqrt{36 - x^2}$;

(c) $R'(x) = \dfrac{3600 - 200x^2}{\sqrt{36 - x^2}}$; (d) $1800   15. (a) $S(x) = -2x^2 + 16x - 2$; (c) $3000; (d) $R'(x) = 14 - 2x$, $C'(x) = 2x - 2$ 17. (a) $[0, 8]$;

(b) $R'(x) = 3x^2 - 32x + 64$; $C'(x) = 18 - 2x$; (c) $\frac{1}{3}(15 - \sqrt{87}) \approx 1.89$ 19. (a) 1625; (b) 67.5 cents; (c) $328.12   21. 37.5 cents

Review Exercises for Chapter 4   (Page 247)

1. $f(0) = 9$, abs max; $f(3) = 0$, abs min   3. 12 mi from point on bank nearest A 5. $\dfrac{445 - 180\sqrt{2}}{\sqrt{409 - 60\sqrt{2}}}$ knots ≈ 10.6 knots   9. $27,225

11. $\dfrac{512}{625\pi}$ in./sec   19. radius $= \frac{3}{2}r$ in.; altitude $= 3h$ in.   21. $\frac{3}{2}$ sec; velocity of horizontal particle $= 1$ ft/sec; velocity of vertical

particle $= 3$ ft/sec   23. decreasing at a rate of $\frac{864}{172}$ lb/ft² per min   25. (a) increasing at a rate of $10,400 per year; (b) increasing at a

rate of $800 per year   27. $f\left(\frac{8}{5}\right) = \dfrac{839,808}{3125}$, rel max; $f(4) = 0$, rel min; pts. of infl. at $x = -2$ and $x = \frac{1}{5}(8 \pm 3\sqrt{6})$; f increasing on

$(-\infty, \frac{8}{5}]$ and $[4, +\infty)$; f decreasing on $[\frac{8}{5}, 4]$; graph concave upward for $-2 < x < \frac{1}{5}(8 - 3\sqrt{6})$ and $\frac{1}{5}(8 + 3\sqrt{6}) < x < +\infty$; graph concave

downward for $-\infty < x < -2$ and $\frac{1}{5}(8 - 3\sqrt{6}) < x < \frac{1}{5}(8 + 3\sqrt{6})$ 29. no relative extrema; pt. of infl. at $x = 3$; f increasing on

$(-\infty, +\infty)$; graph concave upward for $3 < x < +\infty$; graph concave downward for $-\infty < x < 3$ 35. (a) $P(x) = \dfrac{36 - 4x}{x + 3}$;

(b) $R(x) = \dfrac{3600x - 400x^2}{x + 3}$; (c) $R'(x) = -\dfrac{400(x + 9)(x - 3)}{(x + 3)^2}$; (d) 1200   37. 1000, $11   39. $(h^{2/3} + w^{2/3})^{3/2}$ ft   41. $a = 3, b = -3, c = 1$

Exercises 5.1   (Page 255)

1. (a) $3x^2 \Delta x + 3x(\Delta x)^2 + (\Delta x)^3$; (b) $3x^2 \Delta x$; (c) $3x(\Delta x)^2 + (\Delta x)^3$ 3. (a) $\sqrt{x + \Delta x} - \sqrt{x}$; (b) $\dfrac{\Delta x}{2\sqrt{x}}$; (c) $-(2\sqrt{x})^{-1}(\sqrt{x} - \sqrt{x + \Delta x})^2$

5. (a) $(6x^2 + 6x) \Delta x + (6x + 3)(\Delta x)^2 + 2(\Delta x)^3$; (b) $(6x^2 + 6x) \Delta x$; (c) $(6x + 3)(\Delta x)^2 + 2(\Delta x)^3$ 7. (a) 0.0309; (b) 0.03; (c) 0.0009

9. (a) -0.875; (b) -1.5; (c) 0.625   11. (a) -0.00248; (b) -0.00250; (c) 0.00002   13. 6.125   15. 3.009   17. 0.0993   19. $\frac{76}{375}$

21. (a) 6.75 in.³; (b) 0.3 in.²   23. $\frac{5}{4}\pi$ ft³   25. 10 ft³   27. 4%

Exercises 5.2   (Page 259)

1. $6(3x - 1)(3x^2 - 2x + 1)^2 \, dx$ 3. $\frac{2}{3}(7x^2 + 9x)(2x + 3)^{-2/3} \, dx$ 5. $(x - 1)^{-1/2}(x + 1)^{-3/2} \, dx$ 7. $2(x^2 + 1)^{-3/2} \, dx$ 9. $\dfrac{-9x^2}{8y}$

11. $-y^{1/2}x^{-1/2}$ 13. $\dfrac{4x^3 - 9x^2y + 4y^3}{3x^3 - 12xy^2 - 4y^3}$ 15. $\dfrac{9x^2 - 2xy + 2y^2 - 6x}{x^2 - 4xy + 3y^2 - 2y}$ 17. $18t^5 - 56t^3 + 38t$ 19. $(2t - 1)[1 - \frac{3}{2}(t^2 - t + 4)^{-1/2}]$

21. $6t^5 - 4t^3 - 2t - 9t(t^2 + 1)^{1/2} + 6t(t^2 + 1)^{-1/2}$ 23. $\dfrac{8t(16t^4 - 8t^2y + 8t^2 - 2y + 1)}{16t^4 + 8t^2 - y^2 + 1}$

Exercises 5.3   (Page 267)

1. $\frac{3}{5}x^5 + C$ 3. $\frac{1}{3}t^3 - t^2 + 3t + C$ 5. $5x - \dfrac{1}{x^2} - \dfrac{3}{x} + C$ 7. $\frac{2}{3}\sqrt{2x^3} - \sqrt{2x} + C$ 9. $\frac{2}{9}(x^3 - 1)^{3/2} + C$ 11. $\frac{1}{3}\sqrt{3s^2 + 1} + C$

13. $-\dfrac{8}{5}\left(1 + \dfrac{1}{2x}\right)^{5/2} + \dfrac{8}{3}\left(1 + \dfrac{1}{2x}\right)^{3/2} + C$ 15. $-\frac{1}{6}x^9 + \frac{12}{7}x^7 - \frac{48}{5}x^5 + \frac{64}{3}x^3 + C$ 17. $2[\frac{1}{3}(t + 3)^{3/2} - 3(t + 3)^{1/2}] + C$ 19. $-\frac{2}{7}(3 - x)^{7/2}$

$+ \frac{12}{5}(3 - x)^{5/2} - 6(3 - x)^{3/2} + C$ 21. $\frac{2}{3}(x^3 + 3x^2 + 1)^{1/2} + C$ 23. $\frac{3}{4}(3 - y)^{4/3} - 18(3 - y)^{1/3} + C$ 25. $\frac{3}{5}(r^{1/3} + 2)^5 + C$

27. (a) $2x^4 + 4x^3 + 3x^2 + x + C$; (b) $\frac{1}{8}(2x + 1)^4 + C$ 29. g is not differentiable on $(-1, 1)$

Exercises 5.4   (Page 272)

1. $y = x^3 + x^2 - 7x + C$ 3. $3x^2y + Cy + 2 = 0$ 5. $2\sqrt{1 + y^2} = 3x^2 + C$ 7. $12y = 5x^4 + 6x^2 + C_1x + C_2$ 9. $3y = x^3 - 3x^2 - 12x + 18$

11. $x^2 = 4y^2$ 13. $y = 3x^4 + 4x^3 + 2x^2 + 2x$ 15. $y = x^2 - 3x + 2$ 17. $3y = -2x^3 + 3x^2 + 2x + 6$ 19. $12y = -x^4 + 6x^2 - 20x + 27$

21. $x^2 + 2y^2 = C$

Exercises 5.5   (Page 276)

1. $v = 2 + 5t - t^2$; $s = 2t + \frac{5}{2}t^2 - \frac{1}{3}t^3$ 3. $1600s = v^2 + 1200$ 5. $\frac{5}{4}$ sec; 20 ft/sec; $\frac{5}{8}$ sec; $\frac{25}{4}$ ft   7. 3.4 sec; 99 ft/sec

9. $v^2 = -64s + 1600$; 24 ft/sec   11. $\frac{77}{18}$ ft/sec²   13. $\frac{11}{3}$ sec; $\frac{1210}{9}$ ft   15. $\dfrac{300\sqrt{2}}{11}$ mi/hr

Exercises 5.6   *(Page 279)*

1. $R(x) = 12x - \frac{3}{2}x^2$ 3. $px(x + 5) = -18x - 4x^2$ 5. x in $[0, 4]$; $R(x) = 16x - x^3$; $p = 16 - x^2$ 7. $C(x) = x^3 + 4x^2 + 4x + 6$ 9. $325

Review Exercises for Chapter 5   *(Page 280)*

1. $-\frac{4}{3}x^{-1/4} + C$ 3. $\frac{5}{9}(2 + 3x^2)^{3/2} + C$ 5. $\frac{1}{420}(4x + 3)^{3/2}(30x^2 - 18x + 79) + C$ 7. $\frac{1}{2}(y^2 - 1)^{-1} = x^{-1} + C$ 9. $y + y^{-1} = -x + C$

11. (a) -0.16; (b) -0.64 13. $y = 10x - 2x^2 - 9$ 15. 0   17. $\dfrac{dx}{dt} = \left(\dfrac{4y - 24x^2}{81y^2 - 4x}\right)\left(\dfrac{3t^2 + 2tx}{3x^2 - t^2}\right)$ 19. (a) $\dfrac{(x^3 + 1)^3}{9} + C$;

(b) $\dfrac{x^9}{9} + \dfrac{x^6}{3} + \dfrac{x^3}{3} + C$ 21. $y = \frac{4}{15}(x + 4)^{5/2} + \frac{1}{3}(6 - 32\sqrt{2})x - \frac{1}{15}(75 - 128\sqrt{2})$ 23. 1 sec; 80 ft/sec   25. $25\sqrt{3}$ sec ≈ 43.3 sec

27. an error of $\frac{5}{24}$ in. allowed   29. an error of approximately $\pi^2/1610t$ sec   33. $R(x) = \dfrac{ab}{x + b} + a$; $px^2 + apx - ax = ab + a^2$

Exercises 6.1   *(Page 287)*

1. 51   3. $\frac{73}{12}$ 5. $\frac{63}{4}$ 7. $\frac{7}{12}$ 17. 10,400   19. $10(10^n - 1)$ 21. $\frac{100}{101}$ 23. $n^4 - \frac{2}{3}n^3 - 3n^2 - \frac{1}{3}n$ 25. $3^{2n} - \frac{1}{9}(3^{-2n}) - \frac{20}{9}n - \frac{8}{9}$

Exercises 6.2   *(Page 294)*

1. $\frac{8}{3}$ sq units   3. 15 sq units   5. $\frac{5}{3}$ sq units   7. 9 sq units   9. $\frac{3}{8}$ sq units   11. $\frac{17}{4}$ sq units   13. $\frac{1}{2}m(b^2 - a^2)$ sq units
15. $\frac{1}{2}h(b_1 + b_2)$ sq units

Exercises 6.3   *(Page 303)*

1. $\frac{247}{32}$ 3. $\frac{1469}{1320}$ 5. 0.835   7. $\frac{8}{3}$ 9. $\frac{15}{4}$ 11. 66   13. 4   15. 20 sq units   17. $\frac{5}{3}$ sq units   19. $\frac{395}{6}$ sq units

21. $\displaystyle\int_0^2 x^2\, dx$ 23. $\displaystyle\int_0^1 \frac{1}{x^2}\, dx$

Exercises 6.4   *(Page 312)*

9. 0; 64   11. 0; 27   13. 0; 576   15. -3; $\frac{3}{2}$ 17. 0; 6

Exercises 6.5   *(Page 318)*

1. $c = \frac{1}{3}(1 + \sqrt{5})$ 3. $c = -4$ 5. f discontinuous at -2 7. f discontinuous at 1   9. $\frac{1}{2}\sqrt[3]{30}$ 11. $-2 + \sqrt{21}$ 13. 0
15. $32t$; 32   17. π

Exercises 6.6   *(Page 326)*

1. $\frac{200}{3}$ 3. $\frac{140}{3}$ 5. -8 7. $2 - \sqrt[3]{2}$ 9. $\frac{104}{9}$ 11. $\frac{29}{5}$ 13. $\frac{2}{3}\sqrt{2}$ 15. $\frac{41}{6}$ 17. $\frac{6215}{12}$ 19. $\sqrt{4 + x^6}$ 21. $\dfrac{2}{3 + x^2}$

23. $\frac{22}{3}$ sq units   25. $\frac{52}{3}$ sq units   27. $\frac{1}{3}(40\sqrt{5} - 20)$ sq units   29. $\frac{32}{3}$; $\dfrac{4(3 - \sqrt{3})}{3}$ 31. $\dfrac{42,304}{175}$ 35. $4,933.33

Review Exercises for Chapter 6   *(Page 328)*

1. $-\frac{27}{4}$ 3. 4,100,656,560   7. $\frac{4374}{7}$ 9. $\frac{2}{3}(\sqrt{14} - \sqrt{2})$ 11. $\frac{2}{27}(40\sqrt{10} - \frac{64}{5})$ 13. $\frac{652}{15}$ 15. $\frac{313}{2}$

19. $4\sqrt{5} \le \displaystyle\int_1^4 \sqrt{5 + 4x - x^2}\, dx \le 9$ 21. 18 sq units   23. $\frac{224}{3}$ sq units   25. $\dfrac{22,304}{175}$ 29. $1072

Exercises 7.1   *(Page 338)*

1. $\frac{32}{3}$ sq units   3. $\frac{32}{3}$ sq units   5. $\frac{12}{5}$ sq units   7. $\frac{9}{2}$ sq units   9. $\frac{8}{3}\sqrt{2}$ sq units   11. $\frac{5}{12}$ sq units   13. $\frac{27}{10}$ sq units
15. $\frac{64}{3}$ sq units   17. $\frac{253}{12}$ sq units   19. $\frac{7}{3}$ sq units   21. 12 sq units   23. $\frac{128}{5}$ sq units   25. 64 sq units   27. (a) $\frac{16}{3}p^2$ sq units;

(b) 32   29. $-\dfrac{8}{m^4}$

Exercises 7.2   *(Page 344)*

1. 64π cu units   3. $\frac{704}{7}\pi$ cu units   5. $\frac{384}{7}\pi$ cu units   7. $\frac{3456}{35}\pi$ cu units   9. $\frac{4}{3}\pi r^3$ cu units   11. $\frac{128}{7}\pi$ cu units
13. $\frac{1250}{3}\pi$ cu units   15. $\frac{64}{5}\pi$ cu units   17. 180π cu units   19. $\frac{16}{3}\pi$ cu units

Exercises 7.3   *(Page 348)*

9. $\frac{1}{2}\pi$ cu units   11. $\frac{3}{10}\pi$ cu units   13. $\frac{8}{5}\pi$ cu units   15. $\frac{48}{30}\pi$ cu units   17. $\frac{32}{15}\pi a^3$ cu units   19. $\frac{7}{2}\pi$ cu units   21. $\frac{224}{3}\pi$ cu units

Exercises 7.4   *(Page 352)*

1. $\frac{4}{3}\sqrt{3}r^3$ cu units   3. $\frac{8}{3}r^3$ cu units   5. $\frac{1}{6}abc$ cu units   7. 1944 in.³   9. $\frac{2}{3}r^3$ in.³

Exercises 7.5   *(Page 355)*

1. 180 in.-lb   3. 12,000 in.-lb   5. 6562.5w ft-lb   7. 256πw ft-lb   9. 100,000 ft-lb   11. 5500 ft-lb   13. $2\sqrt{3}$ ft   15. $\frac{144}{55}w$ sec

Exercises 7.6   *(Page 359)*

1. 320w lb   3. 64w lb   5. 2.25w lb   7. $\frac{1250}{3}w$ lb   9. 96w lb   11. 11,250$\sqrt{3}w$ lb   13. 250$\sqrt{409}w$ lb

Exercises 7.7   *(Page 364)*

1. 4   3. 6   5. 171 slugs; 5.92 in. from one end   7. 25 slugs; 5.33 ft from left end   9. 16 slugs; $\frac{16}{5}$ ft from one end

11. $\frac{20}{L^2}x^2$ slugs/ft

Exercises 7.8   *(Page 373)*

1. $(2, \frac{1}{3})$ 5. $(0, \frac{8}{5})$ 7. $(0, \frac{12}{5})$ 9. $(\frac{16}{15}, \frac{64}{21})$ 11. $(\frac{1}{2}, -\frac{3}{2})$ 13. $\frac{5}{3}p$ 15. 2.25w lb   17. 100,000w ft-lb   19. $(2, 0)$

23. The point on the bisecting radial line whose distance from the center of the circle is $4/3\pi$ times the radius.   25. $\frac{1}{2}r^3[\pi + \frac{4}{3}]$

Exercises 7.9   *(Page 380)*

1. $(0, \frac{8}{5}, 0)$ 3. $(\frac{1}{2}, 0, 0)$ 5. $(\frac{16}{5}, 0, 0)$ 7. $(2, \frac{10}{7}, 0)$ 9. $(0, \frac{7}{3}, 0)$ 11. $(0, \frac{13}{5}, 0)$ 13. $(\frac{5}{16}, 4, 0)$ 15. $(2, \frac{5}{8}p, 0)$

17. on axis, $\frac{3}{4}h$ units from vertex   19. $(\frac{10}{3}, 0, 0)$

Exercises 7.10   *(Page 387)*

1. $\frac{14}{3}$ 3. $\frac{33}{16}$ 5. $\frac{1}{27}(97^{3/2} - 125)$ 7. 12   9. $\dfrac{8a^3 - (a^2 + 3b^2)^{3/2}}{8(a^2 - b^2)}$ 11. $4\sqrt{3}$

Review Exercises for Chapter 7   *(Page 387)*

1. $\frac{256}{15}$ sq units   3. 1024 in.³   5. $\dfrac{13,600}{3}w\pi$ ft-lb   7. $\frac{7}{3}$ sq units   9. 3π cu units   11. $\frac{16}{3}\sqrt{3}$ 13. $(\frac{39}{13}, \frac{29}{13})$ 15. $(\frac{8}{5}, \frac{1}{2})$

17. 28 slugs; $\bar{x} = \frac{18}{7}$ 19. $\frac{25}{6}\pi$ cu units   21. 90 ft³   23. $\frac{2752}{3}w\pi$ ft-lb   25. 400 ft-lb   27. $\frac{1}{5320}[(2251)^{3/2} - \frac{1}{8}(10999)^{3/2}]$

29. 756 lb   31. $\frac{1}{3}\pi r^2 h$ cu units   33. $(0, \frac{4}{3})$

Exercises 8.1   *(Page 399)*

1. $\dfrac{8x}{1 + 4x^2}$ 3. $\dfrac{-x}{4 - x^2}$ 5. $\dfrac{1 + \ln x^2}{x \ln x}$ 7. $\dfrac{3x^2}{x^3 + 1}$ 9. $\frac{1}{2}(1 + \sqrt{x+1})^{-1}$ 11. $\frac{1}{5}(x^7 + 1)^{-6/5}(8x^9 - 4x^7 + 15x^2 + 10)$

13. $\frac{3}{2}(3x + 4)[(x + 1)(x + 2)]^{-3/2}$ 15. $\dfrac{x \ln(x^2 - 1)}{\sqrt{x^2 + 1}} + \dfrac{2x\sqrt{x^2 + 1}}{x^2 - 1}$ 17. $-\dfrac{xy + y}{xy + x}$ 19. $\ln|3 - 2x|^{-1/2} + C$ 21. $\ln|\ln x| + C$

23. $\frac{1}{3}\ln^3 3x + C$ 25. $x^2 + 4\ln|x^2 - 4| + C$ 27. $\ln 5$ 29. $\frac{1}{2}\ln\frac{7}{4}$ 31. sgn $t(1 - e^{-|t|})$

Exercises 8.2   *(Page 403)*

11. $2 - 2\ln 2 = x - 2y$ 13. $\ln 4$ sq units   15. $2000 \ln 2$ lb/ft²   17. $\ln x = -\frac{1}{2}$ 19. $\ln 16$ slugs; $\bar{x} = \dfrac{6}{\ln 16} - 1$

Exercises 8.3   *(Page 414)*

1. $f^{-1}(x) = \sqrt[3]{x}$; domain: $(-\infty, +\infty)$ 3. no inverse   5. $f^{-1}(x) = \dfrac{1}{2 - x}$; domain: $(-\infty, 2)$ and $(2, +\infty)$ 7. no inverse

9. (a) $f_1(x) = \sqrt{9 - x^2}$; $f_2(x) = -\sqrt{9 - x^2}$; (b) neither has an inverse; (c) $D_x y = -\dfrac{x}{y}$, $D_y x = -\dfrac{y}{x}$ 11. (a) $f(x) = \dfrac{4}{x}$; (b) $f^{-1}(x) = \dfrac{4}{x}$; domain:

$(-\infty, 0)$ and $(0, +\infty)$; (c) $D_x y = -\dfrac{y}{x}$, $D_y x = -\dfrac{x}{y}$ 13. (a) $f(x) = \dfrac{2x^2 + 1}{3x}$; (b) no inverse; (c) $D_x y = \dfrac{4x - 3y}{3x}$, $D_y x = \dfrac{3x}{4x - 3y}$

15. domain: $[0, +\infty)$; range: $[4, +\infty)$ 17. domain: $(-\infty, +\infty)$; range: $(0, +\infty)$ 19. domain: $(-\infty, +\infty)$; range: $(-\infty, +\infty)$

21. $f^{(-1)\prime}(x) = \dfrac{1}{\sqrt{1 - (f^{-1}(x))^4}}$ 23. $f'(x) = \begin{cases} x & \text{if } x < 1 \\ \sqrt{x} & \text{if } 1 \le x \le 81 \\ \dfrac{x^2}{729} & \text{if } x > 81 \end{cases}$

Exercises 8.4   (Page 422)

5. $-6xe^{-3x^2}$ 7. $\dfrac{2e^{2x}(x-1)}{x^3}$ 9. $\dfrac{4}{(e^x + e^{-x})^2}$ 11. $2x$ 13. $x^x(\ln x + 1)$ 15. $\dfrac{e^x(1 - e^y)}{e^y(e^x - 1)}$ 17. $-\dfrac{y^2 + 2ye^{2x}}{2e^{2x} + 3xy}$ 19. $-\tfrac{1}{5}e^{(2-5x)} + C$

21. $e^x - e^{-x} + C$ 23. $\dfrac{1}{6(1 - 2e^{3x})} + C$ 25. $e^x - 3\ln(e^x + 3) + C$ 27. e^2 29. $\tfrac{1}{2}(e^4 - 1)$ 33. $2y + x = 1 + \ln 2$

35. $\tfrac{1}{2}(e^2 - e^{-2} - 4)$ cu units ≈ 1.627 cu units   37. -9.17 lb/ft² per sec   39. $\dfrac{6}{10^3}$ 41. $(e^3 + \tfrac{1}{2})$ ft ≈ 20.586 ft

43. $\tfrac{1}{2}\pi w(e^{-2} - e^{-8})$ ft-lb

Exercises 8.5   (Page 429)

9. $(5 \ln 3)3^{5x}$ 11. $2^{5x}3^{4x^2}(5 \ln 2 + 8x \ln 3)$ 13. $\dfrac{\log_{10}\dfrac{e}{x}}{x^2}$ 15. $\dfrac{\log_a e}{2x\sqrt{\log_a x}}$ 17. $\dfrac{(\log_{10} e)^2}{(x+1)\log_{10}(x+1)}$ 19. $x^{\sqrt{x} - (1/2)}(1 + \tfrac{1}{2}\ln x)$

21. $x^{e^x}e^x\left(\ln|x| + \dfrac{1}{x}\right)$ 23. $4^{3x}e^{3x^2}(6x + 6 \ln 2)$ 25. $\dfrac{3^{2x}}{2 \ln 3} + C$ 27. $\dfrac{a^x e^x}{1 + \ln a} + C$ 29. $\dfrac{10^{x^3}}{3 \ln 10} + C$ 31. $\dfrac{2^{e^x}3^{e^x}}{\ln 6} + C$

33. $(4 \ln 2 + 1)x - (8 \ln 2 + 4)y + 4 = 0$ 35. (a) 61 sales per day; (b) 2.26 sales per day   37. 2.999

Exercises 8.6   (Page 435)

1. $8000\sqrt{2} \approx 11{,}300$ 3. 43.9 g   5. 68.4 years   7. 69.9   9. 102 sec; (b) 42.1°   11. (a) 96%; (b) 66%   13. 118.7

15. 15.9 years   17. 15,000 years

Review Exercises for Chapter 8   (Page 436)

1. $\dfrac{4 \ln x^2}{x}$ 3. $\dfrac{\log_{10} e}{\sqrt{\log_{10}\dfrac{1+x}{1-x}}\,(1 - x^2)}$ 5. 0   7. $(x)^{x(e^x)}+e^x\left[\dfrac{1}{x} + e^x \ln^2|x| + \dfrac{1}{x}e^x \ln|x|\right]$ 9. $\tfrac{3}{2}\ln(1 + e^{2x}) + C$

11. $\dfrac{1}{3}\left(e^{3x} + \dfrac{a^{3x}}{\ln a}\right) + C$ 13. $\dfrac{2}{3 \ln 2}(3 \cdot 2^x + 4)^{1/2} + C$ 15. $\tfrac{1}{3}(e^8 - 1)$ 17. $\tfrac{3}{4}\ln 4$ 19. $-\dfrac{ye^x + e^y + 1}{e^x + xe^y + 1}$ 21. $\ln 5$ slugs;

$\dfrac{4 - \ln 5}{\ln 5}$ ft from one end   23. $v = e^t - e^{-t} + 1$; $s = e^t + e^{-t} + t$ 25. $\tfrac{1}{2}\pi(1 - e^{-2b})$; $\tfrac{1}{2}\pi$ 27. 8212 years   29. $g(x) = -e^x$; domain:

$(-\infty, +\infty)$ 31. $f^{-1}(x) = \sqrt[3]{\dfrac{x+2}{8x}}$; domain: $(-\infty, 0)$ and $(0, +\infty)$ 35. $3000 \ln \tfrac{3}{2}$ in.-lb   37. 8.66 years

Exercises 9.1   (Page 446)

7. $\sin 3t = 3 \sin t - 4 \sin^3 t$ 9. (a) $\sqrt{2} - \sqrt{3}$; (b) $\tfrac{1}{2}\sqrt{2} + \sqrt{3}$ 11. (a) $\tfrac{1}{2}\sqrt{2} + \sqrt{3}$; (b) $\tfrac{1}{2}\sqrt{2} - \sqrt{3}$ 13. (a) $-\cos t$; (b) $-\cos(\tfrac{1}{2}\pi - t)$;

(c) $-\cos t$; (d) $\cos(\tfrac{1}{2}\pi - t)$ 15. (a) $\cos(\tfrac{1}{2}\pi - t)$; (b) $-\cos t$; (c) $-\cos(\tfrac{1}{2}\pi - t)$; (d) $-\cos t$ 17. (a) $t = (2n + \tfrac{1}{2})\pi$, where n is any

integer; (b) $t = 2n\pi$, where n is any integer   19. (a) $t = (2n + \tfrac{1}{8})\pi$ or $(2n + \tfrac{5}{8})\pi$, where n is any integer; (b) $t = (2n \pm \tfrac{1}{3})\pi$, where n is

any integer

Exercises 9.2   (Page 454)

1. 4   3. $\tfrac{9}{7}$ 5. $\tfrac{1}{4}$ 7. 12   9. $6 \cos 2x$ 11. $3 \cos 6x$ 13. $-\dfrac{\sin\sqrt{t}}{\sqrt{t}}$ 15. $5\dfrac{\cos 5x}{\sin 5x}$ 17. $\dfrac{1 + 2 \cos x}{(2 + \cos x)^2}$ 19. $3 \cos x \cos 2x$

21. $(\sin x^2)^{4x}\left(4 \ln |\sin x^2| + 8x^2 \dfrac{\cos x^2}{\sin x^2}\right)$ 23. $(\cos x)^{\sin x}\left(-\dfrac{\sin^2 x}{\cos x} + \cos x \ln |\cos x|\right)$ 25. $\dfrac{\cos^4 x + 2 \sin^2 x \cos^2 x + 2 \sin^2 x + 1}{\cos^4 x\sqrt{1 + \cos^2 x}}$

27. $\dfrac{\sin(x - y)}{\sin(x - y) - 1}$ 35. decreasing at the rate of $\tfrac{1}{48}$ rad/sec   37. $1/\sqrt{1 + k^2}$

Exercises 9.3   (Page 459)

1. $2 \sin x - 3 \cos x + C$ 3. $-e^{\cos x} + C$ 5. $\cos(\cos x) + C$ 7. $\tfrac{1}{3}\cos^3 x - \cos x + C$ 9. $\tfrac{3}{8}x - \tfrac{1}{4}\sin 2x + \tfrac{1}{32}\sin 4x + C$

11. $\frac{1}{2}x + \frac{1}{2}\sin x + C$ 13. $-\frac{1}{3}\cos^3 x + \frac{2}{5}\cos^5 x - \frac{1}{7}\cos^7 x + C$ 15. $\frac{1}{8}t - \frac{1}{96}\sin 12t + C$ 17. $\frac{1}{2}\sin^{2/3} 3x - \frac{1}{8}\sin^{8/3} 3x + C$

19. $\frac{1}{14}\sin 7x + \frac{1}{2}\sin x + C$ 21. $x - \sin x - \frac{1}{8}\sin 4x + \frac{1}{5}\sin 5x - \frac{1}{12}\sin 6x + C$ 23. 1   25. $\frac{2}{3}$ 27. $\frac{1}{8}$ 35. $\frac{4}{\pi}$ volts

37. 2 sq units   39. $\frac{5}{8}\pi^2$ cu units

Exercises 9.4   (Page 469)

3. $2x \sec x^2 \tan x^2$ 5. $2\tan 2x$ 7. $-\dfrac{3\csc^2 3r}{2\sqrt{\cot 3r}}$ 9. $2\sec^3 x - \sec x$ 11. $-3t^2 \csc(t^3 + 1)\cot(t^3 + 1)$ 13. $4\cot t \csc^2 t$

15. $5\sec 5x$ 17. $3^x \sec x(\ln 3 + \tan x)$ 19. $(\sin x)^{\tan x}(\sec^2 x \ln|\sin x| + 1)$ 21. $\dfrac{1}{\sqrt{1 - \cot^2 x}}(\sec^2 x + \sin^2 x - 3\cos^2 x)$

23. $-\csc^2(x + y)$ 25. $\sec^2 x \tan x \sin^2 y \tan y$ 31. $y = \sqrt{2}(x + 1 - \frac{1}{4}\pi)$ 33. $5\sqrt{5}$ ft

Exercises 9.5   (Page 473)

1. (a) $\frac{1}{2}$; (b) $\frac{10}{11}$; (c) $-\frac{7}{4}$; (d) $\frac{7}{31}$; (e) $\frac{7}{26}$ 3. $27°, 45°, 108°$ 5. $3x - y + 7 = 0; x + 3y - 11 = 0$ 9. $-\frac{19}{3} - \frac{1}{3}\sqrt{370}$

13. $(\frac{1}{4}(1 + 4n)\pi, \frac{1}{2}\sqrt{2})$, where n is any even integer; $(\frac{1}{4}(1 + 4n) - \frac{1}{2}\sqrt{2})$ where n is any odd integer; $109° 30'$

Exercises 9.6   (Page 478)

1. $\frac{1}{2}\ln|\sec 2x| + C$ 3. $\frac{1}{10}\ln|\csc 5x^2 - \cot 5x^2| + C$ 5. $-\frac{1}{2}\csc^2 x - \ln|\sin x| + C$ 7. $-\frac{1}{6}\cot 6x + C$ 9. $\frac{1}{7}\tan^7 x + \frac{1}{9}\tan^9 x + C$

11. $-\frac{1}{3}\cot^3 3x - \frac{1}{15}\cot^5 3x + C$ 13. $\frac{1}{3}(\tan 3x - \cot 3x) + C$ 15. $x - 2\tan\frac{1}{2}x + \frac{2}{3}\tan^3\frac{1}{2}x + C$ 17. $-\frac{1}{10}\cot^5 2t + \frac{1}{6}\cot^3 2t - \frac{1}{2}\cot 2t$

$- t + C$ 19. $u - 2\tan\frac{1}{4}u + C$ 21. $-\frac{1}{3}\csc^3 x + C$ 23. $\frac{1}{8}\ln 2$ 25. $\frac{56}{15}$ 27. $\frac{1}{5}$ 31. $\ln(2 + \sqrt{3})$ 33. $\frac{4}{3}\pi$ cu units

Exercises 9.7   (Page 484)

1. (a) $-\frac{1}{2}\pi$; (b) π; (c) $-\frac{1}{4}\pi$; (d) $\frac{3}{4}\pi$; (e) π; (f) $-\frac{1}{2}\pi$ 3. (a) $\frac{2}{3}\sqrt{2}$; (b) $\frac{1}{4}\sqrt{2}$; (c) $2\sqrt{2}$; (d) $\frac{3}{4}\sqrt{2}$; (e) 3   5. (a) $-\frac{2}{5}\sqrt{5}$; (b) $\frac{1}{5}\sqrt{5}$; (c) $-\frac{1}{2}$; (d) $\sqrt{5}$;

(e) $-\frac{1}{5}\sqrt{5}$ 7. (a) $\sqrt{3}$; (b) $\frac{1}{7}\sqrt{21}$ 9. (a) $\frac{1}{2}\pi$; (b) $-\frac{1}{4}\pi$; (c) π; (d) $\frac{3}{4}\pi$ 11. $\frac{119}{169}$ 13. $\frac{2}{9}(1 + \sqrt{10})$ 15. $\frac{1}{39}(48 - 25\sqrt{3})$

17. $\frac{1}{15}(4\sqrt{10} + \sqrt{5})$

Exercises 9.8   (Page 489)

3. $\dfrac{1}{\sqrt{4 - x^2}}$ 5. $\dfrac{1}{|t|\sqrt{25t^2 - 1}}$ 7. $\dfrac{4}{4 + x^2}$ 9. $\sin^{-1} 2y + \dfrac{2y}{\sqrt{1 - 4y^2}}$ 11. $\csc^{-1}\dfrac{1}{x} + \dfrac{x}{\sqrt{1 - x^2}}$ 13. $2\sqrt{4 - x^2}$ 15. $\dfrac{a - t}{\sqrt{a^2 - t^2}}$

17. $-\dfrac{\cos x}{|\cos x|}$ 19. 0   21. $\cot^{-1} x$ 23. $-e^x - \dfrac{1}{\sqrt{1 - x^2}}$ 25. $\dfrac{(1 + y^2)(3x^2 + \sin y)}{1 - x\cos y(1 + y^2)}$ 27. $\frac{52}{3}\pi$ mi/min   29. 0.078 rad/sec

31. 8 ft/sec   33. $\dfrac{6}{x\sqrt{x^2 - 64}}$

Exercises 9.9   (Page 493)

7. $\frac{1}{5}\tan^{-1}\dfrac{x}{5} + C$ 9. $\dfrac{\sqrt{5}}{5}\sin^{-1}\dfrac{\sqrt{10}}{2}x + C$ 11. $\frac{1}{6}\sin^{-1}(\frac{3}{4}r^2) + C$ 13. $\dfrac{1}{\sqrt{7}}\tan^{-1}\left(\dfrac{e^x}{\sqrt{7}}\right) + C$ 15. $2\tan^{-1}\sqrt{x} + C$

17. $\dfrac{2}{\sqrt{7}}\tan^{-1}\left(\dfrac{2x - 1}{\sqrt{7}}\right) + C$ 19. $\cos^{-1}\left(\dfrac{1 - x}{4}\right) + C$ 21. $\cos^{-1}\left(\dfrac{1 + x}{2}\right) - \sqrt{3 - 2x - x^2} + C$ 23. $\sin^{-1}\left(\dfrac{1 + x}{\sqrt{5}}\right) - \sqrt{4 - 2x - x^2} + C$

25. $\frac{1}{2}(x + 2)^2 + \frac{5}{4}\ln(2x^2 - 4x + 3) - \frac{1}{2}\sqrt{2}\tan^{-1}\sqrt{2}(x - 1) + C$ 27. $\frac{1}{4}\pi + \frac{1}{2}\ln 2$ 29. $\frac{1}{3}\pi$ 31. $\tan^{-1} e - \frac{1}{4}\pi$ 33. $\frac{1}{4}\pi$

35. $\bar{x} = \dfrac{4\ln 2}{\pi}$ 37. $2\pi r$ 39. $s = 5\cos 4t$; amplitude $= 5$, period $= \frac{1}{2}\pi$

Exercises 9.10   (Page 501)

17. $\frac{4}{5}\operatorname{sech}^2\dfrac{4x + 1}{5}$ 19. $e^x(\cosh x + \sinh x)$ 21. $2\operatorname{csch} 2t$ 23. $2x\operatorname{sech} x^2$ 25. $x^{\sinh x - 1}(x\cosh x \ln|x| + \sinh x)$

31. $\frac{1}{2}\ln^2 \cosh x + C$ 33. $\frac{1}{224}\sinh 28x + \frac{1}{28}\sinh 14x + \frac{3}{8}x + C$ 35. $\frac{1}{3}\tanh 3x - \frac{1}{9}\tanh^3 3x + C$ 37. $2\cosh\sqrt{x} + C$

39. $\frac{1}{3}\cosh^3 2 - \cosh 2 + \frac{2}{3}$ 43. $a^2\sinh\dfrac{x_1}{a}$ sq units   45. $v = e^{-ct/2}[(B - \frac{1}{2}cA)\sinh t + (A - \frac{1}{2}cB)\cosh t]$;

$a = e^{-ct/2}[(A - cB + \frac{1}{4}c^2A)\sinh t + (B - cA + \frac{1}{4}c^2B)\cosh t]$; $a = K, s + K_2v$, where $K_1 = 1 - \frac{1}{4}c^2$ and $K_2 = -c$

Exercises 9.11   (*Page 507*)

11. $\ln(\frac{1}{4} + \frac{1}{4}\sqrt{17})$ 13. $\frac{1}{2}\ln 3$ 15. $\dfrac{2x}{\sqrt{x^4 + 1}}$ 17. $\dfrac{4}{1 - 16x^2}$ 19. $-\dfrac{1}{2x + 3x^2}$ 21. $2x\left(\cosh^{-1} x^2 + \dfrac{x^2}{\sqrt{x^4 - 1}}\right)$ 23. $|\sec x|$

25. $-\csc x \cot x/|\cot x|$

Review Exercises for Chapter 9   (*Page 507*)

1. $\frac{1}{3}$ 3. 4   7. $\dfrac{\cos 4x}{(\sin 4x)^{3/4}}$ 9. $\cos\dfrac{1}{x} + \dfrac{1}{x}\sin\dfrac{1}{x}$ 11. $\dfrac{2^x \ln 2}{1 + 2^{2x}}$ 13. $2w\sinh^{-1} 2w + \dfrac{2w^2}{\sqrt{4w^2 + 1}}$

15. $\dfrac{(\tan x)^{1/x^2}(x\sec^2 x - 2\tan x \ln|\tan x|)}{x^3 \tan x}$ 17. $\dfrac{6xy - 9y^4 - x^4 y^2}{3x^2 + 18xy^3 + 2x^5 y}$ 19. $\frac{1}{16}x - \frac{1}{24}\sin^3 x - \frac{1}{32}\sin 2x + C$ 21. $\dfrac{2}{\sqrt{31}}\tan^{-1}\dfrac{4x + 3}{\sqrt{31}} + C$

23. $t - \frac{1}{3}\tan\frac{3}{2}t + C$ 25. $\frac{1}{4}\cos 2x - \frac{1}{16}\cos 8x + C$ 27. $\frac{848}{105}$ 29. $\frac{2}{3}\pi + \sqrt{3} - 2$ 31. $\ln(2 + \sqrt{3})$ 33. $106°, 90°, 112°, 52°$

35. $\frac{7}{10}\pi$ hr; he walks all the way.   39. $\sqrt{3} + \frac{1}{8}\pi$ 41. $\frac{1}{2}\pi - 1$ 43. $v^2 = 4(5 - s)(s - 3); a = 4(4 - s)$ 45. (a) 120 rad/hr;

(b) 60 rad/hr   47. $\frac{7}{12}$ 49. $T = 2\pi, P = 200$ 51. $\sqrt{A^2 + B^2}$

Exercises 10.2   (*Page 516*)

1. $x(\ln x - 1) + C$ 3. $x\tan x + \ln|\cos x| + C$ 5. $x\sin^{-1} x + \sqrt{1 - x^2} + C$ 7. $\frac{1}{2}\tan^{-1} x(x^2 + 1) - \frac{1}{2}x + C$

9. $\frac{1}{2}e^x(\cos x + \sin x) + C$ 11. $-x^2\sqrt{1 - x^2} - \frac{2}{3}(1 - x^2)^{3/2} + C$ 13. $(x^2 + 2)\cosh x - 2x\sinh x + C$ 15. $\frac{1}{4}\sec^3 x \tan x$

$+ \frac{3}{8}[\sec x \tan x + \ln|\sec x + \tan x|] + C$ 17. $\frac{9}{16}$ 19. $\frac{1}{4}(3e^4 + 1)$ 21. $\frac{4}{25}(e^{3\pi/4} + 1)$ 23. $\frac{4}{3}\pi - \sqrt{3}$ 25. $(e^2 + 1)$ sq units

27. $\frac{1}{2}\pi(3e^4 + 1)$ cu units   29. $2(1 - e^{-6})$ slugs; $\dfrac{e^6 - 7}{e^6 - 1}$ ft from one end   31. $(4 - \frac{1}{4}\pi)w$ lb   33. $\frac{1}{4}(1 - 9e^{-8})\pi w$ ft-lb   35. $42,400

Exercises 10.3   (*Page 521*)

1. $-\dfrac{(4 - x^2)^{1/2}}{4x} + C$ 3. $-\dfrac{(9 - x^2)^{1/2}}{x} - \sin^{-1}\dfrac{x}{3} + C$ 5. $\dfrac{1}{5}\ln\left|\dfrac{5 - \sqrt{25 - x^2}}{x}\right| + C$ 7. $\frac{1}{2}(\sin^{-1} u + u\sqrt{1 - u^2}) + C$

9. $32\sin^{-1}(\frac{1}{4}x) - \frac{1}{4}(16 - x^2)^{1/2}(8x - x^3) + C$ 11. $-\frac{1}{9}x(4x^2 - 9)^{-1/2} + C$ 13. $\ln|x + 2 + \sqrt{4x + x^2}| + C$ 15. $\dfrac{x + 2}{9\sqrt{5 - 4x - x^2}} + C$

17. $\dfrac{\tan x}{4\sqrt{4 - \tan^2 x}} + C$ 19. $\frac{128}{3} - 24\sqrt{3}$ 21. $\dfrac{6 - 2\sqrt{3}}{27}$ 23. $\frac{1}{2}\cos^{-1}\frac{1}{3} - \frac{1}{8}\pi$ 25. $\frac{625}{16}\pi$ 27. $(\ln 3 - \frac{4}{5})$ sq units

29. $\ln\frac{1}{3}(2\sqrt{5} + \sqrt{10} - \sqrt{2} - 1) + \sqrt{10} - \sqrt{2}$ 31. $\left(0, \dfrac{\ln\frac{5}{3} - \frac{8}{25}}{6(\frac{4}{3} - \sec^{-1}\frac{5}{3})}, 0\right)$ 33. $s = \dfrac{c}{k}\sin kt$ 35. $(\frac{8}{3}\pi + 3\sqrt{3})w$ lb

Exercises 10.4   (*Page 529*)

1. $\dfrac{1}{4}\ln\left|\dfrac{x - 2}{x + 2}\right| + C$ 3. $\ln|C(x - 2)^2(x + 2)^3|$ 5. $\dfrac{1}{4}\ln\left|\dfrac{Cx^4(2x + 1)^3}{(2x - 1)}\right|$ 7. $\dfrac{1}{9}\ln\left|\dfrac{x + 3}{x}\right| - \dfrac{1}{3x} + C$ 9. $-\frac{1}{2}(x + 2)^{-2} + C$

11. $\dfrac{3}{x + 1} + \ln|x + 1| - \dfrac{1}{2}\ln|2x + 3| + C$ 13. $\dfrac{x^2}{2} + 2x - \dfrac{3}{x - 1} - \ln[(x + 3)^4(x - 1)^2] + C$ 15. $-\ln(3x + 2)^{2/3}(x - 1)^2$

$- \dfrac{1}{3(3x + 2)} - \dfrac{3}{x - 1} + C$ 17. $4\ln\frac{4}{3} - \frac{3}{2}$ 19. $-2 + \ln\frac{27}{4}$ 21. $-4\ln 5 + 13\ln 2$ 23. $\ln\frac{7}{2} - \frac{1}{6}$ 25. $\ln 4.5$ sq units

27. $2\pi(2 + 6\ln 3 - 2\ln 2)$ cu units   29. $\left(\dfrac{8\ln 3 - 8}{2 - \ln 3}, \dfrac{2}{9(2 - \ln 3)}\right)$ 31. $\frac{31}{19}$ 33. 7.4 lb

Exercises 10.5   (*Page 533*)

1. $\dfrac{1}{2}\ln\left(\dfrac{Cx^2}{2x^2 + 1}\right)$ 3. $\dfrac{1}{8}\ln\left|\dfrac{2x - 1}{2x + 1}\right| - \dfrac{1}{4}\tan^{-1} 2x + C$ 5. $\ln|x - 1| + \tan^{-1} x + C$ 7. $\dfrac{1}{2}\left(\ln\dfrac{Cx^2}{x^2 + x + 1}\right) - \dfrac{1}{\sqrt{3}}\tan^{-1}\left(\dfrac{2x + 1}{\sqrt{3}}\right)$

9. $\ln\left(\dfrac{Cx^2}{x^2 + 1}\right) - \dfrac{1}{2}\tan^{-1} x - \dfrac{1}{2}x(x^2 + 1)^{-1}$ 11. $\dfrac{5}{162}\ln|9x^2 + 3x + 1| - \dfrac{2}{81}\ln|3x - 1| + \dfrac{5}{9\sqrt{35}}\tan^{-1}\left(\dfrac{6x + 1}{\sqrt{35}}\right) + C$ 13. $\frac{1}{6}\tan^{-1}\frac{2}{3}x$

$+ x(4x^2 + 9)^{-1} + C$ 15. $\ln|1 + \tan x| + \dfrac{2}{\sqrt{3}}\tan^{-1}\left(\dfrac{2\tan x - 1}{\sqrt{3}}\right) + C$ 17. $6\ln 2$ 19. $\ln\frac{12}{5} + \frac{3}{2}\ln\frac{20}{13}$ 21. $\frac{1}{4}\pi$ 23. $\frac{3}{4}\ln 2 + \frac{5}{8}\pi$

25. $(\frac{1}{3}\ln 2 + \frac{1}{9}\sqrt{3}\pi)$ sq units   27. $\frac{3}{4}k\ln 2$ slugs   29. $\dfrac{3}{50}\ln\dfrac{(t_1 + 2)^2}{4(t_1^2 + 1)} - \dfrac{7}{5}(t_1 + 2)^{-1} - \dfrac{4}{25}\tan^{-1} t_1 + \dfrac{7}{10}$

Exercises 10.6   (Page 538)

1. $\sinh^{-1}\frac{1}{2}x + C = \ln\frac{1}{2}(x + \sqrt{x^2+4}) + C$ 3. $\frac{1}{2}\cosh^{-1}x^2 + C = \frac{1}{2}\ln(x^2 + \sqrt{x^4-1}) + C$

5. $\begin{cases} -\frac{1}{12}\tanh^{-1}(\frac{3}{4}x) + C & \text{if } |x| < \frac{4}{3} \\ -\frac{1}{12}\coth^{-1}(\frac{3}{4}x) + C & \text{if } |x| > \frac{4}{3} \end{cases} = \frac{1}{24}\ln\left|\frac{4-3x}{4+3x}\right| + C$ 7. $\sinh^{-1}\frac{\sin x}{\sqrt{3}} + C = \ln(\sin x + \sqrt{4 - \cos^2 x}) + C$

9. $\begin{cases} \frac{1}{\sqrt{6}}\tanh^{-1}\left(\frac{x+2}{\sqrt{6}}\right) + C & \text{if } |x+2| < \sqrt{6} \\ \frac{1}{\sqrt{6}}\coth^{-1}\left(\frac{x+2}{\sqrt{6}}\right) + C & \text{if } |x+2| > \sqrt{6} \end{cases} = \frac{1}{2\sqrt{6}}\ln\left|\frac{\sqrt{6}+2+x}{\sqrt{6}-2-x}\right| + C$ 11. $\ln\left(\frac{5+\sqrt{21}}{3+\sqrt{5}}\right)$ 13. $\ln 3$ 15. $\frac{1}{3}\ln\frac{7+\sqrt{40}}{4+\sqrt{7}}$

Exercises 10.7   (Page 541)

1. $\frac{2}{3}\tan^{-1}(\frac{1}{3}\tan\frac{1}{2}x) + C$ 3. $-\ln|1 - \tan\frac{1}{2}x| + C$ 5. $\frac{1}{2}\ln|\tan\frac{1}{2}x| - \frac{1}{4}\tan^2\frac{1}{2}x + C$ 7. $2\sqrt{2}\ln\left|\frac{\sqrt{2}+\tan x}{\sqrt{2}-\tan^2 x}\right| + C$

9. $\frac{5}{3}\tan^{-1}\left(\tan\frac{1}{2}x\right) - \frac{\sqrt{5}}{3}\ln\left(\frac{\sqrt{5}+\tan\frac{1}{2}x}{\sqrt{5}-\tan\frac{1}{2}x}\right) + C$ 11. $2\tan^{-1}(2 + \tan\frac{1}{2}x) + C$ 13. $\frac{1}{4}\ln 3$ 15. $2\sqrt{3}\ln(1 + \sqrt{3})$

17. $\frac{1}{2}\sqrt{3}\ln(1 + \frac{1}{2}\sqrt{3})$

Exercises 10.8   (Page 543)

1. $\frac{2}{3}x^{3/2} - 3x + 18\sqrt{x} - 54\ln(3 + \sqrt{x}) + C$ 3. $\ln\left|\frac{\sqrt{1+4x}-1}{\sqrt{1+4x}+1}\right| + C$ 5. $-2\sqrt{1+x} + 2\sqrt{2}\ln\left|\frac{\sqrt{1+x}+2}{1-x}\right| + C$ 7. $\frac{3}{2}(x-2)^{2/3}$

$-3(x-2)^{1/3} + 3\ln|1 + (x-2)^{1/3}| + C$ 9. $2\sqrt{2x} + 2\sqrt{x+4} + 4\sqrt{2}\ln\left|\frac{(2\sqrt{2}-\sqrt{x+4})(\sqrt{x}-2)}{x-4}\right| + C$

11. $3\tan^{-1}\sqrt[6]{x} + \frac{3\sqrt[6]{x}}{1+\sqrt[3]{x}} + C$ 13. $2\tan^{-1}(x + \sqrt{x^2+2x-1}) + C$ 15. $\ln\left(\frac{Cx}{x+2+2\sqrt{1+x+x^2}}\right)$ 17. $4 - 2\ln 3$ 19. $\ln\frac{11}{10}$

21. $\frac{1}{9}(54 - 2\sqrt[3]{3})$

Exercises 10.9   (Page 548)

1. approx: 0.695; exact: $\ln 2 \approx 0.693$ 3. approx: 4.250; exact: 4   5. approx: 0.880; exact: $\ln(1 + \sqrt{2}) \approx 0.881$ 7. approx: 1.954;

exact: 2   9. 0.248   11. 1.481   13. 3.694   15. $-0.007 \le \epsilon_T \le -0.001$ 17. $-0.5 \le \epsilon_T \le 0$ 19. $-\frac{1}{50}e \le \epsilon_T \le -\frac{1}{150}$

21. 0.882   23. 3.090

Exercises 10.10   (Page 554)

1. by Simpson's rule: $\frac{8}{3}$; exact: $\frac{8}{3}$ 3. by Simpson's rule: 0.881; exact: $\ln(1 + \sqrt{2}) \approx 0.881$ 5. by Simpson's rule: 0.6045; exact:

$\frac{1}{9}\pi\sqrt{3} \approx 0.6044$ 7. $\epsilon_s = 0$ 9. $-\frac{\pi^5}{233,280} \le \epsilon_s \le 0$ 11. 1.445   13. 0.883   15. 1.402   17. $\pi r^2 h$ 19. $\frac{1}{3}\pi h_1(r_1^2 + r_2^2 + r_1 r_2)$

21. (a) -0.0962; (b) -0.0950; (c) -0.0991

Review Exercises for Chapter 10   (Page 555)

1. $\frac{1}{8}x - \frac{1}{128}\sin 16x + C$ 3. $-2\sqrt{4 - e^x} + C$ 5. $(x+1)\tan^{-1}\sqrt{x} - \sqrt{x} + C$ 7. $\frac{1}{2}x + \frac{3}{4}\sin\frac{2}{3}x + C$ 9. $\ln|x-1| - 2(x-1)^{-1}$

$-(x-1)^{-2} + C$ 11. $\frac{1}{4}\sin 2x - \frac{1}{8}\sin 4x + C$ 13. $3\ln\left|\frac{x^{1/3}}{1+x^{1/3}}\right| + C$ 15. $\frac{1}{3}\tan 3x - \frac{1}{3}\cot 3x + \frac{2}{3}\ln|\tan 3x| + C$

17. $2t + \ln\frac{t^2}{(t+2)^{10}} - \frac{15}{t+2} + C$ 19. $x - \tan^{-1}x + \frac{1}{2}\ln\left|\frac{x-1}{x+1}\right| + C$ 21. $\frac{1}{16}x - \frac{1}{192}\sin 12x - \frac{1}{144}\sin^3 6x + C$ 23. $\sin^{-1}\left(\frac{r+2}{\sqrt{7}}\right) + C$

25. $x\sinh x - \cosh x + C$ 27. $\frac{2}{17}e^{t/2}(4\sin 2t + \cos 2t) + C$ 29. $\frac{1}{4}\tan^{-1}(\frac{1}{2}\sin^2 x) + C$

31. $\begin{cases} \frac{1}{n}\left(-\cos nx + \frac{2}{3}\cos^3 nx - \frac{1}{5}\cos^5 nx\right) + C & \text{if } n \ne 0 \\ C & \text{if } n = 0 \end{cases}$ 33. $-\frac{1}{4}\csc^3 x \cot x - \frac{3}{8}\csc x \cot x + \frac{3}{8}\ln|\csc x - \cot x| + C$

35. $2\ln|y-2| - 8(y-2)^{-1} - \frac{9}{2}(y-2)^{-2} + C$ 37. $-\tan^{-1}(\cos x) + C$ 39. $2\sin^{-1}\left(\frac{t-2}{2}\right) + \frac{1}{2}(t-2)(4t - t^2)^{1/2} + C$

41. $\frac{1}{3}\ln\left|1 - \frac{1}{x^3}\right| + C$ 43. $\frac{1}{3}\sin^{-1}(\frac{3}{2}e^x) + C$ 45. $-\frac{1}{15}\cot^5 3x - \frac{1}{9}\cot^3 3x + C$ 47. $\frac{1}{3}x^3\sin^{-1}x + \frac{1}{9}(x^2 + 2)\sqrt{1-x^2} + C$

49. $\tan^{-1}(\cos x) + C$ 51. $\frac{2}{3}\sec^{-1}|2\sin 3t| + C$ 53. $-\frac{(x^2 + a^2)^{3/2}}{3a^2x^3} + C$ 55. $\sqrt{2t} - \sqrt{1 - 2t}\sin^{-1}\sqrt{2t} + C$

57. $\frac{4}{3}\sqrt{2 + \sqrt{x-1}}(\sqrt{x-1} - 4) + C$ 59. $\frac{\sqrt{2}}{4}\ln\left|\frac{\tan x - \sqrt{2}\tan x + 1}{\tan x + \sqrt{2}\tan x + 1}\right| + \frac{\sqrt{2}}{2}\tan^{-1}(\sqrt{2}\tan x - 1) + \frac{\sqrt{2}}{2}\tan^{-1}(\sqrt{2}\tan x + 1) + C$

61. $\begin{cases}\dfrac{x^{n+1}\ln x}{n+1} - \dfrac{x^{n+1}}{(n+1)^2} + C & \text{if } n \neq -1 \\ \frac{1}{2}\ln^2 x + C & \text{if } n = -1\end{cases}$ 63. 4   65. $\frac{1}{2} + 2\ln\frac{8}{5}$ 67. $\frac{16}{3} - \frac{8}{3}\sqrt{2}$ 69. $\frac{4}{3}\sqrt{3} - \frac{1}{2}\pi$ 71. $\frac{e^2 - 1}{e^2 + 1}$ 73. $\frac{1}{2} - \frac{1}{4}\ln 2$

75. $a^2(\frac{1}{2}\pi - \frac{2}{3}\sqrt{3})$ 77. $\frac{1}{2}\ln\frac{9}{2} - \frac{1}{6}\pi$ 79. 5   81. $\frac{1}{8} + \ln\frac{3}{2}$ 83. $\frac{4}{3}$ 85. $1 - \frac{1}{2}\ln 3$ 87. $\frac{1}{24}\pi$ 89. $\sqrt{3} - \frac{1}{2}\ln(2 + \sqrt{3})$

91. $\frac{1}{5}\ln\frac{3}{2}$ 93. $\frac{256}{15}$ 95. (a) 1.624; (b) 1.563   99. $9\sqrt{2} - 3\sqrt{5} + \frac{3}{2}\ln(2\sqrt{10} + 3\sqrt{5} - 4\sqrt{2} - 6)$ 101. $\left(\frac{e^2 - 3}{2e^2 - 2}, 0, 0\right)$ 103. $3w$ lb

105. $\bar{x} = \frac{4}{9}\left(\frac{2e^3 + 1}{e^2 + 1}\right); \bar{y} = \frac{2}{27}\left(\frac{5e^3 - 2}{e^2 + 1}\right)$ 107. (a) $x = 300\left(\frac{18^t - 17^t}{3 \cdot 18^t - 2 \cdot 17^t}\right)$; (b) 35.94 lb

Exercises 11.1   (Page 563)

1. (a) $(-4, \frac{5}{4}\pi)$; (b) $(4, -\frac{1}{4}\pi)$; (c) $(-4, -\frac{3}{4}\pi)$ 3. (a) $(-2, \frac{3}{2}\pi)$; (b) $(2, -\frac{3}{2}\pi)$; (c) $(-2, -\frac{1}{2}\pi)$ 5. (a) $(-\sqrt{2}, \frac{3}{4}\pi)$; (b) $(\sqrt{2}, -\frac{1}{4}\pi)$;
(c) $(-\sqrt{2}, -\frac{5}{4}\pi)$ 7. $(3, \frac{4}{3}\pi)$; $(-3, \frac{1}{3}\pi)$ 9. $(-4, -\frac{7}{6}\pi)$; $(4, -\frac{1}{6}\pi)$ 11. $(-2, \frac{3}{4}\pi)$; $(2, \frac{7}{4}\pi)$ 13. (a) $(-3, 0)$; (b) $(-1, -1)$;
(c) $(2, -2\sqrt{3})$; (d) $(0, 2)$; (e) $(-\sqrt{2}, \sqrt{2})$; (f) $(\frac{1}{2}\sqrt{3}, -\frac{1}{2})$ 15. $r = |a|$ 17. $r = \frac{2}{1 - \cos\theta}$ 19. $r^2 = 4\cos 2\theta$

21. $r = \frac{3a\sin 2\theta}{2(\sin^3\theta + \cos^3\theta)}$ 23. $(x^2 + y^2)^2 = 4xy$ 25. $(x^2 + y^2)^3 = x^2$ 27. $(x^2 + y^2)^2 = 4(x^2 - y^2)$ 29. $4x^2 - 5y^2 - 36y - 36 = 0$

Exercises 11.2   (Page 571)

41. $\theta = \frac{2}{3}\pi, \theta = \frac{1}{3}\pi$ 43. $\theta = \frac{1}{4}\pi, \theta = \frac{3}{4}\pi$ 45. -1

Exercises 11.3   (Page 576)

1. $(\frac{3}{2}, \frac{1}{6}\pi)$; $(\frac{3}{2}, \frac{5}{6}\pi)$ 3. pole; $(\sqrt{2}, \frac{1}{4}\pi)$ 5. $(\frac{1}{2}\pi, \frac{1}{6}\pi)$; $(-\frac{1}{2}\pi, -\frac{1}{6}\pi)$ 7. $(1, \frac{3}{2}\pi)$; $(1, \frac{1}{2}\pi)$; $(\frac{1}{2}, \frac{1}{6}\pi)$; $(\frac{1}{2}, \frac{5}{6}\pi)$; pole   9. pole; $(\frac{1}{2}\sqrt{2}$,
$(2n + 1)\pi)$, where $n = 0, 1, \ldots, 7$ 11. pole; $(\sqrt{15}, \cos^{-1}\frac{1}{4})$; $(\sqrt{15}, \pi - \cos^{-1}\frac{1}{4})$ 13. $(6, \frac{1}{6}\pi)$; $(6, \frac{5}{6}\pi)$; $(2, \frac{7}{6}\pi)$; $(2, \frac{11}{6}\pi)$
15. pole; $(\frac{1}{2}\sqrt{2}, \frac{1}{6}(2n + 1)\pi)$, where $n = 0, 1, 2, 3, 4, 5$

Exercises 11.4   (Page 579)

1. $\frac{3}{4}\pi$ 3. 153° 26′   5. 38° 9′   7. $\frac{5}{8}\pi$ 9. $\frac{1}{2}\pi$ 11. $\frac{1}{3}\pi$ 13. 0 at pole; $\frac{1}{2}\pi$ at $(1, \pi)$; $\frac{1}{2}\pi$ at $(1, 0)$ 15. 0° at $(0, \frac{1}{2}\pi)$; 79° 6′ at
$(\frac{1}{2}\sqrt{3}, \frac{1}{6}\pi)$; 79° 6′ at $(-\frac{1}{2}\sqrt{3}, \frac{5}{6}\pi)$

Exercises 11.5   (Page 584)

1. $\frac{3}{4}\pi$ 3. 4π 5. 4   7. $\frac{9}{8}\pi$ 9. $\frac{11}{4}\pi - \frac{11}{2}\sin^{-1}\frac{1}{3} - 3\sqrt{2}$ 11. $\frac{19}{3}\pi - \frac{11}{2}\sqrt{3}$ 13. $\frac{9}{2}\pi - 9$ 15. $a^2(2 - \frac{1}{4}\pi)$ 17. $\frac{1}{2}(\pi + 1)$
19. 4   21. $16a^2\pi^3$

Review Exercises for Chapter 11   (Page 584)

1. $r = 9\cos\theta - 8\sin\theta$ 3. $4x^4 + 8x^2y^2 + 4y^4 + 36x^3 + 36xy^2 - 81y^2 = 0$ 9. $\theta = \frac{1}{2}\pi$ 11. $a^2(\frac{1}{3}\pi + \frac{1}{2}\sqrt{3})$ 13. $\frac{e^{4k\pi} - 1}{4k}$

15. $r = \frac{\pi^2}{\sin\theta - \pi\cos\theta}$ 17. no points of intersection   19. $\frac{1}{6}\pi, \frac{1}{6}\pi, \frac{1}{2}\pi$ 21. $16\pi - 24\sqrt{3}$; $32\pi + 24\sqrt{3}$

25. (a) $4r\sin\theta - r^2\cos^2\theta = 4$; (b) $x^2 = 4y - 4$

Exercises 12.1   (Page 590)

1. $3x^2 - 24x + 4y^2 = 0$ 3. $8x^2 - 24x - y^2 + 4y - 4 = 0$ 5. $16x^2 + 4xy + 19y^2 - 152x + 116y + 496 = 0$ 9. $e = 1: y = 0; e < 1:$
$\frac{x^2}{?} + \frac{y^2}{b^2} = 1; e > 1: \frac{x^2}{a^2} - \frac{y^2}{b^2} = 1$

Exercises 12.2   (Page 597)

1. (a) 1; (b) parabola; (c) $r\cos\theta = -2$ 7. (a) $\frac{1}{2}$; (b) ellipse; (c) $r\sin\theta = 5$ 9. (a) $\frac{2}{3}$; (b) ellipse; (c) $r\cos\theta = -3$ 11. (a) $\frac{6}{5}$;
(b) hyperbola; (c) $2r\sin\theta = -3$ 13. (a) $\frac{2}{7}$; (b) ellipse; (c) $r\sin\theta = -5$ 15. $r = \frac{8}{1 - \sin\theta}$ 17. $r = \frac{3}{1 + 2\sin\theta}$

19. $\frac{16}{3}\sqrt{3}\pi$ sq units   21. (a) $r = \dfrac{40{,}000{,}000}{1 - \cos\theta}$; (b) 20,000,000 miles   23. $r^2 = \dfrac{a^2(1 - e^2)}{1 - e^2\cos^2\theta}$

Exercises 12.3   (Page 603)

1. vertices: $(\pm 3, 0)$; foci: $(\pm\sqrt{5}, 0)$; directrices: $x = \pm\frac{9}{5}\sqrt{5}$; $e = \frac{1}{3}\sqrt{5}$; ends of minor axis: $(0, \pm 2)$ 3. vertices: $(\pm 3, 0)$; foci: $(\pm\sqrt{3}, 0)$; directrices: $x = \pm 3\sqrt{3}$; $e = \frac{1}{3}\sqrt{3}$; ends of minor axis: $(0, \pm\sqrt{6})$ 5. vertices: $(\pm 2, 0)$; foci: $(\pm\sqrt{13}, 0)$; directrices: $x = \pm\frac{4}{13}\sqrt{13}$; $e = \frac{1}{2}\sqrt{13}$; $2a = 4$; $2b = 6$ 7. vertices: $(\pm\frac{4}{3}, 0)$; foci: $(\pm\frac{5}{12}, 0)$; directrices: $x = \pm\frac{8}{15}$; $e = \frac{5}{4}$; $2a = \frac{8}{3}$; $2b = \frac{1}{2}$ 9. $9x^2 - 4y^2 = 36$
11. $16x^2 + 25y^2 = 100$ 13. $32x^2 - 33y^2 - 380 = 0$ 15. $2x + 3y - 12 = 0$ 17. $7x^2 - 4y^2 = 28$ 19. $16\frac{2}{5}$ ft   21. 98π in.^{3}
23. the right branch of the hyperbola $16x^2 - 9y^2 = 14400$ 25. $\frac{4}{3}\pi ab^2$ 27. $2400w$ ft-lb

Exercises 12.4   (Page 611)

1. $e = \frac{1}{3}\sqrt{3}$; center: $(2, 3)$; foci: $(2 \pm\sqrt{3}, 3)$; directrices: $x = 2 \pm 3\sqrt{3}$ 3. $e = \frac{1}{5}\sqrt{10}$; center: $(0, \frac{1}{2})$; foci: $(0, \frac{1}{2} \pm\frac{1}{10}\sqrt{170})$; directrices:
$y = \frac{1}{2} \pm\frac{1}{4}\sqrt{170}$ 5. point-circle $(-\frac{5}{2}, 4)$ 7. $3x^2 + 4y^2 = 300$ 9. $\dfrac{(x-4)^2}{25} + \dfrac{(y+2)^2}{9} = 1$ 11. $\dfrac{(y-3)^2}{64} + \dfrac{(x+1)^2}{48} = 1$

15. $\dfrac{(x-1)^2}{64} + \dfrac{(y+5)^2}{39} = 1$ 17. $18\pi w$ lb

Exercises 12.5   (Page 618)

1. $e = \sqrt{3}$; center: $(-3, -1)$; foci: $(-3, -1 \pm\frac{2}{3}\sqrt{6})$; directrices: $y = -1 \pm\frac{2}{3}\sqrt{6}$; asymptotes: $\pm\sqrt{2}x + 2y \pm 3\sqrt{2} = 0$ 3. $e = \frac{1}{2}\sqrt{7}$; center:
$(-1, 4)$; foci: $(-1, -3)$, $(-1, 11)$; directrices: $y = 0, y = 8$; asymptotes: $\pm 2x + \sqrt{3}y \pm 2 - 4\sqrt{3} = 0$ 5. $e = \frac{1}{3}\sqrt{13}$; center: $(1, -2)$; foci:
$(1, -2 \pm\sqrt{13})$; directrices: $y = -2 \pm\frac{9}{13}\sqrt{13}$; asymptotes: $3x + 2y + 1 = 0, 3x - 2y - 7 = 0$ 7. $25x^2 - 144y^2 = 14{,}400$
9. $\dfrac{(y+1)^2}{144} - \dfrac{(x+2)^2}{81} = 1$ 11. $\dfrac{(x+3)^2}{36} - \dfrac{(y-1)^2}{81} = 1$ 15. $\dfrac{(y-5)^2}{4} - \dfrac{(x-2)^2}{12} = 1$ 17. $(3, 4)$

Exercises 12.6   (Page 623)

3. $16\bar{y}^2 - 9\bar{x}^2 = 36$ 5. $\bar{x}^2 - \bar{y}^2 = 16$ 7. $9\bar{x}^2 + 4\bar{y}^2 = 36$ 9. $3\bar{x}'^2 + \bar{y}'^2 = 18$ 11. $\bar{x}'^2 + 4\bar{y}'^2 = 16$ 13. $\bar{x}'^2 - 4\bar{y}'^2 = 16$

Review Exercises for Chapter 12   (Page 623)

1. $9(x - 1)^2 + 5(y - 2)^2 = 180$ 3. $3\bar{x}^2 - \bar{y}^2 - 3 = 0$ 5. $49(x + \frac{5}{7})^2 + 16(y - 3)^2 = 576$ 7. $r = \dfrac{8}{1 - 3\cos\theta}$ 9. $r = \dfrac{6}{1 - \sin\theta}$
11. (a) $e = \frac{1}{2}$; (b) ellipse; (c) $r\sin\theta = -2$ 13. (a) $e = \frac{3}{2}$; (b) hyperbola; (c) $3r\cos\theta = 4$ 15. $e = \frac{1}{2}\sqrt{3}$; center: $(-3, 8)$; foci:
$(-3, 8 \pm 2\sqrt{3})$; directrices: $y = 8 \pm\frac{8}{3}\sqrt{3}$ 17. $e = \sqrt{26}$; center: $(-1, 3)$; foci: $(-1 \pm\sqrt{26}, 3)$; directrices: $x = -1 \pm\frac{1}{26}\sqrt{26}$; asymptotes:
$5x + y + 2 = 0, 5x - y + 8 = 0$ 19. $21\bar{x}'^2 - 49\bar{y}'^2 = 72$ 21. $r = \dfrac{1}{1 - \cos\theta}$ 23. $4\sqrt{3}\pi a^2 b$ 25. 600 miles   27. $(3 \pm\frac{3}{4}\sqrt{6})$ million
miles   29. the left branch of the hyperbola $16x^2 - 9y^2 = 1{,}440{,}000$

Exercises 13.1   (Page 633)

1. $\frac{4}{3}$ 3. $\frac{1}{2}\pi$ 5. 1   7. 2   9. 0   11. $-\frac{1}{8}$ 13. $\ln\frac{2}{3}$ 15. $\frac{1}{6}$ 17. 1   19. $\frac{3}{5}$ 21. 2   23. -1 25. $\dfrac{Et}{L}$

Exercises 13.2   (Page 638)

1. 0   3. 0   5. 1   7. $\frac{1}{2}$ 9. 1   11. $\frac{1}{2}$ 13. 1   15. e^2 17. e^a 19. e^2 21. $e^{-1/3}$ 23. $\frac{1}{2}$ 25. 9   27. 2

Exercises 13.3   (Page 642)

1. 1   3. $-\dfrac{1}{\ln 25}$ 5. 1   7. divergent   9. 2   11. 1   13. divergent   15. (a) divergent; (b) 0   17. (a) 0   19. $\frac{1}{2}\pi$
21. $\frac{1}{2}\pi$ 23. $n = \frac{3}{2}; \frac{3}{4}\ln\frac{7}{16}$

Exercises 13.4   (Page 646)

1. 2   3. divergent   5. divergent   7. divergent   9. divergent   11. divergent   13. 0   15. divergent   17. 0   19. $\frac{1}{3}\pi$
21. (a) divergent; (b) 0   23. $n > -1; \dfrac{1}{n + 1}$ 25. $n > -1; \dfrac{2}{(n + 1)^3}$

Exercises 13.5 *(Page 652)*

1. $P_3(x) = \frac{1}{2} + \frac{1}{2}\sqrt{3}(x - \frac{1}{6}\pi) - \frac{1}{4}(x - \frac{1}{6}\pi)^2 - \frac{1}{12}\sqrt{3}(x - \frac{1}{6}\pi)^3$; $R_3(x) = \frac{1}{24}\sin\xi(x - \frac{1}{6}\pi)^4$, ξ between $\frac{1}{6}\pi$ and x 3. $P_4(x) = x + \frac{1}{6}x^3$;
$R_4(x) = \frac{1}{120}\cosh\xi x^5$, ξ between 0 and x 5. $P_3(x) = x - 1 - \frac{1}{2}(x-1)^2 + \frac{1}{3}(x-1)^3$; $R_3(x) = -\frac{1}{4}\xi^{-4}(x-1)^4$, ξ between 1 and x
7. $P_3(x) = -\ln 2 - \sqrt{3}(x - \frac{1}{3}\pi) - 2(x - \frac{1}{3}\pi)^2 - \frac{4}{3}\sqrt{3}(x - \frac{1}{3}\pi)^3$; $R_3(x) = -\frac{1}{12}(2\sec^2\xi\tan^2\xi + \sec^4\xi)(x - \frac{1}{3}\pi)^4$, ξ between $\frac{1}{3}\pi$ and x
9. $P_3(x) = 1 + \frac{3}{2}x + \frac{3}{8}x^2 - \frac{1}{16}x^3$; $R_3(x) = \frac{3}{128}(1+\xi)^{-5/2}x^4$, ξ between 0 and x 11. 2.71828   13. 0.515   15. 0.1823   19. $\frac{55\sqrt{2}}{672}$;
$|\text{error}| < \frac{1}{7680}\sqrt{2}$ 21. $x \approx \dfrac{\pi}{2(1+m)}$

Review Exercises for Chapter 13 *(Page 653)*

1. ∞ 3. $\frac{1}{3}$ 5. $+\infty$ 7. 1   9. 0   11. 1   13. e 15. divergent   17. $\frac{1}{2}$ 19. divergent   21. $\frac{1}{4}\pi$ 23. divergent
25. $P_6(x) = 1 - \frac{1}{2}x^2 + \frac{1}{24}x^4 - \frac{1}{720}x^6$; $R_6(x) = \frac{1}{30240}\sin\xi x^7$ 27. $f'(0) = \frac{1}{2}$ 29. (a) no; (b) 0   31. $|R_3(\frac{1}{2})| < \frac{1}{192} \approx 0.005$ 33. $+\infty$
35. $\frac{64}{3}$ sq units   37. \$152,500   39. (b) 0

Exercises 14.1 *(Page 661)*

5. $\frac{1}{2}$ 7. divergent   9. 0   11. 1   13. divergent   15. divergent   17. $e^{1/3}$ 19. 1

Exercises 14.2 *(Page 668)*

1. increasing   3. not monotonic   5. decreasing   7. not monotonic   9. increasing   11. decreasing

Exercises 14.3 *(Page 678)*

1. $s_n = \dfrac{n}{2n+1}; \frac{1}{2}$ 3. $s_n = \ln\left(\dfrac{1}{n+1}\right)$; divergent   5. $s_n = \dfrac{n(n+2)}{(n+1)^2}; 1$ 7. $\displaystyle\sum_{n=1}^{+\infty} \dfrac{2}{(3n-2)(3n+1)}; \frac{2}{3}$ 9. $\dfrac{1}{2} - \displaystyle\sum_{n=2}^{+\infty} \dfrac{1}{2^n}; 0$
13. divergent   15. 2   17. 1   19. $\dfrac{1}{e-1}$ 21. divergent   23. $\frac{3}{2}$ 25. divergent   27. $\frac{137}{111}$ 29. $\frac{47}{101}$

Exercises 14.4 *(Page 687)*

1. convergent   3. convergent   5. divergent   7. convergent   9. divergent   11. convergent   13. divergent
15. convergent   17. convergent

Exercises 14.5 *(Page 691)*

1. divergent   3. convergent   5. convergent   7. convergent   9. convergent   11. divergent

Exercises 14.6 *(Page 699)*

1. convergent   3. convergent   5. convergent   7. convergent   9. $|R_4| < \frac{1}{5}$ 11. $|R_4| < \frac{1}{81}$ 13. 0.113   15. 0.406
17. absolutely convergent   19. absolutely convergent   21. divergent   23. absolutely convergent   25. absolutely convergent
27. divergent

Exercises 14.7 *(Page 706)*

1. $(-\infty, +\infty)$ 3. $[-\frac{1}{2}, \frac{1}{2}]$ 5. 0   7. $(-9, 9]$ 9. $(0, 2]$ 11. $\left(-\dfrac{1}{e^2}, \dfrac{1}{e^2}\right)$ 13. $(-1, 1]$ 15. $(-e, e)$ 17. $[4, 6)$
19. $[-1, 1]$

Exercises 14.8 *(Page 714)*

1. (a) $r = 1$; $[-1, 1]$; (b) $\displaystyle\sum_{n=1}^{+\infty} \dfrac{x^{n-1}}{n}$; $r = 1$; (c) $[-1, 1)$ 3. (a) $r = 1$; $[-1, 1)$; (b) $\displaystyle\sum_{n=1}^{+\infty} \sqrt{n}x^{n-1}$; $r = 1$; (c) $(-1, 1)$ 5. (a) $r = +\infty$; $(-\infty, +\infty)$;
(b) $\displaystyle\sum_{n=1}^{+\infty} (-1)^{n-1} \dfrac{x^{2n-2}}{(2n-2)!}$; (c) $(-\infty, +\infty)$ 7. (a) $r = 3$; $[-2, 4)$; (b) $\displaystyle\sum_{n=1}^{+\infty} \dfrac{(x-1)^{n-1}}{3^n}$; $r = 3$; (c) $(-2, 4)$ 9. $\frac{1}{2}\displaystyle\sum_{n=2}^{+\infty} n(n-1)x^{n-2}$
11. $\displaystyle\sum_{n=0}^{+\infty} (-1)^n(n+1)x^n$ 13. 0.60653   15. (a) $\displaystyle\sum_{n=0}^{+\infty} \dfrac{x^{2n+1}}{(2n+1)!}$; (b) $\displaystyle\sum_{n=0}^{+\infty} \dfrac{x^{2n}}{(2n)!}$ 17. 2   19. (a) $\displaystyle\sum_{n=0}^{+\infty} (-1)^n \dfrac{x^{n+2}}{n!}$ 21. $\displaystyle\sum_{n=0}^{+\infty} \dfrac{x^n}{n!}$

Exercises 14.9   (*Page 722*)

1. 0.4854   3. 0.7468   5. 0.2483   7. 1.3179   9. 0.2450   11. $\displaystyle\sum_{n=0}^{+\infty} \frac{x^{2n+1}}{2n+1}$ 15. $\displaystyle\sum_{n=0}^{+\infty} \frac{(-1)^n x^{2n+1}}{(2n+1)!}$; $+\infty$

Exercises 14.10   (*Page 730*)

7. $\ln 2 + \displaystyle\sum_{n=1}^{+\infty} (-1)^{n-1} \frac{(x-2)^n}{n2^n}$ 9. $\displaystyle\sum_{n=1}^{+\infty} (-1)^{n-1} \frac{(x-1)^n}{n}$; $R=1$ 11. $2 + \frac{1}{4}(x-4) + 2 \displaystyle\sum_{n=2}^{+\infty} (-1)^{n-1} \frac{1\cdot 3\cdot 5\cdot\ldots\cdot(2n-3)(x-4)^n}{2\cdot 4\cdot 6\cdot\ldots\cdot(2n)\cdot 4^n}$;

$R=4$ 13. $\frac{1}{2} - \frac{1}{2}\sqrt{3}(x - \frac{1}{3}\pi) - \frac{1}{4}(x - \frac{1}{3}\pi)^2 + \frac{1}{12}\sqrt{3}(x - \frac{1}{3}\pi)^3 + \frac{1}{48}(x - \frac{1}{3}\pi)^4 - \cdots$; $R=+\infty$ 15. $\frac{1}{2}\displaystyle\sum_{n=1}^{+\infty} \frac{(-1)^{n-1}(2x)^{2n}}{(2n)!}$

17. (a) $x + \frac{1}{3}x^3 + \frac{2}{15}x^5$; (b) $1 + x^2 + \frac{2}{3}x^4$; (c) $\frac{1}{2}x^2 + \frac{1}{12}x^4 + \frac{1}{45}x^6$ 19. 0.5299   21. 1.97435   23. −0.2231   25. 0.0415   27. 0.0048
29. 0.2398   31. $a_4 = 3$; $a_3 = -5$; $a_2 = 2$; $a_1 = -1$; $a_0 = 6$

Exercises 14.11   (*Page 735*)

1. $1 + \displaystyle\sum_{n=1}^{+\infty} \frac{(-1)^n(-1)\cdot 1\cdot 3\cdot\ldots\cdot(2n-3)}{2^n n!} x^n$; 1   3. $\displaystyle\sum_{n=0}^{+\infty} \frac{(-1)^n x^n}{x^{n+2}}$; 2   5. $1 + \displaystyle\sum_{n=1}^{+\infty} \frac{(-1)^n\cdot 1\cdot 3\cdot 5\cdot\ldots\cdot(2n-1)}{2^n n!} x^{n+2}$; 1

7. $x + \displaystyle\sum_{n=1}^{+\infty} \frac{(-1)^n\cdot 1\cdot 3\cdot 5\cdot\ldots\cdot(2n-1)}{2^n n!(2n+1)} x^{2n+1}$ 9. 4.8989   11. 5.010   13. 0.3361   15. 0.5082

Review Exercises for Chapter 14   (*Page 735*)

1. $1, \frac{3}{2}, \frac{9}{5}, 2$; 3   3. $0, \frac{1}{3}, \frac{4}{5}, \frac{15}{17}$; 1   5. $1, 3, 1, 3$; no limit   7. convergent; 3   9. divergent   11. convergent; $4 + 2\sqrt{3}$
13. convergent; $\frac{1}{6}$ 15. convergent   17. divergent   19. convergent   21. divergent   23. convergent   25. divergent
27. absolutely convergent   29. conditionally convergent   31. divergent   33. absolutely convergent   35. $[-1, 1)$ 37. $[-3, 3]$
39. $x = 3$ 41. $(-7, 5)$ 43. 0.1973   45. 5.0658   47. 0.9986   49. 0.0124   51. $\displaystyle\sum_{n=0}^{+\infty} \frac{(\ln a)^n}{n!} x^n$; $(-\infty, +\infty)$
53. $\frac{3}{4}\displaystyle\sum_{n=1}^{+\infty} (-1)^{n-1} \frac{(3^{2n}-1)}{(2n+1)!} x^{2n+1}$; $(-\infty, +\infty)$ 55. $\displaystyle\sum_{n=1}^{+\infty} (-1)^n \frac{(3x+\pi)^{2n-1}}{(2n-1)!}$

Exercises 15.1   (*Page 741*)

1. 5   3. 2   5. $\sqrt{11}$ 7. $(3, 9)$ 9. $(3, 0)$ 11. $(\frac{1}{6}, -\frac{1}{6})$ 13. $\langle 2, -3\rangle$ 15. $\langle -2, -7\rangle$ 17. $\langle 5, 6\rangle$ 19. $(-4, 3)$
21. $(12, -5)$

Exercises 15.2   (*Page 748*)

1. $\langle -1, 9\rangle$ 3. $\langle 1, -5\rangle$ 5. $\langle -2, 2\rangle$ 7. $\langle 7, 3\rangle$ 9. $\langle -9, -4\rangle$ 11. $\langle \sqrt{2}, \sqrt{3}\rangle$ 17. (a) $\langle 1, -2\rangle$; (b) $\langle 1, -2\rangle$ 19. $\langle -2, 7\rangle$
21. $\sqrt{74}$ 23. $\sqrt{1061}$ 25. $-2i + 4j$ 27. $\sqrt{221}$ 29. $\sqrt{13} + \sqrt{17}$ 31. $3\sqrt{13} - 2\sqrt{17}$ 33. $\frac{11}{\sqrt{137}}i + \frac{4}{\sqrt{137}}j$ 35. $h=2$,
$k=3$ 37. (a) $\frac{1}{2}\sqrt{2}i - \frac{1}{2}\sqrt{2}j$; (b) $-\frac{1}{2}i + \frac{1}{2}\sqrt{3}j$; (c) $-i$; (d) j

Exercises 15.3   (*Page 755*)

1. 10   3. −1   11. $\frac{1}{10}\sqrt{2}$ 13. $-\frac{16}{65}$ 15. $10, -\frac{2}{5}$ 17. (a) 0; (b) no k 19. $\dfrac{-240 + \sqrt{85683}}{407}$ 21. $-\frac{4}{17}\sqrt{17}i + \frac{1}{17}\sqrt{17}j$; $\frac{4}{17}\sqrt{17}i$
$-\frac{1}{17}\sqrt{17}j$ 23. $-\frac{112}{17}i + \frac{96}{17}j$ 25. $\frac{23}{50}\sqrt{50}$ 27. (a) 24 ft-lb; (b) $24\sqrt{3}$ ft-lb

Exercises 15.4   (*Page 763*)

1. $(-\infty, 0)$ and $(0, 4]$ 3. $[-1, 1]$ 5. all real numbers not in $(-4, 3)$ 7. $\frac{4}{3}t$; $\frac{4}{9}$ 9. $\dfrac{1 + \ln t}{te^t(2+t)}$; $\dfrac{(2+t) - (1 + \ln t)(2 + 4t + t^2)}{t^3 e^{2t}(2+t)^3}$

11. $-\frac{b}{a}\cot t$; $-\frac{b}{a^2}\csc^3 t$ 13. $(y-1)^2 = x$ 15. $25x^2 - 9y^2 = 225$ 17. $y=1$; $x=-1$ 19. $2y + 5\sqrt{3}x = 20$ 21. $\dfrac{dy}{dx} = 0$;

$\dfrac{d^2y}{dx^2} = -\dfrac{1}{4a}$; $\dfrac{d^3y}{dx^3} = 0$ 25. $x^{2/3} + y^{2/3} = a^{2/3}$ 31. $3\pi a^2$

Exercises 15.5   *(Page 770)*

1. $4\mathbf{j}$ 3. $2\mathbf{i}$ 5. $\mathbf{R}'(t) = 2t\mathbf{i} + 2\mathbf{j}$; $\mathbf{R}''(t) = 2\mathbf{i}$ 7. $\mathbf{R}'(t) = 2e^{2t}\mathbf{i} + t^{-1}\mathbf{j}$; $\mathbf{R}''(t) = 4e^{2t}\mathbf{i} - t^{-2}\mathbf{j}$ 9. $\mathbf{R}'(t) = (1 + t^2)^{-1}\mathbf{i} + (\ln 2)2^t\mathbf{j}$;
$\mathbf{R}''(t) = -2t(1 + t^2)^{-2}\mathbf{i} + (\ln 2)^2 2^t\mathbf{j}$ 11. $(2t - 3)(2t^2 - 6t + 5)^{-1/2}$ 13. $20t$ 15. $8 \sin 4t$ 19. $\ln|\sec t|\mathbf{i} - \ln|t|\mathbf{j} + \mathbf{C}$
21. $(t \ln t - t)\mathbf{i} + \frac{1}{3}t^3\mathbf{j} + \mathbf{C}$ 23. $\frac{1}{2}(-\pi + t - \frac{1}{2}\sin 2t)\mathbf{i} + (-\pi + t + \frac{1}{2}\sin 2t)\mathbf{j}$ 25. $x^2 + y^2 = 1$; 0

Exercises 15.6   *(Page 776)*

1. $1 + \frac{1}{2}\sqrt{2}\ln(1 + \sqrt{2})$ 3. $\frac{2}{27}[(40)^{3/2} - (13)^{3/2}]$ 5. $6a$ 7. $a[\ln \cosh 2 + \ln \cosh 1]$ 9. $2\pi a$ 11. $2\pi a$ 13. 12
15. $\frac{1}{2}a(\theta_1 - \frac{3}{2}\sin \frac{2}{3}\theta_1)$

Exercises 15.7   *(Page 783)*

1. (a) $2t\mathbf{i} + \mathbf{j}$; (b) $2\mathbf{i}$; (c) $\sqrt{37}$; (d) 2 3. (a) $\mathbf{i} + \tan t\mathbf{j}$; (b) $\sec^2 t\mathbf{j}$; (c) $\sqrt{2}$; (d) 2 5. (a) $\cos t\mathbf{i} + \sec^2 t\mathbf{j}$; (b) $-\sin t\mathbf{i} + 2 \sec^2 t \tan t\mathbf{j}$;
(c) $\frac{1}{6}\sqrt{91}$; (d) $\frac{1}{18}\sqrt{849}$ 7. (a) $2\mathbf{i} + 6\mathbf{j}$; (b) $2\mathbf{j}$; (c) $2\sqrt{10}$; (d) 2 9. (a) $3\mathbf{j}$; (b) $-4\mathbf{i}$; (c) 3; (d) 4 11. (a) $\mathbf{i} + \sqrt{3}\mathbf{j}$; (b) $-\sqrt{3}\mathbf{i} + \mathbf{j}$; (c) 2; (d) 2
13. $\dfrac{2t - 3}{t - 1}\mathbf{i} + \dfrac{4 - 2t - t^2}{2}\mathbf{j}$ 15. (a) $\dfrac{390{,}625}{2}$ ft; (b) $\dfrac{390{,}625}{8}$ ft; (c) $1250\sqrt{2}\mathbf{i} - 1250\sqrt{2}\mathbf{j}$ 17. $(25 + \sqrt{631})$ sec; $(20{,}000\sqrt{3} + 800\sqrt{1893})$ ft
19. $40° 8'$ 21. 283 ft/sec

Exercises 15.8   *(Page 788)*

1. $\mathbf{T}(t) = \dfrac{t^2 - 1}{t^2 + 1}\mathbf{i} + \dfrac{2t}{t^2 + 1}\mathbf{j}$; $\mathbf{N}(t) = \dfrac{2t}{t^2 + 1}\mathbf{i} + \dfrac{1 - t^2}{t^2 + 1}\mathbf{j}$ 3. $\mathbf{T}(t) = \dfrac{e^{2t}}{\sqrt{e^{4t} + 1}}\mathbf{i} - \dfrac{1}{\sqrt{e^{4t} + 1}}\mathbf{j}$; $\mathbf{N}(t) = \dfrac{1}{\sqrt{e^{4t} + 1}}\mathbf{i} + \dfrac{e^{2t}}{\sqrt{e^{4t} + 1}}\mathbf{j}$
5. $\mathbf{T}(t) = -\sin kt\mathbf{i} + \cos kt\mathbf{j}$; $\mathbf{N}(t) = -\cos kt\mathbf{i} - \sin kt\mathbf{j}$ 7. $\mathbf{T}(t) = -(1 + \cot^4 t)^{-1/2}\mathbf{i} + (1 + \tan^4 t)^{-1/2}\mathbf{j}$;
$\mathbf{N}(t) = \dfrac{-\cos^2 t}{\sqrt{\sin^4 t + \cos^4 t}}\mathbf{i} - \dfrac{\sin^2 t}{\sqrt{\sin^4 t + \cos^4 t}}\mathbf{j}$ 9. $\frac{27}{185}\sqrt{37}$ 13. $x = 2 + \cos s$; $y = 3 + \sin s$ 15. $x = a\left(\dfrac{3a - 2s}{3a}\right)^{3/2}$;
$y = a\left(\dfrac{2s}{3a}\right)^{3/2}$

Exercises 15.9   *(Page 795)*

1. $\frac{1}{8}\sqrt{2}$ 3. $\frac{1}{4}\sqrt{2}$ 5. $\dfrac{\sqrt{2}|1 - t^2|^3}{(1 + 6t^2 + t^4)^{3/2}}$; $\sqrt{2}$ 7. $\frac{1}{2}$ 9. $\frac{1}{4}\sqrt{2}$ 11. $\frac{4}{49}\sqrt{7}$ 13. $\dfrac{(2 - x^2)^{3/2}}{|x|}$ 15. $\dfrac{2(x + y)^{3/2}}{a^{1/2}}$ 17. $4|a \sin \frac{1}{2}t|$
21. $(3, 9)$ 23. $(-3, -1)$ 25. $\frac{23}{98}\sqrt{7}$ 27. $\dfrac{1}{16|a|}$ 31. $(0, -\frac{1}{2})$; 2 33. $\left(3x + 2p, -\dfrac{y^3}{4p^2}\right)$ 35. $\left(\dfrac{a^2 - b^2}{a}\cos^3 t, \dfrac{b^2 - a^2}{b}\sin^3 t\right)$

Exercises 15.10   *(Page 799)*

1. $\mathbf{V}(t) = 2\mathbf{i} + 2t\mathbf{j}$; $\mathbf{A}(t) = 2\mathbf{j}$; $\mathbf{T}(t) = \dfrac{1}{\sqrt{1 + t^2}}\mathbf{i} + \dfrac{t}{\sqrt{1 + t^2}}\mathbf{j}$; $\mathbf{N}(t) = \dfrac{-t}{\sqrt{1 + t^2}}\mathbf{i} + \dfrac{1}{\sqrt{1 + t^2}}\mathbf{j}$; $|\mathbf{V}(t)| = 2\sqrt{1 + t^2}$; $A_T(t) = \dfrac{2t}{\sqrt{1 + t^2}}$;
$A_N(t) = \dfrac{2}{\sqrt{1 + t^2}}$; $K(t) = \dfrac{1}{2(1 + t^2)^{3/2}}$; $\mathbf{V}(2) = 2\mathbf{i} + 4\mathbf{j}$; $\mathbf{T}(2) = \dfrac{1}{\sqrt{5}}\mathbf{i} + \dfrac{2}{\sqrt{5}}\mathbf{j}$; $\mathbf{A}(2) = 2\mathbf{j}$; $\mathbf{N}(2) = \dfrac{-2}{\sqrt{5}}\mathbf{i} + \dfrac{1}{\sqrt{5}}\mathbf{j}$; $|\mathbf{V}(2)| = 2\sqrt{5}$; $A_T(2) = \dfrac{4}{\sqrt{5}}$;
$A_N(2) = \dfrac{2}{\sqrt{5}}$; $K(2) = \dfrac{1}{10\sqrt{5}}$ 3. $\mathbf{V}(t) = -15 \sin 3t\mathbf{i} + 15 \cos 3t\mathbf{j}$; $\mathbf{A}(t) = -45 \cos 3t\mathbf{i} - 45 \cos 3t\mathbf{j}$; $\mathbf{T}(t) = -\sin 3t\mathbf{i} + \cos 3t\mathbf{j}$;
$\mathbf{N}(t) = -\cos 3t\mathbf{i} - \sin 3t\mathbf{j}$; $|\mathbf{V}(t)| = 15$; $A_T(t) = 0$; $A_N(t) = 45$; $K(t) = \frac{1}{5}$; $\mathbf{V}(\frac{1}{3}\pi) = -15\mathbf{j}$; $\mathbf{A}(\frac{1}{3}\pi) = 45\mathbf{i}$; $\mathbf{T}(\frac{1}{3}\pi) = -\mathbf{j}$; $\mathbf{N}(\frac{1}{3}\pi) = \mathbf{i}$; $|\mathbf{V}(\frac{1}{3}\pi)| = 15$
5. $\mathbf{V}(t) = e^t\mathbf{i} - e^{-t}\mathbf{j}$; $\mathbf{A}(t) = e^t\mathbf{i} + e^{-t}\mathbf{j}$; $\mathbf{T}(t) = \dfrac{e^{2t}}{\sqrt{e^{4t} + 1}}\mathbf{i} - \dfrac{1}{\sqrt{e^{4t} + 1}}\mathbf{j}$; $\mathbf{N}(t) = \dfrac{1}{\sqrt{e^{4t} + 1}}\mathbf{i} + \dfrac{e^{2t}}{\sqrt{e^{4t} + 1}}\mathbf{j}$; $|\mathbf{V}(t)| = \dfrac{\sqrt{e^{4t} + 1}}{e^t}$; $A_T(t) = \dfrac{e^{4t} - 1}{e^t\sqrt{e^{4t} + 1}}$;
$A_N(t) = \dfrac{2e^t}{\sqrt{e^{4t} + 1}}$; $K(t) = \dfrac{2e^{3t}}{(e^{4t} + 1)^{3/2}}$; $\mathbf{V}(0) = \mathbf{i} - \mathbf{j}$; $\mathbf{A}(0) = \mathbf{i} + \mathbf{j}$; $\mathbf{T}(0) = \dfrac{1}{\sqrt{2}}\mathbf{i} - \dfrac{1}{\sqrt{2}}\mathbf{j}$; $\mathbf{N}(0) = \dfrac{1}{\sqrt{2}}\mathbf{i} + \dfrac{1}{\sqrt{2}}\mathbf{j}$; $|\mathbf{V}(0)| = \sqrt{2}$; $A_T(0) = 0$;
$A_N(0) = \sqrt{2}$; $K(0) = \dfrac{1}{\sqrt{2}}$ 7. $\mathbf{R} = 2\mathbf{i} + 4\mathbf{j}$; if k = constant speed, $\mathbf{V} = \dfrac{k}{\sqrt{2}}\mathbf{i} + \dfrac{k}{\sqrt{2}}\mathbf{j}$; $\mathbf{A} = \dfrac{k^2}{16}\mathbf{i} - \dfrac{k^2}{16}\mathbf{j}$; $\mathbf{T} = \dfrac{1}{\sqrt{2}}\mathbf{i} + \dfrac{1}{\sqrt{2}}\mathbf{j}$; $\mathbf{N} = \dfrac{1}{\sqrt{2}}\mathbf{i} - \dfrac{1}{\sqrt{2}}\mathbf{j}$;
$A_T = 0$; $A_N = \dfrac{k^2\sqrt{2}}{16}$

Review Exercises for Chapter 15   *(Page 799)*

1. $-25\mathbf{i} + 63\mathbf{j}$ 3. $-22\mathbf{i} + 50\mathbf{j}$ 5. 92 7. $\dfrac{9}{\sqrt{106}}\mathbf{i} - \dfrac{5}{\sqrt{106}}\mathbf{j}$ 9. $h = -\frac{1}{2}$; $k = \frac{1}{2}$ 11. $\dfrac{-38}{\sqrt{50}}$ 13. (a) all real numbers in $[0, +\infty)$

except $t = 1$; (b) $\frac{1}{2}\mathbf{i} + \frac{1}{2}\mathbf{j}$; (c) $\dfrac{-1}{(t+1)^2}\mathbf{i} + \dfrac{2t^{1/2} - t - 1}{2t^{1/2}(t-1)^2}\mathbf{j}$ 15. $x = 12$; $y = 16$; $y = -16$ 17. $\frac{3}{2}\sqrt{37} + \frac{1}{4}\ln(6 + \sqrt{37})$ 23. $|at|$

25. $\dfrac{dy}{dx} = -\tan t$; $\dfrac{d^2y}{dx^2} = \dfrac{1}{3a}\sec^4 t \csc t$ 27. $A_T = \dfrac{-8 + 4t}{\sqrt{25 - 16t + 4t^2}}$; $A_N = \dfrac{6}{\sqrt{25 - 16t + 4t^2}}$ 29. $\mathbf{T}(t) = \dfrac{e^t - e^{-t}}{e^t + e^{-t}}\mathbf{i} + \dfrac{2}{e^t + e^{-t}}\mathbf{j}$;

$\mathbf{N}(t) = \dfrac{2}{e^t + e^{-t}}\mathbf{i} + \dfrac{e^{-t} + e^t}{e^t + e^{-t}}\mathbf{j}$ 31. $x = 2(3s + 17\sqrt{17})^{2/3} - 34$; $y = \frac{1}{3}\{(3s + 17\sqrt{17})^{2/3} - 16\}^{3/2}$ 33. $h = \frac{1}{64}(v_0 \sin \alpha)^2$

37. $\mathbf{V}(t) = 2\sinh 2t\mathbf{i} + 2\cosh 2t\mathbf{j}$; $\mathbf{A}(t) = 4\cosh 2t\mathbf{i} + 4\sinh 2t\mathbf{j}$; $|\mathbf{V}(t)| = 2\sqrt{\cosh 4t}$; $A_T = \dfrac{4\sinh 4t}{\sqrt{\cosh 4t}}$; $A_N(t) = \dfrac{4}{\sqrt{\cosh 4t}}$

Exercises 16.1   (*Page 808*)

1. (b) $(7, 2, 0)$, $(0, 0, 3)$, $(0, 2, 0)$, $(0, 2, 3)$, $(7, 0, 3)$, $(7, 0, 0)$; (c) $\sqrt{62}$ 3. (b) $(2, 1, 2)$, $(-1, 3, 2)$, $(-1, 1, 5)$, $(2, 3, 2)$, $(-1, 3, 5)$, $(2, 1, 5)$; (c) $\sqrt{22}$ 5. (b) $3\sqrt{77}$; (c) $(0, 0, 0)$; $(15, 18, 12)$, $(15, 0, 0)$, $(15, 18, 0)$, $(0, 18, 0)$, $(0, 18, 12)$, $(0, 0, 12)$, $(15, 0, 12)$
7. (a) $\frac{13}{2}$; (b) $(\frac{5}{4}, -1, 2)$ 9. (a) $\frac{23}{2}$; (b) $(\frac{3}{2}, \frac{1}{4}, \frac{1}{2})$ 11. $(\pm 4\sqrt{6}, 4, 2)$ 17. sphere with center at $(4, -2, -1)$ and $r = 5$ 19. the point $(0, 0, 3)$ 21. no real locus   23. $x^2 + (y - 1)^2 + (z + 4)^2 = r^2$, $|r| > 0$

Exercises 16.2   (*Page 814*)

7. $\langle 21, -13, -2 \rangle$ 9. $\langle -25, -26, 5 \rangle$ 11. $7\sqrt{59} - 5\sqrt{41}$ 13. $\langle -19, -16, -1 \rangle$ 15. $\langle -6\sqrt{91}, -8\sqrt{91}, -2\sqrt{91} \rangle$ 17. $a = b = 0$
19. $\dfrac{4}{\sqrt{89}}$; $\dfrac{3}{\sqrt{89}}$; $\dfrac{8}{\sqrt{89}}$ 21. $-\dfrac{6}{\sqrt{89}}$; $-\dfrac{1}{\sqrt{89}}$; $-\dfrac{7}{\sqrt{89}}$ 23. $\langle \frac{13}{3}, 0, -\frac{4}{3} \rangle$ 25. $7(-\frac{6}{7}\mathbf{i} + \frac{2}{7}\mathbf{j} + \frac{3}{7}\mathbf{k})$ 27. $\sqrt{14}\left(-\dfrac{2}{\sqrt{14}}\mathbf{i} + \dfrac{1}{\sqrt{14}}\mathbf{j} - \dfrac{3}{\sqrt{14}}\mathbf{k}\right)$
29. $\cos^{-1}\dfrac{1}{\sqrt{3}}$ or $\cos^{-1}\left(-\dfrac{1}{\sqrt{3}}\right)$ 31. $\langle \frac{1}{9}, \frac{8}{9}, \frac{4}{9} \rangle$ 33. (c) $r = 8$, $s = -7$, $t = 5$

Exercises 16.3   (*Page 819*)

5. -44 7. -468 9. $\langle -88, 196, 128 \rangle$ 11. $-\frac{13}{54}\sqrt{6}$ 13. (a) -3; (b) $\langle 2, 1, -2 \rangle$ 19. $\frac{1}{11}\sqrt{4422}$ 21. $\frac{7}{2}\sqrt{3}$ 23. $\frac{5}{3}\sqrt{6}$ ft-lb
25. $\frac{2}{5}$

Exercises 16.4   (*Page 825*)

1. $x + 2y - 3z + 1 = 0$ 3. $x - 3y - 4z - 3 = 0$ 5. $3x + 2y + 6z = 23$ 7. $\langle \frac{2}{3}, -1, \frac{2}{3} \rangle$; $\langle -\frac{2}{3}, 1, -\frac{2}{3} \rangle$ 9. $\langle \frac{4}{13}, \frac{3}{13}, -\frac{12}{13} \rangle$; $\langle -\frac{4}{13}, -\frac{3}{13}, \frac{12}{13} \rangle$
11. $\left\langle \dfrac{3}{\sqrt{13}}, 0, \dfrac{2}{\sqrt{13}} \right\rangle$; $\left\langle -\dfrac{3}{\sqrt{13}}, 0, -\dfrac{2}{\sqrt{13}} \right\rangle$ 13. $5x - 3y + 7z + 14 = 0$ 15. $2x - y - z + 1 = 0$ 17. $4y - 3z - 1 = 0$ and $z = 1$
19. $-\frac{16}{45}$ 21. $\frac{16}{15}\sqrt{6}$ 23. $\frac{3}{2}$

Exercises 16.5   (*Page 831*)

1. $x = 1 + 4t$, $y = 2 - 3t$, $z = 1$; $\dfrac{x-1}{4} = \dfrac{y-2}{-3}$, $z = 1$ 3. $x = 4 + t$, $y = -5 + 3t$, $z = 20 - 6t$; $\dfrac{x-4}{1} = \dfrac{y+5}{3} = \dfrac{z-20}{-6}$ 5. $\dfrac{x}{13} = \dfrac{y}{-12} = \dfrac{z}{-8}$
9. $8x - y - 66 = 0$; $13x - 5z - 102 = 0$; $13y - 40z + 42 = 0$ 11. $4x + y + 3 = 0$; $3x - z + 4 = 0$; $3y + 4z - 7 = 0$ 13. $\frac{5}{18}\sqrt{6}$
15. $4x + 7y - 3z + 7 = 0$ 17. $4x + 2y - 3z + 5 = 0$ 19. $\dfrac{x-3}{1} = \dfrac{y-6}{2} = \dfrac{z-4}{1}$ 21. $\frac{2}{5}\sqrt{70}$

Exercises 16.6   (*Page 841*)

1. $\langle 7, 13, -11 \rangle$ 3. -490 11. $\langle 9, -1, -23 \rangle$ 19. $\frac{2}{3}\sqrt{2}$ 21. $\sqrt{89}$ 23. $9\sqrt{29}$ 27. $\dfrac{1}{\sqrt{3}}(\mathbf{i} + \mathbf{j} - \mathbf{k})$ 29. 20
31. $5x - 2y + 7z = 0$ 33. $\dfrac{38}{3\sqrt{78}}$

Exercises 16.7   (*Page 847*)

9. $x^2 + z^2 = 4y$ 11. $x^2 + 4y^2 + 4z^2 = 16$ 13. $y^2 + z^2 = \sin^2 x$ 15. $x^2 - z^2 = 4$; z axis   17. $z = \sqrt{|y|}$; y axis

Exercises 16.8   (*Page 854*)

1. ellipsoid   3. elliptic hyperboloid of one sheet   5. elliptic cone   7. elliptic paraboloid   9. hyperbolic paraboloid
11. elliptic hyperboloid of two sheets   13. (a) $|k| > 1$; (b) $|k| < 1$. 15. $\frac{96}{25}\pi$ 17. $\frac{4}{3}\pi abc$

Exercises 16.9   (Page 862)

1. $T(t) = (5 + 9t^4)^{-1/2}(i - 3t^2j - 2k)$ 3. $T(t) = \frac{1}{3}\sqrt{3}[(\cos t - \sin t)i + (\cos t + \sin t)j + k]$ 5. $\sqrt{21} + \frac{3}{2} + \frac{5}{4}\ln(4 + \sqrt{21})$
7. $\sqrt{3}(e^3 - 1)$ 11. $R(t) = ti + e^tj + te^tk$ 13. $T(1) = \frac{1}{14}\sqrt{14}i + \frac{1}{7}\sqrt{14}j + \frac{3}{14}\sqrt{14}k$; $N(1) = -\frac{11}{266}i - \frac{4}{133}\sqrt{266}j + \frac{9}{266}\sqrt{266}k$;
$B(1) = \frac{3}{266}\sqrt{14}i - \frac{3}{266}\sqrt{14}j + \frac{3}{266}\sqrt{14}k$; $K(1) = \frac{1}{98}\sqrt{266}$ 15. $T(-1) = \frac{1}{3}(i + 2j - 2k)$; $N(-1) = \frac{2}{15}\sqrt{5}i - \frac{1}{3}\sqrt{5}j - \frac{4}{15}\sqrt{5}k$;
$B(-1) = -\frac{2}{5}\sqrt{5}i - \frac{1}{5}\sqrt{5}k$; $K(-1) = \frac{2}{27}\sqrt{5}$ 17. $T(0) = \frac{1}{3}\sqrt{3}(i + j + k)$; $N(0) = -\frac{1}{2}\sqrt{2}(i - j)$; $B(0) = -\frac{1}{6}\sqrt{6}(i + j - 2k)$; $K(0) = \frac{1}{3}\sqrt{2}$
19. $V(\frac{1}{2}\pi) = -ai + k$; $A(\frac{1}{2}\pi) = -aj$; $|V(\frac{1}{2}\pi)| = \sqrt{a^2 + 1}$ 21. $V(1) = 2e^2i - 2e^{-2}j + 3e^2k$; $A(1) = 4e^2i + 4e^{-2}j + 8e^2k$;
$|V(1)| = \sqrt{13e^4 + 4e^{-4}}$ 27. 2

Exercises 16.10   (Page 867)

1. (a) $(0, 3, 5)$; (b) $(-\frac{7}{2}, \frac{7}{2}\sqrt{3}, -4)$; (c) $(\cos 1, \sin 1, 1)$ 3. (a) $(\sqrt{6}, \sqrt{2}, 2\sqrt{2})$; (b) $(0, 2\sqrt{3}, 2)$; (c) $(\frac{1}{2}\sqrt{3}, \frac{3}{2}, -\sqrt{3})$
5. (a) $(2, \frac{2}{3}\pi, -2\sqrt{3})$; (b) $(0, \frac{3}{4}\pi, -\sqrt{2})$; (c) $(\sqrt{6}, \frac{1}{4}\pi, \sqrt{6})$ 7. ellipsoid; $r^2 + 4z^2 = 16$ 9. elliptic cone; $r^2 \cos 2\theta = 3z^2$ 11. sphere;
$\rho^2 - 9\rho \cos \phi = 0$ 13. right circular cylinder; $\rho^2 \sin^2 \phi = 9$ 15. (a) right circular cylinder; $x^2 + y^2 = 16$; (b) plane through z axis;
$y = x$ 17. $x^2 - y^2 = z^3$ 19. (a) sphere; $x^2 + y^2 + z^2 = 81$; (b) plane through z axis; $x = y$; (c) cone with vertex at origin, $z = \sqrt{x^2 + y^2}$
21. $x\sqrt{x^2 + y^2 + z^2} = 2y$ 25. $2\pi\sqrt{a^2 + 1}$

Review Exercises for Chapter 16   (Page 869)

3. the x axis   5. the circle in the xz plane with center at the origin and radius 2   7. the plane perpendicular to the xy plane and
intersecting the xy plane in the line $y = x$ 9. the solid of revolution generated by revolving $y^2 = 9z$ about the z axis   11. the solid
of revolution generated by revolving $y = x$ about the x axis   13. $i + 26j - 16k$ 15. -3 17. $7\sqrt{1270}$ 19. 16
21. $\langle -60, -40, 80\rangle$ 23. 295   25. $(x + 2)^2 + (y + 1)^2 + (z - 3)^2 = 17$ 27. 3   29. $\frac{47}{10}\sqrt{2}$ 31. $x - 6y - 10z + 23 = 0$ 33. 3
35. $\frac{1}{3}\sqrt{3}$ 37. $\frac{x}{4} = \frac{y}{-3} = \frac{z}{1}$; $x = 4t$, $y = -3t$, $z = t$ 39. 24   41. $V(\frac{1}{2}\pi) = -\frac{1}{2}\pi i + j + k$; $A(\frac{1}{2}\pi) = -2i - \frac{1}{2}\pi j$; $|V(\frac{1}{2}\pi)| = \frac{1}{2}\sqrt{8 + \pi^2}$
43. (a) $z = r^2(1 + \sin 2\theta) + 1$; (b) $r^2(25 \cos^2 \theta + 4 \sin^2 \theta) = 100$

Exercises 17.1   (Page 879)

1. (a) $-\frac{1}{7}$; (b) $\frac{x^2 + y^2}{x^2 - y^2}$; (c) $\frac{x^2 + 2xy + y^2}{x^2 - 2xy + y^2}$; (d) 0; (e) the set of all points (x, y) in R_2 except those on the line $x = y$; (f) $(-\infty, +\infty)$
3. domain: set of all points (x, y) in R_2 interior to and on the circumference of the circle $x^2 + y^2 = 25$ except those on the line $x = 0$;
range: $(-\infty, +\infty)$ 5. domain: set of all points (x, y) in R_2 interior to the circle $x^2 + y^2 = 25$ and all points on the y axis except $(0, 5)$
and $(0, -5)$; range: $(-\infty, +\infty)$ 7. domain: set of all points (x, y) in R_2 except those on the line $x = y$; range: $(-\infty, +\infty)$
9. domain: set of all points (x, y) in R_2 except those on the x axis; range: $(-\infty, +\infty)$ 11. domain: set of all points (x, y) in R_2 for
which $xy > 1$; range: $(-\infty, +\infty)$ 13. domain: set of all points (x, y, z) in R_3 for which $|x| \leq 1$ and $|y| \leq 1$; range: $(-\pi, 2\pi)$
15. domain: set of all points (x, y) in R_2; range: $[0, +\infty)$ 17. domain: set of all points (x, y) in R_2; range: $(-\infty, 16]$ 19. domain:
set of all points (x, y) in R_2 for which $x + y^2 \leq 10$; range: $[0, +\infty)$ 27. $h(x, y) = \sin^{-1}\sqrt{1 - x^2 - y^2}$; domain: set of all points (x, y)
in R_2 interior to and on the circle $x^2 + y^2 = 1$ 29. (a) 2; (b) 6; (c) $\sqrt{x - y^2}$; (d) $|x - y|$; (e) $|x - y|$

Exercises 17.2   (Page 890)

1. $\delta = \frac{1}{7}\epsilon$ 3. $\delta = \min(1, \frac{1}{6}\epsilon)$ 5. $\delta = \min(1, \frac{1}{8}\epsilon)$ 17. 0   19. 2   21. $\frac{1}{4}\pi$ 23. $\frac{1}{2}$ 25. limit exists and equals 0
27. limit does not exist   29. limit exists and equals 0

Exercises 17.3   (Page 895)

1. continuous at every point in R_2 3. continuous at every point $(x, y) \neq (0, 0)$ in R_2 5. continuous at every point in R_2
9. all points (x, y) in R_2 which are interior to the circle $x^2 + y^2 = 16$ 11. all points (x, y) in R_2 which are exterior to the ellipse
$4x^2 + 9y^2 = 36$ 13. all points (x, y) in R_2 which are in either the first or third quadrant   15. all points (x, y) in R_2 for which
$|xy| \geq 1$ 17. all points in R_2 19. removable; $f(0, 0) = 0$ 21. essential   23. continuous at every point (x, y, z) in R_3 for
which $x^2 + y^2 + z^2 > 1$ 25. continuous at all points in R_3

Exercises 17.4   (Page 903)

1. 6   3. $3x - 2y$ 5. $\dfrac{x}{\sqrt{x^2 + y^2}}$ 7. $x^2 - 6xy + 2z$ 9. $xy + yt + zt$ 11. 4   13. $\dfrac{x}{\sqrt{x^2 + y^2}}$ 15. $-2 \sin 3\theta \sin 2\phi$

17. $\dfrac{e^{u/x}}{xy}\left(y \ln \dfrac{x^2}{y} - x\right)$ 19. $\dfrac{-z}{(x^2 + y^2 + z^2)^{3/2}}$ 21. $4xy + \dfrac{1}{z}$ 23. $xze^{xyz} + \dfrac{3xz^2}{z^4 + 9x^2y^2}$ 25. $-\ln \sin x; \ln \sin y$ 29. (a) 1;

(b) 1   31. (a) -2; (b) 0   33. 4   35. -4 deg/ft; -8 deg/ft   37. (a) $\dfrac{100}{i^2}\left[\dfrac{9i + 1}{(1 + i)^9} - 1\right]$; (b) $\dfrac{1}{0.0036}\left[\dfrac{1.54}{(1.06)^9} - 1\right] \approx -24.4$;

(c) $\dfrac{5000 \ln 1.06}{3(1.06)^t}$; (d) $-\dfrac{5000 \ln 1.06}{3(1.06)^8} \approx -61$

Exercises 17.5   (Page 916)

1. (a) 0.5111; (b) 0.54   3. (a) 0.2141 (b) 0.214   5. (a) $2(x_0 y_0 - y_0)\, \Delta x + (x_0{}^2 - 2x_0)\, \Delta y + (y_0\, \Delta x + \Delta x\, \Delta y)\, \Delta x + 2(x_0\, \Delta x - \Delta x)\, \Delta y$;

(b) $\epsilon_1 = y_0\, \Delta x + \Delta x\, \Delta y$; $\epsilon_2 = 2(x_0\, \Delta x - \Delta x)$ 7. (a) $\dfrac{2x_0 y_0\, \Delta x + y_0(\Delta x)^2 - x_0{}^2\, \Delta y}{y_0{}^2 + y_0\, \Delta y}$; (b) $\epsilon_1 = \dfrac{y_0{}^2\, \Delta x}{y_0{}^3 + y_0{}^2\, \Delta y}$; $\epsilon_2 = \dfrac{x_0{}^2\, \Delta y - 2x_0 y_0\, \Delta x}{y_0{}^3 + y_0{}^2\, \Delta y}$

15. $\xi_1 = \frac{1}{3}\sqrt{156}$ 17. $\xi_2 = \sqrt{5} - 1$ 21. (a) $(y_0 - z_0)\, \Delta x + x_0\, \Delta y + (2z_0 - x_0)\, \Delta z - \Delta z\, \Delta x + \Delta x\, \Delta y + \Delta z\, \Delta z$; (b) $\epsilon_1 = -\Delta z$, $\epsilon_2 = \Delta x$,

$\epsilon_3 = \Delta z$ 25. 0.14 in.; 1.4%   27. $\frac{13}{1600}$; 0.325%   29. \$1200

31. $D_1 f(xy) = \begin{cases} 2x \sin \dfrac{1}{\sqrt{x^2 + y^2}} - \dfrac{x}{\sqrt{x^2 + y^2}} \cos \dfrac{1}{\sqrt{x^2 + y^2}} & \text{if } (x, y) \neq (0, 0) \\ 0 & \text{if } (x, y) = (0, 0) \end{cases}$

$D_2 f(x, y) = \begin{cases} 2y \sin \dfrac{1}{\sqrt{x^2 + y^2}} - \dfrac{y}{\sqrt{x^2 + y^2}} \cos \dfrac{1}{\sqrt{x^2 + y^2}} & \text{if } (x, y) \neq (0, 0) \\ 0 & \text{if } (x, y) = (0, 0) \end{cases}$

Exercises 17.6   (Page 924)

1. $\dfrac{\partial u}{\partial r}$: (a) $6x - 2y$; (b) $16r - 10s$; $\dfrac{\partial u}{\partial s}$: (a) $-2x - 4y$; (b) $-10r - 6s$ 3. $\dfrac{\partial u}{\partial r}$: (a) $\dfrac{2e^{u/x}}{x^2}(2x \sin t - y \cos t)$; (b) 0;

$\dfrac{\partial u}{\partial s}$: (a) $\dfrac{2re^{u/x}}{x^2}(y \sin t + 2x \cos t)$; (b) $2e^{2\tan t} \sec^2 t$ 5. $\dfrac{\partial u}{\partial r} = \dfrac{6re^s + s \cos rs}{\sqrt{1 - (3x + y)^2}}$; $\dfrac{\partial u}{\partial s} = \dfrac{3r^2 e^s + r \cos rs}{\sqrt{1 - (3x + y)^2}}$ 7. $\dfrac{\partial u}{\partial r} = \dfrac{6s}{x^2} \sinh \dfrac{y}{x}(xe^r - ry)$;

$\dfrac{\partial u}{\partial s} = \dfrac{3}{x^2} \sinh \dfrac{y}{x}(2xe^r - yr^2) = 0$ 9. $\dfrac{\partial u}{\partial r} = 2x \sin \phi \cos \theta + 2y \sin \phi \sin \theta + 2z \cos \phi$; $\dfrac{\partial u}{\partial \phi} = 2xr \cos \phi \cos \theta + 2yr \cos \phi \sin \theta - 2zr \sin \phi$;

$\dfrac{\partial u}{\partial \theta} = -2xr \sin \phi \sin \theta + 2yr \sin \phi \cos \theta$ 11. (a) $e^x(\cos t - y \sin t) + e^y(x \cos t - \sin t)$; (b) $e^{\cos t}(\cos t - \sin^2 t) + e^{\sin t}(\cos^2 t - \sin t)$

13. (a) $\dfrac{x \sec^2 t - y \sin t + z \cos t}{\sqrt{x^2 + y^2 + z^2}}$; (b) $\tan t \sec t$ 15. $\dfrac{txe^t - y}{t(x^2 + y^2)}$ 17. $\dfrac{x + y + 2t}{t(y + t)^2}$ 19. $\dfrac{\partial z}{\partial x} = \dfrac{3y - 6x - 4z}{2z + 4x}$; $\dfrac{\partial z}{\partial y} = \dfrac{3x - 2y}{2z + 4x}$

21. $\dfrac{\partial z}{\partial x} = -\dfrac{z}{x}$; $\dfrac{\partial z}{\partial y} = \dfrac{xyz - 1}{xy^2 - 3xy \tan 3xz}$ 27. $\dfrac{\partial u}{\partial v} = \cos w \sinh v \dfrac{\partial u}{\partial x} + \sin w \cosh v \dfrac{\partial u}{\partial y}$; $\dfrac{\partial u}{\partial w} = -\sin w \cosh v \dfrac{\partial u}{\partial x} + \cos w \sinh v \dfrac{\partial u}{\partial y}$

29. decreasing at a rate of $\frac{8}{61}$ rad/sec   31. increasing at a rate of 16 in.³/sec

Exercises 17.7   (Page 932)

1. $2\sqrt{2}x + 5\sqrt{2}y$ 3. $3x + \sqrt{2}y + 4z$ 5. -42 7. -2 9. $-3e^{\pi/4} \cos \frac{1}{12}\pi$ 11. (a) $(-4, -4)$; (b) $-2 - 2\sqrt{3}$

13. (a) $\langle -12, 2, 14 \rangle$; (b) $\frac{6}{7}$ 17. $\frac{3}{20}\pi + \frac{2}{5}; \frac{1}{4}\sqrt{\pi^2 + 4}$ 19. $-\frac{29}{11}; \sqrt{21}$ 21. $\theta = \tan^{-1} \dfrac{3}{3\pi + 1}$ 23. (a) -1; (b) $-\mathbf{j}$; 2

25. (a) direction of $\dfrac{3}{\sqrt{10}}\mathbf{i} - \dfrac{1}{\sqrt{10}}\mathbf{j}$; (b) climbing at 60 ft per ft; (c) descending at $20\sqrt{2}$ ft per ft; (d) direction of $\dfrac{1}{\sqrt{10}}\mathbf{i} + \dfrac{3}{\sqrt{10}}\mathbf{j}$ or

$-\dfrac{1}{\sqrt{10}}\mathbf{i} - \dfrac{3}{\sqrt{10}}\mathbf{j}$

Exercises 17.8   (Page 936)

1. $2x - 2y + 3z = 17$; $\dfrac{x - 2}{2} = \dfrac{y + 2}{-2} = \dfrac{z - 3}{3}$ 3. $4x + 8y + 3z + 22 = 0$; $\dfrac{x + 2}{4} = \dfrac{y + 4}{8} = \dfrac{z - 6}{3}$ 5. $ex - y = 0$; $\dfrac{x - 1}{-e} = \dfrac{y - e}{1}$, $z = 0$

7. $x - y - 3 = 0; \dfrac{x-6}{1} = \dfrac{y-3}{-1}, z = 3$ 9. $x + 2y + 2z - 8 = 0; \dfrac{x-4}{1} = \dfrac{y-1}{2} = \dfrac{z-1}{2}$ 11. $3x - 2y - 6z + 84 = 0;$

$\dfrac{x+8}{-3} = \dfrac{y-27}{2} = \dfrac{z-1}{6}$ 13. $\dfrac{x-2}{4} = \dfrac{y+2}{-1} = \dfrac{z}{20}$ 15. $x = 4, y = 16$ 17. surfaces are tangent

Exercises 17.9   (Page 942)

1. (a) $\dfrac{2}{y} - \dfrac{6y}{x^4}$; (b) $\dfrac{2x^2}{y^3}$ 3. (a) $4e^{2x}\sin y$; (b) $-e^{2x}\sin y$ 5. (a) $2\tan^{-1}\dfrac{y}{x} - \dfrac{2xy}{x^2+y^2}$; (b) $2\tan^{-1}\dfrac{y}{x} + \dfrac{2xy}{x^2+y^2}$ 7. (a) $3y\cosh x$;

(b) $4x\sinh y$ 9. (a) 0; (b) e^y 11. (a) $12r + 4s$; (b) $4r - 30s$ 13. (a) $\dfrac{320rst}{(r^2+4s^2-5t^2)^3}$; (b) $\dfrac{16r(5t^2+12s^2-r^2)}{(r^2+4s^2-5t^2)^3}$ 21. neither exist

23. $f_{12}(0,0) = -1; f_{21}(0,0) = 1$ 27. $6se^{r-s}(2+r) - 8e^{-2s}$ 29. $10\cos^2\theta + 8$ 31. $-10r\sin 2\theta$

Exercises 17.10   (Page 954)

1. no relative extrema; $(1,-2)$ a saddle point   3. $\tfrac{3}{2}\sqrt{3}$, rel max at $(\tfrac{1}{3}\pi, \tfrac{1}{3}\pi)$; $-\tfrac{3}{2}\sqrt{3}$, rel min at $(\tfrac{5}{3}\pi, \tfrac{5}{3}\pi)$ 5. no relative extrema; $(0,\tfrac{1}{2})$ and $(0,-\tfrac{1}{2})$ saddle points   7. $(\tfrac{3}{2},-\tfrac{3}{2})$ 9. $(0,0)$ and $(0,4)$ 11. $(\tfrac{6}{7},-\tfrac{4}{7},\tfrac{2}{7})$ 17. $\tfrac{1}{3}N, \tfrac{1}{3}N, \tfrac{1}{3}N$ 19. $l:w:h = 1:1:\tfrac{1}{2}$

21. hottest at $(\pm\tfrac{1}{2}\sqrt{3}, -\tfrac{1}{2})$; coldest at $(0,\tfrac{1}{2})$ 23. $\left(0, \dfrac{1}{\sqrt{17}}, -\dfrac{4}{\sqrt{17}}\right)$ and $\left(0, -\dfrac{1}{\sqrt{17}}, \dfrac{4}{\sqrt{17}}\right)$; 1   25. 2 ft by 3 ft by $2\tfrac{2}{3}$ ft   27. $\tfrac{65}{4}$

Exercises 17.11   (Page 963)

1. $\dfrac{\partial x}{\partial p} = -1; \dfrac{\partial x}{\partial q} = -2; \dfrac{\partial y}{\partial p} = -2; \dfrac{\partial y}{\partial q} = -1$; complementary   3. $\dfrac{\partial x}{\partial p} = -3; \dfrac{\partial x}{\partial q} = 5; \dfrac{\partial y}{\partial p} = 2; \dfrac{\partial y}{\partial q} = -4$; substitutes   5. $\dfrac{\partial x}{\partial p} = -3; \dfrac{\partial x}{\partial q} = -2;$

$\dfrac{\partial y}{\partial p} = 1; \dfrac{\partial y}{\partial q} = -2$; neither   7. $\dfrac{\partial x}{\partial p} = -0.4p^{-1.4}q^{0.5}; \dfrac{\partial x}{\partial q} = 0.5p^{-0.4}q^{-0.5}; \dfrac{\partial y}{\partial p} = 0.4p^{-0.6}q^{-1.5}; \dfrac{\partial y}{\partial q} = -1.5p^{0.4}q^{-2.5}$; substitutes   9. $-qp^{-2}; p^{-1};$

$2pq^{-1}; -p^2q^{-2}$; substitutes   11. $x = qp^{-1}, y = p^2q^{-1}$ 13. 250 units of first sold at $7.50 per unit and 300 units of second sold at $11.50 per sq unit   17. $6400

Review Exercises for Chapter 17   (Page 964)

1. $\dfrac{2x}{3y^2}; \dfrac{y-2x^2}{3y^3}; -\dfrac{4x}{3y^3}$ 3. $t^2\cos st^2 + te^s; 2st\cos st^2 + e^s; 2t(\cos st^2 - st^2\sin st^2) + e^s$ 5. $\dfrac{1}{uw^2}; -\dfrac{2}{uw^3}; \dfrac{2}{u^2w^3}$

7. (a) $\dfrac{\partial u}{\partial t} = \dfrac{6y(x+y)}{x^2+y^2} + 3\ln(x^2+y^2); \dfrac{\partial u}{\partial s} = \dfrac{4y(x-y)}{x^2+y^2} - 2\ln(x^2+y^2)$; (b) $\dfrac{\partial u}{\partial t} = (3t-2s)\dfrac{18t}{4s^2+9t^2} + 3\ln(8s^2+18t^2);$

$\dfrac{\partial u}{\partial s} = (3t-2s)\dfrac{8s}{4s^2+9t^2} - 2\ln(8s^2+18t^2)$ 9. (a) $3x\cos t - 4(y+2x)\sin t$; (b) $12\cos^2 t - 12\sin^2 t - 32\sin t\cos t$

11. $(-5,-14,26)$ 13. all (x,y) such that $|x| > \tfrac{1}{2}\sqrt{y}$; $(0,+\infty)$ 15. all (x,y) such that $|x| > |y|$; $(0,\tfrac{1}{2}\pi)$ 17. all (x,y,z) such that $z > 0$; $(-\infty,+\infty)$ 19. all (x,y,z) except $y = \pm z$; $(-\infty,+\infty)$ 21. $\delta = \min(1, \tfrac{1}{35}\epsilon)$ 23. limit exists and equals 0   25. continuous at every point in R_2 27. continuous at all points (x,y) in R_2 not on the lines $x = \pm 2y$ 29. continuous at all points (x,y) in R_2 except $(x,y) = (2n+1, 2m+1)$, where n and m are any integers   33. $2y + 5z - 12 = 0; x = 2, \dfrac{y-1}{2} = \dfrac{z-2}{5}$ 35. $2\tfrac{1}{4}°$ at $(-\tfrac{1}{4}, \tfrac{1}{4})$; $0°$ at $(\tfrac{1}{2}, 0)$ 37. 24 class A, 8 class B 39. 73 cents   47. $(9, 11, 15)$ rel max

Exercises 18.1   (Page 973)

1. 50   3. 1368   5. 704   7. $\tfrac{203}{4}$ 9. 1376   11. 68.6

Exercises 18.2   (Page 981)

1. 42   3. $\tfrac{1}{2}$ 5. $\tfrac{1}{5}$ 7. $\tfrac{1}{3}$ 9. $\tfrac{152}{3}$ 11. $\tfrac{3}{2}\pi$ 13. $\tfrac{864}{5}$ 15. $\tfrac{512}{3}$ cu units   17. $\tfrac{16}{3}$ cu units   19. $(\tfrac{1}{3}\pi - \tfrac{4}{15})$ cu units

21. $\tfrac{1}{12}$ sq units   23. 72 sq units   25. $\dfrac{c}{ab}\displaystyle\int_{-a}^{a}\int_{-(b/a)\sqrt{a^2-x^2}}^{(b/a)\sqrt{a^2-x^2}} \sqrt{a^2b^2 - b^2x^2 - a^2y^2}\, dy\, dx$ 27. (b) $\tfrac{2}{3}a^3$; (c) $\dfrac{2}{3}\displaystyle\int_{0}^{a}\int_{0}^{\sqrt{a^2-y^2}} (2x+y)\, dx\, dy$

29. $\tfrac{337}{30}$ cu units   31. $1 - \cos 1$

Exercises 18.3   (Page 987)

1. 12 slugs; $(2, \tfrac{3}{2})$ 3. $\tfrac{176}{15} k$ slugs; $(\tfrac{35}{22}, \tfrac{102}{77})$ 5. $\tfrac{2}{3}ka^3$ slugs; $(\tfrac{3}{32}a(2+\pi), \tfrac{3}{32}a(2+\pi))$ 7. $\dfrac{1}{4}k\pi$ slugs; $\left(\dfrac{\pi}{2}, \dfrac{16}{9\pi}\right)$ 9. $\tfrac{4}{3}$ slugs; $(\tfrac{6}{5}, \tfrac{6}{5})$

11. 9ρ slug-ft^2 13. $\frac{1}{2}\pi\rho a^4$ slug-ft^2 15. $\frac{96}{35}\rho$ slug-ft^2 17. (a) $14\frac{1}{5}$ slug-ft^2; (b) 54 slug-ft^2; (c) $\frac{2}{5}\sqrt{15}$ ft; $14\frac{1}{5}$ slug-ft^2
19. (a) $\frac{3}{32}\pi k$ slug-ft^2; (b) $\frac{1}{24}\pi(2\pi^2-3)k$ slug-ft^2; (c) $\frac{1}{4}\sqrt{6}$ ft; (d) $(\frac{1}{12}\pi^3-\frac{3}{32}\pi)k$ slug-ft^2 21. $\frac{1}{12}b\sqrt{6}$ ft

Exercises 18.4   *(Page 993)*

1. 6π sq units   3. $\frac{1}{4}a^2(8+\pi)$ sq units   5. $(4\pi+12\sqrt{3})$ sq units   7. 4π cu units   9. $\frac{128}{9}(3\pi-4)$ cu units   11. $\frac{7}{2}\pi$ cu units
13. $\frac{40}{3}\pi k$ slugs; $(0,\frac{21}{10})$ 15. $\frac{22}{3}k\pi$ slugs; $(-\frac{57}{44},0)$ 17. $\frac{20}{3}k$ slugs; $(\frac{23}{25},\frac{531}{1280}\pi)$ 19. $11\frac{1}{3}\pi k$ slugs; $(0,-\frac{24}{7})$ 21. $\frac{3}{64}k\pi$ slug-ft^2
23. $\frac{11}{16}k\pi a^4$ slug-ft^2 25. $\frac{1}{4}\sqrt{2\pi}$ ft   27. $\pi e(e^8-1)$

Exercises 18.5   *(Page 999)*

1. $\sqrt{6}$ sq units   3. 9 sq units   5. 8π sq units   7. 12π sq units   9. $\pi b\sqrt{a^2+b^2}$ sq units   11. $2\pi a^2(1-e^{-1})$ sq units
13. 12π sq units   15. $\frac{72}{5}[2+\sqrt{2}\ln(1+\sqrt{2})]$ sq units

Exercises 18.6   *(Page 1004)*

1. $\frac{1}{10}$ 3. $\frac{1}{2}\pi-1$ 5. $\frac{15}{2}$ 7. $\frac{1}{24}$ 9. $\frac{648}{5}$ 11. $\frac{1}{4}$ cu units   13. $\frac{3}{2}\pi$ cu units   15. 4π cu units   17. $\frac{4}{3}\pi abc$ cu units
19. $\frac{1}{28}k$ slugs   21. $\frac{2}{5}(2\sqrt{2}-1)$ slugs

Exercises 18.7   *(Page 1011)*

1. $\frac{1}{8}a^3$ 3. πa^3 5. $\frac{4}{3}\pi a^3$ 7. $\frac{4}{5}a^5\pi k$ slugs   9. $1250\pi k$ slug-ft^2 11. $(0,0,\frac{2}{5}a)$ 13. $\frac{512}{75}k$ slug-ft^2 15. $(0,0,\frac{1}{2})$
17. $\frac{56}{9}\pi a^3 k$ slug-ft^2 19. 18π 21. $\frac{1}{15}\pi(2\sqrt{2}-1)$

Review Exercises for Chapter 18   *(Page 1012)*

1. $\frac{1}{40}$ 3. $\frac{1}{8}\pi$ 5. $\frac{1}{8}e^4-\frac{3}{4}e^2+e-\frac{3}{8}$ 7. $\frac{3}{4}\pi$ 9. $\frac{1}{8}$ 11. $\frac{1}{3}$ 13. $\frac{1}{2}\pi\ln 2$ 15. $\frac{1}{2}(1-\cos 1)$ 17. 3π 19. $\frac{8}{3}$ sq units
21. $\frac{1104}{35}$ cu units   23. 18 sq units   25. $(\frac{1}{2}\pi-\frac{2}{3})$ sq units   27. $(2,\frac{2}{3})$ 29. $\frac{1}{108}(3\pi-7)$ 31. $\frac{1}{64}(7e^8+1)$ slug-ft^2
33. $k(\pi+\frac{8}{3})$ slug-ft^2 35. $2k\pi$ slug-ft^2; $\frac{1}{2}\sqrt{2\pi}$ ft   37. $65k\pi$ slugs   39. $\frac{32}{5}\pi k$ slug-ft^2

Index

74 75 76 9 8 7 6